FUNDAMENTAL FORMULAS *of* PHYSICS

Donald H. Menzel
EDITOR

NEW YORK
Prentice-Hall, Inc.
1955

The St-Catherine Press Ltd., Bruges.

PREFACE

A survey of physical scientists, made several years ago, indicated the need for a comprehensive reference book on the fundamental formulas of mathematical physics. Such a book, the survey showed, should be broad, covering, in addition to basic physics, certain cross-field disciplines where physics touches upon chemistry, astronomy, meteorology, biology, and electronics.

The present volume represents an attempt to fill the indicated need. I am deeply indebted to the individual authors, who have contributed time and effort to select and assemble formulas within their special fields. Each author has had full freedom to organize his material in a form most suitable for the subject matter covered. In consequence, the styles and modes of presentation exhibit wide variety. Some authors considered a mere listing of the basic formulas as giving ample coverage. Others felt the necessity of adding appreciable explanatory text.

The independence of the authors has, inevitably, resulted in a certain amount of overlap. However, since conventional notation may vary for the different fields, the duplication of formulas should be helpful rather than confusing.

In the main, authors have emphasized the significant formulas, without attempting to develop them from basic principles. Apart from this omission, each chapter stands as a brief summary or short textbook of the field represented. In certain instances, the authors have included material not heretofore available.

The book, therefore, should fill needs other than its intended primary function of reference and guide for research. A student may find it a handy aid for review of familiar field or for gaining rapid insight into the techniques of new ones. The teacher will find it a useful guide in the broad field of physics. The chemist, the astronomer, the meteorologist, the biologist, and the engineer should derive valuable aid from the general sections as well as from the cross-field chapters in their specialties. For example, the chapter on Electromagnetic Theory has been designed to meet the needs of both engineers and physicists. The handy conversion factors facilitate rapid conversion from Gaussian to MKS units or vice versa.

In a work of this magnitude, some errors will have inevitably crept in. I should appreciate it, if readers would call them to my attention.

DONALD H. MENZEL
Harvard College Observatory
Cambridge, Mass.

CONTENTS

Chapter 1

BASIC MATHEMATICAL FORMULAS

By Philip Franklin

Professor of Mathematics
Massachusetts Institute of Technology

Certain parts of pure mathematics are easily recognized as necessary tools of theoretical physics, and the results most frequently applied may be summarized as a compilation of formulas and theorems. But any physicist who hopes or expects that any moderate sized compilation of mathematical results will satisfy all his needs is doomed to disappointment. In fact no collection, short of a library, could begin to fulfill all the demands that the physicist will make upon the pure mathematician. And these demands grow constantly with the increasing size of the field of mathematical physics.

The following compilation of formulas is, therefore, intended to be representative rather than comprehensive. To conserve space, certain elementary formulas and extensive tables of indefinite integrals have been omitted, since these are available in many well-known mathematical handbooks.

A select list of reference books, arranged by subject matter, is given at the end of Chapter 1. This bibliography may assist the reader in checking formulas, or in pursuing details or extensions beyond the material given here.

As a preliminary check on the formulas to be included, a tentative list was submitted to a number of physicists. These included all the authors of the various chapters of this book. They contributed numerous suggestions, which have been followed as far as space requirements have permitted.

1. Algebra

1.1. Quadratic equations. If $a \neq 0$, the roots of

$$ax^2 + bx + c = 0 \tag{1}$$

are

$$x_1 = \frac{-b + (b^2 - 4ac)^{1/2}}{2a} = \frac{-2c}{b - (b^2 - 4ac)^{1/2}} \tag{2}$$

$$x_2 = \frac{-b - (b^2 - 4ac)^{1/2}}{2a} = \frac{2c}{-b + (b^2 - 4ac)^{1/2}} \tag{3}$$

When $b^2 \gg |4ac|$, the second form for x_1 when $b > 0$, and for x_2 when $b < 0$ is easier to compute with precision, since it involves the sum, instead of the difference, of two nearly equal terms.

1.2. Logarithms. Let ln represent natural logarithm, or $\log_e$ where $e = 2.71828$. Then for $M > 0$, $N > 0$:

$$\left.\begin{array}{lll} \ln MN = \ln M + \ln N, & \ln M^p = p \ln M, & \ln 1 = 0 \\ \ln \dfrac{M}{N} = \ln M - \ln N, & \ln \dfrac{1}{N} = -\ln N, & \ln e = 1 \end{array}\right\} \quad (1)$$

In this book $\log_{10}$ will be written simply log. For conversion between base e and base 10

$$\ln M = 2.3026 \log M, \qquad \log M = 0.43429 \ln M \quad (2)$$

1.3. Binomial theorem. For n any positive integer,

$$(a+b)^n = a^n + na^{n-1}b + \frac{n(n-1)}{2!}a^{n-2}b^2 + \frac{n(n-1)(n-2)}{3!}a^{n-3}b^3 + \ldots + nab^{n-1} + b^n \quad (1)$$

or

$$(a+b)^n = \sum_{r=0}^{n} {}^nC_r a^{n-r}b^r = \sum_{r=0}^{n} \frac{n!}{r!(n-r)!} a^{n-r}b^r \quad (2)$$

where $n!$ (factorial n) is defined by

$$n! = 1\cdot 2\cdot 3\cdot \ldots \cdot(n-1)n \quad \text{for} \quad n > 1 \quad \text{and} \quad 1! = 1, \quad 0! = 1 \quad (3)$$

1.4. Multinomial theorem. For n any positive integer, the general term in the expansion of $(a_1 + a_2 + \ldots + a_k)^n$ is

$$\frac{n!}{r_1!r_2!r_3!\ldots r_k!} a_1^{r_1} a_2^{r_2} a_3^{r_3} \ldots a_k^{r_k} \quad (1)$$

where $r_1, r_2, \ldots r_k$ are positive integers such that $r_1 + r_2 + \ldots + r_k = n$.

1.5. Proportion

$$\frac{a}{A} = \frac{b}{B} \quad \text{or} \quad \frac{a}{b} = \frac{A}{B} \quad \text{if and only if} \quad aB = bA. \quad (1)$$

If $a/A = b/B = c/C = k$, then for any weighting factors p, q, r each fraction equals

$$k = \frac{pa + qb + rc}{pA + qB + rC} \quad (2)$$

1.6. Progressions. Let l be the last term. Then the sum of the arithmetic progression to n terms

$$s = a + (a + d) + (a + 2d) + \dots + [a + (n - 1)d]$$

is

$$s = \frac{n}{2}(a + l), \tag{1}$$

where $l = a + (n - 1)d$, and the sum of the geometric progression to n terms

$$s = a + ar + ar^2 + \dots + ar^{n-1} = a\left(\frac{1 - r^n}{1 - r}\right) \tag{2}$$

1.7. Algebraic equations. The general equation of the nth degree

$$P(x) = a_0x^n + a_1x^{n-1} + a_2x^{n-2} + \dots + a_{n-1}x + a_n = 0 \tag{1}$$

has n roots. If the roots of $P(x) = 0$, or zeros of $P(x)$, are $r_1, r_2, \dots, r_n$, then

$$P(x) = a_0(x - r_1)(x - r_2) \dots (x - r_n)$$

and the symmetric functions of the roots

$$\sum r_i = -\frac{a_1}{a_0}, \quad \sum r_ir_j = \frac{a_2}{a_0}, \quad \sum r_ir_jr_k = -\frac{a_3}{a_0}, \quad \dots,$$

$$r_1r_2 \dots r_n = (-1)^n \frac{a_n}{a_0} \tag{2}$$

If m roots are equal to r, then r is a multiple root of order m. In this case $P(x) = (x - r)^mQ_1(x)$ and $P'(x) = (x - r)^{m-1}Q_2(x)$, where $P'(x) = dP/dx$, § 3.1. Thus r will be a multiple root of $P'(x) = 0$ of order $m - 1$. All multiple or repeated roots will be zeros of the greatest common divisor of $P(x)$ and $P'(x)$.

If r is known to be a zero of $P(x)$, so that $P(r) = 0$, then $(x - r)$ is a factor of $P(r)$, and dividing $P(x)$ by $(x - r)$ will lead to a depressed equation with degree lowered by one.

When $P(a)$ and $P(b)$ have opposite signs, a real root lies between a and b. The interpolated value $c = a - P(a)(b - a)/[P(b) - P(a)]$, and calculation of $P(c)$ will lead to new closer limits.

If c_1 is an approximate root, $c_2 = c_1 - P(c)/P'(c)$ is Newton's improved approximation. We may repeat this process. Newton's procedure can be applied to transcendental equations. If an approximate complex root can be found, it can be improved by Newton's method.

1.8. Determinants. The determinant of the nth order

$$D = \begin{vmatrix} a_{11} & a_{12} & \dots & a_{1n} \\ a_{21} & a_{22} & \dots & a_{2n} \\ \dots & \dots & \dots & \dots \\ a_{n1} & a_{n2} & \dots & a_{nn} \end{vmatrix} \tag{1}$$

is defined to be the sum of $n!$ terms

$$D = \Sigma\,(\pm)\, a_{1i}a_{2j}a_{3k} \dots a_{nl} \tag{2}$$

In each term the second subscripts $ijk \dots l$ are one order or permutation of the numbers $123 \dots n$. The even permutations, which contain an even number of inversions, are given the plus sign. The odd permutations, which contain an odd number of inversions, are given the minus sign.

The cofactor A_{ij} of the element a_{ij} is $(-1)^{i+j}$ times the determinant of the $(n-1)$st order obtained from D by deleting the ith row and jth column.

The value of a determinant D is unchanged if the corresponding rows and columns are interchanged, or if, to each element of any row (or column), is added m times the corresponding element in another row (or column).

If any two rows (or columns) are interchanged, D is multiplied by (-1). If each element of any one row (or column) is multiplied by m, then D is multiplied by m.

If any two rows (or columns) are equal, or proportional, $D = 0$.

$$D = a_{1j}A_{1j} + a_{2j}A_{2j} + \dots + a_{nj}A_{nj} \tag{3}$$

$$0 = a_{1j}A_{1k} + a_{2j}A_{2k} + \dots + a_{nj}A_{nk}, \quad k \neq j \tag{4}$$

where j and k are any two of the integers $1, 2, \dots, n$.

1.9. Linear equations. The solution of the system

$$\begin{aligned} a_{11}x_1 + a_{12}x_2 + \dots + a_{1n}x_n &= c_1 \\ a_{21}x_1 + a_{22}x_2 + \dots + a_{2n}x_n &= c_2 \\ \dots \quad \dots \quad \dots \quad \dots & \dots \\ a_{n1}x_1 + a_{n2}x_2 + \dots + a_{nn}x_n &= c_n \end{aligned} \tag{1}$$

is unique if the determinant of §1.8, $D \neq 0$. The solution is

$$x_1 = \frac{C_1}{D}, \qquad x_2 = \frac{C_2}{D}, \qquad \dots, \qquad x_n = \frac{C_n}{D} \tag{2}$$

where C_k is the nth order determinant obtained from D by replacing the elements of its kth column $a_{1k}, a_{2k}, \dots, a_{nk}$ by $c_1, c_2, \dots, c_n$.

When all the $c_j = 0$, the system is homogeneous. In this case, if $D = 0$, but not all the A_{ij} are zero, the ratios of the x_i satisfy

$$\frac{x_1}{A_{11}} = \frac{x_2}{A_{12}} = \dots = \frac{x_n}{A_{1n}} \tag{3}$$

A homogeneous system has no nonzero solutions if $D \neq 0$.

2. Trigonometry

2.1. Angles. Angles are measured either in degrees or in radians, units such that

$$2 \text{ right angles} = 180 \text{ degrees} = \pi \text{ radians}$$

where $\pi = 3.14159$. For conversion between degrees and radians,

$$1 \text{ degree} = 0.017453 \text{ radian}; \quad 1 \text{ radian} = 57.296 \text{ degrees}$$

2.2. Trigonometric functions. For a single angle A, the equations

$$\left.\begin{aligned} \tan A &= \frac{\sin A}{\cos A}, & \cot A &= \frac{\cos A}{\sin A}, \\ \sec A &= \frac{1}{\cos A}, & \csc A &= \frac{1}{\sin A} \end{aligned}\right\} \tag{1}$$

define the tangent, cotangent, secant, and cosecant in terms of the sine and cosine. Between the six functions we have the relations

$$\left.\begin{aligned} \sin^2 A + \cos^2 A &= 1, & \cot A &= \frac{1}{\tan A} \\ \sec^2 A &= 1 + \tan^2 A, & \csc^2 A &= 1 + \cot^2 A \end{aligned}\right\} \tag{2}$$

2.3. Functions of sums and differences

$$\left.\begin{aligned} \sin (A + B) &= \sin A \cos B + \cos A \sin B \\ \sin (A - B) &= \sin A \cos B - \cos A \sin B \\ \cos (A + B) &= \cos A \cos B - \sin A \sin B \\ \cos (A - B) &= \cos A \cos B + \sin A \sin B \end{aligned}\right\} \tag{1}$$

$$\tan (A + B) = \frac{\tan A + \tan B}{1 - \tan A \tan B}, \qquad \tan (A - B) = \frac{\tan A - \tan B}{1 + \tan A \tan B} \tag{2}$$

2.4. Addition theorems

$$\left.\begin{aligned} \sin A + \sin B &= 2 \sin \tfrac{1}{2} (A + B) \cos \tfrac{1}{2} (A - B) \\ \sin A - \sin B &= 2 \cos \tfrac{1}{2} (A + B) \sin \tfrac{1}{2} (A - B) \\ \cos A + \cos B &= 2 \cos \tfrac{1}{2} (A + B) \cos \tfrac{1}{2} (A - B) \\ \cos A - \cos B &= -2 \sin \tfrac{1}{2} (A + B) \sin \tfrac{1}{2} (A - B) \end{aligned}\right\} \tag{1}$$

2.5. Multiple angles

$$\sin 2A = 2\sin A\cos A, \qquad \cos 2A = \cos^2 A - \sin^2 A \tag{1}$$

$$\sin^2 A = \tfrac{1}{2} - \tfrac{1}{2}\cos 2A, \qquad \cos^2 A = \tfrac{1}{2} + \tfrac{1}{2}\cos 2A \tag{2}$$

$$\sin\frac{A}{2} = \pm\sqrt{\frac{1-\cos A}{2}}, \qquad \cos\frac{A}{2} = \pm\sqrt{\frac{1+\cos A}{2}} \tag{3}$$

$$\left.\begin{aligned} \tan 2A &= \frac{2\tan A}{1-\tan^2 A}, \\ \tan\frac{A}{2} &= \pm\sqrt{\frac{1-\cos A}{1+\cos A}} = \frac{1-\cos A}{\sin A} = \frac{\sin A}{1+\cos A} \end{aligned}\right\} \tag{4}$$

$$\left.\begin{aligned} \sin 3A &= 3\sin A - 4\sin^3 A, \\ \cos 3A &= 4\cos^3 A - 3\cos A \end{aligned}\right\} \tag{5}$$

$$\left.\begin{aligned} \sin 4A &= \sin A(8\cos^3 A - 4\cos A), \\ \cos 4A &= 8\cos^4 A - 8\cos^2 A + 1 \end{aligned}\right\} \tag{6}$$

$$\left.\begin{aligned} \sin^4 A &= \tfrac{1}{8}(3 - 4\cos 2A + \cos 4A), \\ \cos^4 A &= \tfrac{1}{8}(3 + 4\cos 2A + \cos 4A) \end{aligned}\right\} \tag{7}$$

$$\cos nA\cos mA = \tfrac{1}{2}\cos(n-m)A + \tfrac{1}{2}\cos(n+m)A \tag{8}$$

$$\sin nA\sin mA = \tfrac{1}{2}\cos(n-m)A - \tfrac{1}{2}\cos(n+m)A \tag{9}$$

$$\cos nA\sin mA = \tfrac{1}{2}\sin(n+m)A - \tfrac{1}{2}\sin(n-m)A \tag{10}$$

2.6. Direction cosines. The direction cosines of a line in space are the cosines of the angles α, β, γ which a parallel line through the origin O makes with the coordinate axes OX, OY, OZ. For the line segment P_1P_2, joining the points $P_1 = (x_1, y_1, z_1)$ and $P_2 = (x_2, y_2, z_2)$ the direction cosines are

$$\cos\alpha = \frac{x_2 - x_1}{d}, \qquad \cos\beta = \frac{y_2 - y_1}{d}, \qquad \cos\gamma = \frac{z_2 - z_1}{d} \tag{1}$$

where d is the distance between P_1 and P_2, so that

$$d = \sqrt{(x_2 - x_1)^2 + (y_2 - y_1)^2 + (z_2 - z_1)^2} \tag{2}$$

For any set of direction cosines, $\cos^2\alpha + \cos^2\beta + \cos^2\gamma = 1$.

If a, b, c are direction ratios for a line, or numbers proportional to the direction cosines, then

$$\left.\begin{aligned} \cos\alpha &= \frac{a}{\sqrt{a^2+b^2+c^2}}, \qquad \cos\beta = \frac{b}{\sqrt{a^2+b^2+c^2}}, \\ \cos\gamma &= \frac{c}{\sqrt{a^2+b^2+c^2}} \end{aligned}\right\} \quad (3)$$

The angle θ between two lines with direction angles $\alpha_1, \beta_1, \gamma_1$ and $\alpha_2, \beta_2, \gamma_2$ may be found from

$$\cos\theta = \cos\alpha_1\cos\alpha_2 + \cos\beta_1\cos\beta_2 + \cos\gamma_1\cos\gamma_2 \quad (4)$$

The equation of a plane is $Ax + By + Cz = D$. A, B, C are direction ratios for any normal line perpendicular to the plane. The distance from the plane to $P_1 = (x_1, y_1, z_1)$ is

$$\frac{Ax_1 + By_1 + Cz_1 - D}{\sqrt{A^2+B^2+C^2}} \quad (5)$$

The equations of a straight line with direction ratios A, B, C through the point $P_1 = (x_1, y_1, z_1)$ are

$$\frac{x - x_1}{A} = \frac{y - y_1}{B} = \frac{z - z_1}{C} \quad (6)$$

The angle θ between two planes whose normals have direction ratios A_1, B_1, C_1 and A_2, B_2, C_2, or between two lines with these direction ratios may be found from

$$\cos\theta = \frac{A_1A_2 + B_1B_2 + C_1C_2}{\sqrt{A_1^2+B_1^2+C_1^2}\ \sqrt{A_2^2+B_2^2+C_2^2}} \quad (7)$$

2.7. Plane right triangle. $C = 90°$, opposite c.

$$\left.\begin{aligned} c &= \sqrt{a^2+b^2}, \qquad A = \tan^{-1}\frac{b}{a} \\ b &= c\cos A, \qquad a = c\sin A \end{aligned}\right\} \quad (1)$$

2.8. Amplitude and phase

$$a\cos\omega t + b\sin\omega t = c\sin(\omega t + A) \quad (1)$$

where the *amplitude* c and *phase* A are related to the constants a and b by the equations of §2.7.

2.9. Plane oblique triangle. Sides a, b, c opposite A, B, C.

$$A + B + C = 180 \text{ degrees} \quad \text{or} \quad \pi \text{ radians}$$

Law of sines :
$$\frac{a}{\sin A} = \frac{b}{\sin B} = \frac{c}{\sin C} \qquad (1)$$

Law of cosines :
$$c^2 = a^2 + b^2 - 2ab \cos C \qquad (2)$$

$$\text{Area } K = \tfrac{1}{2}ab \sin C = \sqrt{s(s-a)(s-b)(s-c)} \qquad (3)$$

where $s = \frac{1}{2}(a + b + c)$.

2.10. Spherical right triangle. $C = 90°$, opposite c.

$$\sin a = \sin A \sin c, \qquad \sin b = \sin B \sin c \qquad (1)$$

$$\sin a = \tan b \cot B, \qquad \sin b = \tan a \cot A \qquad (2)$$

$$\cos A = \cos a \sin B, \qquad \cos B = \cos b \sin A \qquad (3)$$

$$\cos A = \tan b \cot c, \qquad \cos B = \tan a \cot c \qquad (4)$$

$$\cos c = \cot A \cot B, \qquad \cos c = \cos a \cos b \qquad (5)$$

2.11. Spherical oblique triangle. Sides a, b, c opposites A, B, C.

$$0° < a + b + c < 360°, \qquad 180° < A + B + C < 540°$$

Law of sines :
$$\frac{\sin a}{\sin A} = \frac{\sin b}{\sin B} = \frac{\sin c}{\sin C} \qquad (1)$$

Law of cosines :
$$\cos c = \cos a \cos b + \sin a \sin b \cos C \qquad (2)$$

$$\cos C = -\cos A \cos B + \sin A \sin B \cos c \qquad (3)$$

Spherical excess :
$$E = A + B + C - 180°$$

If R is the radius of the sphere upon which the triangle lies, its area $K = \pi R^2 E/180$. If

$$s = \tfrac{1}{2}(a + b + c),$$

$$\tan \frac{E}{4} = \sqrt{\tan \tfrac{1}{2}s \tan \tfrac{1}{2}(s-a) \tan \tfrac{1}{2}(s-b) \tan \tfrac{1}{2}(s-c)} \qquad (4)$$

2.12. Hyperbolic functions. For a single number x, the equations

$$\sinh x = \frac{e^x - e^{-x}}{2}, \qquad \cosh x = \frac{e^x + e^{-x}}{2} \qquad (1)$$

define the hyperbolic sine and hyperbolic cosine in terms of the exponential function. And the equations

$$\left.\begin{aligned} \tanh x &= \frac{\sinh x}{\cosh x}, \qquad & \coth x &= \frac{\cosh x}{\sinh x}, \\ \operatorname{sech} x &= \frac{1}{\cosh x}, \qquad & \operatorname{csch} x &= \frac{1}{\sinh x} \end{aligned}\right\} \tag{2}$$

define the hyperbolic tangent, hyperbolic cotangent, hyperbolic secant and hyperbolic cosecant, respectively, in terms of the hyperbolic sine and hyperbolic cosine. The four functions $\sinh x$, $\tanh x$, $\coth x$, and $\operatorname{csch} x$ are odd functions, so that $\sinh(-x) = -\sinh x$ and $\tanh(-x) = -\tanh x$. The functions $\cosh x$ and $\operatorname{sech} x$ are even, so that $\cosh(-x) = \cosh x$. Between the six hyperbolic functions we have the relations

$$\left.\begin{aligned} \cosh^2 x - \sinh^2 x &= 1, \qquad & \coth x &= \frac{1}{\tanh x} \\ \operatorname{sech}^2 x + \tanh^2 x &= 1, \qquad & \coth^2 x - \operatorname{csch}^2 x &= 1 \end{aligned}\right\} \tag{3}$$

2.13. Functions of sums and differences

$$\left.\begin{aligned} \sinh(x+y) &= \sinh x \cosh y + \cosh x \sinh y \\ \sinh(x-y) &= \sinh x \cosh y - \cosh x \sinh y \\ \cosh(x+y) &= \cosh x \cosh y + \sinh x \sinh y \\ \cosh(x-y) &= \cosh x \cosh y - \sinh x \sinh y \end{aligned}\right\} \tag{1}$$

2.14. Multiple arguments

$$\sinh 2x = 2 \sinh x \cosh x, \qquad \cosh 2x = \cosh^2 x + \sinh^2 x \tag{1}$$

$$\sinh^2 x = \tfrac{1}{2}\cosh 2x - \tfrac{1}{2}, \qquad \cosh^2 x = \tfrac{1}{2}\cosh 2x + \tfrac{1}{2} \tag{2}$$

2.15. Sine, cosine, and complex exponential function. $i^2 = -1$.

$$e^{ix} = \cos x + i \sin x, \qquad e^{-ix} = \cos x - i \sin x \tag{1}$$

$$\cos x = \frac{e^{ix} + e^{-ix}}{2}, \qquad \sin x = \frac{e^{ix} - e^{-ix}}{2i} \tag{2}$$

2.16. Trigonometric and hyperbolic functions

$$\left.\begin{aligned} \cos ix &= \cosh x, \qquad & \cosh ix &= \cos x \\ \sin ix &= i \sinh x, \qquad & \sinh ix &= i \sin x \\ \tan ix &= i \tanh x, \qquad & \tanh ix &= i \tan x \end{aligned}\right\} \tag{1}$$

2.17. Sine and cosine of complex arguments

$$\sin (x + iy) = \sin x \cosh y + i \cos x \sinh y \tag{1}$$

$$\cos (x + iy) = \cos x \cosh y - i \sin x \sinh y \tag{2}$$

$$e^{x+iy} = e^x \cos y + ie^x \sin y \tag{3}$$

2.18. Inverse functions and logarithms

$$\cos^{-1} x = -i \ln(x + i\sqrt{1 - x^2}), \qquad \cosh^{-1} x = \ln(x + \sqrt{x^2 - 1}) \tag{1}$$

$$\sin^{-1} x = -i \ln(ix + \sqrt{1 - x^2}), \qquad \sinh^{-1} x = \ln(x + \sqrt{x^2 + 1}) \tag{2}$$

$$\tan^{-1} x = -\frac{1}{2} \ln \frac{1 + ix}{1 - ix}, \qquad \tanh^{-1} x = \frac{1}{2} \ln \frac{1 + x}{1 - x} \tag{3}$$

3. Differential Calculus

3.1. The derivative. Let $y = f(x)$ be a function of x. Then the derivative dy/dx is defined by the equation

$$\frac{dy}{dx} = \lim_{\Delta x \to 0} \frac{\Delta y}{\Delta x} = \lim_{\Delta x \to 0} = \frac{f(x + \Delta x) - f(x)}{\Delta x} \tag{1}$$

Alternative notations for the derivative are $f'(x)$, $D_x y$, y', and $\dot{y}$ is used for dy/dt, when $y = F(t)$.

3.2. Higher derivatives. The second derivative is

$$\frac{d^2y}{dx^2} = \frac{d}{dx}\left(\frac{dy}{dx}\right) = \frac{d}{dx} f'(x) = f''(x) \tag{1}$$

The nth derivative is

$$\frac{d^ny}{dx^n} = \frac{d}{dx}\left(\frac{d^{n-1}y}{dx^{n-1}}\right) = \frac{d}{dx} f^{(n-1)}(x) = f^{(n)}(x) \tag{2}$$

3.3. Partial derivatives. Let $z = f(x,y)$ be a function of two variables. Then the partial derivative $\partial z/\partial x$ is defined by the equation

$$\frac{\partial z}{\partial x} = \lim_{\Delta x \to 0} \frac{f(x + \Delta x, y) - f(x,y)}{\Delta x} = f_x(x,y) = z_x = \left.\frac{\partial z}{\partial x}\right|_y \tag{1}$$

Similarly the derivative $\partial z/\partial y$ is formed with y varying and x fixed.

The second partial derivatives are defined by

$$\frac{\partial^2 z}{\partial x^2} = \frac{\partial}{\partial x}\left(\frac{\partial z}{\partial x}\right), \qquad \frac{\partial^2 z}{\partial y^2} = \frac{\partial}{\partial y}\left(\frac{\partial z}{\partial y}\right),$$

$$\frac{\partial^2 z}{\partial x\, \partial y} = \frac{\partial}{\partial x}\left(\frac{\partial z}{\partial y}\right) = \frac{\partial}{\partial y}\left(\frac{\partial z}{\partial x}\right) = \frac{\partial^2 z}{\partial y\, \partial x} \tag{2}$$

The same process defines partial derivatives of any order, and when the highest derivatives involved are continuous, the result is independent of the order in which the differentiations are performed.

For a function of more than two variables, we may form partial derivatives by varying the independent quantities one at a time. Thus for $u = f(x,y,z)$ the first derivatives are $\partial u/\partial x$, $\partial u/\partial y$, $\partial u/\partial z$.

3.4. Derivatives of functions

Inverse functions:

$$y = y(x), \qquad x = x(y), \qquad \frac{dy}{dx} = \frac{1}{dx/dy}, \qquad \frac{d^2y}{dx^2} = \frac{-\,d^2x/dy^2}{(dx/dy)^3} \tag{1}$$

Chain rule: $\quad y = f(u), \qquad u = g(x), \qquad \dfrac{dy}{dx} = \dfrac{dy}{du}\dfrac{du}{dx}$ (2)

Implicit function: $\quad f(x,y) = 0, \qquad \dfrac{dy}{dx} = -\dfrac{\partial f/\partial x}{\partial f/\partial y}$ (3)

Parameter: $\quad y = y(t), \qquad x = x(t)$

Let $\quad \dot{y} = \dfrac{dy}{dt}, \qquad \dot{x} = \dfrac{dx}{dt}$ (4)

Then $\quad \dfrac{dy}{dx} = \dfrac{\dot{y}}{\dot{x}}, \qquad \dfrac{d^2y}{dx^2} = \dfrac{\dot{x}\ddot{y} - \dot{y}\ddot{x}}{\dot{x}^3}$

Linearity: $\quad \dfrac{d}{dx}(au + bv) = a\dfrac{du}{dx} + b\dfrac{dv}{dx}$ (5)

3.5. Products

$$(uv)' = uv' + vu', \qquad (uv)'' = uv'' + 2u'v' + vu'' \tag{1}$$

Leibniz rule:

$$(uv)^{(n)} = uv^{(n)} + {}^nC_1 u'v^{(n-1)} + \ldots + {}^nC_r u^{(r)}v^{(n-r)} + \ldots + u^{(n)}v \tag{2}$$

The ${}^nC_r$ are defined in §1.3.

3.6. Powers and quotients

$$(u^n)' = nu^{n-1}u', \qquad \left(\frac{1}{v}\right)' = (v^{-1})' = \frac{-v'}{v^2}, \qquad \left(\frac{u}{v}\right)' = \frac{vu' - uv'}{v^2} \tag{1}$$

3.7. Logarithmic differentiation $\dfrac{d(\ln y)}{dx} = \dfrac{y'}{y}$.

$$y = \frac{uv}{w}, \qquad y' = y\frac{d(\ln y)}{dx} = y\left(\frac{u'}{u} + \frac{v'}{v} - \frac{w'}{w}\right) \tag{1}$$

$$y = \frac{u^a v^b}{w^c}, \qquad y' = y\frac{d(\ln y)}{dx} = y\left(a\frac{u'}{u} + b\frac{v'}{v} - c\frac{w'}{w}\right) \tag{2}$$

$$y = u^v, \qquad \frac{d}{dx}(u^v) = u^v(v \ln u)' = u^v\left(v\frac{u'}{u} + v' \ln u\right) \tag{3}$$

3.8. Polynomials

$$\frac{da}{dx} = 0, \qquad \frac{d(bx)}{dx} = b, \qquad \frac{d(cx^n)}{dx} = ncx^{n-1} \tag{1}$$

$$\frac{d}{dx}(a_n x^n + \dots + a_r x^r + \dots + a_1 x + a_0)$$
$$= na_n x^{n-1} + \dots + ra_r x^{r-1} + \dots + a_1 \tag{2}$$

3.9. Exponentials and logarithms. We write ln for $\log_e$, where $e = 2.71828$, as in §1.2.

$$\frac{de^x}{dx} = e^x, \qquad \frac{da^x}{dx} = (\ln a)a^x \tag{1}$$

$$\frac{d \ln x}{dx} = \frac{1}{x}, \qquad \frac{d \log_a x}{dx} = \frac{\log_a e}{x} \tag{2}$$

3.10. Trigonometric functions

$$\frac{d}{dx}\sin x = \cos x, \qquad \frac{d}{dx}\tan x = \sec^2 x, \qquad \frac{d}{dx}\sec x = \tan x \sec x \tag{1}$$

$$\frac{d}{dx}\cos x = -\sin x, \qquad \frac{d}{dx}\cot x = -\csc^2 x, \qquad \frac{d}{dx}\csc x = -\cot x \csc x \tag{2}$$

3.11. Inverse trigonometric functions

$$\frac{d}{dx}\sin^{-1} x = \frac{1}{\sqrt{1 - x^2}}, \qquad \frac{d}{dx}\tan^{-1} x = \frac{1}{1 + x^2} \tag{1}$$

$$\frac{d}{dx}\cos^{-1} x = \frac{-1}{\sqrt{1 - x^2}}, \qquad \frac{d}{dx}\cot^{-1} x = \frac{-1}{1 + x^2} \tag{2}$$

3.12. Hyperbolic functions

$$\left.\begin{array}{ll}\frac{d}{dx}\sinh x = \cosh x, & \frac{d}{dx}\tanh x = \operatorname{sech}^2 x, \\ \frac{d}{dx}\operatorname{sech} x = -\tanh x \operatorname{sech} x & \end{array}\right\} \quad (1)$$

$$\left.\begin{array}{ll}\frac{d}{dx}\cosh x = \sinh x, & \frac{d}{dx}\coth x = -\operatorname{csch}^2 x, \\ \frac{d}{dx}\operatorname{csch} x = -\coth x \operatorname{csch} x & \end{array}\right\} \quad (2)$$

3.13. Inverse hyperbolic functions

$$\frac{d}{dx}\sinh^{-1} x = \frac{1}{\sqrt{x^2+1}}, \qquad \frac{d}{dx}\tanh^{-1} x = \frac{1}{1-x^2} \quad (1)$$

$$\frac{d}{dx}\cosh^{-1} x = \frac{1}{\sqrt{x^2-1}}, \qquad \frac{d}{dx}\coth^{-1} x = \frac{-1}{x^2-1} \quad (2)$$

3.14. Differential. Let $y = f(x)$, and Δx be the increment in x. Then

$$dx = \Delta x \qquad \text{and} \qquad dy = f'(x)dx = \left(\frac{dy}{dx}\right)dx \quad (1)$$

Parameter :

$$y = y(t), \qquad x = x(t), \qquad dx = \dot{x}\,dt, \qquad dy = \dot{y}\,dt \quad (2)$$

First differentials are independent of the choice of independent variable.

3.15. Total differential. For two independent variables $z = f(x,y)$,

$$dz = \frac{\partial z}{\partial z}dx + \frac{\partial z}{\partial y}dy \qquad \text{and} \qquad \frac{dz}{dt} = \frac{\partial z}{\partial x}\frac{dx}{dt} + \frac{\partial z}{\partial y}\frac{dy}{dt} \quad (1)$$

For three variables, $u = f(x,y,z)$,

$$du = \frac{\partial u}{\partial x}dx + \frac{\partial u}{\partial y}dy + \frac{\partial u}{\partial z}dz \quad (2)$$

$$\frac{du}{dt} = \frac{\partial u}{\partial x}\frac{dx}{dt} + \frac{\partial u}{\partial y}\frac{dy}{dt} + \frac{\partial u}{\partial z}\frac{dz}{dt}, \qquad \frac{\partial u}{\partial v} = \frac{\partial u}{\partial x}\frac{\partial x}{\partial v} + \frac{\partial u}{\partial y}\frac{\partial y}{\partial v} + \frac{\partial u}{\partial z}\frac{\partial z}{\partial v} \quad (3)$$

and similarly for functions of more variables.

3.16. Exact differential. The condition that as in § 3.15 for some $f(x,y)$,

$$A(x,y)dx + B(x,y)dy = dz,$$

with $z = f(x,y)$ is

$$\frac{\partial A}{\partial y} = \frac{\partial B}{\partial x} \quad (1)$$

for some $f(x,y,z)$ to make

$$A(x,y,z)dx + B(x,y,z)dy + C(x,y,z)dz = du,$$

with $u = f(x,y,z)$, the condition is

$$\frac{\partial C}{\partial y} = \frac{\partial B}{\partial z}, \qquad \frac{\partial A}{\partial z} = \frac{\partial C}{\partial x}, \qquad \frac{\partial B}{\partial x} = \frac{\partial A}{\partial y} \tag{2}$$

3.17. Maximum and minimum values. Let $y = f(x)$ be regular in the interval a, b. Then at a relative maximum, $f(x_1)$ with $a < x_1 < b$, $f'(x)$ decreases from plus to minus as x increases through x_1. At a relative minimum, $f(x_2)$ with $a < x_2 < b$, $f'(x)$ increases from minus to plus as x increases through x_2. Thus the largest and smallest values of $f(x)$ will be included in the set $f(a)$, $f(b)$, and $f(x_k)$, where $f'(x_k) = 0$.

3.18. Points of inflection. The graph of $y = f(x)$ is concave downward in any interval throughout which $f''(x)$ is negative. The graph is concave upward in any interval throughout which $f''(x)$ is positive. At any point $y_3 = f(x_3)$ such that $f''(x)$ changes sign as x increases through x_3, the graph of $y = f(x)$ is said to have a point of inflection.

3.19. Increasing absolute value. Let $OP = s(t)$, the distance along OX. Then the velocity $v = ds/dt = \dot{s}$, and the acceleration $a = dv/dt = \dot{v} = d^2s/dt^2 = \ddot{s}$. Then s increases when v is positive, and v increases when a is positive. The distance from O, or $|s|$ increases when $|s|^2 = s^2$ increases, so that $|s|$ increases when $s\dot{s}$ is positive, or when s and v have the same sign. The speed or $|v|$ increases when $|v|^2 = v^2$ increases, so that $|v|$ increases when $v\dot{v}$ is positive, or when v and a have the same sign.

3.20. Arc length. In the triangle formed by dx, dy, and ds, the differential of arc length, the angle opposite dy is the slope angle, and the angle opposite ds is $90°$. Thus

$$dx = ds \cos \tau, \qquad dy = ds \sin \tau, \qquad \frac{dy}{dx} = \tan \tau, \text{ and } ds^2 = dx^2 + dy^2, \tag{1}$$

$$ds = \sqrt{1 + y'^2}\, dx = \sqrt{\dot{x}^2 + \dot{y}^2}\; dt \tag{2}$$

In polar coordinates, $r = r(\theta)$,

$$ds^2 = dr^2 + r^2 d\theta^2$$

and

$$ds = \sqrt{r'^2 + r^2}\, d\theta = \sqrt{\dot{r}^2 + r^2\dot{\theta}^2}\; dt \tag{3}$$

3.21. Curvature. $R = ds/d\tau$ is the radius of curvature, and the curvature $K = 1/R$ is given by

$$K = \frac{1}{R} = \frac{y''}{(1 + y'^2)^{3/2}} = \frac{\dot{x}\ddot{y} - \dot{y}\ddot{x}}{(\dot{x}^2 + \dot{y}^2)^{3/2}} \tag{1}$$

In polar coordinates $r = r(\theta)$,

$$K = \frac{r^2 + 2r'^2 - rr''}{(r^2 + r'^2)^{3/2}} \tag{2}$$

3.22. Acceleration in plane motion. The velocity vector has x and y components $\dot{x} = dx/dt$ and $\dot{y} = dy/dt$, and magnitude $v = \sqrt{\dot{x}^2 + \dot{y}^2}$. The acceleration vector has x and y components $\ddot{x} = d^2x/dt^2$ and $\ddot{y} = d^2y/dt^2$. It has a tangential component $\dot{v} = dv/dt$ and a normal component v^2/R. As in § 3.21, $1/R = K$. The magnitude of the acceleration is

$$a = \sqrt{\ddot{x}^2 + \ddot{y}^2} = \sqrt{\dot{v}^2 + \frac{v^4}{R^2}} \tag{1}$$

3.23. Theorem of the mean. Let $f(x)$ and $F(x)$ be regular in the interval a, b. Then for at least one value x_k with $a < x_k < b$,

Rolle's theorem:

If $$f(a) = 0, \quad f(b) = 0, \quad f'(x_1) = 0 \tag{1}$$

Law of the mean:

$$f(b) = f(a) + (b - a)f'(x_2) \tag{2}$$

Cauchy's mean value theorem:

If $$F'(x) \neq 0 \text{ inside } a, b, \tag{3}$$

$$\frac{f(b) - f(a)}{F(b) - F(a)} = \frac{f'(x_3)}{F'(x_3)}$$

3.24. Indeterminate forms. Let $f(x)$ and $F(x)$ each approach zero as x approaches a. We briefly describe the evaluation of $\lim f(x)/F(x)$ as the indeterminate form 0/0. When $f(x)$ and $F(x)$ are each analytic at a, and series in terms of powers of $(x - a)$ can be easily found, the limit may be found by using these series.

l'Hospital's rule: If the limit on the right exists, then when $f(x) \to 0$, $F(x) \to 0$,

$$\lim_{x \to a} \frac{f(x)}{F(x)} = \lim_{x \to a} \frac{f'(x)}{F'(x)} \tag{1}$$

In this rule x may approach a from one side, $x \to a+$ or $x \to a-$, and it applies when in place of $x \to a$, $x \to +\infty$, or $x \to -\infty$. The rule in any form also applies when as $x \to a$, $f(x)$ and $F(x)$ each tend to infinity. This is the indeterminate from ∞/∞.

By writing $f = 1/(1/f)$ for one of the factors, we may reduce the form $0 \cdot \infty$ to $0/0$ or ∞/∞ and then use l'Hospital's rule. A similar procedure with each term sometimes reduces the form $\infty - \infty$ to $0/0$.

If the evaluation of $\lim f^F$ leads to an indeterminate form 0^0, 1^∞, ∞^0, the evaluation of $L = \lim F \ln f$ leads to a form $0 \cdot \infty$ or $\infty \cdot 0$. This may be found as indicated above, and then $\lim f^F = e^L$.

3.25. Taylor's theorem. Let $f(x)$ be analytic at a. Then

$$f(x) = f(a) + f'(a)\frac{(x-a)}{1!} + f''(a)\frac{(x-a)^2}{2!} + f'''(a)\frac{(x-a)^3}{3!} + \dots + f^{(n-1)}(a)\frac{(x-a)^{n-1}}{(n-1)!} + \dots \tag{1}$$

For real values, the remainder after the term with $f^{(n-1)}(a)$ is

$$R_n = f^{(n)}(x_1)\frac{(x-a)^n}{n!} \tag{2}$$

where x_1 is a suitably chosen value in the interval a, x. An alternative form is

$$f(a+h) = f(a) + f'(a)\frac{h}{1!} + f''(a)\frac{h^2}{2!} + f'''(a)\frac{h^3}{3!} + \dots + f^{(n)}(a)\frac{h^n}{n!} + \dots \tag{3}$$

The special case when $a = 0$ is called Maclaurin's series.

$$f(x) = f(0) + f'(0)\frac{x}{1!} + f''(0)\frac{x^2}{2!} + f'''(0)\frac{x^3}{3!} + \dots + f^{(n)}(0)\frac{x^n}{n!} + \dots \tag{4}$$

For computation these series are usually used with $(x - a)$ or h small, and the remainder has the order of magnitude of the first term neglected.

Let $f(x,y)$ be analytic at (a,b). Then in the notation of § 3.3,

$$f(x,y) = f(a,b) + (x-a)f_x(a,b) + (y-b)f_y(a,b) + \frac{1}{2!}[(x-a)^2 f_{xx}(a,b) + 2(x-a)(y-b)f_{xy}(a,b) + (y-b)^2 f_{yy}(a,b)] + \dots + \frac{1}{n!}\left[(x-a)\frac{\partial}{\partial X} + (y-b)\frac{\partial}{\partial Y}\right]^n f(X,Y)\Bigg|_{\substack{X=a\\Y=b}} + \dots \tag{5}$$

An alternative form is

$$f(a+h,\ y+k) = f(a,b) + hf_x(a,b) + kf_y(a,b) + \dots + \frac{1}{n!}\left(h\frac{\partial}{\partial x} + k\frac{\partial}{\partial y}\right)^n f(x,y)\Big|_{\substack{x=a\\ y=b}} + \dots \qquad (6)$$

The special case when $a = 0$, $b = 0$, Maclaurin's series is

$$f(x,y) = f(0,0) + xf_x(0,0) + yf_y(0,0) + \dots + \frac{1}{n!}\left(h\frac{\partial}{\partial x} + k\frac{\partial}{\partial y}\right)^n f(x,y)\Big|_{\substack{x=0\\ y=0}} + \dots \qquad (7)$$

And similar expansions hold for any number of variables.

3.26. Differentiation of integrals

$$\frac{d}{dx}\int_a^x f(x)dx = \frac{d}{dx}\int_a^x f(t)dt = f(x), \qquad \frac{d}{dx}\int_x^b f(t)dt = -f(x) \qquad (1)$$

$$\frac{d}{dx}\int_a^b f(x,t)dt = \int_a^b \frac{\partial}{\partial x} f(x,t)dt \qquad (2)$$

$$\frac{d}{dx}\int_a^x f(x,t)dt = f(x,x) + \int_a^x \frac{\partial}{\partial x} f(x,t)dt \qquad (3)$$

If $f(x,x)$ is infinite or otherwise singular one may use

$$\frac{d}{dx}\int_a^x f(x,t)dt = \frac{1}{x-a}\int_a^x \left[(x-a)\frac{\partial f}{\partial x} + (t-a)\frac{\partial f}{\partial t} + f\right] dt \qquad (4)$$

$$\frac{d}{dx}\int_{u(x)}^{v(x)} f(x,t)dt = v'(x)f[x,v(x)] - u'(x)f[x,u(x)] + \int_{u(x)}^{v(x)} \frac{\partial}{\partial x} f(x,t)dt \qquad (5)$$

4. Integral Calculus

4.1. Indefinite integral. With respect to x, the indefinite integral of $f(x)$ is $F(x)$ provided that $dF/dx = F'(x) = f(x)$. The indefinite integral of the differential $f(x)dx$ is $F(x)$ if $dF(x) = f(x)dx$.

$$\int f(x)dx = F(x) \quad \text{if} \quad F'(x) = f(x) \quad \text{or} \quad dF(x) = f(x)dx \qquad (1)$$

For any constant C, $F(x) + C$ is also a possible indefinite integral. By using all values of C, and any one $F(x)$, we obtain all possible indefinite integrals :

$$\int f(x)dx = F(x) + C.$$

4.2. Indefinite integrals of functions

$$\int dF(x) = F(x) + C, \quad d\int f(x)dx = f(x)dx \tag{1}$$

Linearity:

$$\int (au + bv)dx = a\int u\, dx + b\int v\, dx \quad (a \text{ and } b \text{ not both zero}) \tag{2}$$

Integration by parts:

$$\int u\, dv = uv - \int v\, du \tag{3}$$

$$\int u \frac{dv}{dx} dx = uv - \int v \frac{du}{dx} dx \tag{4}$$

Substitution:

$$\int f(y)\, dx = \int f(y) \frac{dx}{dy} dy = \int \frac{f(y)}{dy/dx} dy \tag{5}$$

4.3. Polynomials

$$\int 0 \cdot dx = C, \quad \int a\, dx = ax + C, \quad \int bx^n\, dx = \frac{1}{n+1} bx^{n+1} \tag{1}$$

$$\left. \begin{aligned} &\int (a_n x^n + \dots + a_r x^r + \dots + a_1 x + a_0)dx \\ &\quad = \frac{1}{n+1} a_n x^{n+1} + \dots + \frac{1}{r+1} a_r x^{r+1} + \dots \frac{1}{2} a_1 x^2 + a_0 x + C \end{aligned} \right\} \tag{2}$$

4.4. Simple rational fractions

$$\int \frac{A}{x-r} dx = A \ln |x - r| + C, \quad \int \frac{A}{(x-r)^k} dx = A \frac{(x-r)^{1-k}}{1-k} + C \tag{1}$$

$$\left. \begin{aligned} \int \frac{2A(x-a) - 2Bb}{(x-a)^2 + b^2} dx &= 2 \operatorname{Re} \int \frac{A + Bi}{x - a - bi} dx \\ &= A \ln [(x-a)^2 + b^2] - 2B \tan^{-1} \frac{x-b}{b} + C \end{aligned} \right\} \tag{2}$$

$$\int \frac{dx}{x^2 + a^2} = \frac{1}{a} \tan^{-1} \frac{x}{a} + C, \quad \int \frac{dx}{x^2 - a^2} = \frac{1}{2a} \ln \left| \frac{x-a}{x+a} \right| + C \tag{3}$$

$$\frac{dx}{x} = \ln |x| + C \tag{4}$$

4.5. Rational functions. To integrate $R(x)dx$ where $R(x)$ is a rational function of x, first write $R(x)$ as the quotient of two polynomials $P_1(x)/D(x)$.

If the degree of $P_1(x)$ is the same or greater than the degree of $D(x)$, by division find polynomials $Q(x)$ and $P(x)$ such that

$$\int R(x)dx = \int \frac{P_1(x)}{D(x)}\,dx = \int Q(x)dx + \int \frac{P(x)}{D(x)}\,dx \tag{1}$$

where $P(x)/D(x)$ is a proper fraction, that is, has the degree of $P(x)$ less than the degree of $D(x)$. Integrate $Q(x)dx$ as in § 4.3.

To integrate the proper fraction $P(x)/D(x)$, decompose it into partial fractions as follows. Suppose first that the roots of $D(x) = 0$ are all distinct. Les $D(x)$ be of the nth degree and call the roots $r_1, r_2, \ldots, r_n$. Then

$$\frac{P(x)}{D(x)} = \frac{A_1}{x - r_1} + \frac{A_2}{x - r_2} + \ldots + \frac{A_n}{x - r_n} \quad \text{with} \quad A_k = \frac{P(r_k)}{D'(r_k)} \tag{2}$$

Assume that $P(x)$ and $D(x)$ have real coefficients. Then either r and A are real and we use the first equation of § 4.4, or complex roots occur in conjugate pairs, $a + bi$, $a - bi$, with conjugate numerators $A + Bi$, $A - Bi$, and we use the third equation (2) of § 4.4.

If the equation $D(x) = 0$ has multiple roots, each factor $(x - r)^m$ in $D(x)$ will lead to a series of fractions

$$\frac{P(x)}{D(x)} = \frac{P(x)}{(x - r)^m D_1(x)} = \frac{A'}{(x - r)} + \frac{A''}{(x - r)^2} + \ldots + \frac{A^{(m)}}{(x - r)^m} + \ldots \tag{3}$$

To determine the m constants, solve the system of equations

$$P(r) = A^{(m)} D_1(r), \quad P'(r) = A^{(m)} D_1{\cdot}(r) + A^{(m-1)} \tag{4}$$

$$P''(r) = A^{(m)} D_1''(r) + 2A^{(m-1)} D_1'(r) + 2{\cdot}1 A^{(m-2)} D_1(r), \quad \ldots \tag{5}$$

$$\left.\begin{aligned} P^{(m-1)}(r) = A^{(m)} D_1{}^{(m-1)}(r) &+ (m - 1) A^{(m-1)} D_1'(r) \\ &+ (m - 1)(m - 2) A^{(m-2)} D_1''(r) \\ &+ \ldots + (m - 1)!\, A' D_1{}^{(m-1)}(r) \end{aligned}\right\} \tag{6}$$

To integrate the simple fractions, use the first and second equations (1) of § 4.4. Conjugate complex roots will lead to conjugate fractions which may be combined in pairs to give a real result after integration.

4.6. Trigonometric functions

$$\int \sin ax\,dx = -\frac{1}{a}\cos ax + C, \quad \int \sin^2 ax\,dx = \frac{x}{2} - \frac{\sin 2ax}{4a} + C \tag{1}$$

$$\int \cos ax\,dx = \frac{1}{a}\sin ax + C, \quad \int \cos^2 ax\,dx = \frac{x}{2} + \frac{\sin 2ax}{4a} + C \tag{2}$$

$$\left.\begin{aligned}\int \frac{dx}{\sin ax} = \int \csc ax\, dx &= \frac{1}{a} \ln \left| \tan \frac{ax}{2} \right| + C \\ &= \frac{1}{a} \ln | \csc ax - \cot ax | + C\end{aligned}\right\} \quad (3)$$

$$\left.\begin{aligned}\int \frac{dx}{\cos ax} = \int \sec ax\, dx &= \frac{1}{a} \ln \left| \tan \left(\frac{ax}{2} + \frac{\pi}{4} \right) \right| + C \\ &= \frac{1}{a} \ln | \sec ax + \tan ax | + C\end{aligned}\right\} \quad (4)$$

$$\left.\begin{aligned}&\int \frac{dx}{\sin^2 ax} = \int \csc^2 ax\, dx = -\frac{1}{a} \cot ax + C \\ &\int \tan ax\, dx = -\frac{1}{a} \ln | \cos ax | + C\end{aligned}\right\} \quad (5)$$

$$\left.\begin{aligned}&\int \frac{dx}{\cos^2 ax} = \int \sec^2 ax\, dx = \frac{1}{a} \tan ax + C \\ &\int \cot ax\, dx = \frac{1}{a} \ln | \sin ax | + C\end{aligned}\right\} \quad (6)$$

4.7. Exponential and hyperbolic functions

$$\int e^{ax}\, dx = \frac{1}{a} e^{ax} + C, \quad \int b^{ax}\, dx = \frac{1}{a \ln b} b^{ax} + C \quad (1)$$

$$\int \sinh ax\, dx = \frac{1}{a} \cosh ax + C, \quad \int \cosh ax\, dx = \frac{1}{a} \sinh ax + C \quad (2)$$

4.8. Radicals

$$\int \frac{dx}{\sqrt{a^2 - x^2}} = \sin^{-1} \left(\frac{x}{a} \right) + C = -\cos^{-1} \left(\frac{x}{a} \right) + C_1 \quad (1)$$

$$\int \frac{dx}{\sqrt{x^2 + A}} = \ln | x + \sqrt{x^2 + A} |^* + C \quad (2)$$

$$\int \sqrt{a^2 - x^2}\, dx = \frac{x}{2} \sqrt{a^2 - x^2} + \frac{a^2}{2} \sin^{-1} \frac{x}{a} + C \quad (3)$$

$$\int \sqrt{x^2 + A}\, dx = \frac{x}{2} \sqrt{x^2 + A} + \frac{A}{2} \ln | x + \sqrt{x^2 + A} |^* + C \quad (4)$$

* For A positive, $A = a^2$, $\ln (x + \sqrt{x^2 + a^2}) = \sinh^{-1} x/a + \ln a$ (5)
For A negative, $A = -a^2$, $\ln (x + \sqrt{x^2 - a^2}) = \cosh^{-1} x/a + \ln a$ (6)
In each case $\ln a$ or $(A/2) \ln a$ may be combined with the constant C.

4.9. Products

$$\int e^{ax} \sin bx \, dx = \frac{1}{a^2 + b^2} e^{ax}(a \sin bx - b \cos bx) + C \tag{1}$$

$$\int e^{ax} \cos bx \, dx = \frac{1}{a^2 + b^2} e^{ax}(a \cos bx + b \sin bx) + C \tag{2}$$

$$\int xe^{ax} \, dx = \frac{1}{a^2} e^{ax}(ax - 1) + C, \quad \int \ln ax \, dx = x \ln ax - x + C \tag{3}$$

We may use § 2.15 to express factors like $\sin ax$, $\cos bx$ in terms of complex exponentials. And we may use § 2.12 to express factors like $\sinh ax$, $\cosh bx$ in terms of exponentials. Thus any product of such factors, or product times e^{kx}, may be reduced to a sum of exponential terms like that in the first equation of § 4.7. If powers of x are also present we are led to

$$\int x^n e^{ax} \, dx = \frac{1}{a} x^n e^{ax} - \frac{n}{a} \int x^{n-1} e^{ax} \, dx \tag{4}$$

This reduction formula may be used repeatedly until the power of x disappears when n is a positive integer.

Let $f(x)$ be the natural logarithm, an inverse trigonometric function, or an inverse hyperbolic function of some simple function of x, for example, $\ln (ax + b)$, $\sin^{-1} x$, $\tanh^{-1} x^2$. Then for $n = 0, 1, 2, \ldots$ the equation

$$\int x^n f(x) dx = \frac{1}{n + 1} x^{n+1} f(x) - \frac{1}{n + 1} \int x^{n+1} f'(x) dx \tag{5}$$

often leads to a simpler integral.

4.10. Trigonometric or exponential integrands. Any rational function of trigonometric functions of x may be written in the form $R(\sin x, \cos x)$, and the substitution $t = \tan x/2$ makes

$$R(\sin x, \cos x)dx = R\left(\frac{2t}{1 + t^2}, \frac{1 - t^2}{1 + t^2}\right) \frac{2dt}{1 + t^2} \tag{1}$$

The new integrand is a rational function of t, discussed in § 4.5. If the integrand is a rational function of e^{ax}, let $t = e^{ax}$ and

$$R(e^{ax})dx = R(t) \frac{1}{at} dt \tag{2}$$

This may be applied to $R(\sin x, \cos x)$ with $a = i$, if § 2.15 is used.

4.11. Algebraic integrands. Let p and q be integers and $a \neq 0$; then the substitution $t = (ax + b)^{1/q}$ makes

$$R[x, (ax + b)^{p/q}]dx = R\left(\frac{t^q - b}{a}, t^p\right) \frac{q}{a} t^{q-1}\, dt \tag{1}$$

The new integrand is a rational function of t, discussed in § 4.5.

For certain integrands of the form $R(x, \sqrt{px^2 + qx + r})$ the following transformations are useful.

$y = \dfrac{1}{x}$ makes

$$\frac{dx}{x\sqrt{px^2 + qx + r}} = -\frac{dy}{\sqrt{ry^2 + qy + p}} \tag{2}$$

$y = \dfrac{1}{x - s}$ makes

$$\frac{dx}{(x - s)\sqrt{px^2 + qx + r}} = -\frac{dy}{\sqrt{(ps^2 + qs + r)y^2 + (2ps + q)y + p}} \tag{3}$$

$y = x + \dfrac{q}{2p}$ makes

$$R(x, \sqrt{px^2 + qx + r})dx = R\left(y - \frac{q}{2p}, \sqrt{py^2 + \frac{4pr - q^2}{4p}}\right)dy \tag{4}$$

Simple integrals of this type are given in § 4.8. Also note that

$$R(x, \sqrt{a^2 - x^2})\, dx = R(a \sin t, a \cos t)a \cos t\, dt \quad \text{if} \quad x = a \sin t \tag{5}$$

$$R(x, \sqrt{x^2 - a^2})\, dx = R(a \sec t, a \tan t)a \tan t \sec t\, dt \quad \text{if} \quad x = a \sec t \tag{6}$$

$$R(x, \sqrt{x^2 + a^2})\, dx = R(a \tan t, a \sec t)a \sec^2 t\, dt \quad \text{if} \quad x = a \tan t \tag{7}$$

The new integrands in t are essentially those treated in § 4.10.

4.12. Definite integral. Let $x_1, x_2, \ldots x_{n-1}$ be points of subdivision of the interval a,b such that $x_k < x_{k+1}$, with $a = x_0$, $b = x_n$. Let $\delta_k = x_k - x_{k-1}$, and d_M be the maximum value of δ_k. Then

$$\int_a^b f(x)dx = \lim_{d_M \to 0} [f(\xi_1)\delta_1 + f(\xi_2)\delta_2 + \ldots + f(\xi_n)\delta_n] \tag{1}$$

For each choice of n, and the x_k, the ξ_k are any values such that $x_{k-1} \leqq \xi_k \leqq x_k$. The limit exists for $f(x)$ regular on a, b:

$$\int_a^b f(x)dx = \left[\int f(x)dx\right]_a^b = F(x)\Big|_a^b = F(b) - F(a) \tag{2}$$

where $F(x)$ is any function whose derivative with respect to x is $f(x)$, as in § 4.1.

4.13. Approximation rules. Let the interval a,b be divided into n equal parts each of length h so that $b - a = nh$. And let $f(a + kh) = y_k$; $k = 0, 1, 2, \ldots, n$. Then the *trapezoidal rule* is

$$\int_a^b f(x)dx = \frac{h}{2}(y_1 + 2y_2 + 2y_3 + \ldots + 2y_{n-1} + y_n) - R_n \tag{1}$$

where

$$R_n = \tfrac{1}{12}(b - a)h^2 f''(x_1) \tag{2}$$

for some suitable x_1 in a,b.

The more accurate *Simpson's rule* requires that n be even, and is

$$\left.\begin{aligned}\int_a^b f(x)dx = \frac{h}{3}(y_1 + 4y_2 + 2y_3 + 4y_4 \\ + \ldots + 2y_{n-2} + 4y_{n-1} + y_n) - R_n\end{aligned}\right\} \tag{3}$$

where

$$R_n = \tfrac{1}{90}(b - a)h^4 f^{\text{IV}}(x_2) \tag{4}$$

for some suitable x_2 in a,b.

In Gauss' Method we let $x = \frac{1}{2}(a + b) + \frac{1}{2}(b - a)w$. Then

$$\int_a^b f(x)dx = \frac{b-a}{2}\int_{-1}^1 g(w)dw = \sum_{m=1}^n R_m g(w_m) \tag{5}$$

The w_m are the n roots of

$$P_n(x) = 0 \tag{6}$$

(see § 8.2), and for $r = 0, 1, 2, \ldots n - 1$.

$$\sum_{m=1}^n R_m \left(\frac{1 + w_m}{2}\right)^r = \frac{1}{r + 1} \tag{7}$$

In particular,

$n = 2:\quad w_1 = -w_2 = 0.57735, \quad R_1 = R_2 = \frac{1}{2}, \quad E(x^4) = \frac{4}{45}$

$n = 3:\quad w_1 = -w_3 = 0.77460, \quad w_2 = 0,$
$R_1 = R_3 = \frac{5}{18}, \quad R_2 = \frac{4}{9}, \quad E(x^6) = \frac{4}{175}$

$n = 4:\quad w_1 = -w_4 = 0.86114, \quad w_2 = -w_3 = 0.33998,$
$R_1 = R_4 = 0.17393, \quad R_2 = R_3 = 0.32607, \quad E(x^8) = \frac{64}{11{,}025}$

The formula is exact if $f(x)$ is a polynomial of degree not exceeding $2n - 1$. The error for a higher degree polynomial may be estimated from the given value of

$$E(x^{2n}) = \frac{1}{2}\int_{-1}^1 w^{2n}\,dw - \sum_{m=1}^n R_m w_m^{\ 2n}$$

4.14. Linearity properties. *Linearity* in the *integrand:*

$$\int_a^b [Af(x) + Bg(x)]dx = A \int_a^b f(x)dx + B \int_a^b g(x)dx \tag{1}$$

Linearity with respect to the *interval:*

$$\int_a^b f(x)dx = - \int_b^a f(x)dx$$

$$\int_a^b f(x)dx = \int_a^c f(x)dx + \int_c^b f(x)dx \tag{2}$$

4.15. Mean values. The mean value of $f(x)$ on the interval a,b is

$$\bar{f} = \frac{1}{b-a} \int_a^b f(x)dx \tag{1}$$

If $f(x)$ is *continuous* on a,b then for some x_1 on a,b the mean value

$$\bar{f} = f(x_1) \quad \text{or} \quad \int_a^b f(x)dx = (b-a)f(x_1) \quad \textit{mean value theorem} \tag{2}$$

The root-mean-square value of $f(x)$ on the interval a,b is

$$\bar{\bar{f}} = \sqrt{\frac{1}{b-a} \int_a^b [f(x)]^2 dx} \tag{3}$$

4.16. Inequalities. Assume that $a < b$. If $f(x) < g(x)$ in a,b, then

$$\int_a^b f(x)dx < \int_a^b g(x)dx \tag{1}$$

If $m < f(x) < M$ in a,b then

$$m(b-a) < \int_a^b f(x)dx < M(b-a) \tag{2}$$

If $|f(x)| \leqq M$ in a,b (or on the complex path of integration C of length L), then

$$\left| \int_a^b f(x)dx \right| \leqq M(b-a) \quad \text{or} \quad \left| \int_C f(z)dz \right| \leqq ML$$

Schwarz's inequality:

$$\left[\int_a^b f(x)g(x)dx \right]^2 \leqq \int_a^b [f(x)]^2 dx \int_a^b [g(x)]^2 dx$$

With the notation of §4.15, and

$$p = fg, \quad \bar{p} \leqq \bar{\bar{f}}\bar{\bar{g}}, \quad \text{and} \quad \bar{f} \leqq \bar{\bar{f}}$$

4.17. Improper integrals

$$\left.\begin{aligned}\int_a^\infty f(x)dx &= \lim_{t\to\infty}\int_a^t f(x)dx\\ \int_{-\infty}^b f(x)dx &= \lim_{t\to\infty}\int_{-t}^b f(x)dx\end{aligned}\right\} \qquad (1)$$

$$\int_{-\infty}^\infty f(x)dx = \int_{-\infty}^c f(x)dx + \int_c^\infty f(x)dx \qquad (2)$$

If $f(x)$ becomes infinite or has a singularity at $x = b$ with $b \neq a$,

$$\int_a^b f(x)dx = \lim_{h\to 0}\int_a^{b-h} f(x)dx \qquad (3)$$

4.18. Definite integrals of functions. Let $u(x)$ and $v(x)$ be continuous in a,b. Then

$$\int_a^b du(x) = u(b) - u(a) \qquad (1)$$

$$\int_a^b u(x)v'(x)dx = u(x)v(x)\Big|_a^b - \int_a^b v(x)u'(x)dx \qquad (2)$$

Let $t = g(u)$, $a = g(c)$, $b = g(d)$, and $g'(u)$ maintain its sign in c,d. Then

$$\int_a^b f(t)dt = \int_c^d f[g(u)]g'(u)du \qquad (3)$$

4.19. Plane area

$$A = \iint dx\,dy = \int_{x_1}^{x_2} dx\int_{y_1(x)}^{y_2(x)} dy = \int_{x_1}^{x_2}(y_2 - y_1)dx \qquad (1)$$

$$A = \iint r\,dr\,d\theta = \int_{\theta_1}^{\theta_2} d\theta\int_{r_1(\theta)}^{r_2(\theta)} r\,dr = \frac{1}{2}\int_{\theta_1}^{\theta_2}(r_2^2 - r_1^2)d\theta \qquad (2)$$

4.20. Length of arc. See § 3.20. For a plane curve,

$$s = \int_{x_1}^{x_2}\sqrt{1 + y'^2}\,dx = \int_{t_1}^{t_2}\sqrt{\dot{x}^2 + \dot{y}^2}\,dt \qquad (1)$$

$$s = \int_{\theta_1}^{\theta_2}\sqrt{r'^2 + r^2}\,d\theta = \int_{t_1}^{t_2}\sqrt{\dot{r}^2 + r^2\dot{\theta}^2}\,dt \qquad (2)$$

4.21. Volumes. With suitable limits on the iterated and triple integrals,

$$V = \int_{x_1}^{x_2} A(x)dx = \int dx\int[z_2(x,y) - z_1(x,y)]dy = \int d\theta\int(z_2 - z_1)\,r\,dr \qquad (1)$$

$$V = \iiint dx\,dy\,dz = \iiint r\,dr\,d\theta\,dz = \iiint r^2\sin\phi\,d\theta\,d\phi\,dr \qquad (2)$$

4.22. Curves and surfaces in space

$$s = \int_{t_1}^{t_2} \sqrt{\dot{x}^2 + \dot{y}^2 + \dot{z}^2}\, dt \tag{1}$$

where $x = x(t)$, $y = y(t)$, $z = z(t)$.

$$A = \iint \sqrt{f_x{}^2 + f_y{}^2 + 1}\, dx\, dy \tag{2}$$

where $z = f(x,y)$.

4.23. Change of variables in multiple integrals. If

$$F[x(u,v), y(u,v)] = G(u,v) \tag{1}$$

and the limits are suitably related, then

$$\iint F(x,y) dx\, dy = \iint G(u,v) \frac{\partial(x,y)}{\partial(u,v)} du\, dv \tag{2}$$

Similarly if

$$F[x(u,v,w), y(u,v,w), z(u,v,w)] = G(u,v,w) \tag{3}$$

then

$$\iiint F(x,y,z) dx\, dy\, dz = \iiint G(u,v,w) \frac{\partial(x,y,z)}{\partial(u,v,w)} du\, dv\, dw \tag{4}$$

The Jacobians inserted here are

$$\frac{\partial(x,y)}{\partial(u,v)} = \begin{vmatrix} x_u & y_u \\ x_v & y_v \end{vmatrix} = x_u y_v - x_v y_u, \quad \frac{\partial(x,y,z)}{\partial(u,v,w)} = \begin{vmatrix} x_u & y_u & z_u \\ x_v & y_v & z_v \\ x_w & y_w & z_w \end{vmatrix} \tag{5}$$

If the Jacobian determinant is not zero, the transformation $x = x(u,v)$, $y = y(u,v)$ has an inverse transformation. When there is a functional relation

$$F[x(u,v), y(u,v)] = 0 \tag{6}$$

the Jacobian $\partial(x,y)/\partial(u,v)$ is identically zero. Also

$$\frac{\partial(x,y)}{\partial(X,Y)} \frac{\partial(X,Y)}{\partial(u,v)} = \frac{\partial(x,y)}{\partial(u,v)}, \quad \frac{\partial(x,y)}{\partial(u,v)} = \frac{1}{\partial(u,v)/\partial(x,y)} \tag{7}$$

Similar results hold for any number of variables.

4.24. Mass and density. Let ρ be the variable (or constant) density of a curve, area, or volume. Then the total mass is given by

$$M = \int dm$$

where $dm = \rho\, ds$, $dm = \rho\, dA$, or $dm = \rho\, dV$. For the differentials ds, dA, dV, use the integrands from §§ 4.19-4.22. Mean density is

$$\bar{\rho} = \frac{\int \rho\, ds}{\int ds}, \quad \bar{\rho} = \frac{\int \rho\, dA}{\int dA}, \quad \bar{\rho} = \frac{\int \rho\, dV}{\int dV}$$

4.25. Moment and center of gravity. Let x, y, z be the coordinates of the center of gravity of one of the elements of mass dm of § 4.24. Then the moments about the coordinate planes are

$$M_{yz} = \int x\, dm, \quad M_{zx} = \int y\, dm, \quad M_{xy} = \int z\, dm \tag{1}$$

And the center of gravity of M is $\bar{x}$, $\bar{y}$, $\bar{z}$ where

$$\bar{x} = \frac{\int x\, dm}{\int dm}, \quad \bar{y} = \frac{\int y\, dm}{\int dm}, \quad \bar{z} = \frac{\int z\, dm}{\int dm} \tag{2}$$

For a mass M composed of several, e.g., three, parts M_1, M_2, M_3, the masses and moments are additive so that

$$\bar{x} = \frac{M_{yz}}{M} = \frac{\bar{x}_1 M_1 + \bar{x}_2 M_2 + \bar{x}_3 M_3}{M_1 + M_2 + M_3} \tag{3}$$

and similarly for $\bar{y}$ and $\bar{z}$.

4.26. Moment of inertia and radius of gyration. Let x, y, z represent root-mean-square values of coordinates for any one of the elements of mass dm of § 4.24. Then the second moments about the coordinate planes are

$$I_{yz} = \int x^2\, dm, \quad I_{zx} = \int y^2\, dm, \quad I_{xy} = \int z^2\, dm \tag{1}$$

The moments of inertia about the coordinate axes are

$$I_x = I_{zx} + I_{xy} = \int (y^2 + z^2) dm \tag{2}$$

and similarly for I_y and I_z. For a figure in the xy plane, $z = 0$, $I_{xy} = 0$, and if $I_z = I_0$,

$$I_0 = I_x + I_y = \int (x^2 + y^2) dm = \int r^2\, dm \tag{3}$$

For any moment of inertia, as I_x, the corresponding radius of gyration k is defined by

$$Mk^2 = I_x \quad \text{or} \quad k = \sqrt{I_x/M} \tag{4}$$

For a mass M composed of several, e.g., three, parts M_1, M_2, M_3, the masses and moments of inertia are additive, so that

$$k = \sqrt{\frac{k_1{}^2 M_1 + k_2{}^2 M_2 + k_3{}^2 M_3}{k_1{}^2 + k_2{}^2 + k_3{}^2}} \tag{5}$$

If I is the moment of inertia of M about any axis, and I_g is the moment of inertia of M about a parallel axis through the center of gravity, and the distance between the parallel axes is d, then

$$I = I_g + Md^2 \tag{6}$$

5. Differential Equations

5.1. Classification. Any equation that involves differentials or derivatives is a *differential equation.* If the equation contains any partial derivatives, it is a *partial differential equation.* If it does not, it is an *ordinary differential equation.*

The *order* of the differential equation is the same as the order of the derivative of highest order in the equation.

Suppose that a differential equation is reducible to a form in which each member is a polynomial in all the derivatives that occur. Then the *degree* of the equation is the largest exponent of the highest derivative in the reduced form.

A differential equation is *linear* if it is a first-degree algebraic equation in the set of variables made up of the dependent variables together with all of their derivatives.

5.2. Solutions. Consider a single ordinary differential equation with dependent variable y and independent variable x. Then $y = f(x)$ is an explicit solution of the differential equation if this equation is identically satisfied in x when we substitute $f(x)$, $f'(x)$, etc. for y, dy/dx, etc. therein. Any implicit relation $F(x,y) = 0$ is a solution if when solved for y it leads to explicit solutions. Every ordinary differential equation of the nth order admits of a *general solution* containing n independent constants.

5.3. First-order and first degree. Consider an ordinary differential equation of the first order and first degree. Any such equation may be written in one of the forms

$$M\,dx + N\,dy = 0, \quad M + N\frac{dy}{dx} = 0, \quad \text{or} \quad \frac{dy}{dx} = -\frac{M}{N} \tag{1}$$

where $M(x,y)$ and $N(x,y)$ are functions of x and y. We indicate how to recognize and solve certain special types in §§ 5.4-5.8.

5.4. Variables separable. Here the M and N in § 5.3 are products of factors, where each factor is either a function of x alone, or a function of y

alone. Divide the equation by the factor of M containing y and by the factor of N containing x. Then the differential equation is

$$f(x)dx = g(y)dy \tag{1}$$

in which the variables are *separated*. The solution is

$$\int f(x)dx = \int g(y)dy + c \quad \text{or} \quad \int_{x_0}^{x} f(x)dx = \int_{y_0}^{y} g(y)dy \tag{2}$$

if $y = y_0$ when $x = x_0$.

5.5. Linear in *y*. Here N in § 5.3 is a function of x alone, and M is a first-degree polynomial in y. Thus the equation is

$$A(x)\frac{dy}{dx} + B(x)y = C(x) \quad \text{or} \quad \frac{dy}{dx} + P(x)y = Q(x) \tag{1}$$

after division by $A(x)$ and with a new notation. Calculate

$$\int P(x)dx \quad \text{and} \quad I(x) = e^{\int P dx} \tag{2}$$

with any constant in the integral. The solution of the equation is

$$y = \frac{1}{I(x)}\left[\int I(x)Q(x)dx + c\right] \tag{3}$$

If $y = y_0$ when $x = x_0$, the solution is found from

$$I(x)y - I(x_0)y_0 = \int_{x_0}^{x} I(x)Q(x)dx \tag{4}$$

5.6. Reducible to linear. To solve the Bernoulli equation

$$A(x)\frac{dy}{dx} + B(x)y = C(x)y^n, \quad n \neq 1 \quad \text{or} \quad 0 \tag{1}$$

multiply by $(1 - n)y^{-n}/A(x)$ and make the substitution

$$u = y^{1-n}, \quad \frac{du}{dx} = (1 - n)y^{-n}\frac{dy}{dx} \tag{2}$$

The resulting equation is like that of § 5.5, with u in place of y.

If M in § 5.3 is a function of y alone, and M is a first-degree polynomial in x, the differential equation is

$$A(y)\frac{dx}{dy} + B(y)x = C(y) \tag{3}$$

and may be solved as in § 5.5 with the roles of x and y interchanged.

Whenever we observe new variables $u(x,y)$ and $t(x,y)$ which reduce a given differential equation to the form

$$A(t)\frac{du}{dt} + B(t)u = C(t) \tag{4}$$

we may solve as in § 5.5 with t and u in the roles of x and y.

5.7. Homogeneous. Here the M and N in § 5.3 are each homogeneous of the same degree, that is of the same dimension when x and y are each assigned the dimension one. In this case use

$$y = vx, \quad dy = v\,dx + x\,dv \tag{1}$$

to eliminate y and dy. The new equation in x and v will be separable as in § 5.4. If more convenient, let $x = uy$.

5.8. Exact equations. The equation of § 5.3 will be exact if

$$\partial M/\partial y = \partial N/\partial x$$

Integrate $M\,dx$, regarding y as constant and adding an unknown function of y, say $f(y)$. Differentiate the result with respect to y and equate the new result to N. From the resulting equation determine the unknown function of y. The solution is then

$$\int M\,dx + f(y) + c = 0 \tag{1}$$

If more convenient, interchange M and N and also x and y in the above process.

5.9. First order and higher degree. The general differential equation of the first order is

$$F\left(x,y,\frac{dy}{dx}\right) = 0, \quad \text{or} \quad F(x,y,p) = 0 \tag{1}$$

if we write a single letter p in place of dy/dx. For special solvable types see §§ 5.10-5.11.

5.10. Equations solvable for p. Some equations § 5.9 may be easily solved for p. The resulting first-degree equations may often be integrated by the methods of §§ 5.3-5.8.

5.11. Clairaut's form. Clairaut's equation is

$$y = x\frac{dy}{dx} + f\left(\frac{dy}{dx}\right) \quad \text{or} \quad y = px + f(p) \tag{1}$$

where f is any function of one variable. The general solution is

$$y = cx + f(c) \tag{2}$$

This represents a family of straight lines. They usually have an envelope given in terms of the parameter c by

$$x = -f'(c), \quad y = f(c) - cf'(c) \tag{3}$$

These are the parametric equations of the *singular solution.*

5.12. Second order. The general differential equation of the second order is

$$F\left(x, y, \frac{dy}{dx}, \frac{d^2y}{dx^2}\right) = 0 \tag{4}$$

If either of the letters x or y is absent from the function F, the substitution $dy/dx = p$ reduces the equation to one of the first order. If the letter y is missing, we put

$$\frac{dy}{dx} = p, \quad \frac{d^2y}{dx^2} = \frac{dp}{dx} \tag{5}$$

and

$$F\left(x, \frac{dy}{dx}, \frac{d^2y}{dx^2}\right) = 0 \quad \text{becomes} \quad F\left(x, p, \frac{dp}{dx}\right) = 0 \tag{6}$$

The solution of this first-order equation in the variables x and p may be found as in § 5.3 or § 5.9. Suppose it is written in the form $p = G(x,c_1)$; then

$$y = \int G(x,c_1)dx + c_2 \tag{7}$$

is the general solution of the second-order equation with y missing.

If the letter x is missing, we put

$$\frac{dy}{dx} = p, \quad \frac{d^2y}{dx^2} = p\frac{dp}{dy} \tag{8}$$

and

$$f\left(y, \frac{dy}{dx}, \frac{d^2y}{dx^2}\right) = 0 \quad \text{becomes} \quad F\left(y, p, p\frac{dp}{dy}\right) = 0 \tag{9}$$

The solution of this first-order equation in the variables y and p may be found as in § 5.3 and § 5.9. Suppose it is written in the form $p = G(y,c_1)$; then

$$x = \int \frac{dy}{G(y,c_1)} + c_2 \tag{10}$$

is the general solution of the second-order equation with x missing.

5.13. Linear equations. The general linear differential equation of the second order is

$$A(x)\frac{d^2y}{dx^2} + B(x)\frac{dy}{dx} + C(x)y = E(x), \quad \text{with} \quad A(x) \neq 0 \tag{1}$$

We get the corresponding homogeneous equation by replacing $E(x)$ by zero. Two solutions u_1, u_2 of the homogeneous equation are linearly independent and constitute a fundamental system if their Wronskian determinant $W(x)$ is not zero, where

$$W(x) = u_1u_2' - u_2u_1' = \begin{vmatrix} u_1 & u_2 \\ u_1' & u_2' \end{vmatrix} \tag{2}$$

When $W(x) \neq 0$, u_1 and u_2 constitute a *fundamental system* of solutions of the homogeneous equation. And if u is any particular solution of the nonhomogeneous equation with $E(x)$ present, the general solution of this equation is given by

$$y = u + c_1u_1 + c_2u_2 \tag{3}$$

In this form c_1 and c_2 are arbitrary constants, u is called the *particular integral*, and $c_1u_1 + c_2u_2$ is the *complementary function.*

Similarly for the linear equation of the nth order

$$A_n(x)\frac{d^ny}{dx^n} + A_{n-1}(x)\frac{d^{n-1}y}{dx^{n-1}} + \ldots + A_1(x)\frac{dy}{dx} + A_0(x)y = E(x) \tag{4}$$

the general solution is

$$y = u + c_1u_1 + c_2u_2 + \ldots + c_nu_n \tag{5}$$

Here u, the particular integral, is any solution of the given equation, and $u_1, u_2, \ldots, u_n$ form a fundamental system of solutions of the homogeneous equation obtained by replacing $E(x)$ by zero, or a set of solutions of the homogeneous equation whose Wronskian determinant $W(x)$ is not zero, where

$$W(x) = \begin{vmatrix} u_1 & u_2 & \cdots & u_n \\ u_1' & u_2' & \cdots & u_n' \\ \cdots & \cdots & \cdots & \cdots \\ u_1^{(n-1)} & u_2^{(n-1)} & \cdots & u_n^{(n-1)} \end{vmatrix} \tag{6}$$

For any n functions u_j, $W(x) = 0$ if some one u is linearly dependent on the others, as $u_n = k_1u_1 + k_2u_2 + \ldots + k_{n-1}u_{n-1}$ with the coefficients k_i constant.

And for n solutions of a linear differential equation of the nth order, if $W(x)$ is not zero, the solutions are linearly independent.

5.14. Constant coefficients. To solve the homogeneous equation

$$A\frac{d^2y}{dx^2} + B\frac{dy}{dx} + Cy = 0 \tag{1}$$

where A, B, and C are constants, find the roots of the auxiliary equation $Ap^2 + Bp + C = 0$. If the roots are unequal quantities r and s, the solution is $y = c_1e^{rx} + c_2e^{sx}$.

When the coefficients A, B, C are real, and the roots are complex, they will occur as a conjugate pair $a + bi$ and $a - bi$. In this case the real form of the solution is $y = e^{ax}(c_1 \cos bx + c_2 \sin bx)$ or by § 2.8, $y = C_1e^{ax} \sin (bx + C_2)$.

If the roots are equal and are r,r the solution is $y = e^{rx}(c_1 + c_2x)$.

Similarly, to solve the homogeneous equation of the nth order

$$A_n\frac{d^ny}{dx^n} + A_{n-1}\frac{d^{n-1}y}{dx^{n-1}} + \ldots + A_1\frac{dy}{dx} + A_0 = 0$$

where A_n, A_{n-1}, ..., A_0 are constants, find the roots of the auxiliary equation

$$A_np^n + A_{n-1}p^{n-1} + \ldots + A_1p + A_0 = 0 \tag{2}$$

For each distinct root r there is a term ce^{rx} in the solution. The terms of the solution are to be added together.

When r occurs twice among the n roots of the auxiliary equation, the corresponding term is $e^{rx}(c_1 + c_2x)$.

When r occurs three times, the corresponding term is $e^{rx}(c_1 + c_2x + c_3x^2)$, and so forth.

When there is a pair of conjugate complex roots $a + bi$ and $a - bi$, the real form of the terms in the solution is $e^{ax}(c_1 \cos bx + c_2 \sin bx)$.

When the same pair occurs twice, the corresponding term is $e^{ax}[(c_1 + c_2x) \cos bx + (d_1 + d_2x) \sin bx]$, and so forth.

Consider next the general nonhomogeneous linear differential equation of order n, with constant coefficients, or

$$A_n\frac{d^ny}{dx^n} + A_{n-1}\frac{d^{n-1}y}{dx^{n-1}} + \ldots + A_1\frac{dy}{dx} + A_0 = E(x)$$

By § 5.13 we may solve this by adding any particular integral to the complementary function, or general solution of the homogeneous equation obtained by replacing $E(x)$ by zero. The complementary function may be found from the rules just given in this section. And the particular integral may then be found by the methods of §§ 5.15-5.16.

5.15. Undetermined coefficients. In the last equation of § 5.14 let the right member $E(x)$ be a sum of terms each of which is of the type

$$k, \quad k \cos bx, \quad k \sin bx, \quad ke^{ax}, \quad kx \tag{1}$$

or, more generally,

$$kx^m e^{ax}, \quad kx^m e^{ax} \cos bx, \quad \text{or} \quad kx^m e^{ax} \sin bx \tag{2}$$

Here m is zero or a positive integer, and a and b are any real numbers. Then the form of the particular integral I may be predicted by the following rules.

Case I. $E(x)$ is a single term T. Let D be written for d/dx, so that the given equation is $P(D)y = E(x)$, where

$$P(D) = A_n D^n + A_{n-1} D^{n-1} + \dots + A_1 D + A_0 \tag{3}$$

With the term T associate the simplest polynomial $Q(D)$ such that $Q(D)T = 0$. For the particular types k, etc., $Q(D)$ will be

$$D, \quad D^2 + b^2, \quad D^2 + b^2, \quad D - a, \quad D^2 \tag{4}$$

and for the general types $kx^m e^{ax}$, etc., $Q(D)$ will be

$$(D - a)^{m+1}, \quad (D^2 - 2aD + a^2 + b^2)^{m+1}, \quad (D^2 - 2aD + a^2 + b^2)^{m+1} \tag{5}$$

Thus $Q(D)$ will always be some power of a first- or second-degree factor,

$$Q(D) = F^q, \quad F = D - a, \quad \text{or} \quad F = D^2 - 2aD + a^2 + b^2 \tag{6}$$

Use § 5.14 to find the terms in the solution of $P(D)y = 0$, and also the terms in the solution of $Q(D)P(D)y = 0$. Then assume that the particular integral I is a linear combination with unknown coefficients of those terms in the solution of $Q(D)P(D)y = 0$ which are not in the solution of $P(D)y = 0$. Thus if $Q(D) = F^q$, and F is *not* a factor of $P(D)$, assume

$$I = (Ax^{q-1} + Bx^{q-2} + \dots + L)e^{ax} \tag{7}$$

when $F = D - a$, and

$$I = (Ax^{q-1} + Bx^{q-2} + \dots + L)e^{ax} \cos bx$$

$$+ (Mx^{q-1} + Nx^{q-2} + \dots + R)e^{ax} \sin bx$$

when

$$F = D^2 - 2aD + a^2 + b^2 \tag{8}$$

When F *is* a factor of $P(D)$ and the highest power of F which is a divisor of $P(D)$ is F^p, try the I above multiplied by x^p.

Case II. $E(x)$ is a sum of terms. With each term in $E(x)$ associate a polynomial $Q(D) = F^q$ as before. Arrange in one group all terms that have the same F. The particular integral of the given equation will be the sum of solutions of equations each of which has one group on the right. For any one such equation, the form of the particular integral is given as for Case I with q the highest power of F associated with any term of the group on the right.

After the form has been found, in Case I or Case II, the unknown coefficients follow when we substitute back in the given differential equation, equating coefficients of like terms, and solve the resulting system of simultaneous equations.

5.16. Variation of parameters. Whenever a fundamental system of solutions $u_1, u_2, \ldots, u_n$ for the homogeneous equation is known, a particular integral of

$$A_n(x)\frac{d^n y}{dx^n} + A_{n-1}(x)\frac{d^{n-1}y}{dx^{n-1}} + \ldots + A_1(x)\frac{dy}{dx} + A_0(x)y = E(x) \tag{1}$$

may be found in the form

$$y = \sum_{k=1}^{n} v_k u_k \tag{2}$$

Here the v_k are functions of x found by integrating their derivatives v_k', and these derivatives are the solutions of the following n simultaneous equations :

$$\left.\begin{aligned} &\sum_{k=1}^{n} v_k' u_k = 0, \quad \sum_{k=1}^{n} v_k' u_k' = 0, \quad \sum_{k=1}^{n} v_k' u_k'' = 0, \quad \ldots, \\ &\sum_{k=1}^{n} v_k' u_k^{(n-2)} = 0, \quad A_n(x)\sum_{k=1}^{n} v_k' u_k^{(n-1)} = E(x) \end{aligned}\right\} \tag{3}$$

To find the v_k from $v_k = \int v_k'\, dx + c_k$, any choice of the constants will lead to a particular integral. The special choice

$$v_k = \int_0^x v_k'\, dx$$

leads to the particular integral having $y, y', y'', \ldots, y^{(n-1)}$ each equal to zero when $x = 0$.

5.17. The Cauchy-Euler "homogeneous linear equation." This has the form

$$k_n x^n \frac{d^n y}{dx^n} + k_{n-1} x^{n-1} \frac{d^{n-1} y}{dx^{n-1}} + \dots + k_1 x \frac{dy}{dx} + k_0 y = F(x) \tag{1}$$

The substitution $x = e^t$, which makes

$$x \frac{dy}{dx} = \frac{dy}{dt}, \quad x^k \frac{d^k y}{dx^k} = \left(\frac{d}{dt} - k + 1\right) \dots \left(\frac{d}{dt} - 2\right)\left(\frac{d}{dt} - 1\right)\frac{dy}{dt} \tag{2}$$

transforms this into a linear differential equation with constant coefficients. By §§ 5.14 to 5.16 its solution may be found in the form $y = g(t)$, leading to $y = g(\ln x)$ as the solution of the given Cauchy-Euler equation.

5.18. Simultaneous differential equations. A system of two equations in x, y depending on t, if linear and with constant coefficients, may be written

$$\left.\begin{aligned} f_1(D)x + g_1(D)y &= E_1(t) \\ f_2(D)x + g_2(D)y &= E_2(t) \end{aligned}\right\} \tag{1}$$

where $D = d/dt$. By §§ 5.14 to 5.16 find the solution of

$$[g_2(D)f_1(D) - g_1(D)f_2(D)]x = g_2(D)E_1(t) - g_1(D)E_2(t) \tag{2}$$

in the form

$$x = u + c_1 u_1 + c_2 u_2 + \dots + c_m u_m, \tag{3}$$

and the solution of

$$[g_2(D)f_1(D) - g_1(D)f_2(D)]y = f_1(D)E_2(t) - f_2(D)E_1(t) \tag{4}$$

in the form

$$y = v + c_1' u_1 + c_2' u_2 + \dots + c_m' u_m \tag{5}$$

Here u, v, u_1, ..., u_m are functions of t. The constants c_k and c_k' are not independent, and the relations between them must be found by substitution of x and y in the original equations. In the general case, and the usual choice of u and v, these relations may be used to determine the c_k' in terms of the c_k.

Consider the special homogeneous linear system of n equations of the first order, with the coefficients c_{ks} constant,

$$\frac{dy_k}{dt} = c_{k1} y_1 + c_{k2} y_2 + \dots + c_{kn} y_n, \quad k = 1, 2, \dots, n \tag{6}$$

Let the equation

$$\begin{vmatrix} c_{11}-r & c_{12} & \dots & c_{1n} \\ c_{21} & c_{22}-r & \dots & c_{2n} \\ \dots & \dots & \dots & \dots \\ c_{n1} & c_{n2} & \dots & c_{nn}-r \end{vmatrix} = 0 \tag{7}$$

have n distinct roots $r_1, r_2, \dots, r_n$. Then the solution is

$$y_k = a_{k1}e^{r_1t} + a_{k2}e^{r_2t} + \dots + a_{kn}e^{r_nt} \tag{8}$$

where for each s the ratios of the coefficients a_{ks} are found from

$$\left.\begin{aligned} (c_{11}-r_s)a_{1s} + c_{12}a_{2s} + \dots + c_{1n}a_{ns} &= 0 \\ c_{21}a_{1s} + (c_{22}-r_s)a_{2s} + \dots + c_{2n}a_{ns} &= 0 \\ \dots \quad \dots \quad \dots \quad \dots \quad \dots &\quad \dots \\ c_{n1}a_{1s} + c_{n2}a_{2s} + \dots + (c_{nn}-r_s)a_{ns} &= 0 \end{aligned}\right\} \tag{9}$$

5.19. First-order partial differential equations. When linear in the derivatives of the two dependent variables, the equation is

$$A(x,y,u)p + B(x,y,u)q = C(x,y,u) \tag{1}$$

where

$$p = \frac{\partial u}{\partial x} = u_x \quad \text{and} \quad q = \frac{\partial u}{\partial y} = u_y \tag{2}$$

The system of differential equations for the characteristic curves is

$$\frac{dx}{A} = \frac{dy}{B} = \frac{du}{C} \tag{3}$$

If this is solved in the form

$$f(x,y,u) = c_1 \quad \text{and} \quad g(x,y,u) = c_2 \tag{4}$$

the solution of the partial differential equation is given by

$$F(f,g) = 0, \quad f = G(g), \quad \text{or} \quad g = H(f) \tag{5}$$

where F, G, H are arbitrary functions.

5.20. Second-order partial differential equations. When linear in the second derivatives of the two dependent variables, the equation is

$$R(x,y)r + 2S(x,y)s + T(x,y)t = V(x,y,p,q,u) \tag{1}$$

where

$$p = u_x, \quad q = u_y, \quad r = u_{xx}, \quad s = u_{xy}, \quad t = u_{yy} \tag{2}$$

The ordinary differential equation for the characteristics is

$$R\left(\frac{dy}{dx}\right)^2 - 2S\frac{dy}{dx} + T = 0 \tag{3}$$

By § 5.10 its solution may be found in the form

$$f(x,y) = a, \quad g(x,y) = b \tag{4}$$

These are the equations of the two families of characteristic curves.

The type of equation depends on the sign of the determinant

$$\begin{vmatrix} R & S \\ S & T \end{vmatrix} = RT - S^2 \tag{5}$$

for any x,y region under consideration. If $RT - S^2 < 0$, or $RT < S^2$, the equation is hyperbolic. In this case the characteristics are real, and if the parameters a and b are used as new variables, we obtain the first normal form

$$u_{ab} = F(a,b,u,u_a,u_b) \tag{6}$$

A second normal form for the hyperbolic type results from the substitution

$$a = X + Y, \quad b = X - Y \tag{7}$$

This is

$$u_{XX} - u_{YY} = G(X,Y,u,u_X,u_Y) \tag{8}$$

If $RT - S^2 = 0$, or $RT = S^2$, the equation is parabolic. In this case the two families of characteristics are real and coincident. We here use $X = a = b$ and Y any second independent function of x,y as new variables. This gives the normal form

$$u_{XX} = F(X,Y,u,u_X,u_Y) \tag{9}$$

If $RT - S^2 > 0$, or $RT > S^2$, the equation is elliptic. Here the characteristics are not real, but use of the substitution

$$a = X + iY, \quad b = X - iY \tag{10}$$

leads to the real normal form

$$u_{XX} + u_{YY} = G(X,Y,u,u_X,u_Y) \tag{11}$$

The wave equation, $u_{tt} - c^2u_{xx} = 0$, is hyperbolic and admits the general solution

$$u = f(x - ct) + g(x + ct) \tag{12}$$

The heat equation

$$a^2u_{xx} = u_t \tag{13}$$

is parabolic and admits no general solution in terms of arbitrary functions.

Laplace's equation, $u_{xx} + u_{yy} = 0$, is elliptic and admits the general solution

$$u = f(x + iy) + g(x - iy). \tag{14}$$

5.21. Runge-Kutta method of finding numerical solutions. For the differential equation $dy/dx = f(x,y)$ of § 5.3 the solution may be found step by step. We start with x_0, y_0, first compute x_1, y_1, then x_2, y_2, and so on up to x_N, y_N. Here $x_{n+1} - x_n = h$ is small, and at each step we find

$$k_1 = f(x_n, y_n)h, \quad k_2 = f\left(x_n + \frac{h}{2}, y_n + \frac{k_1}{2}\right)h,$$

$$k_3 = f\left(x_n + \frac{h}{2}, y + \frac{k_2}{2}\right)h, \quad k_4 = f(x_n + h, y_n + k_3)h.$$

Then

$$x_{n+1} = x_n + h, \quad y_{n+1} = y_n + \Delta y,$$

where

$$\Delta y = \tfrac{1}{6}(k_1 + 2k_2 + 2k_3 + k_4)$$

6. Vector Analysis

6.1. Scalars. A scalar S is a real number capable of representation by a signed coordinate on a scale.

6.2. Vectors. A vector V is a quantity which is determined by a length and a direction. The vector V may be graphically represented by any line segment having this length and this direction $V = OA$.

6.3. Components. Let $\boldsymbol{i}, \boldsymbol{j}, \boldsymbol{k}$ represent three vectors of unit length along the three mutually perpendicular lines OX, OY, OZ, respectively, which are taken as the positive coordinate axes. Let $\boldsymbol{V}$ be a vector in space, and a, b, c the projections of $\boldsymbol{V}$ on the three lines OX, OY, OZ. Then

$$\boldsymbol{V} = a\boldsymbol{i} + b\boldsymbol{j} + c\boldsymbol{k} \tag{1}$$

where a, b, c are the components of $\boldsymbol{V}$, while $a\boldsymbol{i}$, $b\boldsymbol{j}$, $c\boldsymbol{k}$ are the component vectors. The magnitude of $\boldsymbol{V}$ is

$$|\boldsymbol{V}| = V = \sqrt{a^2 + b^2 + c^2} \tag{2}$$

And the direction cosines of $\boldsymbol{V}$ are $a/|\boldsymbol{V}|$, $b/|\boldsymbol{V}|$, $c/|\boldsymbol{V}|$ when $|\boldsymbol{V}| \neq 0$. When $|\boldsymbol{V}| = 0$, we have the null vector

$$0 = 0\boldsymbol{i} + 0\boldsymbol{j} + 0\boldsymbol{k} \tag{3}$$

which has length zero and no determinate direction.

6.4. Sums and products by scalars. These may be formed by corresponding operations on the components. Thus if

$$V_1 = a_1 i + b_1 j + c_1 k \quad \text{and} \quad V_2 = a_2 i + b_2 j + c_2 k \tag{1}$$

$$V_1 + V_2 = (a_1 + a_2)i + (b_1 + b_2)j + (c_1 + c_2)k \tag{2}$$

$$SV = VS = (Sa)i + (Sb)j + (Sc)k \tag{3}$$

$$(S_1 + S_2)V = S_1V + S_2V, \quad S(V_1 + V_2) = SV_1 + SV_2 \tag{4}$$

6.5. The scalar or dot product, $V_1 \cdot V_2$. This is defined as

$$V_1 \cdot V_2 = |V_1|\,|V_2| \cos\theta \tag{1}$$

where θ is any angle from V_1 to V_2.

$$V_1 \cdot V_2 = V_2 \cdot V_1 = a_1a_2 + b_1b_2 + c_1c_2, \quad V_1 \cdot V_1 = |V_1|^2 \tag{2}$$

$$V_1 \cdot (V_2 + V_3) = V_1 \cdot V_2 + V_1 \cdot V_3 \tag{3}$$

$$(V_1 + V_2) \cdot V_3 = V_1 \cdot V_2 + V_2 \cdot V_3 \tag{4}$$

$$i \cdot i = j \cdot j = k \cdot k = 1, \quad i \cdot j = j \cdot k = k \cdot i = j \cdot i = k \cdot j = i \cdot k = 0 \tag{5}$$

6.6. The vector or cross product, $V_1 \times V_2$. This is defined as

$$V_1 \times V_2 = |V_1|\,|V_2| \sin\theta\, u$$

where θ is some angle not exceeding 180° from V_1 to V_2 and u is a unit vector perpendicular to the plane of V_1 and V_2 and so directed that a right-threaded screw along u will advance when turned through the angle θ. For $\theta = 0$ or 180°, V_1 and V_2 do not determine a plane, but $\sin\theta = 0$ makes the product the null vector.

$$\left.\begin{aligned} V_1 \times V_2 = -V_2 \times V_1 &= \begin{vmatrix} i & j & k \\ a_1 & b_1 & c_1 \\ a_2 & b_2 & c_2 \end{vmatrix} \\ &= (b_1c_2 - b_2c_1)i + (c_1a_2 - c_2a_1)j + (a_1b_2 - a_2b_1)k \end{aligned}\right\} \tag{1}$$

$$V_1 \times (V_2 + V_3) = V_1 \times V_2 + V_1 \times V_3 \tag{2}$$

$$(V_1 + V_2) \times V_3 = V_1 \times V_3 + V_2 \times V_3 \tag{3}$$

$$V_1 \times (V_2 \times V_3) = (V_1 \cdot V_3)V_2 - (V_1 \cdot V_2)V_3 \tag{4}$$

$$(V_1 \times V_2) \times V_3 = (V_1 \cdot V_3)V_2 - (V_2 \cdot V_3)V_1 \tag{5}$$

$$\left.\begin{aligned} i \times i = 0, \quad j \times j = 0, \quad k \times k = 0, \quad i \times j = k, \quad j \times k = i, \\ k \times i = j, \quad j \times i = -k, \quad k \times j = -i, \quad i \times k = -j \end{aligned}\right\} \tag{6}$$

6.7. The triple scalar product. The volume of the parallelepiped having V_1, V_2, V_3 as three of its edges is

$$V_1 \cdot (V_2 \times V_3) = (V_1 \times V_2) \cdot V_3 = V_2 \cdot (V_3 \times V_1) = \begin{vmatrix} a_1 & a_2 & a_3 \\ b_1 & b_2 & b_3 \\ c_1 & c_2 & c_3 \end{vmatrix} \tag{1}$$

if we so number the vectors that the cross product makes an acute angle with the vector outside the parenthesis.

6.8. The derivative. Let a vector $\boldsymbol{r}$ have its components variable but functions of a parameter t, so that

$$\boldsymbol{r}(t) = x(t)\boldsymbol{i} + y(t)\boldsymbol{j} + z(t)\boldsymbol{k} \quad \text{or} \quad \boldsymbol{r} = x\boldsymbol{i} + y\boldsymbol{j} + z\boldsymbol{k} \tag{1}$$

To differentiate $\boldsymbol{r}$, we merely differentiate each component. Thus

$$\frac{d\boldsymbol{r}}{dt} = \boldsymbol{r}'(t) = x'(t)\boldsymbol{i} + y'(t)\boldsymbol{j} + z'(t)\boldsymbol{k} = \frac{dx}{dt}\boldsymbol{i} + \frac{dy}{dt}\boldsymbol{j} + \frac{dz}{dt}\boldsymbol{k} \tag{2}$$

For two vectors,

$$\boldsymbol{r}_1 = x_1\boldsymbol{i} + y_1\boldsymbol{j} + z_1\boldsymbol{k} \quad \text{and} \quad \boldsymbol{r}_2 = x_2\boldsymbol{i} + y_2\boldsymbol{j} + z_2\boldsymbol{k},$$

$$\frac{d}{dt}(\boldsymbol{r}_1 + \boldsymbol{r}_2) = \frac{d\boldsymbol{r}_1}{dt} + \frac{d\boldsymbol{r}_2}{dt} \tag{3}$$

$$\frac{d}{dt}(\boldsymbol{r}_1 \cdot \boldsymbol{r}_2) = \boldsymbol{r}_2 \cdot \frac{d\boldsymbol{r}_1}{dt} + \boldsymbol{r}_1 \cdot \frac{d\boldsymbol{r}_2}{dt} \tag{4}$$

$$\frac{d}{dt}(\boldsymbol{r}_1 \times \boldsymbol{r}_2) = \frac{d\boldsymbol{r}_1}{dt} \times \boldsymbol{r}_2 + \boldsymbol{r}_1 \times \frac{d\boldsymbol{r}_2}{dt} = -\boldsymbol{r}_2 \times \frac{d\boldsymbol{r}_1}{dt} + \boldsymbol{r}_1 \times \frac{d\boldsymbol{r}_2}{dt} \tag{5}$$

$$\boldsymbol{r} \cdot \frac{d\boldsymbol{r}}{dt} = |\boldsymbol{r}| \frac{d|\boldsymbol{r}|}{dt} \tag{6}$$

Hence if $|\boldsymbol{r}|$ is constant, $\boldsymbol{r} \cdot d\boldsymbol{r}/dt = 0$

6.9. The Frenet formulas. Let P_0 be a fixed and P a variable point on a curve in space. Take s, the arc length P_0P, as the parameter. Then the vector from the origin O to P is

$$\overrightarrow{OP} = \boldsymbol{r}(s) = x(s)\boldsymbol{i} + y(s)\boldsymbol{j} + z(s)\boldsymbol{k} \tag{1}$$

With each point P we associate three mutually perpendicular unit vectors $\boldsymbol{t}, \boldsymbol{p}$, and $\boldsymbol{b}$. These satisfy the equations:

$$\frac{d\boldsymbol{r}}{ds} = \boldsymbol{t}, \quad \frac{d\boldsymbol{t}}{ds} = \frac{1}{\rho}\boldsymbol{p}, \quad \frac{d\boldsymbol{b}}{ds} = -\frac{1}{\tau}\boldsymbol{p}, \quad \frac{d\boldsymbol{p}}{ds} = \frac{1}{\tau}\boldsymbol{b} - \frac{1}{\rho}\boldsymbol{t} \tag{2}$$

The tangent vector $\boldsymbol{t}$ has the direction of $\boldsymbol{r}'(s)$, the principal normal vector $\boldsymbol{p}$ has the direction of $\boldsymbol{r}''(s)$, and the binormal vector $\boldsymbol{b}$ has the direction of $\boldsymbol{t} \times \boldsymbol{p} = \boldsymbol{b}$. The curvature $1/\rho$ is the length of $\boldsymbol{r}''(s) = d\boldsymbol{t}/ds$. The torsion $1/\tau$ is determined from $d\boldsymbol{b}/ds = -\boldsymbol{p}/\tau$.

6.10. Curves with parameter t. When the parameter is t,

$$\overrightarrow{OP} = \boldsymbol{r}(t) = x(t)\boldsymbol{i} + y(t)\boldsymbol{j} + z(t)\boldsymbol{k} \tag{1}$$

Using dots for t derivatives we form

$$\dot{\boldsymbol{r}} = \dot{x}\boldsymbol{i} + \dot{y}\boldsymbol{j} + \dot{z}\boldsymbol{k} \quad \text{and} \quad \dot{\boldsymbol{r}} \times \ddot{\boldsymbol{r}} = \begin{vmatrix} \dot{y} & \dot{z} \\ \ddot{y} & \ddot{z} \end{vmatrix} \boldsymbol{i} + \begin{vmatrix} \dot{z} & \dot{x} \\ \ddot{z} & \ddot{x} \end{vmatrix} \boldsymbol{j} + \begin{vmatrix} \dot{x} & \dot{y} \\ \ddot{x} & \ddot{y} \end{vmatrix} \boldsymbol{k} \tag{2}$$

Then for the unit vectors of § 6.9, the tangent $\boldsymbol{t}$ has the direction of $\dot{\boldsymbol{r}}$, the binormal $\boldsymbol{b}$ has the direction of $\dot{\boldsymbol{r}} \times \ddot{\boldsymbol{r}}$, and the principal normal $\boldsymbol{p}$ has the direction of $(S_1\dot{\boldsymbol{r}} \times \ddot{\boldsymbol{r}}) \times (S_2\dot{\boldsymbol{r}})$, where S_1 and S_2 are any scalar factors. The curvature and torsion may be found from

$$\frac{1}{\rho} = \frac{\dot{\boldsymbol{r}} \times \ddot{\boldsymbol{r}}}{\dot{\boldsymbol{r}}^3}, \quad \frac{1}{\tau} = \frac{(\dot{\boldsymbol{r}} \times \ddot{\boldsymbol{r}} \cdot \dddot{\boldsymbol{r}})}{\dot{\boldsymbol{r}}^2} \tag{3}$$

When the parameter t is the time, the velocity vector $\boldsymbol{v} = v\boldsymbol{t} = \dot{\boldsymbol{r}}$, the speed

$$v = |\boldsymbol{v}| = \sqrt{\dot{x}^2 + \dot{y}^2 + \dot{z}^2} \tag{4}$$

and the acceleration vector

$$\boldsymbol{a} = \dot{\boldsymbol{v}} = \ddot{\boldsymbol{r}} = \dot{v}\boldsymbol{t} + \frac{v^2}{\rho}\boldsymbol{p}$$

6.11. Relative motion. A varying coordinate system with fixed origin O is instantaneously rotating about some line OL with angular velocity ω. Let $\boldsymbol{w}$ be a vector of length ω along OL. For a variable point P and $\boldsymbol{i}, \boldsymbol{j}, \boldsymbol{k}$ in the moving system

$$\overrightarrow{OP} = \boldsymbol{r} = x\boldsymbol{i} + y\boldsymbol{j} + z\boldsymbol{k} \quad \text{and} \quad \dot{\boldsymbol{r}} = \boldsymbol{v}_{\text{rel}} = \dot{x}\boldsymbol{i} + \dot{y}\boldsymbol{j} + \dot{z}\boldsymbol{k} \tag{1}$$

The absolute velocity of P, $\boldsymbol{v}_{\text{abs}}$ is given by

$$\boldsymbol{v}_{\text{abs}} = \boldsymbol{v}_{\text{rel}} + \boldsymbol{w} \times \boldsymbol{r} = \dot{\boldsymbol{r}} + \boldsymbol{w} \times \boldsymbol{r} \tag{2}$$

where $\boldsymbol{v}_{\text{rel}}$ is the velocity relative to the moving system.

6.12. The symbolic vector del. The equation

$$\boldsymbol{\nabla} = \frac{\partial}{\partial x}\boldsymbol{i} + \frac{\partial}{\partial y}\boldsymbol{j} + \frac{\partial}{\partial z}\boldsymbol{k} \tag{1}$$

defines the vector differential operator $\boldsymbol{\nabla}$, read *del.*

The *gradient* of a scalar function $f(x,y,z)$, $\boldsymbol{\nabla} f$ or grad f is

$$\text{grad}\, f = \boldsymbol{\nabla} f = \frac{\partial f}{\partial x}\boldsymbol{i} + \frac{\partial f}{\partial y}\boldsymbol{j} + \frac{\partial f}{\partial z}\boldsymbol{k} \tag{2}$$

The gradient $\boldsymbol{\nabla} f$ extends in the direction in which the derivative df/ds is a maximum, and $|\boldsymbol{\nabla} f|$ is equal to that maximum. In a direction making an angle θ with the gradient, $df/ds = |\boldsymbol{\nabla} f| \cos\theta$.

We may apply del to a vector function of position $\boldsymbol{Q}$,

$$\boldsymbol{Q}(x,y,z) = Q_1(x,y,z)\boldsymbol{i} + Q_2(x,y,z)\boldsymbol{j} + Q_3(x,y,z)\boldsymbol{k} \tag{3}$$

The *divergence* of the vector function $\boldsymbol{Q}$, $\boldsymbol{\nabla}\cdot\boldsymbol{Q}$ or div $\boldsymbol{Q}$ is

$$\text{div}\,\boldsymbol{Q} = \boldsymbol{\nabla}\cdot\boldsymbol{Q} = \frac{\partial Q_1}{\partial x}\boldsymbol{i} + \frac{\partial Q_2}{\partial y}\boldsymbol{j} + \frac{\partial Q_3}{\partial z}\boldsymbol{k} \tag{4}$$

For a fluid, let $\boldsymbol{Q}$ equal the velocity vector multiplied by the scalar density. Then div $\boldsymbol{Q}$ is the rate of flow outward per unit volume at a point.

The curl or rotation of the vector function $\boldsymbol{Q}$, $\boldsymbol{\nabla}\times\boldsymbol{Q}$ is

$$\left.\begin{aligned} \text{curl}\,\boldsymbol{Q} = \text{rot}\,\boldsymbol{Q} = \boldsymbol{\nabla}\times\boldsymbol{Q} &= \begin{vmatrix} \boldsymbol{i} & \boldsymbol{j} & \boldsymbol{k} \\ \dfrac{\partial}{\partial x} & \dfrac{\partial}{\partial y} & \dfrac{\partial}{\partial z} \\ Q_1 & Q_2 & Q_3 \end{vmatrix} \\ &= \left(\frac{\partial Q_3}{\partial y} - \frac{\partial Q_2}{\partial z}\right)\boldsymbol{i} + \left(\frac{\partial Q_1}{\partial z} - \frac{\partial Q_3}{\partial x}\right)\boldsymbol{j} + \left(\frac{\partial Q_2}{\partial x} - \frac{\partial Q_1}{\partial y}\right)\boldsymbol{k} \end{aligned}\right\} \tag{5}$$

For a fluid, let $\boldsymbol{Q}$ equal the velocity vector times the density. When the motion is analyzed into a dilatation and a rigid displacement, for the latter the angular velocity at a point or vorticity is $\frac{1}{2}$ curl $\boldsymbol{Q}$.

In terms of del the Laplacian operator is ∇^2, and

$$\boldsymbol{\nabla}^2 f = \boldsymbol{\nabla}\cdot\boldsymbol{\nabla} f = \text{div grad}\, f = \frac{\partial^2 f}{\partial x^2} + \frac{\partial^2 f}{\partial y^2} + \frac{\partial^2 f}{\partial z^2} \tag{6}$$

$$\boldsymbol{\nabla}\cdot(\boldsymbol{\nabla}\times\boldsymbol{Q}) = \text{div curl}\,\boldsymbol{Q} = 0, \quad \boldsymbol{\nabla}\times(\boldsymbol{\nabla} f) = \text{curl grad}\, f = 0 \tag{7}$$

And $\boldsymbol{\nabla}\times\boldsymbol{Q} = \text{curl}\,\boldsymbol{Q} = 0$ is a necessary and sufficient condition for $\boldsymbol{Q}$ to be the gradient of some function f,

$$\boldsymbol{Q} = \boldsymbol{\nabla} f \tag{8}$$

$$\text{curl curl}\,\boldsymbol{Q} = \nabla \times (\nabla \times \boldsymbol{Q}) = \text{grad div}\,\boldsymbol{Q} - \nabla^2\boldsymbol{Q} = \nabla(\nabla \cdot \boldsymbol{Q}) - \nabla \cdot \nabla\boldsymbol{Q} \quad (9)$$

where

$$\nabla^2\boldsymbol{Q} = \nabla \cdot \nabla\boldsymbol{Q} = (\nabla^2 Q_1)\boldsymbol{i} + (\nabla^2 Q_2)\boldsymbol{j} + (\nabla^2 Q_3)\boldsymbol{k} \quad (10)$$

6.13. The divergence theorem. Let S consist of one or more closed surfaces that collectively bound a Volume V. Then

$$\int_V \text{div}\,\boldsymbol{Q}\,dV = \int_V \nabla \cdot \boldsymbol{Q}\,dV = \int_S \boldsymbol{Q} \cdot \boldsymbol{n}\,dS \quad (1)$$

where $\boldsymbol{n}$ is the unit normal to S, drawn outward.

6.14. Green's theorem in a plane. Let B be a simple closed curve in the x,y plane which bounds an area A, with the positive direction so chosen that it and the inner normal are related like OX and OY. Then

$$\int_B (M\,dx + N\,dy) = \int_A \left(\frac{\partial N}{\partial x} - \frac{\partial M}{\partial y}\right) dA \quad (2)$$

for M and N any two functions of x and y.

6.15. Stokes's theorem. Let S be a portion of a surface in space bounded by a simple closed curve B. If $\boldsymbol{m}$ is the direction into S perpendicular to B, the positive direction for B is related to $\boldsymbol{m}$ and $\boldsymbol{n}$, the positive normal to S, like OX, OY, and OZ. Then

$$\int_S (\text{curl}\,\boldsymbol{Q}) \cdot \boldsymbol{n}\,dS = \int_S \boldsymbol{n} \cdot (\nabla \times \boldsymbol{Q})dS = \int_B \boldsymbol{Q} \cdot d\boldsymbol{s} \quad (1)$$

6.16. Curvilinear coordinates. For an orthogonal system

$$ds^2 = h_1{}^2du^2 + h_2{}^2dv^2 + h_3{}^2dw^2, \quad dV = h_1h_2h_3du\,dv\,dw \quad (1)$$

In terms of three unit vectors $\boldsymbol{i}_1$, $\boldsymbol{i}_2$, $\boldsymbol{i}_3$ in the direction of increasing u, v, w, respectively, we have

$$\text{grad}\,f = \nabla f = \frac{1}{h_1}\frac{\partial f}{\partial u}\boldsymbol{i}_1 + \frac{1}{h_2}\frac{\partial f}{\partial v}\boldsymbol{i}_2 + \frac{1}{h_3}\frac{\partial f}{\partial w}\boldsymbol{i}_3 \quad (2)$$

$$\text{div}\,\boldsymbol{Q} = \nabla \cdot \boldsymbol{Q} = \frac{1}{h_1h_2h_3}\left[\frac{\partial}{\partial u}(h_2h_3Q_1) + \frac{\partial}{\partial v}(h_3h_1Q_2) + \frac{\partial}{\partial w}(h_1h_2Q_3)\right] \quad (3)$$

$$\left.\begin{aligned}\operatorname{curl} \boldsymbol{Q} = \boldsymbol{\nabla} \times \boldsymbol{Q} &= \frac{1}{h_1 h_2 h_3} \begin{vmatrix} h_1 \boldsymbol{i}_1 & h_2 \boldsymbol{i}_2 & h_3 \boldsymbol{i}_3 \\ \dfrac{\partial}{\partial u} & \dfrac{\partial}{\partial v} & \dfrac{\partial}{\partial w} \\ h_1 Q_1 & h_2 Q_2 & h_3 Q_3 \end{vmatrix} \\ &= \frac{\boldsymbol{i}_1}{h_2 h_3} \left[\frac{\partial(h_3 Q_3)}{\partial v} - \frac{\partial(h_2 Q_2)}{\partial w} \right] \\ &+ \frac{\boldsymbol{i}_2}{h_3 h_1} \left[\frac{\partial(h_1 Q_1)}{\partial w} - \frac{\partial(h_3 Q_3)}{\partial u} \right] + \frac{\boldsymbol{i}_3}{h_1 h_2} \left[\frac{\partial(h_2 Q_2)}{\partial u} - \frac{\partial(h_1 Q_1)}{\partial v} \right] \end{aligned}\right\} \quad (4)$$

6.17. Cylindrical coordinates. These are r, θ, and z, where

$$x = r \cos \theta, \quad y = r \sin \theta \qquad (1)$$

Here

$$h_r = 1, \quad h_\theta = r, \quad h_z = 1$$

$$ds^2 = dr^2 + r^2 d\theta^2 + dz^2, \quad dV = r\, dr\, d\theta\, dz \qquad (2)$$

$$\nabla^2 f = \frac{1}{r} \frac{\partial}{\partial r} \left(r \frac{\partial f}{\partial r} \right) + \frac{1}{r^2} \frac{\partial^2 f}{\partial \theta^2} + \frac{\partial^2 f}{\partial z^2} \qquad (3)$$

6.18. Spherical coordinates. These are r, θ, ϕ, where

$$x = r \sin \phi \cos \theta, \quad y = r \sin \phi \sin \theta, \quad z = r \cos \phi \qquad (1)$$

Here

$$h_r = 1, \quad h_\phi = r, \quad h_\theta = r \sin \phi, \quad ds^2 = dr^2 + r^2 d\phi^2 + r^2 \sin^2 \phi\, d\theta^2 \qquad (2)$$

$$dV = r^2 \sin \phi\, dr\, d\phi\, d\theta \qquad (3)$$

$$\nabla^2 f = \frac{1}{r^2} \frac{\partial}{\partial r} \left(r^2 \frac{\partial f}{\partial r} \right) + \frac{1}{r^2 \sin \phi} \frac{\partial}{\partial \phi} \left(\sin \phi \frac{\partial f}{\partial \phi} \right) + \frac{1}{r^2 \sin^2 \phi} \frac{\partial^2 f}{\partial \theta^2} \qquad (4)$$

Some authors transpose the meaning of θ and ϕ as given here.

6.19. Parabolic coordinates. These are u, v, θ, where

$$\left.\begin{aligned} x = uv \cos \theta, \quad y = uv \sin \theta, \quad z = \tfrac{1}{2}(u^2 - v^2) \\ \sqrt{x^2 + y^2 + z^2} = \tfrac{1}{2}(u^2 + v^2) \end{aligned}\right\} \qquad (1)$$

Here

$$h_u = h_v = \sqrt{u^2 + v^2}, \quad h_\theta = uv \qquad (2)$$

$$ds^2 = (u^2 + v^2)(du^2 + dv^2) + u^2 v^2 d\theta^2, \quad dV = uv(u^2 + v^2) du\, dv\, d\theta \qquad (3)$$

$$\nabla^2 f = \frac{1}{u^2 + v^2} \frac{1}{u} \frac{\partial}{\partial u} \left(u \frac{\partial f}{\partial u} \right) + \frac{1}{v} \frac{\partial}{\partial v} \left(v \frac{\partial f}{\partial v} \right) + \left(\frac{1}{u^2} + \frac{1}{v^2} \right) \frac{\partial^2 f}{\partial \theta^2} \qquad (4)$$

7. Tensors

7.1. Tensors of the second rank. A tensor of the second rank, or second order, has nine components in each coordinate system. Let these be A_{pq} in one system and $\bar{A}_{pq}$ in a second system, where $p = 1, 2$, or 3 and $q = 1, 2$, or 3. If two arbitrary vectors have components U_p and V_p in the first system and $\bar{U}_p$ and $\bar{V}_p$ in the second system,

$$\sum_{p,q} U_p A_{pq} V_q = \sum_{p,q} \bar{U}_p \bar{A}_{pq} \bar{V}_q \qquad (1)$$

is a scalar invariant, the same in all coordinate systems.

7.2. Summation convention. In equations involving tensors, like that in §7.1 the summation signs are often omitted in view of the convention that summation occurs on any index that appears twice.

7.3. Transformation of components. If, for the vector components,

$$\bar{U}_r = \sum_{p} m_{pr} U_p, \quad \bar{U}_r \bar{V}_s = \sum_{p,q} m_{pr} m_{qs} U_p V_q \qquad (1)$$

the tensor components A_{pq} transform like the product $U_p V_q$ and

$$\bar{A}_{rs} = \sum_{p,q} m_{pr} m_{qs} A_{pq}$$

7.4. Matrix notation. We may write the nine A_{pq} as a square array

$$\left\| \begin{matrix} A_{11} & A_{12} & A_{13} \\ A_{21} & A_{22} & A_{23} \\ A_{31} & A_{32} & A_{33} \end{matrix} \right\| \qquad (1)$$

This is a matrix, abbreviated as $\| A_{pq} \|$ or A. Sometimes the double vertical bars are replaced by parentheses, or omitted. (See pages 85-89.)

A vector U_p may be written as a 1 by 3 row matrix $\vec{U}_p$, or a 3 by 1 column matrix $U_p\!\uparrow$. Thus

$$\vec{U}_p = \| U_1 \quad U_2 \quad U_3 \| \quad U_p\!\uparrow = \left\| \begin{matrix} U_1 \\ U_2 \\ U_3 \end{matrix} \right\| \qquad (2)$$

7.5. Matrix products. Let the number of columns of the matrix A_{pq} be the same as the number of rows of the matrix B_{qr}. Then the product matrix, in the order indicated, $C = AB$,

$$\| C_{pr} \| = \| A_{pq} \| \, \| B_{qr} \| \quad \text{has} \quad C_{pr} = \sum_{q} A_{pq} B_{qr} \qquad (1)$$

as its elements, and a number of rows the same as A_{pq}, a number of columns the same as B_{qr}. Matrix multiplication is associative, $(AB)C = A(BC)$ may be written ABC. But the multiplication is not commutative. The dimensions may not allow both AB and BA to be formed, and even if they both exist they will in general be different.

7.6. Linear vector operator. From any vector U, a tensor A_{pq} may be used to generate a new vector by multiplication on the right,

$$V_p = \sum_q A_{pq} U_q \quad \text{or} \quad V_p\uparrow = \| A_{pq} \| \, U_q\uparrow \tag{1}$$

Similarly by multiplication on the left

$$W_q = \sum_p U_p A_{pq} \quad \text{or} \quad \vec{W}_q = \vec{U}_p \, \| A_{pq} \| \tag{2}$$

7.7. Combined operators. If the first process of § 7.5 is applied with a tensor A_{pq}, and then repeated on V_p with a tensor B_{pq}, the result is equivalent to a single operation with C_{pq}, where

$$C_{pq} = \sum_r B_{pr} A_{rq} \quad \text{or} \quad \| C_{pq} \| = \| B_{pr} \| \, \| A_{rq} \| \tag{1}$$

Similarly for the second operation of §7.5, where the result is equivalent to a single operation with D_{pq}, where

$$D_{pq} = \sum_r A_{pr} B_{rq} \quad \text{or} \quad \| D_{pq} \| = \| A_{pr} \| \, \| B_{rq} \| \tag{2}$$

7.8. Tensors from vectors. The products of components of two vectors, or sums of such products form a tensor. Thus

$$A_{pq} = B_p L_q + C_p M_q + D_p N_q \tag{1}$$

Any tensor may be built up of not more than three such products. For A_{pq} any tensor and $\boldsymbol{B}$, $\boldsymbol{C}$, $\boldsymbol{D}$ three noncoplanar or linearly independent vectors, values of $\boldsymbol{L}$, $\boldsymbol{M}$, and $\boldsymbol{N}$ can be found to satisfy the equation just written.

7.9. Dyadics. Write $\boldsymbol{i}_1$, $\boldsymbol{i}_2$, $\boldsymbol{i}_3$ for $\boldsymbol{i}$, $\boldsymbol{j}$, $\boldsymbol{k}$. Then

$$\boldsymbol{B} = \sum_p B_p \boldsymbol{i}_p, \quad \boldsymbol{L} = \sum_q L_q \boldsymbol{i}_q \quad \text{and} \quad \boldsymbol{BL} = \sum_{p,q} B_p L_q \boldsymbol{i}_p \boldsymbol{i}_q \tag{1}$$

The tensor of § 7.8 may be generated from

$$\sum_{p,q} A_{pq}\boldsymbol{i}_p\boldsymbol{i}_q = \boldsymbol{BL} + \boldsymbol{CM} + \boldsymbol{DN} \tag{2}$$

The first operation of § 7.7 may be effected by dot products using the right-hand factors,

$$V = \sum_p V_p\boldsymbol{i}_p = \sum_{p,q} A_{pq}\boldsymbol{i}_p(\boldsymbol{i}_q \cdot \boldsymbol{U}) = \boldsymbol{B}(\boldsymbol{L}\cdot\boldsymbol{U}) + \boldsymbol{C}(\boldsymbol{M}\cdot\boldsymbol{U}) + \boldsymbol{D}(\boldsymbol{N}\cdot\boldsymbol{U}) \tag{3}$$

Similarly the second operation of § 7.7 may be effected by dot products using the left-hand factors,

$$W = \sum_q W_q\boldsymbol{i}_q = \sum_{p,q} A_{pq}(\boldsymbol{U}\cdot\boldsymbol{i}_p)\boldsymbol{i}_q = (\boldsymbol{U}\cdot\boldsymbol{B})\boldsymbol{L} + (\boldsymbol{U}\cdot\boldsymbol{C})\boldsymbol{M} + (\boldsymbol{U}\cdot\boldsymbol{D})\boldsymbol{N} \tag{4}$$

Products of vectors, or sums of such products, used as above to generate tensors and form linear vector functions are called dyadics.

7.10. Conjugate tensor. Symmetry. If A_{pq} is a tensor, then the conjugate $A'_{pq} = A_{qp}$ is also a tensor. A tensor is symmetric if it is equal to its conjugate,

$$A_{pq} = A_{qp} \tag{1}$$

A tensor is alternating, or skew-symmetric if it is equal to the negative of its conjugate,

$$A_{pq} = -A_{qp} \tag{2}$$

Any tensor may be represented as the sum of two tensors one of which is symmetric and the other alternating by means of the identity

$$A_{pq} = \tfrac{1}{2}(A_{pq} + A'_{pq}) + \tfrac{1}{2}(A_{pq} - A'_{pq}) \tag{1}$$

7.11. Unit, orthogonal, unitary. The unit matrix has

$$A_{pq} = \delta_{pq} = 0 \quad \text{if} \quad p \neq q, \quad \text{and} \quad \delta_{pq} = 1 \quad \text{if} \quad p = q \tag{2}$$

A square matrix is singular if its determinant is zero. Each nonsingular square matrix has a reciprocal matrix $A^{-1}{}_{pq}$ such that

$$\| A_{pq} \| \, \| A^{-1}{}_{qr} \| = \| \delta_{pr} \| \quad \text{and} \quad \| A^{-1}{}_{pq} \| \, \| A_{qr} \| = \delta_{pr} \tag{3}$$

A matrix is orthogonal if its conjugate and reciprocal are equal,

$$A'_{pq} = A^{-1}{}_{pq} \quad \sum_q A_{pq}A_{qr} = \sum_q A_{qp}A_{rq} = \delta_{pr} \tag{4}$$

For a matrix with complex elements A_{pq} obtain its Hermitian conjugate $\tilde{A}_{pq}$ from A'_{pq} by replacing each element $a + bi$ by its complex conjugate $a - bi$. A matrix is unitary, or Hermitian orthogonal, if its Hermitian conjugate equals its reciprocal, $\tilde{A}_{pq} = A^{-1}{}_{pq}$.

For Cartesian coordinates the matrix m_{pq} of §7.3 is orthogonal.

7.12. Principal axes of a symmetric tensor. For any symmetric tensor A_{pq} there are three mutually perpendicular directions such that when these are taken as a new coordinate system, the new components of the tensor have the form $\bar{A}_{pq} = R_p\delta_{pq}$. The R_p are the roots of

$$\begin{vmatrix} A_{11} - R & A_{12} & A_{13} \\ A_{21} & A_{22} - R & A_{23} \\ A_{31} & A_{32} & A_{33} - R \end{vmatrix} = -R^3 + S_1R^2 - S_2R + S_3 = 0 \tag{1}$$

When this has three distinct roots, the directions of the new axes in the old coordinate system are found by solving

$$\left.\begin{aligned} A_{11}x_p + A_{12}y_p + A_{13}z_p &= R_px_p \\ A_{21}x_p + A_{22}y_p + A_{23}z_p &= R_py_p \\ A_{31}x_p + A_{32}y_p + A_{33}z_p &= R_pz_p \end{aligned}\right\} \tag{2}$$

for the ratio of x_p, y_p, z_p where p is 1, 2, or 3.

The trace

$$S_1 = A_{11} + A_{22} + A_{33} \tag{3}$$

S_3 is the determinant $|A_{pq}|$ and

$$S_2 = A_{22}A_{33} + A_{33}A_{11} + A_{11}A_{22} - A_{23}{}^2 - A_{31}{}^2 - A_{12}{}^2 \tag{4}$$

S_1, S_2, S_3 known as the first, second, and third scalar invariants of the symmetric tensor A_{pq} have the same value in all coordinate systems.

7.13. Tensors in *n*-dimensions. In two systems of coordinates, let a point P have coordinates $(x^1,x^2,\ldots,x^n)$ in the first system and $(\bar{x}^1,\bar{x}^2,\ldots,\bar{x}^n)$ in the second system, with relations

$$\bar{x}^p = f^p(x^1,x^2,\ldots,x^n), \quad x^p = F^p(\bar{x}^1,\bar{x}^2,\ldots,\bar{x}^n), \quad p = 1, 2, \ldots, n \tag{1}$$

If $(A^1,A^2,\ldots,A^n)$ are related to $(\bar{A}^1, \bar{A}^2,\ldots,\bar{A}^n)$ by the equations

$$\bar{A}^p = \sum_{i=1}^{n} \frac{\partial \bar{x}^p}{\partial x^i} A^i, \quad \text{or} \quad \bar{A}^p = \frac{\partial \bar{x}^p}{\partial x^i} A^i \tag{2}$$

by § 7.2, the A's are the components of a contravariant vector, or a tensor of rank one.

Similarly the relation

$$\bar{A}_p = \left(\frac{\partial x^i}{\partial \bar{x}^p}\right) A_i \tag{3}$$

holds for the components of a covariant vector, or a covariant tensor of rank one.

The expressions $d\bar{x}^m$ and dx^i are the components of a contravariant vector, and if $\phi(x^i) = \bar{\phi}(\bar{x}^m)$ is any scalar point function, the gradient with components $\partial\bar{\phi}/\partial\bar{x}^m$ and $\partial\bar{\phi}/\partial x^i$ is a covariant vector.

7.14. Tensors of any rank. The scalar ϕ is a tensor of rank zero. The transformation $\bar{A}^{pq} = (\partial\bar{x}^p/\partial x^i)(\partial\bar{x}^q/\partial x^j)A^{ij}$ defines a contravariant tensor of rank two. The transformation $\bar{A}_{pq} = (\partial x^i/\partial\bar{x}^p)(\partial x^j/\partial\bar{x}^q)A_{ij}$ defines a covariant tensor of rank two. And the transformation $\bar{A}_q{}^p = (\partial\bar{x}^p/\partial x^i)(\partial x^j/\partial\bar{x}^q)A_j{}^i$ defines a mixed tensor of rank two.

Tensors of higher order are defined similarly.

7.15. The fundamental tensor. This is the symmetric covariant tensor g_{mn} such that in the Riemannian space the element of arc length is $ds^2 = g_{ij}dx^i\,dx^j$. In the determinant of the g_{ij}, let G_{ij} be the cofactor of g_{ij}, § 1.8, and let g be the value of the determinant. Then $g^{ij} = G_{ij}/g$ is a contravariant tensor. Then $g_{im}g^{jm} = \delta_i{}^j$ is a mixed tensor, where $\delta_i{}^j$ is the δ_{ij} of § 7.11.

The fundamental tensors g_{ij}, g^{ij} may be used to change covariant indices to contravariant ones and conversely. For example,

$$A^p = g^{pq}A_q, \quad A_p = g_{pq}A^q, \quad A_p{}^q = g^{iq}A_{pi} \tag{1}$$

7.16. Christoffel three-index symbols. These symbols (themselves not tensors) are defined in terms of the fundamental tensor by

$$\Gamma_{i\cdot rs} = \begin{bmatrix} r\,s \\ i \end{bmatrix} = \frac{1}{2}\left(\frac{\partial g_{ir}}{\partial x^s} + \frac{\partial g_{is}}{\partial x^r} - \frac{\partial g_{rs}}{\partial x^i}\right) \tag{1}$$

$$\Gamma^i{}_{rs} = \begin{Bmatrix} r\,s \\ i \end{Bmatrix} = \frac{1}{2}\,g^{ij}\Gamma_{j\cdot rs} \tag{2}$$

They are used to form tensors by covariant differentiation, as

$$A^i{}_{;p} = \frac{\partial A^i}{\partial x^p} + \Gamma^i{}_{pj}A^j \tag{3}$$

and

$$A^t_{\ s;r} = \frac{\partial A_s^{\ t}}{\partial x^r} - \Gamma^i_{\ sr} A_i^{\ t} + \Gamma^t_{\ jr} A_s^{\ j} \tag{4}$$

The equations of the geodesic lines in the Riemannian space are

$$\frac{d^2x^i}{ds^2} + \Gamma^i_{\ pq} \frac{dx^p}{ds} \frac{dx^q}{ds} = 0 \tag{5}$$

7.17. Curvature tensor. The Riemann-Christoffel curvature tensor is

$$R^i_{\ jhk} = \frac{\partial}{\partial x^h} \Gamma^i_{\ jk} - \frac{\partial}{\partial x^k} \Gamma^i_{\ jh} + \Gamma^i_{\ rh} \Gamma^r_{\ jk} - \Gamma^i_{\ rk} \Gamma^r_{\ jh} \tag{1}$$

This leads to R_{ik}, the second-rank curvature tensor,

$$R_{ik} = \frac{\partial}{\partial x^r} \Gamma^r_{\ ik} - \frac{\partial}{\partial x^k} \Gamma^r_{\ ir} + \Gamma^s_{\ rs} \Gamma^r_{\ ik} - \Gamma^s_{\ ri} \Gamma^r_{\ ks} \tag{2}$$

and to R, the curvature scalar,

$$R = g^{ik} R_{ik}. \tag{3}$$

All the components of each of these curvature tensors are zero for a Euclidean, or flat space.

8. Spherical Harmonics

8.1. Zonal harmonics. In spherical coordinates, for functions independent of θ, by § 7.1 Laplace's equation is

$$\frac{\partial}{\partial r}\left(r^2 \frac{\partial f}{\partial r}\right) + \frac{1}{\sin\phi} \frac{\partial}{\partial \phi}\left(\sin\phi \frac{\partial f}{\partial \phi}\right) = 0 \tag{1}$$

This admits as particular solutions the solid zonal harmonic functions

$$r^n P_n(\cos\phi) \quad \text{and} \quad r^{-(n+1)} P_n(\cos\phi) \tag{2}$$

if $P_n(\cos\phi)$ satisfies a certain differential equation. With $\cos\phi = x$, and $P_n = y$, the equation takes the form

$$(1 - x^2) \frac{d^2y}{dx^2} - 2x \frac{dy}{dx} + n(n+1)y = 0 \tag{3}$$

which is Legendre's differential equation.

The factor $P_n(\cos\phi)$ is called a zonal harmonic.

8.2. Legendre polynomials. For n zero or a positive integer, the only solution of Legendre's differential equation of § 8.1, which is regular at 1 and -1 reduces to a polynomial. This polynomial, multiplied by the factor which makes it 1 when $x = 1$ is called the nth Legendre polynomial and is denoted by $P_n(x)$. The first few Legendre polynomials are

$$\left.\begin{aligned} &P_0(x) = 1, \quad P_1(x) = x, \quad P_2(x) = \tfrac{1}{2}(3x^2 - 1) \\ &P_3(x) = \tfrac{1}{2}(5x^3 - 3x), \quad P_4(x) = \tfrac{1}{8}(35x^4 - 30x^2 + 3) \end{aligned}\right\} \quad (1)$$

The general expression is

$$\left.\begin{aligned} P_n(x) = \frac{(2n-1)(2n-3)\dots 3 \cdot 1}{n!} &\left[x^n - \frac{n(n-1)}{2(2n-1)} x^{n-2}\right. \\ &\left. + \frac{n(n-1)(n-2)(n-3)}{2 \cdot 4(2n-1)(2n-3)} x^{n-4} - \dots\right] \end{aligned}\right\} \quad (2)$$

8.3. Rodrigues's formula

$$P_n(x) = \frac{1}{2^n n!} \frac{d^n(x^2-1)^n}{dx^n} \quad (1)$$

8.4. Particular values

$$P_n(1) = 1, \quad P_n(-x) = (-1)^n P_n(x) \quad (1)$$

$$P_{2n+1}(0) = 0, \quad P_{2n}(0) = (-1)^n \frac{1 \cdot 3 \cdot 5 \dots (2n-1)}{2 \cdot 4 \cdot 6 \dots 2n} \quad (2)$$

$$\left[\frac{dP_{2n+1}(x)}{dx}\right]_{x=0} = (-1)^n \frac{3 \cdot 5 \cdot 7 \dots (2n+1)}{2 \cdot 4 \cdot 6 \dots 2n} \quad (3)$$

8.5. Trigonometric polynomials. In terms of ϕ and multiples of ϕ, where as in § 8.1 we put $\cos\phi = x$, the first few polynomials are

$$\left.\begin{aligned} &P_0(\cos\phi) = 1, \quad P_1(\cos\phi) = \cos\phi, \quad P_2(\cos\phi) = \tfrac{1}{4}(3\cos 2\phi + 1) \\ &P_3(\cos\phi) = \tfrac{1}{8}(5\cos 3\phi + 3\cos\phi) \\ &P_4(\cos\phi) = \tfrac{1}{64}(35\cos 4\phi + 20\cos 2\phi + 9) \end{aligned}\right\} \quad (1)$$

The general expression is

$$\left.\begin{aligned} P_n(\cos\phi) = 2\frac{1 \cdot 3 \cdot 5 \dots (2n-1)}{2^n n!} &\left[\cos n\phi + \frac{1}{1}\frac{n}{2n-1}\cos(n-2)\phi\right. \\ &+ \frac{1 \cdot 3}{1 \cdot 2}\frac{n(n-1)}{(2n-1)(2n-3)}\cos(n-4)\phi \\ &\left.+ \frac{1 \cdot 3 \cdot 5}{1 \cdot 2 \cdot 3}\frac{n(n-1)(n-2)}{(2n-1)(2n-3)(2n-5)}\cos(n-6)\phi + \dots\right] \end{aligned}\right\} \quad (2)$$

8.6. Generating functions. If $r < 1$ and $x < 1$,

$$(1 - 2rx + r^2)^{-1/2} = P_0(x) + rP_1(x) + r^2P_2(x) + r^3P_3(x) + \dots \qquad (1)$$

and if $r > 1$ and $x < 1$,

$$(1 - 2rx + r^2)^{-1/2} = \frac{1}{r}P_0(x) + \frac{1}{r^2}P_1(x) + \frac{1}{r^3}P_2(x) + \dots \qquad (2)$$

8.7. Recursion formula and orthogonality

$$nP_n(x) + (n-1)P_{n-2}(x) - (2n-1)xP_{n-1}(x) = 0 \qquad (1)$$

$$\int_{-1}^{1} P_m(x)P_n(x)\,dx = 0 \quad \text{for } m \neq n, \quad \int_{-1}^{1} [P_n(x)]^2\,dx = \frac{2}{2n+1} \qquad (2)$$

8.8. Laplace's integral

$$P_n(x) = \frac{1}{\pi}\int_0^{\pi} \frac{du}{(x + \sqrt{x^2-1}\cos u)^{n+1}} = \frac{1}{\pi}\int_0^{\pi} (x + \sqrt{x^2-1}\cos u)^n\,du \quad (1)$$

8.9. Asymptotic expression. If $\epsilon > 0$ and $\epsilon < \phi < \pi - \epsilon$,

$$P_n(\cos\phi) = \sqrt{\frac{2}{\pi n \sin\phi}}\sin\left[\left(n + \frac{1}{2}\right)\phi + \frac{\pi}{4}\right] + O\left(\frac{1}{n^{3/2}}\right) \qquad (1)$$

where O means " of the order of " for large n.

8.10. Tesseral harmonics. In spherical coordinates, by § 6.18 Laplace's equation is

$$\frac{\partial}{\partial r}\left(r^2\frac{\partial f}{\partial r}\right) + \frac{1}{\sin\phi}\frac{\partial}{\partial\phi}\left(\sin\phi\frac{\partial f}{\partial\phi}\right) + \frac{1}{\sin^2\phi}\frac{\partial^2 f}{\partial\theta^2} = 0 \qquad (1)$$

This admits as particular solutions the solid spherical harmonic functions

$$\left.\begin{aligned} &r^n \sin m\theta\, P_n^m(\cos\phi), \quad r^n \cos m\theta\, P_n^m(\cos\phi) \\ &r^{-(n+1)}\sin m\theta\, P_n^m(\cos\phi), \quad \text{and} \quad r^{-(n+1)}\cos m\theta\, P_n^m(\cos\phi) \end{aligned}\right\} \qquad (2)$$

if $P_n^m(\cos\phi)$ satisfies a certain differential equation. With $\cos\phi = x$, and $P_n^m = y$, the equation takes the form

$$(1 - x^2)\frac{d^2y}{dx^2} - 2x\frac{dy}{dx} + \left[n(n+1) - \frac{m^2}{1-x^2}\right]y = 0 \qquad (3)$$

which is the associated Legendre equation.

The factor $(\sin m\theta)P_n^m(\cos\phi)$ or $(\cos m\theta)P_n^m(\cos\phi)$ is called a tesseral harmonic. When $m = n$, it reduces to a sectorial harmonic. And when

$m = 0$, that involving $\cos m\theta$ reduces to $P_n^0(\cos\phi = P_n(\cos\phi)$, a zonal harmonic.

Solid harmonics are often combined in series or integrals which for fixed r and ϕ reduce to Fourier series or integrals of known functions of θ. (See §§ 14.10 to 14.16.)

8.11. Legendre's associated functions. Let m and n be each zero or a positive integer with $n \geqq m$. Then there is only one solution of the equation of § 8.10 which does not have logarithmic singularities at 1 or -1. With proper scale factor this solution is called the associated Legendre function and is denoted by $P_n^m(x)$.

$$P_n^m(x) = (1 - x^2)^{m/2} \frac{d^m P_n(x)}{dx^m} = \frac{1}{2^n n!} (1 - x^2)^{m/2} \frac{d^{n+m}}{dx^{n+m}} (x^2 - 1)^n \tag{1}$$

$$\left.\begin{aligned} P_n^m(x) = \frac{(2n)!}{2^n n!(n-m)!} (1 - x^2)^{m/2} \Bigg[x^{n-m} - \frac{(n-m)(n-m-1)}{2(2n-1)} x^{n-m-2} \\ + \frac{(n-m)(n-m-1)(n-m-2)(n-m-3)}{2 \cdot 4(2n-1)(2n-3)} x^{n-m-4} - \dots \Bigg] \end{aligned}\right\} \tag{2}$$

8.12. Particular values

$$\left.\begin{aligned} &P_n^0(x) = P_n(x), \quad P_n^m(-x) = (-1)^n P_n^m(x) \\ &P_n^n(x) = \frac{(2n)!}{2^n n!} (1 - x^2)^{n/2} = 1 \cdot 3 \cdot 5 \dots (2n-1)(1 - x^2)^{n/2} \end{aligned}\right\} \tag{1}$$

With $x = \cos\phi$, the sectorial harmonic

$$P_n^n(\cos\phi) = 1 \cdot 3 \cdot 5 \cdot \dots (2n-1) \sin^n\phi \tag{2}$$

8.13. Recursion formulas

$$(n - m)P_n^m(x) + (n + m - 1)P_{n-2}^m(x) - (2n - 1)xP_{n-1}^m(x) = 0 \tag{1}$$

$$\left.\begin{aligned} P_n^{m+2}(x) + (n - m)(n + m + 1)P_n^m(x) \\ - 2(m + 1) \frac{x}{\sqrt{1 - x^2}} P_n^{m+1}(x) = 0 \end{aligned}\right\} \tag{2}$$

8.14. Asymptotic expression. If $\epsilon > 0$ and $\epsilon < \phi < \pi - \epsilon$,

$$\left.\begin{aligned} &P_n^m(\cos\phi) \\ &= (-n)^m \sqrt{\frac{2}{n\pi \sin\phi}} \sin\left[\left(n + \frac{1}{2}\right)\phi + \frac{\pi}{4} + \frac{m\pi}{2}\right] + O(n^{m-3/2}) \end{aligned}\right\} \tag{1}$$

where O means "of the order of" for n large compared with m.

8.15. Addition theorem. Let γ be defined by

$$\cos\gamma = \cos\phi\cos\phi' + \sin\phi\sin\phi'\cos(\theta - \theta') \tag{1}$$

Thus γ is the distance on the unit sphere between the points with spherical polar coordinates $(1,\theta,\phi)$ and $(1,\theta',\phi')$. Then

$$P_n(\cos\gamma) = P_n(\cos\phi)P_n(\cos\phi') + 2\sum_{m=1}^{n}\frac{(n-m)!}{(n+m)!}P_n^m(\cos\phi)\,P_n^m(\cos\phi')\cos m(\phi - \phi')$$

8.16. Orthogonality

$$\int_{-1}^{1} P_n^m(x)\,P_k^m(x)\,dx = 0 \quad \text{for } k \neq n, \qquad \int_{-1}^{1} P_n^m(x)^2\,dx = \frac{2}{2n+1}\,\frac{(n+m)!}{(n-m)!} \tag{1}$$

9. Bessel Functions

9.1. Cylindrical harmonics. In cylindrical coordinates, by § 6.17 Laplace's equation is

$$\frac{1}{r}\frac{\partial}{\partial r}\left(r\frac{\partial f}{\partial r}\right) + \frac{1}{r^2}\frac{\partial^2 f}{\partial\theta^2} + \frac{\partial^2 f}{\partial z^2} = 0 \tag{1}$$

This admits as particular solutions the harmonic functions

$$\left.\begin{matrix} e^{-az}\sin n\theta\,J_n(ar), & e^{-az}\cos n\theta\,J_n(ar) \\ e^{az}\sin n\theta\,J_n(ar), & e^{az}\cos n\theta\,J_n(ar) \end{matrix}\right\} \tag{2}$$

if $J_n(ar)$ satisfies a certain differential equation. With $ar = x$ and $J_n = y$, the equation takes the form

$$x^2\frac{d^2y}{dx^2} + x\frac{dy}{dx} + (x^2 - n^2)y = 0 \tag{3}$$

which is Bessel's differential equation.

9.2. Bessel functions of the first kind. Only one solution of the equation (3) of § 9.1 is finite for $x = 0$. With proper scale factor it is called the Bessel function of the first kind and is denoted by $J_n(x)$, where $n \geqq 0$. For n zero or a positive integer

$$J_n(x) = \sum_{k=0}^{\infty}\frac{(-1)^k(x/2)^{n+2k}}{k!(n+k)!} \tag{1}$$

In particular,

$$J_0(x) = 1 - \frac{x^2}{2^2} + \frac{x^4}{2^4(2!)^2} - \frac{x^6}{2^6(3!)^2} + \frac{x^8}{2^8(4!)^2} - \cdots \tag{2}$$

$$J_1(x) = \frac{x}{2} - \frac{x^3}{2^3 2!} + \frac{x^5}{2^5 2!3!} - \frac{x^7}{2^7 3!4!} + \frac{x^9}{2^9 4!5!} - \cdots \tag{3}$$

The expression involving the gamma function of § 13.1.

$$J_p(x) = \sum_{k=0}^{\infty} \frac{(-1)^k x^{p+2k}}{2^{p+2k} k!\, \Gamma(p+k+1)} \tag{4}$$

reduces to the above when $p = n$, zero or a positive integer, and for other positive p defines the Bessel function of order p.

9.3. Bessel functions of the second kind. When p is positive and not an integer

$$J_{-p}(x) = \sum_{k=0}^{\infty} (-1)^k \frac{x^{-p+2k}}{2^{-p+2k} k!\, \Gamma(-p+k+1)} \tag{1}$$

is a second solution of Bessel's equation of order p. Or we may use

$$Y_p(x) = N_p(x) = \frac{1}{\sin p\pi} [\cos p\pi\, J_p(x) - J_{-p}(x)] \tag{2}$$

For $n = 0$ or a positive integer, $J_{-n}(x) = (-1)^n J_n(x)$, but as $p \to n$, the limiting value of $Y_p(x)$ is $Y_n(x)$, where

$$\left.\begin{aligned} Y_n(x) = \frac{1}{\pi} \Bigg[2J_n(x) \ln \frac{x}{2} - \sum_{k=0}^{\infty} \frac{(-1)^k x^{n+2k}}{2^{n+2k} k!(n+k)!} [\psi(k+n) + \psi(k)] \\ - \sum_{r=0}^{n-1} \frac{(n-r-1)!x^{-n+2r}}{2^{-n+2r} r!} \Bigg] \end{aligned}\right\} \tag{3}$$

$$\psi(k) = -0.5772157 + 1 + \frac{1}{2} + \frac{1}{3} + \ldots + \frac{1}{k} \tag{4}$$

9.4. Hankel functions. The Hankel functions, sometimes called Bessel functions of the third kind, are defined by

$$H_p^{(1)}(x) = J_p(x) + iY_p(x) = \frac{i}{\sin p\pi} [e^{p\pi i} J_p(x) - J_{-p}(x)] \tag{1}$$

$$H_p^{(2)}(x) = J_p(x) - iY_p(x) = \frac{i}{\sin p\pi} [e^{p\pi i} J_p(x) - J_{-p}(x)] \tag{2}$$

In terms of the Hankel functions

$$J_p(x) = \frac{1}{2}[H_p^{(2)}(x) + H_p^{(1)}(x)], \quad Y_p(x) = \frac{1}{2}[H_p^{(2)}(x) - H_p^{(1)}(x)] \tag{3}$$

Let A be a path in the complex plane made up of a small circuit of the point 1 in the positive direction and two lines parallel to the imaginary axis in the upper half plane extending to infinity. Thus A starts at infinity with an angle $-3\pi/2$, and ends at infinity with an angle $\pi/2$ (see § 20.3.) Then for z with positive real part

$$H_p^{(1)}(z) = \frac{\Gamma(\frac{1}{2} - p)}{2^p \pi^{3/2} i} \int_A e^{izu}(u^2 - 1)^{p-1/2}\, du \tag{4}$$

Similarly for B a path made up of a small negative circuit of the point -1 and two lines parallel to the imaginary axis in the upper half plane to infinity, starting with an angle $\pi/2$ and ending with an angle $-3\pi/2$,

$$H_p^{(2)}(z) = \frac{\Gamma(\frac{1}{2} - p)}{2^p \pi^{3/2} i} \int_B e^{izu}(u^2 - 1)^{p-1/2}\, du \tag{5}$$

The Hankel functions are complex for real values of x. But

$$i^{p+1}H_p^{(1)}(iy) \quad \text{and} \quad i^{-(p+1)}H_p^{(2)}(-iy) \tag{6}$$

are both real when y is real and positive.

When the imaginary part of z goes to plus infinity, $H_p^{(1)}(z)$ approaches zero. And when the imaginary part of z goes to minus infinity, $H_p^{(2)}(z)$ approaches zero.

9.5. Bessel's differential equation. Let $Z_p(x)$ be a solution of

$$x^2 \frac{d^2y}{dx^2} + x\frac{dy}{dx} + (x^2 - p^2)y = 0 \tag{1}$$

For p nonintegral,

$$Z_p(x) = c_1 J_p(x) + c_2 J_{-p}(x) \tag{2}$$

and for any positive or zero value of p,

$$Z_p(x) = c_1 J_p(x) + c_2 Y_p(x) \tag{3}$$

or

$$Z_p(x) = c_1 H_p^{(1)}(x) + c_2 H_p^{(2)}(x) \tag{4}$$

give general solutions with c_1, c_2 arbitrary constants.

9.6. Equation reducible to Bessel's. The equation

$$\left.\begin{aligned} x^2 \frac{d^2y}{dx^2} &+ [(1 - 2A)x - 2BCx^{C+1}]\frac{dy}{dx} \\ &+ [(A^2 - E^2p^2) + BC(2A - C)x^C + B^2C^2x^{2C} + E^2D^2x^{2E}]y = 0 \end{aligned}\right\} \tag{1}$$

becomes Bessel's equation of order p, in Z and X if

$$y = x^A e^{Bx^C} Z, \quad X = Dx^E \tag{2}$$

and so has as its solution $y = x^A e^{Bx^C} Z_p(Dx^E)$.

And in particular $y = x^A Z_p(Dx^E)$ is the solution of

$$x^2 \frac{d^2y}{dx^2} + (1 - 2A)x \frac{dy}{dx} + [(A^2 - E^2p^2) + E^2D^2x^{2E}]y = 0 \tag{3}$$

The solution of $d^2y/dx^2 + Bxy = 0$ is

$$y = \sqrt{x}\, Z_{1/3}\left(\frac{2}{3}\sqrt{B}\, x^{3/2}\right) \tag{4}$$

9.7. Asymptotic expressions. For x large compared with p,

$$H_p^{(1)}(z) = i^{-p-1/2} 2^{1/2} (\pi z)^{-1/2} e^{iz}\, S_p(-2iz) \tag{1}$$

$$H_p^{(2)}(z) = i^{p+1/2} 2^{1/2} (\pi z)^{-1/2} e^{-iz}\, S_p(2iz) \tag{2}$$

where the asymptotic series for S_p is given by

$$\left.\begin{aligned} S_p(t) = 1 + \frac{4p^2 - 1}{1!\,4t} &+ \frac{(4p^2-1)(4p^2-9)}{2!\,(4t)^2} \\ &+ \frac{(4p^2-1)(4p^2-9)(4p^2-25)}{3!\,(4t)^3} + \cdots \end{aligned}\right\} \tag{3}$$

If

$$\phi_p = x - \frac{2p+1}{4}\pi \quad \text{and} \quad S_p(2ix) = P_p(x) - iQ_p(x) \tag{4}$$

with the series P_p and Q_p real,

$$J_p(x) = 2^{1/2}(\pi x)^{-1/2}(P_p \cos\phi_p - Q_p \sin\phi_p) \tag{5}$$

$$Y_p(x) = 2^{1/2}(\pi x)^{-1/2}(P_p \sin\phi_p + Q_p \cos\phi_p) \tag{6}$$

Using the leading terms only, and O meaning "of the order of,"

$$\left.\begin{aligned} J_p(x) &= 2^{1/2}(\pi x)^{-1/2} \cos\phi_p + O\left(\frac{1}{x^{3/2}}\right) \\ Y_p(x) &= 2^{1/2}(\pi x)^{-1/2} \sin\phi_p + O\left(\frac{1}{x^{3/2}}\right) \end{aligned}\right\} \tag{7}$$

9.8. Order half an odd integer. Let p have the form

$$p = \frac{2n+1}{2} = n + \frac{1}{2} \tag{1}$$

n an integer or zero.

The expressions of § 9.7 assume a closed form. The first few are

$$\left.\begin{aligned} J_{1/2}(x) &= 2^{1/2}(\pi x)^{-1/2}\sin x \\ J_{-1/2}(x) &= -Y_{-1/2}(x) = 2^{1/2}(\pi x)^{-1/2}\cos x \end{aligned}\right\} \tag{2}$$

$$J_{3/2}(x) = 2^{1/2}(\pi x)^{-1/2}\left(-\cos x + \frac{\sin x}{x}\right) \tag{3}$$

$$J_{-3/2}(x) = Y_{3/2}(x) = 2^{1/2}(\pi x)^{-1/2}\left(-\sin x - \frac{\cos x}{x}\right) \tag{4}$$

$$Y_p(x) = (-1)^{n+1}J_{-p}(x) \quad \text{if} \quad p = n + \frac{1}{2} \tag{5}$$

9.9. Integral representation

$$J_n(x) = \frac{1}{\pi}\int_0^\pi \cos(x\cos u - nu)du \tag{1}$$

9.10. Recursion formula

$$J_{p-1}(x) + J_{p+1}(x) = \frac{2p}{x}J_p(x), \quad Y_{p-1}(x) + Y_{p+1}(x) = \frac{2p}{x}Y_p(x) \tag{1}$$

9.11. Derivatives

$$\frac{dJ_p}{dx} = -\frac{p}{x}J_p + J_{p-1} = \frac{p}{x}J_p - J_{p+1} = \frac{1}{2}J_{p-1} - \frac{1}{2}J_{p+1} \tag{1}$$

$$\frac{d}{dx}[x^p J_p(ax)] = ax^p J_{p-1}(ax), \quad \frac{d}{dx}[x^{-p}J_p(ax)] = -ax^{-p}J_{p+1}(ax) \tag{2}$$

and $Y_p(x)$ satisfies similar relations.

9.12. Generating function

$$e^{(x/2)(t-1/t)} = \sum_{n=-\infty}^{\infty} J_n(x)t^n \tag{1}$$

9.13. Indefinite integrals

$$\int xJ_p(ax)J_p(bx)dx = \frac{bxJ_p(ax)J_{p-1}(bx) - axJ_{p-1}(ax)J_p(bx)}{a^2 - b^2} \tag{1}$$

$$\int x[J_p(ax)]^2\,dx = \frac{x^2}{2}\{[J_p(ax)]^2 - J_{p-1}(ax)J_{p+1}(ax)\} \tag{2}$$

9.14. Modified Bessel functions. We define

$$I_p(x) = i^{-p}J_p(ix), \quad \text{where} \quad i^{-p} = e^{-pi\pi/2} = \cos\frac{p\pi}{2} - i\sin\frac{p\pi}{2} \tag{1}$$

$$\frac{d}{dx}[x^p I_p(x)] = x^p I_{p-1}(x), \quad \frac{d}{dx}[x^{-p}I_p(x)] = x^{-p}I_{p+1}(x) \tag{2}$$

$$\frac{dI_p}{dx} = \frac{1}{2}(I_{p-1} + I_{p+1}), \quad I_{p-1} - I_{p+1} = \frac{2p}{x}I_p \tag{3}$$

For p not zero or an integer we define

$$K_p(x) = \frac{\pi}{2 \sin p\pi}[I_{-p}(x) - I_p(x)] \tag{4}$$

For $p = n$, zero, or an integer,

$$\left.\begin{aligned} K_n(x) &= (-1)^{n+1} I_n(x) \ln \frac{x}{2} + \frac{1}{2} \sum_{r=0}^{n-1} \frac{(n-r-1)!\,(-1)^r}{2^{-n+2r} r!} x^{-n+2r} \\ &\quad + (-1)^n \frac{1}{2} \sum_{k=0}^{\infty} \frac{x^{n+2k}}{2^{n+2k} k!(n+k)!} [\psi(k+n) - \psi(k)] \end{aligned}\right\} \tag{5}$$

where $\psi(k)$ is that of (4) of § 9.3. For all values of p,

$$\frac{dK_p}{dx} = -\frac{1}{2}(K_{p-1} + K_{p+1}), \quad K_{p-1} - K_{p+1} = -\frac{2p}{x} K_p, \quad K_{-p} = K_p \tag{6}$$

The general solution of the differential equation

$$x^2 \frac{d^2y}{dx^2} + x \frac{dy}{dx} - (x^2 + p^2)y = 0$$

is

$$y = c_1 I_p(x) + c_2 K_p(x) \tag{7}$$

and the general solution of the differential equation

$$x^4 \frac{d^4y}{dx^4} + 2x^3 \frac{d^3y}{dx^3} - (2p^2 + 1)x^2 \frac{d^2y}{dx^2} + (2p^2 + 1)x \frac{dy}{dx} + (p^4 - 4p^2 - x^4)y = 0$$

is

$$y = c_1 J_p(x) + c_2 Y_p(x) + c_3 I_p(x) + c_4 K_p(x) \tag{8}$$

10. The Hypergeometric Function

10.1. The hypergeometric equation. The differential equation

$$x(1-x) \frac{d^2y}{dx^2} + [c - (a + b + 1)x] \frac{dy}{dx} - aby = 0 \tag{1}$$

has one solution regular at the origin. With a scale factor making it 1 when $x = 0$, this solution is called the hypergeometric function and is denoted by $F(a,b;c;x)$.

10.2. The hypergeometric series. For $|x| < 1$, $F(a,b;c;x)$ equals

$$\left.\begin{aligned} &1 + \frac{a \cdot b}{1 \cdot c} x + \frac{a(a+1)b(b+1)}{1 \cdot 2 \cdot c(c+1)} x^2 \\ &\quad + \frac{a(a+1)(a+2)b(b+1)(b+2)}{1 \cdot 2 \cdot 3 \cdot c(c+1)(c+2)} x^3 + \cdots \end{aligned}\right\} \tag{1}$$

With $\Gamma(c)$ as in § 13.1,

$$\left.\begin{aligned}\lim_{c\to -n}\frac{F(a,b;c;x)}{\Gamma(c)} = \frac{a(a+1)\ldots(a+n)(b+1)\ldots(b+n)}{(n+1)!}\,x^{n+1}\\ F(a+n+1,b+n+1;n+2;x)\end{aligned}\right\} \quad (2)$$

10.3. Contiguous functions. In general, a second solution of the differential equation of § 10.1 is given by

$$x^{1-c}F(a+1-c,b+1-c;2-c;x) \quad (1)$$

There are other functions related to $F(a,b;c;x)$ making in all a set of 24, and a number of linear relations connecting them. They form six groups of four, each set of four being equal except perhaps for sign.

For example,

$$\left.\begin{aligned}F(a,b;c;x) &= (1-x)^{c-a-b}F(c-a,c-b;c;x)\\ &= (1-x)^{-a}F\left(a,c-b;c;\frac{x}{x-1}\right)\\ &= (1-x)^{-b}F\left(b,c-a;c;\frac{x}{x-1}\right)\end{aligned}\right\} \quad (2)$$

is one set of four. As six distinct ones we may take

$$\left.\begin{gathered}F(a,b;c;x)\\ x^{1-c}F(a+1-c,b+1-c;2-c;x)\\ F(a,b;a+b+1-c;1-x)\\ (1-x)^{c-a-b}F(c-a,c-b;c+1-a-b;1-x)\\ x^{-a}F\left(a,a+1-c;a+1-b;\frac{1}{x}\right)\\ x^{-b}F\left(b,b+1-c;b+1-a;\frac{1}{x}\right)\end{gathered}\right\} \quad (3)$$

$$\left.\begin{aligned}F(a,b;c;x) &= \frac{\Gamma(c)\Gamma(c-a-b)}{\Gamma(c-a)\Gamma(c-b)}F(a,b;a+b+1-c;1-x)\\ &+ (1-x)^{c-a-b}\frac{\Gamma(c)\Gamma(a+b-c)}{\Gamma(a)\Gamma(b)}F(c-a,c-b;c+1-a-b;1-x)\end{aligned}\right\} \quad (4)$$

$$F(a,b;c;x) = \frac{\Gamma(c)\Gamma(b-a)}{\Gamma(b)\Gamma(c-a)}(-x)^{-a}F\left(a,a+1-c;a+1-b;\frac{1}{x}\right) \quad (5)$$

10.4. Elementary functions

$$(1 + x)^n = F(-n,b\,;b\,;-x) \tag{1}$$

$$\ln(1 + x) = xF(1,1\,;2\,;-x) \tag{2}$$

$$e^x = \lim_{b\to\infty} F(1,b\,;1\,;x/b) \tag{3}$$

$$\cos nx = F(\tfrac{1}{2}n, -\tfrac{1}{2}n\,; \tfrac{1}{2}\,; \sin^2 x) \tag{4}$$

$$\sin nx = n(\sin x)F\left(\frac{1+n}{2}, \frac{1-n}{2}\,; \frac{3}{2}\,; \sin^2 x\right) \tag{5}$$

$$\ln\left(\frac{1+x}{1-x}\right) = 2xF\left(\frac{1}{2}, 1\,; \frac{3}{2}\,; x^2\right) \tag{6}$$

$$\sin^{-1} x = xF\left(\frac{1}{2}, \frac{1}{2}\,; \frac{3}{2}\,; x^2\right) \tag{7}$$

$$\tan^{-1} x = xF\left(\frac{1}{2}, 1\,; \frac{3}{2}\,; -x^2\right) \tag{8}$$

10.5. Other functions. For polynomials, see § 10.7. For the $P_n^{\ m}(x)$ of § 8.11 :

$$P_n^{\ m}(x) = \frac{(x+1)^{m/2}}{(x-1)^{m/2}} \frac{1}{\Gamma(1-m)} F\left(-n, n+1\,; 1-m\,; \frac{1-x}{2}\right) \tag{1}$$

$$K(k) = \int_0^{\pi/2} \frac{d\phi}{\sqrt{1-k^2 \sin^2\phi}} = \frac{\pi}{2} F\left(\frac{1}{2}, \frac{1}{2}\,; 1\,; k^2\right) \tag{2}$$

$$E(k) = \int_0^{\pi/2} \sqrt{1-k^2 \sin^2\phi}\, d\phi = \frac{\pi}{2} F\left(-\frac{1}{2}, \frac{1}{2}\,; 1\,; k^2\right) \tag{3}$$

10.6. Special relations

$$\frac{d}{dx} F(a,b\,;c\,;x) = \frac{ab}{c} F(a+1, b+1\,; c+1\,; x) \tag{1}$$

$$F(a,b\,;c\,;1) = \frac{\Gamma(c)\Gamma(c-a-b)}{\Gamma(c-a)\Gamma(c-b)} \tag{2}$$

$$F(a,b\,;c\,;x) = \frac{\Gamma(c)}{\Gamma(b)\Gamma(c-b)} \int_0^1 u^{b-1}(1-u)^{c-b-1}(1-ux)^{-a}\, du \tag{3}$$

$$\left.\begin{aligned} &F(-n+m+1, 2m+2+k\,; 2m+2\,; x) \\ &\quad = \frac{(2m+1)!}{(2m+k+1)!} \frac{1}{x^{2m+1}} \frac{d^k}{dx^k}[x^{2m+k+1}(1-x)^{n-m-1}] \end{aligned}\right\} \tag{4}$$

10.7. Jacobi polynomials or hypergeometric polynomials

$$\left.\begin{aligned} J_n(p,q;x) &= F(-n, p+n; q; x) \\ &= \frac{x^{1-q}(1-x)^{q-p}}{q(q+1)\dots(q+n-1)}\frac{d^n}{dx^n}[x^{q+n-1}(1-x)^{p+n-q}] \end{aligned}\right\} \quad (1)$$

For $q > 0$, $p > q - 1$, these form a set of polynomials orthogonal with a weight function $w(x) = x^{q-1}(1-x)^{p-q}$ as in § 14.19 on 0,1. They satisfy

$$x(1-x)\frac{d^2y}{dx^2} + [q-(p+1)x]\frac{dy}{dx} + n(p+n)y = 0 \quad (2)$$

For

$$P_n(x) = J_n\left(1, 1; \frac{1-x}{2}\right) = F\left(-n, n+1; 1; \frac{1-x}{2}\right), \quad w(x) = 1 \quad (3)$$

and the Legendre polynomials of § 8.2 are orthogonal on —1,1. For

$$\left.\begin{aligned} T_n(x) &= \cos(n\cos^{-1}x) = J_n\left(0, \frac{1}{2}; \frac{1-x}{2}\right) \\ &= F\left(-n, n; \frac{1}{2}; \frac{1-x}{2}\right), \quad w(x) = \frac{2}{\sqrt{1-x^2}} \end{aligned}\right\} \quad (4)$$

and the Tschebycheff poylnomials $T_n(x)$ are orthogonal with weight function $1/\sqrt{1-x^2}$ on —1, 1.

10.8. Generalized hypergeometric functions. Let $(a)_0 = 1$, $(a)_n = a(a+1)(a+2)\dots(a+n-1)$. And define

$$\left.\begin{aligned} &{}_pF_q(a_1, a_2, \dots, a_p; b_1, b_2, \dots, b_q; x) \\ &= \sum_{n=0}^{\infty}\frac{(a_1)_n(a_2)_n\dots(a_p)_n}{(b_1)_n(b_2)_n\dots(b_q)_n}\cdot\frac{x^n}{n!} \\ &= 1 + \frac{a_1a_2\dots a_p}{b_1b_2\dots b_q}x + \frac{a_1(a_1+1)a_2(a_2+1)\dots a_p(a_p+1)}{b_1(b_1+1)b_2(b_2+1)\dots b_q(b_q+1)}\cdot\frac{x^2}{2!} + \dots \end{aligned}\right\} \quad (1)$$

For example,

$$e^x = {}_1F_1(b; b; x) \cdot {}_2F_1(a, b; c; x) = F(a, b; c; x) \quad (2)$$

of § 10.1.

The Bessel function of § 9.2,

$$J_p(x) = \frac{e^{-ix}(x/2)^p}{(p+1)}\,{}_1F_1\left(n+\frac{1}{2}; 2n+1; 2ix\right) \quad (3)$$

$$\left.\begin{aligned}&{}_3F_2(a, b, c\,; a+1-b, a+1-c\,; x)\\&\quad= (1-x)^{-a}{}_3F_2\left(\frac{a}{2}, \frac{a+1}{2}, a+1-b-c\,;\right.\\&\qquad\qquad\left. a+1-b, a+1-c\,; \frac{-4x}{(1-x)^2}\right)\end{aligned}\right\} \quad (4)$$

$$\left.\begin{aligned}&{}_3F_2(a, b, c\,; a+1-b, a+1-c\,; 1)\\&\quad= \frac{\Gamma(a/2+1)\Gamma(a+1-b)\Gamma(a+1-c)\Gamma(a/2+1-b-c)}{\Gamma(a+1)\Gamma(a/2+1-b)\Gamma(a/2+1-c)\Gamma(a+1-b-c)}\end{aligned}\right\} \quad (5)$$

10.9. The confluent hypergeometric function. $M(a,c,x) = {}_1F_1(a\,;c\,;x)$ is a solution of

$$x\frac{d^2y}{dx^2} + (c-x)\frac{dy}{dx} - ay = 0 \quad (1)$$

11. Laguerre Functions

11.1. Laguerre polynomials. The differential equation

$$x\frac{d^2y}{dx^2} + (1-x)\frac{dy}{dx} + ny = 0 \quad (1)$$

has polynomial solutions known as Laguerre polynomials and denoted by $L_n(x)$. The first few are

$$\left.\begin{aligned}&L_0(x) = 1, \quad L_1(x) = -x+1, \quad L_2(x) = x^2 - 4x + 2\\&L_3(x) = -x^3 + 9x^2 - 18x + 6\end{aligned}\right\} \quad (2)$$

In general

$$L_n(x) = (-1)^n\left(x^n - \frac{n^2}{1!}x^{n-1} + \frac{n^2(n-1)^2}{2!}x^{n-2} + \dots + (-1)^n n!\right) \quad (3)$$

$$L_n(x) = e^x\frac{d^n(x^n e^{-x})}{dx^n} = n!\,{}_1F_1(-n\,;1\,;x) \quad (4)$$

11.2. Generating function

$$\frac{e^{-xt/(1-t)}}{1-t} = \sum_{n=0}^{\infty} L_n(x)\frac{t^n}{n!} \quad (1)$$

11.3. Recursion formula

$$L_{n+1}(x) - (2n+1-x)L_n(x) + n^2L_{n-1}(x) = 0 \quad (1)$$

11.4. Laguerre functions. The Laguerre functions $e^{-x/2}L_n(x)$ satisfy the differential equation

$$x\frac{d^2y}{dx^2}+\frac{dy}{dx}+\left(\frac{1}{2}-\frac{x}{4}+n\right)y=0 \qquad (1)$$

These functions are orthogonal on the range 0, ∞, and

$$\int_0^\infty e^{-x}L_n(x)L_m(x)dx=0 \quad \text{if} \quad m\neq n; \quad \int_0^\infty e^{-x}[L_n(x)]^2dx=(n!)^2 \qquad (2)$$

11.5. Associated Laguerre polynomials. These are the derivatives

$$L_r{}^s(x)=\frac{d^s}{dx^s}[L_r(x)]=\frac{\Gamma(r+s+1)}{\Gamma(s+1)}\,{}_1F_1(-r\,;s+1\,;x) \qquad (1)$$

They satisfy the differential equation

$$x\frac{d^2y}{dx^2}+(s+1-x)\frac{dy}{dx}+(r-s)y=0 \qquad (2)$$

11.6. Generating function

$$(-1)^s\frac{e^{-xt/(1-t)}}{(1-t)^{s+1}}t^s=\sum_{r=s}^{\infty}L_r{}^s(x)\frac{t^r}{r!} \qquad (1)$$

11.7. Associated Laguerre functions. In § 11.5 put $r=n+k$ and $s=2k+1$. Then the associated Laguerre functions are defined as

$$e^{-x/2}x^kL_{n+k}{}^{2k+1}(x) \qquad (1)$$

For x, the r of spherical coordinates, the volume element involves $x^2\,dx$, and with this element the functions are orthogonal.

$$\int_0^\infty e^{-x}x^{2k}L_{n+k}{}^{2k+1}L_{m+k}{}^{2k+1}x^2dx=0 \quad \text{if} \quad m\neq n \qquad (2)$$

$$\int_0^\infty e^{-x}x^{2k}L_{n+k}{}^{2k+1}x^2dx=\frac{2n[(n+k)!]^3}{(n-k-1)!} \qquad (3)$$

12. Hermite Functions

12.1. Hermite polynomials. The differential equation

$$\frac{d^2y}{dx^2}-2x\frac{dy}{dx}+2ny=0 \qquad (1)$$

has polynomial solutions known as Hermite polynomials and denoted by $H_n(x)$.

The first few are

$$\left.\begin{aligned} &H_0(x) = 1, \quad H_1(x) = 2x, \quad H_2(x) = 4x^2 - 2 \\ &H_3(x) = 8x^3 - 12x, \quad H_4(x) = 16x^4 - 48x^2 + 12 \end{aligned}\right\} \tag{2}$$

In general, with K equal to the biggest integer in $n/2$,

$$H_n(x) = \sum_{k=0}^{K} (-1)^k \frac{1}{k!} n(n-1) \dots (n-2k+1)(2x)^{n-2k} \tag{3}$$

$$H_n(x) = (-1)^n e^{x^2} \frac{d^n e^{-x^2}}{dx^n} \tag{4}$$

$$H_{2n} = (-1)^n 2^n (2n-1)(2n-3) \dots 3 \cdot 1 \, {}_1F_1\left(-n; \frac{1}{2}; x^2\right) \tag{5}$$

$$H_{2n+1} = (-1)^n 2^{n+1} (2n+1)(2n-1) \dots 3 \cdot 1 \, x {}_1F_1\left(-n; \frac{3}{2}; x^2\right) \tag{6}$$

12.2. Generating function

$$e^{-t^2+2tx} = e^{x^2} e^{-(t-x)^2} = \sum_{n=0}^{\infty} H_n(x) \frac{t^n}{n!} \tag{1}$$

12.3. Recursion formula

$$H_{n+1}(x) - 2xH_n(x) + 2nH_{n-1}(x) = 0 \tag{1}$$

12.4. Hermite functions. The Hermite functions $e^{-x^2/2}H_n(x)$ satisfy the differential equation

$$\frac{d^2y}{dx^2} + (2n + 1 - x^2)y = 0 \tag{1}$$

These functions are orthogonal on the range $-\infty$, ∞, and

$$\left.\begin{aligned} &\int_{-\infty}^{\infty} e^{-x^2} H_n(x) H_m(x) dx = 0 \quad \text{if} \quad m \neq n \\ &\int_{-\infty}^{\infty} e^{-x^2} [H_n(x)]^2 \, dx = 2^n n! \sqrt{\pi} \end{aligned}\right\} \tag{2}$$

13. Miscellaneous Functions

13.1. The gamma function. For p positive the integral

$$\Gamma(p) = \int_0^{\infty} x^{p-1} e^{-x} \, dx \tag{1}$$

defines the gamma function.

The infinite products

$$\frac{1}{\Gamma(z)} = e^{\gamma(z-1)} \prod_{n=1}^{\infty} \left(1 + \frac{z-1}{n}\right) e^{-(z-1)/n} = z e^{\gamma z} \prod_{n=1}^{\infty} \left(1 + \frac{z}{n}\right) e^{-z/n} \qquad (2)$$

define the function for all complex values of z.

$$\gamma = 0.577216 \qquad (3)$$

$$\Gamma(z) = \lim_{n\to\infty} \frac{(1 \cdot 2 \cdot 3 \ldots n) n^z}{z(z+1)(z+2)\ldots(z+n+1)} \qquad (4)$$

13.2. Functional equations

$$\Gamma(z+1) = z\Gamma(z), \quad \Gamma(z)\Gamma(1-z) = \frac{\pi}{\sin \pi z} \qquad (1)$$

$$\Gamma\left(\frac{z}{n}\right)\Gamma\left(\frac{z+1}{n}\right) \ldots \Gamma\left(\frac{z+n-1}{n}\right) n^{z-1/2} = (2\pi)^{(n-1)/2}\Gamma(z) \qquad (2)$$

$$\Gamma\left(\frac{z}{2}\right)\Gamma\left(\frac{z+1}{2}\right) 2^{z-1} = \sqrt{\pi}\,\Gamma(z) \qquad (3)$$

13.3. Special values

$$\Gamma(1) = 0! = 1, \quad \Gamma(n) = (n-1)! = 1 \cdot 2 \cdot 3 \ldots (n-1) \qquad (1)$$

for n a positive integer.

$$\Gamma\left(\frac{1}{2}\right) = \sqrt{\pi} \qquad (2)$$

13.4. Logarithmic derivative

$$\psi(z) = \frac{d \ln \Gamma(z)}{dz} = -\gamma + \sum_{n=1}^{\infty} \left(\frac{1}{n} - \frac{1}{z+n-1}\right) \qquad (1)$$

$$\psi'(z) = \frac{d\psi(z)}{dz} = \sum_{n=0}^{\infty} \frac{1}{(z+n)^2} \qquad (2)$$

If the terms of a convergent series are rational functions of n, by a partial fraction decomposition the series may be summed in terms of ψ and its derivatives by the series of this section.

13.5. Asymptotic expressions. If O means "of the order of,"

$$\ln \Gamma(x) = \ln [\sqrt{2\pi}\, x^{x-1/2} e^{-x}] + \frac{1}{12x} + O\left(\frac{1}{x^3}\right) \qquad (1)$$

$$x! = \Gamma(x+1) = \sqrt{2\pi}\, x^{x+1/2} e^{-x} \left[1 + \frac{1}{12x} + O\left(\frac{1}{x^2}\right) \right] \tag{2}$$

The first term of this, $\sqrt{2\pi}\, n^{n+1/2}\, e^{-n}$, is Stirling's formula for factorial n, and for large n may be used to evaluate ratios involving factorials.

13.6. Stirling's formula

$$\lim_{n\to\infty} \frac{n!}{\sqrt{2\pi}\, n^{n+1/2}\, e^{-n}} = 1 \tag{1}$$

13.7. The beta function. For p and q positive

$$B(p,q) = \int_0^1 x^{p-1}(1-x)^{q-1}\, dx = 2\int_0^{\pi/2} \cos^{2q-1}\theta \sin^{2p-1}\theta\, d\theta \tag{1}$$

In terms of the gamma function

$$B(p,q) = \frac{\Gamma(p)\Gamma(q)}{\Gamma(p+q)} \tag{2}$$

$$B(p+1, q) = \frac{p}{p+q} B(p, q), \quad B(p, 1-p) = \frac{\pi}{\sin \pi p} \tag{3}$$

13.8. Integrals. In the following integrals, the constants are such as to make all arguments of gamma functions positive.

$$\int_0^1 x^a \left(\ln \frac{1}{x}\right)^b dx = \frac{\Gamma(b+1)}{(a+1)^{b+1}}, \quad \int_0^\infty x^a e^{-bx^c} dx = \frac{1}{c} b^{-(a+1)/c}\, \Gamma\left(\frac{a+1}{c}\right) \tag{1}$$

The double integral of $x^P y^Q$ over the first quadrant of $(x/a)^A + (y/b)^B = 1$ is

$$\int_0^a dx \int_0^{b[1-(x/a)^A]^{1/B}} x^P y^Q\, dy = \frac{a^{P+1} b^{Q+1}}{AB} \frac{\Gamma\left(\frac{P+1}{A}\right)\Gamma\left(\frac{Q+1}{B}\right)}{\Gamma\left(\frac{P+1}{A} + \frac{Q+1}{B} + 1\right)} \tag{2}$$

The triple integral of $x^P y^Q z^R$ over the first octant of

$$\left.\begin{aligned} &\left(\frac{x}{a}\right)^A + \left(\frac{y}{b}\right)^B + \left(\frac{z}{c}\right)^C = 1 \\ &\text{is} \\ &\frac{a^{P+1} b^{Q+1} c^{R+1}}{ABC} \frac{\Gamma\left(\frac{P+1}{A}\right)\Gamma\left(\frac{Q+1}{B}\right)\Gamma\left(\frac{R+1}{C}\right)}{\Gamma\left(\frac{P+1}{A} + \frac{Q+1}{B} + \frac{R+1}{C} + 1\right)} \end{aligned}\right\} \tag{3}$$

13.9. The error integral

$$\operatorname{Erf} x = \frac{2}{\sqrt{\pi}} \int_0^x e^{-t^2} dt \tag{1}$$

The factor outside makes $\operatorname{Erf}(\infty) = 1$. For small x,

$$\operatorname{Erf} x = \frac{2}{\sqrt{\pi}} \left(x - \frac{x^3}{1!3} + \frac{x^5}{2!5} - \dots \right) \tag{2}$$

For large x the asymptotic expression is

$$\operatorname{Erf} x = 1 - \frac{1}{\sqrt{\pi}\, x} e^{-x^2} \left(1 - \frac{1}{2x^2} + \frac{1 \cdot 3}{(2x^2)^2} - \frac{1 \cdot 3 \cdot 5}{(2x^2)^3} + \dots \right) \tag{3}$$

$$\int_0^\infty e^{-h^2x^2} dx = \frac{\sqrt{\pi}}{2h}, \quad \int_0^\infty x e^{-h^2x^2} dx = \frac{1}{2h^2} \tag{4}$$

$$\int_0^\infty x^2 e^{-h^2x^2} dx = \frac{\sqrt{\pi}}{4h^3}, \quad \int_0^\infty x^n e^{-h^2x^2} dx = \frac{1}{2h^{n+1}} \Gamma\left(\frac{n+1}{2} \right) \tag{5}$$

13.10. The Riemann zeta function.

For $z = x + iy$, $x > 1$,

$$\zeta(z) = \sum_{n=1}^{\infty} \frac{1}{n^z} = \prod_{\text{prime}} (1 - p^{-z})^{-1} \tag{1}$$

where the product extends over all prime integers p.

For $x > 1$,

$$\zeta(z) = \frac{1}{\Gamma(z)} \int_0^\infty \frac{t^{z-1}}{e^t - 1} dt \tag{2}$$

For $x > 0$,

$$\zeta(z) = \frac{1}{(1 - 2^{1-z})} \frac{1}{\Gamma(z)} \int_0^\infty \frac{t^{z-1}}{e^t + 1} dt \tag{3}$$

14. Series

14.1. Bernoulli numbers.

These are generated by

$$\frac{x}{e^x - 1} = \sum_{k=0}^{\infty} B_k \frac{x^k}{k!} \tag{1}$$

$$\left.\begin{aligned} &B_0 = 1, \quad B_1 = \tfrac{1}{2}, \quad B_2 = \tfrac{1}{6}, \quad B_3 = 0, \quad B_4 = -\tfrac{1}{30}, \quad B_5 = 0, \quad B_6 = \tfrac{1}{42} \\ &B_7 = 0, \quad B_8 = -\tfrac{1}{30}, \quad B_9 = 0, \quad B_{10} = \tfrac{5}{66}, \quad B_{11} = 0, \quad B_{12} = -\tfrac{691}{2730} \end{aligned}\right\} \tag{2}$$

14.2. Positive powers. For m any positive integer, the finite sum

$$1^m + 2^m + 3^m + \ldots + n^m = \frac{(B+n)^{m+1} - B^{m+1}}{m+1} \tag{1}$$

where on the right is meant the result of expanding by the binomial theorem § 1.3 and then replacing powers B^k by the Bernoulli numbers B_k of § 14.1. In particular

$$1 + 2 + 3 + \ldots + n = \tfrac{1}{2} n(n+1) \tag{2}$$

$$1^2 + 2^2 + 3^2 + \ldots + n^2 = \tfrac{1}{6} n(n+1)(2n+1) \tag{3}$$

$$1^3 + 2^3 + 3^3 + \ldots + n^3 = \tfrac{1}{4} n^2(n+1)^2 \tag{4}$$

14.3. Negative powers. The sum of reciprocal even powers

$$1 + \frac{1}{2^{2m}} + \frac{1}{3^{2m}} + \frac{1}{4^{2m}} + \ldots = \frac{(-1)^m (2\pi)^{2m} B_{2m}}{2(2m)!} = \zeta(2m) \tag{1}$$

In particular,

$$\zeta(2) = \frac{\pi^2}{6}, \quad \zeta(4) = \frac{\pi^4}{90}, \quad \zeta(6) = \frac{\pi^6}{945} \tag{2}$$

This shows that for large m, the numerical value B_{2m} becomes infinite like

$$\frac{2(2m)!}{(2\pi)^{2m}} \tag{3}$$

which exceeds $(m/10)^m$.

14.4. Euler-Maclaurin sum formula. For m and n positive integers,

$$\left.\begin{aligned}\sum_{k=0}^{m} f(k) &= \int_0^m f(t)dt + \frac{1}{2}[f(0) + f(m)] \\ &+ \sum_{k=1}^{n} \frac{B_{2k}}{(2k)!}[f^{(2k-1)}(m) - f^{(2k-1)}(0)] + \frac{mB_{2n+2}}{(2n+2)!} f^{(2n+2)}(\theta m)\end{aligned}\right\} \tag{1}$$

where θ is a suitable number in the interval $0 < \theta < 1$.

14.5. Power series. For simple functions power series may be obtained by use of Taylor's theorem of § 3.25. For the series listed, the expression following a series indicates a region in which the series converges. No expression is added if the series converges for all values of x.

14.6. Elementary functions

$$\left.\begin{aligned}(1+x)^n = 1 + nx + \frac{n(n-1)}{2!}x^2 + \frac{n(n-1)(n-2)}{3!}x^3 + \dots \\ + \frac{n!}{(n-k)!k!}x^k + \dots, \quad |x| < 1\end{aligned}\right\} \tag{1}$$

$$e^x = 1 + x + \frac{x^2}{2!} + \frac{x^3}{3!} + \dots \tag{2}$$

$$\ln(1+x) = x - \frac{x^2}{2} + \frac{x^3}{3} - \frac{x^4}{4} + \dots, \quad |x| \leq 1 \tag{3}$$

$$\sin x = x - \frac{x^3}{3!} + \frac{x^5}{5!} - \frac{x^7}{7!} + \dots \tag{4}$$

$$\cos x = 1 - \frac{x^2}{2!} + \frac{x^4}{4!} - \frac{x^6}{6!} + \dots \tag{5}$$

$$\tan x = x + \frac{x^3}{3} + \frac{2x^5}{15} + \frac{17x^7}{315} + \frac{62x^9}{2835} + \dots, \quad |x| < \frac{\pi}{2} \tag{6}$$

$$\sec x = 1 + \frac{x^2}{2!} + \frac{5x^4}{4!} + \frac{61x^6}{6!} + \frac{1385x^8}{8!} + \dots, \quad |x| < \frac{\pi}{2} \tag{7}$$

$$\sin^{-1} x = x + \frac{x^3}{6} + \frac{1 \cdot 3}{2 \cdot 4} \cdot \frac{x^5}{5} + \frac{1 \cdot 3 \cdot 5}{2 \cdot 4 \cdot 6} \cdot \frac{x^7}{7} + \dots, \quad |x| < 1 \tag{8}$$

$$\tan^{-1} x = x - \frac{x^3}{3} + \frac{x^5}{5} - \frac{x^7}{7} + \dots, \quad |x| < 1 \tag{9}$$

$$\sqrt{1-x^2}\,\sin^{-1} x = x - \frac{x^3}{3} - \frac{2x^5}{3 \cdot 5} - \frac{2 \cdot 4x^7}{3 \cdot 5 \cdot 7} - \dots, \quad |x| < 1 \tag{10}$$

$$\frac{\sin^{-1} x}{\sqrt{1-x^2}} = x + \frac{2x^3}{3} + \frac{2 \cdot 4x^5}{3 \cdot 5} + \frac{2 \cdot 4 \cdot 6x^7}{3 \cdot 5 \cdot 7} + \dots, \quad |x| < 1 \tag{11}$$

$$\sinh x = x + \frac{x^3}{3!} + \frac{x^5}{5!} + \frac{x^7}{7!} + \dots \tag{12}$$

$$\cosh x = 1 + \frac{x^2}{2!} + \frac{x^4}{4!} + \frac{x^6}{6!} + \dots \tag{13}$$

$$\tanh x = x - \frac{x^3}{3} + \frac{2x^5}{15} - \frac{17x^7}{315} + \frac{62x^9}{2835} - \dots, \quad |x| < \frac{\pi}{2} \tag{14}$$

$$\left.\begin{aligned}\sinh^{-1} x &= x - \frac{1}{2}\cdot\frac{x^3}{3} + \frac{1\cdot 3}{2\cdot 4}\cdot\frac{x^5}{5} - \frac{1\cdot 3\cdot 5}{2\cdot 4\cdot 6}\cdot\frac{x^7}{7} + \ldots,\\ &\qquad |x| < 1\end{aligned}\right\} \tag{15}$$

$$\left.\begin{aligned}\sinh^{-1} x &= \ln 2x + \frac{1}{2}\cdot\frac{1}{2x^2} - \frac{1\cdot 3}{2\cdot 4}\cdot\frac{1}{4x^4} + \frac{1\cdot 3\cdot 5}{2\cdot 4\cdot 6}\cdot\frac{1}{6x^6} - \ldots,\\ &\qquad |x| > 1\end{aligned}\right\} \tag{16}$$

$$\left.\begin{aligned}\cosh^{-1} x &= \ln 2x - \frac{1}{2}\cdot\frac{1}{2x^2} - \frac{1\cdot 3}{2\cdot 4}\cdot\frac{1}{4x^4} - \frac{1\cdot 3\cdot 5}{2\cdot 4\cdot 6}\cdot\frac{1}{6x^6} - \ldots,\\ &\qquad |x| > 1\end{aligned}\right\} \tag{17}$$

$$\tanh^{-1} x = x + \frac{x^3}{3} + \frac{x^5}{5} + \frac{x^7}{7} + \ldots, \quad |x| < 1 \tag{18}$$

14.7. Integrals

$$\int_0^x e^{-x^2}\,dx = x - \frac{x^3}{3} + \frac{x^5}{5\cdot 2!} - \frac{x^7}{7\cdot 7!} + \ldots \tag{1}$$

$$\int_0^x \cos(x^2)dx = x - \frac{x^5}{5\cdot 2!} + \frac{x^9}{9\cdot 4!} - \frac{x^{13}}{13\cdot 6!} + \ldots \tag{2}$$

$$\int_0^x \sin(x^2)dx = \frac{x^3}{3} - \frac{x^7}{7\cdot 3!} + \frac{x^{11}}{11\cdot 5!} - \frac{x^{15}}{15\cdot 7!} + \ldots \tag{3}$$

$$\int_0^x \frac{\sin x}{x}\,dx = x - \frac{x^3}{3\cdot 3!} + \frac{x^5}{5\cdot 5!} - \ldots \tag{4}$$

$$-\int_x^\infty \frac{\cos t}{t}\,dt = 0.577216 + \ln x - \frac{x^2}{2\cdot 2!} + \frac{x^4}{4\cdot 4!} - \ldots, \quad x > 0 \tag{5}$$

$$\int_x^\infty e^{-t}\frac{dt}{t} = -0.577216 - \ln x + x - \frac{x^2}{2\cdot 2!} + \frac{x^3}{3\cdot 3!} - \ldots, \quad x > 0 \tag{6}$$

14.8. Expansions in rational fractions. In this section the prime on a summation means that the term for $n = 0$ is to be omitted

$$\cot z = \frac{1}{z} + \sum_{n=-\infty}^{\infty}{}' \left[\frac{1}{z - n\pi} + \frac{1}{n\pi}\right] = \frac{1}{z} + \sum_{n=1}^{\infty} \frac{2z}{z^2 - n^2\pi^2} \tag{1}$$

$$\csc z = \frac{1}{z} + \sum_{n=-\infty}^{\infty}{}' (-1)^n \left[\frac{1}{z - n\pi} + \frac{1}{n\pi}\right] = \frac{1}{z} + \sum_{n=1}^{\infty} (-1)^n \frac{2z}{z^2 - n^2\pi^2} \tag{2}$$

$$\csc^2 z = \sum_{n=-\infty}^{\infty} \frac{1}{(z - n\pi)^2}, \quad \sec z = \sum_{n=1}^{\infty} (-1)^{n-1} \frac{4(2n-1)\pi}{(2n-1)^2\pi^2 - 4x^2} \tag{3}$$

14.9. Infinite products for the sine and cosine. The prime means omit $n = 0$.

$$\sin z = z \prod_{n=-\infty}^{\infty}{}' \left(1 - \frac{z}{n\pi}\right) e^{z/n} = z \prod_{n=1}^{\infty} \left(1 - \frac{z^2}{n^2\pi^2}\right) \tag{1}$$

$$\cos z = \prod_{n=1}^{\infty} \left[1 - \frac{4z^2}{(2n-1)^2\pi^2}\right] \tag{2}$$

14.10. Fourier's theorem for periodic functions. The function $f(x)$ is periodic of period p if

$$f(x + p) = f(x) \tag{1}$$

The period p and frequence ω are related by the equations

$$\omega = \frac{2\pi}{p} \quad \text{and} \quad p = \frac{2\pi}{\omega} \tag{2}$$

Then for any constant c, the Fourier coefficients are

$$\left.\begin{aligned} a = \frac{1}{p}\int_c^{c+p} f(x)dx, \quad a_n = \frac{2}{p}\int_c^{c+p} f(x)\cos n\omega x\, dx \\ b_n = \frac{2}{p}\int_c^{c+p} f(x)\sin n\omega x\, dx \end{aligned}\right\} \tag{3}$$

It is often convenient to take $c = 0$, or $c = -p/2$.

The Fourier series for $f(x)$ is

$$f(x) = a + \sum_{n=1}^{\infty} (a_n \cos n\omega x + b_n \sin n\omega x) \tag{4}$$

A regular arc is a continuous curve with finite arc length. The function $f(x)$ is piecewise regular if its graph on any finite interval is made up of a finite number of pieces, each of which is a regular arc or an isolated point. For any piecewise regular periodic function the Fourier series will converge to $f(x)$ at all points of continuity, and to $\frac{1}{2}[f(x+) + f(x-)]$ at all points of discontinuity. Here $f(x+)$ is the limit approached from the right, and $f(x-)$ is the limit approached from the left, at x.

14.11. Fourier series on an interval. For any function $f(x)$, defined for $c < x < c + p$, but not necessarily periodic, the relations of § 14.10 may be used to find a Fourier series of period p which represents $f(x)$ on the interval $c, c + p$.

14.12. Half-range Fourier series. For any function $f(x)$, piecewise regular on $0,L$ the Fourier cosine series of period $2L$ which represents $f(x)$ for $0 < x < L$ is

$$f(x) = a + \sum_{n=1}^{\infty} a_n \cos n\omega x \tag{1}$$

where

$$a = \frac{1}{L}\int_0^L f(x)dx, \quad a_n = \frac{2}{L}\int_0^L f(x)\cos n\omega x\, dx, \quad \omega = \frac{\pi}{L} \tag{2}$$

The Fourier sine series of period $2L$ for $f(x)$ is

$$f(x) = \sum_{n=1}^{\infty} b_n \sin n\omega x \tag{3}$$

where

$$b_n = \frac{2}{L}\int_0^L f(x)\sin n\omega x\, dx, \quad \omega = \frac{\pi}{L} \tag{4}$$

14.13. Particular Fourier series. For $0 < x < L$,

$$1 = \frac{4}{\pi}\left(\sin\frac{\pi x}{L} + \frac{1}{3}\sin\frac{3\pi x}{L} + \frac{1}{5}\sin\frac{5\pi x}{L} + \dots\right) \tag{1}$$

$$x = \frac{2L}{\pi}\left(\sin\frac{\pi x}{L} - \frac{1}{2}\sin\frac{2\pi x}{L} + \frac{1}{3}\sin\frac{3\pi x}{L} - \dots\right) \tag{2}$$

$$x = \frac{L}{2} - \frac{4L}{\pi^2}\left(\cos\frac{\pi x}{L} + \frac{1}{3^2}\cos\frac{3\pi x}{L} + \frac{1}{5^2}\cos\frac{5\pi x}{L} + \dots\right) \tag{3}$$

$$\left.\begin{aligned} Ax + B = \frac{1}{\pi}\Bigg[&(4B + 2LA)\sin\frac{\pi x}{L} - \frac{2LA}{2}\sin\frac{2\pi x}{L} \\ &+ \frac{4B + 2LA}{3}\sin\frac{3\pi x}{L} - \frac{2LA}{4}\sin\frac{4\pi x}{L} + \dots\Bigg] \end{aligned}\right\} \tag{4}$$

If

$$\left.\begin{aligned} &f(x) = H \text{ for } c < x < c + w, \\ &f(x) = 0 \text{ for } c + w < x < c + 2L, \\ \text{and}\quad &f(x + 2L) = f(x); \end{aligned}\right\} \tag{5}$$

then for this periodic square pulse,

$$f(x) = \frac{Hw}{2L} + \frac{2H}{\pi}\sum_{n=1}^{\infty}\frac{1}{n}\sin\frac{n\pi w}{2L}\cos\frac{n\pi}{L}\left(x - c - \frac{w}{2}\right) \tag{6}$$

For $0 < x < \pi$,

$$\frac{\pi}{4} = \sin x + \frac{\sin 3x}{3} + \frac{\sin 5x}{5} + \frac{\sin 7x}{7} + \dots \tag{7}$$

$$-\frac{x}{2} + \frac{\pi}{4} = \frac{\sin 2x}{2} + \frac{\sin 4x}{4} + \frac{\sin 6x}{6} + \dots \tag{8}$$

$$-\frac{\pi x}{4} + \frac{\pi^2}{8} = \cos x + \frac{\cos 3x}{3^2} + \frac{\cos 5x}{5^2} + \frac{\cos 7x}{7^2} + \dots \tag{9}$$

$$\frac{x^2}{4} - \frac{\pi x}{4} + \frac{\pi^2}{24} = \frac{\cos 2x}{2^2} + \frac{\cos 4x}{4^2} + \frac{\cos 6x}{6^2} + \dots \tag{10}$$

$$-\frac{\pi x^2}{8} + \frac{\pi^2 x}{8} = \sin x + \frac{\sin 3x}{3^3} + \frac{\sin 5x}{5^3} + \frac{\sin 7x}{7^3} + \dots \tag{11}$$

$$\frac{x^3}{12} - \frac{\pi x^2}{8} + \frac{\pi^2 x}{24} = \frac{\sin 2x}{2^3} + \frac{\sin 4x}{4^3} + \frac{\sin 6x}{6^3} + \dots \tag{12}$$

$$\ln \left| \sin \frac{x}{2} \right| = -\ln 2 - \frac{\cos x}{1} - \frac{\cos 2x}{2} - \frac{\cos 3x}{3} - \dots \tag{13}$$

$$\ln \left| \cos \frac{x}{2} \right| = -\ln 2 + \frac{\cos x}{1} - \frac{\cos 2x}{2} + \frac{\cos 3x}{3} - \dots \tag{14}$$

$$\int_0^x \ln \left| \tan \frac{u}{2} \right| du = -2\left(\frac{\sin x}{1^2} + \frac{\sin 3x}{3^2} + \frac{\sin 5x}{5^2} + \dots \right) \tag{15}$$

$$\int_0^x \ln | 2 \sin u | \, du = -2\left(\frac{\sin 2x}{2^2} + \frac{\sin 4x}{4^2} + \frac{\sin 6x}{6^2} + \dots \right) \tag{15}$$

$$\frac{1}{2} \tan^{-1} \frac{2r \sin x}{1 - r^2} = \sum_{n=1}^{\infty} \frac{r^{2n-1}}{2n-1} \sin (2n-1)x, \quad |r| < 1 \tag{17}$$

$$\frac{1}{2} \tan^{-1} \frac{2r \cos x}{1 - r^2} = \sum_{n=1}^{\infty} (-1)^{n-1} \frac{r^{2n-1}}{2n-1} \cos (2n-1)x, \quad |r| < 1 \tag{18}$$

For $-\pi < x < \pi$,

$$e^{ax} = \frac{2 \sinh a\pi}{\pi} \left[\frac{1}{2a} + \sum_{n=1}^{\infty} (-1)^n \frac{a \cos nx - n \sin nx}{a^2 + n^2} \right] \tag{19}$$

$$\sin ax = \frac{2 \sin a\pi}{\pi} \left[\frac{\sin x}{1^2 - a^2} - \frac{2 \sin 2x}{2^2 - a^2} + \frac{3 \sin 3x}{3^2 - a^2} - \dots \right] \tag{20}$$

$$\cos ax = \frac{2a \sin a\pi}{\pi}\left[\frac{1}{2a^2} + \frac{\cos x}{1^2 - a^2} - \frac{\cos 2x}{2^2 - a^2} + \frac{\cos 3x}{3^2 - a^2} - \cdots\right] \tag{21}$$

$$\sinh ax = \frac{2 \sinh a\pi}{\pi}\left[\frac{\sin x}{1^2 + a^2} - \frac{2 \sin 2x}{2^2 + a^2} + \frac{3 \sin 3x}{3^2 + a^2} - \cdots\right] \tag{22}$$

$$\cosh ax = \frac{2a \sinh a\pi}{\pi}\left[\frac{1}{2a^2} - \frac{\cos x}{1^2 + a^2} + \frac{\cos 2x}{2^2 + a^2} - \frac{\cos 3x}{3^2 + a^2} + \cdots\right] \tag{23}$$

14.14. Complex Fourier series. The Fourier series of § 14.10 may be written in complex form as

$$f(x) = \sum_{n=-\infty}^{\infty} C_n e^{in\omega x} \tag{1}$$

where

$$C_n = \frac{1}{p}\int_c^{c+p} f(x) e^{-in\omega x}\, dx, \quad \omega = \frac{2\pi}{p} \tag{2}$$

The complex C_n are related to the coefficients of § 14.10 by

$$C_0 = a, \quad C_n = \frac{a_n - ib_n}{2}, \quad C_{-n} = \frac{a_n + ib_n}{2} \tag{3}$$

$$\frac{(1 - r \cos \omega x) + ir \sin \omega x}{1 + 2r \cos \omega x + r^2} = \sum_{n=0}^{\infty} r^n e^{in\omega x}, \quad |r| < 1 \tag{4}$$

$$\left.\begin{aligned} \ln \frac{1}{\sqrt{1 - 2r \cos \omega x + r^2}} + i \tan^{-1} \frac{r \sin \omega x}{1 - r \cos \omega x} = \sum_{n=1}^{\infty} \frac{1}{n} r^n e^{in\omega x} \\ |r| < 1 \end{aligned}\right\} \tag{5}$$

14.15. The Fourier integral theorem. Let $f(x)$ be piecewise regular, so redefined at points of discontinuity that

$$f(x) = \tfrac{1}{2}[f(x+) + f(x-)] \tag{1}$$

and such that $\int_{-\infty}^{\infty} |f(x)|\, dx$ is finite. Then

$$f(x) = \frac{1}{\pi}\int_0^{\infty} du \int_{-\infty}^{\infty} \cos u(x - t) f(t)\, dt \tag{2}$$

In complex form,

$$f(x) = \lim_{A\to\infty} \frac{1}{2}\int_{-A}^{A} du \int_{-\infty}^{\infty} e^{iu(x-t)} f(t)\, dt \tag{3}$$

14.16. Fourier transforms. The Fourier transform of $f(x)$ is

$$F(u) = \int_{-\infty}^{\infty} e^{-iut} f(t)\, dt \tag{1}$$

and by § 14.15,

$$f(x) = \lim_{A\to\infty} \frac{1}{2\pi} \int_{-A}^{A} e^{iux} F(u)\, du \tag{2}$$

In a linear system, if $R(x,u)$ is the response to e^{iux}, the response to $f(x)$ is

$$R(x) = \lim_{A\to\infty} \frac{1}{2\pi} \int_{-A}^{A} R(x,u)F(u)\, du \tag{3}$$

14.17. Laplace transforms. If $f(t) = 0$ for $t < 0$, its Laplace transform is

$$F(p) = \int_0^{\infty} e^{-pt} f(t)\, dt \tag{1}$$

We write $F(p) = \text{Lap}\, f(t)$.
For derivatives,

$$\text{Lap}\, f'(t) = -f(0+) + p\, \text{Lap}\, f(t) \tag{2}$$

$$\text{Lap}\, f''(t) = -f'(0+) - pf(0+) + p^2\, \text{Lap}\, f(t) \tag{3}$$

and so on. These relations reduce a linear differential equation with constant coefficients to an algebraic equation in the transform. We have

$$\text{Lap}\, \frac{t^n}{n!} = \frac{1}{p^{n+1}}, \quad \text{Lap}\, e^{-at} \sin kt = \frac{k}{(p+a)^2 + k^2} \tag{5}$$

$$\text{Lap}\, e^{-at} \cos kt = \frac{p+a}{(p+a)^2 + k^2}, \quad \text{Lap}\, 1 = \frac{1}{p} \tag{6}$$

If

$$\left.\begin{aligned} h(t) &= \int_0^t f(u) g(t-u)\, du, \\ \text{Lap}\, h(t) &= [\text{Lap}\, f(t)]\, [\text{Lap}\, g(t)] \end{aligned}\right\} \tag{7}$$

For examples of the use of Laplace transforms to solve systems of differential equations, see Franklin, P., *Fourier Methods*, McGraw-Hill Book Company, Inc., New York, 1949, Chap. 5.

14.18. Poisson's formula. For small x, the right member converges rapidly and may be used to compute the value of the left member in

$$\frac{1}{2} + \sum_{n=1}^{\infty} e^{-(nx)^2} = \frac{\sqrt{\pi}}{x} \left(\frac{1}{2} + \sum_{n=1}^{\infty} e^{-(n\pi/x)^2} \right) \tag{1}$$

14.19. Orthogonal functions. Many eigenvalue problems arising from differential systems or integral equations have eigenfunctions which form a complete orthogonal set. For these functions $\phi_n(x)$

$$\int \phi_n(x)\phi_m(x)dx = 0 \quad \text{if} \quad m \neq n; \qquad \int [\phi_n(x)]^2\, dx = N_n \tag{1}$$

and for sufficiently regular functions $f(x)$,

$$f(x) = \sum_{n=1}^{\infty} c_n \phi_n(x) \tag{2}$$

where

$$c_n = \frac{1}{N_n} \int f(x)\phi_n(x)\, dx \tag{3}$$

The integrals are all taken over the fundamental interval for the problem, and the expansion holds in this interval. Except for special conditions sometimes required at the ends of the interval, or at infinity when the interval is infinite or semi-infinite, the regularity conditions are usually similar to those for Fourier series.

It is possible to create a set of orthogonal functions $\phi_n(x)$ from any linearly independent infinite set $f_n(x)$ by setting

$$\phi_1(x) = f_1(x), \quad \phi_2(x) = f_2(x) - \left[\frac{1}{N_1}\int \phi_1(x) f_2(x)dx\right]\phi_1(x) \tag{4}$$

$$\phi_n(x) = f_n(x) - \sum_{i=1}^{n-1}\left[\frac{1}{N_i}\int \phi_i(x) f_n(x)dx\right]\phi_i(x) \tag{5}$$

Examples are $P_n(x)$ on $-1,1$ of § 8.8 ; $P_n^m(x)$ for fixed m on $-1,1$ of § 8.16 ; $x^{1/2}J_p(a_{pn}x)$ where $J_p(a_{pn}) = 0$ for fixed positive p on 0,1 of § 9.13 ; $e^{-x/2}L_n(x)$ on $0, \infty$ of § 11.4 ; $e^{-x/2}x^{k+1}L_{n+k}^{2k+1}(x)$ for fixed k on $0, \infty$ of § 11.7; $e^{-x^2/2}H_n(x)$ on $-\infty, \infty$ of § 12.4; $\sqrt{x^{q-1}(1-x)^{p-q}}\,J_n(p,q;x)$ on 0,1 of § 10.7; $1/(\sqrt[4]{1-x^2})T_n(x)$ on $-1,1$ of § 10.7.

14.20. Weight functions. The functions $g_n(x)$ are orthogonal with a weighting factor $w(x)$ when

$$\int w(x)g_n(x)g_m(x)dx = 0 \quad \text{if} \quad m \neq n \tag{1}$$

For such functions the expansion is

$$F(x) = \sum_{n=1}^{\infty} C_n g_n(x) \tag{2}$$

where

$$C_n = \frac{1}{M_n}\int w(x)F(x)g_n(x)dx, \quad M_n = \int w(x)[g_n(x)]^2\, dx \tag{3}$$

Illustrations related to some of the examples mentioned at the end of § 14.19 are $J_p(a_{pn}x)$ with $w(x) = x$; $L_n(x)$ with $w(x) = e^{-x}$; $H_n(x)$ with $w(x) = e^{-x^2}$; $J_n(p,q;x)$ with $w(x) = x^{q-1}(1-x)^{p-q}$; $T_n(x)$ with $w(x) = 1/\sqrt{1-x^2}$.

15. Asymptotic Expansions

15.1. Asymptotic expansion. Let the expression

$$a_0 + \frac{a_1}{x} + \frac{a_2}{x^2} + \frac{a_3}{x^3} + \dots \tag{1}$$

be related to a function $F(x)$ in such a way that for any fixed n

$$\lim_{x\to\infty} x^n \left[F(x) - a_0 - \frac{a_1}{x} - \dots - \frac{a_n}{x^n} \right] = 0 \tag{2}$$

The limit holds in some sector of the complex plane. The expression in general is a divergent series, since it can converge only if $F(z)$ is analytic at infinity. In any case it is called an asymptotic expansion for the function. The terms asymptotic or semiconvergent series are also used.

The error committed when we employ a finite number of terms in place of $f(x)$ is frequently of the same order of magnitude as the numerical value of the next following term. Thus asymptotic expressions can be used in computation like convergent alternating series as long as the terms remain small. For examples see §§ 8.9, 8.14, 9.7, 13.5, and 13.9.

If the function $F(x)$ is an infinite series of terms $\Sigma\, u_k(x)$, an asymptotic series may sometimes be found by taking $u_k(x)$ as the $f(k)$ in the Euler-Maclaurin sum formula of § 14.4.

15.2. Borel's expansion. Let

$$\phi(t) = \sum_{n=0}^{\infty} A_n t^n$$

be any function for which the integral

$$I(x) = \int_0^\infty e^{-tx} t^p \phi(t) dt \tag{1}$$

converges. Then the expansion

$$I(x) = \frac{\Gamma(p+1)}{x^{p+1}} \left[A_0 + (p+1)\frac{A_1}{x} + (p+1)(p+2)\frac{A_2}{x^2} + \dots \right] \tag{2}$$

is usually an asymptotic series for $I(x)$. One extension is

$$m \int_0^\infty e^{-(xt)^m} t^{m-1} \phi(t)\, dt = \sum_{n=0}^{\infty} A_n\, \Gamma\left(\frac{n}{m} + 1\right) \frac{1}{x^{n+m}} \tag{3}$$

15.3. Steepest descent. If the path C is suitably chosen in the complex plane (see § 20.3) the integral

$$F(x) = \int_C e^{-xg(t)} h(t)dt \tag{1}$$

may be transformed into integrals whose expansion can be found by § 15.2. The path C is one along which $g(t)$ remains real and changes most rapidly. It will pass through a saddle point of the surface $R(u,v)$ where $t = u + iv$ and $g(t) = R(u,v) + iI(u,v)$. At this saddle point t_0, $g(t_0) = 0$ and $g'(t_0) = 0$, and expanding about it

$$s = g(t) = (t - t_0)^2[g_0 + g_1(t - t_0) + g_2(t - t_0)^2 + \dots] \tag{2}$$

The path C consists of two parts L_1 and L_2. On L_1, we find $t_1(s)$ by integrating dt_1 between 0 and s to obtain $t_1 - t_0$. And on L_2, we get $t_2(s)$ by integrating dt_2 between 0 and s to obtain $t_2 - t_0$. Here

$$\frac{dt_1}{ds} = \frac{1}{2} s^{-1/2} \sum_{n=0}^{\infty} a_n s^{n/2}, \qquad \frac{dt_2}{ds} = \frac{1}{2} s^{-1/2} \sum_{n=0}^{\infty} (-1)^{n+1} a_n s^{n/2}$$

where in terms of the coefficients g_k,

$$a_0 = g_0^{-1/2}, \quad a_1 = g_0^{-1}\left(-\frac{g_1}{g_0}\right), \quad a_2 = g_0^{-3/2}\left(-\frac{3g_2}{2g_0} + \frac{3 \cdot 5g_1^2}{8g_2^2}\right)$$

$$a_3 = g_0^{-2}\left(-\frac{2g_3}{g_0} + \frac{6g_1g_2}{g_0^2} - \frac{4g_1^3}{g_0^3}\right)$$

Then in terms of s,

$$F(x) = \int_{L_1} e^{-xs} h(t_1) \frac{dt_1}{ds}\, ds + \int_{L_2} e^{-xs} h(t_2) \frac{dt_2}{ds}\, ds$$

Since s is real, if s runs from 0 to infinity on the path $C = L_1 + L_2$, the sum of these integrals in general has an asymptotic expansion which follows from Borel's expansion (2) of § 15.2.

16. Least Squares

16.1. Principle of least squares. Let $n > r$, so that the n observation equations

$$f_k(a_1, a_2, \dots, a_r) = s_k, \quad k = 1, 2, \dots n \tag{1}$$

form an overdetermined system for the determination of the r unknown constants a_q. Then when the n observed quantities s_k have comparable accuracy, the kth residual is taken as

$$v_k = f_k(a_1, a_2, \dots, a_r) - s_k \tag{2}$$

The principle of least square asserts that the best approximation to the a_q is the set for which the sum of the squares of the residuals is a minimum. Necessary conditions for

$$S = \sum_{k=1}^{n} v_k^2 \tag{3}$$

to be a minimum are

$$\frac{\partial S}{\partial a_1} = 0, \quad \frac{\partial S}{\partial a_2} = 0, \quad \ldots, \quad \frac{\partial S}{\partial a_r} = 0 \tag{4}$$

These constitute the normal equations. In general they determine a unique solution for a_q which gives the desired best approximation.

16.2. Weights. When the relative accuracy of the s_k in § 16.1 is known to be different, we assign weights w_k such that the quantities $w_k s_k$ have comparable accuracy. Then the residual v_k is taken as

$$v_k = w_k f_k(a_1, a_2, \ldots, a_r) - w_k s_k \tag{5}$$

and otherwise the principle is applied as in § 16.1.

16.3. Direct observations. When the s_k are direct observations of a quantity a_1, the residual v_k is $a_1 - s_k$, and the principle gives the average

$$a_1 = \frac{1}{n}(s_1 + s_2 + \ldots + s_n) \tag{1}$$

as the best approximation for a_1.

16.4. Linear equations. When linear in the a_q, the n observation equations may be written

$$\sum_{q=1}^{r} A_{kq} a_q = s_k, \quad k = 1, 2, \ldots, n \tag{1}$$

In this case the normal equations are

$$\sum_{q=1}^{r} \sum_{k=1}^{n} A_{kp} A_{kq} a_q = \sum_{k=1}^{n} A_{kp} s_k, \quad p = 1, 2, \ldots, r \tag{2}$$

16.5. Curve fitting. Suppose the n points (x_k, y_k) follow approximately a straight line. To find the best line when we regard y_k as the observed value corresponding to x_k, we write

$$a_1 + a_2 x_k = y_k \tag{1}$$

as the observation equation. And we determined a_1 and a_2 by solving the two simultaneous normal equations

$$\left.\begin{aligned} na_1 + \left(\sum_{k=1}^{n} x_k\right)a_2 &= \sum_{k=1}^{n} y_k \\ \left(\sum_{k=1}^{n} x_k\right)a_1 + \left(\sum_{k=1}^{n} x_k^2\right)a_2 &= \sum_{k=1}^{n} x_k y_k \end{aligned}\right\} \quad (2)$$

Similarly, to find the best parabola we use

$$a_1 + a_2 x_k + a_3 x_k^2 = y_k \quad (3)$$

as the observation equations, and proceed as in § 16.4, or we may use a polynomial of the mth degree, with the observation equations

$$a_1 + a_2 x_k + a_3 x_k^2 + \ldots + a_{m+1} x_k^m = y_k \quad (4)$$

16.6. Nonlinear equations. When the functions f_k are not linear in the a_q, we get a first approximation $\bar{a}_q$ by graphical means when $r = 2$, or by solving some set of r of the observation equations. Then we expand in Taylor's series about $\bar{a}_q$, and neglect second-order terms. The result is

$$f_k(\bar{a}_1,\bar{a}_2,\ldots,\bar{a}_r) + \sum_{q=1}^{r} \frac{\partial f_k}{\partial \bar{a}_q} \Delta a_k = s_k \quad (1)$$

We treat these as observation equations in the unknown Δa_k. With

$$\partial f_k/\partial \bar{a}_q \text{ for } A_{kq}, \quad \Delta a_q \text{ for } a_q, \quad s_k - f_k(\bar{a}_1,\bar{a}_2,\ldots,\bar{a}_r) \text{ for } s_k,$$

they have the form (1) discussed in § 16.4.

17. Statistics

17.1. Average. The average of a finite set of observed values $s_1, s_2, \ldots, s_n$ is

$$\mu_1(s) = \bar{s} = \frac{1}{n}(s_1 + s_2 + \ldots + s_n) \quad (1)$$

17.2. Median. When a sequence is arranged in order of magnitude the number in the central position, or the average of the two nearest to a central position, is called the median. Essentially, there are as many numbers in the sequence larger than the median as there are smaller than the median.

17.3. Derived averages. The kth moment is the average of the kth powers so that

$$\mu_k(s) = \overline{s^k} = \frac{1}{n}(s_1{}^k + s_2{}^k + \dots + s_n{}^k) \tag{1}$$

17.4. Deviations. To the set of observed values $s_1, s_2, \dots, s_n$ corresponds an average $\bar{s}$, § 17.1, and a set of deviations

$$d_1 = s_1 - \bar{s}, \quad d_2 = s_2 - \bar{s}, \quad \dots, \quad d_n = s_n - \bar{s} \tag{1}$$

The average of a set of deviations is zero, $\mu_1(d) = \bar{d} = 0$.

For the mean-square deviation § 17.3,

$$\mu_2(d) = \mu_2(s) - [\mu_1(s)]^2 \quad \text{or} \quad \overline{d^2} = \overline{s^2} - (\bar{s})^2 \tag{2}$$

The square root of $\mu_2(d)$, or root-mean-square value of the deviation is called the standard deviation σ.

$$\sigma = \sqrt{\mu_2(d)} = \sqrt{\frac{1}{n}\Sigma d_r{}^2} \tag{3}$$

17.5. Normal law. The deviations are samples of a continuous variable x, whose distribution function may frequently be taken as the normal law of error

$$y = \frac{h}{\sqrt{\pi}} e^{-h^2x^2} \tag{1}$$

That is $P_{a,b}$ the probability that an error is between a and b, is

$$P_{a,b} = \frac{h}{\sqrt{\pi}} \int_a^b e^{-h^2x^2} dx \tag{2}$$

In terms of the error function of § 13.9.

$$P_{a,b} = \tfrac{1}{2}(\text{Erf } hb - \text{Erf } ha) \quad \text{and} \quad P_{-b,b} = \text{Erf } hb \tag{3}$$

For a given normal distribution, h is called the measure of precision.

17.6. Standard deviation. For the normal law of § 17.5 the second moment is

$$\mu_2(x) = \int_{-\infty}^{\infty} x^2 \frac{h}{\sqrt{\pi}} e^{-h^2x^2} dx = \frac{1}{2h^2} \tag{1}$$

Thus the standard deviation is

$$\sigma = \sqrt{\mu_2(x)} = \frac{1}{\sqrt{2}h} \quad \text{and} \quad h = \frac{1}{\sqrt{2}\sigma} = \frac{0.7071}{\sigma} \tag{2}$$

All the odd moments, $\mu_{2k+1}(x) = 0$, and for the higher even moments

$$\mu_{2k}(x) = 1 \cdot 3 \cdot 5 \cdot \ldots (2k-1) \frac{1}{2^k h^{2k}} = 1 \cdot 3 \cdot 5 \cdot \ldots (2k-1)\sigma^{2k} \qquad (3)$$

17.7. Mean absolute error. For the normal law of § 17.5 the mean absolute error is

$$\mu_1(|\,x\,|) = 2\int_0^\infty x \frac{h}{\sqrt{\pi}} e^{-h^2x^2} dx = \frac{1}{h\sqrt{\pi}} \qquad (1)$$

Thus the mean absolute error

$$\mu = \frac{1}{h\sqrt{\pi}} \quad \text{and} \quad h = \frac{1}{\mu\sqrt{\pi}} = \frac{0.5643}{\mu} \qquad (2)$$

17.8. Probable error. For the normal law of § 17.5 the particular error which is just as likely to be exceeded as not is called the probable error, ϵ. Thus

$$\tfrac{1}{2} = P_{-\varepsilon,\varepsilon} = \text{Erf}\, h\epsilon \quad \text{and} \quad h\epsilon = 0.4769 \qquad (1)$$

And the probable error

$$\epsilon = \frac{0.4769}{h} = 0.6745\sigma = 0.8453\mu \qquad (2)$$

17.9. Measure of dispersion. To find a measure of precision h which makes the normal law fit a set of deviations, we identify the standard deviation of § 17.6 with $\sqrt{n/(n-1)}$ times that of § 17.4. Thus

$$\frac{1}{\sqrt{2}h} = \sigma = \sqrt{\frac{1}{n-1}\Sigma d_r^{\,2}} \quad \text{and} \quad \epsilon = \frac{0.6745}{\sqrt{n-1}}\sqrt{\Sigma d_r^{\,2}} \qquad (1)$$

Or, we may identify the mean absolute error of § 17.7 with $\sqrt{n/(n-1)}$ times that formed from the d_r, $\mu_1(|\,d_r\,|)$. Thus

$$\frac{1}{h\sqrt{\pi}} = \mu = \frac{1}{\sqrt{n(n-1)}}\Sigma|\,d_r\,| \quad \text{and} \quad \epsilon = \frac{0.8453}{\sqrt{n(n-1)}}\Sigma|\,d_r\,| \qquad (2)$$

These are easier to calculate, but slightly less accurate, than the values found from the standard deviation. In some cases both values are found, and a rough agreement is considered a check on the normal character of the distribution. In either case the probable error of the mean is taken as $1/\sqrt{-}$ times that for a single observation, $\epsilon_m = \epsilon/\sqrt{n}$.

17.10. Poisson's distribution. A variable taking on integral values only, $k = 1, 2, 3, \ldots$ has Poisson's distribution law if the probability that the variable equals k is

$$P_k = \frac{a^k e^{-a}}{k!} \tag{1}$$

For this distribution the average value of the variable

$$\mu_1(k) = a \tag{2}$$

and the standard deviation

$$\sigma = \sqrt{\mu_2(k)} = \sqrt{a}, \quad a = \sigma^2 \tag{3}$$

These relations may be used to find the parameter a from the average or standard deviation of a sample set of observations which follow this law.

17.11. Correlation coefficient. Let x and y be two variables for each of which the deviations from the average have a normal distribution. Then for a set of corresponding pairs $x_1, y_1; x_2, y_2; \ldots; x_n, y_n$ the correlation coefficient of the sample is

$$r = \frac{\Sigma(x_i - \bar{x})(y_i - \bar{y})}{\sqrt{\Sigma(x_i - \bar{x})^2 \cdot \Sigma(y_i - \bar{y})^2}} = \frac{\Sigma d_i D_i}{\sqrt{\Sigma d_i^2 \cdot \Sigma D_i^2}} \tag{1}$$

where

$$\bar{x} = \mu_1(x) = \frac{1}{n}\Sigma x_i, \quad d_i = x_i - \bar{x} \tag{2}$$

$$\bar{y} = \mu_1(y) = \frac{1}{n}\Sigma y_i, \quad D_i = y_i - \bar{y} \tag{3}$$

For $r = 0$ there is no correlation. For $r = 1$ there is strict proportionality $y = Cx$ with a positive C, and for $r = -1$ with a negative C. For $|r|$ near 1, the ellipses of equal probability for the distribution of points x_i, y_i are long and thin, approximating a straight line. The constant c determined from

$$\tan 2\phi = \frac{2\Sigma d_i D_i}{\Sigma d_i^2 - \Sigma D_i^2}, \quad c = \tan\phi \tag{4}$$

leads to the straight line $y = cx$ such that the sum of the squares of the distances to all the observed points x_i, y_i is a minimum.

18. Matrices

18.1. Matrix. The elements of a matrix are a system of mn numbers $a_{ik} (i = 1,2,\ldots,m; k = 1,2,\ldots,n)$. These form a matrix when written as a rectangular array of m rows and n columns

$$\begin{Vmatrix} a_{11} & a_{12} & \cdots & a_{1n} \\ a_{21} & a_{22} & \cdots & a_{2n} \\ \cdots & \cdots & \cdots & \cdots \\ a_{m1} & a_{m2} & \cdots & a_{mn} \end{Vmatrix} \tag{1}$$

We use the abbreviations $\| a_{ik} \|$ or a single letter A. The double bars are sometimes replaced by parentheses. (See §§ 7.4, 7.5.)

18.2. Addition. The relation

$$A = B \qquad \text{means} \quad a_{ik} = b_{ik} \tag{1}$$

$$A + B = C \quad \text{means} \quad a_{ik} + b_{ik} = c_{ik} \tag{2}$$

$$sA = A \qquad \text{means} \quad sa_{ik} = b_{ik}, \text{ where } s \text{ is a scalar} \tag{3}$$

In each of these relations all the matrices involved must have the same dimensions. If these are m by n the matrix equation is equivalent to mn scalar equations.

18.3. Multiplication. Two matrices A and B, taken in this order, are said to be conformable if the number of columns of A equals the number of rows of B. Let A be m by N and B be N by n. Then the product $C = AB$ is an m by n matrix with

$$c_{ik} = \sum_{j=1}^{N} a_{ij} b_{jk} \tag{1}$$

If $n \neq m$, then B and A will not be conformable, and there is no product BA.

If A is m by n and B is n by m, then AB is an m by m matrix and BA is an n by n matrix, of different dimensions if $m \neq n$.

When A and B are each n by n, or square matrices of order n, the product AB and BA will each be n by n, but in general will not be the same. Matrix multiplication is not commutative.

Matrix multiplication is associative,

$$A(BC) = (AB)C = ABC \tag{2}$$

18.4. Linear transformations. Let $X\uparrow = \| x_k \|$ be a 1 by n column matrix, $Y\uparrow = \| y_j \|$ be a 1 by N column matrix, and $Z\uparrow = \| z_i \|$ be a 1 by m column matrix. Then if A is m by N, and B is N by n, in matrix form the transformation

$$y_j = \sum_{k=1}^{n} b_{jk} x_k \quad \text{is} \quad Y\uparrow = BX\uparrow \tag{1}$$

and the transformation

$$z_i = \sum_{j=1}^{N} a_{ij} y_j \quad \text{is} \quad Z\uparrow = AY\uparrow \tag{2}$$

If the transformation which takes the x_k into the z_i directly is

$$z_i = \sum_{k=1}^{n} c_{ik}x_k \quad \text{is} \quad Z\uparrow = CX\uparrow, \quad \text{then} \quad C = AB \quad \text{and} \quad Z\uparrow = ABX\uparrow \tag{3}$$

18.5. Transposed matrix. If $A = \| a_{ij} \|$ is m by N, the transposed matrix $A' = \| a_{ji} \|$ is N by m. For a product $C = AB$, the transposed matrix is $C' = B'A'$.

For $X\uparrow$, $Y\uparrow$, $Z\uparrow$ the column matrices of § 18.4 with a single column, the transposed matrices will be row matrices with a single row. We denote them by $\vec{X}$, $\vec{Y}$, $\vec{Z}$. Then the transformations of § 18.4 may be written in terms of row matrices as

$$\vec{Y} = \vec{X}B', \quad \vec{Z} = \vec{Y}A', \quad \vec{Z} = \vec{X}C', \quad \text{or} \quad \vec{Z} = \vec{X}B'A', \quad \text{since } C' = B'A'$$

18.6. Inverse matrix. The unit matrix is a square matrix with ones on the main diagonal and the remaining elements zero. Its elements are $\delta_{ik} = 0$ if $i \neq k$, and $= 1$ if $i = k$.

A square matrix is singular if its determinant is zero. Each nonsingular square matrix has a reciprocal matrix A^{-1} such that

$$AA^{-1} = \| \delta_{ik} \| \quad \text{and} \quad A^{-1}A = \| \delta_{ik} \| \tag{1}$$

Let $| A |$ denote the determinant $| a_{ik} |$, and A_{ik} the cofactor of a_{ik} or product of $(-1)^{i+k}$ by the determinant obtained from $| a_{ik} |$ by striking out the ith row and kth column. (See § 1.8.) Then explicitly A^{-1} has as elements

$$a^{-1}{}_{ik} = \frac{A_{ki}}{| A |} \tag{2}$$

18.7. Symmetry. For square matrices symmetry and skew-symmetry are defined as for tensors in § 7.10. Orthogonal and unitary, or Hermitian orthogonal matrices are defined in § 7.11.

18.8. Linear equations. The set of n linear equations in n unknowns x_k,

$$\sum_{k=1}^{n} a_{ik}x_k = b_i, \quad i = 1,2,\ldots,n \tag{1}$$

determine a square matrix $A = \| a_{ik} \|$ and two column matrices $B\uparrow = \| B_i \|$ and $X\uparrow = \| x_i \|$. In matrix form we may write

$$AX\uparrow = B\uparrow \tag{2}$$

If A is nonsingular, find its solution by premultiplying by the inverse matrix A^{-1} of § 18.6.

$$X\uparrow = A^{-1}B\uparrow \quad \text{or} \quad x_i = \frac{1}{|A|}\sum_{k=1}^{n} A_{ki}b_k \tag{3}$$

18.9. Rank. For a rectangular matrix we get a subdeterminant of the qth order by selecting those elements in some set of q rows and some set of q columns. If at least one subdeterminant of order r is not zero, but all the subdeterminants of order $r + 1$ and hence those of higher order vanish, the matrix is of rank r.

With any set of m linear equations in n unknowns x_k,

$$\sum_{k=1}^{n} a_{ik}x_k = b_i, \quad i = 1,2,\ldots,m \tag{1}$$

$$\text{or} \quad AX\uparrow = B\uparrow \quad \text{with} \quad A = \| a_{ik} \|, \quad X\uparrow = \| x_k \|, \quad B\uparrow = \| b_i \| \tag{2}$$

we associate two matrices. The matrix of the system is the m by n matrix A, and we obtain from A the augmented matrix, which is an m by $(n + 1)$ matrix, by adding an $(m + 1)$st column whose elements are those of $B\uparrow$. Then the condition that the system of equations is consistent in the sense of having one or more sets of solutions for the unknown x_k is that the matrix and augmented matrix have the same rank.

18.10. Diagonalization of matrices. Let $A = \| a_{ij} \|$ be a square n by n matrix, and $\| \delta_{ij} \|$ be the unit matrix of § 18.6. Then $\| \lambda\delta_{ij} - a_{ij} \|$ is the characteristic matrix of A. The roots of the characteristic equation, $| \lambda\delta_{ij} - a_{ij} | = 0$ are the eigenvalues of A. Suppose that they are all distinct, $\lambda_1, \lambda_2, \ldots, \lambda_n$. Find solutions of

$$\sum_{k=1}^{n} a_{ik}x_{kj} = \lambda_j x_{ij}.$$

The ratios of the x_{ij}, for each j, are determined, § 18.9. They may be scaled to make the vector $x_{1j}, x_{2j}, \ldots, x_{nj}$ have unit length. For distinct λ_j, any two of these vectors are orthogonal. The orthogonal (§ 7.11) matrix $X = \| x_{ij} \|$ is such that $X^{-1}AX = \| \lambda_i\delta_{ij} \|$, a diagonal matrix.

When the eigenvalues are not all distinct, a reduction to diagonal form may not be possible, and we are led into the theory of elementary divisors.

Whether all eigenvalues are distinct or not, whenever A is symmetric, § 7.10, unitary, § 7.11, or Hermitian, $\tilde{H} = H$, a unitary matrix U can be found such that $U^{-1}AU = \| \lambda_i \delta_{ij} \|$, a diagonal matrix. Here $U = \| u_{ij} \|$, where if λ_j is a root of $| \lambda \delta_{ij} - a_{ij} |$ of multiplicity m, so that $\lambda_j = \lambda_{j+1} = \ldots = \lambda_{j+m-1}$, the columns of u_{ij} from j to $j + m - 1$, u_{is}, are found from the m linearly independent vector solutions of

$$\sum_{k=1}^{n} a_{ij} x_{kt} = \lambda_j x_{it}$$

We take $v_{i1} = x_{i1}$,

$$v_{i2} = x_{i2} - \frac{1}{V_1} \left(\sum_{p-1}^{n} \bar{v}_{p1} x_{p2} \right) v_{i1}$$

where the bar means complex conjugate

$$v_{it} = x_{it} - \sum_{k=1}^{t-1} \frac{1}{V_k} \left(\sum_{p=1}^{n} \bar{v}_{pk} x_{pt} \right) v_{ik}$$

Here

$$V_k = \sum_{p=1}^{n} \bar{v}_{pk} v_{pk}$$

Then $u_{i,j+t-1} = (1/\sqrt{V_t}) v_{it}$.

The eigenvalues of a real symmetric or of a Hermitian matrix, $\tilde{H} = H$, are all real. The eigenvalues of a real orthogonal or of a unitary matrix are all of absolute value 1, ± 1 or $e^{i\phi}$.

19. Group Theory

19.1. Group. Let a rule of combination be given which determines a third mathematical object C from two given objects A and B, taken in that order. We call the rule " multiplication " ; call C the " product," and write $C = AB$. Then a system composed of a set of elements $A, B, \ldots$, and this one rule of combination is called a group if the following conditions are satisfied.

I. If A and B are any elements of the set, whether distinct or not, the product $C = AB$ is also an element of the set.

II. The associative law holds ; that is if A, B, C are any elements of the set, $(AB)C = A(BC)$ and may be written ABC.

III. The set contains an identity or unit element I which is such that every element is unchanged when combined with it,

$$IA = AI = A \tag{1}$$

IV. If A is any element, the set contains an inverse element A^{-1}, such that

$$A^{-1}A = AA^{-1} = I \tag{2}$$

19.2. Quotients. For any two elements A and B there is a left-hand quotient of B by A, such that $AX = B$. This $X = A^{-1}B$. There is also a right-hand quotient of B by A, such that $YA = B$. This $Y = BA^{-1}$. Let F be a fixed element of the set, and V be a variable element taking on all possible values successively. Then V^{-1}, VF, FV, $V^{-1}F$, and FV^{-1} each runs through all possible values.

19.3. Order. If there is an infinite number of elements in the set, the group is an infinite or group of infinite order. If there is a finite number, g, of elements in the set, the group is a finite group of order g.

19.4. Abelian group. If the rule of combination is commutative so that all cases $AB = BA$, the group is an Abelian group. In particular a finite group whose elements are all powers of a single element A, such as A, A^2, A^3, ..., $A^g = I$ is necessarily Abelian and is called a cyclic group.

19.5. Isomorphy. We use a single capital letter to indicate either a group or its set of elements. Two groups G and G' are isomorphic if it is possible to establish a one-to-one correspondence between their elements G and G$'$ of such a sort that if A, B are elements of G and A', B', are the corresponding elements of G', then AB corresponds to $A'B'$.

If it is possible to establish an m-to-one correspondence between the elements G and G' of this sort, the group G is multiply isomorphic to the group G'.

19.6. Subgroup. Let G be a finite group of order g. Let the elements H be a subset of the elements G such that if A_H and B_H are any two elements in H, their product A_HB_H is also in H. Then the system composed of the elements H and the rule of combination for G is a group in the sense of § 19.1. We call this group H a subgroup of the group G. The order of the subgroup H, h, is a divisor of g. And the integral quotient $j = g/h$ is called the index of H with respect to G.

19.7. Normal divisor. The elements $A^{-1}HA$, where A is any fixed element of G and H takes on all the elements of some subgroup H, themselves form a subgroup of G, which is said to be conjugate to the subgroup H. If, as A takes on all possible values as an element of G, the resulting conjugate subgroups of H are all identical, then the subgroup H is called a normal divisor of the group G.

19.8. Representation. Let M be a set of h-rowed square matrices, each of which is nonsingular, which form a group when the rule of combination is matrix multiplication as defined in § 18.3. If the group M is simply or multiply isomorphic to a group G, the group M is called a representation of G in terms of matrices or linear transformations, § 18.4. The number of rows in the matrix, or of variables in the linear transformations, h, is called the degree or dimension of the representation.

Two representations M' and M are equivalent if for some fixed matrix A, $M' = A^{-1}MA$. If for some $p + q = h$, each matrix M consists of two square matrices of p and q rows, respectively, on the main diagonal, surrounded by a p by q and a q by p rectangle of zeros, the representation M is reducible. Otherwise it is irreducible. For each finite group G of order g there are a finite number c of irreducible representations not equivalent to one another. If these have dimensions $h_1, h_2, \ldots, h_c$, each of the h_n is a divisor of g, and

$$h_1^2 + h_2^2 + \ldots + h_c^2 = g$$

19.9. Three-dimensional rotation group. The elements of this infinite group are real three by three orthogonal matrices, § 7.11, $B = \| b_{ij} \|$. As in § 18.4, $Y = BX$, where $x_1, x_2, x_3 = x, y, z$ of a first coordinate system and $y_1, y_2, y_3 = x', y', z'$ of a second rotated coordinate system. The particular matrices

$$R_z(\alpha) = \begin{Vmatrix} \cos\alpha & \sin\alpha & 0 \\ -\sin\alpha & \cos\alpha & 0 \\ 0 & 0 & 1 \end{Vmatrix}, \quad R_y(\beta) = \begin{Vmatrix} \cos\beta & 0 & -\sin\beta \\ 0 & 1 & 0 \\ \sin\beta & 0 & \cos\beta \end{Vmatrix} \tag{1}$$

correspond to rotations about $0Z$ through α and about $0Y$ through β. For a suitable choice of the Euler angles α, β, and γ any matrix of the rotation group $B = R(\alpha,\beta,\gamma) = R_z(\gamma)\, R_y(\beta)\, R_z(\alpha)$.

Consider next the unimodular matrices of order two, or unitary matrices with determinant unity,

$$U = \begin{Vmatrix} a + bi & c + di \\ -c + di & a - bi \end{Vmatrix} \tag{2}$$

where $a^2 + b^2 + c^2 + d^2 = 1$. As in § 7.11, $U_{pq} = U^{-1}{}_{pq}$. These make up the special unitary group.

The Pauli spin matrices are defined by

$$P_1 = \begin{Vmatrix} 0 & 1 \\ 1 & 0 \end{Vmatrix}, \quad P_2 = \begin{Vmatrix} 0 & i \\ -i & 0 \end{Vmatrix}, \quad P_3 = \begin{Vmatrix} 1 & 0 \\ 0 & -1 \end{Vmatrix} \tag{3}$$

The Hermitian matrix with $x^2 + y^2 + z^2 = 1$,

$$\begin{Vmatrix} z & x + iy \\ x - iy & -z \end{Vmatrix} = H(x,y,z) = xP_1 + yP_2 + zP_3 \tag{4}$$

has $\tilde{H} = H$. And for any unimodular matrix U, if

$$U^{-1}HU = x'P_1 + y'P_2 + z'P_3,$$

the transformation from x,y,z to x',y',z' is a three-dimensional rotation. The rotations $R_z(\alpha)$ and $R_y(\beta)$ correspond to $U_1(\alpha)$ and $U_2(\beta)$ where

$$U_1(\alpha) = \begin{Vmatrix} e^{i\alpha/2} & 0 \\ 0 & e^{-i\alpha/2} \end{Vmatrix}, \quad U_2(\beta) = \begin{Vmatrix} \cos\dfrac{\beta}{2} & -\sin\dfrac{\beta}{2} \\ \sin\dfrac{\beta}{2} & \cos\dfrac{\beta}{2} \end{Vmatrix} \tag{5}$$

Thus $R(\alpha,\beta,\gamma)$ correspond to $U(\alpha,\beta,\gamma) = U_1(\gamma)U_2(\beta)U_1(\alpha)$, or

$$U(\alpha,\beta,\gamma) = \begin{Vmatrix} e^{i(\alpha+\gamma)/2}\cos\dfrac{\beta}{2} & -e^{-i(\alpha-\gamma)/2}\sin\dfrac{\beta}{2} \\ e^{i(\alpha-\gamma)/2}\sin\dfrac{\beta}{2} & e^{-i(\alpha+\gamma)/2}\cos\dfrac{\beta}{2} \end{Vmatrix} \tag{6}$$

The irreducible representations, § 19.8, by matrices of order $(2j + 1)$, of the special unitary U group are given by

$$\left.\begin{aligned} U_{pq}{}^{(j)}(\alpha,\beta,\gamma) &= \sum_m \frac{(-1)^{m-q-p}\sqrt{(j+p)!\,(j-p)!\,(j+q)!\,(j-q)!}}{(j-p-m)!\,(j+q-m)!\,(m+p-q)!\,m!} \\ &\qquad \times e^{iq\alpha}\cos^{2j+q-p-2m}\frac{\beta}{2}\sin^{p+2m-q}\frac{\beta}{2}\,e^{ip\gamma} \end{aligned}\right\} \tag{7}$$

Here $p,q = -j, -j+1, \ldots, j-1, j,$ and $m = 0, 1, 2, \ldots$ where we stop the summation by putting $1/(-N)! = 0$; and $j = 0, \frac{1}{2}, 1, \frac{3}{2}, 2, \ldots$.

The group characters, or traces, § 7.12, of these matrices are

$$\chi^{(j)}(\alpha) = 1 + 2\cos\alpha + \ldots + 2\cos j\alpha = \frac{\sin(j+\frac{1}{2})\alpha}{\sin\alpha/2} \tag{8}$$

for $j = 0, 1, 2, 3, \ldots$.

For $j = \frac{1}{2}, \frac{3}{2}, \frac{5}{2}, \ldots,$

$$\chi^{(j)}(\alpha) = 2\cos\frac{\alpha}{2} + 2\cos\frac{3\alpha}{2} + \ldots + 2\cos j\alpha = \frac{\sin(j+\frac{1}{2})\alpha}{\sin\alpha/2} \tag{9}$$

Each matrix $R(\alpha,\beta,\gamma)$ corresponds to two U matrices, namely, $U(\alpha,\beta,\gamma)$ and $U(\alpha + 2\pi, \beta, \gamma)$. The group $R(\alpha,\beta,\gamma)U(\alpha,\beta,\gamma)$ is simply isomorphic with $U(\alpha,\beta,\gamma)$ and has all the matrices $U_{pq}{}^{(j)}$ given above as representations.

But for the group $R(\alpha,\beta,\gamma)$ the matrices $U_{pq}{}^{(j)}$ and characters $\chi^{(j)}(\alpha)$ with $j = 0, 1, 2, 3, \ldots$ give a complete representation.

20. Analytic Functions

20.1. Definitions. Consider the complex variable $z = x + iy$ where $i^2 = -1$. We associate $z = x + iy$ with the point (x,y). The single-valued function $f(z)$ has a derivative $f'(z)$ at z if

$$f'(z) = \lim_{\Delta z \to 0} \frac{[f(z+\Delta z) - f(z)]}{z}$$

where $\Delta z \to 0$ through any complex values.

Let z be a variable and z_0 a fixed point in R, any open (boundary excluded) simply connected region. The function $f(z)$ is analytic in R if and only if any of the following four conditions hold.

a. $f(z)$ has a derivative $f'(z)$ at each point of R.

b. $f(z)$ may be integrated in R in the sense that the integral $\oint f(z)\,dz = 0$ about every closed path in R. Thus

$$F(z) = \int_{z_0}^{z} f(z)\,dz$$

is a single-valued analytic function of z independent of the path in R.

c. $f(z)$ has a Taylor's series expansion, §§ 3.25, 20.4, in powers of $(z - z_0)$ about each point z_0 in R.

d. $f(z) = u(x,y) + iv(x,y)$, where both $u(x,y)$ and $v(x,y)$ have continuous partial derivatives that satisfy the Cauchy-Riemann differential equations,

$$\frac{\partial u}{\partial x} = \frac{\partial v}{\partial y}, \quad \frac{\partial u}{\partial y} = -\frac{\partial v}{\partial x} \tag{1}$$

The functions u and v are conjugate potential functions, and each satisfies Laplace's equation

$$\frac{\partial^2 u}{\partial x^2} + \frac{\partial^2 u}{\partial y^2} = 0 \tag{2}$$

20.2. Properties. If $f(z)$ is analytic at all points of some circle with center S, but not at S, then $z_0 = S$ is an isolated singular point. It is a pole of order n if n is the smallest positive integer for which $(z - z_0)^n f(z)$ is bounded. If there is no such n, then z_0 is an essential singularity.

The function $f(x + iy) = u(x,y) + iv(x,y)$ effects a mapping from the x,y to the u,v plane. At any point where $f'(z) \neq 0$, the mapping is conformal, preserving angles of image curves and shapes and ratios of distances for infinitesimal figures.

20.3. Integrals. The integral

$$\left.\begin{aligned} \int_a^b f(z)\,dz &= \int_a^b (u + iv)\,(dx + i\,dy) \\ &= \int_a^b (u\,dx - v\,dy) + i \int_a^b (v\,dx + u\,dy) \end{aligned}\right\} \quad (1)$$

Each of the real differentials $(u\,dx - v\,dy)$ and $(v\,dx + u\,dy)$ is exact. The integral

$$\int_a^b f(z) dz$$

is not changed when the path from a to b is continuously varied without crossing any singular point. And

$$\oint f(z) dz = \int_a^a f(z) dz = 0$$

over any closed path not enclosing any singular point. For the same type of path enclosing t, traversed in the positive sense, Cauchy's integral formula asserts that

$$f(t) = \frac{1}{2\pi i} \oint \frac{f(z)}{z - t}\,dz \quad (2)$$

20.4. Laurent expansion. Let $f(z)$ be analytic for $0 < |z - z_0| < r$. Then for z in this range,

$$\left.\begin{aligned} f(z) &= \sum_{m=-\infty}^{\infty} a_m (z - z_0)^m \\ &= \ldots + \frac{a_{-2}}{(z - z_0)^2} + \frac{a_{-1}}{z - z_0} + a_0 + a_1(z - z_0) + a_2(z - z_0)^2 + \ldots \end{aligned}\right\} \quad (1)$$

$$a_m = \frac{1}{2\pi i} \oint_C (z - z_0)^{-m-1} f(z) dz \quad (2)$$

where C is a circle $|z - z_0| = a$ with $a < r$ traversed in the positive direction. When $f(z)$ is analytic at z_0, all the a_m with negative subscripts are zero, and the expansion reduces to Taylor's series, § 3.25, with $a_n = (1/n!)f^{(n)}(z)$.

When $f(z)$ has a pole of order n at z_0, § 20.2, the a_m are zero for $m < -n$. In this case the residue a_{-1} may be found from

$$a_{-1} = \frac{1}{(n-1)!}\frac{d^{n-1}}{dz^{n-1}}[(z-z_0)^n f(z)]\bigg|_{z=z_0} \tag{3}$$

In particular for a pole of the first order, $n = 1$, the residue a_{-1} may be found from

$$a_{-1} = \lim_{z \to z_0} [(z-z_0)f(z)] \tag{4}$$

For an isolated essential singularity, § 20.2, there are an infinite number of negative powers in the expansion, and we still call a_{-1} the residue.

20.5. Laurent expansion about infinity. Similarly let $f(z)$ be analytic for $|z| > r$. Then for z in this range,

$$f(z) = \sum_{m=-\infty}^{\infty} a_m z^m, \quad a_m = \frac{1}{2\pi i}\oint z^{-m-1} f(z) dz \tag{1}$$

where C is a circle $|z| = a$ with $a > r$ traversed in the positive direction. In this case for $z = \infty$, $f(z)$ is analytic if there are no positive powers, $f(z)$ has a pole of order n if all the a_m are zero for $m > n$, and $f(z)$ has an isolated essential singularity if there are an infinite number of positive powers.

20.6. Residues. About a circle C, $|z - z_0| = a$ as in 20.4,

$$\oint_C (z-z_0)^m dz = 0 \tag{1}$$

when $m = 0, 1, \pm 2, \pm 3, \ldots$, except for $m = 1$, when

$$\oint_C \frac{dz}{z - z_0} = 2\pi i \tag{2}$$

Termwise integration of the Laurent series of § 20.5 over C gives $\oint_C f(z)\, dz = 2\pi i a_{-1}$. And about any closed contour passing through regular points only, but enclosing singular points z_k, $\oint f(z)\, dz = 2\pi i[\Sigma R(z_k)]$, where $R(z_k)$ is the residue a_{-1} or coefficient of $1/(z - z_k)$ in the Laurent expansion appropriate to z_k. For poles the residues may be found as indicated in § 20.4.

For a number of examples of the use of this residue theorem to compute real integrals see Franklin, *Methods of Advanced Calculus*, Chap 5.

21. Integral Equations

21.1. Fredholm integral equations. Fredholm's integral equation (F) is

$$U(x) = f(x) + \lambda \int_a^b K(x,t)U(t)dt \tag{1}$$

The kernel $K(x,t)$ and $f(x)$ are given functions, and $U(x)$ is to be found. We assume that

$$\int_a^b \int_a^b [K(x,t)]^2 \, dx \, dt = W$$

is finite. With (F) we associate the homogeneous equation (F_h), which is

$$U(x) = \lambda \int_a^b K(x,t)U(t)dt$$

and the transposed equation (F_t), which is

$$\tilde{U}(x) = f(x) + \lambda \int_a^b K(t,x)\tilde{U}(t)dt.$$

The homogeneous transposed equation (F_{ht}) is

$$\tilde{U}(x) = \int_a^b K(t,x)\tilde{U}(t)dt.$$

The number ρ of linearly independent solutions $u_1(x)$, $u_2(x)$, ..., $u_\varrho(x)$ of (F_h) is finite and equal to the number of linearly independent solutions $u_1(x)$, $u_2(x)$, ..., $u_\varrho(x)$ of (F_{ht}). The number ρ is the defect of the kernel $K(x,t)$ for the value λ. The general solution of (F_h) is

$$c_1u_1(x) + c_2u_2(x) + \ldots + c_\varrho u_\varrho(x).$$

If $\rho = 0$, then (F) and (F_t) each has a unique solution for any $f(x)$. There is a solving kernel, or resolvent, $\Gamma(x,t;\lambda)$ such that

$$U(x) = f(x) + \lambda \int_a^b \Gamma(x,t;\lambda)f(t)dt \quad \text{for } (F),$$

and

$$\tilde{U}(x) = f(x) + \lambda \int_a^b \Gamma(t,x;\lambda)f(t)dt \quad \text{for } (F_t).$$

Fredholm's form of the resolvent is

$$\Gamma(x,t;\lambda) = \frac{D(x,t;\lambda)}{D(\lambda)} \tag{2}$$

where

$$D(x,t;\lambda) = K(x,t) + \sum_{n=1}^{\infty} (-1)^n D_n(x,t) \frac{\lambda^n}{n!}$$

and

$$D(\lambda) = \sum_{n=0}^{\infty} (-1)^n D_n \frac{\lambda^n}{n!}$$

The D's are found in succession from

$$D_m = \int_a^b D_{m-1}(x,x)dx, \quad D_m(x,t) = D_m K(x,t) - m \int_a^b K(x,s)D_{m-1}(s,t)ds.$$

These series converge for all λ.

For sufficiently small λ, we have the Neumann series

$$\Gamma(x,t;\lambda) = K(x,t) + \lambda K_2(x,t) + \lambda^2 K_3(x,t) + \ldots + \lambda^n K_{n+1}(x,t) + \ldots \quad (3)$$

The iterated kernels $K_m(x,t)$ are found in succession from

$$K_1(x,t) = K(x,t) \quad \text{and} \quad K_m(x,t) = \int_a^b K(x,s)K_{m-1}(s,t)ds \quad (4)$$

If $\rho > 0$, then (F) has a solution only it

$$\int_a^b u_i(t)f(t)dt = 0$$

for $i = 1, 2, \ldots, \rho$. The general solution of (F) is one solution plus the general solution of (F_h).

21.2. Symmetric kernel. In § 21.1 let $K(x,t) = K(t,x)$. Then (F_h) has nonzero solutions for certain determined discrete values $\lambda_1, \lambda_2, \ldots, \lambda_n, \ldots$, called the eigenvalues, for which the defect $\rho > 0$. The corresponding solutions $u_i(x)$ of (F_h) are the eigenfunctions. For any λ, $\rho \leqq \lambda^2 W$. For W see § 21.1.

Every symmetric kernel, not identically zero, has at least one and at most a denumerable infinity of eigenvalues, with no finite limit point. These eigenvalues are all real if $K(x,t)$ is real and symmetric. At most A^2W eigenvalues have numerical values not exceeding A, and $\lambda_n^2 \geqq 1/W$. Also

$$\sum_{n=1}^{\infty} \frac{1}{\lambda_n^2} \leqq W$$

where each eigenvalue of defect ρ is counted ρ times.

The ρ functions for a λ of defect ρ may be taken as of norm, the N_n of § 14.19, unity, and orthogonal to one another. Then if the functions for a λ

with $\rho = 1$ are taken as of norm 1, the totality of eigenvalues will form a real normal and orthogonal set as in § 14.19. Thus

$$\int_a^b [u_n(x)]^2\, dx = 1, \quad \int_a^b u_n(x)u_m(x)dx = 0, \quad m \neq n.$$

The bilinear series

$$K(x,t) = \sum_{n=1}^{\infty} \frac{u_n(x)u_n(t)}{\lambda_n} \tag{5}$$

converges for a Mercer kernel with only a finite number of positive, or only a finite number of negative eigenvalues. Otherwise it converges in the mean,

$$\lim_{n\to\infty} \int (K - S_n)^2 dx = 0$$

where S_n is the sum to n terms.

If (F) has a solution, it is given by the Schmidt series

$$U(x) = f(x) + \lambda \sum_{n=1}^{\infty} \frac{f_n}{\lambda_n - \lambda} u_n(x) \tag{6}$$

where

$$f_n = \int_a^b f(t)u_n(t)dt.$$

Any function which is sourcewise representable,

$$F(x) = \int_a^b K(x,t)\phi(t)dt \tag{7}$$

has an absolutely and uniformly convergent series development

$$F(x) = \sum_{n=1}^{\infty} F_n u_n(x) \quad \text{where} \quad F_n = \int_a^b F(t)u_n(t)dt. \tag{8}$$

21.3. Volterra integral equations. Volterra's integral equation

$$(V) \quad \text{is} \quad U(x) = f(x) + \lambda \int_0^x K(x,t)U(t)dt \tag{1}$$

This always has a solution

$$U(x) = f(x) + \lambda \int_0^x \Gamma(x,t;\lambda)f(t)dt \tag{2}$$

where the resolvent

$$\Gamma(x,t;\lambda) = K(x,t) + \lambda K_2(x,t) + \lambda^2 K_3(x,t) + \ldots + \lambda^n K_{n+1}(x,t) + \ldots \tag{3}$$

The iterated kernels $K_m(x,t)$ are found in succession from

$$K_1(x,t) = K(x,t), \quad K_m(x,t) = \int_0^x K(x,s)K_{m-1}(s,t)ds \tag{4}$$

This Neumann series converges for all values of x.

If $H(x,x) \neq 0$, we may reduce the solution of the equation of the first kind,

$$g(x) = \lambda \int_0^x H(x,t)U(t)dt \tag{5}$$

to the solution of an equation of type (V). Differentiation with respect to x leads to

$$g'(x) = \lambda \int_0^x \frac{\partial H}{\partial x} U(t)dt + \lambda H(x,x)U(x) \tag{6}$$

This is of type (V) with

$$f(x) = \frac{g'(x)}{\lambda H(x,x)}, \quad K(x,t) = \frac{-1}{\lambda H(x,x)} \frac{\partial H}{\partial x} \tag{7}$$

21.4. The Abel integral equation. Abel's equation is

$$g(x) = \int_a^x \frac{U(t)}{(x-t)^q} dt, \quad \text{with} \quad 0 < q < 1 \quad \text{and} \quad g(a) = 0 \tag{1}$$

For this kernel, singular at $t = x$, the unique continuous solution is

$$U(t) = \frac{\sin q\pi}{\pi} \frac{d}{dt} \int_a^t \left[\frac{f(x)}{(t-x)^{1-q}} dx \right] \tag{2}$$

21.5. Green's function. Let $L(y) = E(x)$ be the general linear differential equation of the nth order (4) of § 5.13. The solution satisfying given boundary conditions may often be written as

$$y(x) = \int_a^b G(x,t)E(t)dt \tag{1}$$

where $G(x,t)$ is the Green's function for the given equation and boundary conditions. This function satisfies $L(G) = 0$ except at $x = t$. At $x = t$, $G(x,t)$ as a function of x is continuous, together with its first $(n-2)$ derivatives, but

$$\frac{d^{n-1}G}{dx^{n-1}} \Bigg|_{x=t-}^{x=t+} = -\frac{1}{A_n}$$

where, as in (4) of § 5.13, A_n is the coefficient of d^ny/dx^n in $L(y)$. The Green's function $G(x,t)$ must also satisfy the same given boundary conditions as were imposed on $y(x)$.

The solution of the differential equation $L(y) + \lambda w(x)y = F(x)$ satisfying the given boundary conditions satisfies the Fredholm equation (*F*) of § 21.1

$$y(x) = \lambda \int_a^b G(x,t)w(t)y(t)dt + \int_a^b G(x,t)F(t)dt \tag{2}$$

If $[vL(u) - uL(v)]dx$ is an exact differential, $L(y)$ is self-adjoint, and the Green's function, if it exists, is necessarily symmetric, so that $G(x,t) = G(t,x)$. In this case let

$$U(x) = y(x)\sqrt{w(x)}, \quad f(x) = \sqrt{w(x)} \int_a^b G(x,t)F(t)dt$$

Then

$$U(x) = \lambda \int_a^b G(x,t)\sqrt{w(x)w(t)}\,U(t)dt + f(x) \tag{3}$$

which is an integral equation with symmetric kernel like (*F*) of § 21.2 with $K(x,t) = G(x,t)\sqrt{w(x)w(t)}$.

All the conclusions of § 21.2 apply, and in particular any n times differentiable function satisfying the boundary conditions can be developed in a series in terms of the $u_n(x)$. Hence there are an infinite number of eigenvalues and the eigenfunctions form a complete set.

21.6. The Sturm - Liouville differential equation. If $L(u) = (pu')' - qu$, then

$$[vL(u) - uL(v)]dx = d[p(vu' - uv')] \tag{1}$$

Thus the Sturm-Liouville equation

$$L(u) + \lambda wu = 0, \quad \text{or} \quad (pu')' - qu + \lambda wu = 0 \tag{2}$$

is self-adjoint, and the theory of §§ 21.5 and 21.2 applies to it.

We describe a number of important particular examples. We write $p(x)$ and $q(x)$ in place of p and q when p and q are used as parameters with other meanings.

a. Let the boundary conditions be $u(-1)$ and $u(1)$ finite. With $p = 1 - x^2$, $q = 0$, $w = 1$, we have the Legendre equation of § 8.1 with eigenvalues $n(n + 1)$ and eigenfunctions the polynomials $P_n(x)$ of § 8.2. With

$$p = 1 - x^2, \quad q = \frac{m^2}{1 - x^2}, \quad w = 1 \tag{3}$$

we have the associated Legendre equation of § 8.10 with eigenvalues $n(n + 1)$, $n \geqq m$, and eigenfunctions the polynomials $P_n{}^m(x)$ of § 8.11. With

$$p(x) = x^q(1 - x)^{p-q}, \quad q(x) = 0, \quad w(x) = x^{q-1}(1 - x)^{p-q} \tag{4}$$

we have the Jacobi equation of § 10.7 with eigenvalues $n(p+n)$ and eigenfunctions the polynomials $J_n(p,q;x)$. With

$$p = (1 - x^2)^{1/2}, \quad q = 0, \quad w = (1 - x^2)^{-1/2} \tag{5}$$

we have the Tschebycheff equation of § 10.7 with eigenvalues n^2 and eigenfunctions the polynomials $T_n(x)$.

b. Let the boundary conditions be $u(0)$ finite, and appropriate behavior at plus infinity. With

$$p = xe^{-x}, \quad q = 0, \quad w = e^{-x} \tag{6}$$

we have the Laguerre equation of § 11.1 with eigenvalues n and eigenfunctions the polynomials $L_n(x)$. With

$$p = x, \quad q = \frac{x}{4} - \frac{1}{2}, \quad w = 1 \tag{7}$$

we have the Laguerre equation of § 11.4 with eigenvalues n and eigenfunctions $e^{-x/2}L_n(x)$. With

$$p = x^{s-1}e^{-x}, \quad q = 0, \quad w = x^s e^{-x} \tag{8}$$

we have the associated Laguerre equation of § 11.5 with eigenvalues $r - s$ and eigenfunctions the polynomials $L_r^{\,s}$.

c. Let the boundary conditions be appropriate behavior at plus infinity and at minus infinity. With

$$p = e^{-x^2}, \quad q = 0, \quad w = e^{-x^2} \tag{9}$$

we have the Hermite equation of § 12.1 with eigenvalues $2n$ and eigenfunctions the polynomials $H_n(x)$. With

$$p = 1, \quad q = x^2 - 1, \quad w = 1 \tag{10}$$

we have the Hermite equation of § 12.4 with eigenvalues $2n$ and eigenfunctions $e^{-x^2/2}H_n(x)$.

d. Let the boundary conditions be $u(0)$ finite, $u(1) = 0$. With

$$p = x, \quad q = \frac{n^2}{x}, \quad w = x, \quad \lambda = a^2 \tag{11}$$

we have an equivalent of the modified Bessel equation

$$x^2u'' + xu' + (-n^2 + a^2x^2)u = 0,$$

which is satisfied by $Z_n(ax)$ by §§ 9.5 and 9.6. The eigenvalues are $a_{nr}^{\,2}$, where $J_n(a_{nr}) = 0$, and the eigenfunctions are the $J_n(a_{nr}x)$, § 9.2. Here n is fixed, and the eigenvalues and eigenfunctions correspond to $r = 1, 2, 3, \ldots$. For

$$p = x^c(1-x)^{a+b+1-c}, \quad q = 0, \quad w = x^{c-1}(1-x)^{a+b-c}, \quad \lambda = -ab \tag{12}$$

the Sturm-Liouville equation reduces to the hypergeometric equation of § 10.1.

21.7. Examples of Green's function. In each of the following examples, the Green's function $G(x,t) = G_1(x,t)$ for $x \leqq t$ and $G(x,t) = G_1(t,x)$ for $x \geqq t$. Here G_{1m} means a modified Green's function.

a. Let the boundary conditions be $u(0) = 0$, $u(1) = 0$.

For $$L(u) = u'', \quad G_1(x,t) = (1-t)x \tag{1}$$

For $$L(u) = u'' + k^2u, \quad G_1(x,t) = \frac{\sin kx \sin k(1-t)}{k \sin k} \tag{2}$$

For $$L(u) = u'' - k^2u, \quad G_1(x,t) = \frac{\sinh kx \sinh k(1-t)}{k \sinh k} \tag{3}$$

b. Let the boundary conditions be $u(-1) = u(1)$, $u'(-1) = u'(1)$.

For $$L(u) = u'', \quad G_{1m}(x,t) = \frac{1}{4}(x-t)^2 + \frac{1}{2}(x-t) + \frac{1}{6} \tag{4}$$

For $$L(u) = u'' + k^2u, \quad G_1(x,t) = -\frac{\cos k(x-t+1)}{2k \sin k} \tag{5}$$

For $$L(u) = u'' - k^2u, \quad G_1(x,t) = \frac{\cosh k(x-t+1)}{2k \sinh k} \tag{6}$$

c. Let the boundary conditions be $u(0) = 0$, $u'(1) = 0$.

For $$L(u) = u'', \quad G_1(x,t) = x \tag{7}$$

For $$L(u) = u'' + k^2u, \quad G_1(x,t) = \frac{\sin kx \cos k(1-t)}{k \cos k} \tag{8}$$

For $$L(u) = u'' - k^2u, \quad G_1(x,t) = \frac{\sinh kx \cosh k(1-t)}{k \cosh k} \tag{9}$$

d. Let the boundary conditions be $u(-1) = 0$, $u(1) = 0$.

For $$L(u) = u'', \quad G_1(x,t) = \frac{1}{2}(1 + x - t - xt) \tag{10}$$

e. Let the boundary conditions be

$$u(0) = -u(1), \quad u'(0) = -u'(1). \tag{11}$$

For $\quad L(u) = u'', \quad G_1(x,t) = \frac{1}{4} + \frac{x-t}{2} \qquad (12)$

f. Let the boundary conditions be $u(+\infty)$ and $u(-\infty)$ finite.

For $\quad L(u) = u'' - u, \quad G_1(x,t) = \frac{1}{2}e^{t-x} \qquad (13)$

g. Let the boundary conditions be $u(0) = 0$, $u'(0) = 0$, $u(1) = 0$, $u'(1) = 0$.

For $\quad L(u) = u^{iv}, \quad G_1(x,t) = \frac{1}{6}x^2(1-t)^2(2xt + x - 3t) \qquad (14)$

h. Let the boundary conditions be $u(-1)$ and $u(1)$ finite.

For $\quad L(u) = [(1-x^2)u']', \qquad (15)$

$$G_1(x,t) = -\frac{1}{2}\ln(1-x)(1-t) + \ln 2 - \frac{1}{2} \tag{16}$$

With this $L(u)$, Legendre's equation of § 8.1 is

$$L(y) + n(n+1)y = 0 \tag{17}$$

For $\quad L(u) = [(1-x^2)u']' - \frac{m^2u}{1-x^2}, \quad m \neq 0,$

$$G_1(x,t) = \frac{1}{2m}\left[\frac{(1+x)(1-t)}{(1-x)(1+t)}\right]^{m/2} \tag{18}$$

With this $L(u)$, the associated Legendre equation of § 8.10 is

$$L(y) + n(n+1)y = 0 \tag{19}$$

i. Let the boundary, conditions be $u(0)$ finite, $u(1) = 0$.

For $\quad L(u) = (xu')', \quad G_1(x,t) = -\ln x \qquad (20)$

With this $L(u)$, Bessel's equation (3) of § 9.1 for $n = 0$ is

$$L(y) + xy = 0 \tag{21}$$

For $\quad L(u) = (xu')' - \frac{n^2}{x}u, \quad n \neq 0, \quad G_1(x,t) = \frac{1}{n}\left[\left(\frac{x}{t}\right)^n - (xt)\right]^n \qquad (22)$

With this $L(u)$, Bessel's equation (3) of § 9.1 is

$$L(y) + xy = 0 \tag{23}$$

Bibliography

1. Algebra

FINE, H. B., *College Algebra*, Ginn & Company, Boston, 1905.
RICHARDSON, M., *College Algebra*, Prentice-Hall, Inc., New York, 1947.

2. Trigonometry and space geometry

BRENKE, W. C., *Plane and Spherical Trigonometry*, The Dryden Press, Inc., New York, 1943.
FINE, H. B. and THOMPSON, H. D., *Coordinate Geometry*, The Macmillan Company, New York, 1918.

3. and 4. Calculus

DE HAAN, B., *Nouvelles tables d'intégrales définies*, P. Engels, Leyden, 1867.
DE HAAN, B., *Tables d'intégrales définies*, P. Engels, Leyden, 1858-1864.
DWIGHT, H. B., *Tables of Integrals and Other Mathematical Data*, The Macmillan Company, New York, 1947.
FINE, H. B., *Calculus*, The Macmillan Company, New York, 1937.
FRANKLIN, P., *Differential and Integral Calculus*, McGraw-Hill Book Company, Inc., New York, 1953.
FRANKLIN, P., *Methods of Advanced Calculus*, McGraw-Hill Book Company, Inc., New York, 1944.
PIERCE, B. O., *A Short Table of Integrals*, Ginn & Company, Boston, 1929.
WIDDER, D. V., *Advanced Calculus*, Prentice-Hall, Inc., New York, 1947.

5. Differential equations

FORSYTH, A. R., *Treatise on Differential Equations*, Macmillan and Co., Ltd., London, 1885.
INCE, E. L., *Ordinary Differential Equations*, Longmans, Green & Co., London, 1927.
MORRIS, M. and BROWN, O. E., *Differential Equations*, 3d ed., Prentice-Hall, Inc., New York, 1952.

6. Vector analysis

PHILLIPS, H. B., *Vector Analysis*, John Wiley & Sons, Inc., New York, 1933.

7. Tensors

BRAND, L., *Vector and Tensor Analysis*, John Wiley & Sons, Inc., New York, 1947.
EDDINGTON, A. S., *The Mathematical Theory of Relativity*, Cambridge University Press, London, 1930.
EISENHART, L. P., *Riemannian Geometry*, Princeton University Press, Princeton, 1926.
KRON, G., *Short Course in Tensor Analysis for Electrical Engineers*, John Wiley & Sons, Inc., New York, 1942.
MCCONNELL, A. J., *Applications of the Absolute Differential Calculus*, Blackie & Son, Ltd., London, 1931.
WILLS, A. P., *Vector and Tensor Analysis*, Prentice-Hall, Inc., New York, 1938.

8. to 15. Special functions

CARSLAW, H. S., *Theory of Fourier Series and Integrals*, Macmillan and Co., Ltd., London, 1921.

COURANT, R. and HILBERT, D., *Methoden der mathematischen Physik*, Vol. 1, Julius Springer, Berlin, 1931.

FRANKLIN, P., *Fourier Methods*, McGraw-Hill Book Company, Inc., New York, 1949.

GRAY, A., MATHEWS, G. B. and MACROBERT, T. M., *A Treatise on Bessel Functions*, Macmillan and Co., Ltd., London, 1931.

HOBSON, E. W., *The Theory of Spherical and Ellipsoidal Harmonics*, Cambridge University Press, London, 1931.

KNOPP, K., *Theory and Application of Infinite Series*, trans. Young, R. C., Blackie & Son, Ltd., London, 1928.

MCLACHLAN, N. W., *Bessel Functions for Engineers*, Clarendon Press, Oxford, 1934.

MARGENAU, H. and MURPHY, G. M., *The Mathematics of Physics and Chemistry*, D. Van Nostrand Company, Inc., New York, 1943.

WATSON, G. N., *Theory of Bessel Functions*, Cambridge University Press, London, 1944.

WHITTAKER, E. T. and WATSON, G. N., *A Course of Modern Analysis*, Cambridge University Press, London, 1927.

18. Matrices

BÔCHER, M., *Introduction to Higher Algebra*, The Macmillan Company, New York, 1907.

DICKSON, L. E., *Modern Algebraic Theories*, Benjamin H. Sanborn and Co., Chicago, 1926.

FRAZER, R. A., DUNCAN, W. J. and COLLAR, A. R., *Elementary Matrices*, Cambridge University Press, London, 1938.

TURNBULL, H. W. and AITKEN, A. C., *The Theory of Canonical Matrices*, Blackie & Son, Ltd., London, 1932.

19. Groups

SPEISER, A., *Theorie der Gruppen von endlicher Ordnung*, Julius Springer, Berlin, 1927.

WEYL, H., *The Classical Groups*, Princeton University Press, Princeton, 1939.

WEYL, H., *Theory of Groups and Quantum Mechanics*, Methuen & Co., Ltd., London, 1931.

WIGNER, E., *Gruppentheorie und ihre Anwendung auf Quantenmechanik der Atomspektren*, F. Vieweg und Sohn, Braunschweig, 1931.

20. Analytic functions

HURWITZ, A. and COURANT, R., *Vorlesungen über allgemeine Funktionentheorie und elliptische Funktionen*, Julius Springer, Berlin, 1925.

PIERPONT, J., *Functions of a Complex Variable*, Ginn & Company, Boston, 1914.

21. Integral Equations

FRANK, P. and VON MISES, R., *Differential- und Integralgleichungen der Mechanik und Physik*, M. S. Rosenberg, New York, 1943.

Collections of formulas

ADAMS, E. P. and HIPPISLEY, R. L., *Smithsonian Mathematical Formulae and Tables of Elliptic Functions*, Smithsonian Institution, Washington, 1922.

JAHNKE, E. and EMDE, F., *Funktionentafeln mit Formeln und Kurven*, B. G. Teubner, Leipzig, 1938.

MADELUNG, E., *Die mathematischen Hilfsmittel des Physikers*, Julius Springer, Berlin, 1936.

Chapter 2

STATISTICS

By Joseph M. Cameron

Statistical Engineering Laboratory
National Bureau of Standards

This chapter on statistics was added, at the special request of numerous physicists, to elaborate some of the formulas of mathematical statistics as given in abbreviated form in Chapter 1. Experimental physicists have become increasingly aware of the importance of assigning to their measures some parameter such as mean error, probable error, or limit of error to represent the precision of their measurements and to serve as a yardstick for judging differences. Nevertheless, the literature of physics abounds with examples where the scientist has failed to take full advantage of modern statistical methods. This chapter represents an attempt to give the major formulas of mathematical statistics in a form directly useful for the research student.

1. Introduction

1.1. Characteristics of a measurement process. A sequence of measurements on the same subject derived from the same measurement process (i.e. with the evironmental conditions and procedures maintained throughout the sequence) tends to cluster about some central value for the sequence. If, as the number of measurements is increased indefinitely, the average for the sequence approaches, in the probability sense, a value μ, then μ is the limiting mean of the sequence.

An individual value x_i differs from the limiting mean μ because of uncontrolled or random fluctuations in the environmental conditions or procedures. These individual values will follow some frequency distribution about the limiting mean. The specification of this distribution is made in terms of a mathematical frequency law involving several parameters including the limiting mean μ, a measure of the dispersion about the limiting mean, and other parameters as necessary.

The dispersion of values about the mean is measured in terms of the square root of the second moment about the mean, called the standard deviation, σ. This standard deviation is the limit, in the probability sense, of the square root of the average value of the squared deviation of the individual values from the mean as the number of values is increased indefinitely.

Formulas for estimating the parameters of a distribution from a finite set of data, and methods of making statistical tests of hypothesis concerning these parameters are presented in this chapter.

1.2. Statistical estimation. The experimenter has at hand only a finite set of measurements which are considered a subset of an infinite sequence. He will, therefore, be in ignorance of the *parameters* of the process such as the limiting mean μ, the standard deviation σ, and any other parameters that may exist. The finite set of data is to be used to estimate the unknown parameters. For example, the average or the median may be used to estimate the limiting mean. The function of the data used for estimation is called an *estimator*; the numerical value obtained by using this estimator on a set of data is called an *estimate*.

Estimators of parameters may be either point estimators, such as median or average, or may be interval estimators, such as confidence limits.

A sequence of estimates, generated by use of an estimator on small sets of values randomly selected from some distribution, will have a limiting mean, a standard deviation, and follow some distribution. Just as one technique of measurement may show superiority over another, so also may one method of estimation (i.e., one estimator) show superiority over another in terms of bias and precision.

The exact form of the underlying distribution of the basic measurements cannot be settled, and upon the appropriate choice of the form of the distribution depends the correctness of the inferences drawn from the data.

1.3. Notation. Unless otherwise stated in the formulas that follow:

Individual measurements are indicated by

$$x_1 \quad x_2 \quad x_3 \quad \cdots \quad x_i \quad \cdots \quad x_n$$

where the subscript refers to the order in which the measurements were made.

Each x_i is assumed to be independent in the statistical sense from all other measurements in the set, and all x_i are assumed to follow the same distribution.

Measurements ranked in order of magnitude are indicated by

$$x_{(1)}, \quad x_{(2)}, \quad \cdots \quad x_{(i)} \quad \cdots \quad x_{(n)}$$

such that $$x_{(1)} \leq x_{(2)} \leq \ldots \leq x_{(n)}$$

Parameters of distributions are indicated by Greek letters, μ, σ, β, etc., while estimates of these parameters are indicated by italic letters $\bar{x}$, s, b, etc.

2. Standard Distributions

2.1. The normal distribution.* A variate that follows the frequency function

$$f(x) = \frac{1}{\sigma\sqrt{2\pi}} e^{-(x-\mu)^2/2\sigma^2} \qquad -\infty < x < \infty \tag{1}$$

is said to be normally distributed with

$$\text{mean value of } x = \mu \qquad \text{variance of } x = \sigma^2$$

The normal distribution is quite often a fairly good approximation to the distribution of random fluctuations in physical phenomena. This general applicability of the normal distribution is verified by experience and supported in part by theory.

By virtue of the *central limit theorem*, which states that for certain conditions the sum of a large number of independent random variables is asymptotically normally distributed, the distribution of the random fluctuations in a measurement process tends toward normality because the variations are due to a multitude of minor random variations in the process.†

2.2. Additive property. If $x_1, x_2, \ldots, x_n$ are normally and independently distributed with means $\mu_1, \mu_2, \ldots, \mu_n$, and variances $\sigma_1^2, \sigma_2^2, \ldots, \sigma_n^2$, then

$$c_1x_1 + c_2x_2 + \ldots + c_nx_n$$

where the c_i are arbitrary constants and will be normally distributed with

$$\text{mean} \sum_{i=1}^{n} c_i\mu_i \quad \text{and} \quad \text{variance} \sum_{i=1}^{n} c_i^2\sigma_i^2$$

* Tables of the standardized normal distribution

$$\frac{1}{\sqrt{2\pi}} \int_{-x}^{x} e^{-t^2/2} dt$$

to 15 decimals are given in *Tables of Normal Probability Functions*, National Bureau of Standards, Applied Mathematics Series, No. 23, 1953.

† Cramer, H., *Mathematical Methods of Statistics*, Princeton University Press, 1946, pp. 213-220; and *Random Variables and Probability Distributions*, Cambridge Tracts in Mathematics, No. 36, 1937, p. 113.

2.3. The logarithmic-normal distribution. If $y = \ln x$ is normally distributed with mean μ, and standard deviation σ, then x will have mean ξ

$$\xi = e^{\mu+\sigma^2/2} \tag{1}$$

and variance $\sigma_x{}^2$.

$$\sigma_x{}^2 = e^{2\mu+\sigma^2}(e^{\sigma^2} - 1) = \xi^2(e^{\sigma^2} - 1) \tag{2}$$

Note : The use of the average of the x's as an estimate of ξ is inefficient when the variance of the y's is greater than 0.7. The use of s^2 as an estimate of $\sigma_x{}^2$ is inefficient when the variance of the y's is greater than 0.1. For efficient estimators see FINNEY, D. J., *Supplement to Journal of the Royal Statistical Society*, Vol. 7, No. 2, 1941, pp. 155-161.

2.4. Rectangular distribution. If the probability that x lies in the interval $x_0 + dx$ is the same for all values of x_0 and x is restricted to the interval (α, β), then x follows the rectangular distribution with frequency function

$$f(x) = \frac{1}{\beta - \alpha} \qquad (\alpha < x < \beta) \tag{1}$$

$$\text{mean value of } x = \frac{\beta + \alpha}{2}, \qquad \text{variance of } x = \frac{(\beta - \alpha)^2}{12}$$

2.5. The χ^2 distribution. The sum of squares of n independent normal variates having mean zero and variance unity follow the χ^2 distribution for n degrees of freedom. The χ^2 distribution enters in statistical tests of goodness of fit, homogeneity, and a variety of other purposes because the standardized variable

$$\frac{\text{estimate of mean} - \text{mean}}{\text{standard deviation of estimate of mean}}$$

tends to be asymptotically normal with mean zero and variance unity. The χ^2 distribution for n degrees of freedom has frequency function

$$f(\chi^2) = \frac{1}{2^{n/2}\Gamma(n/2)} e^{-\chi^2/2}(\chi^2)^{(n-2)/2} \qquad (0 < \chi^2 < \infty) \tag{1}$$

$$\text{mean of } \chi^2 = n, \qquad \text{variance of } \chi^2 = 2n$$

The χ^2 distribution has the *additive property* that the sum of k independent χ^2 variates based on $n_1, n_2, n_3, \ldots, n_k$ degrees of freedom respectively follows a χ^2 distribution for

$$\sum_{i=1}^{k} n_i$$

degrees of freedom.

A table of values of χ^2 exceeded with probability P is given in most texts on statistics.

2.6. Student's *t*-distribution. In sets of size $(n + 1)$ from a normal distribution the ratio of the average to standard deviation $(t = \bar{x}/s)$ follows Student's t-distribution with n degrees of freedom. Frequency function for the t-distribution is

$$f(t) = \frac{\Gamma[(n+1)/2]}{\Gamma(n/2)} \cdot \frac{1}{\sqrt{n\pi}} \cdot \frac{1}{(1 + t^2/n)^{(n+1)/2}} \qquad (-\infty < t < \infty) \qquad (1)$$

$$\text{mean value of } t = 0 \qquad \text{variance of } t = \frac{n}{n-2} \qquad (n > 2)$$

Tables of the values of t exceeded in absolute value with probability α are given in most modern texts on statistics, i.e., t_0 for which

$$\int_{-t_0}^{t_0} f(t)dt = 1 - \alpha$$

2.7. The *F* distribution. If s_1^2 and s_2^2 based on m and n degrees of freedom, respectively, are two independent estimates of the same σ^2 for a normal distribution, $F = s_1^2/s_2^2$ will follow the F distribution for (m,n) degrees of freedom (the number of degrees of freedom for the numerator is always quoted first).

The frequency function of F is

$$(F) = \frac{\Gamma[(m+n)/2]}{\Gamma(m/2)\Gamma(n/2)} \left(\frac{m}{n}\right)^{m/2} \cdot \frac{F^{(m-2)/2}}{[1 + (m/n)F]^{(m+n)/2}} \qquad (0 < F < \infty) \qquad (1)$$

$$\text{mean of } F = \frac{n}{n-2} \qquad (n > 2)$$

$$\text{variance of } F = \left(\frac{n}{n-2}\right)^2 \left[\frac{2(m+n-2)}{m(n-4)}\right] \qquad (n > 4)$$

Tables of values of F exceeded with probability 0.05 and 0.01 are given in G. W. SNEDECOR, *Statistical Methods*, Iowa University Press, 4th edition (1946), and in a number of recent texts on statistics.

2.8. Binomial distribution. If on any single trial, the probability of occurrence of an event is P and the probability of nonoccurrence of the event is $1 - P$, the probability of $k = 0, 1, \ldots, n$ occurrences in n trials is given by the successive terms in the expansion of

$$[(1 - P) + P]^n = (1 - P)^n + n(1 - P)^{n-1}P + \ldots \qquad (1)$$

The average number of occurrences in n trials will be

$$nP$$

and the standard deviation of the number of occurrences will be

$$\sqrt{nP(1-P)}$$

Tables of individual terms and cumulative terms for $P = .01(01).50$ and $n = 1(1)49$ are given in *Tables of the Binomial Probability Distribution*, National Bureau of Standards Applied Mathematics Series, No. 6, 1950.

2.9. Poisson distribution. If the probability of the occurrence of an event in an interval (of time, space, etc.) of length dx is proportional to the length of the interval, i.e., probability of occurrence is equal to, say, $\lambda\, dx$, the probability of k independent occurrences in an interval of length x is given by (for $\mu = \lambda x$)

$$\frac{e^{-\mu}\mu^k}{k!}$$

The average number of occurrences is μ; the standard deviation of the number of occurrences is $\sqrt{\mu}$. Additive property: If $k_1, k_2, \ldots, k_n$ independently follow Poisson distributions with means $\mu_1, \mu_2, \ldots, \mu_n$, then

$$\sum_{i=1}^{n} k_i$$

also follows a Poisson distribution, with mean $\sum_{i=1}^{n} \mu_i$.

Note: For P small (less than 0.1) the Poisson may be used as an approximation to the binomial taking $\mu = nP$.

Tables of individual terms and cumulative sums are given in MOLINA, E. C., *Poissons' Exponential Binomial Limit*, D. Van Nostrand Company, Inc., 1947.

3. Estimators of the Limiting Mean

3.1. The average or arithmetic mean. Symbol $\bar{x}$.

$$\bar{x} = \frac{1}{n}\sum_{i=1}^{n} x_i$$

If the x_i have limiting mean μ and standard deviation σ,

$$\text{limiting mean of } \bar{x} = \mu$$

$$\text{s.d. of } \bar{x} = \sigma/\sqrt{n}$$

3.2. The weighted average. If each x_i has assigned to it a weight of w_i, the weighted mean is defined as

$$\frac{\sum_{i=1}^{n} w_i x_i}{\sum_{i=1}^{n} w_i} \tag{1}$$

If the x_i have same limiting mean μ and standard deviation σ,

$$\text{limiting mean of weighted average} = \mu$$

$$\text{s.d. of weighted mean} = \sigma \frac{\sqrt{\sum_{i=1}^{n} w_i^2}}{\sum_{i=1}^{n} w_i}$$

3.3. The median. The median is that value that divides the set of values $x_{(i)}$ into two equal halves. The median of n values is

$$x_{(n+1)/2} \quad \text{for } n \text{ odd}$$

$$\tfrac{1}{2}(x_{(n/2)} + x_{(n/2+1)}) \quad \text{for } n \text{ even}$$

If the x_i have limiting mean μ and standard deviation σ and if the distribution of the x's is symmetrical about μ,

$$\text{limiting mean of the median} = \mu$$

If the x_i follow a normal distribution the standard deviation of the median approaches, for large n,

$$\sqrt{\frac{\pi}{2}} \cdot \frac{\sigma}{\sqrt{n}} = 1.2533 \frac{\sigma}{\sqrt{n}} \tag{1}$$

For values of $n < 10$ the s.d. is approximately $1.2\,\sigma/\sqrt{n}$.

4. Measures of Dispersion

4.1. The Standard deviation. Symbol s.

$$s = \sqrt{\frac{\sum_{i=1}^{n}(x_i - \bar{x})^2}{n-1}} \tag{1}$$

If the x_i follow a normal distribution with limiting mean μ and standard deviation σ,

$$\left.\begin{aligned}\text{limiting mean of } s &= \left[\frac{\Gamma(n/2)}{\Gamma[(n-1)/2]}\sqrt{\frac{2}{n-1}}\right]\sigma \\ &= a\sigma \sim \sqrt{1-\frac{1}{2(n-1)}}\,\sigma\end{aligned}\right\} \tag{2}$$

$$\text{s.d. of } s = \sqrt{1-a^2}\,\sigma \sim \frac{\sigma}{\sqrt{2(n-1)}} \tag{3}$$

The distribution of s is approximately normal for $n > 30$.

Note: In all statistical analysis involving comparing of averages or precision of two processes, the square of the standard deviation, or variance, is used. If such analysis is intended, the estimator s is to be preferred over other estimators of standard deviation because s^2 has a limiting mean σ^2, the other estimators do not. These alternate estimates are :

a. The estimator

$$\sqrt{\frac{\sum_{i=1}^{n}(x_i-\bar{x})^2}{n}} = \sqrt{\frac{n-1}{n}}\,s \tag{4}$$

for which, if the x_i follow a normal distribution,

$$\text{limiting mean of } \sqrt{\frac{n-1}{n}}\,s = \sqrt{\frac{n-1}{n}}\,a\sigma$$

$$\text{s.d. of } \sqrt{\frac{n-1}{n}}\,s = \sqrt{\frac{n-1}{n}}\sqrt{1-a^2}\,\sigma$$

b. The estimator

$$\frac{1}{a}\,s = \frac{\Gamma[(n-1)/2]}{\Gamma(n/2)}\sqrt{\frac{n-1}{2}}\sqrt{\frac{\sum_{i=1}^{n}(x_i-\bar{x})^2}{n-1}} \tag{5}$$

for which, if the x_i follow a normal distribution,

$$\text{limiting mean of } \frac{1}{a}\,s = \sigma$$

$$\text{s.d. of } \frac{1}{a}\,s = \sqrt{\frac{1}{a^2}-1}\,\sigma$$

c. The estimator

$$0.67449 \sqrt{\frac{\sum_{i=1}^{n} (x_i - \bar{x})^2}{n}}$$

the so-called "probable error." For the case of a normal distribution has mean value

$$0.67449 \sqrt{\frac{n-1}{n}}\, a\sigma$$

and standard deviation

$$0.67449 \sqrt{\frac{n-1}{n}} \sqrt{1-a^2}\, \sigma$$

For a normal distribution with mean μ and standard deviation σ, the interval $(\mu - 0.67449\,\sigma, \mu + 0.67449\,\sigma)$ will include 50 per cent of the frequency distribution. When σ is estimated from finite sets of data such an exact probability statement cannot be made (see tolerance limits).

4.2. The variance $s^2 = \sum_{i=1}^{n} (x_i - \bar{x})^2/(n-1)$. Whatever the distribution of x's, the limiting mean of $s^2 = \sigma^2$.

If the x's follow a normal distribution with standard deviation σ,

$$\text{standard deviation of } s^2 = \sqrt{\frac{2}{n-1}}\,\sigma^2 \tag{1}$$

and $(n-1)s^2/\sigma^2$ follows a χ^2 distribution with $(n-1)$ degrees of freedom.

4.3. Average deviation, $\frac{1}{n}\sum_{i=1}^{n} |x_i - \bar{x}|$

If the x_i are normally distributed, limiting mean μ and standard deviation σ,

$$\text{limiting mean of average deviation} = \sqrt{\frac{2}{\pi}} \sqrt{\frac{n-1}{n}}\,\sigma \tag{1}$$

$$\left.\begin{aligned} \text{s.d. of average deviation} &= \sqrt{\frac{2}{\pi}\frac{\sqrt{n-1}}{n}\left[\frac{\pi}{2} + \sqrt{n(n-2)} - n\right.} \\ &\quad \overline{\left. + \sin^{-1}\frac{1}{n-1}\right]^{1/2}}\sigma \sim \frac{\sigma}{\sqrt{n}}\sqrt{1-\frac{2}{\pi}} \end{aligned}\right\} \tag{2}$$

for large n. Note that in comparing two average deviations, account must be taken of any difference in the number of observations in the two estimates.

4.4. Range: difference between largest and smallest value in a set of observations, $x_{(n)} = x_{(1)}$. If the x_i follow a normal distribution with limiting mean μ and standard deviation σ,

$$\text{limiting mean of range} = (\text{constant})\ \sigma$$

Note: Tables of this constant for different values of n are given in *Biometrika*, Vol. 24, p. 416, along with values of the standard deviation of the range. With the use of these tables an estimate of the standard deviation can be obtained by dividing the range of the data by this constant. For example: for sets of 5 measurements the constant is 2.33,
10 measurements the constant is 3.08,
20 measurements the constant is 3.73,
30 measurements the constant is 4.09,
100 measurements the constant is 5.02.

5. The Fitting of Straight Lines

5.1. Introduction. When the mathematical relationship or law between two variates is known or assumed to be linear, and exact knowledge of the relationship is obscured by random errors in the measurement of one or both of the variates, the formulas of this section are applicable.

A clear distinction must be made between the case of estimating the parameters of a linear *physical law* and the case of estimating the parameters of *linear regression.* In the physical law case there are two mathematical variables, X and Y, related by a linear equation. Our inability to measure without error obscures this relationship. In the linear regression case the average values of y for given x's are related to x by a linear equation. In the linear regression case there is a bivariate distribution of x and y. There are two distinct regression lines (that of $\bar{y}$ on x and $\bar{x}$ on y) and there is a correlation between x and y. The regression lines and the correlation are properties of the underlying bivariate distribution.

5.2. The case of the underlying physical law. Let X and Y represent the variables of the physical law, and:

a. The two variables X and Y are related by a law of the form $Y = \alpha + \beta X$ or its converse $X = (-\alpha/\beta) + (1/\beta)Y$.

b. At any X_i repeated measurements y_i of the variable Y, are dispersed about $Y_i = \alpha + \beta X_i$ with a standard deviation to be called σ_{y_i}, the functional form of the error distribution being the same at all X_i.

c. At any Y_i repeated measurements, x_i, of the variate X are dispersed about $X_i = -\alpha/\beta + (1/\beta)Y_i$ with a standard deviation to be called σ_{x_i}, the functional form of the distribution of errors being the same at all Y_i.

d. In practice there are obtained n paired values (x_i, y_i) which correspond to paired values (X_i, Y_i) from the linear law. The problem is to obtain the best estimate, $Y = a + bX$ of the linear law $Y = \alpha + \beta X$ from the n values (x_i, y_i).

If one variable, X, is known to be measured without error, the following tables (pages 118-119) are applicable.

If both variates are subject to error, i.e., if $\sigma_{y_i} = \sigma_y$ and $\sigma_{x_i} = \sigma_x$ and the error distribution is normal, the following technique is applicable.

Step 1. Arrange the n paired values (x_i, y_i) in order of magnitude according to one of the variates, say x.

Step 2. Divide this ranked set of n values into three nearly equal groups, so that in the two extreme groups there are the same number, say k. Thus the center has $n - 2k$.

Step 3. Compute the averages, $\bar{x}_1$ and $\bar{y}_1$ of x's and y's in the first group, the averages $\bar{x}_3$ and $\bar{y}_3$ of the x's and y's in the third group, and the grand averages $\bar{x}$ and $\bar{y}$.

Estimator of slope $$b' = \frac{\bar{y}_3 - \bar{y}_1}{\bar{x}_3 - \bar{x}_1}$$

Estimator of intercept $$a = \bar{y} - b'\bar{x}$$

Estimator of error in y's,

$$s_y = \sqrt{\left[\sum_{i=1}^{n} (y_i - \bar{y})^2 - b' \sum_{i=1}^{n} (x_i - \bar{x})(y_i - \bar{y})\right] / -1}$$

Estimator of error in x's,

$$s_x = \sqrt{\left[\sum_{i=1}^{n} (x_i - \bar{x})^2 - (1/b') \sum_{i=1}^{n} (x_i - \bar{x})(y_i - \bar{y})\right] / n - 1}$$

The distributions of the estimators depend on the value of the unknown slope β. See WALD, A., *Annals of Mathematical Statistics*, Vol. 11, 1940, p. 284; BARTLETT, M. S., *Biometrics*, Vol. 5, 1949, p. 207.

ERROR DISTRIBUTION OF y'S THE SAME FOR ALL X, i.e., $\sigma_{y_i}{}^2 = \sigma^2$

Parameter	Estimator when $\alpha = 0$	Estimator when $\alpha \neq 0$
β	$b = \dfrac{\sum_{i=1}^{n} x_i y_i}{\sum_{i=1}^{n} x_i^2}$	$b = \dfrac{\sum_{i=1}^{n} (x_i - \bar{x})(y_i - \bar{y})}{\sum_{i=1}^{n} (x_i - \bar{x})^2}$
α	$a = 0$	$a = \bar{y} - b\bar{x}$
σ^2	$s = \dfrac{\sum_{i=1}^{n} y_i^2 - \dfrac{\left[\sum_{i=1}^{n} x_i y_i\right]^2}{\sum_{i=1}^{n} x_i^2}}{n - 1}$	$s = \dfrac{\sum_{i=1}^{n} (y_i - \bar{y})^2 - \dfrac{\left[\sum_{i=1}^{n} (x_i - \bar{x})(y_i - \bar{y})\right]^2}{\sum_{i=1}^{n} (x_i - \bar{x})^2}}{n - 2}$
s.d. of estimate of slope : σ_b	$s_b = \dfrac{s}{\sqrt{\sum_{i=1}^{n} x_i^2}}$	$s_b = \dfrac{s}{\sqrt{\sum_{i=1}^{n} (x_i - \bar{x})^2}}$
s.d. of estimate of intercept : σ_a	$\sigma_a = 0$	$s_a = s\sqrt{\dfrac{1}{n} + \dfrac{\bar{x}^2}{\sum_{i=1}^{n} (x_i - \bar{x})^2}}$
s.d. of Y_0, a point on the line at $X = X_0 : \sigma_{Y_0}$	$s_{Y_0} = \dfrac{sX_0}{\sqrt{\sum_{i=1}^{n} x_i^2}}$	$s_{Y_0} = s\sqrt{\dfrac{1}{n} + \dfrac{(X_0 - \bar{x})^2}{\sum_{i=1}^{n} (x_i - \bar{x})^2}}$

Parameter	Estimator when $\alpha = 0$	Estimator when $\alpha \neq 0$
β	$b = \dfrac{\sum_{i=1}^{n} w_i^2 x_i y_i}{\sum_{i=1}^{n} w_i^2 x_i^2}$	$b = \dfrac{\sum_{i=1}^{n} w_i^2 x_i y_i - \left[\left(\sum_{i=1}^{n} w_i^2 x_i\right)\left(\sum_{i=1}^{n} w_i^2 y_i\right) \Big/ \sum_{i=1}^{n} w_i^2\right]}{\sum_{i=1}^{n} w_i^2 x_i^2 - \left[\left(\sum_{i=1}^{n} w_i^2 x_i\right)^2 \Big/ \sum_{i=1}^{n} w_i^2\right]}$
α	$\alpha = 0$	$a = \dfrac{\sum_{i=1}^{n} w_i^2 y_i}{\sum_{i=1}^{n} w_i^2} - b\dfrac{\sum_{i=1}^{n} w_i^2 x_i}{\sum_{i=1}^{n} w_i^2}$
σ^2	$s^2 = \dfrac{1}{n-1}\left[\sum_{i=1}^{n} w_i^2 y_i^2 - \dfrac{\left(\sum_{i=1}^{n} w_i^2 x_i y_i\right)^2}{\sum_{i=1}^{n} w_i^2 x_i^2}\right]$	$s = \dfrac{1}{n-2}\left\{\sum_{i=1}^{n} w_i^2 y_i^2 - \dfrac{\left(\sum_{i=1}^{n} w_i^2 y_i\right)^2}{\sum_{i=1}^{n} w_i^2} - \dfrac{\left[\sum_{i=1}^{n} w_i^2 x_i y_i - \dfrac{\left(\sum_{i=1}^{n} w_i^2 x_i\right)\left(\sum_{i=1}^{n} w_i^2 y_i\right)}{\sum_{i=1}^{n} w_i^2}\right]^2}{\sum_{i=1}^{n} w_i^2 x_i^2 - \left[\left(\sum_{i=1}^{n} w_i^2 x_i\right)^2 \Big/ \sum_{i=1}^{n} w_i^2\right]}\right\}$
s.d. of estimate of slope : σ_b	$s_b = \dfrac{}{\sqrt{\sum_{i=1}^{n} w_i x^2{}_i^2}}$	$s_b = \dfrac{s}{\sqrt{\sum_{i=1}^{n} w_i^2 x_i^2 - \dfrac{\left(\sum_{i=1}^{n} w_i^2 x_i\right)^2}{\sum_{i=1}^{n} w_i^2}}}$

Note: One of the estimates, s_y^2 or s_x^2, can be negative. Such negative values are to be expected more often when n is small, or when the parameter (σ_x^2 or σ_y^2) being estimated is near zero. The distribution of the estimates has not been worked out.

6. Linear Regression

6.1. Linear regression. If two variates x and y vary concurrently (as for example, the height and weight of men age 30) and a linear relation exists between the average value of y and the corresponding value of x, and also a linear relation between the average value of x and the corresponding y, the formulas of this section are applicable.

Parameter	Estimator	Variance
α	$a = \bar{y} - b\bar{x}$	—
β	$b = \dfrac{\sum_{i=1}^{n} (x_i - \bar{x})(y_i - \bar{y})}{\sum_{i=1}^{n} (x_i - \bar{x})^2}$	$\dfrac{1}{n-3} \dfrac{\sigma_y^2}{\sigma_x^2}(1 - \rho^2)$
ρ	$r = \dfrac{\sum_{i=1}^{n} (x_i - \bar{x})(y_i - \bar{y})}{\sqrt{\sum_{i=1}^{n} (x_i - \bar{x})^2 \sum_{i=1}^{n} (y_i - \bar{y})^2}}$	$\dfrac{1}{n}(1 - \rho^2)^2$ for large n
α'	$a' = \bar{x} - b'\bar{y}$	—
β'	$b' = \dfrac{\sum_{i=1}^{n} (x_i - \bar{x})(y_i - \bar{y})}{\sum_{i=1}^{n} (y_i - \bar{y})^2}$	$\dfrac{1}{n-3} \dfrac{\sigma_x^2}{\sigma_y^2}(1 - \rho^2)$
σ_y^2	$s_y^2 = \dfrac{1}{n-1} \sum_{i=1}^{n} (y_i - \bar{y})^2$	—
σ_x^2	$s_x^2 = \dfrac{1}{n-1} \sum_{i=1}^{n} (x_i - \bar{x})^2$	—

For a given x_i, the y's have a variance σ_y^2, and mean value

$$\bar{y}_i = \alpha + \beta x_i$$

and for a given y_i, the x's have a variance σ_x^2, and mean value

$$\bar{x}_i = \alpha' + \beta' y_i$$

where $\bar{y}$ and $\bar{x}$ are the averages of an infinite number of values at y and x, respectively. Thus there are two lines to determine, and further there is the parameter ρ, the correlation between x and y.

7. The Fitting of Polynomials

7.1. Unequal intervals between the x's. Let n paired values (x_i, y_i) be observed. If the variate x is measured without error and the variate y is related to x by the equation

$$y = \alpha_0 + \alpha_1 x + \alpha_2 x^2 + \alpha_3 x^3 + \dots \tag{1}$$

and the errors in y follow a distribution with mean zero and standard deviation σ, the constants are estimated by minimizing the sum of squares of the y deviations, i.e., the estimates $a_0, a_1, a_2, \dots$ of $\alpha_0, \alpha_1, \alpha_2, \dots$ are those values for which

$$\sum_{i=1}^{n} (y_i - a_0 - a_1 x - a_2 x^2 - \dots)^2 = \text{minimum} \tag{2}$$

This minimization process leads to a set of simultaneous equations :

$$\left.\begin{aligned} \Sigma y - n a_0 - a_1 \Sigma x - a_2 \Sigma x^2 - \dots &= 0 \\ \Sigma xy - a_0 \Sigma x - a_1 \Sigma x^2 - a_2 \Sigma x^3 - \dots &= 0 \\ \Sigma x^2 y - a_0 \Sigma x^2 - a_1 \Sigma x^3 - a_2 \Sigma x^4 - \dots &= 0 \quad \text{etc.} \end{aligned}\right\} \tag{3}$$

where the summations are over $i = 1, 2, \dots, n$.

For the estimators of the parameters of linear equation $y = \alpha_0 + \alpha_1 x$ the solution is

$$a_0 = \frac{\begin{vmatrix} \Sigma y & \Sigma x \\ \Sigma xy & \Sigma x^2 \end{vmatrix}}{D_2} \qquad a_1 = \frac{\begin{vmatrix} n & \Sigma y \\ \Sigma x & \Sigma xy \end{vmatrix}}{D_2} \tag{4}$$

where
$$D_2 = \begin{vmatrix} n & \Sigma x \\ \Sigma x & \Sigma x^2 \end{vmatrix}$$

and the sum of squares of deviation of the y's from the line is

$$S_2^2 = \Sigma y^2 - a_0 \Sigma y - a_1 \Sigma xy.$$

For the estimators of the parameters of a parabola, $y = \alpha_0 + \alpha_1 x + \alpha_2 x^2$,

$$a_0 = \frac{\begin{vmatrix} \Sigma y & \Sigma x & \Sigma x^2 \\ \Sigma xy & \Sigma x^2 & \Sigma x^3 \\ \Sigma x^2 y & \Sigma x^3 & \Sigma x^4 \end{vmatrix}}{D_3} \qquad a_1 = \frac{\begin{vmatrix} n & \Sigma y & \Sigma x^2 \\ \Sigma x & \Sigma xy & \Sigma x^3 \\ \Sigma x^2 & \Sigma x^2 y & \Sigma x^4 \end{vmatrix}}{D_3}$$

$$a_2 = \frac{\begin{vmatrix} n & \Sigma x & \Sigma y \\ \Sigma x & \Sigma x^2 & \Sigma xy \\ \Sigma x^2 & \Sigma x^3 & \Sigma x^2 y \end{vmatrix}}{D_3} \tag{5}$$

where

$$D_3 = \begin{vmatrix} n & \Sigma x & \Sigma x^2 \\ \Sigma x & \Sigma x^2 & \Sigma x^3 \\ \Sigma x^2 & \Sigma x^3 & \Sigma x^4 \end{vmatrix}$$

and the sum of squares of y deviation from the parabola is

$$S_3^2 = \Sigma y^2 - a_0 \Sigma y - a_1 \Sigma xy - a_2 \Sigma x^2 y \tag{6}$$

The extension to polynomials of higher order is obvious. The estimate of the standard deviation σ_1 of the y determination

is $s = \sqrt{\dfrac{S_2^2}{n-2}}$ for the line (7)

is $s = \sqrt{\dfrac{S_3^2}{n-3}}$ for the parabola (8)

and $s = \sqrt{\dfrac{S_k^2}{n-k}}$ for a polynomial of degree $k-1$ (9)

For testing the significance of any of the constants fitted, the reduction in the total sum of squares of the y's is studied as follows :

		Degrees of freedom	Mean square
Total sum of squares . .	$\sum_{i=1}^{n} (y_i - \bar{y})^2 = S_1^2$	$n-1$	—
Deviation from linear	S_2^2	$n-2$	$S_2^2/(n-2)$
Reduction of sum of squares due to linear terms	$S_1^2 - S_2^2$	1	$S_1^2 - S_2^2$
Deviations from quadratic	S_3^2	$n-3$	$S_3^2/(n-3)$
Reduction of sum of squares due to quadratic terms	$S_2^2 - S_3^2$	1	$S_2^2 - S_3^2$
etc.			

To test the significance of a coefficient, a_k, compute

$$F = \frac{S_{k-1}^2 - S_k^2}{S_k^2/(n-k)} \tag{10}$$

If the distribution of errors in the y measurement is normal, F will follow the F distribution for 1, $n-k$ degrees of freedom. If the computed F is greater than the value of F for 1, $n-k$ degrees of freedom exceeded with probability α, the reduction in sum of squares due to fitting the constant a_k (coefficient of x^{k-1}) is regarded as significant at the 100 α per cent level of significance.

Each of the a_k are seen to be a linear function of the y's, so that the standard deviation of any particular a_i can be obtained by writing

$$a_k = \sum_{i=1}^{n} c_i y_i,$$

and using the formula for the variance of a linear function, noting that the mean value of $y_i = \alpha_0 + \alpha_1 x_i + \alpha_2 x_i^2 + \ldots$.

7.2. The case of equal intervals between the x's — the method of orthogonal polynomials. In order to find the best fitting polynomial

$$y = a_0 + a_1 x + a_2 x^2 + \ldots \tag{1}$$

when the x values are evenly spaced, it is convenient to fit instead the polynomial

$$y = A + B\xi_1' + C\xi_2' + \ldots \tag{2}$$

where ξ_1', ξ_2', ξ_3', ... are orthogonal polynomials of degree 1, 2, 3, ...

$$\xi_0 = 1$$

$$\xi_1 = (x - \bar{x})\lambda,$$

$$\xi_2' = \left[(x-\bar{x})^2 - \frac{n^2-1}{12}\right]\lambda_2$$

$$\vdots$$

$$\xi_k' = \left[\xi_1'\xi_n' - \frac{r^2(n^2-r^2)}{4(4r^2-1)}\xi_{n-1}'\right]\lambda_r$$

The λ's are chosen so that all the coefficients of these polynomials are integers. The coefficients of these orthogonal polynomials and a description of the method of analysis are given in FISHER, R. A., and YATES, F., *Statistical Tables*, 4th edition, Hafner Publishing Company, New York, 1953 for ξ_1', to ξ_5', for $n = 3(1)75$.

7.3. Fitting the coefficients of a function of several variables. Just as a distinction was made in the case of the straight line between the underlying physical law situation and the linear regression situation, so also must this distinction be preserved with the extension to this multivariate case.

If Y is related by a physical law to variates $X_1, X_2, \ldots$ by the equation

$$Y = \alpha_0 + \alpha_1 X_1 + \alpha_2 X_2 + \ldots \tag{1}$$

one is interested only in estimating the coefficients α_k. There is no question of the correlation between, say, X_1 and X_3. In the physical law case when X_1, X_2, and X_3 are regarded as free from error and Y as subject to errors following a distribution with mean zero and standard deviation σ, for n values $(y_i, X_{1i}, X_{2i}, \ldots)$ the estimators a_k for the parameter α_k are, for the case of the law $Y = \alpha_0 + \alpha_1 X_1 + \alpha_2 X_2$,

$$\left.\begin{array}{l} a_0 = \dfrac{\begin{vmatrix} \Sigma y & \Sigma X_1 & \Sigma X_2 \\ \Sigma X_1 y & \Sigma X_1^2 & \Sigma X_1 X_2 \\ \Sigma X_2 y & \Sigma X_1 X_2 & \Sigma X_2^2 \end{vmatrix}}{D_3} \qquad a_1 = \dfrac{\begin{vmatrix} n & \Sigma y & \Sigma X_2 \\ \Sigma X_1 & \Sigma X_1 y & \Sigma X_1 X_2 \\ \Sigma X_2 & \Sigma X_2 y & \Sigma X_2^2 \end{vmatrix}}{D_3} \\ \\ \qquad\qquad a_2 = \dfrac{\begin{vmatrix} n & \Sigma X_1 & \Sigma y \\ \Sigma X_1 & \Sigma X_1^2 & \Sigma X_1 y \\ \Sigma X_2 & \Sigma X_1 X_2 & \Sigma X_2 y \end{vmatrix}}{D_3} \end{array}\right\} \tag{2}$$

where

$$D_3 = \begin{vmatrix} n & \Sigma X_1 & \Sigma X_2 \\ \Sigma X_1 & \Sigma X_1^2 & \Sigma X_1 X_2 \\ \Sigma X_2 & \Sigma X_1 X_2 & \Sigma X_2^2 \end{vmatrix}$$

The sum of squares of deviations of y from the fitted equation is

$$S_3^2 = \Sigma y^2 - a_0 \Sigma y - a_1 \Sigma X_1 y - a_2 \Sigma X_2 y \tag{3}$$

The extension to include cases of more variables is straightforward, and the tests of significance of the coefficients is analogous to the case of fitting a polynomial.

7.4. Multiple regression. In the multiple regression case where a number of variates are varying concurrently (as, for example, weight of males age 30, as a function of height, wrist circumference, and waist girth) is treated in R. A. FISHER, *Statistical Methods for Research Workers*, Oliver and Boyd, Section 29. In multiple regression there are partial correlations and partial regression coefficients to be estimated.

8. Enumerative Statistics

8.1. Estimator of parameter of binomial distribution. If in n trials, m occurrences of some event are observed, then the estimator for the parameter P is

$$p = \frac{m}{n}. \tag{1}$$

This estimate will have a standard deviation

$$\text{s.d. of } p = \sqrt{\frac{P(1-P)}{n}}. \tag{2}$$

$100(1-\alpha)$ per cent confidence intervals (P_1, P_2) for the parameter P of the binomial for k occurrences in a sample of n are given by solving

$$\sum_{i=k}^{n} \binom{n}{i} P^i(1-P)^{n-i} = \alpha/2 \tag{3}$$

for P, giving the lower limit P_1, and

$$\sum_{i=0}^{k} \binom{n}{i} P^i(1-P)^{n-i} = \alpha/2 \tag{4}$$

for P, giving the upper limit P_2.

The computation is simplified by using the incomplete beta function (see Mood, A. M., *Introduction to Theory of Statistics*, McGraw-Hill Book Company, Inc., 1950, pp. 233-235).

8.2. Estimator of parameter of Poisson distribution. If in an interval of x units, k occurrences are observed, the estimator for the parameter λ of the Poisson is k/x, which has a standard deviation of $\sqrt{\lambda/x}$.

If n independent estimates of λ, k_1/x_1, k_2/x_n, ..., k_n/x_n are available, the best estimate of λ is

$$\frac{\sum_{i=1}^{n} k_i}{\sum_{i=1}^{n} x_i}$$

which has standard deviation $\sqrt{\lambda \Big/ \sum_{i=1}^{n} x_i}$.

The average of the ratios has standard deviation

$$\sqrt{\frac{\lambda}{n^2}\sum_{i=1}^{n}\left(\frac{1}{x_i}\right)} \geq \sqrt{\frac{\lambda}{\sum_{i=1}^{n} x_i}}$$

To test the conformance of a series of n values of k_i to the Poisson law where the interval length is the same for all determinations, compute

$$\chi^2 = \frac{\sum_{i=1}^{n}(k_i - \bar{k})^2}{\bar{k}} \tag{5}$$

where $\bar{k} = (1/n)\sum_{i=1}^{n} k_i$.

This statistic will have approximately the χ^2 distribution for $n - 1$ degrees of freedom.

8.3. Rank correlation coefficient. N objects are ranked by two methods. Denote the ranking of the ith object by the first method by r_{1i} and its ranking by the second method by r_{2i}, and the difference $d_i = r_{1i} - r_{2i}$. The rank correlation coefficient is defined as

$$1 - \frac{6\sum_{i=1}^{N} d_i^2}{N(N^2 - 1)}$$

For a complete treatment of rank correlation see KENDALL, M. G., *Rank Correlation Methods*, Charles Griffin & Co., Ltd., London, 1948.

9. Interval Estimation

9.1. Confidence interval for parameters. Instead of a point estimator of a parameter, an interval estimator may be used. A random interval (L_1,L_2), depending only on the observed set of data having the property that $100(1 - 2\alpha)$ per cent of such intervals computed will include the value of the parameter being estimated, is called the $100(1 - 2\alpha)$ *per cent confidence interval.*

No probability statement can be made regarding an individual confidence interval since a particular interval either includes the parameter, or it does not. It is the method of estimation that carries with it the probability of correctly bracketing the parameter.

For a given distribution of measurements it is possible to set down the distribution of estimates of a parameter derived by using a given estimator and a sequence of random sets from the original distribution. For example, the probability that $\bar{x}$ based on n measurements lies in the interval $(\mu - 1.96\,\sigma/\sqrt{n},\ \mu + 1.96\,\sigma/\sqrt{n})$ is 0.95. From this it follows that the random interval $(\bar{x} - 1.96\,\sigma/\sqrt{n}, \bar{x} + 1.96\,\sigma/\sqrt{n})$ will include the parameter μ with probability 0.95, and the interval $(\bar{x} - 1.96\,\sigma/\sqrt{n},\ \bar{x} + 1.96\,\sigma/\sqrt{n})$ is therefore the 95 per cent confidence interval estimator of μ.

9.2. Confidence interval for the mean of a normal distribution. For a set of n measurements from a normal population the interval (L_1,L_2) where

$$L_1 = \bar{x} - t_{(2\alpha,n-1)}\frac{s}{\sqrt{n}} \tag{1}$$

and

$$L_2 = \bar{x} + t_{(2\alpha,n-1)}\frac{s}{\sqrt{n}} \tag{2}$$

where $t_{(2\alpha,n-1)}$ is the value of Student's t for $n - 1$ degrees of freedom exceeded in absolute value with probability 2α, defines the $100(1 - 2\alpha)$ per cent confidence interval for μ, the mean of a normal distribution.

9.3. Confidence interval for the standard deviation of a normal distribution. From a set of n measurement (i.e., an estimate of standard deviation based on $n - 1$ degrees of freedom) from a normal distribution the interval (L_1,L_2) where

$$L_1 = \sqrt{\frac{(n-1)s^2}{\chi^2_{(\alpha,n-1)}}} \tag{1}$$

and

$$L_2 = \sqrt{\frac{(n-1)s^2}{\chi^2_{(1-\alpha,n-1)}}} \tag{2}$$

and where $\chi^2_{(\alpha,n-1)}$ is the value of χ^2 for $df = n - 1$ exceeded with probability α, defines the $100(1 - 2\alpha)$ per cent confidence interval for σ.

Note: (L_1^2,L_2^2) defines the $100(1 - 2\alpha)$ per cent confidence interval for σ^2.

9.4. Confidence interval for slope of straight line. If the variate x is free from errors and the variate y_i,

$$y_i = (\alpha + \beta x_i) + \epsilon_i \tag{1}$$

where ϵ_i is a random variable, normally distributed with mean 0 and standard deviation σ for all i, then (L_1, L_2) is the $100(1 - 2\alpha)$ per cent confidence interval for β, the slope of the line.

$$L_1 = b - t_{(2\alpha, n-2)} s_b \tag{2}$$

$$L_2 = b + t_{(2\alpha, n-2)} s_b \tag{3}$$

where $t_{(2\alpha, n-2)}$ is the value of Student's t, exceeded in absolute value with probability 2α.

Note: If the intercept is known to be zero, replace $t_{(2\alpha, n-2)}$ by $t_{(2\alpha, n-1)}$ in the formulas for L_1 and L_2.

9.5. Confidence interval for intercept of a straight line. Under the same conditions required for a confidence interval for the slope,

$$L_1 = a - t_{(2\alpha, n-2)} s_a \tag{1}$$

$$L_2 = a + t_{(2\alpha, n-2)} s_a \tag{2}$$

define the $100(1 - 2\alpha)$ per cent confidence interval estimator for α, the intercept of a straight line.

9.6. Tolerance limits. Limits between which a given percentage, P, of the values of a distribution lie are called tolerance limits. For example, for the normal distribution with mean μ and standard deviation σ, 95 per cent of the values lie between the limits $\mu - 1.96\sigma$ and $\mu + 1.96\sigma$. If $\bar{x}$ and s are estimates of μ and σ, it cannot be stated that the limits $\bar{x} - 1.96s$ and $\bar{x} + 1.96$ include 95 per cent of the population. Here $\bar{x} + Ks$ (where K is a constant) is a random variable which is approximately normally distributed with mean $\mu + Ks$ and approximate standard deviation $\sigma\sqrt{1/n + K^2/2(n-1)}$ where n is the number of observations upon which $\bar{x}$ is based and $(n - 1)$ is the number of degrees of freedom in the estimate s.

The value of K can be adjusted so that the limits $(\bar{x} - Ks)$ and $(\bar{x} - ks)$ will in a given percentage γ of the cases include a given proportion P of the original distribution. See *Techniques of Statistical Analysis*, edited by C. Eisenhart, M. W. Hastay, and W. A. Wallis, McGraw-Hill Book Company, Inc., 1947, Chapter 2, for tables of values of K for various n, γ, and P.

10. Statistical Tests of Hypothesis

10.1. Introduction. Investigations are concerned not only with estimating certain parameters, but also with comparing the estimates obtained with certain assumed values or with other estimates. For example, an average value for a certain quantity is derived from two separate experiments. The question is asked: Can the averages be considered in agreement? In this case the hypothesis to be tested, called the *null hypothesis*, is that the limiting means of the distribution from which the averages arose are identical.

The specification of the statistical test requires a statement of the *alternate hypothesis* against which the null hypothesis is tested. The statistical test will lead to either acceptance or rejection of the null hypothesis.

Any statistical test may result in a wrong decision. Errors of two kinds may be committed: *Type I error:* rejecting the null hypothesis when it is in fact true and, *Type II error:* accepting the null hypothesis when it is in fact false. For any statistical test the risk α of making a Type I error can be made as small as desired.

A statistic T, some function of the observed value, is chosen in the light of the null and alternate hypotheses. When the null hypothesis is true this statistic will tend to fall within a certain range; when the alternate hypothesis is true the statistic T will tend to fall in some other range. These ranges will in general overlap. The value selected to serve as the boundary between these ranges determines the risks of making a wrong decision.

The null hypothesis is rejected if an observed value of a test statistic exceeds the critical value. In this section the critical value specified is such that there is a chance α of wrongly rejecting the null hypothesis. The test is said to be conducted at the 100α per cent *level of significance.*

If in conducting a test of a hypothesis at the 100α per cent level, a value is obtained that falls short of the critical value, the statement can be made that "there is no evidence of a difference." If the observed value of a test statistic exceeds the critical value, the statement can be made that "there is evidence of a difference since as divergent a set of values as found would occur by chance only 100α per cent of the time if no real difference existed."

10.2. Test of whether the mean of a normal distribution is greater than a specified value.

a. *Observed values:* $\bar{x}$ and s based on n measurements considered as a set of values from a normal distribution with mean μ, and standard deviation σ.

b. *Null hypothesis :* $\mu = \mu_0$

c. *Alternate hypothesis :* $\mu > \mu_0$

d. *Test statistic :* $$t = \frac{\bar{x} - \mu_0}{s/\sqrt{n}}$$

t follows Student's t-distribution for $n - 1$ degrees of freedom if null hypothesis is true.

e. *Rejection criterion :* Reject the null hypothesis if the observed value of t is greater than the value of t for $n - 1$ degrees of freedom, exceeded with probability α.

10.3. Test of whether the mean of a normal distribution is different from some specified value.

a. *Observed values :* $\bar{x}$ and s based on n measurements considered as a set of values from a normal distribution with mean μ, and standard deviation σ.

b. *Null hypothesis :* $\mu = \mu_0$

c. *Alternate hypothesis :* $\mu \neq \mu_0$

d. *Test statistic :* $$t = \frac{|\bar{x} - \mu_0|}{s/\sqrt{n}}$$

t follows Student's t-distribution for $n - 1$ degrees of freedom if null hypothesis is true.

e. *Rejection criterion :* Reject the null hypothesis if the observed value of t is greater than the value of t for $n - 1$ degrees of freedom, exceeded in absolute value with probability α. (This is equivalent to the value of t exceeded with probability $\alpha/2$).

10.4. Test of whether the mean of one normal distribution is greater than the mean of another normal distribution.

a. *Observed values :* $\bar{x}_1$ and s_1 based on n measurements considered as a set of values from a normal distribution with mean μ_1, and standard deviation σ, and $\bar{x}_2$ and s_2 based on m measurements considered as a set of values from a normal distribution with mean μ_2 and standard deviation σ.

b. *Null hypothesis :* $\mu_1 = \mu_2$

c. *Alternate hypothesis :* $\mu_1 > \mu_2$

d. *Test statistic :*

$$t = \frac{\bar{x}_1 - \bar{x}_2}{\sqrt{(m+n)/mn}\ \sqrt{[(n-1)s_1^2 + (m-1)s_2^2]/(m+n-2)}}$$

t follows Student's t-distribution for $(n + m - 2)$ degrees of freedom when null hypothesis is true.

e. *Rejection criterion :* Reject the null hypothesis if the observed value of t is greater than the value of t for $(n + m - 2)$ degrees of freedom exceeded with probability α.

10.5. Test of whether the means of two normal distributions differ.

a. *Observed values :* $\bar{x}_1$ and s_1 based on n measurements considered as a set of values from a normal distribution with mean μ_1, and standard deviation σ, and $\bar{x}_2$ and s_2 based on m measurements considered as a set of values from a normal distribution with mean μ_2 and standard deviation σ.

b. *Null hypothesis :* $\mu_1 = \mu_2$

c. *Alternate hypothesis :* $\mu_1 \neq \mu_2$

d. *Test statistic :*

$$t = \frac{|x_1 - x_2|}{\sqrt{(m+n)/n}\ \sqrt{[(n-1)s_1^2 + (m-1)s_2^2]}}$$

t follows Student's t-distribution for $(m + n - 2)$ degrees of freedom when the null hypothesis is true.

e. *Rejection criterion :* Reject the null hypothesis if the observed value of t is larger than the value of t for $(m + n - 2)$ degrees of freedom exceeded in absolute value with probability α.

Note : For the case where the distributions do not have the same standard deviation, see FISHER, R. A. and YATES, F., *Statistical Tables*, 4th edition, Hafner Publishing Company, New York, 1953, pp. 3-4.

10.6. Tests concerning the parameters of a linear law. In the case where X is free from error and the errors in the observed values of y follow a normal distribution with mean zero and standard deviation σ, the statistics

$$t = \frac{b - \beta_0}{s_b} \tag{1}$$

and

$$t = \frac{a - \alpha_0}{s_a} \tag{2}$$

follow Student's t-distribution for degrees of freedom equal to the number of degrees of freedom in the estimate of s_b and s_a, (which will be $n-2$ for both when the line does not pass through the origin, and $n-1$ for s_b when it is assumed a priori that $\alpha = 0$) when the null hypothesis $\beta = \beta_0$ and $\alpha = \alpha_0$ are true.

The tests of hypothesis concerning β can therefore be made in the same manner as tests regarding the mean of a normal distribution.

10.7. Test of the homogeneity of a set of variances. Let $s_1^2, s_2^2, \ldots, s_k^2$ be k variance estimates based on $n_1, n_2, \ldots, n_k$ observations respectively. Then the statistic

$$B = \frac{2.30259}{c}\left[N \log S^2 - \sum_{i=1}^{k}(n_i - 1)\log s_i^2\right] \tag{1}$$

where

$$N = \sum_{i=1}^{k}(n_i - 1)$$

$$S^2 = \frac{\sum_{i=1}^{k}(n_i - 1)s_i^2}{N}$$

$$c = 1 + \frac{\sum_{i=1}^{k}[1/(n_i - 1)] - 1/N}{3(k-1)}$$

has approximately the χ^2 distribution for $k-1$ degrees of freedom under the null hypothesis that the s_i^2 are all estimates of a common σ^2. The null hypothesis is rejected if the observed value of B is greater than the value of χ^2 for $(k-1)$ degrees of freedom exceeded with probability α.

10.8. Test of homogeneity of a set of averages. If $\bar{x}_1, \bar{x}_2, \ldots, \bar{x}_n$ are n averages, each based on k measurements each, the statistic

$$F = \frac{\left[k\sum_{i=1}^{n}(\bar{x} - \bar{\bar{x}})^2\right]/(n-1)}{\left[\sum_{i=1}^{n}\sum_{j=1}^{k}(x_{ij} - \bar{x}_i)^2\right]/[n(k-1)]} \tag{1}$$

where

$$\bar{\bar{x}} = \frac{1}{n}\sum_{i=1}^{n}\bar{x}_i$$

follows the F distribution for $(n - 1)$, and $n(k - 1)$ degrees of freedom under the null hypothesis that limiting mean of $\bar{x}_i$ is the same for all i. Reject the null hypothesis if the observed value of F is greater than the value of F for $n - 1$, $n(k - 1)$ degrees of freedom exceeded with probability α.

10.9. Test of whether a correlation coefficient is different from zero. If r is the observed correlation coefficient found in the linear regression case, assumed to be an estimate of ρ of a bivariate normal distribution, then in order to test the *null hypothesis* that $\rho = 0$ against the *alternative hypothesis* that $\rho \neq 0$ compute the statistic

$$t = \frac{r\sqrt{n-2}}{\sqrt{1-r^2}} \tag{1}$$

When the null hypothesis is true t follows Student's t-distribution for $(n - 2)$ degrees of freedom. Reject the null hypothesis if the observed value of t is greater than the value of Student's t-distribution exceeded in absolute value with probability α.

10.10. Test of whether the correlation coefficient ρ is equal to a specified value. Let

$$\left.\begin{aligned} z &= \frac{1}{2}\log\frac{1+r}{1-r} \\ \zeta &= \frac{1}{2}\log\frac{1+\rho}{1-\rho} \end{aligned}\right\} \tag{1}$$

where r is the observed correlation found in the linear regression case and assumed to be an estimate of ρ of a bivariate normal distribution, then $(z - \zeta)$ is approximately normally distributed with mean zero and standard deviation approximately $\sqrt{1/(n-3)}$.

Thus a test for the significance of the difference of r from any arbitrary ρ is given by computing the statistic

$$t = \frac{\frac{1}{2}\log\left(\frac{1+r}{1-r}\right) - \frac{1}{2}\log\left(\frac{1+\rho_0}{1-\rho_0}\right)}{\sqrt{1/(n-3)}} \tag{2}$$

Under the null hypothesis that $\rho = \rho_0$, t will be approximately normally distributed with mean zero and standard deviation $\sigma = 1$.

Reject the null hypothesis if t is greater than the standardized normal deviate exceeded with probability $\alpha/2$ when the alternate hypothesis is that $\rho \neq \rho_0$.

11. Analysis of Variance

11.1. Analysis of Variance. Consider a two-way classification of data as shown in the table.

		Column 1	2	j	c	Row averages
Row	1	x_{11}	x_{12}	x_{1j}	x_{1c}	$\bar{x}_{R1}$
	2	x_{21}				$\bar{x}_{R2}$
				$\vdots$		
	i	x_{i1}	$\cdots$	x_{ij}	$\cdots$	$\bar{x}_{Ri}$
				$\vdots$		
	r	x_{r1}		x_{rj}	x_{rc}	$\bar{x}_{Rr}$
column averages		$\bar{x}_{C1}$	$\bar{x}_{C2}$	$\bar{x}_{Cj}$	$\bar{x}_{Cc}$	$\bar{x}$ = grand average

It is a property of numbers that

$$\sum_{i=1}^{r}\sum_{j=1}^{c}(x_{ij}-\bar{x})^2$$

can be broken up into three components as follows :

$$c\,(\text{Deviation of row averages about grand average}) = c\sum_{i=1}^{r}(\bar{x}_{Ri}-\bar{x})^2 \tag{1}$$

$$r\,(\text{Deviation of column averages about grand average}) = r\sum_{j=1}^{c}(\bar{x}_{Cj}-\bar{x})^2 \tag{2}$$

$$\text{Residue} = \sum_{i=1}^{r}\sum_{j=1}^{c}(x_{ij}-\bar{x}_{Ri}-\bar{x}_{Cj}+\bar{x})^2 \tag{3}$$

It is assumed in what follows that the x_{ij} are normally independently distributed with variance σ^2, about means μ_{ij}

$$\mu_{ij}=\mu_0+\delta_{Ri}+\delta_{Cj} \tag{3}$$

where μ_0, is the grand mean, δ_{Ri} and δ_{Cj} are the deviations of the row and column means, respectively, from the grand mean. Two models of analysis of variance are possible.

a. *Model I. The parameters* δ_{Ri} *and* δ_{Cj} *are fixed constants.*

For example, if the rows represent different machines and the columns different operators then the δ_{Ri} are the deviations of the individual machines performance from the grand mean, and δ_{Cj} are the operator biases.

The row averages and column averages are estimators of $\mu_0 + \delta_{Ri}$ and $\mu_0 + \delta_{Cj}$, respectively.

In order to test the hypothesis that the row means are all identical or that the column means are all identical, the following computations are made :

	Sum of squares	Degrees of freedom	Mean square	Mean square is estimate of
eviation of row averages . . .	$R = c \sum_{i=1}^{r} (\bar{x}_{Ri} - \bar{x})^2$	$r - 1$	$\dfrac{R}{r-1}$	$\sigma^2 + c \dfrac{\sum_{i=1}^{r} \delta_{Ri}^2}{r-1}$
eviation of column averages .	$C = r \sum_{j=1}^{c} (\bar{x}_{Cj} - \bar{x})^2$	$c - 1$	$\dfrac{C}{c-1}$	$\sigma^2 + r \dfrac{\sum_{j=1}^{c} \delta_{Cj}^2}{c-1}$
sidue	$T - R - C$	$(r-1)(c-1)$	$\dfrac{T-R-C}{(r-1)(c-1)}$	σ^2
tal	T	$rc - 1$	—	—

To test the null hypothesis that the row means are identical, that is, that

$$\sum_{i=1}^{r} \delta_{Ri}^2 = 0$$

compute the statistic

$$F = \frac{R/(r-1)}{(T-R-C)/[(r-1)(c-1)]} \tag{4}$$

Under the null hypothesis F follows the F distribution for $r-1$, $(r-1)(c-1)$ degrees of freedom. A similar test can be made for the column means.

b. *Model II. The parameters are components of variance.*

For example, if the rows represent different samples of the same material and the columns represent different days on which the tests were conducted, then δ_{Ri} and δ_{Cj} are random variables. These random variables will have mean zero and variances σ_R^2 and σ_C^2, respectively, and in that which follows are assumed to be normally distributed. The computations are the same as shown in Model I.

	Sum of squares	Degrees of freedom	Mean square	Mean square is estimate of
Deviation of row averages	R	$r-1$	$\frac{R}{r-1}$	$\sigma^2 + c\sigma_R^2$
Deviation of column averages	C	$c-1$	$\frac{C}{c-1}$	$\sigma^2 + r\sigma_C^2$
Residue	$T-R-C$	$(r-1)(c-1)$	$\frac{T-R-C}{(r-1)(c-1)}$	σ^2
Total	T	$rc-1$	—	—

The parameters σ_R^2 and σ_C^2 are estimated by

$$s_R^2 = \frac{1}{c}\left[\frac{R}{r-1} - \frac{T-R-C}{(r-1)(c-1)}\right] \tag{5}$$

and

$$s_C^2 = \frac{1}{r}\left[\frac{C}{c-1} - \frac{T-R-C}{(r-1)(c-1)}\right] \tag{6}$$

The test of the null hypothesis that $\sigma_R^2 = 0$ is made by computing the statistic

$$F = \frac{R/(r-1)}{(T-R-C)/[(r-1)(c-1)]} \tag{7}$$

which, if the null hypothesis is true, follows the F distribution with $r-1$, $(r-1)(c-1)$ degrees of freedom.

A test of the hypothesis that $\sigma_C^2 = 0$ is conducted in a similar manner.

The analysis of variance technique of which the above are examples can be extended to n-fold classifications. The technique is also valuable in ascertaining whether the effect of a factor is maintained over different levels of other factors, i.e., for detecting the presence of interactions. See ANDERSON, R. L., and BANCROFT, T. A., *Statistical Theory in Research*, McGraw-Hill

Book Co., Inc. New York, 1952; FISHER, R. A., *Statistical Methods for Research Workers*, 11th edition, Oliver & Boyd, Ltd., London, 1950.

12. Design of Experiments

12.1. Design of experiments. The validity of inferences that can be drawn from an experiment depend upon the manner in which the experiment was conducted. In a comparison of a number of objects it has long been realized that identical conditions should be maintained during the testing of all the objects. Often this is not possible, since not all the objects to be compared can be tested in a short enough interval that conditions can be regarded as identical for all tests.

The scheduling of the tests to achieve unbiased estimates of parameters, and maximum efficiency in the testing of the hypotheses that the experimenter set out to test; the search for an optimum combination of a number of factors each of which may be at several levels; or an investigation of the influence of several factors individually and jointly on some physical quantity are treated in COCHRAN, W. G., and COX, G. M., *Experimental Designs*, John Wiley & Sons, Inc., New York, 1950; and FISHER, R. A., *The Design of Experiments*, 5th edition, Oliver & Boyd, Ltd., London, 1949.

13. Precision and Accuracy

13.1. Introduction. A measurement process is regarded as *precise* if the dispersion of values is regarded as small, i.e., σ small.

A measurement process is regarded as *accurate* if the values cluster closely about the correct value c.

The *precision of an individual measurement* is the same as the precision for the process generating the measurements.

By *accuracy of an individual measurement* or of an average of n measurements is usually meant the maximum possible error (constant and/or random) that could affect the observed value and is frequently thought of in terms of the number of significant figures to which the value can be regarded as correct.

13.2. Measure of precision. It is suggested that the measure for representing precision of an individual measurement in a set of n measurements be

$$s = \sqrt{\frac{\sum_{i=1}^{n} (x - \bar{x})^2}{n - 1}} \tag{1}$$

and for the precision of an average,

$$s_{\bar{x}} = \frac{s}{\sqrt{n}}. \tag{2}$$

13.3. Measurement of accuracy. Limits on possible constant errors due to known sources of inaccuracy can be set down from a study of the method of conducting the experiment. Such limits on errors represent a judgment on the part of the experimenter and no probability statements can be attached thereto. The setting down of the upper limit and lower limit for a quantity should involve the possible uncertainties due to any constant error plus some component due to random errors.

Suggested form for reporting results of n determinations of some quantity :

Average $\bar{x}$	=
Number of measurements n	=
s.d. of average $s/\sqrt{n}$	=
Maximum possible constant errors ; E, $-E'$	=
Lower limit to quantity : $x - E' - Ks/\sqrt{n}$	=
Lower limit to quantity : $\bar{x} + E + Ks/\sqrt{n}$	=

where K is either Student's t, $K = 2$ or 3 for approximation to 2σ or 3σ limits (for n large), or any other specified constant.

The upper and lower limit to a quantity express the experimenter's best judgment of the range within which the true value of the quantity being measured lies. A value could then be said to be accurate to as many significant figures as the upper and lower limits agree.

14. Law of Propagation of Error

14.1. Introduction. If x follows a distribution with mean μ and standard deviation σ, and $F(x)$ is some function of x, then the mean μ_F and variance $\sigma_F{}^2$ of $F(x)$, where x is the average of n values, is approximated by

$$\mu_F = F(\mu) \tag{1}$$

$$\sigma_F{}^2 = [F'(\mu)]^2\sigma^2 \tag{2}$$

provided $F(x)$, $F'(x)$ are continuous and nonzero in the neighborhood of the point $x = \mu$.

Caution must be exercised in the application of the formula. It is valid when two conditions are satisfied : (a) if the Taylor expansion

$$F(x) = F(\mu) + F'(\mu)(x - \mu) + \frac{F''(\mu)}{2!}(x - \mu)^2 + \dots \tag{3}$$

is such that $F^k(\mu)$ for $k = 2, 3, \ldots$ is small, and (b) if the expected value of $(x - \mu)^k$, for $k = 3, 4, \ldots$ is small (i.e., that the third and higher moments of the distribution of x be small). There are cases where condition (a) is not satisfied, yet the formula is valid because condition (b) holds, or where neither condition holds but the product of $F^k(\mu)$ and the kth moment is small for $k > 2$.

EXAMPLE: Let x be normally distributed with mean μ and standard deviation σ. Then the mean and variance of $y = x^2$ are according to the above formula

$$\text{mean of } y = \mu^2$$

$$\text{variance of } y = 4\mu^2\sigma^2$$

The exact answer for the mean is $\mu^2 + \sigma^2$, and for the variance, $4\mu^2\sigma^2 + 2\sigma^4$. When σ is large the " propagation of error formula " can be seriously in error in this case.

EXAMPLE: Let x have mean $\xi = e^{\mu+1/2\sigma^2}$, and variance $\xi^2(e^{\sigma^2} - 1)$, and with third moment, or average value of $(x - \xi)^3 = \xi^3(e^{3\sigma^2} - 3e^{\sigma^2} + 2)$, fourth moment, or average value of $(x - \xi)^4 = \xi^4(e^{6\sigma^2} - 4e^{3\sigma^2} + 6e^{\sigma^2} - 3)$, etc., such that $y = \log x$ is normally distributed with mean μ and standard deviation σ. The approximation gives

for the mean of y:

$$\log \xi = \mu + \tfrac{1}{2}\sigma^2$$

for the variance of y:

$$\frac{1}{\xi^2}\, \xi^2 \,(e^{\sigma^2} - 1) = e^{\sigma^2} - 1 = \sigma^2 + \frac{\sigma^4}{2!} + \frac{\sigma^6}{3!} + \cdots$$

If σ is large, the approximate formula can be seriously in error, in this case because the third and higher moments of the original distribution are not small.

If $H(x_1, x_2, x_3, \ldots)$ is a function of $x_1, x_2, x_3, \ldots$ which have mean values $\mu_1, \mu_2, \mu_3, \ldots$ and variances $\sigma_1^2, \sigma_2^2, \sigma_3^2, \ldots$ and correlations $\rho_{12}, \rho_{13}, \rho_{23}, \ldots$, then the variance, σ_H^2, of $H(x_1, x_2, x_3, \ldots)$ is given by

$$\left.\begin{aligned} \sigma_H^2 &= [H_{x_1}']^2\sigma_1^2 + [H_{x_2}']^2\sigma_2^2 + [H_{x_3}']^2\sigma_3^2 + \ldots \\ &\quad - 2\rho_{12}\sigma_1\sigma_2 H_{x_1}' H_{x_2}' - 2\rho_{13}\sigma_1\sigma_3 H_{x_1}' H_{x_3}' - 2\rho_{23}\sigma_2\sigma_3 H_{x_2}' H_{x_3}' - \ldots \end{aligned}\right\} \quad (4)$$

all derivatives being evaluated at $\mu_1, \mu_2, \mu_3, \ldots$.

The restrictions on the validity of this formula are analogous to the restrictions applying to $F(x)$.

14.2. Standard deviation of a ratio of normally distributed variables. If $z = x/y$ where x is normally distributed with mean μ_x and standard deviation σ_x; y is normally distributed with mean μ_y and standard deviation σ_y; the correlation between x and y is ρ and μ_y/σ_y is sufficiently large (say greater than 5) then z will be approximately normally distributed with mean of $z = \mu_x/\mu_y$, and standard deviation of

$$z = \frac{\mu_x}{\mu_y}\sqrt{\frac{\sigma_x^2}{\mu_x^2} + \frac{\sigma_y^2}{\mu_y^2} - 2\rho\frac{\sigma_x\sigma_y}{\mu_x\mu_y}} \tag{1}$$

[FIELLER, E. C., *Biometrika*, Vol. 24 (1932), p. 428.]

14.3. Standard deviation of a product of normally distributed variables. If x and y are normally distributed with means μ_x and μ_y and standard deviations σ_x and σ_y, then $w = xy$ will have mean $\mu_x\mu_y$ and standard deviation

$$\sqrt{\mu_x^2\sigma_y^2 + \mu_y^2\sigma_x^2 + \sigma_x^2\sigma_y^2}$$

[CRAIG, C. C., *Annals of Mathematical Statistics*, Vol. 7 (1936), p. 1.]

Chapter 3

NOMOGRAMS

BY DONALD H. MENZEL

Professor of Astrophysics at Harvard University
Director of Harvard College Observatory

1. Nomographic Solutions

1.1. A nomogram (or nomograph) furnishes a graphical procedure for solving certain types of equations, primarily those containing three variables, say α, β, and γ. If any two of these quantities are known the third follows directly from the conditioning equation between the three parameters. The determinant,

$$\begin{vmatrix} x_1 & y_1 & 1 \\ x_2 & y_2 & 1 \\ x_3 & y_3 & 1 \end{vmatrix} = 0 \tag{1}$$

represents the equation:

$$\frac{y_1 - y_2}{x_1 - x_2} = \frac{y_2 - y_3}{x_2 - x_3} \tag{2}$$

The three points $(x_1 y_1)$, $(x_2 y_2)$, and $(x_3 y_3)$ are collinear because the two segments possess identical slopes and because they have a point, (x_2, y_2) in common.

Now, suppose that we can write

$$\begin{aligned} x_1 &= \phi_1(\alpha) & y_1 &= \psi_1(\alpha) \\ x_2 &= \phi_2(\beta) & y_2 &= \psi_2(\beta) \\ x_3 &= \phi_3(\gamma) & y_3 &= \psi_3(\gamma) \end{aligned} \tag{3}$$

Equations (3) define three curves, in parametric form, whose points we can label in terms of our basic parameters α, β, and γ. Thus, if we know α and β, for example, a straight line from the appropriate points on the α and β curves will intersect the γ curve at the value of γ that satisfies the equations, as indicated in Fig. 1, which represents the artificial equation

$$\begin{aligned} &2 \ln \beta \sin \alpha + 1.5\alpha \cos (\pi/2)\gamma + 2\beta^2 + 1.5\beta^2 \sin^2 (\pi/2)\gamma \\ &\qquad - 1.5 \cos (\pi/2)\gamma \ln \beta - 4 \sin \alpha - 3 \sin \alpha \sin (\pi/2)\gamma - \alpha\beta^2 = 0 \end{aligned}$$

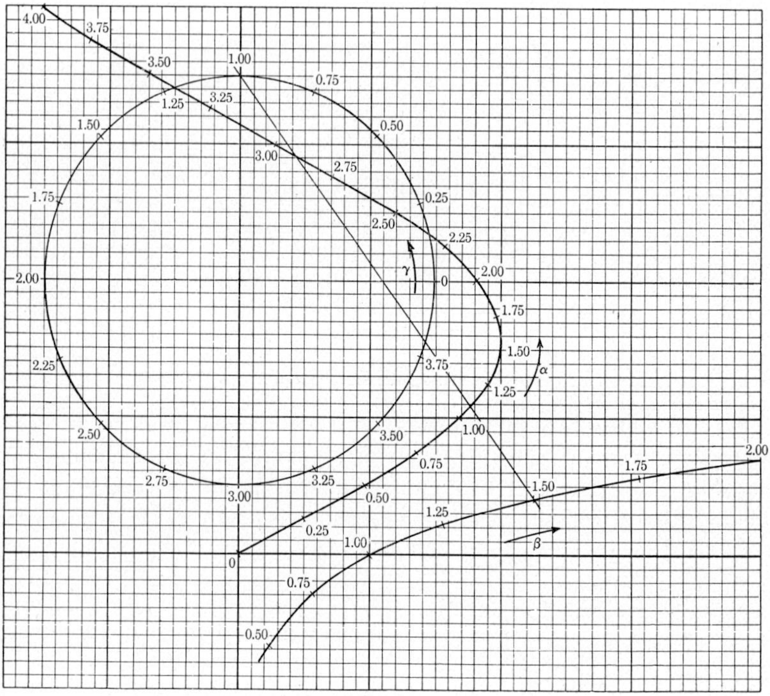

FIGURE 1

This equation fits the determinant (1), with

$$x_1 = 2 \sin \alpha, \qquad y_1 = \alpha$$

$$x_2 = \beta^2, \qquad y_2 = \ln \beta$$

$$x_3 = 1.5 \cos (\pi/2)\gamma, \quad y_3 = 2.0 + 1.5 \sin (\pi/2)\gamma$$

The line connecting given points $\beta = 1.5$ and $\gamma = 1$ intersects the α curve twice. There are thus two roots, approximately at $\alpha = 1.1$ and 2.9. By increasing the number of coordinates marking the values of α, β, γ, we can read as closely as desired. In many examples, of course, some of these curves are straight lines.

To represent an equation nomographically we must first find an equivalent determinant which we then transform by standard rules until we obtain our equation in the form of (1), viz.,

$$\begin{vmatrix} \phi_1(\alpha) & \psi_1(\alpha) & 1 \\ \phi_2(\beta) & \psi_2(\beta) & 1 \\ \phi_3(\gamma) & \psi_3(\gamma) & 1 \end{vmatrix} = 0 \tag{4}$$

We must separate the variables, as above.

Although this equation satisfies the initial condition, the diagram resulting from it is by no means the most general one possible. Let $a, b, c, d, e, f, g, h, i$ represent nine arbitrary constants. Then, using the transformation properties of a zero-valued determinant, we obtain the general form, which expansion will prove to be equivalent to (4).

$$\begin{vmatrix} \dfrac{a\phi_1 + b\psi_1 + c}{g\phi_1 + h\psi_1 + i} & \dfrac{d\phi_1 + e\psi_1 + f}{g\phi_1 + h\psi_1 + i} & 1 \\ \dfrac{a\phi_2 + b\psi_2 + c}{g\phi_2 + h\psi_2 + i} & \dfrac{d\phi_2 + e\psi_2 + f}{g\phi_2 + h\psi_2 + i} & 1 \\ \dfrac{a\phi_3 + b\psi_3 + c}{g\phi_3 + h\psi_3 + i} & \dfrac{d\phi_3 + e\psi_3 + f}{g\phi_3 + h\psi_3 + i} & 1 \end{vmatrix} = 0 \tag{5}$$

By choosing these constants $a - i$ appropriately, we can control the positions and scales of the α, β, and γ curves in order to achieve maximum accuracy for the desired range of variables.

The diagram representing Eq. (5) is a linear transformation of the diagram representing Eq. (4). In other words, (5) is a mere projection of (4) upon some arbitrary plane. Two of the constants, in effect, fix the scales of x and y. Two more determine the choice of origin, including the possibility of shifting any specific point to infinity. Four more define some specific line in the plane and the remaining constant fixes the degree of rotation of the original diagram about this arbitrary line as an axis. The nine constants thus completely determine the projection scheme. Some experimenting with constants is generally necessary to produce the best diagram for a given problem.

A few examples follow. The simple additive nomogram

$$f_1(\alpha) + f_2(\beta) + f_3(\gamma) = 0 \tag{6}$$

yields the basic determinant:

$$\begin{vmatrix} f_1 & 1 & 1 \\ -f_2 & 1 & 0 \\ -f_3 & 0 & 1 \end{vmatrix} = \begin{vmatrix} f_1 & 1 & 2 \\ -f_2 & 1 & 1 \\ -f_3 & 0 & 1 \end{vmatrix} = \begin{vmatrix} \frac{1}{2}f_1 & \frac{1}{2} & 1 \\ -f_2 & 1 & 1 \\ -f_3 & 0 & 1 \end{vmatrix} = 0 \tag{7}$$

The third determinant defines three parallel straight lines. The γ scale fits along the y axis, the β scale along the line $y = 1$, with the α scale halfway between. Now, transforming the determinant by (5) we can get a general form, wherein the three lines may no longer be parallel.

The multiplicative form

$$f_1(\alpha)f_2(\beta) = f_3(\gamma) \tag{8}$$

assumes the form of (6) if we take logarithms. However we often find the following more useful.

$$\begin{vmatrix} f_1 & 0 & 1 \\ 1 & f_2 & 0 \\ 0 & -f_3 & 1 \end{vmatrix} = \begin{vmatrix} f_1 & 0 & 1+f_1 \\ 1 & f_2 & 1 \\ 0 & -f_3 & 1 \end{vmatrix} = \begin{vmatrix} f_1/(1+f_1) & 0 & 1 \\ 1 & f_2 & 1 \\ 0 & -f_3 & 1 \end{vmatrix} = 0 \tag{9}$$

Here the γ scale coincides with the negative part of the y axis. The β scale extends in the positive direction along $y = 1$. The α scale lies along the x axis. By projecting this diagram we can make it assume a Z-shape, with the two arms of the Z not necessarily parallel.

For four variables several alternatives arise. Occasionally the nomograms for four variables are identical in form with those for three, except that one (or more) of the scales are shifted. A sort of sliderule index, to set for the fourth variable, gives the necessary flexibility.

Sometimes we may treat one of the variables as a constant, calculating a different nomogram for each value of the fourth parameter. One can then interpolate between various curves to select the appropriate point.

In still other cases, as for example, in the equations,

$$f_1(\alpha)f_2(\beta) = f_3(\gamma)f_4(\delta) = f_5(\zeta) \tag{10}$$

involving the four variables, we may introduce an arbitrary variable ζ, as above. Now we can compile two independent nomograms, one involving α, β, and ζ and the other γ, δ, and ζ. With the ζ scale identical on both, we can make a single diagram with a common ζ scale. Then, if we are given, say α, β, and γ, and wish to find δ, we first join α and β with a straight line that intersects ζ at some special point. Then connect this point with the value of δ. The intersection of this line with the γ axis determines γ.

Bibliography

1. D'OCAGNE, M., *Traité de Nomographie*, 2nd ed. Gauthier-Villars et Cie, Paris, 1921. The standard work and most complete reference.
2. DOUGLASS, R. D. and ADAMS, D. P., *Elements of Nomography*, McGraw-Hill Book Company, Inc. New York, 1947.

Chapter 4

PHYSICAL CONSTANTS

BY JESSE W. M. DUMOND

Professor of Physics, California Institute of Technology

AND E. RICHARD COHEN

Physicist, North American Aviation Inc., Downey, California

1. Constants and Conversion Factors of Atomic and Nuclear Physics *

It is an interesting paradox that whereas the physical constants, and particularly those associated with the atom, fixed as they are by nature rather than by man, are believed to be the most invariable things known to science, the best methods of arriving at reliable numerical values for these constants have undergone more change in recent years than has been seen in almost any other branch of physics. Recent rapid advances in new techniques and in our theoretical understanding have resulted in new, entirely different, and very superior approaches for ascertaining the best values. These improvements at each stage usually render quite obsolete most of the methods of the preceding stage or era, not because the earlier methods were wrong in principle, but because they admitted of so much less accuracy in practice that they are no longer worth considering in competition with the newer methods. Recently this pace has been markedly accelerated so that, in the span of only a little over four years, completely new experimental methods growing out of the development of microwave and atomic beam techniques have so greatly improved the precision of our knowledge of the atomic constants as to warrant a complete re-evaluation of the entire situation. There has resulted an improvement in accuracy of approximately tenfold as regards our knowledge of the constants and conversion factors. No guarantee can be given that another two or three years hence an equally radical revolution may not have rendered the present methods equally obsolete. It is a fortunate and reassuring fact, however, that with all these

* Values as of November, 1952.

changes in *method* the *results* obtained, *the values* of these constants and conversion factors, give every indication of tending to settle down within narrower and narrower limits of uncertainty toward stable and definite results.

Because of this ephemeral character of the methods of determining these constants, we shall say here only enough about these methods to clarify certain important points bearing on the use of the table of values. The reader who wishes to study our present methods in detail will find them described in a paper by the present authors [*Rev. Mod. Phys.*, **25**, 691 (1953)]. A list of references at the end of this chapter also indicates some of the key papers bearing on this subject over the last twenty-five years. The outstanding work of R. T. Birge during this period in this field has been undoubtedly the greatest single factor in bringing about its present high state of development.

The appended table of values of constants and conversion factors of atomic and nuclear physics was computed by means of formulas (given with each constant in the table), all of which can be expressed directly in terms of the values of the following five key quantities combined with certain other accurately known auxiliary constants. The five key quantities (which we call our " primitive unknowns ") are N, Avogadro's number; e, the electronic charge; α, Sommerfeld's fine structure constant; c, the velocity of light; and λ_g/λ_s, the conversion factor from the Siegbahn arbitrary scale of x-ray wavelengths (x units) to absolute (or " grating ") wavelengths in milliangstroms (10^{-11} cm). The computation of the table of values from these five primary values is a straightforward process on which we need not dwell. The computation of the values of the five primitive unknowns from various experimental data is accomplished by the following general method. A number of " observational equations " (in the present instance thirteen) is set up to express the results of experimental measurements. It is a peculiarity of the atomic constants that in but few instances are the directly measured numerical quantities which result from experimental work capable of determining a single primitive unknown (such as e or N). In most cases, it is some function of two or more of the primitive unknowns that experiments determine. The number of such determined independent functions of the unknowns should exceed the number of unknowns as much as possible to afford a considerable degree of overdetermination in order to furnish a check (the only one in fact available) on the interconsistency of the data and its freedom from systematic errors. The mathematical tool especially developed for just such a situation as this is the method of least squares.* This permits us to compute a set of " adjusted " or compromise values of the

* See Chapter 2.

unknowns that do the least violence to all the input data, according to a systematic rule for minimizing such violence. This rule allows greater latitude for deviation to the less accurate determinations. In the present instance, a judgment of the violence done to the input data by the process of least-squares adjustment can be obtained from the statement that the ratio of our " precision measure by external consistency " (a measure of the compatibility of the overdetermined input equations) to our " precision measure by internal consistency " (based on estimates of the experimental accuracy of the input data) was $r_e/r_i = 2.55$.

A rather delicate point of novel character arises, in the present least-squares adjustment. In order to minimize the numerical work, which piles up with appalling rapidity as the number of unknowns increases, an effort is made to formulate the observational equations as compactly as possible. A result of this is that, unless care is taken to avoid such a condition, the numerical values (the results of experimental measurements), to each of which is equated some function of the unknowns in each observational equation, may not always be *single* measurements but may be *a function of several* independent measurements. If, furthermore, the same independent measurement may have been used as a contributing factor in computing the numerics for several different observational equations, these numerics may thus become " observationally correlated." Great care and attention must be given either (1) to formulate the equations so these correlations are absent or at most insignificant, or (2) to take account of them by an extension of the method of least-squares which has been especially developed for this purpose.

Two scales of atomic weights exist, the physical and chemical scales. On the physical scale the O^{16} isotope of oxygen has, by definition, the atomic weight 16. On the chemical scale, atomic weight 16 is assigned to the average atomic weight of a mixture of the oxygen isotopes in their naturally occurring abundance ratios. Unfortunately, if we are interested in the highest accuracy, the chemical scale is ambiguous and indefinite now that the precision with which atomic weights can be measured (by mass spectrographic means) is amply sufficient to show that the naturally occurring abundance ratios of the oxygen isotopes is different for different natural sources of oxygen (such as water or iron ore on the one hand and limestone or air on the other). All the atomic weights used in the following table are therefore given on the *physical* scale of atomic weights.

If one wishes to be strictly correct, some care must be used in computing precision measures of quantities depending functionally upon two or more of the numerical values given in the appended tables because these values are not completely uncorrelated in the observational sense. This unavoidable complication and the simple methods of handling it (by means of correlation coefficients and cross-product contributions to the error measure) are explained in an article, [*Rev. Mod. Phys.*, **25**, 691 (1953)].

2. Table of Least-Squares-Adjusted Output Values

(November, 1952)

I. Auxiliary Constants Used:

These auxiliary constants are quantities which are uncorrelated (observationally) with the variables of the least-squares adjustment.

Rydberg wave number for infinite mass: *

$$R_\infty = 109737.309 \pm 0.012 \text{ cm}^{-1}$$

Rydberg wave numbers for the light nuclei:

$$R_{\mathrm{H}} = 109677.576 \pm 0.012 \text{ cm}^{-1}$$

$$R_{\mathrm{D}} = 109707.419 \pm 0.012 \text{ cm}^{-1}$$

$$R_{\mathrm{He}^3} = 109717.345 \pm 0.012 \text{ cm}^{-1}$$

$$R_{\mathrm{He}^4} = 109722.267 \pm 0.012 \text{ cm}^{-1}$$

Atomic mass of neutron:

$$n = 1.008982 \pm 0.000003$$

Atomic mass of hydrogen:

$$\mathrm{H} = 1.008142 \pm 0.000003$$

Atomic mass of deuterium:

$$\mathrm{D} = 2.014735 \pm 0.000006$$

Gas constant per mole (physical scale):

$$R_0 = (8.31662 \pm 0.00038) \times 10^7 \text{ erg mole}^{-1} \text{ deg}^{-1} \text{ C}$$

Standard volume of a perfect gas (physical scale):

$$V_0 = 22420.7 \pm 0.6 \text{ cm}^3 \text{ atm mole}^{-1}$$

* This differs from the value $R_\infty = 109737.311 \pm 0.012$ cm^{-1} given by E. R. Cohen (Ref. 11) and which was used in the least-squares adjustment. In Ref. 11 a tentative value $Nm = 5.48785 \times 10^{-4}$ for the atomic mass of the electron was used with the proviso, p. 359, that " ... an increase of 1 part per million in the electron mass will produce an increase of 0.00005 cm^{-1} in the Rydberg." (The coefficient 0.0005 cm^{-1} in the text is a typographical error.) The present value has therefore been revised, using this coefficient to accord with our present output value of Nm and similar modifications have been made in the Rydberg values of the light nuclei.

II. Least-Squares Adjusted-Output Values:

(The quantity following each $\pm$ sign is the standard error by external consistency.)

Velocity of light:

$$c = 299792.9 \pm 0.8 \text{ km sec}^{-1}$$

Avogadro's constant (physical scale):

$$N = (6.02472 \pm 0.00036) \times 10^{23} \text{ (g mol)}^{-1}$$

Loschmidt's constant (physical scale):

$$L_0 = N/V_0 = (2.68713 \pm 0.00016) \times 10^{19} \text{ cm}^{-3}$$

Electronic charge:

$$e = (4.80288 \pm 0.00021) \times 10^{-10} \text{ esu}$$

$$e' = e/c = (1.60207 \pm 0.00007) \times 10^{-20} \text{ emu}$$

Electron rest mass:

$$m = (9.1085 \pm 0.0006) \times 10^{-28} \text{ g}$$

Proton rest mass:

$$m_p = M_p/N = (1.67243 \pm 0.00010) \times 10^{-24} \text{ g}$$

Neutron rest mass:

$$m_n = n/N = (1.67474 \pm 0.00010) \times 10^{-24} \text{ g}$$

Planck's constant:

$$h = (6.6252 \pm 0.0005) \times 10^{-27} \text{ erg sec}$$

$$\hbar = h/(2\pi) = (1.05444 \pm 0.00009) \times 10^{-27} \text{ erg sec}$$

Conversion factor from Siegbahn x-units to milliangstroms:

$$\lambda_g/\lambda_s = 1.002063 \pm 0.000034$$

Faraday constant (physical scale):

$$F = Ne = (2.89360 \pm 0.00007) \times 10^{14} \text{ esu (g mol)}^{-1}$$

$$F' = Ne/c = (9652.01 \pm 0.25) \text{ emu (g mol)}^{-1}$$

Charge-to-mass ratio of the electron:

$$e/m = (5.27299 \pm 0.00016) \times 10^{17} \text{ esu g}^{-1}$$

$$e'/m = e/(mc) = (1.75888 \pm 0.00005) \times 10^{7} \text{ emu g}^{-1}$$

Ratio h/e:

$$h/e = (1.37943 \pm 0.00005) \times 10^{-17} \text{ erg sec (esu)}^{-1}$$

Fine structure constant:

$$\alpha = e^2/(\hbar c) = (7.29726 \pm 0.00008) \times 10^{-3}$$

$$1/\alpha = 137.0377 \pm 0.0016$$

$$\alpha/2\pi = (1.161396 \pm 0.000013) \times 10^{-3}$$

$$\alpha^2 = (5.32501 \pm 0.00012) \times 10^{-5}$$

$$1 - (1 - \alpha^2)^{1/2} = (0.266254 \pm 0.000006) \times 10^{-4}$$

Atomic mass of the electron (physical scale) :

$$Nm = (5.48760 \pm 0.00013) \times 10^{-4}$$

Ratio of mass of hydrogen to mass of proton : *

$$\mathrm{H/H^+} = \left[1 - \frac{Nm}{\mathrm{H}}(1 - \tfrac{1}{2}\alpha^2)\right]^{-1} = 1.000544610 \pm 0.000000013$$

Atomic mass of proton :

$$\mathrm{H^+} = 1.007593 \pm 0.000003$$

Ratio of proton mass to electron mass :

$$\mathrm{H^+}/Nm = 1836.13 \pm 0.04$$

Reduced mass of electron in hydrogen atom :

$$\mu = m\mathrm{H^+/H} = (9.1035 \pm 0.0006) \times 10^{-28}\ \mathrm{g}$$

Schrödinger constant for a fixed nucleus :

$$2m/\hbar^2 = (1.63844 \pm 0.00016) \times 10^{27}\ \mathrm{erg^{-1}\ cm^{-2}}$$

Schrödinger constant for the hydrogen atom :

$$2\mu/\hbar^2 = (1.63755 \pm 0.00016) \times 10^{27}\ \mathrm{erg^{-1}\ cm^{-2}}$$

First Bohr radius :

$$a_0 = \hbar^2/(me^2) = (5.29171 \pm 0.00006) \times 10^{-9}\ \mathrm{cm} = \alpha/(4\pi R_\infty)$$

Radius of electron orbit in normal H^1, referred to center of mass :

$$a_0' = a_0(1 - \alpha^2)^{1/2} = (5.29157 \pm 0.00006) \times 10^{-9}\ \mathrm{cm}$$

Separation of proton and electron in normal H^1 :

$$a_0'' = a_0' R_\infty / R_\mathrm{H} = (5.29445 \pm 0.00006) \times 10^{-9}\ \mathrm{cm}$$

Compton wavelength of the electron :

$$\lambda_{ce} = h/(mc) = (24.2625 \pm 0.0006) \times 10^{-11}\ \mathrm{cm} = \alpha^2/(2R_\infty)$$

$$\bar{\lambda}_{ce} = \lambda_{ce}/(2\pi) = (3.86150 \pm 0.00009) \times 10^{-11}\ \mathrm{cm} = \alpha^2/(4\pi R_\infty)$$

Compton wavelength of the proton :

$$\lambda_{cp} = h/m_p c = (13.2139 \pm 0.0004) \times 10^{-14}\ \mathrm{cm}$$

$$\bar{\lambda}_{cp} = \lambda_{cp}/(2\pi) = (2.10307 \pm 0.00007) \times 10^{-14}\ \mathrm{cm}$$

Compton wavelength of the neutron :

$$\lambda_{cn} = h/m_n c = (13.1958 \pm 0.0004) \times 10^{-14}\ \mathrm{cm}$$

$$\bar{\lambda}_{cn} = \lambda_{cn}/(2\pi) = (2.10017 \pm 0.00007) \times 10^{-14}\ \mathrm{cm}$$

Classical electron radius :

$$r_0 = e^2/(mc^2) = (2.81784 \pm 0.00010) \times 10^{-13}\ \mathrm{cm} = \alpha^3/(4\pi R_\infty)$$

$$r_0^2 = (7.9402 \pm 0.0005) \times 10^{-26}\ \mathrm{cm^2}$$

* The binding energy of the electron in the hydrogen atom has been included in the quantity. The mass of the electron when found in the hydrogen atom is not m but more correctly $m(1 - \frac{1}{2}\alpha^2 + \ldots)$.

Thompson cross section :

$$\tfrac{8}{3}\pi r_0^2 = (6.65196 \pm 0.0005) \times 10^{-25}\ \mathrm{cm}^2$$

Fine-structure doublet separation in hydrogen :

$$\Delta E_{\mathrm{H}} = \frac{1}{16} R_{\mathrm{H}}\alpha^2 \left[1 + \frac{\alpha}{\pi} + \left(\frac{5}{8} - \frac{5.946}{\pi^2} \right) \alpha^2 \right]$$

$$= 0.365869 \pm 0.000008\ \mathrm{cm}^{-1}$$

$$= 10968.49 \pm 0.25\ \mathrm{mc\ sec}^{-1}$$

Fine-structure separation in deuterium :

$$\Delta E_{\mathrm{D}} = \Delta E_{\mathrm{H}}\, R_{\mathrm{D}}/R_{\mathrm{H}} = 0.365969 \pm 0.000008\ \mathrm{cm}^{-1}$$

$$= 10971.48 \pm 0.25\ \mathrm{mc/sec}^{-1}$$

Zeeman displacement per gauss :

$$(e/mc)/(4\pi c) = (4.66879 \pm 0.00015) \times 10^{-5}\ \mathrm{cm}^{-1}\ \mathrm{gauss}^{-1}$$

Boltzmann's constant :

$$k = R_0/N = (1.38042 \pm 0.00010) \times 10^{-16}\ \mathrm{ergs\ deg}^{-1}$$

$$k = (8.6164 \pm 0.0004) \times 10^{-5}\ \mathrm{ev\ deg}^{-1}$$

$$1/k = 11605.7 \pm 0.5\ \mathrm{deg\ ev}^{-1}$$

First radiation constant :

$$c_1 = 8\pi hc = (4.9919 \pm 0.0004) \times 10^{-15}\ \mathrm{erg\ cm}$$

Second radiation constant :

$$c_2 = hc/k = (1.43884 \pm 0.00008)\ \mathrm{cm\ deg}$$

Atomic specific heat constant :

$$c_2/c = (4.79946 \pm 0.00027) \times 10^{-11}\ \mathrm{sec\ deg}$$

Wein displacement law constant : *

$$\lambda_{\max} T = c_2/(4.96511423) = 0.28979 \pm 0.00005\ \mathrm{cm\ deg}$$

Stefan-Boltzmann constant :

$$\sigma = (\pi^2/60)\,(k^4/\hbar^3 c^2) = (0.56686 \pm 0.00005) \times 10^{-4}\ \mathrm{erg\ cm}^{-2}\ \mathrm{deg}^{-4}\ \mathrm{sec}^{-1}$$

Sackur-Tetrode constant :

$$S_0/R_0 = \tfrac{5}{2} + \ln\,[(2\pi R_0)^{3/2} h^{-3} N^{-4}] = -\,5.57324 \pm 0.00011$$

$$S_0 = -\,(46.3505 \pm 0.0017) \times 10^7\ \mathrm{erg\ mole}^{-1}\ \mathrm{deg}^{-1}$$

Bohr magneton :

$$\mu_0 = he/(4\pi mc) = \tfrac{1}{2} e \lambda\!\!\!^{-}_{ce} = (0.92732 \pm 0.00006) \times 10^{-20}\ \mathrm{erg\ gauss}^{-1}$$

* The numerical constant 4.96511423 is the root of the transcendental equation $x = 5(1 - e^{-x})$.

Anomalous electron-moment correction :

$$\left[1 + \frac{\alpha}{2\pi} - 2.973\frac{\alpha^2}{\pi^2}\right] = \mu_e/\mu_0 = 1.001145356 \pm 0.000000013$$

Magnetic moment of the electron :

$$\mu_e = (0.92838 \pm 0.00006) \times 10^{-20} \text{ erg gauss}^{-1}$$

Nuclear magneton :

$$\mu_n = he/(4\pi m_p c) = \mu_0 Nm/\text{H}^+ = 0.505038 \pm 0.000036) \times 10^{-23} \text{ erg gauss}^{-1}$$

Proton moment :

$$\mu = 2.79277 \pm 0.00006 \text{ nuclear magnetons}$$
$$= (1.41045 \pm 0.00009) \times 10^{-23} \text{ erg gauss}^{-1}$$

Gyromagnetic ratio of the proton in hydrogen, uncorrected for diamagnetism :

$$\gamma' = (2.67520 \pm 0.00008) \times 10^4 \text{ radians sec}^{-1} \text{ gauss}^{-1}$$

Gyromagnetic ratio of the proton (corrected) :

$$\gamma = (2.67527 \pm 0.00008) \times 10^4 \text{ radians sec}^{-1} \text{ gauss}^{-1}$$

Multiplier of (Curie constant)$^{1/2}$ to give magnetic moment per molecule :

$$(3k/N)^{1/2} = (2.62178 \pm 0.00017) \times 10^{-20} (\text{erg mole deg}^{-1})^{1/2}$$

Mass-energy conversion factors :

$$1 \text{ g} = (5.60999 \pm 0.00025) \times 10^{26} \text{ Mev}$$
$$1 \text{ electron mass} = 0.510984 \pm 0.000016 \text{ Mev}$$
$$1 \text{ atomic mass unit} = 931.162 \pm 0.024 \text{ Mev}$$
$$1 \text{ proton mass} = 938.232 \pm 0.024 \text{ Mev}$$
$$1 \text{ neutron mass} = 939.526 \pm 0.024 \text{ Mev}$$

Quantum energy conversion factors :

$$1 \text{ ev} = (1.60207 \pm 0.00007) \times 10^{-12} \text{ erg}$$
$$E/\tilde{\nu} = (1.98620 \pm 0.00016) \times 10^{-16} \text{ erg cm}$$
$$E\lambda_g = (12397.8 \pm 0.5) \times 10^{-8} \text{ ev-cm}$$
$$E\lambda_s = 12372.2 \pm 0.4 \text{ kilovolt-}x \text{ units}$$
$$E/\nu = (6.6252 \pm 0.0005) \times 10^{-27} \text{ erg sec}$$
$$E/\nu = (4.13544 \pm 0.00015) \times 10^{-15} \text{ ev-sec}$$
$$\tilde{\nu}/E = (5.0347 \pm 0.0004) \times 10^{15} \text{ cm}^{-1} \text{ erg}^{-1}$$
$$\tilde{\nu}/E = (8065.98 \pm 0.30) \text{ cm}^{-1} \text{ ev}^{-1}$$
$$\nu/E = (1.50938 \pm 0.00012) \times 10^{26} \text{ sec}^{-1} \text{ erg}^{-1}$$
$$\nu/E = (2.41812 \pm 0.00009) \times 10^{14} \text{ sec}^{-1} \text{ ev}^{-1}$$

de Broglie wavelengths, λ_D of elementary particles : *

Electrons :

$$\lambda_{De} = (7.27373 \pm 0.00016)\ \text{cm}^2\ \text{sec}^{-1}/\text{v}$$
$$= (1.55226 \pm 0.00008) \times 10^{-13}\ \text{cm (erg)}^{1/2}/\sqrt{E}$$
$$= (1.226377 \pm 0.000032) \times 10^{-7}\ \text{cm (ev)}^{1/2}/\sqrt{E}$$

Protons :

$$\lambda_{Dp} = (3.96145 \pm 0.00013) \times 10^{-3}\ \text{cm}^2\ \text{sec}^{-1}/\text{v}$$
$$= (3.62261 \pm 0.00020) \times 10^{-15}\ \text{cm (erg)}^{1/2}/\sqrt{E}$$
$$= (2.86208 \pm 0.00012) \times 10^{-9}\ \text{cm (ev)}^{1/2}/\sqrt{E}$$

Neutrons :

$$\lambda_{Dn} = (3.95599 \pm 0.00013) \times 10^{-3}\ \text{cm}^2\ \text{sec}^{-1}/\text{v}$$
$$= (3.62005 \pm 0.00020) \times 10^{-15}\ \text{cm (erg)}^{1/2}/\sqrt{E}$$
$$= (2.86005 \pm 0.00012) \times 10^{-9}\ \text{cm (ev)}^{1/2}/\sqrt{E}$$

Energy of 2200 m/sec neutron :

$$E_{2200} = 0.0252977 \pm 0.0000006\ \text{ev}$$

Velocity of 1/40 ev neutron :

$$v_{0.025} = 2187.017 \pm 0.028\ \text{m/sec}$$

The Rydberg and related derived constants :

$$R_\infty = 109737.309 \pm 0.012\ \text{cm}^{-1}$$
$$R_\infty c = (3.289847 \pm 0.000008) \times 10^{15}\ \text{sec}^{-1}$$
$$R_\infty hc = (2.17961 \pm 0.00018) \times 10^{-11}\ \text{ergs}$$

$$\frac{R_\infty hc^2 \times 10^{-8}}{e} = 13.6050 \pm 0.0005\ \text{ev}$$

Hydrogen ionization potential :

$$I_0 = 13.5978 \pm 0.0005\ \text{ev} = R_H \frac{hc^2}{e}\left[1 + \frac{\alpha^2}{4} + \ldots\right] \times 10^{-8}$$

* These formulas apply only to nonrelativistic velocities. If the velocity of the particle is not negligible compared to the velocity of light, c, or the energy not negligible compared to the rest mass energy, we must use $\lambda_D = \lambda_c[\epsilon(\epsilon + 2)]^{-1/2}$, where λ_c is the appropriate Compton wavelength, and ϵ is the kinetic energy measured in units of the particle rest-mass.

Bibliography

By R. T. Birge

Revs. Modern. Phys., **1**, 1 (1929).*
Phys. Rev., **40**, 207 (1932).
Phys. Rev., **40**, 228 (1932).
Phys. Rev., **42**, 736 (1932).
Nature, **133**, 648 (1934).
Nature, **134**, 771 (1934).
Phys. Rev., **48**, 918 (1935).
Nature, **137**, 187 (1936).
Phys. Rev., **54**, 972 (1938).
Am. Phys. Teacher, **7**, 351 (1939).
Phys. Rev., **55**, 1119 (1939).
Phys. Rev., **57**, 250 (1940).
Phys. Rev., **58**, 658 (1940).
Phys. Rev., **60**, 766 (1941).*
Reports on Progress in Physics, London, **VIII**, 90 (1942).*
Am. J. Phys., **13**, 63 (1945).*
Phys. Rev., **79**, 193 (1950).
Phys. Rev., **79**, 1005 (1950).

Other References

1. F. G. Dunnington, *Revs. Modern Phys.*, **11**, 65 (1939).
2. J. W. M. DuMond, *Phys. Rev.*, **56**, 153 (1939).
3. *Phys. Rev.*, **58**, 457 (1940).
4. F. Kirchner, *Ergeb. exakt. Naturwiss.*, **18**, 26 (1939).
5. J. W. M. DuMond and E. R. Cohen, *Revs. Modern Phys.*, **20**, 82-108 (1948).
6. J. W. M. DuMond, *Phys. Rev.*, **77**, 411 (1950).
7. J. W. M. DuMond and E. R. Cohen, *American Scientist*, **40**, 447 (1952).
8. J. A. Bearden and H. M. Watts, *Phys. Rev.*, **81**, 73 (1951).
9. Bearden and Watts, *Phys. Rev.*, **81**, 160 (1951).
10. E. R. Cohen, *Phys. Rev.*, **81**, 162 (1951).
11. E. R. Cohen, *Phys. Rev.*, **88**, 353 (1952).
12. J. W. M. DuMond and E. R. Cohen, *Rev. Modern Phys.*, **25**, 691 (1953).
13. E. R. Cohen, *Revs. Modern Phys.*, **25**, 691 (1953).
14. E. S. Dayhoff, S. Triebwasser, and W. Lamb Jr., *Phys. Rev.*, **89**, 106 (1953).
15. S. Triebwasser, E. S. Dayhoff, and W. Lamb Jr., *Phys. Rev.*, **89**, 98 (1953).

* Longer and more important review articles. The first is a classic of considerable importance since it reviews carefully all the constants of physics rather than just the atomic constants. The numerical values of the atomic constants given therein, as well as the methods of determining them, have, however, undergone considerable modification since it was written.

Chapter 5

CLASSICAL MECHANICS

BY HENRY ZATZKIS

Assistant Professor of Mathematics
Newark College of Engineering

The formulas of classical mechanics lie at the base of practically all major fields of modern physics. Although the methods of quantum mechanics are necessary for the understanding of microscopic systems, the methods of even that field are best interpreted in terms of the formulas of classical mechanics, by way of contrast. The following set of formulas, although far from complete, represents an attempt to select from the enormous number of formulas of classical mechanics those that have a particularly modern application.

Notation: A vector quantity will be indicated by bold-face italic type, e.g., $\boldsymbol{a}$. The symbol a will represent the magnitude of $\boldsymbol{a}$. The Cartesian components of $\boldsymbol{a}$ will be denoted by either a_1, a_2, a_3, or a_x, a_y, a_z. The scalar product between two vectors will be denoted by $\boldsymbol{a} \cdot \boldsymbol{b}$, and the vector product by $\mathbf{a} \times \mathbf{b}$. Cartesian coordinates will be denoted by x, y, z, or x_1, x_2, x_3, and time by t. The total time derivative will occasionally also be denoted by a dot over the quantity. The total time derivative of a vector quantity $\boldsymbol{w}(x,y,z,t)$ is given by

$$\dot{\boldsymbol{w}} = \frac{d\boldsymbol{w}}{dt} = \frac{\partial \boldsymbol{w}}{\partial t} + (\boldsymbol{v} \cdot \mathbf{grad})\boldsymbol{w}$$

where $\boldsymbol{v}$ is the velocity with which the material point, which is the carrier of the property $\boldsymbol{w}$, moves.

1. Mechanics of a Single Mass Point and a System of Mass Points

1.1. Newton's laws of motion and fundamental motions.

a. Bodies not subject to internal forces continue in a state of rest or a straight line uniform motion (law of inertia). The equations of motion are

$$\frac{d^2x}{dt^2} = \frac{d^2y}{dt^2} = \frac{d^2z}{dt^2} = 0 \tag{1}$$

Any coordinate system in which Eq. (1) holds simultaneously for all masses, not subject to forces, is called an inertial coordinate system. The collection of all reference frames which move with constant velocity with respect to a given inertial system forms the totality of all inertial frames. The coordinate system anchored in the center of mass of the fixed stars is a good approximation of an inertial system.

b. Bodies which are subject to forces undergo acceleration. The acceleration is parallel to the force and its magnitude is the ratio of the force acting on the body and the (inertial) mass of the body. The mathematical form of the second law is

$$\boldsymbol{f} = m\boldsymbol{a} \tag{2}$$

or

$$f_1 = m\ddot{x}, \quad f_2 = m\ddot{y}, \quad f_3 = m\ddot{z} \tag{3}$$

(force equals mass times acceleration.)

c. To each force exerted by a mass point A on another mass point B corresponds a force exerted by B on A. The second force is equal in magnitude to the first and opposite in direction (law of action and reaction).

$$\boldsymbol{p} = m\boldsymbol{v} \quad [\boldsymbol{v} = (\dot{x},\dot{y},\dot{z})]$$

is called the linear momentum. The force law can also be written

$$\boldsymbol{f} = \frac{d\boldsymbol{p}}{dt} \tag{4}$$

The acceleration $\boldsymbol{a}$ can also be decomposed into a component tangential to the path

$$\boldsymbol{b}_t = \frac{\boldsymbol{v}}{v}\frac{dv}{dt} \tag{5}$$

and a component normal to the path

$$\boldsymbol{b}_n = \frac{\boldsymbol{R}}{R^2}v^2 \tag{6}$$

where $\boldsymbol{R}$ is a vector that has the direction and magnitude of the radius of curvature. The expression $m\boldsymbol{b}_n$ is called the centrifugal force.

If $\boldsymbol{r}$ is the position vector of the mass point m, the vector product $m(\boldsymbol{r} \times \boldsymbol{v})$ is called the angular momentum, and if the force $\boldsymbol{f}$ acts on the mass, the vector product $(\boldsymbol{r} \times \boldsymbol{f})$ is called the torque (or moment of force) inerted by the force $\boldsymbol{f}$.

The work dW done by the force $\boldsymbol{f}$ during a displacement $d\boldsymbol{r}$ is defined by

$$dW = \boldsymbol{f} \cdot d\boldsymbol{r} = (\boldsymbol{f} \cdot \boldsymbol{v})dt = m\left(\frac{d\boldsymbol{v}}{dt} \cdot \boldsymbol{v}\right) = \frac{d}{dt}\left(\frac{mv^2}{2}\right) = dT \tag{7}$$

$$T = \frac{1}{2} mv^2 = \frac{p^2}{2m} \quad \text{is called the kinetic energy.}$$

$$\frac{dW}{dt} = \boldsymbol{f} \cdot \boldsymbol{v} \quad \text{is called the power of the force } \boldsymbol{f}.$$

1.2. Special cases. a. *Central force.* If the force $\boldsymbol{f}(\boldsymbol{r},t)$ is parallel to $\boldsymbol{r}$, then $\boldsymbol{f} \times \boldsymbol{r} = 0$, and therefore

$$m \frac{d}{dt} (\boldsymbol{r} \times \dot{\boldsymbol{r}}) = m(\boldsymbol{r} \times \ddot{\boldsymbol{r}}) = 0 \tag{1}$$

(law of conservation of angular momentum). The vector $\boldsymbol{k} = (\boldsymbol{r} \times \dot{\boldsymbol{r}})$ is a constant, nonlocalized vector (areal velocity vector). In planetary motion Eq. (1) expresses Kepler's second law.

b. *Mass point in a potential field.* If the force $\boldsymbol{f}$ can be written as the negative gradient of a scalar function $U(\boldsymbol{r},t)$, i.e., if

$$\boldsymbol{f} = -\,\mathbf{grad}\, U(\boldsymbol{r},t) \tag{2}$$

U is the potential energy. If U does not depend implicitly on time, i.e.,

$$U = U(\boldsymbol{r}) \tag{3}$$

the force $\boldsymbol{f}$ is called conservative, and

$$\frac{d}{dt} (T + U) = 0 \quad \text{(conservation law of energy)} \tag{4}$$

or

$$T + U = E = \text{constant} = \text{total energy.}$$

c. *Constraints.* The mass points may be constrained to move along certain surfaces or curves, called constraints. These constraints can be replaced by constraint forces $\boldsymbol{f}^*$ which keep the bodies from leaving these constraints but do themselves no work, since the bodies always move at right angles to the constraints. The law of motion for a single mass point under the combined influence of an internal force $\boldsymbol{f}$ and a constraint force $\boldsymbol{f}^*$ is

$$\boldsymbol{f} + \boldsymbol{f}^* = m\boldsymbol{a} \tag{5}$$

If the constraint is given by

$$\phi(x,y,z) = 0 \tag{6}$$

(i.e., the particle is constrained to move on a surface), the force of constraint is

$$\boldsymbol{f}^* = \lambda\, \mathbf{grad}\, \phi \tag{7}$$

The Lagrangian multiplier λ is an unknown function of space and time.

For example, consider a bead that slides frictionless on a straight wire that makes an angle with the horizontal whose tangent is a. We assume the wire in the $x - z$ plane with the positive z axis directed upward. In this case λ is a function of time only :

$$\lambda = \lambda(t)$$

The equations of the constraint is

$$z - Ax - B = 0 \tag{8}$$

The equation of motion are, therefore

$$m\ddot{x} = -A\lambda(t) \tag{9}$$

$$m\ddot{z} = -mg + \lambda(t) \tag{10}$$

We can eliminate λ from both equations and obtain

$$-\frac{m}{A}\ddot{x} = m\ddot{z} + mg \tag{11}$$

But from

$$\ddot{z} = A\ddot{x} \tag{12}$$

and therefore

$$-\frac{m}{A}\ddot{x} = mA\ddot{x} + mg \tag{13}$$

or

$$x = -\sin\alpha\cos\alpha g\frac{t^2}{2} \tag{14}$$

$$z = -\sin^2\alpha g\frac{t^2}{2} \tag{15}$$

and

$$\lambda = -\frac{m}{A}\ddot{x} = g\cos^2\alpha \tag{16}$$

where $x = \text{arc tan } A$, and where we assumed the particle started from rest at the origin.

d. *Apparent or inertial forces.* All the above laws refer to inertial systems. If we refer the equations of motion to accelerated systems, additional terms appear which are called apparent or inertial forces.

The most important cases are :

1. Linearly accelerated systems :

$$\boldsymbol{r} = \boldsymbol{r}^* + \boldsymbol{b}(t) \tag{17}$$

(r refers to the position vector in the inertial frame and $\boldsymbol{r}^*$ to the accelerated frame). The equation of motion is

$$m\ddot{\boldsymbol{r}}^* = \boldsymbol{f} - m\ddot{\boldsymbol{b}} \tag{18}$$

where $\boldsymbol{f}$ is the external force and $-m\ddot{\boldsymbol{b}}$ is the inertial force.

2. Rotating coordinate systems: Let $\boldsymbol{k}$ be a unit vector in the direction of the fixed axis of rotation and ω the angular velocity. The equation of motion is

$$m\ddot{\boldsymbol{r}}^* = \boldsymbol{f} - 2m\omega(\boldsymbol{k} \times \dot{\boldsymbol{r}}^*) - m\omega^2[\boldsymbol{k} \times (\boldsymbol{k} \times \boldsymbol{r}^*)] \tag{19}$$

$-2m\omega(\boldsymbol{k} \times \dot{\boldsymbol{r}}^*)$ is the Coriolis force.

$-m\omega^2[\boldsymbol{k} \times (\boldsymbol{k} \times \boldsymbol{r}^*)]$ is the centrifugal force.

1.3. Conservation laws. We shall assume a system of N mass points which exert central forces on one another and which are in addition subject to external forces $\boldsymbol{f}_n^*(n = 1,2,\ldots,N)$, where $\boldsymbol{f}_n^*$ is the force acting on the nth mass point. The following notations will be used.

$$\boldsymbol{v}_n = \text{velocity of the } n\text{th mass point}$$

$$m_n\boldsymbol{v}_n = \boldsymbol{p}_n = \text{linear momentum of the } n\text{th mass point}$$

$$\boldsymbol{P} = \sum_{n=1}^{N} \boldsymbol{p}_n = \text{total linear momentum}$$

$$\boldsymbol{I} = \sum_{n=1}^{N} m_n(\boldsymbol{r}_n \times \boldsymbol{v}_n) = \text{total angular momentum}$$

$$M = \sum_{n=1}^{N} m_n = \text{total mass of system}$$

$$\boldsymbol{\rho} = \frac{1}{M}\sum_{n=1}^{N} m_n\boldsymbol{r}_n = \text{position of center of mass}$$

$$\boldsymbol{F}^* = \sum_{n=1}^{N} \boldsymbol{f}_n^* = \text{total external force}$$

All quantities are assumed to be taken with respect to a Cartesian inertial reference frame.

The following three conservation laws hold

$$\frac{d\boldsymbol{P}}{dt} = M\frac{d\boldsymbol{\rho}}{dt} = \boldsymbol{F}^* \tag{1}$$

$$\frac{d\boldsymbol{I}}{dt} = M(\boldsymbol{\rho} \times \boldsymbol{F}^*) \tag{2}$$

$$\frac{dE}{dt} = \sum_{n=1}^{N} \boldsymbol{f}_n^* \cdot \boldsymbol{v}_n \tag{3}$$

If the internal forces vanish, the linear momentum, angular momentum, and energy of the system remain constant, hence the name "conservation laws."

1.4. Lagrange equations of the second kind for arbitrary curvilinear coordinates. The equations of motions containing the forces of constraint (see § 1.2*c*) contain supernumerary coordinates, since the constraints actually reduce the number of degrees of freedom. They also use Cartesian coordinates. Often these Lagrange equations of the first kind (as they are called) are difficult to use. The generalized coordinates $q_1, \ldots, q_f$, where f is the true number of degrees of freedom, are often more convenient. All the q_k must be independent of each other, and

$$\left.\begin{aligned} x_i &= x_i(q_1,\ldots,q_f) \\ y_i &= y_i(q_1,\ldots,q_f) \\ z_i &= z_i(q_1,\ldots,q_f) \end{aligned}\right\} \quad (i = 1, 2, \ldots, N) \tag{1}$$

and

$$\dot{x}_i = \sum_{s=1}^{f} \frac{\partial x_i}{\partial q_s} \dot{q}_s \tag{2}$$

etc. The total kinetic energy

$$T = \frac{1}{2} \sum_{i=1}^{N} m_i(\dot{x}_i^2 + \dot{y}_i^2 + \dot{z}_i^2)$$

expressed in terms of the generalized velocities $\dot{q}$, will be a homogeneous quadratic function of the $\dot{q}$, where the coefficients will in general be functions of the q. We assume the system conservative and denote the potential energy by U and define the Lagrange function or the Lagrangian L to be

$$L = T - U \tag{3}$$

The Lagrange equations of the second kind read

$$\frac{d}{dt}\left(\frac{\partial L}{\partial \dot{q}_k}\right) - \frac{\partial L}{\partial q_k} = 0 \tag{4}$$

The quantities $p_k = \partial L/\partial \dot{q}_k$ are called the generalized momenta.

Note : Equation (4) assumes that all forces are conservative. If there exist in addition nonconservative forces F_k (e.g., magnetic forces or friction forces), the Lagrange equations are to be generalized to

$$\frac{d}{dt}\left(\frac{\partial L}{\partial \dot{q}_k}\right) - \frac{\partial L}{\partial q_k} = F_k \tag{5}$$

Sometimes we can find a function M of q and $\dot{q}$ so that even the nonconservative forces F_k appear in the form

$$\frac{d}{dt}\frac{\partial M}{\partial \dot{q}_k} - \frac{\partial M}{\partial q_k} = F_k \tag{6}$$

In that case we introduce a new Lagrangian $L \equiv L + M$, and the equation of motion again assumes the form (4) :

$$\frac{d}{dt}\frac{\partial \bar{L}}{\partial \dot{q}_k} - \frac{\partial \bar{L}}{\partial q_k} = 0 \tag{7}$$

Consider the motion of an electric charge ϵ in an electromagnetic field. In that case

$$M = \frac{\epsilon}{c}(\boldsymbol{A} \cdot \boldsymbol{v}) \tag{8}$$

where $\boldsymbol{A}$ is the so-called magnetic vector potential and $\boldsymbol{v}$ is the velocity of the charge ϵ.

1.5. The canonical equations of motion. If in the Lagrangian L the generalized velocities $\dot{q}$ are expressed in terms of the generalized momenta p, we obtain a function L^* which is numerically equal to L :

$$L^*(q_k,p_k,t) = L(q_k,\dot{q}_k,t) \tag{1}$$

We introduce a new function $H(q_k,p_k,t)$ defined by

$$H(q_k,p_k,t) \equiv -L^*(q_k,p_k,t) + \sum_{s=1}^{f} p_s \dot{q}_s(q_k,p_k,t) \tag{2}$$

The equations of motion (§ 1.4-5) become then

$$\dot{p}_k = -\frac{\partial H}{\partial q_k} \tag{3}$$

$$\dot{q}_k = \frac{\partial H}{\partial p_k} \tag{4}$$

where H is called the Hamiltonian. In Cartesian coordinates the Hamiltonian is

$$H = T + U \tag{5}$$

hence equal to the total energy in a conservative system. The symbolical $2f$-dimensional space of q and p comprises the " phase space." Through each point in phase space passes exactly one mechanical trajectory. The f-dimensional subspace the coordinates q is called the configuration space.

1.6. Poisson brackets. If F is any dynamical variable of the mechanical system, e.g., the angular momentum, assumed to be expressed in terms of q, p, and t, its time rate of change is given by

$$\frac{dF}{dt} = \sum_{k=1}^{f} \left(\frac{\partial F}{\partial q_k} \dot{q}_k + \frac{\partial F}{\partial p_k} \dot{p}_k \right) + \frac{\partial F}{\partial t} = \sum_{k=1}^{f} \left(\frac{\partial F}{\partial q_k} \frac{\partial H}{\partial p_k} - \frac{\partial F}{\partial p_k} \frac{\partial H}{\partial q_k} \right) + \frac{\partial F}{\partial t} \tag{1}$$

An expression such as

$$\sum_{k=1}^{f} \frac{\partial F}{\partial q_k} \frac{\partial H}{\partial p_k} - \frac{\partial F}{\partial p_k} \frac{\partial H}{\partial q_k}$$

is called a Poisson bracket. The Poisson bracket of any two dynamical variables F and G is defined by

$$[F,G] \equiv \sum_{k=1}^{f} \left(\frac{\partial F}{\partial q_k} \frac{\partial G}{\partial p_k} - \frac{\partial F}{\partial p_k} \frac{\partial G}{\partial q_k} \right) \tag{2}$$

Equation (1) can be written

$$\dot{F} = [F,H] + \frac{\partial F}{\partial t} \tag{3}$$

In particular,

$$\dot{H} = [H,H] + \frac{\partial H}{\partial t} = \frac{\partial H}{\partial t} \tag{4}$$

or

$$\frac{dH}{dt} = \frac{\partial H}{\partial t} \tag{5}$$

In a conservative system, in which the energy does not depend explicitly on time, H is constant. Any constant of the motion (or " integral of the motion ") has a vanishing Poisson bracket with H.

The Poisson brackets satisfy the identities

$$[F,G] + [G,F] = 0 \tag{6}$$

and

$$\{F,[G,M]\} + \{G,[M,F]\} + \{M,[F,G]\} = 0 \tag{7}$$

The latter is called Jacobi's identity. The Poisson brackets of the canonical coordinates q and p themselves have the values

$$\left.\begin{aligned} [q_k,q_l] &= 0 \\ [p_k,p_l] &= 0 \\ [q_k,p_k] &= \delta_{kl} \end{aligned}\right\} \tag{8}$$

These Poisson brackets are of fundamental importance in the Heisenberg formulation of quantum mechanics, where they express the fundamental uncertainty principle.

1.7. Variational principles. a. *Hamilton's principle.* The Lagrange equations (§ 1.4-4) are the Euler-Lagrange equations of the variational principle

$$\delta S = \delta \int_{t_1}^{t_2} L\, dt = 0 \tag{1}$$

The variation is taken in configuration space only, subject to the restriction that the time (and therefore also the end points of the path) is not varied. This formulation of the Lagrange equations shows their invariance in configuration space i.e., if $L(q,\dot{q},t) = L^*(q^*,\dot{q}^*,t)$, then in the new coordinate system the same equations hold again :

$$\frac{d}{dt}\left(\frac{\partial L^*}{\partial \dot{q}^*}\right) - \frac{\partial L^*}{\partial q^*} = 0 \tag{2}$$

$$S = \int_{t_1}^{t_2} L(q,\dot{q},t)dt$$

is called the action function, or Hamilton's principal function, and (1) defines Hamilton's "principle of least action," the analogue of Fermat's principle in optics, (see § 1.11).

b. *Variational principle in phase space.* The canonical equations of motion (§ 1.5-3.4) are the Euler-Lagrange equations of the variational principle in phase space (i.e. q and p are considered the coordinates of a point) :

$$\delta \int_{t_1}^{t_2} \left[\sum_{k=1}^{f} p_k\dot{q}_k - H(q_k,p_k,t)\right] dt = 0 \quad [\dot{q}_k = \dot{q}_k(q_k,p_k,t)] \tag{3}$$

The time and the endpoints are again held fixed.

1.8. Canonical transformations. The form of the equations is independent of any specific coordinate system. The basic principle serves as a unifying guide for expressing more general theories, e.g., in the general theory of relativity or quantum mechanics.

Any transformation law from the canonical coordinates q and p to new canonical coordinates $\bar{q}$ and $\bar{p}$, by which the canonical equations remain invariant, is called a canonical transformation. Mathematically the canonical transformations are a special case of the contact transformations. The necessary and sufficient condition that the transformation be canonical is that the two linear differential forms

$$\sum_{k=1}^{f} p_k dq_k - H(q_k,p_k,t)dt \quad \text{and} \quad \sum_{k=1}^{f} \bar{p}_k d\bar{q}_k - \bar{H}(\bar{q}_k,\bar{p}_k,t)dt$$

differ by a total differential, denoted by dV:

$$(\Sigma p_k dq_k - Hdt) - (\Sigma \bar{p}_k d\bar{q}_k - \bar{H}dt) = dV \tag{1}$$

$$\bar{q}_k = \bar{q}_k(q_1 q_2 \cdots p_1 p_2 \cdots t) \tag{2}$$

$$\bar{p}_k = \bar{p}_k(q_1 q_2 \cdots p_1 p_2 \cdots t) \tag{3}$$

where V is called the generating function. The canonical transformations are particular mappings of phase space upon itself. The following choices are possible for the function V.

$$\left.\begin{aligned} &V = V(q,\bar{q},t) \\ &p_k = \frac{\partial V}{\partial q_k}; \quad \bar{p}_k = -\frac{\partial V}{\partial \bar{q}_k}; \quad H = \bar{H} - \frac{\partial V}{\partial t} \end{aligned}\right\} \tag{4}$$

$$\left.\begin{aligned} &V = V(q,\bar{p},t) \\ &p_k = \frac{\partial V}{\partial q_k}; \quad \bar{q}_k = \frac{\partial V}{\partial \bar{p}_k}; \quad H = \bar{H} - \frac{\partial V}{\partial t} \end{aligned}\right\} \tag{5}$$

$$\left.\begin{aligned} &V = V(\bar{q},p,t) \\ &\bar{p}_k = -\frac{\partial V}{\partial \bar{q}_k}; \quad q_k = -\frac{\partial V}{\partial p_k}; \quad H = \bar{H} - \frac{\partial V}{\partial t} \end{aligned}\right\} \tag{6}$$

$$\left.\begin{aligned} &V = V(p,\bar{p},t) \\ &q_k = -\frac{\partial V}{\partial p_k}; \quad \bar{q}_k = \frac{\partial V}{\partial \bar{p}_k}; \quad H = \bar{H} - \frac{\partial V}{\partial t} \end{aligned}\right\} \tag{7}$$

For example,

$$V = q_1\bar{p}_1 + q_2\bar{p}_2 + \ldots \tag{8}$$

leads to the identity transformation

$$q_1 = \bar{q}_1 \qquad p_1 = \bar{p}_1 \qquad \text{etc.}$$

$$V = p_x r \cos\phi + p_y r \sin\phi + p_z z \tag{9}$$

gives us the transformation from Cartesian to cylindrical coordinates:

$$\begin{aligned} x &= r\cos\phi, & p_r &= p_x \cos\phi + p_y \sin\phi \\ y &= r\sin\phi, & p_z &= -p_x r \sin\phi + p_y r \cos\phi \\ z &= z, & p_z &= p_z \end{aligned}$$

The expression $p_x^2 + p_y^2$ goes over into $p_r^2 + p^2/r^2$.

$$V = p_x r \cos\phi \sin\theta + p_y r \sin\phi \sin\theta + p_z r \cos\theta \tag{10}$$

This gives us the transition to polar coordinates:

$$\begin{aligned} x &= r\cos\phi\sin\theta, & p_r &= p_x \cos\phi \sin\theta + p_y \sin\phi \sin\theta + p_z \cos\theta \\ y &= r\sin\phi\sin\theta, & p_z &= -p_x r \sin\phi \sin\theta + p_y r \cos\phi \sin\theta \\ z &= r\cos\theta, & p_\theta &= p_x r \cos\phi \cos\theta + p_y r \sin\phi \cos\theta - p_z r \sin\theta \end{aligned}$$

and

$$p_x^2 + p_y^2 + p_z^2 = p_r^2 + \frac{p_\theta^2}{r^2} + \frac{p_\theta^2}{r^2 \sin^2\theta}$$

Rotation of a Cartesian coordinate system (x_1,x_2,x_3) to $(\bar{x}_1,\bar{x}_2,\bar{x}_3)$:

$$V = \Sigma\alpha_{ik}x_i\bar{p}_k \qquad (i,k = 1,2,3) \tag{11}$$

where

$$\Sigma\alpha_{iy}\alpha_{kj} = \delta_{ik}$$

$$\bar{x}_i = \sum_{r=1}^{3} \alpha_{ir}x_r, \quad \text{and} \quad p_i = \Sigma\alpha_{ir}p_r$$

$$\left.\begin{aligned} V &= \frac{m}{2}\omega q^2 \cot\bar{q} \\ q &= \sqrt{\frac{2\bar{p}}{m\omega}}\sin\bar{q}; \quad p = \sqrt{2m\omega\bar{p}}\cos\bar{q} \end{aligned}\right\} \tag{12}$$

and $p^2/2m + m\omega^2q^2/2$ goes over into $\omega\bar{p}$. This last transformation shows how we can easily find the equations of motion of the linear harmonic oscillator. Since $T = m\dot{q}^2/2$ and $U = kq^2/2 = m\omega^2q^2/2$, we obtain for the Hamiltonian the expression

$$H = \frac{p^2}{2m} + \frac{m\omega^2}{2} q^2$$

We shall call the new canonical variables ϕ and α and thus have the relations :

$$q = \sqrt{\frac{2\alpha}{m\omega}} \sin\phi \qquad p = \sqrt{2m\omega\alpha} \cos\phi$$

Hence the new Hamiltonian is $\bar{H} = \omega\alpha$, and the equations of motion are

$$\alpha = \text{constant} \qquad \phi = \omega t + \beta$$

and therefore

$$q = \sqrt{\frac{2\alpha}{m\omega}} \sin(\omega t + \beta)$$

The canonical transformations were characterized by the fact that they leave a certain integral in phase space, the action integral, invariant. Still other quantities that are invariant in phase space under canonical transformations, include the so-called integral invariants. They are

$$F_1 = \iint \sum_{k=1}^{f} dp_k dq_k \tag{13}$$

taken over an arbitrary two-dimensional submanifold in phase space. Similarly

$$F_2 = \iiiint \Sigma\, dp_i dp_k dq_i dq_k \tag{14}$$

where the summation is taken over every combination of two indices and the integral is again taken over any arbitrary four-dimensional submanifold in phase space. Similarly

$$F_3 = \iiint \iiint \Sigma\, dp_i dp_k dp_l dq_i dq_k dq_l \tag{15}$$

where the summation is taken over every combination of three indices and the integral is taken over any arbitrary six-dimensional submanifold. The last integral in this sequence is

$$F_{2f} = \int \ldots \int dp_1 dp_2 \ldots dp_f dq_1 dq_2 \ldots dq_f \tag{16}$$

The last mentioned integral invariant, known as Liouville's theorem in statistical mechanics, says that the volume in phase space is an invariant. The integral invariants were of great significance in the earlier Bohr-Sommerfeld formulation of quantum theory. They were those dynamical quantities of classical mechanics which had to be quantized.

1.9. Infinitesimal contact transformations.* A transformation

$$\left.\begin{aligned}\bar{q}_k &= q_k + \epsilon\phi_k(q_1q_2\ldots p_1p_2\ldots)\\ \bar{p}_k &= p_k + \epsilon\psi_k(q_1q_2\ldots p_1p_2\ldots)\end{aligned}\right\} \quad (k = 1,2,\ldots,f) \tag{1}$$

is called infinitesimal if ϵ is a small quantity such that its higher powers can be neglected as compared to the first power. Thus if we have a dynamical function $F(\bar{q}_k,\bar{p}_k)$, we can write

$$F(q_k + \epsilon\phi_k, p_k + \epsilon\psi_k) = F(q_k,p_k) + \epsilon\sum_{r=1}^{f}\frac{\partial F}{\partial q_r}\phi_r + \epsilon\sum_{r=1}^{f}\frac{\partial F}{\partial p_r}\psi_r \tag{2}$$

This infinitesimal transformation will be canonical, if

$$\Sigma p_r\delta q_r - \Sigma\bar{p}_r\delta\bar{q}_r = \delta F$$

or

$$\Sigma p_r\delta q_r - \Sigma(p_r + \epsilon\psi_r)(\delta q_r + \epsilon\delta\phi_r) = \delta F$$

or omitting terms containing ϵ^2, if

$$-\epsilon\Sigma p_r\delta\phi_r + \psi_r\delta q_r = \delta F$$

or

$$\epsilon\sum_r\left[\sum_l p_r\left(\frac{\partial\phi_r}{\partial p_l}\delta p_l + \frac{\partial\phi_r}{\partial q_l}\delta q_l\right) + \psi_r\delta q_l\right] = -\delta F$$

If we put $F = \epsilon W$, we obtain

$$\left.\begin{aligned}\psi_r + \sum_l p_l\frac{\partial\phi_l}{\partial q_r} &= -\frac{\partial W}{\partial q_r}\\ \sum_l p_l\frac{\partial\phi_l}{\partial p_r} &= -\frac{\partial W}{\partial p_r}\\ \text{or}\qquad \psi_r + \frac{\partial}{\partial q_r}\sum p_l\phi_l &= -\frac{\partial W}{\partial q_r}\end{aligned}\right\} \tag{3}$$

$$\frac{\partial}{\partial p_r}\sum p_l\phi_l - \phi_r = -\frac{\partial W}{\partial p_r} \tag{4}$$

If we put

$$W + \Sigma p_l\phi_l = V \tag{5}$$

then

$$\psi_r = -\frac{\partial V}{\partial q_r}, \quad \phi_r = \frac{\partial V}{\partial p_r} \tag{6}$$

* See, e. g., HAMEL, G., *Theoretische Mechanik*, Julius Springer, Berlin, 1949, p. 299.

Therefore the infinitesimal canonical transformation is

$$\bar{q}_k - q_k = \Delta q_k = \epsilon \frac{\partial V}{\partial p_k} \tag{7}$$

$$\bar{p}_k - p_k = \Delta p_k = -\epsilon \frac{\partial V}{\partial q_k} \tag{8}$$

where V is the generating function. Therefore we can regard the canonical equations

$$dq_k = \frac{\partial H}{\partial p_k}\, dt \quad \text{and} \quad dp_k = -\frac{\partial H}{\partial p_k}\, dt$$

as infinitesimal transformations with the Hamiltonian H as the generating function. Any finite canonical transformation can be built up out of successive infinitesimal transformations.

Any arbitrary dynamical function $F = F(q,p)$ undergoes during an infinitesimal canonical transformation, a change ΔF.

$$\begin{aligned} \Delta F &= \sum \frac{\partial F}{\partial q_r} \Delta q_r + \sum \frac{\partial F}{\partial p_r} \Delta p_r \\ &= \epsilon \sum \left(\frac{\partial F}{\partial q_r} \frac{\partial V}{\partial p_r} - \frac{\partial F}{\partial p_r} \frac{\partial V}{\partial q_r} \right) = \epsilon [F,V] \end{aligned} \tag{9}$$

This equation brings out again the meaning of the Poisson bracket. If V is the Hamiltonian and if F is a constant of the motion,

$$\Delta F = 0 \tag{10}$$

1.10. Cyclic variables. *The Hamilton-Jacobi partial differential equation.* If the Hamiltonian H does not contain a certain coordinate, e.g., q_1,

$$H = H(p_1, q_2, p_2, \ldots, q_f, p_f, t) \tag{1}$$

then

$$\dot{p}_1 = 0 \tag{2}$$

$$p_1 = \text{constant} \tag{3}$$

Therefore p_1 is a constant of the motion. Helmholtz has introduced the name of cyclic coordinate for such a " hidden " coordinate. We shall try to find such a canonical transformation wherein all the new coordinates are cyclic. We denote the original canonical variables by q_k and p_k and the corresponding new cyclic canonical coordinates and momenta, respectively, by ϕ_k and α_k. Denote the generating function by $S = S(q_1, \ldots, \alpha_1, \ldots, t)$.

Then

$$p_k = \frac{\partial S}{\partial q_k} \quad \text{and} \quad \phi_k = \frac{\partial S}{\partial \alpha_k} \tag{4}$$

(compare § 1.8, Case c).

By appropriately disposing of the time dependence of the generating function, we can always make the new Hamiltonian $\bar{H}$ vanish.* Therefore

$$\bar{H} = H + \frac{\partial S}{\partial t} = 0 \tag{5}$$

or

$$H\left(q_k, \frac{\partial S}{\partial q_k}, t\right) + \frac{\partial S}{\partial t} = 0 \tag{6}$$

This is the Hamilton-Jacobi partial differential equation. Since the ϕ_k are cyclic variables, the equations of motion can be written down at once :

$$\alpha_k = \text{constant} \tag{7}$$

and

$$\phi_k = \omega_k t + \beta_k \tag{8}$$

where

$$\omega_k = \frac{\partial S}{\partial \alpha_k} \tag{9}$$

Since $p_k = \partial S/\partial q_k$, we have

$$dS = \sum_{k=1}^{f} \frac{\partial S}{\partial q_k} dq_k + \frac{\partial S}{\partial t} dt = \sum p_k \dot{q}_k dt + \frac{\partial S}{\partial t} dt = 2T dt + \frac{\partial S}{\partial t} dt$$

We assume furthermore a conservative system. Therefore $H = E$ or $\partial S/\partial t = -E$; since $E = T + U$,

$$\left.\begin{aligned} dS &= 2T\,dt - E\,dt = (T - U)dt = L\,dt \\ S &= \int_{t_1}^{t_2} L\,dt \end{aligned}\right\} \tag{10}$$

This shows that for a conservative system the generating function S is identical with the action function introduced in § 1.7, $S = S(q_1,\ldots,q_f,t)$ which we can write

$$S = S^*(q_1,\ldots,q_f,\alpha_1,\ldots,\alpha_f) - Et \tag{11}$$

$$p_k = \frac{\partial S}{\partial q_k} = \frac{\partial S^*}{\partial q_k} \tag{12}$$

Here S^* is sometimes called the "reduced" action function because it

* See, e.g., BERGMANN, P. G., *Basic Theories of Physics: Mechanics and Electrodynamics*, Prentice-Hall, Inc., New York, 1949, p. 38.

depends only on the coordinates but not on the time. The Hamilton-Jacobi partial differential equation can also be written

$$H(q_1,q_2,\ldots,\frac{\partial S^*}{\partial q_1},\frac{\partial S^*}{\partial q_2},\ldots) = W(\alpha_1,\alpha_2,\ldots,\alpha_f) = E \tag{13}$$

$$\omega_k = \frac{\partial W}{\partial \alpha_k} \tag{14}$$

An important special case arises if the Hamiltonian is " separable," i.e., if

$$H = H_1(q_1,p_1) + H_2(q_2,p_2) + \ldots + H_f(q_f,p_f) \tag{15}$$

Set

$$H_k(q_k,p_k) = W_k$$

where

$$W_1 + W_2 + \ldots + W_f = W \tag{16}$$

If, furthermore,

$$S^*\ (q_1,\ldots,q_f) = S_1^*(q_1) + \ldots + S_f^*(q_f) \tag{17}$$

then

$$p_k = \frac{\partial S^*}{\partial q_k} = \frac{dS_k^*}{dq_k} \tag{18}$$

and instead of the Hamilton-Jacobi partial differential equation we have f ordinary differential equation to solve, each of the type

$$\left(\frac{dS_k^*}{dq_k}\right)^2 + g_k(q_k) = \alpha_k \tag{19}$$

The total energy E of the system is then a function of the $\alpha_1, \ldots, \alpha_f$:

$$E = E(\alpha_1,\ldots,\alpha_f) \tag{20}$$

As an example, consider the motion of a mass point in a central force field $U(r)$. Using the canonical transformation for spherical coordinates, we obtain

$$H = T + U = \frac{1}{2m}\left(p_r^{\ 2} + \frac{p_\theta^{\ 2}}{r^2} + \frac{p^{\ 2}}{r^2 \sin^2\theta}\right) + U(r) \tag{21}$$

We put

$$S^* = S_r^*(r) + S_\theta^*(\theta) + S\ ^*(\phi) \tag{22}$$

and the Hamilton-Jacobi equation

$$\left(\frac{\partial S^*}{\partial r}\right)^2 + \frac{1}{r^2}\left(\frac{\partial S^*}{\partial \theta}\right)^2 + \frac{1}{r^2\sin^2\theta}\left(\frac{\partial S^*}{\partial \phi}\right)^2 + 2m[U(r) - W] = 0 \tag{23}$$

falls apart into three ordinary differential equations :

$$\frac{dS_\phi^*}{d\phi} = \alpha_\phi \tag{24}$$

$$\left(\frac{dS_\theta^*}{d\theta}\right)^2 + \frac{\alpha_\phi^2}{\sin^2\theta} = \alpha_\theta^2 \tag{25}$$

$$\left(\frac{dS_r^*}{dr}\right)^2 + \frac{\alpha_\theta^2}{r^2} + 2m[U(r) - W] = 0 \tag{26}$$

or

$$\frac{dS_r^*}{dr} = p_r = \sqrt{2m[W - U(r)] - \frac{\alpha_\theta^2}{r^2}} \tag{27}$$

$$\frac{dS_\theta^*}{d\theta} = p_\theta = \sqrt{\alpha_\theta^2 - \frac{\alpha_\phi^2}{\sin^2\theta}} \tag{28}$$

$$\frac{dS_\phi^*}{d\phi} = p_\phi = \alpha_\phi \tag{29}$$

The three constants of integration are $\alpha_z = p_z = mr^2 \sin^2\theta\dot{\phi}$, the angular momentum component along the polar axis; α_θ, the total angular momentum ($\alpha_\phi = \alpha_\theta \cos\gamma$) where γ is the angle between the orbital plane and the equatorial plane); and $W = E$, the total energy.

1.11. Transition to wave mechanics. The optical-mechanical analogy. The Hamilton-Jacobi partial differential equation is of central importance in the transition from classical to wave mechanics. Before discussing the analogy with wave optics we shall discuss the relation to the limiting case of wave optics, viz., geometrical optics. Let μ denote the index of refraction, which may be a function of the coordinates. The paths of the light rays are governed by Fermat's principle :

$$\delta\int_{p_1}^{p_2} \mu\, ds = 0 \quad \text{or} \quad \delta\int_{p_1}^{p_2} \frac{ds}{u} = 0 \quad (u = \text{phase velocity}) \tag{1}$$

We shall now consider all trajectories of a particle belonging to the same constant total energy E. According to Hamilton's principle

$$0 = \delta\int_{t_1}^{t_2}(2T - E)dt = \delta\int_{t_1}^{t_2} 2T\, dt = \delta\int_{t_1}^{t_2} mv^2 dt = \delta\int_{p_1}^{p_2} mv\, ds$$

or

$$\delta\int_{p_1}^{p_2} v\, ds = 0 \tag{2}$$

This equation is of the same structure as (1), but the material velocity (or "group velocity") v is inversely proportional to the phase velocity u.

$$v = \sqrt{\frac{2}{m}(E - U)} \tag{3}$$

The index of refraction is defined by

$$\mu = \frac{u_0}{u} = \frac{v}{v_0} = \sqrt{\frac{E - U}{E}} \tag{4}$$

("Vacuum" is here defined as the region where the potential energy $U = 0$). Thus we can associate with a moving mass point a "wave" whose phase velocity is inversely proportional to the velocity of the particle and whose index of refraction is $\sqrt{(E - U)/U}$. It remains now to recover the "wave equation." We shall use Cartesian coordinates. We assume again a single mass point with the total energy E moving in the potential field U. The action function $S = S(x,y,z,t)$ represents at every instant t a surface in space on which the value of S is constant. Let the velocity with which this surface of a fixed value for S propagates itself in space be denoted by $\boldsymbol{u}$. An observer travelling with the same velocity $\boldsymbol{u}$ will not see any change in value of S. Therefore

$$0 = \frac{dS}{dt} = \frac{\partial S}{\partial t} + \boldsymbol{u} \cdot \nabla S = \frac{\partial S}{\partial t} + \boldsymbol{u} \cdot \boldsymbol{p}$$

or

$$-\frac{\partial S}{\partial t} = \boldsymbol{u} \cdot \boldsymbol{p} = m\boldsymbol{u} \cdot \boldsymbol{v} \tag{5}$$

But

$$-\frac{\partial S}{\partial t} = E \tag{6}$$

and

$$E = m\boldsymbol{v} \cdot \boldsymbol{u} \tag{7}$$

But $\boldsymbol{u}$ is parallel to $\boldsymbol{v}$ since $\boldsymbol{u}$ is perpendicular to the surfaces $S =$ constant and $\boldsymbol{p} = \textbf{grad}\, S$, which means that $\boldsymbol{p}$ is also perpendicular to the surfaces $S =$ constant.

Therefore

$$E = mvu \tag{8}$$

or

$$u = \frac{E}{mv} = \frac{E}{\sqrt{2m(E - U)}} \tag{9}$$

If we solve Eq. (9) for U and replace E again by $-\partial S/\partial t$, the Hamilton-Jacobi equation assumes the form

$$\frac{1}{2m}(|\,\textbf{grad}\, S\,|)^2 + U + \frac{\partial S}{\partial t} = 0 \tag{10}$$

or

$$(|\,\mathbf{grad}\,S\,|)^2 = \frac{1}{u^2}\left(\frac{\partial S}{\partial t}\right)^2 \tag{11}$$

This is the " wave equation " of classical mechanics. In optics the law according to which a scalar quantity $g(x,y,z,t)$ (e.g., the component of the electric field strength in an electromagnetic wave) is propagated is governed by the wave equation :

$$\nabla^2 g = \frac{\mu^2}{c^2}\frac{\partial^2 g}{\partial t^2} \tag{12}$$

where $\mu =$ index of refraction, $c =$ velocity of light in empty space. We try a solution of the form

$$g(x,y,z,t) = f(x,y,z)e^{i\phi} \tag{13}$$

The phase ϕ is given by

$$\phi = 2\pi\left(\frac{l}{\lambda} - \nu t\right) = 2\pi\nu\left(\frac{l}{\mu} - t\right) = 2\pi\nu\left(\frac{\mu l}{c} - t\right) \tag{14}$$

where $\nu =$ frequency, $\lambda =$ wavelength, $l =$ geometrical path length of optical path.

We shall assume that the amplitude function $f(x,y,z)$ changes so slowly that we can assume it constant. Substituting Eq. (13) into Eq. (12) we obtain for ϕ,

$$i \operatorname{div} \mathbf{grad}\,\phi - (|\,\mathbf{grad}\,\phi\,|)^2 = i\frac{\mu^2}{c^2}\frac{\partial^2\phi}{\partial t^2} - \frac{\mu^2}{c^2}\left(\frac{\partial\phi}{\partial t}\right)^2 \tag{15}$$

But

$$\frac{\partial\phi}{\partial t} = -2\pi\nu, \qquad \frac{\partial^2\phi}{\partial t^2} = 0$$

We shall assume also that the index of refraction changes very slowly ($\mathbf{grad}\,\mu = 0$) and that the rays are nearly parallel ($\operatorname{div} \boldsymbol{S}_0 = 0$, where $\boldsymbol{S}_0$ is a unit tangent vector along the optical path.) Then Eq. (15) reduces to

$$(\mathbf{grad}\,\phi)^2 = \frac{1}{u^2}\left(\frac{\partial\phi}{\partial t}\right)^2 \tag{16}$$

But this is an equation of the same type as Eq. (11). Schrödinger therefore assumed that S is proportional to ϕ. Since S has the dimension of an action and ϕ is a pure number, Schrödinger put

$$\phi = \frac{2\pi}{h}S = \frac{2\pi}{h}(S^* - Et) \tag{17}$$

since, according to Planck's law,

$$\frac{E}{h} = \nu \tag{18}$$

Schrödinger assumed that the behavior of a particle can also be described by a wave equation :

$$\nabla^2\Psi = \frac{1}{u^2} \cdot \frac{\partial^2\Psi}{\partial t^2} \tag{19}$$

He put

$$\Psi = \psi(x,y,z)e^{-2\pi iEt/h} \tag{20}$$

where

$$\psi(x,y,z) = e^{2\pi iS^*/h}$$

and therefore, if this value (20) is substituted into Eq. (19), we obtain

$$\nabla^2\psi = -\frac{4\pi^2E^2}{h^2u^2}\psi \tag{21}$$

but

$$u^2 = \frac{E^2}{2m(E-U)}$$

and thus we obtain the celebrated Schrödinger equation :

$$\nabla^2\psi + \frac{8\pi^2m}{h^2}(E-U)\psi = 0 \tag{22}$$

1.12. The Lagrangian and Hamiltonian formalism for continuous systems and fields. So far only systems with a finite (or perhaps denumerably many) degrees of freedoms have been considered. We shall deal now with a continuous system, such as a fluid or an elastic solid. The ensuing relations could be derived as limiting cases of the corresponding laws for discrete systems. The classical treatment of continuous systems is a very important preliminary step to the quantization of wave fields, the so-called " second quantization."

The dynamical variables of particle mechanics, which are *functions* of a finite number of degrees of freedom, become now *functionals*, i.e., functions of infinitely many variables, namely the values of the field variables at each space-time point. We shall denote the field variables by $y_A (A = 1,\ldots,N)$. The Cartesian coordinates will be denoted by x_1, x_2, and x_3. The y_A play now the role of the generalized coordinates.

$$y_A = y_A(x_1,x_2,x_3,t) \tag{1}$$

Partial derivatives with respect to spatial coordinate, will be denoted by commas :

$$y_{A,r} \equiv \frac{\partial y_A}{\partial r} \tag{2}$$

and partial derivatives with respect to time by dots :

$$\dot{y}_A \equiv \frac{\partial y_A}{\partial t} \tag{3}$$

The $\dot{y}_A$ play the role of the generalized velocities $\dot{q}$. In the case of the electromagnetic field we have four field variables ($N = 4$), viz., the three components of the vector potential A and the scalar potential ϕ.

We assume again that the " equations of motion " are the Euler-Lagrange equations of a variational principle :

$$\delta L = 0 \tag{4}$$

$$L = \int_{t_1}^{t_2} dt \int_V \mathcal{L}\, dV \tag{5}$$

where dV is an ordinary three-dimensional volume element. The variations are taken only in the interior of the " world-domain " t, V, and the independent variables x, t are not varied. We shall assume that $\mathcal{L}$, (the " Lagrangian density "), is a function of the y_A, $y_{A,r}$, and $\dot{y}_A$ only and not of x and t, or any higher derivatives of the $\dot{y}_A$:

$$\mathcal{L} = \mathcal{L}(y_A, y_{A,r}, \dot{y}_A) \tag{6}$$

The resulting Euler-Lagrange equations are

$$\frac{\partial \mathcal{L}}{\partial y_A} - \sum_{r=1}^{3} \frac{\partial}{\partial x_r}\left(\frac{\partial \mathcal{L}}{\partial y_{A,r}}\right) - \frac{\partial}{\partial t}\frac{\partial \mathcal{L}}{\partial \dot{y}_A} = 0 \tag{7}$$

These equations are called the field equations. One calls

$$\frac{\partial L}{\partial y_A} - \sum_r \frac{\partial}{\partial x_r}\frac{\partial \mathcal{L}}{\partial y_{A,r}} = \frac{\delta \mathcal{L}}{\delta y_A} = \frac{\vartheta L}{\vartheta y_A}$$

the variational derivative of $\mathcal{L}$ with respect to y_A or the functional derivatives of L with respect to y_A. The energy-stress tensor $t_\sigma{}^\varrho$ is defined by

$$t_\sigma{}^\varrho = \mathcal{L}\delta_\sigma{}^\varrho - y_{A,\sigma}\frac{\partial \mathcal{L}}{\partial y_{A,\varrho}} \tag{8}$$

where $\rho, \sigma = 1, 2, 3, 4$. The index 4 refers to the time coordinate t. On account of the field equations (7) the tensor $t_\sigma{}^\varrho$ obeys the conservation laws :

$$\sum_{\varrho=1}^{4} t_\sigma{}^\varrho{}_{,\varrho} = 0 \tag{9}$$

These are four ordinary divergency relations, expressing the conservation of linear momentum ($\sigma = 1, 2, 3$) and energy ($\sigma = 4$).

In analogy to particle mechanics the momentum densities Π_A are defined to be

$$\Pi_A = \frac{\partial \mathcal{L}}{\partial \dot{y}_A} \tag{10}$$

The next step is to define the Hamiltonian density $\mathcal{H}$. The Hamiltonian H itself is then

$$H = \iiint \mathcal{H}\, dV \tag{11}$$

$\mathcal{H}$ is defined the same way as in particle mechanics:

$$\mathcal{H}(\Pi_A, y_A, y_{A,r}) = \sum_{A=1}^{N} \Pi_A \dot{y}_A - \mathcal{L}[y_A, y_{A,r}, \dot{y}_A(y_A, y_{A,r}, \Pi_A)] \tag{12}$$

In this expression we assume that the velocities $\dot{y}_A$ have been expressed in terms of the momenta. The canonical equations are

$$\dot{y}_A = \frac{\partial \mathcal{H}}{\partial \Pi_A} = \frac{\delta H}{\delta \Pi_A} \tag{13}$$

$$\dot{\Pi}_A = -\frac{\partial \mathcal{H}}{\partial y_A} + \frac{\partial}{\partial x_r}\left(\frac{\partial \mathcal{H}}{\partial y_{A,r}}\right) = -\frac{\delta H}{\delta y_A} \quad (r = 1,2,3) \tag{14}$$

If F and G are any two dynamical functionals, i.e.,

$$F = \iiint \mathcal{F}(y_A, y_{A,r}, \Pi_A) dV \tag{15}$$

and

$$G = \iiint \mathcal{G}(y_A, y_{A,r}, \Pi_A) dV \tag{16}$$

then the Poisson bracket of F and G is defined by

$$[F,G] = \iiint \sum_A \left(\frac{\delta \mathcal{F}}{\delta y_A}\frac{\delta \mathcal{G}}{\delta \Pi_A} - \frac{\delta \mathcal{F}}{\delta \Pi_A}\frac{\delta \mathcal{G}}{\delta y_A}\right) dV \tag{17}$$

In particular, the time rate of change of F is given by

$$\frac{dF}{dt} = [F,H] = \iiint \sum_A \left(\frac{\delta \mathcal{F}}{\delta y_A}\frac{\delta H}{\delta \Pi_A} - \frac{\delta \mathcal{F}}{\delta \Pi_A}\frac{\delta H}{\delta y_A}\right) dV \tag{18}$$

For example, in the electromagnetic field in free space, the field variables y_A are A_1, A_2, A_3, ϕ (i.e., the vector and the scalar potential). Maxwell's equations

$$\left.\begin{aligned} &\mathbf{curl}\, \boldsymbol{E} + \frac{1}{c}\frac{\partial \boldsymbol{H}}{\partial t} = 0; \quad \mathbf{curl}\, \boldsymbol{H} - \frac{1}{c}\frac{\partial \boldsymbol{E}}{\partial t} = 0 \\ &\operatorname{div} \boldsymbol{E} = 0; \qquad \operatorname{div} \boldsymbol{H} = 0 \end{aligned}\right\} \tag{19}$$

are the Euler-Lagrange equations belonging to the Lagrangian density

$$\mathcal{L} = \frac{1}{8\pi}\left(\left|\frac{1}{c}\frac{\partial \boldsymbol{A}}{\partial t} + \mathbf{grad}\,\phi\right|\right)^2 - \frac{1}{8\pi}(|\,\mathbf{curl}\, \boldsymbol{A}\,|)^2 \tag{20}$$

The conjugate momentum density to A_1 is Π_1, where

$$\Pi_1 = \frac{1}{4\pi c}\left(\frac{1}{c}\frac{\partial A_1}{\partial t} + \frac{\partial \phi}{\partial x}\right) \tag{21}$$

The conjugate momentum to ϕ vanishes identically since $\partial\phi/\partial t$ does not occur in the Hamiltonian. The Hamiltonian density is

$$H = \mathbf{\Pi} \cdot \frac{\partial \boldsymbol{A}}{\partial t} - \mathcal{L} = 2\pi c^2 \mid \mathbf{\Pi} \mid^2 + \frac{1}{8\pi}(\mid \mathbf{curl}\ \boldsymbol{A} \mid)^2 - c\mathbf{\Pi} \cdot \nabla\phi \tag{22}$$

The canonical equations are

$$\frac{\partial \boldsymbol{A}}{\partial t} = 4\pi c^2 \mathbf{\Pi} - c\ \mathbf{grad}\,\phi \tag{23}$$

and

$$\frac{\partial \mathbf{\Pi}}{\partial t} = -\frac{1}{4\pi}\mathbf{curl}\ \mathbf{curl}\ \boldsymbol{A} \tag{24}$$

These equations give us all of Maxwell equations except the third

$$\mathrm{div}\,\boldsymbol{E} = 0$$

We must require that $\mathrm{div}\,\boldsymbol{E} = 0$ at some instant of time. But then the canonical equations give us automatically the result that this restriction is maintained at all times.

Bibliography

1. Corben, H. C. and Stehle, P., *Classical Mechanics*, John Wiley & Sons, Inc., New York, 1950. An excellent account of the mechanics of continuous systems and fields.
2. Goldstein, H., *Classical Mechanics*, Addison-Wesley Press, Inc., Cambridge, Mass., 1950.
3. Lanczos, C., *The Variational Principles of Mechanics*, University of Toronto Press, Toronto, 1949.
4. Synge, J. L. and Griffith, B. A., *Principles of Mechanics*, 2d ed., McGraw-Hill Book Company, Inc., New York, 1949.
5. Whittaker, E. T., *A Treatise on the Analytical Dynamics of Rigid Bodies*, 4th ed., Cambridge University Press, London, 1937. (Also Dover Publications, New York, 1944.) The standard work.

Chapter 6

SPECIAL THEORY OF RELATIVITY

BY HENRY ZATZKIS

Assistant Professor of Mathematics
Newark College of Engineering

1. The Kinematics of the Space-Time Continuum

1.1. The Minkowski "world." Ordinary three-dimensional space plus the time form the four-dimensional "world." A "world point" is an ordinary point at a certain time. Its four coordinates are the Cartesian coordinates, x, y, z and the time t, which will also be denoted by x^1, x^2, x^3 and x^4. An "event" is a physical occurrence at a certain world point. In what follows, the Einstein summation convention will be used: Whenever an index appears twice, as an upper (contravariant) and a lower (covariant) index, it is to be summed over. If the index is a lower-case Greek letter, the summation extends from 1 to 4; if it is an italic lower-case letter, the summation extends from 1 to 3. (Generally, the indices 1, 2, and 3 will refer to the spatial dimensions and the index 4 to the timelike dimension of the continuum.) Examples are

$$a^\tau b_{\tau\lambda} = a^1 b_{1\lambda} + a^2 b_{2\lambda} + a^3 b_{3\lambda} + a^4 b_{4\lambda}$$

$$a^{\tau r} b_r = a^{\tau 1} b_1 + a^{\tau 2} b_2 + a^{\tau 3} b_3$$

The two most fundamental invariants of the special theory of relativity are the magnitude c of the speed of light in vacuo and the four-dimensional "distance" τ_{12} of any two world points (x_1, y_1, z_1, t_1) and (x_2, y_2, z_2, t_2) defined by

$$\begin{aligned} \tau_{12}{}^2 &= (t_2 - t_1)^2 - \frac{1}{c^2}[(x_2 - x_1)^2 + (y_2 - y_1)^2 + (z_2 - z_1)^2] \\ &= (\Delta t)^2 - \frac{1}{c^2}[(\Delta x)^2 + (\Delta y)^2 + (\Delta z)^2] \end{aligned} \tag{1}$$

All the kinematic properties of the theory are a consequence of these invariants.

1.2. The Lorentz transformation. We introduce a covariant " metric tensor " $\eta_{\mu\nu}$ and its corresponding contravariant tensor $\eta^{\mu\nu}$, defined by

$$\eta^{\mu\lambda}\eta_{\lambda\nu} = \delta_\nu{}^\mu \tag{1}$$

where

$$\delta_\nu{}^\mu = \begin{cases} 1 & \text{if} \quad \mu = \nu \\ 0 & \text{if} \quad \mu \neq \nu \end{cases} \tag{2}$$

and

$$\eta_{\mu\nu} = \begin{bmatrix} -\frac{1}{c^2}, & 0, & 0, & 0 \\ 0, & -\frac{1}{c^2}, & 0, & 0 \\ 0, & 0, & -\frac{1}{c^2}, & 0 \\ 0, & 0, & 0, & +1 \end{bmatrix}$$

and

$$\eta^{\mu\nu} = \begin{bmatrix} -c^2, & 0, & 0, & 0 \\ 0, & -c^2, & 0, & 0 \\ 0, & 0, & -c^2, & 0 \\ 0, & 0, & 0, & +1 \end{bmatrix} \tag{3}$$

In terms of the metric tensor, the " world distance " or " world interval " τ_{12} becomes

$$\tau_{12}{}^2 = \eta_{\mu\nu}\Delta x^\mu \Delta x^\nu \tag{4}$$

When we go from one reference system Σ with the coordinates x^λ to a new system $\overset{*}{\Sigma}$ with the coordinates $\overset{*}{x}{}^\lambda$ the only admissible systems are those resulting from a nonsingular, linear transformation that leaves $\tau_{12}{}^2$ invariant. Since only coordinate differences and not the coordinates themselves are involved, transformation may be homogeneous or inhomogeneous in the coordinates. Usually, only homogeneous transformations are considered: the " Lorentz transformation." Think of them as rotations in the four-dimensional continuum (the inhomogeneous transformations would correspond to rotations plus translations. The transformation equations are

$$\begin{aligned} \overset{*}{x}{}^\lambda &= \gamma^{\lambda\cdot}_{\cdot\tau} x^\tau \\ x^\lambda &= \gamma^{\cdot\lambda}_{\tau\cdot} \overset{*}{x}{}^\tau \end{aligned} \tag{5}$$

where the $\gamma^{\cdot\lambda}_{\tau\cdot}$ denote the coefficients of the inverse transformation and are solutions of the equations

$$\gamma^{\lambda\cdot}_{\cdot\tau}\gamma^{\cdot\tau}_{\nu\cdot} = \delta^\lambda_\nu \tag{6}$$

The $\gamma^{\lambda\cdot}_{\cdot\tau}$ themselves are the solutions of the equations

$$\eta_{\mu\nu}\gamma^{\mu\cdot}_{\cdot\lambda}\gamma^{\nu\cdot}_{\cdot\tau} = \eta_{\lambda\tau} \tag{7}$$

A spatial rotation in three-dimensional space is a special case, characterized by $\gamma^{r\cdot}_{\cdot 4} = 0$ and $\gamma^{4\cdot}_{\cdot 4} = 1$. Another special case, the most important one in the subsequent discussion, is that one giving the relations between a coordinate system Σ at rest and another system $\overset{*}{\Sigma}$ moving in the direction of the positive x axis with the constant speed v and whose origin $\overset{*}{O}$ coincides at the time $t = 0$ with the origin O of Σ. The transformation coefficients $\gamma^{\lambda\cdot}_{\cdot\tau}$ are in this case.

$$\gamma^{\lambda\cdot}_{\cdot\tau} = \begin{bmatrix} \dfrac{1}{\sqrt{1 - v^2/c^2}}, & 0, & 0, & \dfrac{-v}{\sqrt{1 - v^2/c^2}} \\ 0, & 1, & 0, & 0 \\ 0, & 0, & 1, & 0 \\ \dfrac{-v/c^2}{\sqrt{1 - v^2/c^2}}, & 0, & 0, & \dfrac{1}{\sqrt{1 - v^2/c^2}} \end{bmatrix} \tag{8}$$

and their inverse matrix:

$$\gamma^{\cdot\lambda}_{\tau\cdot} = \begin{bmatrix} \dfrac{1}{\sqrt{1 - v^2/c^2}}, & 0, & 0, & \dfrac{v}{\sqrt{1 - v^2/c^2}} \\ 0, & 1, & 0, & 0 \\ 0, & 0, & 1, & 0 \\ \dfrac{v/c^2}{\sqrt{1 - v^2/c^2}}, & 0, & 0, & \dfrac{1}{\sqrt{1 - v^2/c^2}} \end{bmatrix} \tag{9}$$

The relations between the two coordinate systems are

$$\left.\begin{aligned} \overset{*}{x}{}^1 &= \overset{*}{x} = \frac{x - vt}{\sqrt{1 - v^2/c^2}} \\ \overset{*}{x}{}^2 &= \overset{*}{y} = y \\ \overset{*}{x}{}^3 &= \overset{*}{z} = z \\ \overset{*}{x}{}^4 &= \overset{*}{t} = \frac{t - vx/c^2}{\sqrt{1 - v^2/c^2}} \end{aligned}\right\} \tag{10}$$

$$\left.\begin{aligned} x^1 &= x = \frac{\overset{*}{x} + v\overset{*}{t}}{\sqrt{1 - v^2/c^2}} \\ x^2 &= y = \overset{*}{y} \\ x^3 &= z = \overset{*}{z} \\ x^4 &= t = \frac{\overset{*}{t} + v\overset{*}{x}/c^2}{\sqrt{1 - v^2/c^2}} \end{aligned}\right\} \tag{11}$$

The ratio v/c will be denoted by β.

The Lorentz transformations form a group, i.e., if the system $\overset{*}{\Sigma}$ is related to the system Σ by a Lorentz transformation, and if the system $\overset{**}{\Sigma}$ is related to $\overset{*}{\Sigma}$ by another Lorentz transformation, then there exists a third Lorentz transformation which relates $\overset{**}{\Sigma}$ directly to Σ.

Lorentz's transformation laws [*Proceedings of the Academy of Sciences*, Amsterdam, **6**, 809 (1904)] are however, not completely equivalent to Einstein's. His formulas (4) and (5) read :

$$\overset{*}{x} = \frac{x}{\sqrt{1-\beta^2}}; \quad t = \overset{*}{t}\sqrt{1-\beta^2} - \frac{xv/c^2}{\sqrt{1-\beta^2}}$$

Therefore $x^2 - c^2t^2$ is not an invariant, since

$$\overset{*}{x}{}^2 - c^2\overset{*}{t}{}^2 = x^2 - c^2t^2 + 2\beta xct + c^2\beta^2t^2.$$

If the Einstein equations and the original Lorentz equations are expanded in powers of β, they agree in the first powers of β, but not in the second and higher powers. This explains why the original Lorentz electron theory, which still assumed an absolute " ether " at rest, could explain correctly all first-order phenomena, such as aberration, but not second-order phenomena such as the Michelson-Morley experiment without some special *ad hoc* assumptions, e.g., the Lorentz-Fitzgerald contraction.

1.3. Kinematic consequences of the Lorentz transformation.

a. *Relativity of simultaneity. Order of events.* If an event occurs in Σ at the points x_1 and x_2 at the times t_1 and t_2, then

$$\overset{*}{t}_1 = \frac{t_1 - vx_1/c^2}{\sqrt{1-\beta^2}}, \quad \overset{*}{t}_2 = \frac{t_2 - vx_2/c^2}{\sqrt{1-\beta^2}} \tag{1}$$

and therefore

$$\overset{*}{t}_2 - \overset{*}{t}_1 = \frac{t_2 - t_1 - (v/c^2)(x_2 - x_1)}{\sqrt{1-\beta^2}} \tag{2}$$

If $t_2 = t_1$, we obtain

$$\overset{*}{t}_2 - \overset{*}{t}_1 = \frac{(-v/c^2)(x_2 - x_1)}{\sqrt{1-\beta^2}} \neq 0 \tag{3}$$

Thus two events that are simultaneous in Σ are no longer simultaneous in $\overset{*}{\Sigma}$. If the two events in Σ can be connected by a signal whose speed w is less than the speed of light, i.e., if

$$\frac{x_2 - x_1}{t_2 - t_1} = w > c \tag{4}$$

then
$$\overset{*}{t}_2 - \overset{*}{t}_1 = (t_2 - t_1)\frac{1 - vw/c^2}{\sqrt{1 - v^2/c^2}} \tag{5}$$

In other words, $\overset{*}{t}_2 - \overset{*}{t}_1$ will always be positive if $t_2 - t_1$ is positive. The temporal order of events is not destroyed by a Lorentz transformation.

b. *The time dilatation.* If a clock, e.g., an atomic oscillator, vibrates with the period T at a fixed point x, a moving observer will observe the period

$$\overset{*}{T} = \frac{T}{\sqrt{1 - v^2/c^2}} \tag{6}$$

c. *The Lorentz contraction.* The spatial distance between two world points $\overset{*}{P}_1 = (\overset{*}{x}_1, \overset{*}{y}_1, \overset{*}{z}_1, \overset{*}{t})$ and $\overset{*}{P}_2 = (\overset{*}{x}_2, \overset{*}{y}_2, \overset{*}{z}_2, \overset{*}{t})$ is

$$\left.\begin{aligned} \overset{*}{L} &= \sqrt{(\overset{*}{x}_2 - \overset{*}{x}_1)^2 + (\overset{*}{y}_2 - \overset{*}{y}_1)^2 + (\overset{*}{z}_2 - \overset{*}{z}_1)^2} \\ &= \sqrt{(x_2 - x_1)^2(1 - \beta)^2 + (y_2 - y_1)^2 + (z_2 - z_1)^2} \end{aligned}\right\} \tag{7}$$

The linear dimensions in the direction of motion appear contracted in the ratio $1 : \sqrt{1 - \beta^2}$ to a moving observer. Distances orthogonal to the direction of motion remain unchanged. This contraction explains the negative outcome of the Michelson-Morley experiment, historically the starting point for the creation of the theory of relativity. Suppose that an observer on a material system, moving through space with a velocity v, makes observations on the velocity of light, and determines the time taken by light to pass from a point A to a point B at a distance d from A and to be reflected back to A. Let the velocity v of his system be in the direction from A to B. Let the light start from A at time t_1, arrive at B at time t_2, and get back to A at t_3. Then if the light travels through space with velocity c, we have

$$d + v(t_2 - t_1) = c(t_2 - t_1) \tag{8}$$

$$d - v(t_3 - t_2) = c(t_3 - t_2) \tag{9}$$

or
$$t_2 - t_1 = \frac{d}{c - v} \tag{10}$$

$$t_3 - t_2 = \frac{d}{c + v} \tag{11}$$

Hence
$$\Delta t = t_3 - t_1 = \frac{2d}{c(1 - v^2/c^2)} = \frac{2d}{c(1 - \beta^2)} \tag{12}$$

Suppose now that AB is perpendicular to the velocity v. In this case the distance traversed by the light signal, as it travels from A to B and back to A again is

$$2\sqrt{d^2 + \frac{v^2}{4}(t_3' - t_1')^2} = c(t_3' - t_1') = c\Delta t' \tag{13}$$

Therefore

$$\Delta t' = \frac{2d}{c\sqrt{1-\beta^2}} \tag{14}$$

The two time intervals Δt and $\Delta t'$ are not the same. However, because of the Lorentz contraction, the required time Δt is shortened, and becomes

$$\Delta t = \frac{2d\sqrt{1-\beta^2}}{c(1-\beta^2)} = \Delta t' \tag{15}$$

It was experimentally observed that $\Delta t = \Delta t'$.

d. *Velocity addition theorem.* If the velocity of a material particle has the Cartesian components u_1, u_2, and u_3 in Σ, its components in $\overset{*}{\Sigma}$ are given by

$$\overset{*}{u}_1 = \frac{u_1 + v}{1 + vu_1/c^2} \tag{16}$$

$$\overset{*}{u}_2 = \frac{u_2\sqrt{1-\beta^2}}{1 + vu_1/c^2} \tag{17}$$

$$\overset{*}{u}_3 = \frac{u_3\sqrt{1-\beta^2}}{1 + vu_1/c^2} \tag{18}$$

Applications. (1) Assume that a light ray is traveling in the y direction, $u_1 = u_3 = 0$; $u_2 = c$. Then $\overset{*}{u}_1 = -v$; $\overset{*}{u}_2 = c\sqrt{1-\beta^2}$; $\overset{*}{u}_3 = 0$. The angle α which the ray includes with the $\overset{*}{y}$ axis is given by

$$\tan\alpha = \frac{\overset{*}{u}_1}{\overset{*}{u}_2} = -\frac{v}{c\sqrt{1-\beta^2}} = -\beta\left(1 + \frac{\beta^2}{2} + \dots\right) \tag{19}$$

For small values of β, the absolute value of α becomes β (angle of aberration).

(2) Let N be the refractive index of a substance having the velocity v in the x direction. The speed of light in this substance is $u = c/N$. Consequently the speed $\overset{*}{u}$ of a light ray traveling in the $\overset{*}{x}$ direction is

$$\overset{*}{u} = \overset{*}{u}_1 = \frac{u + v}{1 + vu/c^2} = \frac{c}{N} + v\left(1 - \frac{1}{N^2}\right) + \dots \tag{20}$$

the factor $(1 - 1/N^2)$ is called the Fresnel-drag coefficient.

e. *Doppler effect and general formula for the aberration.* If a plane light wave in vacuum travels along a direction which forms an angle $\overset{*}{\theta}$ with the $\overset{*}{x}$ axis and has a frequency $\overset{*}{\nu}$ in the system $\overset{*}{\Sigma}$, an observer in the system Σ will observe the frequency ν and the angle θ, where

$$\nu = \frac{(1 + \beta \cos \overset{*}{\theta})}{\sqrt{1 - \beta^2}} \overset{*}{\nu} \tag{21}$$

$$\cos \theta = \frac{\cos \overset{*}{\theta} + \beta}{1 + \beta \cos \overset{*}{\theta}} \tag{22}$$

$$\sin \theta = \frac{\sqrt{1 - \beta^2} \sin \overset{*}{\theta}}{1 + \beta \cos \overset{*}{\theta}} \tag{23}$$

f. *Reflection at moving mirror.* Let a mirror have the speed u and a plane wave be reflected by it (Fig. 1). If ψ_1 is the angle of incidence, and ψ_2 the angle of reflection,

$$\frac{\tan \psi_2}{\tan \psi_1} = \frac{c - u}{c + u} \tag{24}$$

If ν_1 is the frequency of the incident wave and ν_2 that of the reflected wave,

$$\frac{\nu_2}{\nu_1} = \frac{\sin \psi_1}{\sin \psi_2} \tag{25}$$

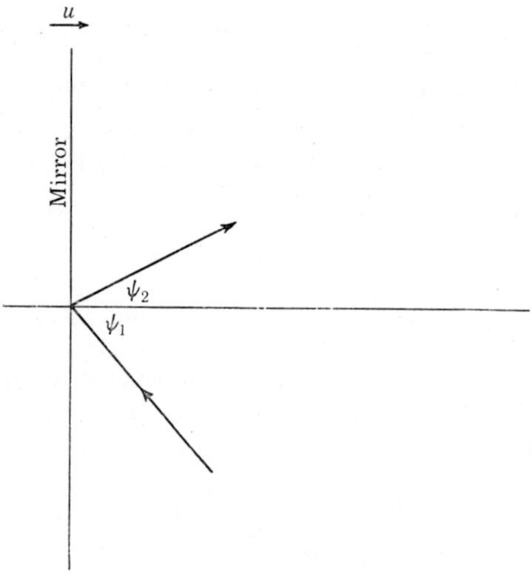

FIGURE 1

If the mirror moves opposite to the incident wave, we note that $\psi_2 < \psi_1$ and $\nu_2 < \nu_1$. These formulas played an important part in Planck's derivation of black-body radiation and in the thermodynamics of cavity radiation.

g. *Graphical representation of the Lorentz transformation.* We project the four-dimensional world upon the x,t plane (Fig. 2) and choose as abscissa

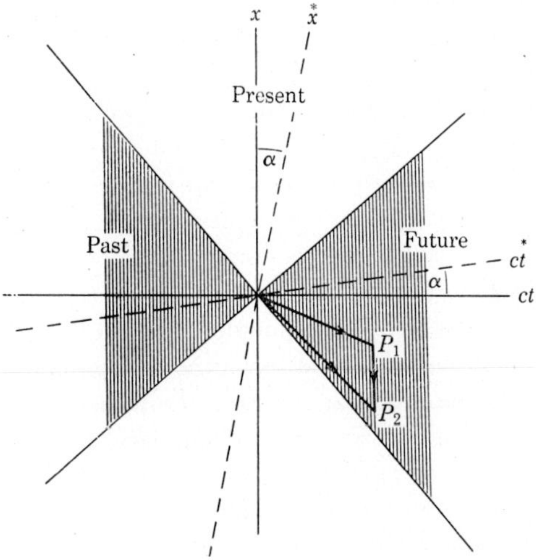

FIGURE 2

not the time t but $\xi_4 = ct$ and as ordinate $x = \xi_1$. The relations between $x' = \xi_1'$ and $\overset{*}{ct} = \overset{*}{\xi}_4$, and ξ_1 and ξ_4 are given by

$$\overset{*}{\xi}_1 = \xi_1 \cos\alpha - i\xi_4 \sin\alpha \tag{26}$$

$$\overset{*}{\xi}_4 = -i\xi_1 \sin\alpha + \xi_4 \cos\alpha \tag{27}$$

or if we put $\xi_1 = \eta_1$ and $i\xi_4 = \eta_4$,

$$\overset{*}{\eta}_1 = \eta_1 \cos\alpha - \eta_4 \sin\alpha \tag{28}$$

$$\overset{*}{\eta}_4 = \eta_1 \sin\alpha + \eta_4 \cos\alpha \tag{29}$$

where $i \tan\alpha = v/c$.

Introducing the imaginary angle γ, defined by $\gamma = i\alpha$, we can rewrite these formulas in the form

$$\overset{*}{\xi}_1 = \xi_1 \cosh \gamma - \xi_4 \sinh \gamma \tag{30}$$

$$\overset{*}{\xi}_4 = - \xi_1 \sinh \gamma + \xi_4 \cosh \gamma \tag{31}$$

The expression $c \tanh \gamma = v$ is the speed with which the reference frame $\overset{*}{\Sigma}$ moves with respect to the reference frame Σ.

A uniform motion of a particle, passing through the origin of either coordinate system at the time zero is represented by a straight line through the origin. Its slope is given by $\tan \phi = w/c$ where w is the speed with respect to the system Σ. Since the speed cannot exceed the speed of light, the two 45° lines passing through the origin represent the motion of a light signal. In the Minkowski world the light signals reaching the origin at the time zero form the surface of a three-dimensional cone with its vertex at the origin. Likewise the light signals leaving O at the time zero form another cone with the vertex at O. This double cone is called the " light cone." Any physical event either in the past or in the future that can be linked to an event happening at the origin at the time zero must take place at a world point located in the interior or on the boundary of the light cone. The left-hand cone represents the past and the right-hand cone the future. All other events are located in the " present," since they can neither have caused nor be the consequence of the event at the origin at time zero. In the sense of the Minkowski metric the " distance " between two points $P_1(\xi_4,\xi_1)$ and $P_2(\xi_4',\xi_1')$ is $d(P_1P_2) = + \sqrt{(\xi_4' - \xi_4)^2 - (\xi_1' - \xi_1)^2}$, where it is assumed that both points lie within the same part of the light cone, i.e., both points lie in the past or in the future. It is an immediate consequence of this definition that

$$d(OP_1) + d(OP_2) \leqq d(OP_2) \tag{32}$$

In other words, the usual triangle-inequality is just reversed. The straight-line connection between two points is not the shortest, but the longest connection.

2. Dynamics

2.1. Conservation laws. Classical mechanics knows two independent conservation laws, the conservation of a vector p^s, the linear momentum, and the conservation of a scalar, the energy E. Relativistic mechanics knows only one conservation law, the conservation of a world vector P^{ϱ}.

More precisely, it states that if there are n particles present with rest masses $\underset{1}{m}, \underset{2}{m}, \ldots, \underset{n}{m}$, then in the absence of external forces four laws of inertia hold :

$$\sum_{k=1}^{n} \underset{k}{P}^{\varrho} = \text{constant} \qquad (\rho = 1,2,3,4) \tag{1}$$

where

$$\underset{k}{P}^{\varrho} = \left(\frac{\underset{k}{m}\underset{k}{u}^{s}}{\sqrt{1 - \underset{k}{u}^2/c^2}}, \frac{\underset{k}{E}}{c^2} \right) \tag{2}$$

The corresponding covariant vector is

$$\underset{k}{P}_{\varrho} = \left(\frac{-\underset{k}{m}\underset{k}{u}^{s}}{c^2\sqrt{1 - \underset{k}{u}^2/c^2}}, \frac{\underset{k}{E}}{c^2} \right) \qquad \underset{k}{E} = \frac{\underset{k}{m}c^2}{\sqrt{1 - \underset{k}{u}^2/c^2}} \tag{4}$$

The relativistic kinetic energy T is defined by

$$T = \frac{mc^2}{\sqrt{1 - u^2/c^2}} - mc^2 \tag{5}$$

which for small velocities becomes the classical value $\frac{1}{2}mu^2$. Since the vector P^{ϱ} is conserved, its magnitude, and hence also the square of its magnitude are also conserved. Thus

$$P^{\varrho}P_{\varrho} = \frac{1}{c^2}\left[\frac{E^2}{c^2} - \sum_{s=1}^{3}(p^s)^2\right] = \text{constant} \tag{6}$$

When the expression for E and p^s are substituted into Eq. (6), one finds that

$$P^{\varrho}P_{\varrho} = \frac{m^2}{c^2} \tag{7}$$

If the rest-mass is zero, e.g., in the case of a photon, we obtain the result that

$$\sum_{s=1}^{3}(p^s)^2 = \frac{E^2}{c^2} \tag{8}$$

In words : the magnitude of the linear momentum p_n is $p = E/c$. On using the Planck relation that $E = h\nu$ (ν is the frequency of the photon), we obtain

$$p = \frac{h\nu}{c} \tag{9}$$

To illustrate the application to the Compton effect, let us assume an electron, of rest-mass m, is initially at rest and struck by a photon of frequency ν.

The scattered photon has the frequency ν' and forms an angle θ with the direction of the incident photon. The electron acquires the velocity v in a direction making an angle ϕ with the direction of the incident photon. The conservation law for the energy states that

$$h\nu = h\nu' + \frac{mc^2}{\sqrt{1 - v^2/c^2}} \tag{10}$$

The conservation law for the momentum states that

$$\frac{h\nu}{c} = \frac{h\nu'}{c} \cos\theta + \frac{mv}{\sqrt{1 - v^2/c^2}} \cos\phi \tag{11}$$

and

$$0 = \frac{h\nu'}{c} \sin\theta - \frac{mv}{\sqrt{1 - v^2/c^2}} \sin\phi \tag{12}$$

By eliminating ϕ, we obtain

$$m(\nu - \nu') - \frac{h}{c^2}(1 - \cos\theta)\nu\nu' = 0 \tag{13}$$

On writing $1 - \cos\theta = 2\sin^2\theta/2$; $\nu = c/\lambda$; $\nu' = c/\lambda'$ we finally obtain

$$\lambda' - \lambda = \frac{2h}{mc} \sin^2\frac{\theta}{2} \tag{14}$$

where h/mc is usually called the Compton wavelength.

2.2. Dynamics of a free mass point. The dynamics of a free mass point of rest mass m follows from a variational principle :

$$I = \int_{t_1}^{t_2} L(x^s, \dot{x}^s)dt, \quad \left(\dot{x}^s = \frac{dx^s}{dt}\right) \tag{1}$$

$$\delta I = 0$$

The variation is to be performed only in the interior, the end points are kept fixed. The Lagrangian function L is given by

$$L = -mc^2\sqrt{1 - v^2/c^2} \tag{2}$$

$$v^2 = \left(\frac{dx^1}{dt}\right)^2 + \left(\frac{dx^2}{dt}\right)^2 + \left(\frac{dx^3}{dt}\right)^2$$

The corresponding Euler-Lagrange equations are

$$\frac{\partial L}{\partial x^s} - \frac{d}{dt}\left(\frac{\partial L}{\partial \dot{x}^s}\right) = 0 \tag{3}$$

The momenta are, as usual, defined by

$$p_s = \frac{\partial L}{\partial \dot{x}^s} = \frac{m\dot{x}^s}{\sqrt{1 - v^2/c^2}} \tag{4}$$

Equations (2.2) and (2.3) can be brought into the canonical form. We introduce the Hamiltonian funtion H, defined by

$$\left.\begin{aligned} H = -L + p_s\dot{x}^s = \frac{mc^2}{\sqrt{1 - u^2/c^2}} = mc^2 \sqrt{1 + \frac{p^2}{m^2c^2}} \\ (p^2 = p_1{}^2 + p_2{}^2 + p_3{}^2) \end{aligned}\right\} \tag{5}$$

The canonical equations are

$$\dot{x}^s = \frac{\partial H}{\partial p_s} = \frac{p_s/m}{\sqrt{1 + p^2/m^2}} \tag{6}$$

$$p_s = -\frac{\partial H}{\partial x^s} = 0 \tag{7}$$

2.3. Relativistic force. The force f_s acting on an accelerated mass point can be defined, just as in classical mechanics, as the time rate change of linear momentum :

$$\left.\begin{aligned} f_s = \frac{d}{dt}\left(\frac{m\dot{x}^s}{\sqrt{1 - v^2/c^2}}\right) = \left(1 - \frac{v^2}{c^2}\right)^{-3/2} m\left[\delta_{st}\left(1 - \frac{v^2}{c^2}\right) + \frac{\dot{x}^s\dot{x}^t}{c^2}\right]\ddot{x}^t \\ (v^2 = \dot{x}^2 + \dot{y}^2 + \dot{z}^2) \end{aligned}\right\} \tag{1}$$

This force is in general not parallel to the acceleration. It is parallel only when the acceleration is either parallel or perpendicular to the velocity. When it is parallel, Eq. (1) takes the form

$$f_s = \left(1 - \frac{v^2}{c^2}\right)^{-3/2} m\ddot{x}^s \tag{2}$$

If the acceleration is orthogonal to the velocity, Eq. (1) takes the form

$$f_s = \left(1 - \frac{v^2}{c^2}\right)^{-1/2} m\ddot{x}^s \tag{3}$$

The coefficients $(1 - v^2/c^2)^{-3/2}m$ and $(1 - v^2/c^2)^{-1/2}m$ are called the " longitudinal mass " and the " transversal mass " in the older literature.

2.4. Relativistic electrodynamics. We introduce the covariant tensor $\phi = (A_s, -c\phi)$,

$$A_s = \text{vector potential}, \quad \phi = \text{scalar potential}$$

the world current-vector $s^{\omega} = (I_s, \rho)$,

$$I_s = \text{current density}, \quad \rho = \text{charge density}$$

and the world force density $F^{\omega} = (k_s, -\lambda/c)$,

$$k_s = \text{ordinary force density}, \quad \lambda = \text{power density}$$

Comma means differentiation, e.g., $\phi_{\varrho,\sigma} = \partial\phi_{\varrho}/\partial x^{\sigma}$ and

$$\phi_{\varrho\sigma} \equiv \frac{\partial\phi_{\varrho}}{\partial x^{\sigma}} - \frac{\partial\phi_{\sigma}}{\partial x^{\varrho}} = \phi_{\varrho,\sigma} - \phi_{\sigma,\varrho} = -\phi_{\sigma\varrho}$$

$$\begin{aligned} \boldsymbol{E} &= (E_1, E_2, E_3) = \text{electric field strength} \\ \boldsymbol{D} &= (D_1, D_2, D_3) = \text{electric displacement vector} \\ \boldsymbol{H} &= (H_1, H_2, H_3) = \text{magnetic field strength} \\ \boldsymbol{B} &= (B_1, B_2, B_3) = \text{magnetic displacement vector} \end{aligned}$$

We finally introduce two antisymmetric tensors $\Phi_{\varrho\sigma}$ and $\Psi^{\varrho\sigma}$:

$$\begin{aligned} (\Phi_{12}, \Phi_{23}, \Phi_{31}) &= (-B_3, -B_1, -B_2) \\ (\Phi_{14}, \Phi_{24}, \Phi_{34}) &= (-cE_1, -cE_2, -cE_3) \\ (\Psi^{12}, \Psi^{23}, \Psi^{31}) &= (-c^4H_3, -c^4H_1, -c^4H_2) \\ (\Psi^{41}, \Psi^{42}, \Psi^{43}) &= (-c^3D_1, -c^3D_2, -c^3D_3) \end{aligned}$$

The fundamental equations of electrodynamics are

$$s^{\lambda}{}_{,\lambda} = 0 \quad \text{or} \quad \operatorname{div} \boldsymbol{I} + \frac{\partial\rho}{\partial t} = 0 \tag{1}$$

$$\phi^{\lambda}{}_{,\lambda} = 0 \quad \text{or} \quad \operatorname{div} \boldsymbol{A} + \frac{1}{c}\frac{\partial\phi}{\partial t} = 0 \tag{2}$$

$$\phi_{\lambda,\varrho} - \phi_{\varrho,\lambda} = -\Phi_{\lambda\varrho} \quad \text{or} \quad \boldsymbol{B} = \textbf{curl}\, \boldsymbol{A}; \qquad \boldsymbol{E} = -\textbf{grad}\, \phi - \frac{1}{c}\frac{\partial \boldsymbol{A}}{\partial t} \tag{3}$$

$$\Phi_{\lambda\varrho,\sigma} + \Phi_{\varrho\sigma,\lambda} + \Phi_{\sigma\varrho,\lambda} = 0 \quad \text{or} \quad \operatorname{div} \boldsymbol{B} = 0; \quad \textbf{curl}\, \boldsymbol{E} = -\frac{1}{c}\frac{\partial \boldsymbol{B}}{\partial t} \tag{4}$$

$$\Psi^{\varrho\lambda}{}_{,\lambda} = -4\pi c^3 s^{\varrho} \quad \text{or} \quad \textbf{curl}\, \boldsymbol{H} = \frac{4\pi \boldsymbol{I}}{c} + \frac{1}{c}\frac{\partial \boldsymbol{D}}{\partial t}; \quad \operatorname{div} \boldsymbol{D} = 4\pi\rho \tag{5}$$

$$F^{\varrho} = \frac{1}{c^4} \Phi^{\varrho\lambda} s_{\lambda} \quad \text{or} \quad \begin{cases} \boldsymbol{k} = \rho \boldsymbol{E} + \frac{1}{c} [\boldsymbol{I} \times \boldsymbol{B}] & (6) \\ \lambda = \boldsymbol{I} \cdot \boldsymbol{E} & (7) \end{cases}$$

In vacuum $\boldsymbol{E} = \boldsymbol{D}$ and $\boldsymbol{H} = \boldsymbol{B}$ and therefore $\Phi^{\varrho\lambda} = \Psi^{\varrho\lambda}$. In this case we can eliminate $\Phi_{\lambda\varrho}$ by combining Eq. (3) and Eq. (5) and utilizing (2) we obtain

$$-\Box \phi^{\varrho} = 4\pi s^{\varrho} \tag{8}$$

where $\Box$ is the wave operator or the " D'Alembertian "

$$\Box = \frac{\partial^2}{\partial x^2} + \frac{\partial^2}{\partial y^2} + \frac{\partial^2}{\partial z^2} - \frac{1}{c^2} \frac{\partial^2}{\partial t^2}$$

If we put

$$\phi^{\varrho} = Z^{\varrho\lambda}{}_{,\lambda} \quad (Z^{\varrho\lambda} = -Z^{\lambda\varrho})$$

$$s^{\varrho} = Q^{\varrho\lambda}{}_{,\lambda} \quad (Q^{\varrho\lambda} = -Q^{\lambda\varrho})$$

we obtain

$$4\pi Q^{\varrho\lambda} = -\Box Z^{\varrho\lambda} \tag{9}$$

where $Z^{\varrho\lambda}$ corresponds to the Hertz vector in electrodynamics.

2.5. Gauge invariance. The Maxwell equations (1), (4) and (5) of the preceding paragraph remain unaltered if the world vector ϕ_{ϱ} is changed into a new world vector $\bar{\phi}_{\varrho}$ by adding to it an arbitrary four-dimensional gradient field $\psi_{,\varrho}$:

$$\bar{\phi}_{\varrho} = \phi_{\varrho} + \psi_{,\varrho} \tag{1}$$

Such a transformation is called gauge transformation. The condition (2.4-2) is not gauge-invariant. But since ψ is arbitrary and does not affect the Maxwell equations, we are permitted to make this choice. The advantage of having the " Lorentz gauge condition " (2.4-2) satisfied is that we can solve for the highest time derivatives of the potentials and thus obtain a system of differential equations of the Cauchy-Kowalewski type. In such a system the initial conditions on a function guarantee its unique continuation into the future (and its past).

If one works with the field strengths $\boldsymbol{E}$ and $\boldsymbol{H}$ themselves (which are the only physically observable quantities), rather than with the potentials, then Maxwell's equations are automatically of the Cauchy-Kowalewski type with respect to the time derivatives, regardless of any gauge condition. We introduce potentials primarily for mathematical convenience.

2.6. Transformation laws for the field strengths

$$\left.\begin{aligned}
\overset{*}{E}_1 &= E_1 & \overset{*}{B}_1 &= B_1 \\
\overset{*}{E}_2 &= \frac{1}{\sqrt{1-\beta^2}}(E_2 - \beta B_3) & \overset{*}{B}_2 &= \frac{1}{\sqrt{1-\beta^2}}(B_2 + \beta E_3) \\
\overset{*}{E}_3 &= \frac{1}{\sqrt{1-\beta^2}}(E_3 + \beta B_2) & \overset{*}{B}_3 &= \frac{1}{\sqrt{1-\beta^2}}(B_3 - \beta E_2) \\
\overset{*}{D}_1 &= D_1 & \overset{*}{H}_1 &= H_1 \\
\overset{*}{D}_2 &= \frac{1}{\sqrt{1-\beta^2}}(D_2 - \beta H_3) & \overset{*}{H}_2 &= \frac{1}{\sqrt{1-\beta^2}}(H_2 + \beta D_3) \\
\overset{*}{D}_3 &= \frac{1}{\sqrt{1-\beta^2}}(D_3 + \beta H_2) & \overset{*}{H}_3 &= \frac{1}{\sqrt{1-\beta^2}}(H_3 - \beta D_2)
\end{aligned}\right\} \quad (1)$$

Here $\beta = v/c$, where v is the velocity of $\overset{*}{\Sigma}$ with respect to Σ and $v = (v,0,0)$. The total charge is an invariant. If the world current vector s^ϱ is purely convective, and if the charge has the velocity u in the system Σ and $\overset{*}{u}$ in Σ, then

$$\left.\begin{aligned}
\overset{*}{\rho}\overset{*}{u}_1 &= \rho\,\frac{u_1 - v}{\sqrt{1-\beta^2}} \\
\overset{*}{\rho}\overset{*}{u}_2 &= \rho u_2 \\
\overset{*}{\rho}\overset{*}{u}_3 &= \rho u_3 \\
\overset{*}{\rho} &= \rho\,\frac{1 - vu_1/c^2}{\sqrt{1-\beta^2}}
\end{aligned}\right\} \quad (2)$$

If the charge is at rest in Σ, i.e., if $u_1 = u_2 = u_3 = 0$, then

$$\overset{*}{\rho} = \frac{\rho}{\sqrt{1-\beta^2}}$$

2.7. Electrodynamics in moving, isotropic ponderable media (Minkowski's equation). The relations between $\Phi^{\varrho\lambda}$ and $\Psi^{\varrho\lambda}$ must be of such a nature that, in a reference system at rest with respect to the medium, the relations must go over into

$$\boldsymbol{D} = \epsilon \boldsymbol{E} \quad (1)$$

$$\boldsymbol{B} = \mu \boldsymbol{H} \quad (2)$$

$$\boldsymbol{I}_c = \sigma \boldsymbol{E} \quad (3)$$

ϵ = dielectric constant, μ = magnetic permeability, σ = electric conductivity, $\boldsymbol{I}_c$, the "metallic" current density, is obtained from the total current density s^ϱ through subtraction of the convective current density $U^\varrho \cdot (s^\lambda U_\lambda)$, where

$$U^\varrho = \left(\frac{u^s}{c\sqrt{1-u^2/c^2}}, \frac{1}{c\sqrt{1-u^2/c^2}}\right)$$

We shall denote the corresponding world vector of $\boldsymbol{I}_c$ by l^ϱ. Therefore

$$l^\varrho = s^\varrho - U^\varrho \cdot (s^\lambda U_\lambda) \tag{3}$$

becomes

$$\boldsymbol{l} = \sigma \boldsymbol{E} \tag{4}$$

We introduce two new world vectors

$$e^\varrho = \Phi^{\varrho\lambda} U_\lambda \quad \text{and} \quad d^\varrho = \Psi^{\varrho\lambda} U_\lambda$$

Then

$$d^\varrho = \epsilon \varepsilon^\varrho \tag{5}$$

is an invariant relation which reduces to $\boldsymbol{D} = \epsilon \boldsymbol{E}$ in a system at rest with respect to the medium. We also introduce two antisymmetric tensors

$$b^{\varrho\lambda\tau} = \Phi^{\varrho\lambda} U^\tau + \Phi^{\lambda\tau} U^\varrho + \Phi^{\tau\varrho} U^\lambda$$

and

$$h^{\varrho\lambda\tau} = \Psi^{\varrho\lambda} U^\tau + \Psi^{\lambda\tau} U^\varrho + \Psi^{\tau\varrho} U^\lambda$$

Then

$$b^{\varrho\tau\lambda} = \mu h^{\varrho\tau\lambda} \tag{6}$$

is another invariant relation, which reduces to $\boldsymbol{B} = \mu \boldsymbol{H}$ in a system with respect to the medium. We introduce certain abbreviations :

$$\left.\begin{aligned} \boldsymbol{E}' &\equiv \boldsymbol{E} + \frac{1}{c}(\boldsymbol{u} \times \boldsymbol{B}) \\ \boldsymbol{D}' &\equiv \boldsymbol{D} + \frac{1}{c}(\boldsymbol{u} \times \boldsymbol{H}) \end{aligned}\right\} \text{(electromotive force)}$$

$$\left.\begin{aligned} \boldsymbol{H}' &\equiv \boldsymbol{H} - \frac{1}{c}(\boldsymbol{u} \times \boldsymbol{D}) \\ \boldsymbol{B}' &\equiv \boldsymbol{B} - \frac{1}{c}(\boldsymbol{u} \times \boldsymbol{E}) \end{aligned}\right\} \text{(magnetomotive force)}$$

Then the Minkowski equations read

$$D' = \epsilon E' \tag{7}$$

$$B' = \mu H' \tag{8}$$

The generalization of Ohm's law is

$$l^\varrho = \sigma \varepsilon^\varrho \tag{9}$$

In vectorial form this means

$$\boldsymbol{I}+\frac{\boldsymbol{u}[(\boldsymbol{u}\cdot\boldsymbol{I})-\rho c^2]}{c^2-u^2}=\frac{\sigma \boldsymbol{E}'}{\sqrt{1-u^2/c^2}} \tag{10}$$

If the current is purely convective, then $\boldsymbol{I}=\rho\boldsymbol{u}$ and $s^\varrho=U^\varrho\cdot(s^\lambda U_\lambda)$, and the Lorentz-force expression becomes

$$k^\varrho=\frac{\rho_0}{c^4}\,\Phi^{\varrho\lambda}U_\lambda \tag{11}$$

where ρ_0 is the rest charge density.

2.8. Field of a uniformly moving point charge in empty space. Force between point charges moving with the same constant velocity. We shall assume a point charge ε moving with the constant speed v in the positive x direction. In a reference system $\overset{*}{\Sigma}$, chosen so that the charge is at rest with respect to it, and permanently at its origin, we have

$$\overset{*}{D}_s=\overset{*}{E}_s=\varepsilon\,\frac{\overset{*}{x}{}^s}{\overset{*}{r}{}^3};\qquad \overset{*}{B}_s=\overset{*}{H}_s=0 \tag{1}$$

Using the transformation equations of F, we obtain

$$\left.\begin{aligned}
E_1&=\overset{*}{E}_1, & H_1&=0\\
E_2&=\frac{\overset{*}{E}_2}{\sqrt{1-\beta^2}}, & H_2&=-\frac{\beta}{\sqrt{1-\beta^2}}\overset{*}{E}_3\\
E_3&=\frac{\overset{*}{E}_3}{\sqrt{1-\beta^2}}, & H_3&=\frac{\beta}{\sqrt{1-\beta^2}}\overset{*}{E}
\end{aligned}\right\} \tag{2}$$

Since $\overset{*}{r}{}^2=\overset{*}{x}{}^2+\overset{*}{y}{}^2+\overset{*}{z}{}^2$ and $\overset{*}{x}=\dfrac{x-vt}{\sqrt{1-\beta^2}};\quad \overset{*}{y}=y;\quad \overset{*}{z}=z$

we obtain

$$\left.\begin{aligned}
E_1&=\frac{\varepsilon}{\sqrt{1-\beta^2}}\cdot\frac{x-vt}{R^3}, & H_1&=0\\
E_2&=\frac{\varepsilon}{\sqrt{1-\beta^2}}\cdot\frac{y}{R^3}, & H_2&=-\frac{\varepsilon\beta}{\sqrt{1-\beta^2}}\cdot\frac{z}{R^3}\\
E_3&=\frac{\varepsilon}{\sqrt{1-\beta^2}}\cdot\frac{z}{R^3}, & H_3&=\frac{\varepsilon\beta}{\sqrt{1-\beta^2}}\cdot\frac{y}{R^3}\\
R^2&=\frac{(x-vt)^2}{1-\beta^2}+y^2+z^2
\end{aligned}\right\} \tag{3}$$

These expressions show that the electromagnetic field is carried rigidly along by the charge (" convective field "). For simplicity, consider the field at the time zero, when the charge passes through the origin. Then

$$R^2 = \frac{x^2}{1-\beta^2} + y^2 + z^2$$

and

$$\left.\begin{aligned} E_1 &= \frac{\varepsilon}{\sqrt{1-\beta^2}} \cdot \frac{x}{R^3}, & H_1 &= 0 \\ E_2 &= \frac{\varepsilon}{\sqrt{1-\beta^2}} \cdot \frac{y}{R^3}, & H_2 &= -\frac{\varepsilon\beta}{\sqrt{1-\beta^2}} \cdot \frac{z}{R^3} \\ E_3 &= \frac{\varepsilon}{\sqrt{1-\beta^2}} \cdot \frac{z}{R^3}, & H_3 &= \frac{\varepsilon\beta}{\sqrt{1-\beta^2}} \cdot \frac{y}{R^3} \end{aligned}\right\} \tag{4}$$

The magnetic field lies entirely in the " equatorial plane," i.e., the plane orthogonal to the direction of motion. Let us compute the electric field strength at a distance s from the origin. If the point of observation lies on the x axis, $R = s/\sqrt{1-\beta^2}$, we obtain

$$E_1 = \frac{\varepsilon(1-\beta^2)}{s^2}; \quad E_2 = E_3 = 0 \tag{5}$$

If the point lies on the y axis at a distance S from the origin, we obtain $R = S$ and

$$E_2 = \frac{\varepsilon}{s^2\sqrt{1-\beta^2}}; \quad E_1 = E_3 = 0 \tag{6}$$

As the speed increases to the speed of light, in the first case $E_1 = E_2 = E_3 = 0$ and in the second case $E_2 = \infty$; $E_1 = E_3 = 0$. At high speeds the electric field tends more and more to crowd in the equatorial plane. The energy density becomes zero outside and infinite inside the equatorial plane in such a manner that the total energy of the field becomes infinite, and therefore also the electromagnetic mass of the charge becomes infinite. The Lorentz force $\boldsymbol{F}$ exerted on a second charge ε' which moves with the same velocity $\boldsymbol{u}$, is

$$\boldsymbol{F} = \varepsilon' \left\{ E + \frac{1}{c}[\boldsymbol{u} \times \boldsymbol{H}] \right\} \tag{7}$$

and can be written

$$\boldsymbol{F} = \mathbf{grad}\, \psi,$$

where

$$\psi = (1-\beta^2)\frac{\varepsilon}{R} \tag{8}$$

Here ψ is called the " convective potential."

The surfaces of constant convective potential are

$$R^2 = x^2 + (1 - \beta^2)(y^2 + z^2) = \text{constant} \tag{9}$$

They are ellipsoids of revolution with the charge at their center. The direction of motion is the axis of revolution and the principal axis is smaller than the two minor axes. These ellipsoids are called the " Heaviside ellipsoids."

If the charge ε' lies on the x axis at a distance s from e, the magnitude of the force exerted on it, is

$$F = \frac{\varepsilon\varepsilon'}{s^2}(1 - \beta^2) \tag{10}$$

If the charge is located on the y axis at a distance s from the charge e, the force is

$$F = \frac{\varepsilon\varepsilon'}{s^2}\sqrt{1 - \beta^2} \tag{11}$$

In either case the force between the two charges tends to zero as their velocity approaches the velocity of light.

2.9. The stress energy tensor and its relation to the conservation laws. We introduce the tensor $M^{\varrho\sigma}$, defined by

$$M^{\varrho\sigma} = \frac{1}{4\pi c^\sigma}\left[\frac{\eta^{\varrho\sigma}}{4}\Phi_{\lambda\mu}\Phi^{\lambda\mu} - \frac{1}{2}(\Phi^{\varrho\lambda}\Psi^{\cdot\sigma\mu} + \Phi^{\sigma\lambda}\Psi^{\cdot\varrho\mu})\eta_{\lambda\mu}\right] \tag{1}$$

$$\Phi_{\lambda\mu}\Psi^{\cdot\lambda\mu} = 2c^4(\boldsymbol{B}\cdot\boldsymbol{H} - \boldsymbol{E}\cdot\boldsymbol{D}) \tag{2}$$

$$M^{rs} = \frac{1}{4\pi}\left[\frac{1}{2}\delta_{rs}(\boldsymbol{B}\cdot\boldsymbol{H} + \boldsymbol{D}\cdot\boldsymbol{E}) - B_r H_s - D_r E_s\right] \tag{3}$$

$$M^{14} = \frac{1}{8\pi c}(\boldsymbol{D}\times\boldsymbol{B} + \boldsymbol{E}\times\boldsymbol{H})_x \tag{4}$$

$$M^{44} = \frac{1}{8\pi c^2}(\boldsymbol{E}\cdot\boldsymbol{D} + \boldsymbol{H}\cdot\boldsymbol{B}) \tag{5}$$

The M^{rs} are the components of the Maxwell stress tensor; c^2M^{4s} are the components of the Poynting vector; c^2M^{44} is the energy density of the electromagnetic field. The energy stress tensor obeys the four conservation laws

$$M^{\varrho\lambda}{}_{,\lambda} = 0 \tag{6}$$

If in addition to the electrodynamic stresses $M^{\varrho\lambda}$ any other stresses $P^{\varrho\lambda}$ of nonelectrical origin are present, the conservation laws take on the form

$$T^{\varrho\lambda}{}_{,\lambda} = 0 \tag{7}$$

where $T^{\varrho\lambda} \equiv P^{\varrho\lambda} + M^{\varrho\lambda} =$ " total stress energy tensor."

As a special example assume matter of constant rest density σ moving with uniform velocity v along the x axis. Assume furthermore that the mechanical stresses are given by the tensor t^{rs}. Then

$$\left.\begin{aligned}
&P'' = \frac{t'' + \sigma v^2}{1 - v^2/c^2}; \quad P^{22} = t^{22}; \quad P^{33} = t^{33}; \quad P^{44} = \frac{\sigma + v^2 t''/c^4}{1 - v^2/c^2} \\
&P^{12} = \frac{t^{12}}{\sqrt{1 - v^2/c^2}}; \quad P^{13} = \frac{t^{13}}{\sqrt{1 - v^2/c^2}}; \quad P^{14} = -\frac{\sigma v + v t''/c^2}{1 - v^2/c^2} \\
&P^{23} = t^{23}; \quad P^{24} = -\frac{v}{c^2} \frac{t^{12}}{1 - v^2/c^2}; \quad P^{34} = -\frac{v}{c^2} \frac{t^{13}}{1 - v^2/c^2}
\end{aligned}\right\} \tag{8}$$

In the case of a perfect fluid of pressure p, we have

$$\left.\begin{aligned}
&t^{rs} = p\delta^{rs}; \quad p^{12} = p^{13} = p^{24} = p^{34} = p^{23} = 0 \\
&p^{11} = \frac{p + \sigma v^2}{1 - v^2/c^2}; \quad p^{22} = p^{33} = p; \quad p^{44} = \frac{\sigma + v^2 p/c^4}{1 - v^2/c^2} \\
&p^{14} = -\frac{\rho v + v p/c^2}{1 - v^2/c^2}
\end{aligned}\right\} \tag{9}$$

3. Miscellaneous Applications

3.1. The ponderomotive equation. The Lorentz-force on a particle of rest-mass m and charge ε can be derived as the Euler-Lagrange equation of the variational principle

$$I = \int_{P_1}^{P_2} L\, dt = \int_{P_1}^{P_2} \left\{ -mc^2 \sqrt{1 - \frac{u^2}{c^2}} - \varepsilon\phi + \frac{\varepsilon}{c} u^s A_s \right\} dt \quad (\delta I = 0) \tag{1}$$

In this variation the end points are kept fixed. The Euler-Lagrange equations belonging to Eq. (1) are

$$\frac{d}{dt}\left(\frac{mu^s}{\sqrt{1 - u^2/c^2}}\right) = \varepsilon E_s + \frac{\varepsilon}{c} u^r H_{sr} \qquad H_{12} = -H_{21} = H_3 \text{ etc.} \tag{2}$$

The " relativistic momenta " p_s are defined by

$$p_s = \frac{\partial L}{\partial u^s} = \frac{mu^s}{\sqrt{1 - u^2/c^2}} + \frac{\varepsilon}{c} A_s \tag{3}$$

The velocities can be expressed in terms of the momenta :

$$u^s = \frac{1}{m}\left(p_s - \frac{\varepsilon}{c} A_s\right)\left[1 + \frac{(p_k - \varepsilon A_k/c)^2}{m^2c^2}\right]^{-1/2} \tag{4}$$

Therefore the Lagrangian L can be written in terms of the momenta and is given by

$$L = \left[1 + \frac{(p_k - \varepsilon A_k/c)^2}{m^2c^2}\right]^{-1/2} \left[- mc^2 + \frac{\varepsilon A_s}{c} \cdot \frac{p_s - (\varepsilon A_s/c)}{m}\right] - \varepsilon\phi \quad (5)$$

The Hamiltonian function H, defined by $H = p_s u^s - L$ is given by

$$H = mc^2 \left[1 + \frac{(p_k - \varepsilon A_k/c)^2}{m^2c^2}\right]^{1/2} + \varepsilon\phi \quad (6)$$

The canonical equations of motion are

$$\dot{u}^s = \frac{\partial H}{\partial p_s} = \frac{1}{m}\left[1 + \frac{(p_k - \varepsilon A_k/c)^2}{m^2c^2}\right]^{-1/2} \left(p_s - \frac{\varepsilon}{c} A_s\right) \quad (7)$$

$$\dot{p}_s = -\frac{\partial H}{\partial x^s} = \frac{\varepsilon}{mc}\left[1 + \frac{(p_k - \varepsilon A_k/c)^2}{m^2c^2}\right]^{-1/2} \left(p_r - \frac{\varepsilon}{c} A_r\right) A_{r,s} - \varepsilon\phi_{,s} \quad (8)$$

Equations (8) are equivalent to Eq. (2).

3.2. Application to electron optics. We consider the motion of a charged particle in a combined stationary electric and magnetic field.

$$\boldsymbol{E} = -\,\mathbf{grad}\,\phi; \quad \boldsymbol{H} = \mathbf{curl}\,\boldsymbol{A} \quad (1)$$

The Lagrangian is

$$L = mc^2 \left(1 - \sqrt{1 - \frac{u^2}{c^2}}\right) - \varepsilon\phi + \frac{\varepsilon}{c}(\boldsymbol{u} \cdot \boldsymbol{A}) \quad (2)$$

The variational principle $\delta \int_{P_1}^{P_2} \leq dt = 0$ yields

$$\frac{d}{dt}\left(\frac{mu}{\sqrt{1 - u^2/c^2}}\right) = -\,\varepsilon\,\mathbf{grad}\,\phi + \frac{\varepsilon}{c}(\boldsymbol{u} \times \mathbf{curl}\,\boldsymbol{A}) \quad (3)$$

The total rate of change of the potential energy ϕ of the particle along its path is given by

$$\frac{d\phi}{dt} = \frac{\partial\phi}{\partial t} + \boldsymbol{u} \cdot \mathbf{grad}\,\phi \quad (4)$$

Since we assume a stationary electromagnetic field,

$$\frac{\partial\phi}{\partial t} = 0 \quad (5)$$

and thus

$$\boldsymbol{u} \cdot \mathbf{grad}\,\phi = \frac{d\phi}{dt} \quad (6)$$

Multiplying both sides of Eq. (3) scalarly by $\boldsymbol{u}$, we obtain

$$mc^2 \frac{d}{dt}\left(\frac{1}{\sqrt{1 - u^2/c^2}}\right) = -\varepsilon \frac{d\phi}{dt} \tag{7}$$

or

$$\frac{d}{dt}\left(\frac{mc^2}{\sqrt{1 - u^2/c^2}} + \varepsilon\phi\right) = 0 \tag{8}$$

Or introducing the relativistic kinetic energy

$$I = \frac{mc^2}{\sqrt{1 - u^2/c^2}} - mc^2$$

Eq. (8) can also be written

$$\frac{d}{dt}\left(\frac{mc^2}{\sqrt{1 - u^2/c^2}} - mc^2 + \varepsilon\phi\right) = 0 \tag{9}$$

And thus one obtains one integral of the motion, the energy E,

$$\frac{mc^2}{\sqrt{1 - u^2/c^2}} - mc^2 + \varepsilon\phi = E \tag{10}$$

or

$$\frac{mc^2}{\sqrt{1 - u^2/c^2}} + \varepsilon\phi = E + mc^2 \tag{11}$$

This equation enables us to rewrite the Lagrangian in the form

$$L = (E - \varepsilon\phi)\left(1 + \sqrt{1 - \frac{u^2}{c^2}}\right) + \frac{\varepsilon}{c}(\boldsymbol{u} \cdot \boldsymbol{A}) - E \tag{12}$$

Since $u = ds/dt$, we obtain from Eq. (10)

$$\frac{ds}{dt} = c\,\frac{\sqrt{(E + 2mc^2 - \varepsilon\phi)(E - \varepsilon\phi)}}{E + mc^2 - \varepsilon\phi} \tag{13}$$

and

$$L\,dt = \left[\frac{1}{c}\sqrt{(\mathrm{E} - \varepsilon\phi)(E + 2mc^2 - \varepsilon\phi)} + \frac{\varepsilon}{c}(\boldsymbol{s} \cdot \boldsymbol{A})\right] ds - E\,dt \tag{14}$$

where $\boldsymbol{s}$ is a unit vector in the direction of the tangent of the trajectory of the particle : $\boldsymbol{u}\,dt = \boldsymbol{s}\,ds$. The variational principle can be reformulated

$$\delta \int_{P_1}^{P_2} \left[\frac{1}{c}\sqrt{(E - \varepsilon\phi)(E + 2mc^2 - \varepsilon\phi)} + \frac{\varepsilon}{c}(\boldsymbol{s} \cdot \boldsymbol{A})\right] ds = 0 \tag{15}$$

since E is a constant and t is not varied, and therefore

$$\delta \int_{P_1}^{P_2} E\,dt = 0.$$

If we call the dimensionless quantity μ

$$\mu = \frac{1}{mc^2}\,[\sqrt{(E - \varepsilon\phi)\,(E + 2mc^2 - \varepsilon\phi)} + \varepsilon(\boldsymbol{s}\cdot\boldsymbol{A})] \tag{16}$$

the variational principle is

$$\delta \int_{P_1}^{P_2} \mu\, ds = 0 \tag{17}$$

This is identical with Fermat's principle in geometrical optics. μ is the " index of refraction." It depends through ϕ and A on the position (x,y,z) and through $\boldsymbol{s}$ also on the direction. The index of refraction is thus seen to be both inhomogeneous and unisotropic. Equation (16) is the fundamental equation of electron optics.

3.3. Sommerfeld's theory of the hydrogen fine structure. We shall assume that an electron of rest-mass m and charge ε moves in the field of a proton which is assumed at rest. Let r be the distance between electron and proton. The energy E is given by

$$mc^2\left(\frac{1}{\sqrt{1 - u^2/c^2}} - 1\right) - \frac{\varepsilon^2}{r} = E \tag{1}$$

The angular momentum

$$I_\theta = \frac{mr^2\dot{\theta}}{\sqrt{1 - u^2/c^2}}$$

is also a constant of the motion. According to Sommerfeld's quantization rule

$$\oint I_\theta d\theta = n_\theta h \tag{2}$$

The integration must be carried out over a complete cycle of the motion, $n_\theta = 1, 2, 3, \ldots$ ($n_\theta = 0$ would imply that the electron penetrates through the nucleus.) Therefore

$$\frac{mr^2\dot{\theta}}{\sqrt{1 - u^2/c^2}}\cdot 2\pi = n_\theta \cdot h \tag{3}$$

or

$$mr^2\dot{\theta} = n_\theta \cdot \hbar\sqrt{1 - u^2/c^2} \qquad \left(\hbar = \frac{h}{2\pi}\right) \tag{4}$$

The radial momentum p_r is given by

$$p_r = \frac{m\dot{r}}{\sqrt{1 - u^2/c^2}} \tag{5}$$

It must again obey the same quantization rule

$$\oint p_r dr = n_r h \qquad (n_r = 0,1,2,\ldots) \tag{6}$$

If Eq. (4) is substituted into Eq. (6) and the integration is carried out, we obtain

$$E = mc^2\left[1 - \frac{1}{\sqrt{1 + \alpha^2/(n_r + \sqrt{n_\theta^2 - \alpha^2})}}\right] \tag{7}$$

where $\alpha = \varepsilon^2/\hbar c$ is the fine-structure constant. If E is expanded in a power series of α, we obtain

$$E = \frac{m\varepsilon^4}{2\hbar^2(n_r + n_\theta)^2}\left[1 + \frac{\alpha^2}{(n_r + n_\theta)^2}\left(\frac{n_r}{n_\theta} + \frac{1}{4}\right) + \ldots\right] \tag{8}$$

Usually $n_r + n_\theta = n$ is called the principal or orbital quantum number, and $n_\theta = k$ the azimuthal quantum number. Hence

$$E = \frac{m\varepsilon^4}{2\hbar^2 n^2}\left[1 + \frac{\alpha^2}{n^2}\left(\frac{n}{k} - \frac{3}{4}\right)\right] \tag{9}$$

Thus the energy depends not only on n, as in the classical theory, but also on k. If the speed of light were infinite, then $\alpha = 0$, and E would depend on n only.

4. Spinor Calculus

4.1. Algebraic properties. The tensor formalism does not include all the objects that form relations that are invariant under Lorentz transformations. Besides the world tensors there exist " spinors " whose transformation group is also Lorentz-covariant and whose representation admits an even larger possibility than that of the tensors. In that sense the spinors are more fundamental than the tensors. In order to facilitate the reading of the literature * we shall change slightly our previous notation. The coordinates (x,y,z,ct) will be denoted by (x^1,x^2,x^3,x^4) and the metric tensor will be assumed

$$\eta^{11} = \eta^{22} = \eta^{33} = 1; \quad \eta^{44} = -1$$

$$\eta_{11} = \eta_{22} = \eta_{33} = 1; \quad \eta_{44} = -1$$

* See especially the paper, " Application of Spinor Analysis to the Maxwell and Dirac Equations," by Laporte, O. and Uhlenbeck, G. E., *Phys. Rev.*, **37**, 1380 (1931). The following discussion follows this paper closely and the reader will find further discussion and applications in it.

We shall call any two-dimensional vector $g = (g_1, g_2)$ a spinor of rank one. Its components obey the following linear transformation law

$$\left.\begin{aligned} \overset{*}{g}_1 &= \alpha_{11} g_1 + \alpha_{12} g_2 \\ \overset{*}{g}_2 &= \alpha_{21} g_1 + \alpha_{22} g_2 \end{aligned}\right\} \tag{1}$$

and where the determinant of the transformation coefficients has the value unity

$$\begin{vmatrix} \alpha_{11} & \alpha_{12} \\ \alpha_{21} & \alpha_{22} \end{vmatrix} = 1 \tag{2}$$

the spinor g will also be denoted by $g_k (k = 1, 2)$. Spinor indices will always be denoted by lower-case italic letters and always assume the values 1 and 2 only. The coefficients $\alpha_{rs} (r = 1,2; s = 1,2)$ can be real or complex numbers.

We shall also define a spinor $f = (f_{\dot{1}}, f_{\dot{2}})$ with dotted indices, which obeys the transformation law

$$\left.\begin{aligned} \overset{*}{f}_{\dot{1}} &= \bar{\alpha}_{11} f_{\dot{1}} + \bar{\alpha}_{12} f_{\dot{2}} \\ \overset{*}{f}_{\dot{2}} &= \bar{\alpha}_{21} f_{\dot{1}} + \bar{\alpha}_{22} f_{\dot{2}} \end{aligned}\right\} \tag{3}$$

This spinor will also be denoted by $f_{\dot{k}} (\dot{k} = 1,2)$. A bar will always denote the conjugate complex.

Spinors of higher ranks are quantities that transform like products of spinors of first rank, e.g., the spinor $a_{kl} (k,l = 1,2)$ shall transform like $a_k b_l$, or the "mixed" spinor $a_{\dot{k}l}$ shall transform like $a_{\dot{k}} b_l$. We raise or lower spin indices in the usual fashion by introducing a metric spinor ϵ_{kl} of second rank, symmetric in its indices, such that

$$\left.\begin{aligned} a^k &= \epsilon^{kl} a_l \\ a_k &= \epsilon_{kl} a^l \end{aligned}\right\} \tag{4}$$

$$\left.\begin{aligned} \epsilon_{kl} = \epsilon_{lk} = \epsilon_{\dot{k}\dot{l}} = \epsilon_{\dot{l}\dot{k}} &= \begin{pmatrix} 0 & -1 \\ 1 & 0 \end{pmatrix} \\ \epsilon^{kl} = \epsilon^{lk} = \epsilon^{\dot{k}\dot{l}} = \epsilon^{\dot{l}\dot{k}} &= \begin{pmatrix} 0 & 1 \\ -1 & 0 \end{pmatrix} \end{aligned}\right\} \tag{5}$$

$$\epsilon^{kl} \epsilon_{lm} = \delta^k{}_m \tag{6}$$

Summations will be performed only over undotted or dotted indices, but not over mixed indices.

Thus e.g., $$a^l b_l = a^1 b_1 + a^2 b_2$$

and $$a^{\dot{l}} b_{\dot{l}} = a^{\dot{1}} b_{\dot{1}} + a^{\dot{2}} b_{\dot{2}}$$

but no summation for $$a^l b_{\dot{l}}$$

From the above definitions follow the fundamental relations

$$\left.\begin{aligned} a^1 &= a_2; \qquad b^{\dot{1}} = b_{\dot{2}} \\ a^2 &= -a_1; \quad b^{\dot{2}} = -b_{\dot{1}} \end{aligned}\right\} \tag{7}$$

This ensures that $a_k b^k$ and $a_{\dot{k}} b^{\dot{k}}$ are invariants. From the above definitions,

$$a_l b^l = -a^l b_l \tag{8}$$

Also, the absolute value of any spinor of odd rank is zero.

$$a_l a^l = 0 \quad \text{or} \quad a_{lmn} a^{lmn} = 0 \tag{9}$$

$$a^l b_l c_m + a_l b_m c^l + a_m b^l c_l = 0 \tag{10}$$

All these rules hold of course also for dotted indices. The positions of dotted and undotted indices may be interchanged without changing the spinor, e.g.,

$$a_{\dot{r}st} = a_{s\dot{r}t} = a_{st\dot{r}} \tag{11}$$

However, the interchange of two dotted or two undotted indices will in general change the spinor unless it possesses certain additional symmetry properties. To obtain the complex conjugate of any spinor equation replace all dotted indices by dotted ones and vice versa.

4.2. Connection between spinors and world tensors. To each contravariant world tensor A^ϱ a mixed spinor $a_{\dot{r}s}$ can be uniquely associated, and vice versa. This permits us to rewrite each tensor equation as a spinor equation and vice versa. The relations are the following :

$$\left.\begin{aligned} A^1 &= A_1 = \frac{1}{2}(a_{\dot{2}1} + a_{\dot{1}2}) \\ A^2 &= A_2 = \frac{1}{2i}(a_{\dot{2}1} - a_{\dot{1}2}) \\ A^3 &= A_3 = \frac{1}{2}(a_{\dot{1}1} - a_{\dot{2}2}) \\ A^4 &= -A_4 = \frac{1}{2}(a_{\dot{1}1} + a_{\dot{2}2}) \end{aligned}\right\} \tag{1}$$

Conversely, we can also express the spinor components in terms of the vector components

$$\left.\begin{aligned} a_{\dot{2}1} &= -a^{\dot{1}2} = A^1 + iA^2 = A_1 + iA_2 \\ a_{\dot{1}2} &= -a^{\dot{2}1} = A^1 - iA^2 = A_1 - iA_2 \\ a_{\dot{1}1} &= +a^{\dot{2}2} = A^3 + A^4 = A_3 - A_4 \\ -a_{\dot{2}2} &= -a^{\dot{1}1} = A^3 - A^4 = A_3 + A_4 \end{aligned}\right\} \quad (2)$$

$$A_\varrho A^\varrho = -\frac{1}{2} a_{\dot{r}t} a^{\dot{r}t} \quad (3)$$

The above scheme also permits to introduce spinor differential operators

$$\left.\begin{aligned} \partial_1^{\dot{1}} &= \partial_{\dot{2}1} = \frac{\partial}{\partial x^1} + i\frac{\partial}{\partial x^2} \\ \partial_2^{\dot{2}} &= \partial_{\dot{1}2} = \frac{\partial}{\partial x^1} - i\frac{\partial}{\partial x^2} \\ -\partial_1^{\dot{2}} &= \partial_{\dot{1}1} = \frac{\partial}{\partial x^3} - \frac{\partial}{\partial x^4} \\ -\partial_2^{\dot{1}} &= -\partial_{\dot{2}2} = \frac{\partial}{\partial x^3} + \frac{\partial}{\partial x^4} \end{aligned}\right\} \quad (4)$$

By means of the relations (4) all the usual vector differential operators that occur in vector analysis can be translated into equivalent spinor relations, e.g., let $\phi_{\dot{r}s}$ be the spinor that corresponds to the world vector ϕ^ϱ; then div $\mathbf{\Phi} \equiv \Phi^\varrho{}_{,\varrho}$ corresponds to $-\frac{1}{2}\,\partial_{\dot{r}s}\phi^{\dot{r}s}$, and if the ordinary scalar S corresponds to the spinor scalar s, then

$$\Box S = \eta^{\varrho\sigma}\frac{\partial^2 S}{\partial x^\varrho \partial x^\sigma} = \nabla_1{}^2 S - \frac{1}{c^2}\frac{\partial_1{}^2 S}{\partial t^2}$$

corresponds to $$-\frac{1}{2}\,\partial_{\dot{r}t}\partial^{\dot{r}t} s$$

4.3. Transformation laws for mixed spinors of second rank. Relation between spinor and Lorentz transformations. Since mixed spinors of rank two are the fundamental " building stones " for world tensors, we shall write out their transformation laws explicity. The symbol $R(\alpha)$ shall denote the real part of α and $I(\alpha)$ shall denote the imaginary part of α. Thus if $\alpha = \beta + i\gamma$, where β and γ are real numbers,

$$R(\alpha) = \beta \quad \text{and} \quad I(\alpha) = \gamma$$

The absolute value of α will be denoted by $|\alpha| = +\sqrt{\beta^2 + \gamma^2}$.

Let $g_{\dot{r}s}$ be a mixed spinor of rank two, and $\overset{*}{g}_{\dot{r}s}$ the corresponding spinor in the new coordinate system. Then

$$\left.\begin{aligned}
\overset{*}{g} &= |\alpha_{11}|^2 g_{\dot{1}1} + \bar{\alpha}_{11}\alpha_{12} g_{\dot{1}2} + \bar{\alpha}_{12}\alpha_{11} g_{\dot{2}1} + |\alpha_{12}|^2 g_{\dot{2}2} \\
\overset{*}{g} &= \bar{\alpha}_{11}\alpha_{21} g_{\dot{1}1} + \bar{\alpha}_{11}\alpha_{22} g_{\dot{1}2} + \bar{\alpha}_{12}\alpha_{21} g_{\dot{2}1} + \bar{\alpha}_{12}\alpha_{22} g_{\dot{2}2} \\
\overset{*}{g} &= \bar{\alpha}_{21}\alpha_{11} g_{\dot{1}1} + \bar{\alpha}_{21}\alpha_{12} g_{\dot{1}2} + \bar{\alpha}_{22}\alpha_{11} g_{\dot{2}1} + \bar{\alpha}_{22}\alpha_{12} g_{\dot{2}2} \\
\overset{*}{g} &= |\alpha_{21}|^2 g_{\dot{1}1} + \bar{\alpha}_{21}\alpha_{22} g_{\dot{1}2} + \bar{\alpha}_{22}\alpha_{21} g_{\dot{2}1} + |\alpha_{22}|^2 g_{\dot{2}2}
\end{aligned}\right\} \quad (1)$$

The relations between the α_{rs} and the coefficients $\gamma^{\lambda\cdot}_{\cdot\tau}$ of the Lorentz transformation follow:

$$\left.\begin{aligned}
\gamma^{1\cdot}_{\cdot 1} &= R(\bar{\alpha}_{11}\alpha_{22}) + R(\bar{\alpha}_{12}\alpha_{21}) \\
\gamma^{2\cdot}_{\cdot 1} &= I(\bar{\alpha}_{11}\alpha_{22}) + I(\alpha_{12}\bar{\alpha}_{21}) \\
\gamma^{3\cdot}_{\cdot 1} &= R(\alpha_{11}\bar{\alpha}_{21}) - R(\bar{\alpha}_{12}\alpha_{22}) \\
\gamma^{4\cdot}_{\cdot 1} &= -R(\alpha_{11}\bar{\alpha}_{21}) - R(\bar{\alpha}_{12}\alpha_{22}) \\
\gamma^{1\cdot}_{\cdot 2} &= I(\bar{\alpha}_{22}\alpha_{11}) + I(\bar{\alpha}_{21}\alpha_{12}) \\
\gamma^{2\cdot}_{\cdot 2} &= R(\bar{\alpha}_{11}\alpha_{22}) - R(\bar{\alpha}_{12}\alpha_{21}) \\
\gamma^{3\cdot}_{\cdot 2} &= I(\bar{\alpha}_{21}\alpha_{11}) + I(\bar{\alpha}_{12}\alpha_{22}) \\
\gamma^{4\cdot}_{\cdot 2} &= I(\bar{\alpha}_{11}\alpha_{21}) + I(\bar{\alpha}_{12}\alpha_{22}) \\
\gamma^{1\cdot}_{\cdot 3} &= R(\bar{\alpha}_{11}\alpha_{12}) - R(\bar{\alpha}_{21}\alpha_{22}) \\
\gamma^{2\cdot}_{\cdot 3} &= I(\bar{\alpha}_{11}\alpha_{12}) + I(\bar{\alpha}_{22}\alpha_{21}) \\
\gamma^{3\cdot}_{\cdot 3} &= \frac{1}{2}(|\alpha_{11}|^2 + |\alpha_{22}|^2 - |\alpha_{12}|^2 - |\alpha_{21}|^2) \\
\gamma^{4\cdot}_{\cdot 3} &= \frac{1}{2}(|\alpha_{21}|^2 + |\alpha_{22}|^2 - |\alpha_{11}|^2 - |\alpha_{12}|^2)
\end{aligned}\right\} \quad (2)$$

$$\left.\begin{aligned}
\gamma^{1\cdot}_{\cdot 4} &= -R(\alpha_{11}\bar{\alpha}_{12}) - R(\bar{\alpha}_{21}\alpha_{22}) \\
\gamma^{2\cdot}_{\cdot 4} &= -I(\alpha_{11}\bar{\alpha}_{12}) + I(\alpha_{21}\bar{\alpha}_{22}) \\
\gamma^{3\cdot}_{\cdot 4} &= \frac{1}{2}(|\alpha_{12}|^2 + |\alpha_{22}|^2 - |\alpha_{11}|^2 - |\alpha_{21}|^2) \\
\gamma^{4\cdot}_{\cdot 4} &= \frac{1}{2}(|\alpha_{11}|^2 + |\alpha_{12}|^2 + |\alpha_{21}|^2 + |\alpha_{22}|^2)
\end{aligned}\right\}$$

The $\gamma^{\lambda\cdot}_{\cdot\tau}$ are quadratic in the α_{rs}. To each Lorentz transformation belong two spinor transformations which differ only in sign. But to each spinor transformation belongs only one Lorentz transformation. In this sense the spinors are more fundamental than the tensors.

Two special examples will illustrate the meaning of Eq. (2).

$$\alpha_{11} = e^{-i\theta/2}; \quad \alpha_{22} = e^{i\theta/2}; \quad \alpha_{12} = \alpha_{21} = 0 \tag{3}$$

This yields

$$\gamma^{1\cdot}_{\cdot 1} = \gamma^{2\cdot}_{\cdot 2} = \cos\theta$$

$$\gamma^{1\cdot}_{\cdot 2} = -\gamma^{2\cdot}_{\cdot 1} = \sin\theta$$

$$\gamma^{3\cdot}_{\cdot 3} = \gamma^{4\cdot}_{\cdot 4} = 1$$

All other γ are zero.

This corresponds to a purely spatial rotation about the z axis through an angle θ.

$$\alpha_{11} = e^{\theta/2}; \quad \alpha_{22} = e^{-\theta/2}; \quad \alpha_{12} = \alpha_{21} = 0 \tag{4}$$

This yields

$$\gamma^{1\cdot}_{\cdot 1} = \gamma^{2\cdot}_{\cdot 2} = 1$$

$$\gamma^{3\cdot}_{\cdot 4} = -\gamma^{4\cdot}_{\cdot 3} = \sinh\theta$$

$$\gamma^{3\cdot}_{\cdot 3} = \gamma^{4\cdot}_{\cdot 4} = \cosh\theta$$

All other γ are zero. This corresponds to a coordinate system $\overset{*}{\Sigma}$ moving in the positive z direction with the velocity v, where $\tan i\theta = iv/c$.

4.4. Dual tensors. We assume the existence of an antisymmetric tensor $F^{\alpha\beta}$ whose components are all assumed real. The dual of $F^{\alpha\beta}$, denoted by $\overset{\Delta}{F}{}^{\alpha\beta}$, is defined by

$$\overset{\Delta}{F}{}^{\alpha\beta} = \eta^{\alpha\varrho}\eta^{\beta\sigma}\overset{\Delta}{F}_{\varrho\sigma} \tag{1}$$

where $\overset{\Delta}{F}_{\varrho\sigma}$ is defined by

$$\overset{\Delta}{F}_{\varrho\sigma} = \frac{i}{2}\,\delta_{\varrho\sigma\lambda\tau}F^{\lambda\tau} \tag{2}$$

Here $\delta_{\varrho\sigma\lambda\tau}$ is either $+1$ or -1, depending on whether the indices $\rho\sigma\lambda\tau$ are an even or odd permutation of the array (1234). If any two or more indices are the same, then $\delta_{\varrho\sigma\lambda\tau} = 0$. From these definitions, we get

$$\left.\begin{aligned} \overset{\Delta}{F}{}^{12} &= iF^{34}; & \overset{\Delta}{F}{}^{14} &= -iF^{23} \\ \overset{\Delta}{F}{}^{23} &= iF^{14}; & \overset{\Delta}{F}{}^{24} &= -iF^{31} \\ \overset{\Delta}{F}{}^{31} &= iF^{24}; & \overset{\Delta}{F}{}^{34} &= -iF^{12} \end{aligned}\right\} \tag{3}$$

The same relations hold true also for a covariant antisymmetric tensor $F_{\varrho\sigma}$ and its dual tensor $\overset{\Delta}{F}_{\varrho\sigma}$. A tensor $F^{\varrho\sigma}$ is self-dual if

$$F^{\varrho\sigma} = \overset{\Delta}{F}{}^{\varrho\sigma}$$

From a given antisymmetric tensor $F^{\varrho\sigma}$ one can always construct a self-dual tensor $G^{\varrho\sigma}$ by forming

$$G^{\varrho\sigma} \equiv F^{\varrho\sigma} + \overset{\Delta}{F}{}^{\varrho\sigma}$$

Whereas an antisymmetric tensor possesses six linearly independent components, a self-dual tensor possesses only three linearly independent components. They can most conveniently be expressed in terms of a three-dimensional, complex-valued vector $k = (k_1,k_2,k_3)$. The components of $G^{\varrho\sigma}$ are then

$$\left.\begin{aligned} (G^{14},G^{24},G^{34}) &= (-ik_1,-ik_2,-ik_3) \\ (G^{23},G^{31},G^{12}) &= (k_1,k_2,k_3) \end{aligned}\right\} \tag{4}$$

We may write the vector k as a complex sum of two real three-dimensional vectors a and b, i.e.,

$$k = a + ib \tag{5}$$

Then

$$\left.\begin{aligned} (G^{14},G^{24},G^{34}) &= (b_1 - ia_1,b_2 - ia_2,b_3 - ia_3) \\ (G^{23},G^{31},G^{12}) &= (a_1 + ib_1,a_2 + ib_2,a_3 + ib_3) \end{aligned}\right\} \tag{6}$$

It is possible to associate with a self-dual tensor $G^{\varrho\sigma}$ a symmetric spinor g_{rs} of rank two which also possesses only three linearly independent components, viz.,

$$\left.\begin{aligned} g_{11} &= 2(k_2 - ik_1) = 2[a_2 + b_1 + i(b_2 - a_1)] \\ g_{22} &= 2(\bar{k}_2 + i\bar{k}_1) = 2[a_2 + b_1 - i(b_2 - a_1)] \\ g_{12} &= g_{21} = 2ik_3 = 2(-b_3 + ia_3) \\ g_{\dot{1}\dot{1}} &= \bar{g}_{11} = 2[a_2 + b_1 - i(b_2 - a_1)] \\ g_{\dot{2}\dot{2}} &= \bar{g}_{22} = 2[a_2 + b_1 + i(b_2 - a_1)] \\ g_{\dot{1}\dot{2}} &= g_{\dot{2}\dot{1}} = \bar{g}_{12} = \bar{g}_{21} = 2(-b_3 - ia_3) \end{aligned}\right\} \quad (7)$$

4.5. Electrodynamics of empty space in spinor form. We construct a self-dual tensor $G^{\varrho\sigma}$, where

$$G^{\varrho\sigma} = \Psi^{\varrho\sigma} + \overset{\Delta}{\Psi}{}^{\varrho\sigma}$$

is the tensor defined in Section 2.4. In our present notation, however, we set $c = 1$. Therefore the vector $\boldsymbol{k}$ is in this case

$$\boldsymbol{k} = -\boldsymbol{H} + i\boldsymbol{E} \quad (2)$$

The corresponding spinor $g_{\dot{r}\dot{s}}$ has the components

$$\left.\begin{aligned} g_{\dot{1}\dot{1}} &= 2[-H_2 + E_1 - i(H_1 + E_2)] \\ g_{\dot{2}\dot{2}} &= 2[-H_2 + E_1 + i(H_1 + E_2)] \\ g_{\dot{1}\dot{2}} &= g_{\dot{2}\dot{1}} = 2(-E_3 + iH_3) \end{aligned}\right\} \quad (3)$$

We also introduce a current-density spinor $s_{\dot{r}s}$ corresponding to the contravariant current-density world-vector $s^\lambda = (I_1, I_2, I_3, \rho)$, viz.,

$$\left.\begin{aligned} s_{\dot{1}1} &= I_3 + \rho \\ s_{\dot{1}2} &= I_1 - iI_2 \\ s_{\dot{2}1} &= I_1 + iI_2 \\ s_{\dot{2}2} &= -I_3 + \rho \end{aligned}\right\} \quad (4)$$

Maxwell's eight equations read then in spinor language

$$\partial^{\dot{r}}_{\cdot l}\, g_{\dot{r}\dot{m}} = 8\pi s_{l\dot{m}} \quad (5)$$

2. Fundamental Relativistic Invariants

1. Speed of light in empty space c
2. Length of a world line element ds:

$$ds^2 = dx^2 + dy^2 + dz^2 - c^2dt^2$$

3. Phase of an electromagnetic wave
4. Rest mass of a particle m
5. Electric charge ε
6. Action integral $\int_{t_1}^{t_2} L\, dt$
7. Planck's constant h
8. Entropy $S = S_0$ (S = entropy of moving system; S_0 = entropy of system at rest)
9. Boltzmann's constant k
10. Rest temperature $T_0 = T/\sqrt{1 - \beta^2}$
11. Heat $Q_0 = Q/\sqrt{1 - \beta^2}$

Bibliography

1. BERGMANN, P. G., *Introduction to the Theory of Relativity*, Prentice-Hall, Inc., New York, 1942. Probably the best modern representation of the subject.
2. EDDINGTON, Sir A. S., *The Mathematical Theory of Relativity*, Cambridge University Press, London, 1923.
3. LANE, M. V., *Das Relativitätsprinzip*, Vol. 1 (special theory), 4th ed., 1921; Vol. 2 (general theory), 2d ed., 1923; F. Vieweg und Sohn, Braunschweig.
4. LORENTZ, A. H., EINSTEIN, A. and MINKOWSKI, H., *Das Relativitätsprinzip*, 4th ed., B. G. Teubner, Leipzig, 1922.
5. PAULI, W., Jr., *Relativitätstheorie*, 4th ed., B. G. Teubner, Leipzig, 1922. (Article in *Enzyklopädie der mathematischen Wissenschaften*, Vol. 5, Part 2, Sec. 4.) An exhaustive treatment of the earlier parts of the theory.
6. WEYL, H., *Raum, Zeit, Materie*, 5th ed., Julius Springer, Berlin, 1923. Discusses the fundamental philosophical principles of space and time. (A translation was published by Dover Publications, New York, under the title *Space, Time, Matter*.)

Chapter 7

THE GENERAL THEORY OF RELATIVITY

BY HENRY ZATZKIS

Assistant Professor of Mathematics
Newark College of Engineering

1. Mathematical Basis of General Relativity

1.1. Mathematical introduction. The world continuum of space-time is no longer considered " flat " or " Euclidean," as was done in the special theory of relativity, but " curved " or " Riemannian." This means there exists a " metric tensor " $g_{\varrho\sigma} = g_{\sigma\varrho}$, such that the distance $d\tau$ between two infinitesimally close world points (x^1,x^2,x^3,x^4) and $(x^1 + dx^1, x^2 + dx^2, x^3 + dx^3, x^4 + dx^4)$ is expressed by

$$\left.\begin{aligned} d\tau^2 &= g_{\varrho\sigma}\, dx^\varrho\, dx^\sigma, \\ g_{\varrho\sigma} &= g_{\sigma\varrho}(x^1,x^2,x^3,x^4), \quad x^4 = t \end{aligned}\right\} \tag{1}$$

whereas in flat space the distance is

$$dt^2 = \eta_{\varrho\sigma}\, dx^\varrho\, dx^\sigma \tag{2}$$

The essential point is that the $g_{\varrho\sigma}$ are functions of the coordinates and that no special coordinate system exists in which $g_{\varrho\sigma}$ would be constant in a finite domain.

It was Einstein's fundamental idea to establish a relation between the metric tensor and the matter distribution in the world continuum. This relation is the content of Einstein's field equations. The $g_{\varrho\sigma}$ play the role of gravitational potentials and are the direct generalization of the Newtonian gravitational potential. More specifically, if the deviation from flatness is small, all $g_{\varrho\sigma}$ vanish, except g_{44}, which then becomes identical with the Newtonian potential of a mass distribution.

Another important geometrical object in a Riemanian manifold, besides the metric tensor, is the Riemanian curvature tensor

$$R_{\lambda\varrho\tau.}{}^{\sigma} = \Gamma^\sigma_{\tau\lambda,\varrho} - \Gamma^\sigma_{\tau\varrho,\lambda} - \Gamma^\sigma_{\omega\lambda}\Gamma^\omega_{\tau\varrho} + \Gamma^\sigma_{\omega\varrho}\Gamma^\omega_{\tau\lambda} \tag{3}$$

A comma denotes as usual the derivative with respect to the corresponding coordinate.

The Γ symbols are called the Christoffel three-index symbols of the second kind, and are defined by

$$\Gamma^{\lambda}_{\varrho\sigma} = \tfrac{1}{2} g^{\lambda\omega}(g_{\varrho\omega,\sigma} + g_{\sigma\omega,\varrho} - g_{\varrho\sigma,\omega}) \tag{4}$$

The Γ's vanish identically if the $g_{\varrho\sigma}$ are constants, i.e., if the space is flat. However, even in flat space the $g_{\varrho\sigma}$ may not be constants as a result of a special choice of coordinates, e.g., if we choose polar coordinates instead of Cartesian coordinates in ordinary three-dimensional Euclidean space. It is therefore useful to have the following criterion for the curvature of a given space: The necessary and sufficient condition for a space to be flat is that all the components of the Riemannian curvature tensor vanish.

From the curvature tensor we can obtain tensors of lower rank by the process of "contraction." Of special interest is the tensor of rank two, denoted by $R_{\lambda\sigma}$ and the completely contracted curvature tensor, which gives us the curvature scalar R.

$$R_{\lambda\sigma} = R_{\sigma\lambda} = R^{\omega}_{\omega\lambda\sigma} \tag{5}$$

$$R = g^{\lambda\sigma} R_{\lambda\sigma} \tag{6}$$

Written in terms of the Christoffel symbols, $R_{\lambda\sigma}$ takes the form

$$R_{\lambda\sigma} = \Gamma^{\omega}_{\sigma\omega,\lambda} - \Gamma^{\omega}_{\sigma\lambda,\omega} - \Gamma^{\omega}_{\tau\omega}\Gamma^{\tau}_{\sigma\lambda} + \Gamma^{\omega}_{\tau\lambda}\Gamma^{\tau}_{\sigma\lambda} \tag{7}$$

For later purposes we need the expression denoted by $G^{\lambda\sigma}$

$$G^{\lambda\sigma} = R^{\lambda\sigma} - \tfrac{1}{2} g^{\lambda\sigma} R \tag{8}$$

By contracting the above expression we obtain

$$g_{\lambda\sigma} G^{\lambda\sigma} = R - (\tfrac{1}{2}) \cdot 4R = -R \tag{9}$$

Therefore

$$G^{\lambda\sigma} = 0 \tag{10}$$

is equivalent to

$$R^{\lambda\sigma} = 0 \tag{11}$$

Finally we shall denote the determinant of the $g_{\varrho\sigma}$ matrix by g.

1.2. The field equations. If matter can be represented by a continuous distribution $\rho = \rho(x,y,z)$ which depends on space but not on time, the gravitational potential G, generated by the mass distribution, is given by Poisson's equation

$$\nabla^2 G = -4\pi\rho \tag{1}$$

In regions where the space is empty, this reduces to Laplace's equation

$$\nabla^2 G = 0 \tag{2}$$

If the matter distribution depended on time also, it would be natural to assume that Eq. (1) should be generalized to the inhomogeneous wave equation

$$\Box G = -4\pi\rho(x,y,z,t) \tag{3}$$

This equation, however, is not Lorentz-covariant, since the right side is not Lorentz-covariant. In order to be so, the right side should read ρ_0 instead ρ, i.e., should include only the rest density. On the other hand, it is an empirical fact that the total mass is responsible for gravitational forces and not only the rest mass. Thus ρ must include the contributions from the kinetic energy as well. But the latter terms are no longer scalars.

Another possibility would have been to introduce four gravitational potentials and choose as the right-hand side the energy-momentum vector. But this is again not feasible. In the presence of matter, the mass density ρ is not a scalar, but one component of a tensor $P^{\lambda\sigma}$ (see the discussion of the stress energy tensor in the special theory of relativity).

In his search for the correct formulation Einstein postulated the field equations

$$G^{\lambda\sigma} = -8\pi K P^{\lambda\sigma} \tag{4}$$

The $G^{\lambda\sigma}$ are the expressions defined by Eq. (8). K is the gravitational constant and $P^{\lambda\sigma}$ is the stress-energy tensor and represents a given distribution of matter. If the gravitating matter is concentrated in small regions, " mass points," and zero elsewhere, the field equations reduce to

$$G^{\lambda\sigma} = 0 \tag{5}$$

which is equivalent to

$$R^{\lambda\sigma} = 0 \tag{6}$$

Equation (4) corresponds to Poisson's equation, and Eq. (5) to Laplace's equation. And just as Laplace's equation has solutions which are regular everywhere, except at the origin, also Eq. (4) possesses solutions $g_{\varrho\sigma}$ which are regular everywhere except for a singularity at the origin.

1.3. The variational principle. Laplace's equation

$$\nabla^2 G = 0 \tag{1}$$

is the Euler-Lagrange equation of the variational principle

$$\delta \int_V (|\,\mathbf{grad}\, G\,|)^2\, dV = 0 \tag{2}$$

As usual, G is varied only in the interior of the three-dimensional volume V and not on its boundary. Similarly, Einstein's field equations for empty space can be derived as the Euler-Lagrange equations of the variational principle

$$\delta \int_D R\sqrt{-g}\, dx^1\, dx^2\, dx^3\, dx^4 = 0 \tag{3}$$

Again the field variables $g_{\varrho\sigma}$ and their derivatives are to be varied only in the interior of the four-dimensional domain D.

If matter is present, the variational principle is to be generalized to

$$\delta \int_D (R + 8\pi KM)\sqrt{-g}\, dx^1\, dx^2\, dx^3\, dx^4 = 0 \tag{4}$$

where M is a function of the undifferentiated $g_{\varrho\sigma}$ and the distribution of matter. If $P^{\varrho\sigma}$ denotes the gravitational part of the stress-energy tensor, then the gravitational part of M, denoted by M_{grav} must obey the relation

$$\frac{\partial(\sqrt{-g}M_{\text{grav}})}{\partial \mathcal{G}^{\varrho\sigma}} = P_{\varrho\sigma} \qquad (\mathcal{G}^{\varrho\sigma} = \sqrt{-g}g^{\varrho\sigma}) \tag{5}$$

The electrodynamic part of M is given by

$$M_{\text{el}} = -\frac{1}{8\pi c^{\sigma}}\, \Phi^{\varrho\sigma}\Phi_{\varrho\sigma} \tag{6}$$

Here $\Phi^{\varrho\sigma}$ is the antisymmetric tensor defined in the chapter on the special theory of relativity. In this case the field variables that are to be varied are the $g_{\varrho\sigma}$ and the electromagnetic potentials. Maxwell's equations are then part of the resulting Euler-Lagrange equations.

1.4. The ponderomotive law. Einstein, Infeld, and Hoffmann * have shown that the motion of bodies (considered as singularities in the field) follows from the field equations alone. This is in strong contrast to the Lorentz theory of electrodynamics where the ponderomotive law is an additional postulate, logically independent of the field equations of Maxwell. In the limiting case where the rest mass of the particle is so small that its contribution to the field is negligible, its motion under the influence of a gravitational field alone becomes indistinguishable from a force-free or

* See Einstein, A. and Infeld, L., *Canadian Journal of Mathematics*, 1, No. 3, 209 (1949).

inertial motion. In curved space, it describes a geodesic line, which corresponds to a straight line in flat space. Therefore its path is

$$\frac{d^2x^\varrho}{d\tau^2} + \Gamma^\varrho_{\lambda\sigma}\frac{dx^\lambda}{d\tau}\frac{dx^\sigma}{d\tau} = 0 \tag{1}$$

the equation of a geodesic in a Riemannian manifold.
If the space is flat, all the Γ vanish and the classical law of inertia results :

$$\frac{d^2x^\varrho}{d\tau^2} = 0 \tag{2}$$

1.5. The Schwarzschild solution. Only a few rigorous solutions of Einstein's field equations are known. One of them is the Schwarzschild solution, which describes the static field of a mass point at rest. Let m be its mass; then the equation of a line element in polar coordinates is

$$d\tau^2 = c^2\left(1 - \frac{2Km}{c^2r}\right)dt^2 - \left(1 - \frac{2Km}{c^2r}\right)^{-1} dr^2 - r^2\, d\theta^2 - r^2 \sin^2\theta\, d\phi^2 \tag{1}$$

We shall introduce dimensionless variables by letting

$$\frac{d\tau}{\alpha} = ds, \quad \frac{c_4}{\alpha} = T, \quad \frac{r}{\alpha} = R, \quad 2\alpha = \frac{2Km}{c^2} = \text{“gravitational radius”}$$

and obtain

$$ds^2 = \left(1 - \frac{2}{R}\right)dT^2 - \left(1 - \frac{2}{R}\right)^{-1} dR^2 - R^2\, d\theta^2 - R^2 \sin^2\theta\, d\phi^2 \tag{2}$$

H. Weyl and T. Levi-Civita * succeeded in finding the static solutions that have only rotational but not spherical symmetry.

1.6. The three “Einstein effects” †

a. *The motion of the perihelion.* Suppose that an infinitesimal particle is moving in the field of a Schwarzschild singularity at the origin. The equation of motion is

$$\frac{d^2x^\varrho}{ds^2} = -\Gamma^\varrho_{\lambda\sigma}\frac{dx^\lambda}{ds}\frac{dx^\sigma}{ds} \tag{1}$$

The Γ can be computed from Eq. (45-2). One obtains a plane motion

* Weyl, H., *Ann. Physik*, **54**, 117 (1917); **59**, 185 (1919). Bach and Weyl, H., *Math. Z.*, **13**, 142 (1921). Levi-Civita, T., *Atti accad. naz. Lincei* (several notes, 1918-1919).

† See Wilson, H. A., *Modern Physics*, 3d ed., Blackie & Son, Ltd., London, 1948, p. 392 (the treatment we follow here).

which can be chosen in the plane $\theta = \pi/2$. Two further integrals of the motion are

$$\frac{h}{\alpha c} = H = R^2 \frac{d\phi}{ds} \qquad \text{(conservation of angular momentum)} \tag{2}$$

and

$$A = \left(1 - \frac{2}{R}\right) \frac{dT}{ds} \qquad \text{(conservation of energy)} \tag{3}$$

With the substitution, $u = 1/R$, we get the equation of the orbit:

$$\frac{d^2u}{d\phi^2} + u = \frac{1}{h^2} + 3u^2 \tag{4}$$

The corresponding Newtonian law is

$$\frac{d^2u}{d\phi^2} + u = \frac{1}{h^2} \tag{5}$$

The solution of Eq. (5) is

$$u = \frac{1}{h^2}(1 + \epsilon \cos \phi) \tag{6}$$

This is an ellipse if $\epsilon < 1$. The Einstein term $3u^2$ is very small compared to $1/h^2$ in planetary motion. Therefore Eq. (4) can be solved by the methods of successive approximations. One substitutes on the right-hand side the Newtonian value of u, and obtains the differential equation

$$\frac{d^2u}{d\phi^2} + u = \frac{1}{H^2} + \frac{3}{H^4}\left(1 + \frac{\epsilon^2}{2} + 2\epsilon \cos \phi + \frac{1}{2}\epsilon^2 \cos^2 \phi\right) \tag{7}$$

The solution is

$$u = \left[\frac{1}{h^2} + \frac{3}{h^4}\left(1 + \frac{\epsilon^2}{2}\right)\right](1 + \epsilon \cos \phi) + \frac{3\epsilon}{h^4}\left(\phi \sin \phi - \frac{1}{6}\epsilon \cos^2 \phi\right) \tag{8}$$

If it were not for the term $\phi \sin \phi$, u would have the period 2π. The actual period is $2\pi + \mathcal{E}$, where $\mathcal{E}$ is a small number. If this value is substituted in Eq. (8) and higher powers of $\mathcal{E}$ are neglected, one obtains

$$\mathcal{E} = \frac{6\pi}{H^2} = \frac{6\pi\alpha c}{H^2} = \frac{6\pi K m}{cH^2} \tag{9}$$

In the case of the planet Mercury, this formula gives for the rotation of the major axis of the orbit in 100 years approximately 43 seconds of arc. This is in good agreement with observation.

As A. Sommerfeld has pointed out, each deviation from the Newtonian or Coulomb potential causes a perihelion motion of the Kepler ellipse. In the theory of the fine structure of the hydrogen spectrum the deviation results from the mass-variability of the orbital electron. However the effect is much smaller than here. The rate of the precession of the perihelion is only about one-sixth of the rate produced here.

b. *Deflection of light rays by the sun.* For a light ray path $ds = 0$. Therefore $h = \infty$. The differential equation for the path becomes

$$\frac{d^2u}{d\phi^2} + u = 3u^2 \tag{10}$$

If the right-hand side were zero, the solution would be

$$u = \frac{1}{p} \cos\phi \tag{11}$$

where ϕ is the angle between r and the x axis, the equation of a straight-line parallel to the y axis at a distance p. Again, we substitute this value for u into the right-hand side of Eq. (10). This gives

$$\frac{d^2u}{d\phi^2} + u = \frac{3}{p^2}\frac{1 + \cos^2\phi}{2} \tag{12}$$

The solution is

$$u = \frac{1}{p}\cos\phi + \frac{3}{p^2}\left(\frac{1}{2} - \frac{1}{6}\cos^2\phi\right) \tag{13}$$

From Eq. (13) $u = 0$, or $r = \infty$ for $\phi = \pm(\pi/2 + \varepsilon)$, where ε is small. To find ε, we have the equation

$$0 = -\frac{\varepsilon}{p} + \frac{3}{p^2}\left(\frac{1}{2} + \frac{1}{6}\right) \tag{14}$$

or

$$\varepsilon = \frac{2}{p} \tag{15}$$

The asymptotic directions of the light ray differ by $2/p$ radians from the undeflected direction. The total deviation of a light ray, starting from infinity where the space is flat, and going off into the opposite direction to infinity, where the space is again flat, is

$$\delta = \frac{4}{p} = \frac{4\alpha}{d} \quad (d = \alpha p) \tag{16}$$

c. *The red shift of spectral lines.* Consider two identical "atomic clocks," one on the surface of the sun and one on the surface of the earth, where the curvature of space may be assumed negligible. If both clocks are at rest, we have

$$dr = d\theta = d\phi = 0 \tag{17}$$

Hence
$$d\tau^2 = c^2\left(1 - \frac{2Km}{c^2r}\right)dt^2 \tag{18}$$

if the proper-time dt/c between two successive signals will be the same on the sun as on the earth. But the observed time intervals dt' (on the sun) and dt'' (on the earth) will have the ratio

$$\frac{dt''}{dt'} = \sqrt{1 - \frac{2Km}{c^2r}} = 1 - \frac{Km}{c^2r} \tag{19}$$

the corresponding frequencies have the ratio

$$\frac{f''}{f'} = 1 + \frac{Km}{c^2r} \tag{20}$$

or
$$\delta f = f'' - f' = \frac{Km}{c^2r} \tag{21}$$

The frequency of the same spectrum line, emitted by an atom on the surface of the sun, appears shifted to the red as compared with the line emitted by the same atom on the surface of the earth.

Bibliography

See references at end of Chapter 6.

Chapter 8

HYDRODYNAMICS AND AERODYNAMICS

By Max M. Munk

Department of Aeronautical Engineering
Catholic University of America

1. Assumptions and Definitions

1.1. Theoretical fluid dynamics deals with continuous fluid masses. Modern physics interprets the continuous properties of such masses as statistical averages. The passage from the general equations governing the fluid motion to specific solutions often involves the replacement of the correct equations by special and simplified equations approaching merely the exact equations asymptotically as special additional conditions are more and more exactly complied with. These simpler and more special equations again lead to specific formulas. The student of hydrodynamics and of aerodynamics is particularly interested in these formulas. One should also recall that the velocity fields of hydrodynamics and of gas dynamics have much in common with the fields of electric theory and of the theory of elasticity, all being the solutions of the basic equations subject to boundary conditions. The student will therefore find comparison of the formulas of this section with those in other allied sections a useful and often profitable occupation.

1.2. We divide the fluid body into small compact portions called fluid particles, which operate under Newton's law of dynamics, notwithstanding the continual loss of identity because of perpetual diffusion.

1.3. We reconcile the exchange of momentum that arises from diffuse convection, § 1.2, by assuming that viscous stresses act within the fluid.

1.4. A pure pressure p, within the fluid, is the mechanism adapting the fluid density to the physical problem.

1.5. A perfect fluid is one free of diffusion and hence free of viscosity stresses.

1.6. The fluid is called perfect in a stricter sense if its density is constant and unchangeable.

1.7. A perfect gas subordinates itself to § 1.5, it obeys the equation of state of a perfect gas.

$$p/\rho = R\theta \tag{1}$$

where $\theta =$ temperature, $R =$ gas constant, $\rho =$ mass density, and its internal energy u per unit mass is proportional to the absolute temperature

$$u = k_V \theta \tag{2}$$

2. Hydrostatics

2.1. The buoyancy of an immersed body is equal to the weight of the displaced fluid.

2.2. The buoyancy force acts along a vertical line passing through the center of gravity (CG) of the displaced fluid.

2.3. The wholly submersed body is in stable equilibrium if it weighs as much as the displaced fluid, and if its center of gravity lies vertically below the center of gravity of the displaced fluid.

2.4. The metacenter of a floating partially submersed body is the point at which the body would have to be suspended to experience moments, when slightly tilted from equilibrium, equal to the hydrostatic moments.

2.5. The distance between the center of gravity of the body and the metacenter is called the metacentric height h.

2.6. Let a denote the vertical distance between the CG of the body and the CG of the displaced fluid, positive if the CG of the body is above the CG of said fluid. Let I denote the axial (not central) moment of inertia

$$I = \int y^2 \, dA \tag{1}$$

of the area A cut by the partially immersed body out of the fluid surface, the CG of said area having the ordinate $y = 0$. The metacentric height is then

$$\text{MCH} = I/V - a \tag{2}$$

where V denotes the volume of the displaced fluid.

2.7. The pressure gradient of standing fluid is vertical and equal to the specific gravity of the fluid.

3. Kinematics

3.1. The bulk or particle velocity $\boldsymbol{v}$ is a vector and a function of the time t and of the space vector $\boldsymbol{r}$. The Cartesian components of $\boldsymbol{r}$ will be designated by x, y, z. The Cartesian components of $\boldsymbol{v}$ parallel to said space vector components respectively will be designated by u, v, w. This way of describing the flow is ordinarily designated as Eulerian.

3.2. The less common Lagrangian description identifies the fluid particles by suitable variables and follows the motion of each individual particle.

3.3. The divergence of a velocity field $\boldsymbol{v}$ is defined by

$$\nabla \cdot \boldsymbol{v} = \partial u/\partial x + \partial v/\partial y + \partial w/\partial z \qquad (1)$$

It is a scalar quantity.

3.4. The rotation or " curl " of a velocity field, also called its vorticity, is defined by the vector whose Cartesian components are

$$\nabla \times \boldsymbol{v} = (u_y - v_x, v_z - w_y, w_x - u_z) \qquad (1)$$

3.5. The gradient of a scalar field p such as the pressure is defined by

$$\mathbf{grad}\, p = \nabla p = (p_x, p_y, p_z) \qquad (1)$$

3.6. The acceleration $\boldsymbol{a}$ of a fluid particle in terms of the Eulerian representation is equal to

$$\boldsymbol{a} = \partial \boldsymbol{v}/\partial t + (\boldsymbol{v} \cdot \nabla)\boldsymbol{v} \qquad (1)$$

The first right-hand term is called the local portion of the acceleration, the second term is called the convection portion. The x component of the convective term is

$$u u_x + v u_y + w u_z \qquad (2)$$

and similarly the y and z components.

3.7. The convective portion of the acceleration can be transformed as follows.

$$(\boldsymbol{v} \cdot \nabla)\boldsymbol{v} = -\tfrac{1}{2}\nabla v^2 + \boldsymbol{v} \times (\nabla \times \boldsymbol{v}) \qquad (1)$$

3.8. A flow is called steady if its velocity and all its other properties are a function of the space coordinates only and not a function of the time t. The local portion of the acceleration $\partial \boldsymbol{v}/\partial t$ is then zero.

3.9. A flow field whose velocity v can be represented as the gradient of a scalar quantity ϕ is called a potential flow, or a nonrotational flow. The quantity ϕ is called the potential of the velocity, or the velocity potential.

3.10. The rotation of a potential flow is zero.

$$\nabla \times \nabla\phi = 0 \tag{1}$$

3.11. A velocity field $\boldsymbol{v}$ that has a potential ϕ is given by the scalar line integral $\phi = -\int d\boldsymbol{r} \cdot \boldsymbol{v}$, taken along any line connecting a reference point with the point in question.

3.12. The scalar line integral $-\int d\boldsymbol{r} \cdot \boldsymbol{v}$ taken along a closed line is called the circulation.

3.13. The scalar integral $\int d\boldsymbol{f} \cdot \boldsymbol{v}$, taken through a surface $\boldsymbol{f}$, bounded or unbounded, is called the flux of $\boldsymbol{v}$ through $\boldsymbol{f}$.

3.14. The flow field of an incompressible fluid has the divergence zero, $\nabla \cdot \boldsymbol{v} = 0$.

3.15. The general equation of continuity for any fluid is

$$\nabla \cdot (\boldsymbol{v}\rho) = -\partial\rho/\partial t \tag{1}$$

3.16. The divergence of the vorticity of any velocity field v is identically zero.

$$\nabla \cdot \nabla \times \boldsymbol{v} = 0 \tag{1}$$

3.17. The substantive rate of change of the circulation of $\boldsymbol{v}$ is that change along a closed line moving with the fluid particles, i.e., along one always occupied by the same fluid particles. This substantive rate of change equals the circulation of the acceleration

$$D/Dt \int d\boldsymbol{r} \cdot \boldsymbol{v} = \int d\boldsymbol{r} \cdot \boldsymbol{a} \tag{1}$$

3.18. In a plane two-dimensional flow of an incompressible fluid, the flux through any line connecting a pair of points is independent of the shape of the line of connection. This flux is called stream function ψ if one of the two points is chosen as a fixed reference point and the other point is varied

$$u = \partial\psi/\partial y, \quad v = -\partial\psi/\partial x \tag{1}$$

The existence of a stream function is equivalent to the absence of divergence.

3.19. Axially symmetric two-dimensional flows have no velocity components at right angles to the meridian plane. They have a stream function ψ if the fluid is incompressible

$$u = \frac{1}{r}\psi_y, \quad v = -\frac{1}{r}\psi_x \tag{1}$$

where r denotes the distance from the axis of symmetry.

3.20. With a steady two-dimensional compressible flow the quantity $\boldsymbol{v}\rho$, called mass flux density, possesses a stream function ψ equivalent to § 3.18 and § 3.19, respectively. If the flow is plane,

$$u\rho = \partial\psi/\partial y, \quad v\rho = -\,\partial\psi/\partial x \tag{1}$$

3.21. The plane having the velocity components u and v of a plane two-dimensional flow as Cartesian coordinates is called the hodograph plane.

3.22. The space vector x, y has a potential L in the hodograph plane u, v, provided the velocity vector u, v has a potential ϕ in the physical plane x, y, and conversely.

$$L = -\phi + u \cdot x + v \cdot y \tag{1}$$

3.23. The stream function of (u, v) is the potential of the flow $v, -u$. The theorem of § 3.22 holds therefore also for the stream function.

3.24. In the following, S denotes space, $dS = dx\,dy\,dz$; O denotes a closed surface, $d\sigma$ an element thereof. A bounded surface is denoted by f.

3.25. The kinetic energy K of the flow v within the space S bounded by the surface O is equal to

$$K = \tfrac{1}{2}\int v^2\rho\, dS \tag{1}$$

3.26. If the flow has a potential ϕ, then K is equal to

$$K = \tfrac{1}{2}\int d\boldsymbol{\sigma} \cdot \boldsymbol{v}\rho\phi \tag{1}$$

3.27. The momentum of the flow is equal to

$$\boldsymbol{M} = \int dS\, \boldsymbol{\nabla} \cdot (\boldsymbol{v}\rho)\boldsymbol{r} + \int d\boldsymbol{\sigma} \cdot \boldsymbol{v}\rho\boldsymbol{r} \tag{1}$$

3.28. The moment of momentum of the flow is equal to

$$\int dS\, \boldsymbol{v}\rho\boldsymbol{r} = \tfrac{1}{2}\int dS(\boldsymbol{\nabla} \times \boldsymbol{v}\rho)\boldsymbol{r} \cdot \boldsymbol{r} - \tfrac{1}{2}\int d\boldsymbol{\sigma} \times (\rho\boldsymbol{v})\boldsymbol{r} \cdot \boldsymbol{r} \tag{1}$$

3.29. Biot Savart

$$\boldsymbol{v} = \frac{1}{4\pi}\iint \frac{dS\, dS'(\boldsymbol{\nabla} \times \boldsymbol{v}) \times (\boldsymbol{r} - \boldsymbol{r}')}{[(\boldsymbol{r} - \boldsymbol{r}') \cdot (\boldsymbol{r} - \boldsymbol{r}')]^{3/2}} \tag{1}$$

4. Thermodynamics

4.1. Notations:

p = pressure
ρ = mass density
V = specific volume
θ = temperature
s = entropy
dQ = heat differential
u = internal energy
i = enthalpy, also designated by h
C_V = specific heat of constant volume
C_p = specific heat of constant pressure

4.2. Notations, perfect gases:

R = gas constant γ = isentropic exponent

4.3. $du = -p\,dV + dQ = -p\,dV + \theta\,ds$

4.4. $dh = di = -V\,dp + \theta\,ds$

4.5. Perfect gases

$$p = R\rho\theta, \quad u = C_V\theta, \quad h = C_p\theta$$

$$R = C_p - C_V = C_p\frac{\gamma - 1}{\gamma} = C_V(\gamma - 1)$$

$$\gamma = \frac{n+2}{n} = \frac{C_p}{C_V} = \frac{C_V + R}{C_V}$$

where n denotes degrees of freedom.

$$s = C_V \ln p - C_p \ln \rho$$

5. Forces and Stresses

5.1. There may act on the fluid external body forces $\boldsymbol{f}$ per unit volume. These forces may have a potential

$$\boldsymbol{f} = -\nabla\phi'$$

5.2. The buoyancy force per unit volume exerted on the fluid particle by a pressure distribution p is $-\nabla p$.

5.3. The force effect per unit volume caused within an incompressible fluid by the simplest type of viscosity is (μ denoting the modulus of viscosity)

$$-\mu\nabla\cdot\nabla\nu = (\mu\nabla\cdot\nabla u, \quad \mu\nabla\cdot\nabla v, \quad \mu\nabla\cdot\nabla w) \tag{1}$$

5.4. The viscosity stress within the incompressible fluid corresponding to the equation in § 5.3 is

$$\Sigma = \mu[\nabla \boldsymbol{v} + \boldsymbol{v}\nabla] =$$

$$\begin{vmatrix} \sigma_{xx} & \sigma_{xy} & \sigma_{xz} \\ \sigma_{yx} & \sigma_{yy} & \sigma_{yz} \\ \sigma_{zx} & \sigma_{zy} & \sigma_{zz} \end{vmatrix} = \mu \begin{vmatrix} u_x & v_x & w_x \\ u_y & v_y & w_y \\ u_z & v_z & w_z \end{vmatrix} + \mu \begin{vmatrix} u_x & u_y & u_z \\ v_x & v_y & v_z \\ w_x & w_y & w_z \end{vmatrix} \tag{1}$$

5.5. The average normal stress $\sigma_{xx} + \sigma_{yy} + \sigma_{zz}$ of the stress § 5.4 is zero.

5.6. The dissipation of kinetic energy into heat in accordance with § 5.4 is, per unit volume,

$$2\mu\nabla \cdot \boldsymbol{a} + \mu(|\nabla \times \boldsymbol{v}|)^2 \tag{1}$$

where $\boldsymbol{a}$ denotes the acceleration of the fluid.

5.7. The same dissipation for a finite portion of space S is

$$2\mu \int d\sigma \cdot \boldsymbol{a} + \mu \int dS(|\nabla \times \boldsymbol{v}|)^2 \tag{1}$$

5.8. If the velocity is, and remains, zero at the boundary of the space portion S, the total dissipation (but not the local dissipation, § 5.4) becomes equal to $\mu/2$ times the integral of the vorticity squared over the space portion.

6. Dynamic Equations

(External forces assumed absent)

6.1. Euler's equation for nonviscous fluids:

$$\partial \boldsymbol{v}/\partial t + (\boldsymbol{v} \cdot \nabla)\boldsymbol{v} = -\frac{\nabla p}{\rho}, \quad \frac{dp}{\rho} + V\,dV = 0 \tag{1}$$

along any streamline.

6.2. Euler's equation for steady potential flows:

$$\frac{\nabla p}{\rho} = -\frac{1}{2}\nabla(u^2 + v^2 + w^2) \tag{1}$$

6.3. For a steady isentropic potential flow of an inviscid gas:

$$h_0 = h + \frac{u^2 + v^2 + w^2}{2} \tag{1}$$

6.4. Stokes-Navier equation for a steady incompressible fluid having viscosity:

$$-\frac{\nabla p}{\rho} = (\boldsymbol{v} \cdot \nabla)\boldsymbol{v} - \frac{\mu}{\rho}\nabla \cdot \nabla \boldsymbol{v} \tag{1}$$

6.5. Helmholtz' theorem: If external body forces and viscosity are absent, individual vortices move with the fluid; i.e., individual vortices always consist of the same fluid particles.

6.6. For plane two-dimensional flow of an incompressible fluid, each fluid particle preserves its vorticity.

6.7. In steady plane two-dimensional flow of a perfect gas along any one streamline, the vorticity is proportional to the pressure.

6.8. Convection and diffusion of vorticity: Plane two-dimensional flow

$$w_T + \boldsymbol{v} \cdot \boldsymbol{\nabla} w = \frac{\mu}{\rho \boldsymbol{\nabla}} \cdot \boldsymbol{\nabla} w \tag{1}$$

6.9. In absence of viscosity and of external body forces, a homogeneous fluid executing a potential flow will continue to do so.

6.10. The continued existence of a potential implies that all dynamic equations and requirements are complied with.

7. Equations of Continuity for Steady Potential Flow of Nonviscous Fluids (see also §§ 3.14, 3.15)

7.1. Laplace's equation for the potential of an incompressible fluid of constant density:

$$\boldsymbol{\nabla} \cdot \boldsymbol{\nabla} \phi = \frac{\partial^2 \phi}{\partial x^2} + \frac{\partial^2 \phi}{\partial y^2} + \frac{\partial^2 \phi}{\partial z^2} = 0 \tag{1}$$

7.2. For plane, two-dimensional flow:

$$\frac{\partial^2 \phi}{\partial x^2} + \frac{\partial^2 \phi}{\partial y^2} = 0 \tag{1}$$

7.3. For polar coordinates, r, θ

$$\phi_{rr} + \frac{1}{r^2} \phi_{\theta\theta} + \frac{\phi_r}{r} = 0 \tag{1}$$

7.4. For spherical polar coordinates:

$$\sin \theta \frac{\partial}{\partial r} (r^2 \phi_r) + \frac{\partial}{\partial \theta} (\sin \theta \phi_\theta) + \frac{1}{\sin \theta} \phi_{\omega\omega} = 0 \tag{1}$$

$$x = r \cos \theta, \quad y = r \sin \theta \cos \omega, \quad z = r \sin \theta \sin \omega \tag{2}$$

7.5. For a plane two-dimensional flow obeying Laplace's equation, the equation for the potential L of (x, y) as a function of (u, v) again obeys Laplace's equation.

$$x = \partial L/\partial u, \qquad y = \partial L/\partial v$$

$$\partial^2 L/\partial u^2 + \partial^2 L/\partial v^2 = 0$$

7.6. The value of a solution ϕ of Laplace's equation (§ 7.1) at any point is the arithmetical mean of its values over any sphere having that point as its center (in three-dimensional flows) or any equivalent circle (in two-dimensional flows).

7.7. Equation of continuity for a steady potential flow of a compressible fluid (see § 6.4).

$$\left.\begin{aligned}\phi_{xx}\left(1-\frac{\phi_x^{\,2}}{c^2}\right)+\phi_{yy}\left(1-\frac{\phi_y^{\,2}}{c^2}\right)+\phi_{zz}\left(1-\frac{\phi_z^{\,2}}{c^2}\right)&\\ -\frac{2}{c^2}\phi_{xy}\phi_x\phi_y-\frac{2}{c^2}\phi_{yz}\phi_y\phi_z-\frac{2}{c^2}\phi_{zx}\phi_z\phi_x&=0\end{aligned}\right\} \quad (1)$$

where c denotes the local velocity of sound.

7.8. For polytropic expansion (γ = expansion exponent):

$$(1-\phi_{xi}\phi_{xi})\nabla\cdot\nabla\phi=\frac{2}{\gamma-1}\phi_{xi}\phi_{xk}\phi_{xixk} \quad (1)$$

$$(i,k = 1, 2, 3)$$

7.9. For two-dimensional flow in plane polar coordinates:

$$\left.\begin{aligned}\left(1-\frac{\gamma+1}{\gamma-1}\phi_r^{\,2}-\frac{\phi_\theta^{\,2}}{r^2}\right)\phi_{rr}+\left(1-\phi_r^{\,2}-\frac{\gamma+1}{\gamma-1}\frac{\phi_\theta^{\,2}}{r^2}\right)\left(\frac{\phi_{\theta\theta}}{r^2}+\frac{\phi_r}{r}\right)&\\ -\frac{4}{\gamma-1}\phi_r\frac{\phi_\theta}{r}\left(\frac{\phi_{\theta r}}{r}-\frac{\phi_\theta}{r^2}\right)&=0\end{aligned}\right\} \quad (1)$$

7.10. In the hodograph plane:

$$\left(1-\frac{w^2}{c^2}\right)w^2\phi_{ww}+w\left(1-2\frac{w^3}{c^3}\frac{dc}{dw}+\frac{w^4}{c^4}\right)\phi_w+\left(1-\frac{w^2}{c^2}\right)^2\phi_{\theta\theta}=0 \quad (1)$$

7.11. The stream function:

$$w^2\psi_{ww}+w\left(1+\frac{w^2}{c^2}\right)\psi_w+\left(1-\frac{w^2}{c^2}\right)\psi_{\theta\theta}=0 \quad (1)$$

7.12. Reciprocal potential, L:

$$\left(1-\frac{v^2}{c^2}\right)L_{uu}+\left(1-\frac{u^2}{c^2}\right)L_{vv}+\frac{2uv}{c^2}L_{uv}=0 \tag{1}$$

8. Particular Solutions of Laplace's Equation

8.1. Sink or source in three dimensions:

$$\phi_1=\frac{1}{4\pi}\frac{1}{r} \tag{1}$$

8.2. Sink or source in two dimensions:

$$\phi_2=\frac{1}{2\pi}\ln r \tag{1}$$

8.3. Rankine flow in three or two dimensions:

$$\phi=x+\phi_1, \qquad x+\phi_2 \tag{1}$$

8.4. Flow past a sphere:

$$\phi=v_0\left(r+\frac{R^3}{2r^2}\right)\cos\theta \tag{1}$$

8.5. Flow past a circle:

$$\phi=v_0\left(r+\frac{R^2}{r}\right)\cos\theta \tag{1}$$

8.6. General solution suitable for solving problems relating to a straight line in two-dimensional flow:

$$\phi=\text{real part of }\frac{1}{i(z-\sqrt{z^2-1})^n} \tag{1}$$

8.7. Complex variables: If $u+iv$ is an analytic function of $x+iy$, then u and v are each solutions of Laplace's equation.

8.8. If $f(x,y,z)$ is a solution of Laplace's equation, then

$$\frac{1}{r}f\left(\frac{x}{r^2},\frac{y}{r^2},\frac{z}{r^2}\right) \tag{1}$$

is also a solution.

8.9. Degree zero: The following is a solution, F and G denoting any analytic function.

$$u=F\left(\frac{x+iy}{r+z}\right)+G\left(\frac{x-iy}{r+z}\right) \quad (r^2=x^2+y^2+z^2) \tag{1}$$

8.10. Degree —1: The following are solutions.

$$v = \frac{1}{r} u \tag{1}$$

where u is given in § 8.9.

8.11. A conformal transformation of the system of lines $\phi =$ constant, $\psi =$ constant in a plane leads again to a solution of Laplace's equation if the initial system represents potential lines and streamlines consistent with that equation.

8.12. The lines of equal potential and the lines of equal stream function form an orthogonal system.

8.13. Fundamental solutions of Laplace's equation in three dimensions:

$$\phi = \frac{\partial^n}{\partial x^n} \frac{1}{r} \tag{1}$$

The factor of r^n expressed as a function of cos ϕ is called a Legendre function.

8.14. Kinetic energy of the potential flow of the incompressible fluid

$$T = \frac{\rho}{2} \int dS \quad v^2 = \frac{\rho}{2} \int d\sigma \cdot \nu\phi \tag{1}$$

8.15. Variational principle: The potential flow of the incompressible fluid has a smaller kinetic energy than any other thinkable potential flow of the incompressible fluid having the same values of the potential at the boundary of the region considered wherever there is a flux different than zero across the boundary.

8.16. Differentiation: The differential quotient $\partial\phi/\partial x$ of a solution ϕ of Laplace's equation with respect to a Cartesian coordinate x is again a solution.

9. Apparent Additional Mass

9.1. An immersed body, moving in a perfect incompressible fluid otherwise at rest, responds to external forces as if its mass were increased by an apparent additional mass. This mass depends on the shape of the body only and is, in general, different for motions in various directions relative to the body. (Translation.)

9.2. The apparent additional mass is equal to the kinetic energy of the fluid, divided by one-half the square of the velocity of advance.

9.3. The apparent additional mass is equal to the momentum transmitted from the body to the fluid from initial rest, divided by the velocity of advance.

9.4. The apparent mass K of a body having the same density as the fluid is equal to the static moment of the sink source system that would induce the fluid motion, multiplied by the density, or

$$K = \rho \int dS\, \mathbf{r} \nabla \cdot \mathbf{v} \tag{1}$$

9.5. The apparent additional mass is equal to the surface integral of the potential, multiplied by the density, or

$$K = \rho \int d\sigma\, \phi \tag{1}$$

9.6. The apparent additional mass, divided by the mass of the displaced fluid, is called the factor of the apparent mass.

9.7. Factor of apparent additional mass: Circular cylinder moving crosswise, 1; sphere, $\frac{1}{2}$.

9.8. Apparent additional mass: Elliptical cylinder of length $L \to \infty$, moving crosswise at a right angle to major axis, a,

$$La^2 \frac{\pi}{4} \rho \tag{1}$$

Flat plate of width a, moving crosswise,

$$La^2 \frac{\pi}{4} \rho \tag{2}$$

Circular disk of diameter r, moving crosswise,

$$\frac{8a^3\rho}{3} \tag{3}$$

9.10. The additional apparent momentum is a symmetric and linear function of the velocity, i.e., at least three principal directions mutually at right angles to each other exist, for which the momentum is parallel to the velocity. The momentum in any other direction (relative to the body) can be computed from the velocity components in the principal directions by simple superposition.

9.11. The momentum transmitted from a body to a barotropically expanding gas surrounding the body, from the time both, the body and the gas, were at rest until the translational motion of the body as well as the motion of the gas has become steady, does not depend on the time history of the motion.

9.12. The energy for subsonic motion has a lower bound, associated with infinitely gradual setting up of the motion.

9.13. The minimum energy is composed of the kinetic energy and of the elastic energy of the gas.

9.14. We can evaluate the elastic energy if the total mass of the gas involved in the motion remains constant for all velocities of advance.

9.15. For polytropic expansion the elastic energy is the space integral of

$$\left.\begin{aligned}&\frac{[1-M_0^2(\gamma-1)v^2/2]^{\gamma/(\gamma-1)}}{\gamma(\gamma-1)}+\frac{[1-M_0^2(\gamma-1)v_0^2/2]^{\gamma/(\gamma-1)}}{\gamma}\\&\qquad-\frac{[1-M_0^2(\gamma-1)v^2/2]^{1/(\gamma-1)}[1-M_0^2(\gamma-1)v_0^2]}{\gamma-1}\end{aligned}\right\} \quad (1)$$

where v_0 = ambient velocity, v = local velocity, M_0 = ambient Mach number, γ = polytropic exponent.

10. Airship Theory

10.1. Assumptions: Perfect incompressible flow, slender airship body with circular section, no fins, small angle of attack, linearization, cross-sectional area, X-axial coordinate.

10.2. Cross force per unit axial length (lift):

$$\frac{dL}{dx}=2\frac{dS}{dx}\frac{v^2\rho}{2}\sin\alpha\cos\alpha=2\frac{dS}{dx}\frac{v^2\rho}{2}\alpha \quad (1)$$

10.3. The total air force of streamlined spindle is zero.

10.4. The total unstable moment of the air force (couple) is

$$M=2\text{ volume }\frac{v^2\rho}{2}\alpha$$

10.5. The total lift of the spindle ending abruptly in a flat base of cross section S is

$$L=2\frac{Sv^2\rho}{2}\alpha$$

10.6. The pressure around any one cross section is proportional to the distance from the diameter normal to the plane of symmetry.

11. Wing Profile Contours; Two-dimensional Flow with Circulation

11.1. The plane two-dimensional flow past such a contour is determined by the ordinary boundary condition of zero flux in conjunction with Kutta's condition that the separation point coincide with the sharp-pointed trailing edge.

11.2. The resulting air force, or lift, acts at right angles to the translational motion of advance. The lift passes through a point of the contour called center of pressure and is proportional to the circulation about the contour.

$$L = v\rho\Gamma \quad \text{per unit span} \tag{1}$$

11.3. The profile possesses a point called areodynamic center. The moment of the air force with respect to this center is not dependent on the angle of attack but is merely proportional to the density and to the square of the velocity of advance.

11.4. The aerodynamic center of a thin contour extending close to a straight line, called the chord, is positioned near the 25 % point of the chord; that is, it is spaced one-quarter chord length downstream from the leading edge.

11.5. The direction of forward motion for zero lift of a slender profile is nearly parallel to the line connecting the trailing edge with the center of the profile, this center being at the 50 % station and equidistant from the upper and lower camber line, or contour boundary.

11.6. Lift coefficient:

$$C_L = 2\pi\alpha = \frac{L}{cv^2\rho/2} \tag{1}$$

where L = lift per unit span, v = velocity of advance, c = chord, ρ = density, α = angle of attack; $dc_L/d\alpha$ is called the lift slope.

11.7. As the angle of attack increases, the CP (center of pressure) approaches the aerodynamic center (AC) with positively cambered profiles.

11.8. If the CP does not travel but is fixed, it coincides with the AC.

11.9. The linearized theory applies to slender airfoil sections. The boundary condition of zero flux at the contour is replaced by prescribing the flow direction along the chord, namely, to be parallel to the average camber direction at the chord station. Only terms linear in the perturbation velocity components are retained.

11.10. The angle of attack of zero lift is given by the integral

$$\alpha = \frac{1}{\pi}\int_{-1}^{+1}\frac{\xi\, dx}{(1-x)\sqrt{1-x^2}} \tag{1}$$

where chord $= 2$, $x =$ chord station, $\xi =$ mean camber.

11.11. The angle of attack for zero moment with respect to the 50 % station is given by the integral

$$\alpha = \frac{2}{\pi}\int_{-1}^{+1}\frac{x\xi\, dx}{\sqrt{1-x^2}} \tag{1}$$

11.12. In actual, slightly viscous air the profiles experience, furthermore, a resistance or drag, called the profile drag.

12. Airfoils in Three Dimensions

12.1. Assumptions: The spanwise extension of the airfoil or airfoils is large when compared with the flowwise extension. The ratio of the square of the span, or maximum span, to the total projected airfoil area is called aspect ratio. Viscosity is absent. The air, having been in contact with the upper airfoil surface, slides sideways over the air having been in contact with the lower airfoil surface. The vortices representing this condition coincide with the streamlines and are assumed to extend straight downstream. There occurs a drag called induced drag.

12.2. The spanwise lift distribution for minimum induced drag requires constant downwash velocity along the span or spans, provided all chordwise distances are reduced to zero; that is, the airfoil or airfoils are replaced by the flowwise projection.

12.3. The minimum induced drag is equal to

$$D_i = \frac{L^2}{v^2\rho\, 4k/2} \tag{1}$$

where k denotes the area of apparent additional mass of the front projection of the airfoils.

12.4. The minimum induced drag of a single airfoil, straight in front view, is

$$D_i = \frac{L^2}{v^2 \rho b^2 \pi / 2} \tag{1}$$

where b denotes the span. The lift slope of the single airfoil is equal to

$$\frac{dC_L}{d\alpha} = \frac{2\pi}{1 + 2S/b^2}$$

12.5. For the single airfoil the relation of the center-of-pressure travel to the variation of the lift coefficient is the same as with the two-dimensional flow (infinite span).

13. Theory of a Uniformly Loaded Propeller Disk

(Incompressible, nonviscous, infinite number of blades)

13.1. The theoretical efficiency, i.e., the upper bound of the uniformly loaded disk of a propeller is

$$\eta = \frac{2}{1 + \sqrt{1 + 8T/v^2 D^2 \pi \rho}} \tag{1}$$

where T = thrust, D = diameter, v = axial forward velocity.

13.2. The minimum power requirement for a hovering propeller ($v = 0$) is equal to

$$P = \sqrt{2T^3/\rho D^2 \pi} \tag{1}$$

13.3. The local slipstream velocity ratio in the region of a propeller is equal to

$$v_s = \frac{1}{2} \sqrt{[1 + (8T/v^2 D^2 \pi) - 1]}$$

14. Free Surfaces

(Incompressible, nonviscous, plane, two-dimensional)

14.1. The intrinsic equation for flow from all sides into an open channel of constant width 4 is

$$s = -\frac{2}{\pi} \ln \cos \frac{\theta}{2} \tag{1}$$

$$y = \frac{1}{\pi} (\theta - \sin \theta) \tag{2}$$

where s = length of curve, θ = direction of curve bounding stream, coefficient of contraction = $\frac{1}{2}$.

14.2. For a slot in a wall of width $2 + 4/\pi$,

$$s = -\frac{2}{\pi} \ln(-\cos\theta) \tag{1}$$

where final width of the jet is 2. The coefficient of contraction is

$$\frac{\pi}{\pi + 2} = 0.611 \tag{2}$$

14.3. For an infinite stream impinging on a strip of width one, with a cavity pressure equal to undisturbed pressure,

$$s = \frac{1}{1 + \pi} \frac{1}{\cos^2 \theta} \tag{1}$$

$$\frac{\text{force}}{\rho v'^2} = \frac{\pi}{\pi + 4} = 0.440 \tag{2}$$

15. Vortex Motion

15.1. The condition for steady vortex motion in the absence of external forces is

$$\nabla \times [\boldsymbol{v} \times (\nabla \times \boldsymbol{v})] = 0 \tag{1}$$

15.2. Bernoulli's equation holds for steady vortex flow, provided all vortices are parallel to the streamlines.

15.3. The force on a cylinder in laminar straight motion of constant vorticity is

$$f = 2\kappa\rho u \tag{1}$$

where κ = circulation of circumference.

15.4. The stagger ratio of stable pairs of vortices (Karman's vortices) is

$$\kappa\pi = b/a, \quad \cosh^2 \kappa\pi = 2, \quad \kappa\pi = 0.8814 \tag{1}$$

where a = distance of vortices in each line, b = distance between the two lines.

15.5. The velocity of translational advance of a circular vortex depends on the local distribution of the vorticity within the region of the ring.

16. Waves

(One-dimensional, weak)

16.1. Group velocity c_g:

$$c_g = c - \lambda \frac{dc}{d\lambda} \tag{1}$$

where c = wave velocity, λ = wavelength, g = acceleration of gravity.

16.2. Surface waves, gravity, infinite depth:

$$c = \sqrt{g\lambda/2\pi} \tag{1}$$

16.3. Capillary waves:

$$c = \sqrt{2\pi k/\rho\lambda} \tag{1}$$

where k = surface tension (force/length).

16.4. Gravity and capillarity in unison:

$$c = \sqrt{\frac{g\lambda}{2\pi} + \frac{2\pi k}{\rho\lambda}} \tag{1}$$

16.5. Tidal waves, shallow depth h:

$$c = \sqrt{gh} \tag{1}$$

16.6. Water jumps associated with tidal waves, steady:

$$v_1 v_2 = \frac{1}{2}(c_1{}^2 + c_2{}^2) \tag{1}$$

16.7. Same, relation between heights:

$$h_2 = h_1\left[\sqrt{2M_1{}^2 + \frac{1}{4}} - \frac{1}{2}\right] \tag{1}$$

where M denotes equivalent Mach number, v/c.

16.8. Progressing wave traveling in one direction only: The kinetic energy is equal to the potential energy.

17. Model Rules

17.1. Froude's rule:

$$Lg/v^2 = \text{constant} \tag{1}$$

where L = length, v = velocity, g = acceleration of gravity.

17.2. Reynolds' rule

$$R = \text{Reynolds' number} = \frac{vL}{\nu} = \frac{vL}{\mu/\rho} = \text{constant} \tag{1}$$

where ρ = density, μ = modulus of viscosity, $\nu = \mu/\rho$ kinematic modulus of viscosity.

17.3. Mach's rule:

$$\text{Mach number} = M = v/c = \text{constant} \tag{1}$$

where v = velocity, c = velocity of sound (see § 23.2).

17.4. Grashoff's rule:

$$\beta L^3 g \Delta\theta/\nu^2\theta = \text{const.} \tag{1}$$

where θ = temperature, β = thermal expansion.

18. Viscosity
(Incompressible)

18.1. Absence of inertia forces:

$$\mu\nabla^2 v = \nabla p, \qquad \nabla\cdot v = 0 \tag{1}$$

18.2. Sphere with radius a advancing with velocity U:

$$P = 6\pi\mu a U \tag{1}$$

where P = resistance.

18.3. Circular disk having radius r moving broadside on

$$R = 16r/9\pi \tag{1}$$

R denotes the radius of the sphere having the same resistance.

18.4. Circular cylinder, two-dimensional flow:

$$R = \frac{4\pi\mu U}{\frac{1}{2} - \gamma - \ln(\mu a/4v)} \tag{1}$$

where γ = resistance per unit length.

18.5. See §§ 5.6 to 5.8; also Section 24.

18.6. Poiseuille flow through straight vertical circular pipe (laminar):

$$\text{Flux} = \frac{\pi a^4}{8\mu}\left(\frac{p_1 - p_2}{l} + \rho g\right) \tag{1}$$

where a = radius of pipe.

18.7. The velocity profile across the diameter of a Poiseuille flow is a parabola.

18.8. Couette flow between two parallel plane walls sliding relatively to each other, steady flow:

$$\text{Tangential force per unit area} = \sigma = \mu v/a \tag{1}$$

where a = distance of walls, v = difference of wall velocities.

19. Gas Flow, One- and Two-Dimensional (Isentropic)

19.1. Velocity of sound:

$$c^2 = dp/d\rho \tag{1}$$

If p is not a function of ρ, both must be varied for the particle considered. With steady flows they have to be varied along the streamline.

19.2. Velocity of sound for a perfect gas:

$$c^2 = \gamma p/\rho = \gamma g^{R\theta} \tag{1}$$

19.3. General equation for sound wave motion:

$$\partial^2\phi/\partial T^2 = c^2\nabla^2\phi \tag{1}$$

19.4. The kinetic energy of a simple, harmonic sound wave is equal to its elastic energy.

19.5. Force necessary to vibrate a sphere (linearized, amplitude $\ll$ radius):

$$f = \frac{4}{3}\pi\rho a^3\left[\frac{2+k^2a^2}{4+k^4a^4}\frac{du}{dT} + \frac{k^3a^3}{4+k^4a^4}\sigma u\right] \tag{1}$$

where a = radius of cylinder, $k = 2\pi$/wavelength, $\sigma = 2\pi$/period.

19.6. Subsonic flow past a circular cylinder (perfect gas):

$$\frac{\phi}{u} = \phi_{00} + M^2\phi_{10} + \ldots = \left(r + \frac{1}{r}\right)\cos\theta \tag{1}$$

$$+ M^2\left[\left(\frac{13}{12}r^{-1} - \frac{1}{2}r^{-3} + \frac{1}{12}r^{-5}\right)\cos\theta + \left(-\frac{1}{4}r^{-1} + \frac{1}{12}r^{-3}\right)\cos 3\theta\right] + \ldots \tag{2}$$

19.7. Characteristic equations for plane two-dimensional potential flows:

$$d\theta \pm dp \frac{\sin\mu \cos\mu}{\rho c^2} = 0 \tag{1}$$

For plane two-dimensional flow:

$$dv/v = \pm \tan\mu \, d\theta, \qquad \sin\mu = 1/M \tag{2}$$

19.8. Same for polytropic expansion, integrated along the Mach line:

$$\mu + \sqrt{\frac{\gamma+1}{\gamma-1}} \tan^{-1} \sqrt{\frac{\gamma+1}{\gamma-1}} \tan\mu \pm \theta = 0 \tag{1}$$

For Prandtl-Meyer flow the characteristic equations (19.7) or (19.8) hold through the entire flow and not merely along any characteristic.

19.9. Characteristic equation for axially symmetric flow:

$$d\theta \pm dp \frac{\sin\mu \cos\mu}{\rho c^2} \mp \frac{dr}{r} \frac{\sin\theta \sin\mu}{\sin(\theta \pm \mu)} = 0 \tag{1}$$

19.10. Characteristic equation for unsteady one-dimensional flow:

$$\frac{2}{\gamma-1} c \pm v = \text{constant} = \frac{2}{\gamma-1} c_0 \tag{1}$$

$$\frac{2}{\gamma-1} c_0 \equiv \text{escape velocity} \tag{2}$$

Equation 19.10 holds throughout centered flow, that is, waves traveling in one direction only.

19.11. Coparallelism: All Mach line systems of plane two-dimensional potential flows of the same polytropic gas are coparallel. That is to say, corresponding sides of the diamonds formed by corresponding pairs of adjacent Mach lines are parallel. Mach lines are corresponding if they are parallel at the same Mach number station. If they are parallel at one Mach number station, they are at all Mach number stations.

20. Gas Flows, Three Dimensional

20.1. Isentropic supersonic flow past a circular cone, symmetric (Taylor-Maccoll):

$$v = u_\omega \tag{1}$$

where $\omega =$ polar angle, $u =$ radial velocity, $v =$ peripheral velocity.

20.2. Velocity component of general linearized conical flow, $M^2 = 2$:

$$u = F\left(\frac{x + iy}{iz + \sqrt{x^2 + y^2 - z^2}}\right) + F\left(\frac{(x - iy)}{iz + \sqrt{x^2 + y^2 - z^2}}\right) \tag{1}$$

(See § 8.9).

20.3. Throat flow:

$$\xi^2 = \frac{2Rr}{\gamma + 1} \tag{1}$$

where $\xi =$ radius of curvature of sonic line, $r =$ throat radius, $R =$ radius of curvature of nozzle wall, $\gamma =$ expansion exponent.

20.4. Reversal theorem for three-dimensional airfoil flow (linearized equations). The lift slope of any airfoil remains unchanged if the velocity of advance is reversed.

20.5. Slender delta wing, having span b. The lift coefficient slope computed with $b^2\pi/4$ and $v^2\rho/2$ as reference quantities is equal to 2.

20.6. Initial lift slope of slender, flat-based, finless missile body of circular cross section (linearized equations). The lift coefficient slope computed with $D^2\pi/4$ and $v^2\rho/2$ as reference quantities is equal to 2. ($D =$ base diameter.)

20.7. Canonical variables: Every steady flow of a polytropic gas can be expressed by four dependent variables u/a, v/a, w/a, and p, where a denotes the ultimate velocity of the streamline in question. That is to say, every streamline pattern serves an infinity of flows, in that the density can be prescribed arbitrarily at one point at each streamline. The flow may include shock waves.

21. Hypothetical Gases

21.1. Chaplygin gas:

$$p = -\frac{A}{\rho} + B, \qquad \gamma = -1 \tag{1}$$

This gas can execute a plane, simple, sound wave of finite magnitude with unchangeable contour. In plane two-dimensional potential flows all Mach line elements along any one Mach line of the conjugate family are parallel. The characteristics in the hodograph are straight. In the hodograph, the equation for the stream function is reducible to Laplace's equation or to the simple wave equation.

21.2. Munk's gas:

$$p = A - \tan^{-1}\frac{1}{\rho} - \frac{\rho}{1+\rho^2} \tag{1}$$

All Mach lines in the plane two-dimensional potential flow are straight. In the hodograph the characteristics are circles passing through the center. In the hodograph, the equation for the Legendre reciprocal potential is reducible to Laplace's equation or to the simple wave equation. This is not a polytropic expansion.

21.3. Isothermal expansion:

$$\gamma = +1 \tag{1}$$

Many equations for polytropic gases do not hold for this special case, but must be replaced by special equations containing logarithmic or exponential expressions. The ultimate velocity for this expansion is infinite, and the velocity of sound is constant. This constant velocity of sound is preferably used as reference velocity. The elastic energy of expansion available is unlimited.

21.4. Any expansion law $p = f(\rho)$ may be replaced by

$$p = f(\rho) + \text{constant} \tag{1}$$

without any change of the dynamics of the gas.

22. Shockwaves

22.1. Steady, normal shock: a. *Rankine-Hugoniot relations:*

$$u_1^2 + h_1 = u_2^2 + h_2 \qquad \text{(energy)} \tag{1}$$

$$u_1\rho_1 = u_2\rho_2 \qquad \text{(continuity)} \tag{2}$$

$$p_1 + \rho_1 u_1^2 = p_2 + \rho_2 u_2^2 \qquad \text{(momentum)} \tag{3}$$

where subscript 1 denotes upstream shockwave; subscript 2 denotes downstream shockwave; *a* denotes ultimate velocity.

b. *Polytropic expansion, perfect gas:*

$$c^{*2} = a_1^2 \frac{\gamma - 1}{\gamma + 1} = a_2^2 \frac{\gamma - 1}{\gamma + 1}$$

$$\theta_{01} = \theta_{02}, \qquad u_1 u_2 = c^{*2}$$

If M_1 is given,

$$M_2^2 = \frac{(\gamma - 1)M_1^2 + 2}{2\gamma M_1^2 - (\gamma - 1)} = \frac{M_1^2 + 5}{7M_1^2 - 1} \quad (\gamma = 1.4) \tag{5}$$

$$\frac{p_2}{p_1} = \frac{2\gamma M_1^2 - (\gamma - 1)}{\gamma + 1} = \frac{7M_1^2 - 1}{6} \quad (\gamma = 1.4) \tag{6}$$

$$\frac{\rho_2}{\rho_1} = \frac{u_1}{u_2} = \frac{(\gamma + 1)M_1^2}{(\gamma - 1)M_1^2 + 2} = \frac{6M_1^2}{M_1^2 + 5} \quad (\gamma = 1.4) \tag{7}$$

$$\frac{\theta_2}{\theta_1} = \frac{p_2 \rho_1}{p_1 \rho_2} \tag{8}$$

$$\frac{\rho_2}{\rho_1} = \frac{(\gamma + 1)(p_2/p_1) + (\gamma - 1)}{(\gamma - 1)(p_2/p_1) + (\gamma + 1)} = \frac{(6p_2/p_1) + 1}{(p_2/p_1) + 6} \quad (\gamma = 1.4) \tag{9}$$

$$\frac{\Delta S}{c_v} = \ln \frac{2\gamma M_1^2 - (\gamma - 1)}{\gamma + 1} - \gamma \ln \frac{(\gamma + 1)M_1^2}{(\gamma - 1)M_1^2 + 2} \tag{10}$$

where $cv = R/\gamma - 1$.

22.2. Oblique shock waves : In equations (22.1*b*-5), (22.1b-6), and (22.1b-7) substitute $M \sin \sigma$ for M. Then

$$\tan \delta = \frac{2M_1^2(\sin \sigma \cos \sigma - \cot \sigma)}{2 + M_1^2(\gamma + 1 - 2 \sin^2 \sigma)} \tag{1}$$

$$v_1 \cos \sigma = v_2 \cos (\sigma - \delta) \tag{2}$$

$$a^2_{\text{oblique}} = a^2_{\text{normal}} + v_1^2 \cos^2 \sigma \tag{3}$$

$$v_1 \sin \sigma \cdot v_2 \sin (\sigma - \delta) = \frac{\gamma - 1}{\gamma + 1} a^2_{\text{normal}} \tag{4}$$

where σ = shock angle, normal shock $\sigma = 90^\circ$, δ = deflection angle.

23. Cooling

23.1. Notation : k = conductivity, c_p = heat capacity (specific heat), μ = modulus of viscosity, L = reference length.

23.2. Prandtl number:

$$\sigma = \mu c/k \tag{1}$$

23.3. Nusselt number:

$$gL/[k(\theta_2 - \theta_1)] \tag{1}$$

23.4. Impact temperature increase (for air) is about

$$\Delta\theta = (MPH/100)^2 \quad \text{centigrade} \tag{1}$$

23.5. Impact temperature increase

$$\Delta\theta = v^2/2c_p, \quad c_p \sim 1000 \text{ m}^2/\text{sec}^2 \quad \text{(air)} \tag{1}$$

24. Boundary layers

24.1. Notations: u = streamwise velocity component, U = undisturbed velocity, x = streamwise coordinate, X = streamwise distance from leading edge, ρ = density, μ = modulus of viscosity, $\nu = \mu/\rho$, R = Reynolds' number = XU/ν, T = local shear, δ = boundary layer thickness, δ_{99} same up to where velocity equals 99 % of undisturbed velocity, δ_d = asymptotic displacement of streamlines, S = " wetted " area.

24.2. Boundary layer equations (incompressible):

$$u_T + uu_x + vu_y = -p_x/\rho + u_{yy}\nu \tag{1}$$

$$u_x + v_y = 0 \tag{2}$$

a. *Boundary layer of flat plate* (*laminar*). Boundary layer is laminar, for R = 350,000 to 500,000.

$$T = 0.332u^2\rho\sqrt{\mu/(U\rho X)} = 1.66\mu u/\delta_{99} \tag{1}$$

$$\delta_{99} = 5\sqrt{\nu x/u} \tag{2}$$

$$\delta_{\text{displ}} = 1.73\sqrt{\nu x/u} \tag{3}$$

Total friction

$$D_f = 1.328 S\rho u^2/(2\sqrt{xu/\nu}) \tag{4}$$

b. *Boundary layer of flat plate* (*turbulent*). The following holds for R = 1,000,000 to 10,000,000.

$$\delta = \frac{0.37x}{\sqrt[5]{ux/\nu}} \tag{1}$$

$$\tau = 0.0228\rho u^2 \sqrt[4]{\frac{\nu}{u\delta}} \tag{2}$$

$$= 0.0294\rho u^2 \sqrt[5]{\frac{\nu}{ux}} \tag{3}$$

$$D_f = 0.072\rho u^2 \frac{S}{2} \sqrt[5]{\frac{\nu}{ux}} \tag{4}$$

Bibliography

1. Bateman, H., *Partial Differential Equations*, Dover Publications, New York, 1944.
2. Courant, R. and Friedrichs, R. O., *Supersonic Flow and Shock Waves*, Interscience Publishers, Inc., New York, 1948. Emphasizes the mathematical aspect of gas dynamics.
3. Durand, W. F., *Aerodynamic Theory*, Julius Springer, Berlin, 1935. Reprinted by California Institute of Technology, 1943. See especially Vols. 1, 2, 6.
4. Goldstein, S., *Modern Developments in Fluid Dynamics*, Clarendon Press, Oxford, 1938.
5. Lamb, H., *Hydrodynamics*, 6th ed., Cambridge University Press, London, 1932. (Also Dover Publications, New York, 1945.) The classical treatise, rich and profound.
6. Sauer, R., *Einführung in die theoretische Gasdynamik*, Julius Springer, Berlin, 1943.
7. Tietjens, O. G., *Applied Hydro- and Aeromechanics* (based on lectures of L. Prandtl; trans. J. P. Den Hartog), McGraw-Hill Book Company, Inc., New York, 1934. Short and clear.
8. Tietjens, O. G., *Fundamentals of Hydro- and Aeromechanics* (based on lectures of L. Prandtl; trans. L. Rosenhead), McGraw-Hill Book Company, Inc., New York, 1934. Short and clear.

Chapter 9

BOUNDARY VALUE PROBLEMS IN MATHEMATICAL PHYSICS

By Henry Zatzkis

Assistant Professor of Mathematics
Newark College of Engineering

1. The Significance of the Boundary

1.1. Introductory remarks. Boundary value problems occupy a central position in mathematical physics. To give a systematic development of this subject would be well beyond the scope of the book, and we shall therefore confine ourselves to the discussion of some of the equations that occur more frequently. Other specifications will appear in other chapters. The major difficulty is not so much to find a solution of the given differential equation (in fact the equations admit always an infinity of solutions), but to find that solution which fits the given boundary values. If the solution depends on space and time, the latter can be treated formally as an additional coordinate in a space of one extra dimension, and the initial conditions thus also form part of the " boundary " conditions.

We are mainly concerned here with the Laplace equation, wave equation, and heat conduction equation. They are all linear, homogeneous, partial differential equations of second order. We plan first to discuss these equations individually and then to describe some of the features common to all which furnish unifying principles for their solutions. Finally, we shall also add some remarks concerning the corresponding inhomogeneous equations. Since any linear, homogeneous, differential equation can be solved by the method of separation of variables, this method furnishes one of the principal tools. However, it is not the only possibility, as will be seen subsequently.

1.2. The Laplace equation. The three-dimensional Laplace equation in Cartesian coordinates is defined by

$$\nabla^2\Phi = \frac{\partial^2\Phi}{\partial x^2} + \frac{\partial\Phi}{\partial y^2} + \frac{\partial^2\Phi}{\partial z^2} = 0 \qquad (1)$$

If Φ is independent of z, we obtain the two-dimensional Laplace equation

$$\nabla^2\Phi = \frac{\partial^2\Phi}{\partial x^2} + \frac{\partial^2\Phi}{\partial y^2} = 0 \tag{2}$$

A function Φ satisfying the Laplace equation is called harmonic. An intuitive interpretation of $\nabla^2\Phi$ is the following. Consider a point P_0 at which Φ has the value Φ_0. Draw a little sphere around P_0 with a radius sufficiently small that we can use the Taylor formula to express the values of Φ on the surface of the sphere and neglect third-order and higher-order terms. If we compute the arithmetic mean of Φ on the spherical surface and denote it by $\overline{\Phi}$, then $\overline{\Phi} - \Phi_0 = (\nabla^2\Phi)_0$. We can therefore say that $\nabla^2\Phi$ is a measure for the deviation of the value of Φ at a given point from its average or " equilibrium " value. This interpretation is especially helpful in understanding the nature of the wave equation or heat conduction equation.

The Laplace equation is fundamental for potential theory; Φ then represents the potential produced by gravitational masses (or electrostatic charges) in a region free from mass (or charge). The simplest boundary value

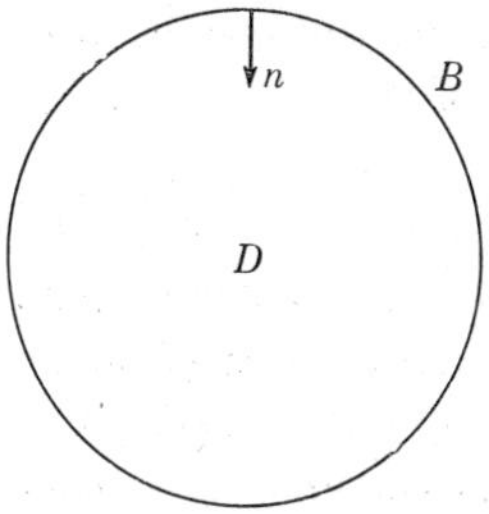

FIGURE 1

problem is the following: Given a simply connected domain D (Fig. 1), bounded by a continuous boundary B, the values of Φ on B are prescribed to be a continuous function $\overline{\Phi}$. We then wish to find the values of Φ in the interior of D, satisfying the Laplace equation and taking on the prescribed boundary values. This is the " inner " Dirichlet problem. In place of the function values $\overline{\Phi}$ themselves, their normal derivatives $\overline{\partial\Phi/\partial n}$ may be prescribed on B. This constitutes the Neumann problem or, finally, a linear combination of the function values and their normal derivatives with constant coefficients may be prescribed on B. This is the " third " problem, which occurs mainly in connection with the heat conduction equation. The condition, imposed on the solution Φ to be harmonic in D, has as a consequence that $\overline{\Phi}$ and $\overline{\partial\Phi/\partial n}$ cannot be prescribed independent of each other and, therefore, cannot be prescribed simultaneously in an arbitrary manner.

If we wanted the solution Φ outside the domain D, with the same boundary conditions, we should speak of the corresponding " outer " problems.

We understand that the positive direction of the normal always extends into the interior of the region D. To give meaning to the concept of " normal, " we must assume that the boundary consists of at least piecewise continuously differentiable sections.

We finally remark that the domain may also be multiply connected.

1.3. Method of separation of variables. Frequently the boundary is of a simple geometrical structure, e.g., a rectangle or a circle. Then we find it useful to employ rectangular or, more generally, curvilinear coordinates in which the boundary consists of sections along which one of the coordinates has a constant value. In case of the rectangle we use of course, the Cartesian coordinates themselves. The boundary consists then of segments, described by equations $x =$ constant and $y =$ constant. In case of a circular boundary of radius a, we use polar coordinates, and the boundary is given by $r = a$. The Laplace equation, after transformation to the new coordinates u, v, w, usually yields to a solution of the form

$$\Phi(u,v,w) = U(u)V(v)W(w) \tag{1}$$

We obtain then a system of ordinary differential equations for the functions U, V, and W. The final step consists of obtaining any appropriate linear combination of the solutions of type Eq. (1) with constant coefficients chosen to satisfy the given boundary conditions. Some examples are the following.

a. *Cartesian coordinates, three-dimensional:*

$$\frac{\partial^2\Phi}{\partial x^2} + \frac{\partial^2\Phi}{\partial y^2} + \frac{\partial^2\Phi}{\partial z^2} = 0 \tag{2}$$

Particular solutions:

$$\Phi_{k,l,m} = (kx + ly + mz), \qquad (k^2 + l^2 + m^2 = 1) \tag{3}$$

b. *Cartesian coordinates, two-dimensional:*

$$\frac{\partial^2\Phi}{\partial x^2} + \frac{\partial^2\Phi}{\partial y^2} = 0 \tag{4}$$

Particular solutions:

$$\Phi_k = e^{\pm k(x \pm iy)} \tag{5}$$

c. *Spherical coordinates* (r,θ,φ) :

$$\frac{1}{r^2}\frac{\partial}{\partial r}\left(r^2\frac{\partial\Phi}{\partial r}\right)+\frac{1}{r^2\sin\theta}\frac{\partial}{\partial\theta}\left(\sin\theta\frac{\partial\Phi}{\partial\theta}\right)+\frac{1}{r^2\sin^2\theta}\frac{\partial^2\Phi}{\partial r^2}=0 \tag{6}$$

Particular solutions :

$$\Phi_{m,k}=\left(Ar^m+\frac{B}{r^{m+1}}\right)e^{\pm ik\varphi}P_m{}^k(\cos\theta) \tag{7}$$

where $P_m{}^k(\cos\theta)=$ associated Legendre polynomial.

d. *Cylindrical coordinates, three-dimensional* (ρ,φ,z) :

$$\frac{\partial^2\Phi}{\partial\rho^2}+\frac{1}{\rho}\frac{\partial\Phi}{\partial\rho}+\frac{1}{\rho^2}\frac{\partial^2\Phi}{\partial\varphi^2}+\frac{\partial^2\Phi}{\partial z^2}=0 \tag{8}$$

Particular solutions :

$$\Phi_{k,m}=e^{\pm i(kz\pm m\varphi)}J_m(ik\rho) \tag{9}$$

where $J_m=$ Bessel function of order m.

e. *Cylindrical coordinates, two-dimensional* (ρ,φ) :

$$\frac{\partial^2\Phi}{\partial\rho^2}+\frac{1}{\rho}\frac{\partial\Phi}{\partial\rho}+\frac{1}{\rho^2}\frac{\partial^2\Phi}{\partial\varphi^2}=0 \tag{10}$$

Particular solutions :

$$\Phi_k=\rho^{\pm k}e^{ik\varphi} \tag{11}$$

f. *Elliptical coordinates* (u_1,u_2,u_3) :

The relations between the Cartesian and elliptical coordinates are :

$$\left.\begin{aligned} x&=\sqrt{\frac{(u_1+a^2)(u_2+a^2)(u_3+a^2)}{(b^2-a^2)(c^2-a^2)}}\\ y&=\sqrt{\frac{(u_1+b^2)(u_2+b^2)(u_3+b^2)}{(c^2-b^2)(a^2-b^2)}}\\ z&=\sqrt{\frac{(u_1+c^2)(u_2+c^2)(u_3+c^2)}{(a^2-c^2)(b^2-c^2)}}\end{aligned}\right\} \tag{12}$$

where $a^2>u_3>b^2>u_2>c^2>u_1$. The surfaces $u_1=$ constant, $u_2=$ constant, $u_3=$ constant represent confocal ellipsoids, hyperboloids of one sheet, and hyperboloids of two sheets, respectively.

Then $u_1 = 0$ in the ellipsoid

$$\frac{x^2}{a^2} + \frac{y^2}{b^2} + \frac{z^2}{c^2} = 1$$

If $$R_i = \sqrt{(u_i + a^2)(u_i + b^2)(u_i + c^2)}, \qquad (i = 1,2,3)$$

the Laplacian reads as follows.

$$\left.\begin{aligned}\nabla^2\Phi = \frac{4}{(u_1 - u_2)(u_2 - u_3)(u_3 - u_1)} \Bigg[&(u_2 - u_3)R_1 \frac{\partial}{\partial u_1}\left(R_1 \frac{\partial\Phi}{\partial u_1}\right) \\ &+ (u_3 - u_1)R_2 \frac{\partial}{\partial u_2}\left(R_2 \frac{\partial\Phi}{\partial u_2}\right) \\ &+ (u_1 - u_2)R_3 \frac{\partial}{\partial u_3}\left(R_3 \frac{\partial\Phi}{\partial u_3}\right)\Bigg] = 0\end{aligned}\right\} \tag{13}$$

As an illustration, let us compute the potential of a charged ellipsoidal conductor, whose surface is given by

$$\frac{x^2}{a^2} + \frac{y^2}{b^2} + \frac{z^2}{c^2} = 1$$

The conductor must be a surface of constant potential. For large distances the potential must fall off as Q/r, where Q is the charge of the conductor. The equipotential surfaces are confocal ellipsoids, i.e., Φ depends only on u_1. The Laplace equation reduces to

$$\frac{d}{du_1}\left(R_1 \frac{d\Phi}{du_1}\right) = 0 \tag{14}$$

The solution is

$$\Phi = k \int_{u_1=0}^{\infty} \frac{d\xi}{R_1(\xi)} \tag{15}$$

where $R_1(\xi) = \sqrt{(\xi + a^2)(\xi + b^2)(\xi + c^2)}$. For large values of $r^2 = x^2 + y^2 + z^2$, the value of ξ approaches r^2, and the potential Φ itself approaches the value

$$\Phi \doteq \frac{2k}{r} \tag{16}$$

Therefore $2k = Q =$ charge of the conductor, and the solution becomes

$$\Phi = \frac{Q}{2} \int_{u_1=0}^{\infty} \frac{d\xi}{R_1(\xi)} \tag{17}$$

1.4. Method of integral equations. We can express the interior Dirichlet problem as the solution of an integral equation. Let Q and T be points on the boundary B and P, and interior point of the domain D; let n be the interior normal of B, and $g(T)$ be the preassigned boundary values of $\Phi(P)$. The solution of the problem is then in the three-dimensional case

$$\Phi(P) = \iint_B f(Q) \frac{\partial}{\partial n_Q} \left(\frac{1}{r_{PQ}}\right) dS_Q \tag{1}$$

where $f(Q)$ is the solution of the integral equation

$$2\pi f(T) + \iint_B f(Q) \frac{\partial}{\partial n_Q} \left(\frac{1}{r_{TQ}}\right) dS_Q = g(T) \tag{2}$$

In the two-dimensional case the corresponding formulas are

$$\Phi(P) = \oint_B f(Q) \frac{\partial}{\partial n_Q} \left(\log \frac{1}{r_{TQ}}\right) dS_Q \tag{3}$$

and

$$\pi f(T) + \oint_B f(Q) \frac{\partial}{\partial n_Q} \left(\log \frac{1}{r_{TQ}}\right) dS_Q = g(T) \tag{4}$$

In the second case B is the curve bounding the area D, dS_Q is a line element, and the line integral has to be taken in the positive sense (the interior of the domain must be to the left of B).

The integral equations for f are Fredholm integral equations of the second kind. For the methods of their solution the reader is referred to any textbook on integral equations or potential theory.

In the special case where the boundary is a sphere or circle of radius 1, an explicit solution can be given. The formulas are known as the Poisson integral formulas:

$$\Phi(P) = \frac{1}{2\pi} \iint_B g(Q) \left[\frac{\partial}{\partial n_Q} \left(\frac{1}{r_{PQ}}\right) - \frac{1}{2l r_{PQ}}\right] d_1 S_Q \tag{5}$$

and

$$\Phi(P) = \frac{1}{\pi} \oint g(Q) \left[\frac{\partial}{\partial n_Q} \left(\log \frac{1}{r_{PQ}}\right) - \frac{1}{2l}\right] dS_Q \tag{6}$$

1.5. Method of Green's function. This method is closely related to the foregoing discussion. The Green function G belonging to the domain D with the boundary B is defined in the following way: G is a function of two points $P(x,y,z)$ and $Q(\xi,\eta,\zeta)$, of which the point P varies in the interior of D, and Q varies in $D + B$. Also, G has the property that, as a function of Q, it is harmonic in $D + B$, with the exception of P. In P, the function G becomes singular, like $1/r_{PQ}$.

Therefore, G can be written

$$G(r_{PQ}) = \frac{1}{r_{PQ}} + \omega(r_{PQ}) \tag{1}$$

where r_{PQ} is harmonic in the closed domain $D + B$. Finally, we assume that, on the boundary, ω takes on the value $-1/r_{PQ}$. In the two-dimensional case, the procedure is identical, except that we replace $1/r_{PQ}$ by $\log(1/r_{PQ})$.

The solution of the interior Dirichlet problem then becomes

$$\Phi(P) = \frac{1}{4\pi}\iint_B g(Q)\frac{\partial G}{\partial n}\,dS_Q \tag{2}$$

in the three-dimensional case, and

$$\Phi(P) = \frac{1}{2\pi}\oint_B g(Q)\frac{\partial G}{\partial n}\,dS_Q \tag{3}$$

in the two-dimensional case. As in the preceding section, the function $g(Q)$ denotes the prescribed boundary values of Φ.

For a sphere and a circle, Green's function can be stated explicitly. Let Q (Fig. 2) be a point on the boundary, and P an interior point whose

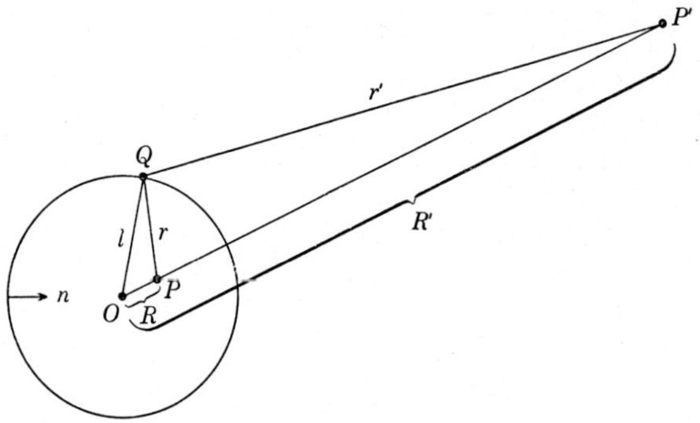

FIGURE 2

distance from the center O is R. Let P' be the " conjugate " point of P with the distance R' from O, i.e., $\overline{OP}\cdot\overline{OP'} = RR' = l^2$ ($l =$ radius). Then

$$G(PQ) = 1/r - l/Rr'$$

for the three-dimensional case, and

$$G(PQ) = \log(1/r) - \log(l/Rr')$$

for the two-dimensional case. W. Thomson's (Lord Kelvin's) method of electrical images is based on these Green functions.

1.6. Additional remarks about the two-dimensional case. The two-dimensional Laplace equation has an important property that any analytic function

$$f(z) = \Phi(x,y) + i\Psi(x,y) \tag{1}$$

is a solution of the Laplace equation. The fact that $f(z)$ is analytic permits us to use all the results of function theory. Especially important is the theorem that an analytic function remains analytic under a conformal mapping. The conjugate functions Φ and Ψ satisfy the Cauchy-Riemann equations

$$\partial\Phi/\partial x = \partial\Psi/\partial y, \qquad \partial\Phi/\partial y = -\partial\Psi/\partial x \tag{2}$$

A consequence of Eq. (2) is that both Φ and Ψ satisfy Laplace's equation. The two families of curves $\Phi =$ constant and $\Psi =$ constant are mutually orthogonal. We can, therefore, interpret them, respectively, as lines of constant potential and lines of force. Under a conformal mapping they will transform into two families of mutually orthogonal curves. We utilize these results in solving problems in electrostatics and in the steady, two-dimensional flow of an incompressible, ideal liquid. If this flow is also irrotational, the velocity distribution can be described by a velocity potential function $\Phi(x,y)$ whose Laplacian is zero. The Cartesian components of the velocity at the point (x,y) are given by

$$u = \partial\Phi/\partial x, \qquad v = \partial\Phi/\partial y \tag{3}$$

As an example let us consider a uniform motion with a constant velocity α in a positive x direction. Then

$$\Phi = \alpha x \tag{4}$$

and, therefore,

$$\Psi = \alpha y \tag{5}$$

or

$$f(z) = \alpha(x + iy) = \alpha z, \qquad (z = x + iy)\ * \tag{6}$$

The mapping $\omega = z^2$ maps the upper half-plane into the upper right-hand quadrant. As we can see from Eq. (8), the new streamlines are hyperbolas with the coordinate axes as asymptotes. The velocity potential takes the form

$$\xi = \alpha^2(x^2 - y^2) \tag{9}$$

The velocity components are

$$u = \partial\xi/\partial x = 2\alpha^2 x, \qquad v = \partial\xi/\partial y = 2\alpha^2 y \tag{10}$$

* The mapping $\omega = z^2$ gives us again a possible flow. If we write

$$\omega = \xi + i\eta \tag{7}$$

the new streamlines are given by

$$\eta = 2\alpha^2 xy = \text{constant} \tag{8}$$

The magnitude of the velocity is

$$\sqrt{u^2 + v^2} = 2\alpha^2 r, \qquad (r^2 = x^2 + y^2) \tag{11}$$

In the plane every analytic function represents a conformal mapping. In three-dimensional space the possibilities of conformal mapping (i.e., angle-preserving mapping) are much more restricted. Aside from the similarity transformations (i.e., rigid rotations, translations, and stretching the x, y, and z axes by the same factor), the only nontrivial conformal mapping of the space upon itself is the inversion at a sphere. If the radius of the sphere is equal to 1, the image point P' of the object point P lies along the infinite half line through the center of the sphere and P, and its distance from the center is given by $\overline{OR} \cdot \overline{OR'} = l^2$. If the center of the sphere is at the origin, the coordinates of the point P′ and P are, therefore,

$$\left.\begin{aligned} x' &= \frac{l^2}{R^2}\,x, \qquad y' = \frac{l^2}{R^2}\,y, \qquad z' = \frac{l^2}{R^2}\,z \\ x &= \frac{l^2}{R'^2}\,x', \qquad y = \frac{l^2}{R'^2}\,y', \qquad z = \frac{l^2}{R'^2}\,z' \end{aligned}\right\} \tag{12}$$

As W. Thomson discovered, we have here also a possibility of obtaining new solutions of the Laplace equation from the original one by conformal mapping. However, we find one difference that distinguishes the three-dimensional from the two-dimensional case. If

$$\frac{\partial^2 F}{\partial x^2} + \frac{\partial^2 F}{\partial y^2} + \frac{\partial^2 F}{\partial z^2} = 0 \tag{13}$$

then $F(x',y',z')$ does not satisfy the Laplace equation, but

$$F' = \frac{l}{R'}\,F(x',y',z') \tag{14}$$

does:

$$\frac{\partial^2 F'}{(\partial x')^2} + \frac{\partial^2 F'}{(\partial y')^2} + \frac{\partial^2 F'}{(\partial z')^2} = 0 \tag{15}$$

Green's function is closely related to the problem of conformal mapping in the two-dimensional case. Let $\zeta = f(x + iy)$ be an analytic function that maps conformally the domain D in the z plane ($z = x + iy$) in such a manner into the unit circle in the y plane, such that the point $\zeta(\xi,\eta)$ in D goes over into the center of the unit circle; then $-(1/2\pi) \log |f(x + iy)|$ is the desired Green function. Thus we know the Green functions for all those domains which can be mapped conformally into the unit circle.

1.7. The one-dimensional wave equation. The fundamental equation for the propagation of a wave in an anisotropic and homogeneous medium is

$$\nabla^2\Phi = \frac{1}{c^2}\frac{\partial^2\Phi}{\partial t^2} \tag{1}$$

where c is the velocity at which a disturbance will travel. If the direction of propagation is in the x direction only, the equation above reduces to

$$\frac{\partial^2\Phi}{\partial x^2} = \frac{1}{c^2}\frac{\partial^2\Phi}{\partial t^2} \tag{2}$$

Just as was the case for the two-dimensional Laplace equation, we can write the general solution at once:

$$\Phi(x,t) = F(x - ct) + G(x + ct) \tag{3}$$

where F represents a disturbance traveling in the positive x direction at velocity c, and G is a disturbance traveling in the negative x direction at the velocity c.

We want to apply this solution to find the motion of a vibrating string which is held fixed at its boundary points $x = 0$ and $x = L$, and whose initial displacement is prescribed to be $\Phi(x,0) = f(x)$, and its initial velocity distribution

$$\left.\frac{\partial\Phi}{\partial t}\right|_{t=0} = g(x)$$

From the initial conditions it follows that

$$\left.\begin{aligned} f(x) &= F(x) + G(x) \\ g(x) &= -cF'(x) + cG'(x) \end{aligned}\right\} \quad \text{for} \quad 0 \leqq x \leqq L \tag{4}$$

where primes denote derivatives with respect to the argument. If the second equation is integrated and combined with the first we obtain

$$\left.\begin{aligned} F(x) &= \frac{1}{2}\left(f(x) - \frac{1}{c}\int_{x_0}^{x} g(u)du\right) \\ G(x) &= \frac{1}{2}\left(f(x) + \frac{1}{c}\int_{x_0}^{x} g(u)du\right) \end{aligned}\right\} \quad \text{for} \quad 0 \leqq x \leqq L \tag{5}$$

The lower limit x_0 is arbitrary, and it will be cancelled out if Eq. (5) is substituted into Eq. (3):

$$\Phi(x,t) = \frac{1}{2}\left[f(x - ct) + f(x + ct) + \frac{1}{c}\int_{x-ct}^{x+ct} g(u)du\right] \tag{6}$$

Since f and g are defined only for values between 0 and L, the formula above is valid only for

$$ct \leqq x \leqq L - ct$$

However, the boundary conditions permit us to extend this range, for we must have

$$\Phi(0,t) = F(-ct) + G(ct) = 0$$

for all t. Therefore,

$$F(-x) = -G(x) \tag{7}$$

Hence the second equation (5) permits us to define $F(x)$ also for the range

$$-L \leqq x \leqq 0$$

Using Eq. (7), Eq. (3) can now be written

$$\Phi(x,t) = F(x - ct) - F(-x - ct) \tag{8}$$

The second boundary condition for $x = L$ now yields

$$\Phi(L,t) = F(L - ct) - F(-L - ct) = 0 \tag{9}$$

or

$$F(L - ct) = F(-L - ct) \tag{10}$$

This result shows that F is a periodic function in x with the period $2L$. Thus, F is defined for all values of x. Furthermore, if t increases by $T = 2L/c$, the function will also repeat itself. Therefore F is also defined for all times.

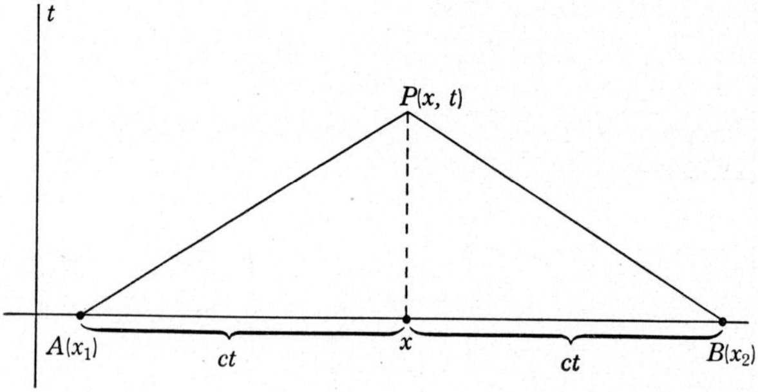

FIGURE 3

Equation (6) has an interesting geometrical interpretation (see Fig. 3). We draw through the point P in the x,t plane the two characteristic lines PA and PB (the characteristic lines are the lines obeying the equations $x = ct =$ constant). It is only those initial data (Cauchy data) which lie on the segment AB that contribute to the disturbance at point P at the time t. In optics the triangular polygon APB is called the retrograde light cone. If the initial velocities are zero, i.e., $g = 0$, then

$$\Phi(x,t) = \tfrac{1}{2}[f(x - ct) + f(x + ct)] \tag{11}$$

This is an expression of Huyghens' principle: The perturbation at x at the time t, originating from the sources at A and B at the time zero, need the retardation time $\tau = (x_2 - x)/c = (x - x_1)/c$ to reach the point x.

1.8. The general eigenvalue problem and the higher-dimensional wave equation. The one-dimensional wave equation is the only one for which the general solution can be given in closed form as in Eq. (3). In all other cases the method of separation of variables must be used. It will, therefore, be useful to consider those features which are common to all these problems and see the common underlying idea. We shall designate the spatial coordinates by x_1, x_2, x_3 (not necessarily Cartesian) and time again by t.

The inhomogeneous wave equation is of the structure

$$L[u] = \rho(x_1,x_2,x_3,\ldots)\frac{\partial^2 u}{\partial t'^2} - F(x_1,\ldots,t), \quad u = u(x_1,\ldots,t) \tag{1}$$

where L is a linear differential operator which operates on the spatial coordinates only. The linearity of L means that L has the property

$$L[au_1 + bu_2] = aL[u_1] + bL[u_2]$$

where a and b are independent of x.

We need also the concept of adjoint and self-adjoint linear differential operators. Let $u = u(x\ldots t)$ and $v = v(x\ldots t)$ be any two sufficiently differentiable functions in x; M is called the adjoint of L if $vL[u] - uM[v]$ can be written as a complete divergence, i.e., there exists a set of functions $f_1(x_1\ldots t)$, $f_2(x_1\ldots t)$, ... such that

$$vL[u] - uM[v] = \frac{\partial f_1}{\partial x_1} + \ldots + \frac{\partial f_n}{\partial x_n}$$

where $n =$ dimensionality of the space, and L is called self-adjoint if $L = M$.

We also need the concept of homogeneous and inhomogeneous boundary conditions. We speak of a problem having a homogeneous character if, with the solution u the function cu is also a solution, where c is a constant. For this to be the case it is necessary not only that the differential equation but also that the boundary conditions, be homogeneous, e.g., $u = 0$ on B, or $\partial u/\partial n = 0$ on B, or $A_1 u + A_2(\partial u/\partial n) = 0$ on B, where A_1 and A_2 are constants.

Now suppose that u satisfies a homogeneous equation but an inhomogeneous boundary condition

$$u = f \quad \text{on } B.$$

It is then possible to continue f in such a manner into the interior of D that $L[f] = g$, where g is a continuous function in D. We can now construct a new function $v = f - u$ which satisfies the inhomogeneous differential equation $L[v] = g$ but satisfies the homogeneous boundary conditions

$$v = 0 \quad \text{on } B.$$

The problem can be reversed in the same manner, and we can state quite generally that a homogeneous differential equation with inhomogeneous boundary conditions is equivalent to an inhomogeneous differential equation with homogeneous boundary conditions.

We shall, from now on, assume L to be self-adjoint (in the case of the wave equation, L is the Laplace operator, which is self-adjoint). If ρ is a function of x only, we can interpret ρ as the mass density, and Eq. (1) represents the dynamical equation for a continuous medium with the restoring force $L[u]$, e.g., an elastic force and an applied, external force F. In the case of equilibrium, after the transient has died and where F is a function of x only, we obtain as a special case Poisson's equation:

$$L[u] = F(x_1, \ldots) \tag{2}$$

The general problem to be solved is *that we assume L, ρ and F are defined in a certain spatial domain D.* On the boundary B of D we prescribe the homogeneous boundary conditions

$$u(x_1, \ldots, 0) = \varphi(x_1, \ldots) \quad \text{and} \quad \left.\frac{\partial u}{\partial t}\right|_{t=0} = \psi(x_1, \ldots) \quad \text{on } B$$

We want to find a solution $u(x_1, \ldots, t)$ of Eq. (1) which satisfies these boundary conditions.

We shall first discuss the homogeneous differential equation

$$L[u] = \rho \frac{\partial^2 u}{\partial t^2} \tag{3}$$

i.e., $F \equiv 0$. Among all the possible solutions of Eq. (3) obeying homogeneous boundary conditions, we are especially interested in the synchronous solutions, i.e., those solutions which can be written

$$u = v(x_1, \ldots, x_n) g(t) \tag{4}$$

Since we are interested in periodic phenomena in time, we assume $g(t)$ of the form

$$g(t) = a \cos \lambda t + b \sin \lambda t \tag{5}$$

We obtain then for v the equation

$$L[v] + \lambda^2 \rho v = 0 \tag{6}$$

where v must now satisfy the boundary conditions imposed on u. Eq. (6) is called a Sturm-Liouville equation. We will find that if D is a finite domain, solutions obeying the boundary conditions will exist only for special values of λ: $\lambda_1, \lambda_2, \ldots$, the so-called characteristic values, or eigenvalues. The solutions belonging to them: $v_1(x), v_2(x), \ldots$, are called the characteristic functions or eigenfunctions. The solution of Eq. (3) is given by

$$u = (a \cos \lambda t + b \sin \lambda t) v(x_1, \ldots, x_n) \tag{7}$$

An eigenvalue λ_i can have several eigenfunctions $u_i^{(1)}, \ldots, u_i^{(k)}$. It is then called a k-fold degenerate. The eigenfunctions can be chosen in such a way that they form a " complete orthonormal " set, i.e.,

$$\int_D \rho u_i u_k d\tau = \delta_{ik} \tag{8}$$

Every function $h(x_1, \ldots)$ which has the degree of differentiability required by the operator L and obeys the required boundary conditions can be written in a generalized Fourier series

$$h = \sum_{n=1}^{\infty} c_n v_n(x) \tag{9}$$

where the constant coefficients c_n are given by

$$c_n = \int_D \rho h v_n d\tau \tag{10}$$

The complete, time-dependent solution of Eq. (3) is found by superposition of the particular solutions

$$u = \Sigma(a_n \cos \lambda t + b_n \sin \lambda t) v_n(x) \tag{11}$$

where

$$a_n = \int_D \rho \varphi v_n d\tau, \qquad b_n = \frac{1}{\lambda_n} \int_D \rho \psi v_n d\tau \tag{12}$$

The inhomogeneous Eq. (1) is solved by quite similar methods. But before discussing these we must introduce the concept of homogeneous and inhomogeneous boundary conditions. We speak of a problem having a homogeneous character if with u the function cu is also a solution, where c is a constant. For this to be the case it is necessary not only that the differential equation but also that the boundary conditions be homogeneous, e.g., $u = 0$ on B and $\partial u/\partial n = 0$ on B, or $Au + B\,\partial u/\partial n = 0$ on B, where A and B are constants.

Now suppose that u satisfies an inhomogeneous boundary condition, e.g., $u = f$ on B, but obeys the homogeneous differential equation $L[u] = 0$. It is then possible to continue the values of u on B in such a manner into the interior of D that $L[f] = g$ in D, where g is a continuous function in D. If we wish now to solve the inhomogeneous Eq. (1), we can without loss of generality assume homogeneous boundary conditions. We expand $F(x_1,\ldots,t)$ in terms of the orthonormal functions v_n:

$$F(x_1,\ldots,t) = \sum_{n=1}^{\infty} F_n(t) v_n(x) \tag{13}$$

and similarly

$$u(x_1,\ldots,t) = \sum_{n=1}^{\infty} \gamma_n(t) v_n(x) \tag{14}$$

If these values are substituted into Eq. (1), we obtain the differential equation for $\gamma_n(t)$:

$$\frac{d^2\gamma_n}{dt^2} + \lambda_n^2 \gamma_n = -F_n \tag{15}$$

A particular solution of Eq. (15) is

$$\gamma_n = \frac{1}{\lambda_n} \int_0^t \sin \lambda_n (t - \tau) F_n(\tau) d\tau \tag{16}$$

Using a series expansion (14) with the coefficients of Eq. (16), we obtain a solution of Eq. (1) and, by a linear superposition, we obtain a solution of Eq. (1) satisfying the prescribed homogeneous boundary conditions.

There exists a close connection between the eigenvalue problem and the calculus of variations. We shall for simplicity state this relation for the one-dimensional case.

Suppose we want to find the function (or functions) $u(x)$ which give the integral

$$\int_a^b \left[A(x) \left(\frac{du}{dx} \right)^2 - B(x) u^2 \right] dx = 0 \tag{17}$$

a stationary value. The function u is subject to the auxiliary condition

$$\int_a^b \rho u^2 dx = \text{constant}, \quad [\rho(x) > 0 \quad \text{for} \quad a \leq x \leq b] \tag{18}$$

and shall also satisfy the homogeneous boundary conditions

$$x(a) = x(b) = 0 \tag{19}$$

The Euler-Lagrange equation belonging to this problem is the Sturm-Liouville equation

$$\frac{d}{dx}\left(A\frac{du}{dx}\right) + Bu + \lambda\rho u = 0 \tag{20}$$

The stationary values of the integral Eq. (17) are achieved if u is one of the characteristic functions with the characteristic value λ. This property of the characteristic values is utilized in the so-called direct methods of the calculus of variations to find the numerical value of the lowest eigenvalue and with it also the eigenfunction itself.

We shall state now the synchronous wave equation in a few typical coordinate systems and its particular solutions. The wave equation is in all cases

$$\nabla^2\Phi + \lambda^2\Phi = 0 \tag{21}$$

a. *Cartesian coordinates, two-dimensional case:*

$$\frac{\partial^2\Phi}{\partial x^2} + \frac{\partial^2\Phi}{\partial y^2} + \lambda^2\Phi = 0 \tag{22}$$

Particular solutions

$$\Phi_{\alpha,\beta} = e^{\pm i(\alpha x+\beta y)} \tag{23}$$

where $\alpha^2 + \beta^2 = \lambda^2$ (plane wave).

$$\Phi_0 = (Ax + B)e^{i\lambda y} \tag{24}$$

b. *Cartesian coordinates, three-dimensional case:*

$$\frac{\partial^2\Phi}{\partial x^2} + \frac{\partial^2\Phi}{\partial y^2} + \frac{\partial^2\Phi}{\partial z^2} + \lambda^2\Phi = 0 \tag{25}$$

Particular solutions

$$\Phi_{k,l,m} = e^{i(kx+ly+mz)} \tag{26}$$

where $k^2 + l^2 + m^2 = \lambda^2$ (plane wave).

c. *Cylindrical coordinates, two-dimensional case:*

$$\frac{\partial^2\Phi}{\partial \rho^2} + \frac{1}{\rho}\frac{\partial\Phi}{\partial \rho} + \frac{1}{\rho^2}\frac{\partial^2\Phi}{\partial \varphi^2} + \lambda^2\Phi = 0 \tag{27}$$

Particular solutions

$$\Phi_k = e^{ik\varphi}\cdot J_k(\lambda\rho), \quad \text{(circular wave)} \tag{28}$$

$$\Phi_0 = (A\varphi + B)J_0(\lambda\rho) \tag{29}$$

d. *Cylindrical coordinates, three-dimensional case:*

$$\frac{\partial^2\Phi}{\partial\rho^2} + \frac{1}{\rho}\frac{\partial\Phi}{\partial\rho} + \frac{1}{\rho^2}\frac{\partial^2\Phi}{\partial\varphi^2} + \frac{\partial^2\Phi}{\partial z^2} + \lambda^2\Phi = 0 \tag{30}$$

Particular solutions (modulated cylindrical wave)

$$\Phi_{k,m} = e^{\pm i(kz+m\varphi)} \cdot J_m(\rho\sqrt{\lambda^2 - k^2}) \tag{31}$$

$$\Phi_{0,0} = (A\varphi + B)(Cz + D)J_0(\lambda\rho) \tag{32}$$

where J_m is the Bessel function of order m.

e. *Spherical coordinates:*

$$\left.\begin{aligned}\frac{1}{r^2}\frac{\partial}{\partial r}\left(r^2\frac{\partial\Phi}{\partial r}\right) + \frac{1}{r^2\sin^2\theta}\frac{\partial}{\partial\theta}\left(\sin\theta\frac{\partial\Phi}{\partial\theta}\right)\\ + \frac{1}{r^2\sin^2\theta}\frac{\partial^2\Phi}{\partial\varphi^2} + \lambda^2\Phi = 0\end{aligned}\right\} \tag{33}$$

Particular solutions

$$\Phi_{m,k} = \frac{1}{\sqrt{r}} J_{m+(1/2)}(\lambda r)e^{\pm ik\varphi}P_m{}^k(\cos\theta) \tag{34}$$

for a modulated spherical wave, and

$$\Phi_0 = \frac{e^{i\lambda r}}{r} \tag{35}$$

for a pure spherical wave.

By using the Fourier integral it is possible to build up either spherical or cylindrical waves out of plane waves, or, conversely, plane waves out of modulated spherical or cylindrical waves.

a. *Spherical wave as a superposition of plane waves:*

$$\left.\Phi = \frac{i\lambda}{2\pi}\int_0^{(\pi/2)-i\sim} d\theta\sin\theta\int_0^{2\pi} d\varphi e^{i\lambda(x\sin\theta\cos\varphi+y\sin\theta\sin\varphi+|z\cos\theta|)} = \frac{e^{i\lambda r}}{r}\right\} \tag{36}$$

b. *Plane wave as a superposition of modulated spherical waves:*

$$\Phi = \sqrt{\frac{2\pi}{\lambda r}}\sum_{n=0}^{\infty}\frac{2n+1}{2}i^n J_{n+(1/2)}(\lambda r)P_n(\cos\theta) = e^{i\lambda r\cos\theta} = e^{i\lambda z} \tag{37}$$

c. *Plane wave as a superposition of circular waves* (two-dimensional case):

$$\sum_{n=-\infty}^{+\infty} i^n J_n(\lambda\rho)e^{in\varphi} = e^{i\lambda\varrho\cos\varphi} = e^{i\lambda x} \tag{38}$$

1.9. Heat conduction equation. Let $T(x,y,z,t)$ be the temperature distribution. In a homogeneous and isotropic medium it obeys the " equation of heat conduction "

$$\nabla^2 T = \frac{1}{a^2}\frac{\partial T}{\partial t} \tag{1}$$

Here $a^2 = k/c\rho$, where k = specific heat conductivity, c = specific heat, ρ = density. If the homogeneous body D with the boundary B is imbedded in an infinite homogeneous medium of constant temperature zero, the boundary condition has the form

$$\frac{\partial T}{\partial n} + \sigma T = 0 \tag{2}$$

where σ is a positive constant and the normal n is directed into the interior of D. We have here again an eigenvalue problem, and the preceeding general principles therefore apply. We write again

$$T = v(x,y,z)g(t) \tag{3}$$

and obtain for v the eigenvalue problem

$$\nabla^2 v + \lambda v = 0 \quad \text{in } D \tag{4}$$

and

$$\frac{\partial v}{\partial n} + \sigma v = 0 \quad \text{in } B \tag{5}$$

The eigenfunction belonging to λ is

$$T = Ave^{-\lambda a^2 t} \tag{6}$$

If $T(x,y,z,0)$ is a prescribed function $\varphi(x,y,z)$, which is twice continuously differentiable and satisfies the boundary conditions, then the solution can be written in terms of the characteristic functions $v_1, v_2, \ldots,$ and their characteristic values $\lambda_1, \lambda_2, \ldots.$

$$T(x,y,z,t) = \sum_{n=1}^{\infty} c_n v_n(x,y,z)e^{-\lambda_n a^2 t} \tag{7}$$

where

$$c_n = \iiint_D \varphi v_n dxdydz \tag{8}$$

If the domain in which the initial temperature $\varphi(x,y,z)$ is prescribed is the entire space, the solution can be written down in closed form:

$$T(x,y,z,t) = \frac{1}{(2a\sqrt{\pi t})^3}\iiint_{-\infty}^{+\infty} \varphi(x',y',z')e^{-\varrho^2/4a^2 t}dx'dy'dz' \tag{9}$$

where

$$\rho^2 = (x-x')^2 + (y-y')^2 + (z-z')^2$$

This solution can be interpreted in the following way. Suppose the initial temperature was zero everywhere, except in a small region around the point, where it had the constant value T_0. Let us assume this region was a small cube of size $\Delta\tau$. We may choose this point P_0 as the origin. The temperature is then

$$T(x,y,z,t) = \frac{T_0\Delta\tau}{(2a\sqrt{\pi t})^3} e^{-\varrho^2/4a^2t} \tag{10}$$

where

$$\rho^2 = x^2 + y^2 + z^2$$

At the time zero there exists a sharp maximum at the origin, which gradually becomes less and less defined caused by the diffusion of the heat. The initial accumulation of heat at the origin is called a heat pole. We may therefore interpret Eq. (9) as the result of a continuous set of heat poles having the strength $\varphi(x,y,z)$.

Another solution of the one-dimensional heat equation

$$\frac{\partial^2 T}{\partial x^2} = \frac{1}{a^2}\frac{\partial T}{\partial t} \tag{11}$$

of geophysical interest is the penetration of heat into the interior of a semi-infinite, homogeneous isotropic medium if the temperature on the surface is a prescribed periodic function of time, e.g., the temperature distribution in the interior of the earth caused by the daily or annual temperature oscillations on its surface.

We shall assume the temperature at the surface $x = 0$ to be $A \cos \omega t$. The temperature $T(x,t)$ for $x > 0$ (in the interior of the medium) is given by

$$T = Ae^{-(1/a)\sqrt{\omega/2}\,x} \cos\left(\omega t - \frac{1}{a}\sqrt{\frac{\omega}{2}}\,x\right) \tag{13}$$

This expression shows that temperature distribution has the shape of a damped oscillation, and that the phase is continuously changing. The solution also has another remarkable property; if we write the phase in the form

$$-\frac{1}{a}\sqrt{\frac{\omega}{2}}\,(x - a\sqrt{2\omega}t) \tag{13}$$

we see that the velocity $a\sqrt{2\omega}$ with which the disturbance travels depends on ω. In other words, we have here a dispersion, which was not the case for the one-dimensional wave equation. This is also the reason why we cannot have here a general solution of the type $f(x \pm ct)$.

Another significant difference between the heat and the wave equation is that the heat equation is not isotropic with respect to the direction of time. The solution for $t > 0$ cannot be continued to values $t < 0$. This is connected with the fact that heat flow is an irreversible flow and is connected with an increase in entropy.

1.10. Inhomogeneous differential equations. Suppose we have density distribution ρ of mass in space, and we assume that ρ is independent of time. The potential Φ then obeys Poisson's equation

$$\nabla^2\Phi = -4\pi\rho \tag{1}$$

Its solution is

$$\Phi(P) = \int \frac{\rho_Q}{r_{PQ}} d\tau_Q \tag{2}$$

where r_{PQ} is the distance between the " field point " P, where we want to compute the potential, and the " source point " Q with mass $\rho d\tau$.

If we assume that ρ is a function of space and time, we obtain the inhomogeneous wave equation for Φ:

$$\nabla^2\Phi - \frac{1}{c^2}\frac{\partial^2\Phi}{\partial t^2} = -4\pi\rho \tag{3}$$

One solution of this equation is

$$\Phi(P) = \int \frac{\rho(\xi,\eta,\zeta,t - R/c)}{R} d\xi d\eta d\zeta \tag{4}$$

where

$$R^2 = (x-\xi)^2 + (y-\eta^2) + (z-\zeta)^2$$

This solution is called the retarded potential, because the contributions to the potential at P are arising from those values of ρ at $Q(\xi,\eta,\zeta)$ which needed the time R/C to reach P.

Bibliography

1. CHURCHILL, R. V., *Fourier Series and Boundary Value Problems*, McGraw-Hill Book Company, Inc., New York, 1941. Emphasizes the expansion in orthogonal functions.
2. COURANT, R. and HILBERT, D., *Methoden der mathematischen Physik*, 2d ed., Vol. 1, 1931; Vol. 2, 1937: Julius Springer, Berlin. (Also Interscience Publishers, Inc., New York, 1943.)
3. FRANK, P. and VON MISES, R., *Die Differential- und Integralgleichungen der Mechanik und Physik*, 2d ed., Vol. 1 (mathematical part), 1930; Vol. 2 (physical part), 1935; F. Viehweg und Sohn, Braunschweig.
4. WEBSTER, A. G., *Partial Differential Equations of Mathematical Physics*, 2d ed., G. E. Stechert & Company, New York, 1936.

Chapter 10

HEAT AND THERMODYNAMICS

By P. W. Bridgman

Higgins University Professor
Harvard University

1. Formulas of Thermodynamics

The derivation of the word thermodynamics, which literally means " concerned with the motion of heat," suggests that the science of thermodynamics deals with the details of the interchange of heat between bodies. As a matter of fact, traditional thermodynamics does not deal with the motion of heat at all, but with the equilibrium conditions reached after heat motion has ceased, and should, therefore, more properly be called thermostatics. The results of thermodynamics are derived from two laws : the laws of the conservation and of the degradation of energy. These two laws are, perhaps, the most sweeping generalization from experiment yet achieved. A mechanistic account of these laws can be given by the methods of statistical mechanics, for which the following chapter should be consulted.

1.1. Introduction. The partial derivatives of thermodynamics are somewhat different from the conventional partial derivatives of mathematics in spite of their apparent identity of form. The conventional derivative $(\partial y/\partial x)_z$ implies by its form that y is a function of x and z. In the corresponding thermodynamic derivative the subscript z indicates the *path* along which the derivative is taken, y and x not necessarily being defined off the path. It follows that such derivatives as $(\partial\tau/\partial p)_Q$, $(\partial\tau/\partial p)_W$, $(\partial Q/\partial p)_\tau$, $(\partial W/\partial\tau)_p$ are thermodynamically meaningful, although Q and W are not possible independent variables.

The ordinary mathematical formulas for the manipulation of first derivatives apply to the path derivatives of thermodynamics. In particular,

$$\left(\frac{\partial x}{\partial y}\right)_z = \frac{1}{(\partial y/\partial x)_z} \tag{1}$$

$$\left(\frac{\partial x}{\partial y}\right)_z \left(\frac{\partial y}{\partial z}\right)_x \left(\frac{\partial z}{\partial x}\right)_y = -1 \tag{2}$$

$$\left(\frac{\partial w}{\partial u}\right)_v = \left(\frac{\partial w}{\partial x}\right)_y \left(\frac{\partial x}{\partial u}\right)_v + \left(\frac{\partial w}{\partial y}\right)_x \left(\frac{\partial y}{\partial u}\right)_v \tag{3}$$

The second path derivatives, however, in general require special treatment. In particular,

$$\frac{\partial}{\partial p}\left[\left(\frac{\partial Q}{\partial \tau}\right)_p\right]_\tau \equiv \frac{\partial^2 Q}{\partial p \partial t} \neq \frac{\partial^2 Q}{\partial \tau \partial p}, \quad \text{etc.} \tag{4}$$

1.2. The laws of thermodynamics. The first law is

$$dE = dQ - dW \tag{1}$$

This formula applies to any thermodynamic system for any infinitesimal change of its state. This formula is a definition for dE, it being assumed that dQ (heat absorbed by the system) and dW (work done by the system) have independent instrumental significance. The first law states that the dE so defined is a perfect differential in the independent variables of state. By integration E may be obtained as a function of the state variables. The E so obtained contains an arbitrary constant of integration, without significance for thermodynamics.

The second law is

$$ds = \frac{dQ}{\tau} \tag{2}$$

The second law states that for any *reversible* absorption of heat there is an integrating denominator τ (absolute temperature) such that ds is a perfect differential in the state variables.

Applied to a Carnot engine (engine working on two isothermals and two adiabatics)

$$Q_1/Q_2 = \tau_1/\tau_2 \tag{3}$$

$$\text{efficiency of Carnot engine} \equiv \frac{Q_1 - Q_2}{Q_1} = \frac{\tau_1 - \tau_2}{\tau_1} \tag{4}$$

The two laws apply to any subsystem that can be carved out of the whole system. It follows that there are fluxes of heat $\boldsymbol{q}$, mechanical energy $\boldsymbol{w}$, total energy $\boldsymbol{e}$, and entropy $\boldsymbol{s}$ such that

$$-\operatorname{div} \boldsymbol{q} = dQ/dt \tag{5}$$

$$\operatorname{div} \boldsymbol{w} = dW/dt \tag{6}$$

$$\boldsymbol{e} = \boldsymbol{q} - \boldsymbol{w} \tag{7}$$

$$\boldsymbol{s} = \boldsymbol{q}/\tau \tag{8}$$

where now Q and W are taken for unit volume, and t denotes time.

1.3. The variables. The variables usually associated with thermodynamic systems are p = pressure, τ = absolute temperature, v = volume, s = entropy, E = energy, $G = E + pv - \tau s$ (Gibbs thermodynamic potential), $F = E - \tau s$ (Helmholtz free energy), $H = E + pv$ (total heat or enthalpy), dW = work done by the system, dQ = heat absorbed by the system. The specific heats are defined as

$$C_p = \left(\frac{\partial Q}{\partial \tau}\right)_p, \qquad C_v = \left(\frac{\partial Q}{\partial \tau}\right)_v$$

These variables are all to be taken in consistent units, which means in particular that heat is usually to be measured in mechanical units. The amount of matter in the system to which these quantities refer may be taken arbitrarily, subject to the demands of consistency. Thus, if v represents the volume of one gram, C_p refers conventionally to one gram of matter, but measured in mechanical units. However, if v is taken more ordinarily as the volume of that amount of substance which occupies one cubic centimeter under standard conditions, then C_p has its conventional value multiplied by the density.

1.4. One-component systems. The state is fixed by two independent variables of which p and τ are a possible pair. $dW = pdv$ (one-phase systems). In such a system any three of the first derivatives can, in general, be assigned without restriction from the laws of thermodynamics (there are many exceptions to this). Any fourth first derivative can then, in general, be expressed in terms of the chosen three with the help of the first and second laws. Normally, a thermodynamic relation involving first derivatives is a relation between any four such derivatives. There are approximately 10^{11} such relationships. Various schemes have been proposed by which any desired one of these 10^{11} relationships may be obtained with comparatively little mathematical manipulation *. No attempt is made to reproduce these schemes here, but in the following a few of the most frequently used relations will be given.

$$\left(\frac{\partial \tau}{\partial v}\right)_s = -\left(\frac{\partial p}{\partial s}\right)_v \tag{1}$$

$$\left(\frac{\partial \tau}{\partial p}\right)_s = \left(\frac{\partial v}{\partial s}\right)_p \tag{2}$$

$$\left(\frac{\partial p}{\partial \tau}\right)_v = \left(\frac{\partial s}{\partial v}\right)_\tau \tag{3}$$

* References 1, 2, 3, 4 and 10 in the Bibliography.

$$\left(\frac{\partial v}{\partial \tau}\right)_p = -\left(\frac{\partial s}{\partial p}\right)_\tau \tag{4}$$

Equations (1)-(4) are the four Maxwell relations.

$$\left(\frac{\partial v}{\partial p}\right)_s = \left(\frac{\partial v}{\partial p}\right)_\tau + \frac{\tau}{C_p}\left(\frac{\partial v}{\partial \tau}\right)_p^2 \tag{5}$$

$$C_p = \tau\left(\frac{\partial s}{\partial \tau}\right)_p = \tau\left(\frac{\partial p}{\partial \tau}\right)_s\left(\frac{\partial v}{\partial \tau}\right)_p \tag{6}$$

$$C_v = \tau\left(\frac{\partial s}{\partial \tau}\right)_v = -\tau\left(\frac{\partial \tau}{\partial v}\right)_s\left(\frac{\partial p}{\partial \tau}\right)_v = \left(\frac{\partial E}{\partial \tau}\right)_v \tag{7}$$

$$C_p - C_v = \tau\left(\frac{\partial p}{\partial \tau}\right)_v\left(\frac{\partial v}{\partial \tau}\right)_p = \frac{-\tau(\partial v/\partial \tau)_p{}^2}{(\partial v/\partial p)_\tau} \tag{8}$$

$$C_p/C_v \equiv \gamma = \frac{(\partial p/\partial v)_s}{(\partial p/\partial v)_\tau} \tag{9}$$

$$\frac{(\partial v/\partial \tau)_s}{(\partial v/\partial \tau)_p} = \frac{1}{1-\gamma} \tag{10}$$

$$\left(\frac{\partial Q}{\partial p}\right)_\tau = -\tau\left(\frac{\partial v}{\partial \tau}\right)_p \tag{11}$$

$$\left(\frac{\partial G}{\partial p}\right)_\tau = v, \qquad \left(\frac{\partial G}{\partial \tau}\right)_p = -s \tag{12}$$

$$\left(\frac{\partial F}{\partial v}\right)_\tau = -p, \qquad \left(\frac{\partial F}{\partial \tau}\right)_v = -s \tag{13}$$

$$\left(\frac{\partial H}{\partial s}\right)_p = \tau, \qquad \left(\frac{\partial H}{\partial p}\right)_s = v \tag{14}$$

$$\left(\frac{\partial E}{\partial s}\right)_v = \tau, \qquad \left(\frac{\partial E}{\partial v}\right)_s = -p \tag{15}$$

$$\left(\frac{\partial E}{\partial v}\right)_\tau = -p + \tau\left(\frac{\partial p}{\partial \tau}\right)_v \tag{16}$$

Equation (16) is the so-called " thermodynamic equation of state."

$$\left.\begin{aligned} \mu &\equiv \left(\frac{\partial \tau}{\partial p}\right)_H, \quad \text{(Joule-Thomson coefficient)} \\ &= \frac{1}{C_p}\left[\tau\left(\frac{\partial v}{\partial \tau}\right)_p - v\right] = -\frac{1}{C_p}\left(\frac{\partial H}{\partial p}\right)_\tau \end{aligned}\right\} \tag{17}$$

$$\left(\frac{\partial C_p}{\partial p}\right)_\tau = -\tau\left(\frac{\partial^2 v}{\partial \tau^2}\right)_p \tag{18}$$

$$\left(\frac{\partial C_v}{\partial v}\right)_\tau = \tau\left(\frac{\partial^2 p}{\partial \tau^2}\right)_v \tag{19}$$

1.5. One-component, usually two-phase systems. The state is fixed by two independent variables of which p and τ are *not* a possible pair, $dW = pdv$. A new variable appears, x, the fraction of the total mass of the system present in phase 1. There are now only two independently assignable first derivatives, of which $dp/d\tau$ and $C_v [\equiv (\partial Q/\partial \tau)_v]$ form a convenient pair; C_v is expressible in terms of the properties of the separate phases.

$$\left.\begin{aligned} C_v = x&\left[C_{p_1} - 2\tau\frac{dp}{d\tau}\left(\frac{\partial v_1}{\partial \tau}\right)_p - \tau\left(\frac{dp}{d\tau}\right)^2\left(\frac{\partial v_1}{\partial p}\right)_\tau\right] \\ &+ (1-x)\left[C_{p_2} - 2\tau\frac{dp}{d\tau}\left(\frac{\partial v_2}{\partial \tau}\right)_p - \tau\left(\frac{dp}{d\tau}\right)^2\left(\frac{\partial v_2}{\partial p}\right)_\tau\right] \end{aligned}\right\} \tag{1}$$

The general thermodynamic relation between first derivatives is a relation between any three derivatives. In these relations the following function of x occurs frequently :

$$\left.\begin{aligned} f(x, 1-x) \equiv x&\left[\left(\frac{\partial v_1}{\partial \tau}\right)_p + \left(\frac{\partial v_1}{\partial p}\right)_\tau \frac{dp}{d\tau}\right] \\ &+ (1-x)\left[\left(\frac{\partial v_2}{\partial \tau}\right)_p + \left(\frac{\partial v_2}{\partial p}\right)_\tau \frac{dp}{d\tau}\right] \end{aligned}\right\} \tag{2}$$

In addition to the following special formulas, many of the formulas of Section 1.4 also apply.

$$\left(\frac{\partial x}{\partial \tau}\right)_s = -\frac{1}{v_1 - v_2}\left[\frac{C_v}{\tau(dp/d\tau)} + f(x, 1-x)\right] \tag{3}$$

$$\left(\frac{\partial x}{\partial \tau}\right)_v = -\frac{f(x, 1-x)}{v_1 - v_2} \tag{4}$$

$$\left(\frac{\partial x}{\partial v}\right)_\tau = \frac{1}{v_1 - v_2} \tag{5}$$

$$\left(\frac{\partial x}{\partial v}\right)_s = \frac{1}{v_1 - v_2}\left[1 + \frac{\tau}{C_v}\frac{dp}{d\tau} f(x, 1-x)\right] \tag{6}$$

$$\left(\frac{\partial x}{\partial \tau}\right)_E = \frac{1}{v_1 - v_2}\left[\frac{C_v}{p - \tau(dp/d\tau)} - f(x, 1-x)\right] \tag{7}$$

$$\left(\frac{\partial x}{\partial E}\right)_G = \frac{-1}{(v_1 - v_2)\,[p - \tau(dp/d\tau)]} \tag{8}$$

$$\left(\frac{\partial x}{\partial \tau}\right)_H = \frac{-1}{v_1 - v_2}\left[f(x, 1-x) + \frac{C_v + v(dp/d\tau)}{\tau(dp/d\tau)}\right] \tag{9}$$

$$\left(\frac{\partial x}{\partial \tau}\right)_F = \frac{-1}{v_1 - v_2}\left[f(x, 1-x) + \frac{s}{p}\right] \tag{10}$$

$$\frac{d\tau}{dp} = \frac{\tau(v_1 - v_2)}{L}, \quad \text{(Clapeyron's equation)} \tag{11}$$

where L is the heat absorbed by the system when it passes from phase 2 to phase 1 (latent heat).

$$\left.\begin{aligned} \frac{d^2\tau}{dp^2} = \frac{-1}{v_1 - v_2}\frac{d\tau}{dp}\Bigg\{ & \frac{C_{p_1} - C_{p_2}}{\tau}\left(\frac{d\tau}{dp}\right)^2 \\ & - 2\left[\left(\frac{dv_1}{\partial\tau}\right)_p - \left(\frac{\partial v_2}{\partial \tau}\right)_p\right]\frac{d\tau}{dp} - \left[\left(\frac{\partial v_1}{\partial p}\right)_\tau - \left(\frac{\partial v_2}{\partial p}\right)_\tau\right]\Bigg\} \end{aligned}\right\} \tag{12}$$

$$\frac{dL}{dp} = \frac{d\tau}{dp}(C_{p_1} - C_{p_2}) + (v_1 - v_2) - \tau\left[\left(\frac{\partial v_1}{\partial \tau}\right)_p - \left(\frac{\partial v_2}{\partial \tau}\right)_p\right] \tag{13}$$

If the phase 1 is a perfect gas,

$$\frac{d \log p}{d\tau} = \frac{L}{R\tau^2} \tag{14}$$

1.6. Transitions of higher orders

$$\frac{dp}{d\tau} = -\frac{\Delta(\partial z/\partial \tau)_p}{\Delta(\partial z/\partial p)_\tau} \tag{1}$$

Here z is any continuous thermodynamic function with discontinuous first derivatives along a line in the p,τ plane. The formula gives the slope of the line of discontinuity. By specializing z, various formulas may be obtained. By identifying z successively with s and v and eliminating $dp/d\tau$, Ehrenfest's formula for a transition of the second kind is obtained:

$$\Delta C_p = -\tau\left[\frac{\Delta(\partial v/\partial\tau)_p{}^2}{\Delta(\partial v/\partial p)_\tau}\right] \tag{2}$$

1.7. Equations of state

$$pv = R\tau, \quad \text{(perfect gas)} \tag{1}$$

If p is measured in dynes/cm², v is the volume in cm³ of one gram molecule, and τ is absolute Kelvin degrees, and $R = 8.3144 \times 10^7$ergs/g-mole-deg.

$$\left(p + \frac{a}{v^2}\right)(v - b) = R\tau, \qquad \text{(van der Waals)} \tag{2}$$

$$\left(p + \frac{a}{\tau v^2}\right)(v - b) = R\tau, \qquad \text{(Berthelot)} \tag{3}$$

$$p(v - b) = R\tau \exp\frac{-C}{R\tau v}, \qquad \text{(Dieterici)} \tag{4}$$

$$p = \frac{R\tau(1-\epsilon)}{v^2}(v + B) - \frac{A}{v^2}, \qquad \text{(Beattie-Bridgeman)} \tag{5}$$

where $\quad A = A_0\left(1 - \dfrac{a}{v}\right), \quad B = B_0\left(1 - \dfrac{b}{v}\right), \quad \epsilon = C/v\tau^3$

and A_0, a, B_0, b, and c are constants.

$$pv = A + \frac{B}{v} + \frac{C}{v^2}\cdots, \qquad \text{(“ virial equation of state ”)} \tag{6}$$

The coefficients A, B, etc., which are functions of temperature, are called the first, second, etc. virial coefficients.

Excepting the perfect gas equation, all these equations have the property of indicating the " critical point " at which vapor and liquid phases are identical. The parameters of the system at the critical point are designated by p_C, τ_C, v_C. The " reduced coordinates " of a system are defined as $p_r = p/p_C$, $\tau_r = \tau/\tau_C$, $v_r = v/v_C$. If the various equations of state are expressed in terms of reduced coordinates, a functional form will be obtained, the same for all substances. In particular, the reduced van der Waals equation of state is

$$p_r = \frac{8\tau_r}{3v_r - 1} - \frac{3R}{(v_r)^2} \tag{7}$$

1.8. One-component, two-variable systems, with $dW = Xdy$. Here X is "generalized force" and y is "generalized displacement." Possible pair of variables, τ and X. The simplest examples of such systems are electrical or magnetic systems, or simple elastic systems with a single stress component not a hydrostatic pressure. All the formulas of § 1.4 apply, replacing p by X and v by y.

1.9. One-component, two-variable systems, with $dW = Xdy$. Here X is generalized force and y is generalized displacement, τ and X *not* a possible pair of variables, X being fixed as a function of τ by the physics of the system. The formulas of § 1.5 apply, replacing p by X and v by y. Special examples are

$$u = \text{constant } \tau^4 \quad \text{(Stefan's law)} \tag{1}$$

where u is the density of black-body radiation.

$$\frac{d\,\text{emf}}{d\tau} = \frac{1}{\tau}\left(\frac{\partial Q}{\partial q}\right)_\tau, \quad \text{(Helmholtz)} \tag{2}$$

the equation for the temperature change of the emf of a reversible cell in terms of the heat absorbed when unit quantity of electricity flows through the cell isothermally.

$$\frac{d\sigma}{d\tau} = -\frac{1}{\tau}\left(\frac{\partial Q}{\partial A}\right)_\tau \tag{3}$$

the temperature derivative of surface tension in terms of the heat absorbed when the surface increases isothermally.

1.10. One-component, multivariable systems, with $dW = \Sigma X_i dy_i$. Here the X_i's are generalized forces and the y_i's are generalized displacements. Much variation is possible in the treatment, depending on the choice of independent variables. The generalized equation of state must be known for such systems. A general method of getting information is to put ds a perfect differential and write the relations on the cross derivatives of the coefficients. The various potential functions may be generalized for such systems. For example,

$$G_{\text{gen}} = E - \tau s + \Sigma Xy \tag{1}$$

This potential function is a minimum at equilibrium for changes at constant τ and X.

1.11. Multicomponent, multivariable systems, $dW = pdv$. A system fixed by composition variables n_i, usually given in gram molecules, plus two others, for example p and τ. In general a composition variable will be needed for each independent component in each homogeneous part (phase) of the system. A complete scheme for obtaining all the possible relations in such a system has been given by Goranson (see Bibliography), analogous to the schemes for dealing with § 1.4. Only a few of the more important relations will be given here. For arbitrary values of the independent variables in multicomponent systems, the system is generally not in equilibrium, and the spontaneous changes of variable which occur as the system settles toward equilibrium are irreversible. At equilibrium

G is a minimum for changes at constant p and τ (1)

F is a minimum for changes at constant v and τ (2)

H is a minimum for changes at constant s and p (3)

E is a minimum for changes at constant s and v (4)

In general all the formulas of § 1.4 apply with the addition of all the n_i's as subscripts. For example,

$$\left(\frac{\partial G}{\partial \tau}\right)_{p_i n_i} = v \tag{5}$$

The new formulas involve derivatives with respect to the n_i's. These derivatives define various " partial " quantities. In particular the " partial chemical potentials " are defined by

$$\mu_i \equiv \left(\frac{\partial G}{\partial n_i}\right)_{\tau_i p_i n_j} \equiv \left(\frac{\partial F}{\partial n_i}\right)_{\tau_i v_i n_j} \equiv \left(\frac{\partial H}{\partial n_i}\right)_{p_i s_i n_j} \equiv \left(\frac{\partial E}{\partial n_i}\right)_{s_i v_i n_j} \tag{6}$$

Here the subscript n_j indicates that all the n's except n_i are held constant during the differentiation. Other typical partial quantities are

$$\bar{v}_i \equiv \left(\frac{\partial v}{\partial n_i}\right) \tag{7}$$

$$\bar{s}_i \equiv \left(\frac{\partial s}{\partial n_i}\right) \tag{8}$$

$$C_{pi} \equiv \left(\frac{\partial C_p}{\partial n_i}\right) \tag{9}$$

No subscripts are indicated in these derivatives. The understanding is that all the other independent variables except n_i, whatever they may be, are held constant during the differentiation.

For the various *extensive* properties of the system there are linear relations on the n's, such as

$$G = \Sigma\, n_i \mu_i \tag{10}$$

$$F = \Sigma\, n_i \mu_i \tag{11}$$

$$v = \Sigma\, n_i \bar{v}_i \tag{12}$$

$$s = \Sigma\, n_i \bar{s}_i \tag{13}$$

Formulas for the various partial quantities hold similar to those for the total quantities. For example,

$$\left(\frac{\partial \mu_i}{\partial \tau}\right)_{p_i n_i} = -\bar{s}_i \tag{14}$$

$$\left(\frac{\partial \mu_i}{\partial p}\right)_{\tau_i n_i} = \bar{v}_i \tag{15}$$

1.12. Homogeneous systems. a. *Gaseous mixtures.* The mole fractions are defined by

$$N_i = \frac{n_i}{\sum_k n_k} \tag{1}$$

$$\Sigma\, N_i = 1 \tag{2}$$

The partial vapor pressures are defined by

$$\bar{p}_i = N_i p \tag{3}$$

$$\Sigma\, \bar{p}_i = p \tag{4}$$

Perfect gaseous mixtures:

$$\bar{v}_i = \left(\frac{\partial \mu_i}{\partial p}\right)_{\tau_i n_i} = \frac{R\tau}{p} N_i \tag{5}$$

$$p = \sum \frac{n_i}{v} R\tau \tag{6}$$

$$\bar{p}_i = \frac{n_i}{v} R\tau \tag{7}$$

$$\left[\frac{\partial(\mu_i/\tau)}{\partial \tau}\right]_{p_i n_i} = -\frac{\bar{H}_i}{\tau^2} \tag{8}$$

If the perfect gases react according to the equation

$$lL + mM \ldots \rightleftarrows qQ + rR \ldots \tag{9}$$

where L, M, etc. represent moles of the reacting species, and l, m, etc. are the numerical coefficients in the reaction equation,

$$\frac{(\bar{p}_Q)^q(\bar{p}_R)^r \cdots}{(\bar{p}_L)^l(\bar{p}_M)^m \cdots} = \bar{K}(\tau), \quad \text{(mass action law for perfect gases)} \tag{10}$$

Here $\bar{K}(\tau)$ is a function of temperature only and is called the *equilibrium constant.*

$$\frac{d \log \bar{K}}{d\tau} = \frac{L_p}{R\tau^2} \tag{11}$$

where L_p is the latent heat at constant pressure of the reaction from left to right.

Imperfect gaseous mixtures: The "fugacity" ($= \bar{p}_i^*$) of the ith component is a quantity closely related to the partial vapor pressure and is defined by the equations

$$\mu_i = \mu_i^{o}(\tau) + R\tau \log \bar{p}_i^* \tag{12}$$

$$\lim_{p \to 0} \bar{p}_i^* = \bar{p}_i \tag{13}$$

$$\left(\frac{\partial \log \bar{p}_i^*}{\partial \tau}\right)_{p_i n_i} = -\frac{\bar{H}_i - \bar{H}_i^{o}}{R\tau^2} \tag{14}$$

where μ_i^{o} and $\bar{H}_i^{o}$ are the limiting values at infinite volume.

If the imperfect gases react according to Eq. (9)

$$\frac{(\bar{p}_Q^*)^q(\bar{p}_R^*)^r \cdots}{(\bar{p}_L^*)^l(\bar{p}_M^*)^m \cdots} = K(\tau) \tag{15}$$

$$\frac{d \log K(\tau)}{d\tau} = \frac{L_p^{o}}{R\tau^2} \tag{16}$$

where L_p^{o} is the heat of reaction at infinite volume.

b. *Ideal solutions:*

$$\mu_i = \mu_i^{o} + R\tau \log N_i \tag{17}$$

where μ_i^{o} is a function of pressure and temperature but not of composition.

$$\frac{\partial \mu_i}{\partial p} = \frac{\partial \mu_i^{o}}{\partial p} = \bar{v}_i \tag{18}$$

$$\frac{\partial(\mu_i/\tau)}{\partial \tau} = \frac{\partial(\mu_i^{o}/\tau)}{\partial \tau} = -\frac{\bar{H}_i}{\tau^2} \tag{19}$$

Ideal solutions of the same solvent mix with no change in volume or total heat content.

1.13. Heterogeneous systems. The phase rule of Gibbs is

$$f = c - n + 2 \tag{1}$$

where f is the number of degrees of freedom (counting intensive variables only), c the number of components, and n the number of phases.

For a liquid or solid solution in equilibrium with a vapor which behaves as a perfect gas

$$\Sigma N_i d(\log \bar{p}_i) = 0, \quad \text{(Duhem-Margules)} \tag{2}$$

for changes in composition at constant p and τ, where N_i refers to the condensed phase and $\bar{p}_i$ to the vapor phase in equilibrium with it.

$$\bar{p}_i = k_i N_i, \quad \text{(Henry's law for ideal solutions)} \tag{3}$$

where k_i is independent of N_i.

$$\bar{p}_0 = \bar{p}_0{}^0 N_0, \quad \text{(Raoult's law for ideal solutions)} \tag{4}$$

Here the subscript 0 denotes the solvent, and $\bar{p}_0{}^0$ the vapor pressure of the pure solvent

$$\Pi = \frac{R\tau}{\bar{v}_0} \log \frac{1}{N_0} = \frac{R\tau}{\bar{v}_0} N_1, \quad \text{(osmotic pressure)} \tag{5}$$

Here Π is the osmotic pressure of the ideal solution of the component N_1 in the solvent N_0.

Depression of the freezing point of an ideal dilute solution

$$\theta = \frac{R\tau_f{}^2}{L_f{}^0} N_1, \quad \text{(van 't Hoff)} \tag{6}$$

where $L_f{}^0$ is the latent heat of freezing of the pure solvent. Raising of the boiling point of the ideal dilute solution

$$\theta = \frac{R\tau_b{}^2}{L_v{}^0} N_1, \quad \text{(van 't Hoff)} \tag{7}$$

where $L_v{}^0$ is the latent heat of vaporization of the pure solvent at the normal boiling point τ_b;

$$\frac{N_i{}^\alpha}{N_i{}^\beta} = K, \quad \text{(Nernst's distribution law for ideal solutions)} \tag{8}$$

where α and β denote different condensed phases, and K depends on solvent, p, and τ, but not on N_i.

Bibliography

1. BRIDGMAN, P. W., *Phys. Rev.*, April, 1914.
2. BRIDGMAN, P. W., *A Condensed Collection of Thermodynamic Formulas*, Harvard University Press, Cambridge, Mass., 1925.
3. CRAWFORD, F. H., *Am. J. Phys.*, **17**, 1-5 (1949).
4. CRAWFORD, F. H., *Proc. Am. Acad. Arts Sci.*, **78**, 165-184 (1950).
5. EPSTEIN, P. S., *Textbook of Thermodynamics*, John Wiley & Sons, Inc., New York, 1937. A comprehensive book for the more advanced student.
6. GORANSON, R. W., *Publication 408*, Carnegie Institution of Washington, Washington, 1930.
7. GUGGENHEIM, E. A., *Thermodynamics*, North Holland Publishing Company, Amsterdam, 1949. Features especially the use of thermodynamic potentials.
8. PRIGOGINE, I. and DEFAY, R., *Thermodynamique chimique*, Éditions Desoer, Liège, 1950. Deals with " open " systems and irreversible processes.
9. SCHOTTKY, W., *Thermodynamik*, Julius Springer, Berlin, 1929. Notable for rigorous examination of fundamentals.
10. SHAW, N., *Trans. Roy. Soc.* (London), 1935, pp. 234, 299.
11. ZEMANSKY, M. W., *Heat and Thermodynamics*, 3d ed., McGraw-Hill Book Company, Inc., New York, 1951. A comprehensive treatment from the elementary point of view.

Chapter 11

STATISTICAL MECHANICS

By Donald H. Menzel

Professor of Astrophysics at Harvard College
Director of Harvard College Observatory

1. Statistics of Molecular Assemblies

1.1. Partition functions. Thermodynamics and statistical mechanics constitute independent approaches to essentially the same problem: the physical properties of assemblies of atoms or molecules. Thermodynamics depends on certain postulates concerning the behavior of an artificially defined quantity called entropy. Statistical mechanics concerns itself with averages over an assembly wherein a certain amount of energy E has been partitioned among the various atomic or molecular systems.

Fowler defines a quantity known as a " partition function," for each component of the assembly. By component we mean each kind of atom, molecule, particle, or " system," whether interacting or not. Thus all atoms of neutral iron comprise one component; those of singly ionized iron a second, etc. In its most general form the partition function, $f(T)$, reduces to a sum:

$$f(T) = \sum_i e^{-\varepsilon_i/kT} \tag{1}$$

where ϵ_i is the energy of state i, k is Boltzmann's constant, and T is the absolute temperature. If a given level is degenerate, consisting of $\tilde{\omega}_i$ states, we sum by multiplying the summand by $\tilde{\omega}_i$, which we term the statistical weight.

For a molecule, we often can break up the total energy of a given state into a number of independent energies, viz., $\epsilon_V =$ potential energy, $\epsilon_T =$ kinetic energy, $\epsilon_r =$ rotational energy, $\epsilon_v =$ vibrational energy, $\epsilon_e =$ internal electronic energy.

Of these energies the last three are usually quantized and, for classical assemblies, the first two are nonquantized. The potential energy is a function of the coordinates q_1, q_2, q_3; the kinetic energy, in turn, depends on the momenta p_1, p_2, p_3.

Writing

$$\epsilon = \epsilon_V + \epsilon_T + \epsilon_r + \epsilon_v + \epsilon_e \tag{2}$$

we see that the partition function factors whenever the energies are independent as above. Then

$$\left.\begin{aligned} f(T) &= \iiint e^{-\varepsilon_V/kT} dq_1 dq_2 dq_3 \iiint e^{-\varepsilon_T/kT} \frac{dp_1 dp_2 dp_3}{h^3} \\ &\quad \times \sum_r e^{-\varepsilon_r/kT} \sum_v e^{-\varepsilon_v/kT} \sum_e e^{-\varepsilon_e/kT} \\ &= V(T)H(T)B_r(T)B_v(T)B_e(T) \end{aligned}\right\} \tag{3}$$

The quantity h is Planck's constant, which we include so that the product $dp_1 dq_1/h$ will be dimensionless. We arbitrarily associate h with the kinetic rather than with the potential energy.

$$V(T) = \iiint e^{-\varepsilon_V/kT} dq_1 dq_2 dq_3 = V \tag{4}$$

the volume, in the absence of an external potential field. Under a constant gravitational acceleration g, the potential is $\epsilon_V = mgz$, where m is the mass of the particle and z the vertical coordinate. Then

$$V(T) = e^{-mgz/kT} V \tag{5}$$

Usually we integrate over only a small volume V of the assembly, wherein we can take ϵ_V constant or zero.

The classical partition function for the kinetic energy becomes

$$H(T) = \int_0^\infty \int_0^\infty \int_0^\infty e^{-(p_1^2+p_2^2+p_3^2)/2mkT} \frac{dp_1 dp_2 dp_3}{h^3} = \frac{(2\pi mkT)^{3/2}}{h^3} \tag{6}$$

A factor $H^{1/3}$ belongs to each degree of freedom of kinetic energy.

For a diatomic molecule, we can write

$$\epsilon_r = hcBJ(J+1) \tag{7}$$

where c is the velocity of light, B the quantity

$$B = h/8\pi^2 cI \tag{8}$$

with I the moment of inertia, and J the quantum number, an integer: 1,2,.... For a given J, we get $2J+1$ states of identical energy. Thus

$$B_r(T) = \sum_{J=1}^{\infty} \frac{2J+1}{\sigma} e^{-J(J+1)hcB/kT} \tag{9}$$

When $hcB/kt \gg 1$ we cannot easily simplify the expression. But when this quantity is small, we can approximate to $B_r(T)$ by an integral

$$\begin{aligned} B_r(T) &\sim \int_0^\infty \frac{2J+1}{\sigma} e^{-J(J+1)hcB/kT} dJ \\ &\sim \frac{1}{B\sigma} \cdot \frac{kT}{hc} = \frac{8\pi^2 IkT}{h^2\sigma} \end{aligned} \tag{10}$$

We call σ the symmetry factor. It is unity for diatomic molecules whose components are unlike, e.g., C^{12}-C^{13}. It is 2 for diatomic molecules whose constituents are identical, e.g., C^{12}-C^{12}. The number of rotational states is halved for a symmetrical molecule.

The spacing of the vibrational levels, if independent of rotation, will usually follow a law similar to

$$\epsilon_v = (v + \tfrac{1}{2})hc\omega_e \tag{11}$$

where ω_e is a basic vibrational wave number and v an integral vibrational quantum number.

Equation (11) measures ϵ_v from the lowest point of the potential energy curve. If, instead, we measure it from the condition of complete dissociation, we get

$$\epsilon_v = \left(v + \frac{1}{2}\right)hc\omega_e - D - \frac{hc\omega_e}{2} = hc\omega_e v - D \tag{12}$$

with D equal to the dissociation energy. Then

$$B_v(T) = \sum_0^\infty e^{D - hc\omega_e v/kT} = \frac{e^{D/kT}}{1 - e^{-hc\omega_e/kT}} \tag{13}$$

We cannot usually express the electronic energy in any simple form. We must therefore merely write

$$B_e(T) = \sum_j \tilde{\omega}_j e^{-\varepsilon_j/kT} \tag{14}$$

with the sum taken over all relevant levels of electronic excitation. For atoms we take the statistical weight of a single state to be unity. If, as in common practice, we represent a level by its inner quantum number, J,

$$\tilde{\omega}_j = 2J + 1 \tag{15}$$

If a complete term, denoted by the orbital and spin quantum numbers L and S, is degenerate,

$$\tilde{\omega}_j = (2S + 1)(2L + 1) \tag{16}$$

etc. (see Chapter 19).

A spining electron has the invariant weight :

$$\tilde{\omega}_j = 2 \tag{17}$$

For molecules we encounter electronic states characterized by the quantum numbers S and Λ. $\Lambda = 0$ corresponds to Σ levels; $\Lambda = 1$ to Π; $\Lambda = 2$ to Δ, etc. If we set $r = 2S + 1$, where r is the multiplicity, we get

$$\left.\begin{aligned} \tilde{\omega}_j &= 2S + 1 = r && \text{for } {}^r\Sigma \text{ levels} \\ \tilde{\omega}_j &= 2(2S + 1) = 2r, && \text{for } {}^r\Pi,\ {}^r\Delta, \text{ etc. levels} \end{aligned}\right\} \tag{18}$$

The complete partition function for a diatomic molecule whose components possess masses m_1 and m_2 becomes

$$f(T) = \frac{[2\pi(m_1 + m_2)kT]^{3/2}}{h^3} V(T) \frac{1}{B\sigma} \cdot \frac{kT}{hc} \cdot \frac{e^{D/kT}}{(1 - e^{-hc\omega_e/kT})} B_e(T) \tag{19}$$

1.2. Equations of state. For a perfect gas, the equation of state becomes

$$p = \frac{2}{3} \cdot \frac{\bar{E}_{\text{kin}}}{V} = NkT \frac{\partial}{\partial V} \ln f(T) \tag{1}$$

Since V usually enters into $f(T)$ only as a multiplicative parameter, we get

$$p = \frac{N}{V} kT = nkT \tag{2}$$

where n is the number of systems per unit volume. If we take V as the volume of a gram molecule and set N equal to the number of atoms per mol,

$$pV = NkT = R_0 T \tag{3}$$

If ρ is the density,

$$p = \rho kT/m_0\mu \tag{4}$$

where m is the mass of an atom of unit atomic weight, and μ the atomic weight of the gas.

For an imperfect gas the best-known equation is that of van der Waals :

$$(p + a/V^2)(V - b) = NkT \tag{5}$$

Berthelot gives an alternative empirical equation :

$$(p + a'/TV^2)(V - b) = NkT \tag{6}$$

and Dieterici still another, viz :

$$p(V - b) = NkTe^{-a'/NkT^sV} \tag{7}$$

where a, a', b, and s are all constants, the last being an exponent.

To the first order in $1/V$ these three equations assume the respective forms,

$$pV = NkT + \frac{(NkTb - a)}{V} \tag{8}$$

$$pV = NkT + \frac{(NkTb - a'/T)}{V} \tag{9}$$

$$pV = NkT + \frac{(NkTb - a'/T^{s-1})}{V} \tag{10}$$

1.3. Energies and specific heats of a one-component assembly. If E is the total energy assigned to the N systems of a one-component assembly,

$$E = NkT^2 \frac{d}{dT} \ln f(T) \tag{1}$$

The mean kinetic energy per particle is

$$\bar{\epsilon} = \frac{E_{\text{kin}}}{N} = kT^2 \frac{d}{dT} \ln H(T) = \frac{3}{2} kT \tag{2}$$

The specific heats per mol at constant volume C_v, and at constant pressure C_p are

$$\left.\begin{aligned} C_V &= \left(\frac{\partial E}{\partial T}\right)_V = \left[\frac{\partial}{\partial T} M_0 kT^2 \frac{\partial}{\partial T} \ln f(T)\right]_V \\ C_p &= \left[\frac{\partial}{\partial T}(E + pV)\right]_p = C_V + \left[\frac{\partial}{\partial T} pV\right]_p \end{aligned}\right\} \tag{3}$$

where the subscripts indicate that V and p are held constant during the respective differentiations; M_0 is the number of particles per mol.

1.4. Adiabatic processes. Let γ be the ratio

$$\gamma = C_p/C_V \tag{1}$$

The so-called adiabatic law, wherein no heat is added or subtracted from a gas is

$$pV^\gamma = \text{constant} \tag{2}$$

$$pT^{\gamma/(1-\gamma)} = \text{constant} \tag{3}$$

$$\rho T^{1/(1-\gamma)} = \text{constant} \tag{4}$$

In each of these equations we regard V as the volume of a mol (or some other conveniently defined mass of gas.)

1.5. Maxwell's and Boltzmann's laws. The number of systems in a given quantum state is

$$N_i = N \frac{\tilde{\omega}_i e^{-\varepsilon_i/kT}}{B(T)} \tag{1}$$

which is Boltzmann's law. Also

$$\frac{N_i}{N_j} = \frac{\tilde{\omega}_i}{\tilde{\omega}_j} e^{-(\varepsilon_i - \varepsilon_j)/kT} \tag{2}$$

In a classical assembly, the number, ϕ of systems in a volume element dV, with components of momenta in dp_1, dp_2, dp_3, becomes

$$\left.\begin{aligned} \phi dp_1 dp_2 dp_3 dV &= \frac{N}{H(T)V} e^{-(p_1{}^2+p_2{}^2+p_3{}^2)/2mkT} \frac{dp_1 dp_2 dp_3 dV}{h^3} \\ &= \frac{N}{V} \cdot \frac{1}{(2\pi mkT)^{3/2}} e^{-(p_1{}^2+p_2{}^2+p_3{}^2)/kT} dp_1 dp_2 dp_3 dV \end{aligned}\right\} \tag{3}$$

normalized to give

$$\int \phi dp_1 dp_2 dp_3 dV = N/V \tag{4}$$

where the integral is over a unit volume, with the respective momenta limits $-\infty$ to $+\infty$.

In terms of Cartesian velocity components, u, v, w, we have the alternative form of Maxwell's equation :

$$\phi du dv dw dV = \frac{N}{V}\left(\frac{m}{2\pi kT}\right)^{3/2} e^{-m(u^2+v^2+w^2)/2kT} du dv dw dV \tag{5}$$

If c is the actual space velocity, such that

$$c^2 = u^2 + v^2 + w^2 \tag{6}$$

the number of systems moving with velocities in dc and within solid angle $d\omega$ are

$$f dc d\omega = \frac{N}{V}\left(\frac{m}{2\pi kT}\right)^{3/2} c^2 e^{-mc^2/2kT} dc d\omega \tag{7}$$

To get the total number per cm^3, with velocities in dc, replace $d\omega$ by 4π.

For additional theorems on kinetic theory of gases see Chapter 20, pp. 288-302.

1.6. Compound and dissociating assemblies. When an assembly consists of more than one component, interacting or not, we write, instead of Eq. (1) of § 1.3,

$$E = \sum_j N_j k T^2 \frac{d}{d\pi} \ln f_j(T) \tag{1}$$

where the subscript j refers to a given component. The partition function is the same as before. For noninteracting components N_j is constant. Otherwise, N_j will depend on T and V according to the dissociation equation. For example, when N_m atoms of component m interact with N_n atoms of component n to form N_s compound molecules of component s, in accord with the symbolic chemical equation

$$M + N \rightleftarrows S \tag{2}$$

where S is a molecule of type MN, the equilibrium conforms to the law

$$\frac{N_m N_n}{N_s} = \frac{f_m(T) f_n(T)}{f_s(T)} \tag{3}$$

In a more general case, when N_m, N_n, N_p, ..., etc., interact to form a compound molecule, so that α atoms of type m, β of type n, γ of type p, etc., are required to form μ compound molecules of type s, according to the reaction

$$\alpha M + \beta N + \gamma P + \ldots = \mu S = \mu[M_{\alpha/\mu} N_{\beta/\mu} P_{\gamma/\mu} \ldots] \tag{4}$$

in ordinary chemical notation. The general dissociation equation becomes

$$\frac{N_m^{\alpha} N_n^{\beta} N_p^{\gamma} \ldots}{N_s^{\mu}} = \frac{(f_m)^{\alpha} (f_n)^{\beta} (f_p)^{\gamma} \ldots}{(f_s)^{\mu}} \tag{5}$$

in which the superscripts α, β, γ, ..., μ are true algebraic exponents. For more detailed forms of these equations, including the Saha " ionization formula," see Chapter 21.

1.7. Vapor pressure. The vapor pressure of a gas in equilibrium with its solid or liquid phase is

$$p = \frac{kT}{V} \cdot \frac{f(T)}{\kappa(T)} \tag{1}$$

For structureless systems, the partition function

$$f(T) = \frac{(2\pi mkT)^{3/2}}{h^3} V e^{-\chi/kT} \tag{2}$$

where χ is the energy required to evaporate an atom from the liquid or solid to the gaseous phase at absolute zero. The partition function for the crystal is

$$\ln \kappa(T) = \int_0^{T/V} \frac{dT}{RT^2} \int_0^T (C_p)_{\text{sol}} dT' \tag{3}$$

where $(C_p)_{\text{sol}}$ is the specific heat of the solid or condensed phase, calculated at the vapor pressure of the gas for the value of T in the integrand; $(C_p)_{\text{sol}}$ also includes heats of transition (melting, evaporation, etc.)

For molecular gases or other gases having internal structure, the appropriate factors relation to rotations, vibrations, electronic energies, etc., must be included in $f(T)$. For many applications we can set, approximately,

$$\kappa(T) \sim H(T) \tag{4}$$

see Eq. (6) of § 1.1.

More generally we note that the empirical relation,

$$p = CT^{\alpha}e^{-X/T} \tag{5}$$

with three disposable constants, C, α, and X usually gives a very accurate representation between any two given transition points.

1.8. Convergence of partition functions. The partition function $B_e(T)$, Eq. (14) of § 1.1, does not converge if we sum over all quantum numbers to $n = \infty$. The presence of neighboring atoms fixes an effective upper limit to the summation, beyond which we regard the electron as free rather than bound. Thus we excluded the volume assigned to other atoms. Denote by the subscript s the lower electronic states of a given atom, and by r the lower electron states of the same atom in the next higher ionization stage. Approximately

$$B(T) \sim \sum_s \tilde{\omega}_s e^{-\varepsilon_s/kT} + \tilde{\omega}_\varepsilon \left[\frac{64}{9\pi}\left(\frac{3}{4\pi}\right)^{1/2} \frac{(Rhc)^{3/2}}{\epsilon^3}\right] \frac{Z^{3/2}}{n_0{}^{1/2}} e^{-\chi_0/kT} \sum \tilde{\omega}_r e^{-\varepsilon_r/kT} \tag{1}$$

The bracketed constant, we shall term Q. Its value is

$$Q \sim 1.02 \times 10^{12}\ \text{cm}^{-3/2} \tag{2}$$

In this equation, $\tilde{\omega}_\varepsilon$ is the electron spin, Z is the effective charge of the higher ionization state involved, χ_0 is the ionization potential, and n_0 is the number of systems per cm^3. Usually only the first or the second term of (1) will dominate.

1.9. Fermi-Dirac and Bose-Einstein statistics. The foregoing formulas, especially those relating to equations of state and partition of kinetic energy, involve the tacit assumption that the energies of such a system are not quantized. This assumption is sufficiently correct at low densities and high temperatures. However, at high densities and low temperatures, we find that even the so-called " continuous states " are quantized and, furthermore, that we can assign only one particle to each state. The Pauli exclusion principle is a consequence of this general law.

For systems whose wave functions are antisymmetric, we get the Fermi-Dirac statistics (indicated by the upper sign in the following formulas). When the wave functions are symmetric, we get the Bose-Einstein statistics (lower signature).

In our given volume V, which contains N systems in all, we find that N_s are assigned to the energy level ϵ_s, whose statistical weight is $\tilde{\omega}_s$. Then

$$N_s = \pm \tilde{\omega}_s \lambda \frac{\partial}{\partial \lambda} \ln (1 \pm \lambda e^{-\varepsilon_s/kT}) = \frac{\tilde{\omega}_s}{\lambda^{-1} e^{\varepsilon_s} \pm 1} \tag{1}$$

The parameter λ follows from the condition that

$$\sum_s N_s = N = \sum_s \frac{\tilde{\omega}_s}{\lambda^{-1} e^{\varepsilon_s/kT} \pm 1} \tag{2}$$

For Bose-Einstein statistics we must have

$$0 < \lambda \leqslant 1 \tag{3}$$

For Fermi-Dirac, we have the condition

$$\lambda > 0 \tag{4}$$

To complete these equations we must have formulas for the separations ϵ_s. For kinetic energy in a cubical volume bounded by a side of length l,

$$\epsilon_s = \frac{p^2}{2m} = \frac{h^2}{8l^2 m} (x^2 + y^2 + z^2) \tag{5}$$

where x, y, and z are integers $0 < x,y,z \leqslant \infty$. Then

$$N = \sum_{x=1}^{\infty} \sum_{y=1}^{\infty} \sum_{z=1}^{\infty} \frac{\tilde{\omega}}{\lambda^{-1} e^{h^2(x^2+y^2+z^2)/8l^2mkT} \pm 1} \tag{6}$$

where $\tilde{\omega}$ is a weight factor set equal to unity for longitudinal and equal to 2 for transverse waves. The quantity $h^2/8l^2mkT = 4.4 \times 10^{-11}$, if $l = 1$ cm and $T = 1^\circ$ K. Hence we can approximate to the sum by an integral

$$\left.\begin{aligned} N &= \int_0^\infty \int_0^\infty \int_0^\infty \frac{\tilde{\omega} dx dy dz}{\lambda^{-1} e^{h^2(x^2+y^2+z^2)/8l^2mkT} \pm 1} \\ &= \int_0^{\pi/2} \int_0^{\pi/2} \int_0^\infty \frac{\tilde{\omega} r^2 \sin\theta \, dr d\theta d\varphi}{\lambda^{-1} e^{h^2 r^2/8l^2mkT} \pm 1} \\ &= \frac{\pi}{2} \int_0^\infty \frac{\tilde{\omega} r^2 dr}{\lambda^{-1} e^{hr^2/8l^2mkT} \pm 1} = \frac{2\pi\tilde{\omega}(2m)^{3/2} V}{h^3} \int_0^\infty \frac{\epsilon_s^{1/2}}{\lambda^{-1} e^{\varepsilon_s/kT} \pm 1} d\epsilon_s \end{aligned}\right\} \tag{7}$$

where we set

$$x^2 + y^2 + z^2 = r^2 \tag{8}$$

and transform from Cartesian to spherical coordinates. We have set $l^3 = V$.

We cannot integrate again in finite terms. However, when $\lambda \ll 1$,

$$N \sim \frac{2\pi\tilde{\omega}(2m)^{3/2}V\lambda}{h^3}\int_0^\infty e^{-\varepsilon_s/kT}\epsilon_s^{1/2}d\epsilon_s = \frac{\tilde{\omega}(2\pi mkT)^{3/2}V\lambda}{h^3} \tag{9}$$

Thus, when

$$\lambda = \frac{N}{\tilde{\omega}V}\cdot\frac{h^3}{(2\pi mkT)^{3/2}} \ll 1 \tag{10}$$

$$N_s = N\frac{2\pi(2m)^{1/2}}{(2\pi mkT)^{3/2}}e^{-\varepsilon_s/kT}\epsilon_s^{1/2}d\epsilon_s \tag{11}$$

a form of Maxwell's law, expressed in terms of energies instead of momenta or velocities as before. Thus, when $\lambda \ll 1$ we recover the classical formulas.

When $\lambda \gg 1$ (for the Fermi-Dirac case only)

$$N \sim \frac{2\pi\tilde{\omega}(2m)^{3/2}V}{h^3}\int_0^{\varepsilon'} \epsilon_s^{1/2}\,d\epsilon_s = \frac{4\pi}{3\pi^{1/2}}\frac{(2\pi mkT)^{3/2}V}{h^3}(\ln\lambda)^{3/2} \tag{12}$$

where ϵ' is defined by

$$\lambda^{-1}e^{\varepsilon'/kT} = 1 \tag{13}$$

For large λ, then, the Fermi-Dirac distribution becomes

$$N_s = 2\pi\tilde{\omega}(2m)^{3/2}V\epsilon_s^{1/2}d\epsilon_s \tag{14}$$

for the energy range below ϵ'. For higher energies, the formula grades into the classical expression.

For the Bose-Einstein case, $\lambda \ll 1$, we get

$$N \sim \frac{\tilde{\omega}(2\pi mkT)^{3/2}V}{h^3}\sum_{j=1}^{\infty}\frac{\lambda^j}{j^{3/2}} \tag{15}$$

1.10. Relativistic degeneracy. At extremely high temperatures we must allow for relativistic change of mass with velocity. The deBroglie wavelength of a particle moving with velocity v is

$$\lambda_v = \frac{h}{m_0 v}\left(1 - \frac{v^2}{c^2}\right)^{1/2} \tag{1}$$

where m_0 is the " rest mass." The kinetic energy is

$$\epsilon_s = m_0c^2\left[\left(1 - \frac{v^2}{c^2}\right)^{-1/2} - 1\right] \tag{2}$$

or

$$\frac{1}{\lambda_v^2} = \frac{2\epsilon_s m_0(1 + \epsilon_s/2m_0c^2)}{h^2} \tag{3}$$

when relativity effects are predominant,

$$\epsilon_s \gg 2m_0c^2 \tag{4}$$

and

$$\epsilon_s = \frac{hc}{\lambda v} = h\nu_s \tag{5}$$

Planck's relation. The energy is independent of m_0.

For Fermi-Dirac statistics we get, for a relativistically degenerate gas,

$$N = \frac{4\pi\tilde{\omega}V}{h^3c^2} \int_0^\infty \frac{\epsilon_s^{\ 2}}{\lambda^{-1}e^{\epsilon_s/kT}+1}\, d\epsilon_s \tag{6}$$

When $\lambda \ll 1$,

$$N \sim 8\pi\tilde{\omega}V\lambda\left(\frac{kT}{hc}\right)^3 \tag{7}$$

When $\lambda \gg 1$,

$$N \sim \frac{4\pi\tilde{\omega}V}{3}\left(\frac{kT}{hc}\ln\lambda\right)^3 \tag{8}$$

1.11. Dissociation laws for new statistics. Let

$$\beta_m = m_m/m\epsilon \tag{1}$$

the ratio of the mass of the system to that of the electron.

For each component m of an assembly find the appropriate value of λ_m according to the conditions of temperature and density.

Classical nonrelativistic:

$$\lambda = \frac{Nm}{\tilde{\omega}_m V} \cdot \frac{h^3}{(2\pi m_m kT)^{3/2}} \tag{2}$$

$$\text{conditions:} \quad \left\{ \begin{array}{l} N_m/V \ll \tilde{\omega}_m/h^3(2\pi m_m kT)^{3/2} = 4.87 \times 10^{15}(\beta_m T)^{3/2} \\ T \ll m_m c^2/k = 5.9 \times 10^9 \beta_m \end{array} \right\}$$

Classical, relativistic:

$$\lambda_m = \frac{N_m}{8\pi\tilde{\omega}_m V}\left(\frac{hc}{kT}\right)^3 \tag{3}$$

$$\text{conditions:} \quad \left\{ \begin{array}{l} N_m/V \ll 4.87 \times 10^{15}(\beta_m T)^{3/2} \\ T \gg 5.9 \times 10^9 \beta_m \end{array} \right\}$$

Fermi-Dirac degeneracy, nonrelativistic:

$$\ln\lambda_m = \frac{h^2}{2m_m kT}\left(\frac{3}{4\pi\tilde{\omega}_m}\frac{N_m}{V}\right)^{2/3} \tag{4}$$

$$\text{conditions:} \quad \left\{ \begin{array}{l} N_m/V \gg 4.87 \times 10^{15}(\beta_m T)^{3/2} \\ T \ll 5.9 \times 10^9 \beta_m \end{array} \right\}$$

Bose-Einstein degeneracy, nonrelativistic:

$$\sum_{j=1}^{\infty} \frac{\lambda_m^{\ j}}{j^{3/2}} = \frac{N_m}{\tilde{\omega}_m V} \frac{h^3}{(2\pi m_m kT)^{3/2}} \tag{5}$$

Conditions : same as for Fermi-Dirac, above.

Fermi-Dirac degeneracy, relativistic (electron gas):

$$\ln \lambda_m = \left(\frac{3N_m}{4\pi\tilde{\omega}_m V}\right)^{1/3} \frac{hc}{kT} \tag{6}$$

$$\text{conditions :} \quad \begin{cases} N_m/V \gg (kT/hc)^3 \, (4\pi\tilde{\omega}_m/3) = 2.86T^3 \\ T \gg 5.9 \times 10^9/\ln \lambda_m \end{cases}$$

These equations ignore internal excitation energies. Now in a reaction such as

$$M + N \rightleftarrows S \tag{7}$$

where S is a molecule of type MN, of dissociation energy Q_s, we can determine the equilibrium from the equation

$$\lambda_s = \lambda_m \lambda_n e^{Q_s/kT} \tag{8}$$

For the more complex reaction

$$\alpha M + \beta N \rightleftarrows \gamma S \tag{9}$$

with α, β, and γ integers, in which the chemical formula for S is $M_{\alpha/\gamma} N_{\beta/\gamma}$, we get

$$\lambda_s^{\gamma} = \lambda_m^{\alpha} \lambda_n^{\beta} e^{Q_s/kT} \tag{10}$$

1.12. Pressure of a degenerate gas. The general equation of state still holds for nonrelativistic statistics :

$$p = \frac{2}{3} \cdot \frac{\bar{E}_{\text{kin}}}{V} \tag{1}$$

$$\bar{E}_{\text{kin}} = \frac{2\pi\tilde{\omega}(2m)^{3/2} V}{h^3} \int_0^{\infty} \frac{\epsilon_s^{\ 3/2}}{\lambda^{-1} e^{\varepsilon_s/kT} \pm 1} \, d\epsilon_s \tag{2}$$

For small λ, we recover the classical expression

$$p = NkT/V \tag{3}$$

For $\lambda \gg 1$, for Fermi-Dirac statistics,

$$p = \frac{4\pi}{15} \frac{h^2\tilde{\omega}}{m} \left(\frac{3}{4\pi\tilde{\omega}} \cdot \frac{N}{V}\right)^{5/3} + \frac{2\pi^3}{9} \frac{m(kT)^2}{h^2} \left(\frac{3}{4\pi\tilde{\omega}} \frac{N}{V}\right)^{1/3} + \cdots \tag{4}$$

Note that the leading term gives a pressure independent of T.

For Bose-Einstein statistics

$$p = \tilde{\omega}\,\frac{(2\pi m)^{3/2}(kT)^{5/2}}{h^3}\sum_1^\infty \frac{\lambda^j}{j^{3/2}} \tag{5}$$

For relativistic statistics,

$$p = \frac{\bar{E}_{\text{kin}}}{3V} \tag{6}$$

$$\bar{E}_{\text{kin}} = \frac{4\pi\tilde{\omega}V}{h^3c^3}\int_0^\infty \frac{\epsilon_s^{\,3}}{\lambda^{-1}e^{\varepsilon_s/kT} \pm 1}\,d\epsilon_s \tag{7}$$

When $\lambda \ll 1$,

$$p = NkT/V \tag{8}$$

When $\lambda \gg 1$, Fermi-Dirac,

$$p = \frac{hc}{4}\left(\frac{3}{4\pi\tilde{\omega}}\right)^{1/3}\left(\frac{N}{V}\right)^{4/3} \tag{9}$$

1.13. Statistics of light quanta. Quanta obey the Bose-Einstein relativistic statistics with $\lambda = 1$. This condition is equivalent to the assumption that total number of quanta are not conserved.

$$\bar{E}_{\text{kin}} = \frac{4\pi\tilde{\omega}Vh}{c^3}\int_0^\infty \frac{\nu^3}{e^{h\nu/kT} - 1}\,d\nu \tag{1}$$

Set $\tilde{\omega} = 2$ for transverse waves. Then the energy density of ν radiation becomes

$$\rho_\nu d\nu = \frac{8\pi h\nu^3}{c^3}\,\frac{1}{e^{h\nu/kT} - 1}\,d\nu \tag{2}$$

For additional radiation formulas, see Chapter 21.

Bibliography

1. Chandrasekhar, S., *Monthly Notices Roy. Astronom. Soc.*, **95**, 225 (1935).
2. Fowler, R. H. and Guggenheim, E. A., *Statistical Mechanics*, Cambridge University Press, London, 1939.

Chapter 12

KINETIC THEORY OF GASES: VISCOSITY, THERMAL CONDUCTION, AND DIFFUSION

By Sydney Chapman

Oxford University

The kinetic theory of gases was the pioneer branch of statistical mechanics, applied to the motion of gas molecules moving freely except during the brief fraction of time occupied by collisions. Kinetic theory thus provides the necessary connection between the microscopic viewpoint of the molecules on one hand and the macroscopic viewpoint of hydrodynamics on the other. The formulas here given were chosen as those most likely to be useful to the working physicist, especially those who like to know the steps leading the mathematicians to the results as well as the results themselves. Some of the following formulas, as, for example, those for diffusion, are not so generally well known as they should be.

1. Preliminary Definitions and Equations for a Mixed Gas, Not in Equilibrium

1.1. $\boldsymbol{r}, x, y, z, t, d\boldsymbol{r}$. Position is indicated by the position vector $\boldsymbol{r}$ or by orthogonal coordinates x, y, z; and time by t. A small volume element enclosing the point $\boldsymbol{r}$ is denoted by $d\boldsymbol{r}$.

1.2. $m, n, \rho, n_{10}, n_{12}, m_0$. A mixed gas of two constituents is considered; suffixes 1,2 refer to the two constituents, e.g., m_1, m_2 denote the molecular masses, n_1, n_2 the number densities (or numbers per cc), ρ_1, ρ_2 the mass densities n_1m_1, n_2m_2. The total number or mass density is denoted by n or ρ.

$$n = n_1 + n_2, \quad \rho = \rho_1 + \rho_2 = n_1m_1 + n_2m_2 \tag{1}$$

Also let

$$n_{10} = n_1/n, \quad n_{20} = n_2/n, \quad n_{12} = n_1/n_2 \tag{2}$$

so that

$$n_{10} + n_{20} = 1 \tag{3}$$

and let

$$m_0 = m_1 + m_2, \quad m = \rho/n \tag{4}$$

so that m_0 is the combined, and m the mean, molecular mass.

Thus the suffix 1 or 2 refers to one constituent only, and without the suffix the reference is to the whole gas (or to a simple gas); this is here called the suffix convention and is to be applied in each subsequent section concluded by (S.C.) meaning *suffix convention.*

1.3. The external forces $\boldsymbol{F}$, X, Y, Z, Ψ. Every molecule is supposed to be subject to an external force $m\boldsymbol{F}$, with components mX, mY, mZ, the same for all those of one kind ($m_1\boldsymbol{F}_1$ or $m_2\boldsymbol{F}_2$). Moreover it is supposed that these are conservative forces with potentials Ψ_1, Ψ_2, so that

$$\boldsymbol{F}_1 = -\operatorname{grad}\Psi_1, \qquad \boldsymbol{F}_2 = -\operatorname{grad}\Psi_2, \qquad \text{(S.C.)} \tag{1}$$

1.4. $\boldsymbol{c}$, u, v, w, $d\boldsymbol{c}$. The velocity of a typical molecule is denoted by $\boldsymbol{c}$, and its components by u, v, w; these may be regarded as specifying a point in a *velocity space*, referring to molecules of one kind only, if suffix 1 or 2 is added, otherwise to molecules of both kinds (or to those of a simple gas). A small volume element in the velocity space, enclosing the *velocity point* $\boldsymbol{c}$, is denoted by $d\boldsymbol{c}$. (S.C.)

1.5. The velocity distribution function f. Each of the $nd\boldsymbol{r}$ molecules in the space volume element $d\boldsymbol{r}$ at time t has its own velocity point; the number of these within the velocity volume element $d\boldsymbol{c}$ is denoted by $fd\boldsymbol{r}d\boldsymbol{c}$, that is, $fd\boldsymbol{r}$ is the number density at $\boldsymbol{c}$ in the velocity space; f is a function of $\boldsymbol{c}$, $\boldsymbol{r}$, t in general, and to indicate this it is also written $f(\boldsymbol{c},\boldsymbol{r},t)$; it is called the *velocity distribution function.* (S.C.)

1.6. Mean values of velocity functions. The average of any function $F(\boldsymbol{c})$, vector or scalar, e.g., $\boldsymbol{c}$ or u or uv or c^2, over all the molecules (of either or both kinds) in $d\boldsymbol{r}$ at $\boldsymbol{r}$, t, is indicated by the function symbol with an overline, e.g., $\bar{\boldsymbol{c}}$, $\overline{F(\boldsymbol{c})}$, $\bar{u}$, $\overline{uv}$, $\bar{c}$. Clearly

$$n\overline{F(\boldsymbol{c})} = \int F(\boldsymbol{c})f(\boldsymbol{c},\boldsymbol{r},t)d\boldsymbol{c} \tag{1}$$

the integral being taken over the whole velocity space. (S.C.)

In consequence of this definition,

$$n\bar{\boldsymbol{c}} = n_1\bar{\boldsymbol{c}}_1 + n_2\bar{\boldsymbol{c}}_2, \quad n\bar{u} = n_1\bar{u}_1 + n_2\bar{u}_2, \quad \text{etc.} \tag{2}$$

1.7. The mean mass velocity $\boldsymbol{c}_0$; u_0, v_0, w_0. The mean momentum per molecule, for the whole gas, is $(n_1m_1\bar{\boldsymbol{c}}_1 + n_2m_2\bar{\boldsymbol{c}}_2)/n$; this is denoted by $m\boldsymbol{c}_0$; and u_0, v_0, w_0 denote the components of $\boldsymbol{c}_0$. Clearly

$$\rho\boldsymbol{c}_0 = \rho_1\bar{\boldsymbol{c}}_1 + \rho_2\bar{\boldsymbol{c}}_2 \tag{1}$$

1.8. The random velocity C; U, V, W; dC. The *random* velocity $\boldsymbol{C}$ of a typical molecule, and its components U, V, W, are defined by

$$\boldsymbol{C} = \boldsymbol{c} - \boldsymbol{c}_0, \quad U = u - u_0, \quad \text{etc.} \tag{1}$$

Clearly

$$\bar{\boldsymbol{C}}_1 = \bar{\boldsymbol{c}}_1 - \boldsymbol{c}_0, \quad \bar{\boldsymbol{C}}_2 = \bar{\boldsymbol{c}}_2 - \boldsymbol{c}_0, \quad \bar{\boldsymbol{C}} = \bar{\boldsymbol{c}} - \boldsymbol{c}_0 \tag{2}$$

If the origin in the velocity space is moved to the velocity point $\boldsymbol{c}_0$, the velocity position vector of a typical molecule is changed to $\boldsymbol{C}$, and the distribution function f can be regarded alternatively as a function of $\boldsymbol{C}$, $\boldsymbol{r}$, t, namely $f(\boldsymbol{C},\boldsymbol{r},t)$; if $d\boldsymbol{C}$ denotes a velocity volume element enclosing the velocity point $\boldsymbol{C}$, the equation for $\overline{F(\boldsymbol{c})}$ in § 1.5 can alternatively be written

$$n\overline{F(\boldsymbol{c})} = \int F(\boldsymbol{c})f(\boldsymbol{C},\boldsymbol{r},t)d\boldsymbol{C}, \quad \text{(S.C.)} \tag{3}$$

1.9. The "heat" energy of a molecule E: its mean value $\bar{E}$. The heat energy E of a molecule is defined to be the energy $\frac{1}{2}mC^2$ of its random translatory energy, together with any additional energy, either rotatory or internal (e.g., vibratory), *which is communicable from one molecule to another on encounter*; for example, this would not include any rotatory energy of a smooth, rigid, elastic, spherical molecule. Its value at $\boldsymbol{r}$, t is denoted by $\bar{E}$. Naturally $\bar{E}$ is a function of the (absolute or Kelvin) temperature T.

1.10. The molecular weight W and the constants m_u, N_L. A molecule of mass m is said to have molecular "weight" W equal to m/m_u, where m_u ($= 1.6603 \times 10^{-24}$ gram), the unit atomic mass, is one-sixteenth the mass of the O^{16} isotope of oxygen. A mass of W grams of a gas of (mean) molecular weight W is called a gram molecule or mole; it contains N_L molecules, where

$$N_L = 1/m_u = 6.023 \times 10^{23} \tag{1}$$

N_L is called Loschmidt's number (or sometimes, less appropriately, Avogadro's number; see § 2.3).

1.11. The constants J, k, R. The following constants are used in later sections, e.g., 1.12.

$J = 4.185 \times 10^7$ ergs per calorie (Joule's mechanical equivalent of heat).
$k = 1.3805 \times 10^{-16}$ erg per degree C (Boltzmann's constant).
$R = kN_L = 8.314 \times 10^7$ ergs per degree C per mole (the gas constant in mechanical units).
$R = kN_L/J = 1.9865$ calorie per degree C per mole (the gas constant in heat units).

1.12. The kinetic theory temperature T is defined by

$$kT = \tfrac{1}{3}m\overline{C^2} \tag{1}$$

whether or not the gas be in thermodynamic equilibrium (see § 2.3).

1.13. The symbols c_v, C_v denote the specific heat at constant volume, per gram (c_v) or per mole (C_v) : that is, the heat required to raise the temperature of this mass of gas by 1° C, at constant volume; this is indicated formally by

$$c_v = (1/m)\,(d\bar{E}/dT)_v,\ C_v = Wc_v = (1/m_u)\,(d\bar{E}/dT)_v = N_L(d\bar{E}/dT)_v \tag{1}$$

If the molecules have no communicable rotatory or internal energy, $\bar{E} = \frac{1}{2}m\overline{C^2} = \frac{3}{2}kT$, and $c_v = 3k/2m$; and $C_v = 3k/2m_u$, the same for all gases. If $\bar{E}$ is a constant multiple (s) of $\frac{1}{2}m\overline{C^2}$, so that $\bar{E} = \frac{3}{2}skT$, $c_v = 3ks/2m$, $C_v = 3ks/2m_u$; for many diatomic molecules at ordinary temperatures $s = \frac{5}{3}$, as they possess rotatory energy of amount two-thirds the random translatory kinetic energy (see § 2.4 for c_p, C_p, γ).

1.14. The stress distribution, p_{xx}, p_{xy}, ... The x, y, z components of the stress (force per unit area) exerted at $\boldsymbol{r}$, t, *upon* the gas on the positive side of a plane through $\boldsymbol{r}$ normal to Ox, *by* the gas on the negative side, are denoted by p_{xx}, p_{xy}, p_{xz}; similarly p_{yx}, p_{yy}, p_{yz}, and p_{zx}, p_{zy}, p_{zz} denote the stress components across planes normal to Oy and Oz. These nine components are the elements of the stress *tensor*; p_{xx}, p_{yy}, p_{zz} are *normal* stresses; the other six are *tangential* stresses.

In the interior of a gas of ordinary low density (e.g., normal air) these stresses arise mainly from the transfer of momentum by molecules crossing the planes concerned; this produces the *kinetic stresses*. In addition there is a much smaller part due to intermolecular forces; a gas in which this part is negligible is called a perfect gas. The gas here considered will be supposed perfect, but the equation of state will be given also for a slightly imperfect gas (§ 2.5).

In a perfect mixed gas the constituents contribute independently to the stresses :

$$\left.\begin{aligned} p_{xx} &= (p_{xx})_1 + (p_{xx})_2, \quad & p_{xy} &= (p_{xy})_1 + (p_{xy})_2, \ \text{etc.} \\ (p_{xx})_1 &= \rho_1\overline{U_1^2}, & (p_{xy})_1 &= \rho_1\overline{U_1V_1}, \ \text{etc.} \end{aligned}\right\} \tag{1}$$

Hence (see § 1.6)

$$p_{xx} = \rho_1\overline{U_1^2} + \rho_2\overline{U_2^2} = \rho\overline{U^2},\quad p_{xy} = \rho\overline{UV},\quad \text{etc.} \tag{2}$$

1.15. The hydrostatic pressure p; the partial pressures p_1, p_2. The hydrostatic pressure p is defined as the mean of the three normal stresses; that is,

$$p = \tfrac{1}{3}(p_{xx} + p_{yy} + p_{zz}) = \tfrac{1}{3}\rho\overline{C^2} = knT \tag{1}$$

using § 1.12. The "partial" pressures p_1, p_2 caused by the separate constituents are similarly given by

$$p_1 = \tfrac{1}{3}\rho_1\overline{C_1^2}, \quad p_2 = \tfrac{1}{3}\rho_2\overline{C_2^2}, \quad p = p_1 + p_2 \tag{2}$$

1.16. Boltzmann's equation for f. Boltzmann showed that each velocity distribution function f_1, f_2, satisfies an integro-differential equation. This (e.g., for f_1) equates the following combination of partial derivatives of f_1,

$$\frac{\partial f_1}{\partial t} + u_1\frac{\partial f_1}{\partial x} + v_1\frac{\partial f_1}{\partial y} + w_1\frac{\partial f_1}{\partial z} + X_1\frac{\partial f_1}{\partial u_1} + Y_1\frac{\partial f_1}{\partial v_1} + Z_1\frac{\partial f_1}{\partial w_1} \tag{1}$$

to a multiple integral (not given here), which involves both f_1 and f_2, and represents the rate of change of f_1 caused by molecular encounters. In a perfect gas only simple encounters, each involving but two molecules, need be considered. The evaluation of this integral naturally, in general, involves knowledge as to the properties of the molecules, that is, as to their modes of interaction in encounters.

1.17. Summational invariants. Certain properties are unchanged by an encounter. These are (1) the number of molecules involved, namely two, (2) their combined momentum, namely $m_1\boldsymbol{c}_1 + m_1\boldsymbol{c}_1'$, $m_2\boldsymbol{c}_2 + m_2\boldsymbol{c}_2'$, or $m_1\boldsymbol{c}_1 + m_2\boldsymbol{c}_2$, according as the encounter is between like or unlike molecules, and (3) their combined energy, $E + E'$, or $\tfrac{1}{2}mC^2 + \tfrac{1}{2}m'C'^2$ (suffix convention) if the molecules have no rotatory or internal energy. These properties (number, $m\boldsymbol{c}$, and E) are called summational invariants of an encounter.

1.18. Boltzmann's H theorem. For a uniform gas whose molecules are spherical and possess only translatory kinetic energy, and are subject to no external forces, the 'differential' side of Boltzmann's equation reduces to $\partial f_1/\partial t$. Boltzmann also considered in this case the variation of the function H defined by $\int f \ln f \, d\boldsymbol{c}$, integrated over the whole velocity space. He showed that $\partial H/\partial t$ is negative or zero, and that in the steady state, when it must be zero, $\ln f$ must be a summational invariant, and consequently (see § 1.16) of the form $a_1 + \boldsymbol{a}_1' . \ m\boldsymbol{c} + a_1''mC^2$, where a_1, $\boldsymbol{a}_1'$, a_1'' are arbitrary (scalar or vector) constants; the middle term is the scalar product of $\boldsymbol{a}_1'$ and $m\boldsymbol{c}$.

2. Results for a Gas in Equilibrium*

2.1. Maxwell's steady-state solutions. Maxwell determined f in three important special cases, of steady or quasi-steady states; Boltzmann improved the proofs by means of his H theorem (§ 1.18). Later he showed that H_0, the space integral of H over a given volume of gas in such a state, satisfies the equation

$$S = -kH_0 + \text{constant}$$

where S denotes the *entropy* of the gas. In all three of Maxwell's special states,

$$f_1 = n_1\left(\frac{m_1}{2\pi kT}\right)^{3/2} e^{-m_1 C_1^2/kT} \tag{1}$$

which is known as the Maxwellian velocity distribution. His three cases are :

a. Uniform steady state of rest or uniform motion under no external forces; n_1, n_2, T, and $\boldsymbol{c}_0$ are all uniform.

b. Steady state at rest under external forces derived from potentials Ψ_1, Ψ_2 (1.3); in this case T and $\boldsymbol{c}_0$ are uniform, but not n_1 and n_2, which are given by

$$n_1 = (n_1)_0 e^{-m_1\Psi_1/kT}, \qquad n_2 = (n_2)_0 e^{-m_2\Psi_2/kT} \tag{2}$$

where $(n_1)_0$, $(n_2)_0$ are constants (the values of n_1 and n_2 at the points, if any, where Ψ_1 or Ψ_2 is zero).

c. A gas in uniform rotation or screw-motion subject to no external force (or to forces whose potentials are constant along the circles or spirals traced out by any point fixed relative to the gas). In this case T must be uniform, but not $\boldsymbol{c}_0$, which is given by

$$\boldsymbol{c}_0 = (\boldsymbol{c}_0)_0 + \omega x \boldsymbol{r}$$

(where ω denotes the angular velocity and $(\boldsymbol{c}_0)_0$ the constant velocity at the origin, and $\omega x \boldsymbol{r}$ denotes the *vector* product of and $\boldsymbol{r}$), nor n_1, n_2, which are given by

$$n_1 = (n_1)_0 e^{-m_1\Psi_0/kT} \tag{3}$$

where $\Psi_0 = -\frac{1}{2}\omega^2 d^2$, and d denotes the distance of the point $\boldsymbol{r}$ from the axis of the rotation or screw. Thus the density distribution is the same as if the gas were at rest in a field of (centrifugal) force with this potential.

* See also Chapters 10 and 11.

2.2. Mean values when f is Maxwellian. In this case the following mean values (§ 1.6) of various functions of $\boldsymbol{C}$ are readily found.

$$\bar{C}_1 = \left(\frac{8kT}{\pi m_1}\right)^{1/2}, \qquad \bar{U}_{1+} = \frac{1}{2}\bar{C}_1 \tag{1}$$

where $\bar{U}_{1+}$ denotes the mean value of any component of $\boldsymbol{C}_1$, e.g., $\boldsymbol{U}_1$, averaged over those molecules 1 for which this component is positive. Also

$$\overline{U_1^2} = \overline{V_1^2} = \overline{W_1^2} = \frac{1}{3}\overline{C_1^2} = \frac{kT}{m_1}, \quad \overline{U_1V_1} = \overline{V_1W_1} = \overline{W_1U_1} = 0 \tag{2}$$

so that

$$\left.\begin{aligned}(p_{xx})_1 = (p_{yy})_1 = (p_{zz})_1 = p_1 = kn_1T\\ (p_{xy})_1 = (p_{yz})_1 = (p_{zx})_1 = 0\end{aligned}\right\} \tag{3}$$

Thus the stress distribution is hydrostatic, that is, normal and equal across all planes through $\boldsymbol{r}$.

The "root-mean-square" speed $\sqrt{\overline{C_1^2}}$ is given by

$$\sqrt{\overline{C_1^2}} = \sqrt{(3kT/m_1)} = 1.086\bar{C}_1 \tag{4}$$

Also

$$\tfrac{1}{2}m_1\overline{C_1^2} = \tfrac{1}{2}m_2\overline{C_2^2} = \tfrac{3}{2}kT \tag{5}$$

thus the mean random kinetic energy is the same for both kinds of molecule; this is a particular case of a very general theorem of *equipartition of energy*.

2.3. The equation of state for a perfect gas. The equation $p = knT$ may be written, in reference to a mass M of the gas, occupying a volume V, so that $n = M/mV$, in the form

$$pV = (kM/m)T \tag{1}$$

This is the *equation of state* for a perfect gas, that is, the equation connecting p, V, and T in the equilibrium state; it includes Boyle's law (pV = constant at any given temperature), and Charles' law (V proportional to T at a given pressure). These laws, however, refer to the thermodynamic temperature, and it is necessary to show that in equilibrium (for which alone the thermodynamic temperature is defined) this is the same as the kinetic theory temperature T. This can be achieved by considering Carnot's cycle for a perfect gas.

The equation $p = knT$ then confirms, for a perfect gas, Avogadro's hypothesis that all gases in equilibrium, at the same p and T, contain the same number N_A of molecules in unit volume. For 1 cc at N.T.P. (0° C and

1 atmosphere pressure namely, 1.013×10^6 dynes/cm²) this number N_A is 2.687×10^{19}; it is known as Avogadro's number (or sometimes, less appropriately, as Loschmidt's number. See § 1.10).

2.4. Specific heats. The symbols c_p and $C_p\,(=Wc_p)$ denote the specific heat at constant pressure, per gram (c_p) or per mole (C_p); see § 1.13. That is, c_p is the heat required to raise 1 gram (containing $1/m$ molecules) by 1° C ($= dT$), at constant pressure. It includes, besides the heat c_v required to increase the mean molecular energy of the molecules, the mechanical energy (pdV/J in heat units) required to increase the volume by dV, against the constant pressure p, according to Charles' law. The equation of state (§ 2.3) gives, for $M = 1$ and $dT = 1°$ C,

$$pdV/J = k/Jm \tag{1}$$

Thus

$$c_p = c_v + \frac{k}{Jm} \tag{2}$$

$$C_p = C_v + \frac{Wk}{Jm} = C_v + \frac{N_L k}{J} = C_v + R \tag{3}$$

or $C_p - C_v = R$ (the same for all perfect gases); R is here expressed in heat units (see § 1.11).

The ratio c_p/c_v or C_p/C_v is denoted by γ; by § 1.13,

$$\gamma = 1 + \frac{k}{Jmc_v} = 1 + \frac{2}{3}s \tag{4}$$

Thus $\gamma = \frac{5}{3}$ for molecules with no rotatory or internal communicable energy, for which $s = 1$; for the diatomic molecules for which (at ordinary temperatures) $s = \frac{5}{3}$, $\gamma = 1.4$.

2.5. Equation of state for an imperfect gas. The simplest generalization of the equation of state $p = knT$ or $pV = (kM/m)T$ for a perfect gas is

$$p + a\rho^2 = knT(1 + b\rho\chi) \tag{1}$$

or, less accurately,

$$(p + a\rho^2)(1 - b\rho) = knT \tag{2}$$

which is van der Waals' equation. These equations allow for both the intermolecular forces and the finite size of molecules. For a simple gas in which the molecules are rigid, elastic, attracting spheres of diameter σ, exerting a force $F(r)$ at distance r,

$$b = \frac{2}{3} \cdot \frac{\pi\sigma^3}{m}, \qquad a = \frac{2}{3} \cdot \frac{\pi}{m^2} \int r^3 F(r)dr \tag{3}$$

and to a first approximation

$$\chi = 1 + \tfrac{5}{8}\rho b \tag{4}$$

2.6. The free path, collision frequency, collision interval, and collision energy (perfect gas). For a mixed gas composed of rigid, elastic, spherical molecules of diameters σ_1, σ_2, (for kinds 1 and 2), the following results are obtained by use of Maxwell's velocity distribution function (§ 2.1).

The number of collisions N_{11}, N_{22}, N_{12} per unit volume per unit time, between like molecules (1 or 2) or unlike molecules, are given by

$$N_{11} = 2n_1^2\sigma_1^2\left(\frac{\pi kT}{m_1}\right)^{1/2}, \quad N_{12} = 2n_1n_2\sigma_{12}^2\left(\frac{2\pi m_0 kT}{m_1m_2}\right)^{1/2} \tag{1}$$

where $\sigma_{12} = \frac{1}{2}(\sigma_1 + \sigma_2)$.

The *collision frequencies*, ν_1, ν_2, or average number of collisions for a molecule 1 or 2 per unit time, are given by

$$\nu_1 = \frac{2N_{11} + N_{12}}{n_1}, \qquad \nu_2 = \frac{2N_{22} + N_{12}}{n_2} \tag{2}$$

The *collision intervals*, τ_1, τ_2, or mean time interval between collisions for a molecule of kind 1 or 2, are

$$\tau_1 = 1/\nu_1, \qquad \tau_2 = 1/\nu_2 \tag{3}$$

The mean free paths l_1, l_2, between collisions for a molecule of kind 1 or 2, are

$$\frac{1}{l_1} = \pi\left[2^{1/2}n_1\sigma_1^2 + \left(\frac{1+m_1}{m_2}\right)^{1/2} n_2\sigma_{12}^2\right] \tag{4}$$

If the gas is simple,

$$l = 0.707/\pi n\sigma^2 \tag{5}$$

The mean free path $l_1(C_1)$ of a molecule of kind 1, moving with random speed C_1 is, for various values of $C_1/\overline{C_1}$, as follows:

$C_1/\overline{C_1}$:	0	0.25	0.50	1	2	3	4	5	6	∞
$l_1(C_1)/l_1$:	0	0.344	0.641	1.026	1.288	1.355	1.380	1.392	1.399	1.414

The probability that a molecule 1 with a particular speed C_1 shall travel a distance at least equal to l is $e^{-l/l_1(C_1)}$.

The probability that a molecule 1 moving with any speed should describe a free path at least equal to l is approximately $e^{-1.04l/l_1}$.

The fraction of the N_{12} collisions per unit volume and unit time, between unlike molecules whose collisional energy (namely, their combined translatory kinetic energy relative to their mass center, before collision) is x_0kT, is $(1 + x_0^2)e^{-x_0^2}$.

The mean value of the collisional energy is $2kT$.

3. Nonuniform Gas

3.1. The second approximation to f. Maxwell's velocity distribution is not correct when T is nonuniform, nor when $\boldsymbol{c}_0$ and the concentration ratio n_1/n_2 vary from point to point, except for his special states (§§ 2.1a and 2.1b). Even so, however, it is a good first approximation to f, if n is 10^{13} or more and if the gradients of T and $\boldsymbol{c}_0$ do not exceed 1°/cm and 1 sec^{-1}, respectively. Also, for these conditions, the second approximation to f gives reasonably accurate expressions for the stress distribution, thermal conduction, and diffusion.

The second approximation has the form

$$f_1 = f_1^{(0)}\,(1 + \Phi_1^{(1)}) \tag{1}$$

where $f_1^{(0)}$ denotes the Maxwellian expression (2.1), and

$$\Phi_1^{(1)} = -A_1(C_1)\boldsymbol{C}_1 \cdot \mathbf{grad} \ln T - D_1(C_1)\boldsymbol{C} \cdot \boldsymbol{d}_{12} - B_1(C_1)B(\boldsymbol{C}_1\boldsymbol{c}_0) \tag{2}$$

where

$$\boldsymbol{d}_{12} = \mathbf{grad}\, n_{10} + \frac{n_1 n_2}{n^2 p\rho}(m_1 - m_2)\boldsymbol{f} - \frac{n_1 n_2}{np}(m_1\boldsymbol{F}_1 - m_2\boldsymbol{F}_2) \tag{3}$$

$$\left.\begin{aligned} B(C_1,c_0) = \frac{1}{3}\,U_1^2\left(2\frac{\partial u_0}{\partial x} - \frac{\partial v_0}{\partial y} - \frac{\partial w_0}{\partial z}\right) + \ldots \\ + V_1W_1\left(\frac{\partial v_0}{\partial z} + \frac{\partial w_0}{\partial y}\right) + \ldots \end{aligned}\right\} \tag{4}$$

and A_1, D_1, B_1, are scalar functions of the random speed C_1, determinable from Boltzmann's equation (§ 1.16) and involving molecular interactions. In $\boldsymbol{d}_{12}$ the vector $\boldsymbol{f}$ denotes the acceleration of the gas at $\boldsymbol{r}$, namely $D\boldsymbol{c}_0/Dt$, where D/Dt denotes the hydrodynamic " mobile operator "

$$\frac{\partial}{\partial t} + \frac{u_0\partial}{\partial x} + \frac{v_0\partial}{\partial y} + \frac{w_0\partial}{\partial z}$$

$\boldsymbol{f}$ is given by

$$\rho\boldsymbol{f} = \rho_1\boldsymbol{F}_1 + \rho_2\boldsymbol{F}_2 - \mathbf{grad}\, p \tag{5}$$

3.2. The stress distribution. From this expression for f_1, and the corresponding one for f_2, the components of the stress distribution are found to be

$$p_{xx} = knT - \frac{2}{3}\mu\left(\frac{2\partial u_0}{\partial x} - \frac{\partial v_0}{\partial y} - \frac{\partial w_0}{\partial z}\right), \quad p_{yz} = \mu\left(\frac{\partial v_0}{\partial z} + \frac{\partial w_0}{\partial y}\right), \quad \text{etc.} \tag{1}$$

where μ is expressible in terms of integrals involving the functions B_1 and B_2 and depends on the mode of molecular interaction.

These expressions for the stress agree with those of the formal theory of viscous stress, so that μ is identified with the coefficient of viscosity. In laminar motion, such that $u_0 = w_0 = 0$, $v_0 = az$, where a is a constant $(= \partial v_0/\partial z)$,

$$p_{xx} = p_{yy} = p_{zz} = knT, \quad p_{xy} = p_{xz} = 0, \quad p_{yz} = -\mu a \tag{2}$$

which is the simplest formal definition of μ.

3.3. Diffusion. In general $\overline{C_1}$ and $\overline{C_2}$ are unequal in a nonuniform mixed gas; that is, the two sets of molecules diffuse through each other. The rate of diffusion is expressible by $\overline{C_1} - \overline{C_2}$, which is independent of any uniform motion of the axes of reference. It is convenient to consider the flux of either type of molecule relative to axes moving with the mean speed $\bar{\mathbf{c}}$ (rather than $\mathbf{c}_0$), in which case

$$n_1\overline{C_1} = -n_2\overline{C_2} = \frac{n_1 n_2}{n}(\overline{C_1} - \overline{C_2}) \tag{1}$$

In this case the expression for $\overline{C_1} - \overline{C_2}$ derived from f_1 and f_2 gives

$$n_1\overline{C_1} = -nD_{12}\mathbf{d}_{12} - nD_T\,\mathbf{grad}\ln T \tag{2}$$

where D_{12} and D_T are expressible in terms of integrals involving the functions A_1 and D_1 and depend on the law of molecular interaction.

This expression shows that diffusion is set up by any of the four following causes: (a) a concentration gradient, (b) acceleration of the gas, (c) unequal external forces on the molecules 1, 2, and (d) a temperature gradient. Diffusion resulting from this last cause is called thermal diffusion. When T is uniform and there is no external force and no acceleration, p and n are uniform (see §§ 3.1-3.5), and (2) reduces to

$$n_1\overline{C_1} = -nD_{12}\,\mathbf{grad}\,n_{10} = -D_{12}\,\mathbf{grad}\,n_1 \tag{3}$$

This is the formal definition of D_{12} as the coefficient of diffusion. This coefficient also governs accelerative and forced diffusion, due to the causes (b) and (c).

Thermal diffusion is governed by a different factor D_T, called the coefficient of thermal diffusion; the ratio D_T/D_{12} is called the thermal diffusion ratio, and denoted by k_T: it has $n_{10}n_{20}$ as a factor, and therefore varies greatly with the concentration ratio. The thermal diffusion factor α, defined by $k_T/n_{10}n_{20}$, is much less dependent on n_1/n_2. Thus

$$n\overline{\boldsymbol{C}_1} = -D_{12}\boldsymbol{d}_{12}' \tag{4}$$

where

$$\boldsymbol{d}_{12}' = n\,\mathbf{grad}\,n_{10} + \frac{n_1 n_2}{np\rho}(m_1 - m_2)\boldsymbol{f}$$

$$-\frac{n_1 n_2}{p}(m_1\boldsymbol{F}_1 - m_2\boldsymbol{F}_2) + nk_T\,\mathbf{grad}\ln T$$

If T is uniform and $\boldsymbol{f}$ zero, and $\boldsymbol{F}_1$ and $\boldsymbol{F}_2$ are derived from potentials Ψ_1 and Ψ_2, diffusion proceeds in the sense which decreases $\boldsymbol{d}_{12}$, and if in the limit diffusion ceases, the condition $\boldsymbol{d}_{12}' = 0$ leads to

$$\mathbf{grad}\ln\frac{n_1}{n_2} = -\mathbf{grad}\frac{m_1\Psi_1 - m_2\Psi_2}{kT} \tag{5}$$

in accordance with Eq. (3) of § 2.1.

3.4. Thermal conduction. Heat conduction in a diffusing mixed gas proves to be expressible most simply by considering the flux relative to axes moving with the molecular mean speed $\bar{\boldsymbol{c}}$ instead of $\boldsymbol{c}_0$ (when there is no diffusion $\bar{\boldsymbol{c}}$ and $\boldsymbol{c}_0$ are identical). In this case the expressions for f_1 and f_2 lead to the equation

$$\boldsymbol{q} = -\lambda\,\mathbf{grad}\,T - np\alpha D_{12}\boldsymbol{d}_{12}' \tag{1}$$

where λ depends on the mode of molecular interaction, through the functions A_1 and D_1, and is identified with the coefficient of thermal conduction in accordance with the formal definition for a nondiffusing gas. The second term in $\boldsymbol{q}$ is proportional to the rate of diffusion; it is an effect inverse to thermal diffusion, and is called the diffusion thermo-effect.

4. The Gas Coefficients for Particular Molecular Models

4.1. Models *a* to *d*. The simplest molecular models are:

a. *Smooth rigid elastic spheres* of diameters σ_1, σ_2; let

$$\sigma_{12} = \tfrac{1}{2}(\sigma_1 + \sigma_2)$$

This is the model already considered in 2.6. For such molecules $E = \frac{1}{2}mC^2$.

b. *Smooth rigid elastic attracting spheres.* This (Sutherland's) model has already been considered in § 2.5. The mutual force is $F(r)$ at distance r between two molecules.

c. *Point centers of repulsive force,* given at distance r by $\kappa r^{-\nu}$; κ is called the force constant and ν the force index. Suffixes 11, 22, or 12 are to be added to κ and ν according as the interacting molecules are both m_1, both m_2, or unlike.

d. *Point centers of repulsive and attractive force,* expressed by $\kappa r^{-\nu} - \kappa' r^{-\nu'}$, where κ' and ν' refer to the attraction. Alternatively the interaction may be expressed by the formula $4\epsilon[(\sigma'/r)^{\nu-1} - (\sigma'/r)^{\nu'-1}]$ for the *mutual potential energy* of the two molecules; σ is the distance at which the force changes sign, and ϵ the potential energy due to either the attractive or repulsive field at this mutual distance. Suffixes 11, 22, or 12 must be added to κ, ν, κ', ν'.

4.2. Viscosity μ and thermal conductivity λ for a simple gas

Model a:

$$\mu = 1.016 \frac{5}{16\sigma^2}\left(\frac{kmT}{\pi}\right)^{1/2} = 0.1792\left(\frac{kmT}{\pi}\right)^{1/2} \propto (mT)^{1/2}$$

$$\lambda = 2.522 \mu c_v$$

Model b (Sutherland's). In this case the expressions for μ and λ are those for Model a, divided by $1 + S/T$. The term S, known as Sutherland's constant, is proportional to the potential energy of attraction of the molecules at contact. The term S/T is only the first in a series of descending powers of T, and when S/T is not small, the neglect of the latter terms impairs this interpretation of S, as found empirically from the variation of μ or λ with T, as the potential energy.

Model c:

$$\mu = \frac{5}{8} C_\nu \left(\frac{kmT}{\pi}\right)^{1/2} \frac{(2kT/\kappa)^s}{A_2(\nu)\Gamma(4-s)} \propto \frac{m^{1/2}T^{1/2+s}}{\kappa^s}$$

where $s = \dfrac{2}{\nu - 1}$, and $C_\nu = 1 + \dfrac{3(\nu-5)^2}{2(\nu-1)(101\nu-113)} + \cdots$

and $A_2(\nu)$ is a function of ν here given for several values of ν.

ν:	2	3	5	7	9	11	15	21	25	∞
s:	2	1	0.5	0.33	0.25	0.2	0.14	0.1	0.08	0
$A_2(\nu)$:			0.436	0.357	0.332	0.319	0.309	0.307	0.306	0.333
$A_1(\nu)$:			0.422	0.385	0.382	0.383	0.393			0.5

Also $\lambda = f\mu c_v$

where $$f = \frac{5}{2}\left(1 + \frac{(\nu - 5)^2}{4(\nu - 1)(11\nu - 13)} + \ldots\right)/C_v$$

and f declines from 2.522 for $\nu = \infty$ (equivalent to Model a) to 2.5 for $\nu = 5$.

Model d. In this case, if the attractive field is weak, the expressions for μ and λ are those for Model c, divided by $1 + S/T^a$, where $a = (\nu - \nu')/(\nu - 1)$, and S is a function of κ, κ', ν, ν'.

In terms of ϵ and σ, an alternative expression for μ is

$$\mu = \frac{5}{16(\sigma')^2}\left(\frac{kmT}{\pi}\right)^{1/2} \chi\frac{(kT)}{\epsilon};$$

if T is large, the repulsive part of the field is dominant, and χ is proportional to $(kT/\epsilon)^s$. If T is small, the attractive field is dominant, and χ is proportional to $(kT/\epsilon)^{s'}$, where $s' = 2/(\nu' - 1)$.

The values $\nu = 13$, $\nu' = 7$ are found to be specially appropriate for many gases. A graph of $\log_{10} \chi$ is given for these values and also for $\nu = 9$, $\nu' = 5$ in the second item of the bibliography.

The preceding formulas all refer to spherically symmetrical models, for which $\gamma = \frac{5}{3}$; this applies to monatomic molecules and also to some diatomic molecules (e.g., H_2) at very low temperatures. For other values of γ, Eucken has given the following empirical formula for f, which is fairly satisfactory.

$$f = \tfrac{1}{4}(9\gamma - 5).$$

4.3. The first approximation to D_{12}. This is independent of the concentration ratio n_1/n_2. Its values for particular molecular models are

Model a:

$$\frac{3}{8n\sigma_{12}^2}\left(\frac{kT(m_1 + m_2)}{2\pi m_1 m_2}\right)^{1/2} \propto \frac{(T/m')^{1/2}}{n\sigma_{12}^2} \tag{1}$$

where $m' = m_1 m_2/(m_1 + m_2)$; m' is called the "reduced" mass of a pair of unlike molecules.

Model b:

$$\frac{3}{8n}\left(\frac{kT}{m_1}\right)^{1/2} \frac{(2kT/\kappa_{12})^s}{A_1(\nu)\Gamma(3 - s)} \propto \frac{T^{1/2+s}}{n\kappa_{12}^s (m_1)^{1/2}} \tag{2}$$

where $A_1(\nu)$ has values as in the preceding table.

The addition of an attracting force to Model a adds a Sutherland factor $1/(1 + S_{12}/T)$ to the D_{12} expression for this model.

The correction to the foregoing first approximations to D_{12} may amount to a few per cent, and it introduces a small dependence of D_{12} upon n_1/n_2.

4.4. Thermal diffusion. The formula for even the first approximation to k_T or α is very complicated, and this approximation is less close to the true value than in the case of μ, λ, and D_{12}. The correction (which is additive) may be as great as 23 per cent for Model a, when m_1/m_2 is very large. For other models it is less. And for Model b, when $\nu = 5$, k_T is zero.

The end values of α, for $n_{10} = 1$ and $n_{10} = 0$, will be denoted by α_1 and α_2. Values of α for $0 < n_{10} < 1$ are generally of similar magnitude, though they do not necessarily lie between α_1 and α_2. For molecules of very nearly equal mass, and with very different values of σ, it is possible for α_1 and α_2 to be of different sign, in which case α is always very small (e.g., 0.1).

Here only the first approximation to α_1 will be given for Model a (that for α_2 is obtained by changing suffix 2 to 1 except in σ_{12}). It is

$$\frac{2^{3/2}m_1(m_0{}^3/m_2)^{1/2}(\sigma_1/\sigma_{12})^2 - m_2(15m_2 - 7m_1)}{(2/5)(\sigma_1/\sigma_{12})^2(2m_0/m_2)^{1/2}} \tag{1}$$

$$= \frac{5m_1m_0 + (5/2^{3/2})(\sigma_{12}/\sigma_1)^2(m_2{}^3/m_0)^{1/2}(7m_1 - 15m_2)}{13m_1{}^2 + 16m_1m_2 + 30m_2{}^2}$$

Unless σ_1 and σ_2 differ greatly, α_1 and α_2 are positive if $m_1 > m_2$. If there is a steady temperature gradient in a gas mixture, and no external forces or acceleration, diffusion will tend to set up a steady state in which

$$\log n_{12} = -\alpha \log T + \text{constant}$$

(treating α as independent of n_{12} and T, which is usually approximately correct). If α is positive, and the suffix 1 refers to the heavier molecules ($m_1 > m_2$), the proportion of gas 1 is enriched in the colder and reduced in the hotter regions, relative to gas 2. Thus the heavier molecules are usually more numerous in the cooler region.

5. Electrical Conductivity in a Neutral Ionized Gas with or without a Magnetic Field

5.1. Definitions and symbols. The gas is supposed to consist of neutral particles, ions (positive and negative) and electrons. These constituents are distinguished by suffixes 1, 2, ... attached to the symbols for their properties; mass m; number density n; charge e; diameter σ; etc. The suffix 1 will refer to the neutral molecules, so that $e_1 = 0$.

The electric intensity is denoted by $\boldsymbol{E}$, and the magnetic by $\boldsymbol{H}$, in the direction of the unit vector $\boldsymbol{h}$. In the presence of a uniform magnetic field alone, a charge e_s will spiral round the lines of force with angular velocity ω_s given by

$$\omega_s = e_s H / m_s$$

The current intensity is denoted by $\boldsymbol{j}$.

5.2. The diameters σ_s. The diameter σ_1 for the neutral molecules, and also the " joint diameter " or effective distance between centers, σ_{1s}, at a collision between a neutral and charged particle ($s \neq 1$), are a moderate multiple of 10^{-8} cm (the factor being 1 to 5, diminishing slightly as T increases). The joint diameter σ_{ei} for a collision between an electron and an ion is of order $10^{-5}\, Z_i\, (300/T)$, where Z_i is the number of unit charges on the ion. For a collision between two ions, it is similarly about $10^{-5} Z_i Z_i' (300/T)$, where Z_i and Z_i' are the charge numbers of the two ions.

Owing to the large magnitude of the effective diameters for collisions between charged particles (due to the slow inverse-square decrease of electrostatic force with increasing distance), the collision frequencies of the charged particles are little affected by the presence of neutral molecules unless these are in large excess, e.g., n_1 more than a hundredfold as great as the number density of all the charged particles, as in a slightly ionized gas (such as the E and F layers of the ionosphere).

5.3. Slightly ionized gas. When n_1/n_s ($s \neq 1$) is large, the different kinds of charged particles each contribute independently to the current and the electric conductivity, their mutual collisions being negligible. If $\boldsymbol{E}$ is *perpendicular* to $\boldsymbol{H}$,

$$\boldsymbol{j} = K\boldsymbol{E} + K' \boldsymbol{h} \times \boldsymbol{E} \tag{1}$$

where
$$K + iK' = \sum_{s \neq 1} \frac{n_s e_s^2 \tau_{1s}}{m_s(1 + i\omega_s \tau_{1s})}$$

or
$$\boldsymbol{j} = \sum \frac{n_s e_s^2 \tau_{1s}}{m_s(1 + \omega_s^2 \tau_{1s}^2)} \quad (\boldsymbol{E} + \omega_s \tau_{1s} \boldsymbol{E} \times \boldsymbol{h})$$

An electric field perpendicular to $\boldsymbol{H}$ hence produces a current in its own direction, for which the conductivity is K, and also a transverse current perpendicular both to $\boldsymbol{E}$ and $\boldsymbol{H}$, for which the conductivity is K'.

If $\boldsymbol{E}$ is along $\boldsymbol{H}$, there is no transverse current, and K is increased to $\sum n_s e_s^2 \tau_{1s}/m_s$.

5.4. Strongly ionized gas. Consider a gas in which n_1 is zero or negligible, and the charged particles are electrons, and ions of two kinds, with very different masses. Let suffixes e, i, and j refer to the electrons and the heavier and lighter ions, and take m_e/m_j, m_j/m_i to be negligible. The electronic contribution to the conductivity is

$$\mathrm{K}_e + i\mathrm{K}_e' = \frac{n_e e^2 \tau_{ie}}{m_e(1 + \tau_{ie}/\tau_{je} + i\omega_e \tau_{ie})} \tag{1}$$

independent of the mutual ionic collisions.

The ion conductivity is similarly given by

$$\frac{n_i n_j (e_i m_j - e_j m_i)^2 \tau_{ij}}{(n_i m_i + n_j m_j) m_i m_j (1 + i\omega_{ij}\tau_{ij})} \tag{2}$$

where $$\omega_{ij} = eH(m_i + m_j)/m_i m_j$$

Bibliography

1. Boltzmann, L., *Vorlesungen über die Gas Theorie* (2 vols.), J. A. Barth, Leipzig, 1910. This pioneer work well shows the nascent ideas of the kinetic theory in their first detailed mathematical development.
2. Chapman, S. and Cowling, T. G., *Mathematical Theory of Non-Uniform Gases*, 2d ed., Cambridge University Press, London, 1953. This severely mathematical work gives the classical kinetic theory in detail, but sets out and explains the formulas in a way designed for the use of the physicist and chemist.
3. Jeans, J. H., *Kinetic Theory of Gases*, Cambridge University Press, London, 1925. This book in its earlier editions stresses the difficulties later met by the quantum theory, and has interesting passages on the statistical mechanical aspects of the kinetic theory.
4. Kennard, E. H., *Kinetic Theory of Gases*, McGraw-Hill Book Company, New York, Inc., 1938. This book is written for the physicist and does not contain the full mathematical theory.
5. Loeb, L. B., *Kinetic Theory of Gases*, 2d ed., McGraw-Hill Book Company, Inc., New York, 1934. See remarks on the Kennard book above.
6. Maxwell, J. C., *Scientific Papers* (2 vols.), Cambridge University Press, London, 1890. See remarks on the Boltzmann book above.

Chapter 13

ELECTROMAGNETIC THEORY

BY NATHANIEL H. FRANK

Professor of Physics, Massachusetts Institute of Technology

AND WILLIAM TOBOCMAN

Research Assistant, Department of Physics, Massachusetts Institute of Technology

1. Definitions and Fundamental Laws

1.1. Primary definitions. The study of mechanics is founded on three basic concepts—space, time, and mass. In the theory of electromagnetism, the additional concept of charge is introduced. Quantity of electric charge is denoted by q, electric current by i, and electric current density by $\boldsymbol{J}$. The mutual interactions of charges and currents are described in terms of fields of electric intensity $\boldsymbol{E}$ and magnetic induction $\boldsymbol{B}$. The force on an element of charge caused by all other charges is represented as the interaction of the element of charge with the field ($\boldsymbol{E}$ and $\boldsymbol{B}$) in its vicinity, the sources of the field being all the other charges. These fields are defined by

$$\text{mks:}\quad \frac{d\boldsymbol{F}}{dq} = \boldsymbol{E} + \boldsymbol{V}\times \boldsymbol{B}, \qquad \text{Gaussian:}\quad \frac{d\boldsymbol{F}}{dq} = \boldsymbol{E} + \frac{\boldsymbol{V}\times \boldsymbol{B}}{c} \tag{1}$$

where $d\boldsymbol{F}$ is force experienced by an element dq of charge, $\boldsymbol{V}$ is the velocity of the element of charge, and c is the velocity of light in vacuum.

The electromagnetic field in a given region of space depends on the kind of matter occupying the region as well as on the distribution of charge giving rise to the field. This phenomenon can be described in nonconducting, nonferromagnetic media by writing the field vectors as products of two quantitities :

$$\text{mks:}\quad \boldsymbol{E} = \frac{\boldsymbol{D}}{\epsilon} = \frac{\boldsymbol{D}}{\kappa_\varepsilon \epsilon_0}, \qquad \text{Gaussian:}\quad \boldsymbol{E} = \frac{\boldsymbol{D}}{\epsilon} = \frac{\boldsymbol{D}}{\kappa_\varepsilon} \tag{2}$$

$$\boldsymbol{B} = \mu \boldsymbol{H} = \mu_0 \kappa_m \boldsymbol{H}, \qquad \boldsymbol{B} = \mu \boldsymbol{H} = \kappa_m \boldsymbol{H} \tag{3}$$

where $\boldsymbol{D}/\epsilon_0$ and $\mu_0\boldsymbol{H}$ are what the electric field $\boldsymbol{E}$ and the magnetic induction $\boldsymbol{B}$ would be in vacuum, and the κ's are quantities characteristic of the medium. In isotropic media the κ's are scalars. $\boldsymbol{D}$ is the electric displacement; $\boldsymbol{H}$ is the magnetic field intensity; κ_ε is the dielectric constant; κ_m is the relative permeability; ϵ_0 and μ_0 are universal constants

mks	Gaussian
$\epsilon_0 = 8.854 \times 10^{-12}\,\dfrac{\text{farad}}{\text{meter}}$,	$\epsilon_0 = 1$
$\mu_0 = 4\pi \times 10^{-7}\,\dfrac{\text{henry}}{\text{meter}}$,	$\mu_0 = 1$

In terms of the above, the following quantities are defined

	mks	Gaussian	
polarization :	$\boldsymbol{P} = \boldsymbol{D} - \epsilon_0\boldsymbol{E}$,	$\boldsymbol{P} = \dfrac{1}{4\pi}(\boldsymbol{D} - \epsilon_0\boldsymbol{E})$	(4)
magnetization :	$\boldsymbol{M} = \dfrac{\boldsymbol{B}}{\mu_0} - \boldsymbol{H}$,	$\boldsymbol{M} = \dfrac{1}{4\pi}\left(\dfrac{\boldsymbol{B}}{\mu_0} - \boldsymbol{H}\right)$	(5)
magnetic susceptibility :	$\chi_m = \dfrac{\lvert\boldsymbol{M}\rvert}{\lvert\boldsymbol{H}\rvert}$,	$\chi_m = \dfrac{\lvert\boldsymbol{M}\rvert}{\lvert\boldsymbol{H}\rvert}$	(6)
electric susceptibility :	$\chi_\varepsilon = \dfrac{\lvert\boldsymbol{P}\rvert}{\epsilon_0\lvert\boldsymbol{E}\rvert}$,	$\chi_\varepsilon = \dfrac{\lvert\boldsymbol{P}\rvert}{\epsilon_0\lvert\boldsymbol{E}\rvert}$	(7)

1.2. Conductors. A conductor is a material within which charge is free to move. Metals and electrolytes are conductors; the flow of charge within a metal or electrolyte is governed by Ohm's law :

$$\boldsymbol{J} = \sigma\boldsymbol{E} \tag{1}$$

where σ (conductivity) is a constant characteristic of the medium, and $\rho = 1/\sigma$ is called the resistivity. The resistance of a conductor of length l and constant cross section A is defined

$$R = \frac{l}{\sigma A} = \frac{l\rho}{A} \tag{2}$$

Clearly it is impossible to maintain a static potential difference between two points of a conductor without flow of charge, so that under electrostatic conditions a conductor is an equipotential. This implies that the tangential component of $\boldsymbol{E}$ must vanish at the surface of a conductor for static situations.

1.3. Ferromagnetic materials. The magnetic induction $\boldsymbol{B}$ within a ferromagnetic medium is not a linear function of the magnetic intensity $\boldsymbol{H}$. The magnetic induction depends not only on the value of the magnetic intensity but also on the previous history of the medium, so that it is possible to have a finite value for $\boldsymbol{B}$ when $\boldsymbol{H} = 0$. In such a case the body has a residual magnetization $M_1 = B/\mu_0$ (in mks units) and acts as a source of magnetic field.

1.4. Fundamental laws. Electromagnetic theory can be based on the definitions above and the following three fundamental laws:

conservation of charge:

mks	Gaussian	
$\nabla \cdot \boldsymbol{J} = -\dfrac{\partial \rho}{\partial t}$,	$\nabla \cdot \boldsymbol{J} = -\dfrac{\partial \rho}{\partial t}$	(1)

Faraday's law:

$$\nabla \times \boldsymbol{E} = -\frac{\partial \boldsymbol{B}}{\partial t}, \qquad \nabla \times \boldsymbol{E} = -\frac{1}{c} \cdot \frac{\partial \boldsymbol{B}}{\partial t} \tag{2}$$

Ampère's law:

$$\nabla \times \boldsymbol{H} = \boldsymbol{J} + \frac{\partial \boldsymbol{D}}{\partial t}, \qquad \nabla \times \boldsymbol{H} = \frac{4\pi \boldsymbol{J}}{c} + \frac{1}{c} \cdot \frac{\partial \boldsymbol{D}}{\partial t} \tag{3}$$

Taking the divergence of both sides of Eq. (2) and (3) and using Eq. (1) there follow Gauss's law:

	mks	Gaussian	
	$\nabla \cdot \boldsymbol{D} = \rho$,	$\nabla \cdot \boldsymbol{D} = 4\pi\rho$	(4)
and	$\nabla \cdot \boldsymbol{B} = 0$,	$\nabla \cdot \boldsymbol{B} = 0$	(5)

Equations (2), (3), (4), and (5) are called Maxwell's equations.

1.5. Boundary conditions. Application of Maxwell's equations to infinitesimal contours and volumes at the boundary between two regions in space yield the following boundary conditions for electromagnetic fields.

mks	Gaussian	
$\boldsymbol{n} \cdot (\boldsymbol{B}_2 - \boldsymbol{B}_1) = 0$,	$\boldsymbol{n} \cdot (\boldsymbol{B}_2 - \boldsymbol{B}_1) = 0$	(1)
$\boldsymbol{n} \times (\boldsymbol{H}_2 - \boldsymbol{H}_1) = \boldsymbol{J}_s$,	$\boldsymbol{n} \times (\boldsymbol{H}_2 - \boldsymbol{H}_1) = \dfrac{4\pi}{c} \boldsymbol{J}_s$	(2)
$\boldsymbol{n} \times (\boldsymbol{E}_2 - \boldsymbol{E}_1) = 0$,	$\boldsymbol{n} \times (\boldsymbol{E}_2 - \boldsymbol{E}_1) = 0$	(3)
$\boldsymbol{n} \cdot (\boldsymbol{D}_2 - \boldsymbol{D}_1) = \sigma_s$,	$\boldsymbol{n} \cdot (\boldsymbol{D}_2 - \boldsymbol{D}_1) = 4\pi\sigma_s$	(4)

where $\boldsymbol{n}$ is a unit vector normal to the boundary and pointing from region 1 into region 2, σ_s is surface charge density and $\boldsymbol{J}_s$ is the surface current density.

1.6. Vector and scalar potentials. From (5) of § 1.4 it follows that

$$\boldsymbol{B} = \nabla \times \boldsymbol{A}, \quad (\boldsymbol{A} = \text{vector potential}) \tag{1}$$

and from (2) of § 1.4 that

mks Gaussian

$$\boldsymbol{E} = -\nabla\varphi - \frac{\partial \boldsymbol{A}}{\partial t}, \quad \boldsymbol{E} = -\nabla\varphi - \frac{1}{c}\cdot\frac{\partial}{\partial t}\boldsymbol{A}, \quad (\varphi = \text{scalar potential}) \tag{2}$$

These definitions leave $\nabla \cdot \boldsymbol{A}$ (the gauge) undetermined, and the potential φ contains an arbitrary additive constant.

From the fact that the fields must always be finite in regions devoid of charge or current, it follows that the potentials must be continuous functions within such regions.

Using the definition

$$\nabla^2 \boldsymbol{V} = \nabla\nabla\cdot\boldsymbol{V} - \nabla\times\nabla\times\boldsymbol{V}, \tag{3}$$

the differential equations relating the potential functions to their sources follow from Eqs. (2), (3) of § 1.4, and (1), (2) of § 1.6; for homogeneous, isotropic media these equations are

mks

$$\nabla^2\varphi = \epsilon\mu\frac{\partial^2\varphi}{\partial t^2} - \frac{\partial}{\partial t}\left(\nabla\cdot\boldsymbol{A} + \epsilon\mu\frac{\partial\varphi}{\partial t}\right) - \frac{\rho}{\epsilon},$$

Gaussian

$$\nabla^2\varphi = \frac{\epsilon\mu}{c^2}\cdot\frac{\partial^2\varphi}{\partial t^2} - \frac{1}{c}\cdot\frac{\partial}{\partial t}\left(\nabla\cdot\boldsymbol{A} + \frac{\epsilon\mu}{c}\cdot\frac{\partial\varphi}{\partial t}\right) - \frac{4\pi\rho}{\epsilon}, \tag{4}$$

mks

$$\nabla^2\boldsymbol{A} = \mu\epsilon\frac{\partial^2}{\partial t^2}\boldsymbol{A} + \nabla\left(\nabla\cdot\boldsymbol{A} + \epsilon\mu\frac{\partial\varphi}{\partial t}\right) - \mu\boldsymbol{J},$$

Gaussian

$$\nabla^2\boldsymbol{A} = \frac{\mu\epsilon}{c^2}\cdot\frac{\partial^2}{\partial t^2}\boldsymbol{A} + \nabla\left(\nabla\cdot\boldsymbol{A} + \frac{\epsilon\mu}{c}\cdot\frac{\partial\varphi}{\partial t}\right) - \frac{4\pi\mu}{c}\boldsymbol{J}, \tag{5}$$

1.7. Bound charge. Combining Eqs. (4) of § 1.1 and (4) of § 1.4 gives for isotropic media

mks Gaussian

$$\nabla\cdot\boldsymbol{E} = \frac{1}{\epsilon_0}(\rho - \nabla\cdot\boldsymbol{P}), \quad \nabla\cdot\boldsymbol{E} = \frac{4\pi}{\epsilon_0}(\rho - \nabla\cdot\boldsymbol{P}) \tag{1}$$

This result has led to the following nomenclature

$-\nabla\cdot\boldsymbol{P}$ = bound charge density

$\boldsymbol{P}\cdot\boldsymbol{n}$ = bound surface charge density

where $\boldsymbol{n}$ is the unit outward normal to surface.

1.8. Amperian currents. Combining Eqs. (5) of § 1.1 and (3) of § 1.4 for a nonferromagnetic isotropic medium gives

$$\text{mks} \qquad\qquad \text{Gaussian}$$

$$\nabla\times \boldsymbol{B} = \mu_0(\boldsymbol{J} + \nabla\times \boldsymbol{M}), \quad \nabla\times \boldsymbol{B} = 4\pi\mu_0(\boldsymbol{J} + \nabla\times \boldsymbol{M}) \tag{1}$$

when $\partial\boldsymbol{D}/\partial t = 0$.

This result provides the justification for the following nomenclature:

$$\nabla\times \boldsymbol{M} = \text{amperian current density}$$

$$\boldsymbol{M}\times \boldsymbol{n} = \text{amperian surface current density}$$

where $\boldsymbol{n}$ is the outward normal to the surface.

2. Electrostatics

2.1. Fundamental laws. For electrostatic situations, Maxwell's equations for the electric field reduce to

$$\text{mks} \qquad\qquad \text{Gaussian}$$

$$\nabla\times \boldsymbol{E} = 0, \qquad \nabla\times \boldsymbol{E} = 0 \tag{1}$$

$$\nabla\cdot \boldsymbol{D} = \rho, \qquad \nabla\cdot \boldsymbol{D} = 4\pi\rho \tag{2}$$

Since $\boldsymbol{E}$ is now irrotational, it can be derived from a scalar potential:

$$\boldsymbol{E} = -\nabla\varphi \tag{3}$$

Combining this result with Eqs. (2) of § 1.1 and (4) of § 1.4, there follows Poisson's equation:

$$\text{mks} \qquad\qquad \text{Gaussian}$$

$$\nabla^2\varphi = -\frac{\rho}{\epsilon}, \qquad \nabla^2\varphi = -\frac{4\pi\rho}{\epsilon} \tag{4}$$

Integration of Poisson's equation by the Green function method gives

$$\varphi = -\frac{1}{4\pi}\int_V \frac{\nabla^2\varphi}{r}\,dV + \frac{1}{4\pi}\int_S \left[\frac{\nabla\varphi}{r} - \varphi\nabla\left(\frac{1}{r}\right)\right]\cdot d\boldsymbol{S} \tag{5}$$

where φ is the potential at a point inside volume V, which is bounded by surface S. Taking S at infinity, where we assume φ vanishes, reduces Eq. (5) to

$$\text{mks} \qquad\qquad \text{Gaussian}$$

$$\varphi = \frac{1}{4\pi\epsilon}\int \frac{\rho dV}{r}, \qquad \varphi = \frac{1}{\epsilon}\int \frac{\rho dV}{r} \tag{6}$$

For a point charge, i.e.,

$$\rho = q\delta(x)\delta(y)\delta(z)$$

equation (6) becomes

$$\text{mks} \qquad\qquad \text{Gaussian}$$

$$\varphi = \frac{q}{4\pi\epsilon r}, \qquad \varphi = \frac{q}{\epsilon r} \tag{7}$$

which is called Coulomb's law.

2.2. Fields of some simple charge distributions. Equations (7) of § 2.1 and (2) of § 2.1 can be used to give the fields due to various simple charge distributions. Let $\zeta = 1$ for mks units, $\zeta = 4\pi$ for Gaussian units.

a. *Line of charge* (τ = linear charge density) :

$$\varphi = -\frac{\zeta\tau}{2\pi\epsilon}\ln R \tag{1}$$

b. *Sphere of charge* (q = total charge; a = radius of the sphere) :

$$\varphi = \frac{\zeta q}{4\pi\epsilon r}, \quad (r \geq a); \qquad \varphi = \frac{\zeta q}{4\pi\epsilon a}, \quad (r \leq a) \tag{2}$$

c. *Ring of charge* Fig. 1 (q = total charge) :

$$\left.\begin{aligned} \varphi &= \frac{\zeta q}{4\pi\epsilon d}\sum_{n=0}^{\infty}\left(\frac{d}{r}\right)^{n+1} P_n(\cos\alpha)P_n(\cos\theta), \quad (r > d \text{ or } \theta \neq \alpha) \\ \varphi &= \frac{\zeta q}{4\pi\epsilon d}\sum_{n=0}^{\infty}\left(\frac{r}{d}\right)^{n} P_n(\cos\alpha)P_n(\cos\theta), \quad (r < d \text{ or } \theta \neq \alpha) \end{aligned}\right\} \tag{3}$$

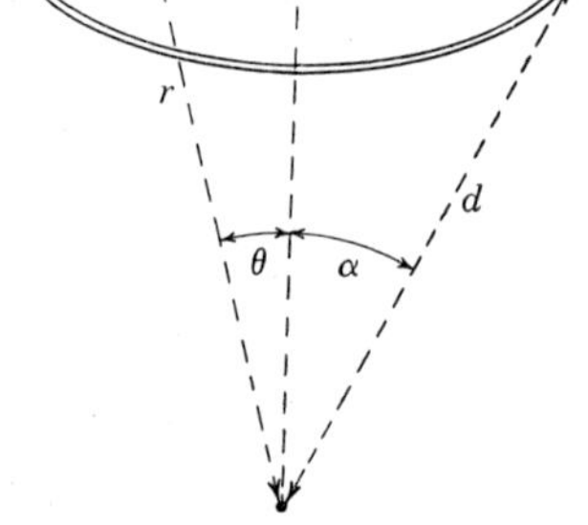

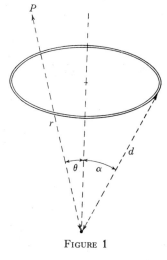

FIGURE 1

where P_n is the Legendre polynomial.

2.3. Electric multipoles; the double layer. A point charge is regarded as a monopole (2^0 pole). A 2^{n+1} pole is defined in terms of a 2^n pole in the following manner. Let

$$\boldsymbol{l}_n = l_n\boldsymbol{u}_n, \qquad |\,\boldsymbol{u}_n\,| = 1$$

be a vector at the origin. At the tip of $\boldsymbol{l}_n$ place the charge singularity characterized by 2^n pole of moment p_n; at the back end of $\boldsymbol{l}_n$ place a 2^n pole of moment $-p_n$; let $l_n \to 0$ and $p_n \to \infty$ in such a way as to keep the product $l_n p_n$ constant.

The resulting charge singularity is called a 2^{n+1} pole of moment

$$p_{n+1} = (n+1)l_n p_n \tag{1}$$

The potential resulting from such a singularity is

$$\varphi_{n+1} = \frac{(-1)^{n+1}}{1/\zeta} \frac{p_{n+1}}{(n+1)!} \boldsymbol{u}_n \cdot \nabla \boldsymbol{u}_{n-1} \cdot \nabla \boldsymbol{u}_{n-2} \cdot \ldots \cdot \boldsymbol{u}_0 \cdot \nabla \left(\frac{1}{r}\right) \tag{2}$$

Accordingly,

$$\varphi_0 = \frac{\zeta}{4\pi\epsilon} \cdot \frac{p_0}{r}, \quad [p_0 = q \quad \text{(monopole)}] \tag{3}$$

$$\varphi_1 = -\frac{\zeta}{4\pi\epsilon} p_1 \boldsymbol{u}_0 \cdot \nabla \left(\frac{1}{r}\right), \quad [p_1 = p_0 l_0 \quad \text{(dipole)}] \tag{4}$$

$$\left.\begin{aligned} \varphi_2 &= \frac{\zeta}{4\pi\epsilon} \cdot \frac{p_2}{2!} \boldsymbol{u}_1 \cdot \nabla \left[\boldsymbol{u}_0 \cdot \nabla \left(\frac{1}{r}\right)\right] \\ &[p_2 = 2l_1 p_1 = 2l_1 p_0 l_0 \quad \text{(quadrupole)}] \end{aligned}\right\} \tag{5}$$

where $\zeta = 1$ in mks units, $\zeta = 4\pi$ in Gaussian units.

The potential at point

$$\boldsymbol{r} = x\boldsymbol{u}_x + y\boldsymbol{u}_y + z\boldsymbol{u}_z$$

of an element of charge $dq = \rho dV$ located at point

$$\boldsymbol{r}_1 = x_1\boldsymbol{i} + y_1\boldsymbol{j} + z_1\boldsymbol{k}$$

when $|\boldsymbol{r}| > |\boldsymbol{r}_1|$ is

$$d\varphi = \frac{\zeta}{4\pi\epsilon} \frac{dq}{|\boldsymbol{r} - \boldsymbol{r}_1|} = \sum_{n=0} d\varphi_n \tag{6}$$

where

$$d\varphi_n = \frac{\zeta(-1)^n}{4\pi\epsilon n!} dq \left[(\boldsymbol{r}_1 \cdot \nabla)_n (\boldsymbol{r}_1 \cdot \nabla)_{n-1} \cdots (\boldsymbol{r}_1 \cdot \nabla)_2 (\boldsymbol{r}_1 \cdot \nabla)_1 \left(\frac{1}{r}\right)\right]$$

$$d\varphi_0 = \frac{\zeta dq}{4\pi\epsilon} \left(\frac{1}{r}\right)$$

by Taylor's theorem. The subscripts simply serve to count the number of factors.

A double layer is a surface distribution of dipoles. Let τ be the dipole moment per unit area; then the potential due to the double layer is

$$\varphi = -\frac{\zeta}{4\pi\epsilon} \int \tau d\Omega \tag{7}$$

where $d\Omega$ is the element of solid angle intercepted by an element of area of the double layer.

2.4. Electrostatic boundary value problems. The electrostatic field potential in a given region must satisfy the following conditions:

a. φ must be a solution of Poisson's equation, Eq. (4) of § 2.1.

b. The change in $(\epsilon \nabla \varphi \cdot \boldsymbol{n})$ must be equal to the surface charge density across any boundary.

c. φ must be constant in a conductor.

d. φ is continuous everywhere (except across a double layer).

e. φ vanishes at least as fast as $1/r$ at infinity if all sources are within a finite region. These conditions determine the field uniquely.

2.5. Solutions of simple electrostatic boundary value problems. Let

$$\zeta = 1 \text{ for the mks system of units,}$$

$$\zeta = 4\pi \text{ for the Gaussian system of units.}$$

a. *Conducting sphere in the field of a point charge*, center at the origin, where

r_1 = radius of sphere
q_1 = net charge on sphere
charge $= q$ at $z = Z > r_1,\ y = 0,\ x = 0$
$r_2 = \sqrt{r^2 + Z^2 - 2rZ \cos \theta}$
Φ = potential at (r,θ,φ)

$$\left.\begin{aligned} \Phi &= \frac{\zeta}{4\pi\epsilon}\left[\frac{q}{r_2} + \frac{r_1\varphi_s}{r} - q\sum_{n=0}^{\infty}\frac{r_1^{2n+1}}{Z^{n+1}}\frac{P_n(\cos\theta)}{r^{n+1}}\right], \quad (r > r_1) \\ \Phi &= \varphi_s = \left(\frac{q_1}{r_1} + \frac{q}{Z}\right)\frac{\zeta}{4\pi\epsilon}, \quad (r < r_1) \end{aligned}\right\} \tag{1}$$

b. *Dielectric sphere of inductive capacity* ϵ_1 *in the field of a point charge* q, both immersed in a medium of inductive capacity ϵ:

$$\Phi = \frac{\zeta}{4\pi\epsilon}\left\{\begin{aligned} &\frac{q}{r_2} + q\sum_{n=0}^{\infty}\left[\frac{n(\epsilon - \epsilon_1)}{n\epsilon_1 + (n+1)\epsilon}\right]\frac{r_1^{2n+1}}{Z^{n+1}}\frac{P_n(\cos\theta)}{r^{n+1}}, \quad (r > r_1) \\ &q\sum_{n=0}^{\infty}\left[\frac{(2n+1)\epsilon}{n\epsilon_1 + (n+1)\epsilon}\right]\frac{r_n}{Z^{n+1}}P_n(\cos\theta), \quad (r < r_1) \end{aligned}\right\} \tag{2}$$

c. *Conducting sphere of radius r_1 in a uniform electric field:*

$$\left.\begin{aligned}\Phi &= -E_0 r\cos\theta + E_0\frac{r_1^3\cos\theta}{r^2} + \frac{q_1\zeta}{r4\pi\epsilon}, \quad (r > r_1)\\ \Phi &= \frac{\zeta q_1}{4\pi\epsilon r_1} \quad (r < r_1)\end{aligned}\right\} \tag{3}$$

where the external field has the potential

$$\Phi_0 = -E_0 r\cos\theta$$

d. *Dielectric sphere of radius r_1 in the uniform electric field:*

$$\left.\begin{aligned}\Phi_0 &= -E_0 r\cos\theta\\ \Phi &= -E_0 r\cos\theta + \frac{\epsilon_1-\epsilon}{\epsilon_1+2\epsilon}r_1^3 E_0\frac{\cos\theta}{r^2}, \quad (r > r_1)\\ \Phi &= -\frac{3\epsilon}{\epsilon_1+2\epsilon}E_0 r\cos\theta \quad (r < r_1)\end{aligned}\right\} \tag{4}$$

Let $\boldsymbol{E}_1$ be the field within the sphere, and let $\boldsymbol{P}_1$ be the polarization of the dielectric sphere (example d). The depolarizing factor L, which is defined by the equation

$$LP_1 = E_0 - E_1 \tag{5}$$

is then

$$L = \frac{\zeta}{3\epsilon_0}\frac{\kappa_1-\kappa}{\kappa(\kappa_1-1)} \tag{6}$$

for a sphere.

2.6. The method of images. For the case of a regularly shaped conductor or dielectric in the field of a simple distribution of charge, it is often possible to construct a potential distribution which satisfies the boundary conditions outside the conductor or dielectric by replacing the dielectric or conductor by a distribution of charges located inside of its boundaries. Since the field so constructed satisfies Poisson's equation as well as the boundary conditions, it must represent the actual field outside the conductor. Such fictitious charge distributions are called image charges.

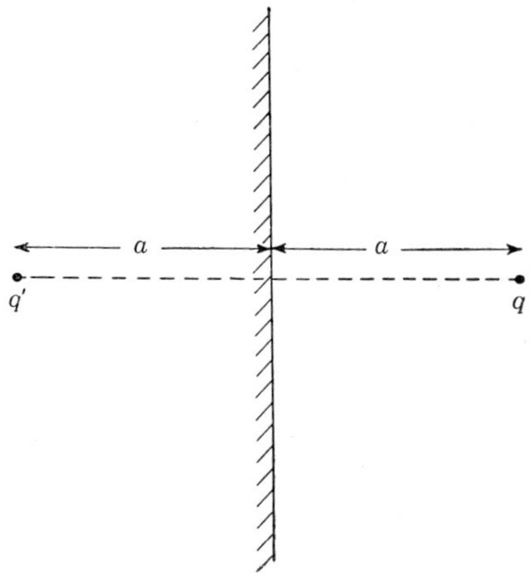

FIGURE 2

Examples:

1. Point charge outside an infinite grounded plane conductor, Fig. 2, p. 315 (q' = image charge = $-q$).

2. Point charge outside a pair of intersecting grounded plane conductors, Fig. 3; (n = integer):

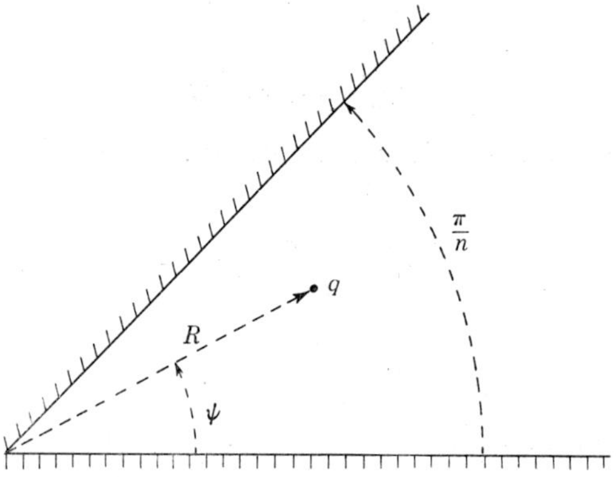

FIGURE 3

Image charges of charge q at

$$\left(R,\psi+\frac{2\pi}{n}\right),\quad \left(R,\psi+\frac{4\pi}{n}\right),\quad \ldots$$

Image charges of charge $-q$ at

$$(R,-\psi),\quad \left(R,-\psi-\frac{2\pi}{n}\right),\quad \left(R,-\psi-\frac{4\pi}{n}\right),\quad \ldots$$

3. Point charge outside a conducting sphere:

$$q' = \text{image charge} = -\frac{qa}{OQ},\quad OR = \frac{a^2}{OQ}\quad \text{(Fig. 4)}$$

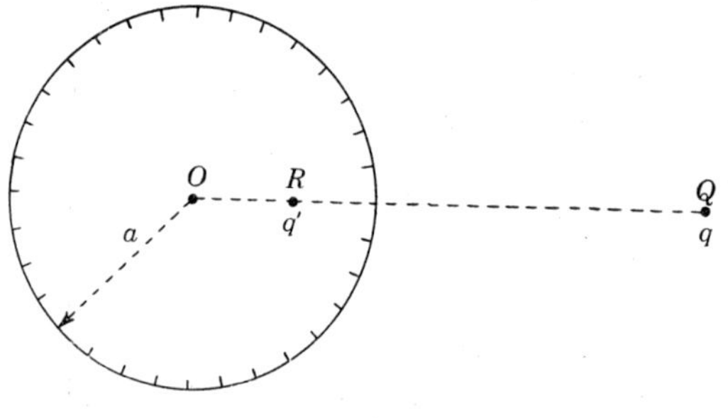

FIGURE 4

4. Line of charge outside a conducting cylinder, Fig. 5; ($\tau =$ charge per unit length):

$$\tau' = -\tau, \qquad \overline{OR} = \frac{a^2}{\overline{OQ}}$$

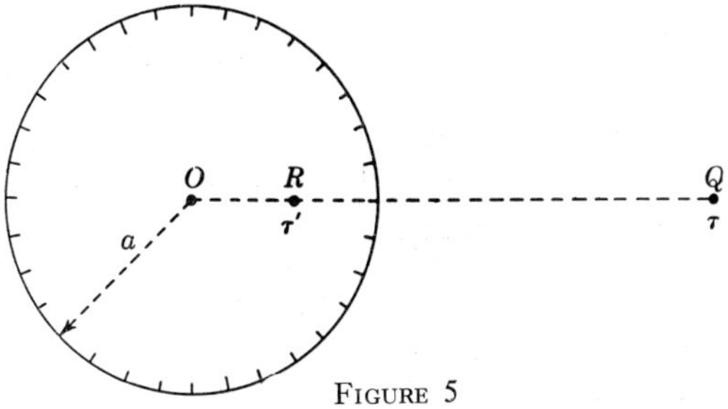

FIGURE 5

5. Point charge near a plane boundary between two semi-infinite dielectrics, Fig. 6; (Let $k = \epsilon_2/\epsilon_1$):

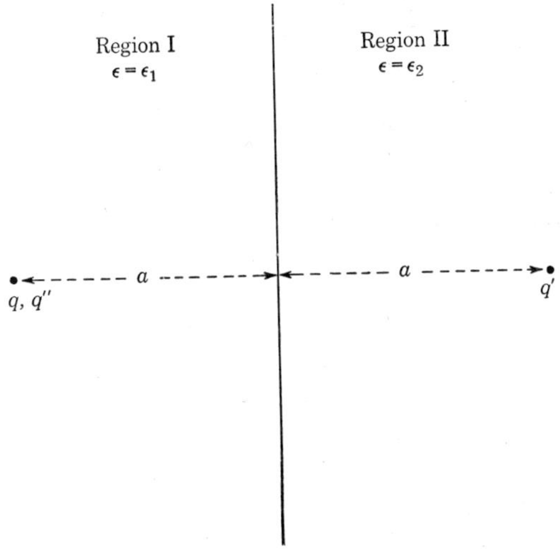

FIGURE 6

The field in region II is given by replacing region I with charge q'':

$$q'' = \frac{2k}{k+1}q$$

The field in region I is given by replacing region II with charge q':

$$q' = \left(\frac{k-1}{k+1}\right)q$$

2.7. Capacitors. A capacitor is a system consisting of two insulated conductors bearing equal and opposite charge. Let $\Delta\varphi$ be the difference of potential between the two conductors, and let q be the magnitude of the charge on each. Then the capacitance of the system is defined to be

$$C = \frac{q}{\Delta\varphi} \tag{1}$$

The capacitance of a single conductor is defined as the limit of the capacitance of a system of two such conductors as their separation becomes infinite. The work required to charge a capacitor is

$$W = \frac{1}{2} C(\Delta\varphi)^2 = \frac{1}{2}\frac{q^2}{C} \tag{2}$$

The capacitances of some simple capacitors may be calculated by the formulas shown below, where $\zeta = 1$ for the mks system, and $\zeta = 4\pi$ for the Gaussian system.

a. *Parallel plates:*

A = area of the plates

d = the separation of the plates

$$C = \frac{A\epsilon}{\zeta d}, \quad (A \gg d^2) \tag{3}$$

b. *Concentric spheres:*

r_1 = radius of inner sphere

r_2 = radius of outer sphere

$$C = \frac{4\pi\epsilon}{\zeta(1/r_1 - 1/r_2)} \tag{4}$$

c. *Concentric circular cylinders:*

r_1 = inner radius

r_2 = outer radius

L = length

$$C = \frac{4\pi\epsilon L}{\zeta 2 \ln r_2/r_1}, \quad (L \gg r_2 - r_1) \tag{5}$$

d. *Parallel circular cylinders:*

Same symbols as in example c. D = separation of centers; positive when the cylinders are external, negative when one cylinder is inside the other

$$C = \frac{1}{2} \cdot \frac{\zeta L}{4\pi\epsilon} \left\{ \cosh^{-1} \left[\pm \frac{(D^2 - r_1^2 - r_2^2)}{2r_1 r_2} \right] \right\}^{-1} \qquad (L \gg D \quad \text{and} \quad |r_1 - r_2|) \tag{6}$$

e. *Two circular cylinders of equal radii :*

$$C = \frac{\zeta}{4\pi\epsilon} \cdot \frac{L}{4} \left(\cosh^{-1} \frac{D}{2r} \right)^{-1}, \quad (L \gg D) \tag{7}$$

f. *Cylinder and an infinite plane :*

$h =$ separation of center of cylinder and plane

$$C = \frac{\zeta}{4\pi\epsilon} \cdot \frac{L}{2} \left[\cosh^{-1} \frac{h}{r} \right], \quad (L \gg h) \tag{8}$$

g. *Circular disk of radius r :*

$$C = \frac{\zeta}{4\pi\epsilon} \cdot \frac{2r}{\pi} \tag{9}$$

2.8. Normal stress on a conductor. Consider an element of surface dA of a conductor. Let the charge density on this element be σ. Then there will be an outward force dF normal to dA :

mks	Gaussian
$dF = \left(\frac{1}{2} \cdot \frac{\sigma}{\epsilon} \right) (\sigma dA),$	$dF = \left(\frac{\sigma 4\pi}{2\epsilon} \right) (\sigma dA)$

The normal stress on such a surface is

mks	Gaussian	
$\frac{dF}{dA} = \frac{\sigma^2}{2\epsilon},$	$\frac{dF}{dA} = \frac{4\pi\sigma^2}{2\epsilon}$	(1)

2.9. Energy density of the electrostatic field. The energy of a static system of charges is just the sum over all the charge of the potential energy of each element of charge due to the field of all the other charge. This energy is related to the field by the equation

mks	Gaussian	
$W = \int \frac{\boldsymbol{E} \cdot \boldsymbol{D}}{2} dv,$	$W = \int \frac{\boldsymbol{E} \cdot \boldsymbol{D}}{8\pi} dv$	(1)

The energy density of the electric field is therefore taken to be

mks	Gaussian	
$u = \frac{\boldsymbol{E} \cdot \boldsymbol{D}}{2},$	$u = \frac{\boldsymbol{E} \cdot \boldsymbol{D}}{8\pi}$	(2)

3. Magnetostatics

3.1. Fundamental laws. For magnetostatic situations Maxwell's equations for the magnetic field reduce to

mks	Gaussian	
$\nabla \times \boldsymbol{H} = \boldsymbol{J},$	$\nabla \times \boldsymbol{H} = \dfrac{4\pi \boldsymbol{J}}{c}$	(1)
$\nabla \cdot \boldsymbol{B} = 0,$	$\nabla \cdot \boldsymbol{B} = 0$	(2)

Since $\boldsymbol{B}$ is divergenceless it may be derived from a vector potential

$$\boldsymbol{B} = \nabla \times \boldsymbol{A} \tag{3}$$

Then for the case of a nonferromagnetic, isotropic, homogeneous medium, Eq. (1) becomes

mks	Gaussian	
$\nabla^2 \boldsymbol{A} = -\mu \boldsymbol{J},$	$\nabla^2 \boldsymbol{A} = -\dfrac{4\pi\mu}{c}\boldsymbol{J}$	(4)

where

$$\nabla^2 \boldsymbol{A} = \nabla\nabla \cdot \boldsymbol{A} - \nabla \times \nabla \times \boldsymbol{A}$$

and we choose $\nabla \cdot \boldsymbol{A} = 0$. Equation (4) can be integrated by the vector analogue of the Green's function method * to give

$$\left.\begin{aligned} \boldsymbol{A} = &-\frac{1}{4\pi}\int_V \nabla^2 \boldsymbol{A}\,dv \\ &-\frac{1}{4\pi}\int_S \left\{ \boldsymbol{n} \times (\nabla \times \boldsymbol{A}) + (\boldsymbol{n} \times \boldsymbol{A}) \times \nabla\left(\frac{1}{r}\right) + \boldsymbol{n} \cdot \boldsymbol{A}\nabla\left(\frac{1}{r}\right) \right\} \cdot dS \end{aligned}\right\} \tag{5}$$

where $\boldsymbol{A}$ is the vector potential at a point inside a volume V bounded by surface $\boldsymbol{S}$, and $\boldsymbol{n}$ is the unit outward normal to the surface. Letting $\boldsymbol{S}$ approach infinity where we assume $\boldsymbol{A}$ must vanish reduces Eq. (5) to

mks	Gaussian	
$\boldsymbol{A} = \dfrac{\mu}{4\pi}\displaystyle\int \boldsymbol{J}\frac{dv}{r},$	$\boldsymbol{A} = \dfrac{\mu}{c}\displaystyle\int \boldsymbol{J}\frac{dv}{r}$	(6)

The potential of the current element $i\boldsymbol{ds} = \boldsymbol{J}dv$ is then

mks	Gaussian	
$d\boldsymbol{A} = \dfrac{\mu}{4\pi r}\, i\boldsymbol{ds},$	$d\boldsymbol{A} = \dfrac{\mu}{cr}\, i\boldsymbol{ds}$	(7)

* Stratton, J. A., *Electromagnetic Theory*, McGraw-Hill Book Co., Inc., New York, 1941, p. 250.

so that

$$\text{mks} \qquad d\mathbf{B} = \frac{\mu i}{4\pi} \cdot \frac{d\mathbf{s} \times \mathbf{r}}{r^3}, \qquad \text{Gaussian} \qquad d\mathbf{B} = \frac{\mu i}{c} \frac{d\mathbf{s} \times \mathbf{r}}{r^3} \tag{8}$$

Equation (8) is called the Biot-Savart law.

3.2. Fields of some simple current distributions. From Eqs. (6) and (8) of § 3.1, we can deduce the fields caused by various simple current distributions. Let $\zeta = 1$ in mks units, $\zeta = 4\pi$ in Gaussian units; let $\xi = 1$ in mks units, $\xi = 1/c$ in Gaussian units.

a. *Infinite straight wire:*

$$H = \zeta\xi \frac{i}{2\pi R} \tag{1}$$

b. *On the axis of a circular current loop* (Fig. 7):

$$H = \zeta\xi \frac{iR^2}{2(x^2 + R^2)^{3/2}} \tag{2}$$

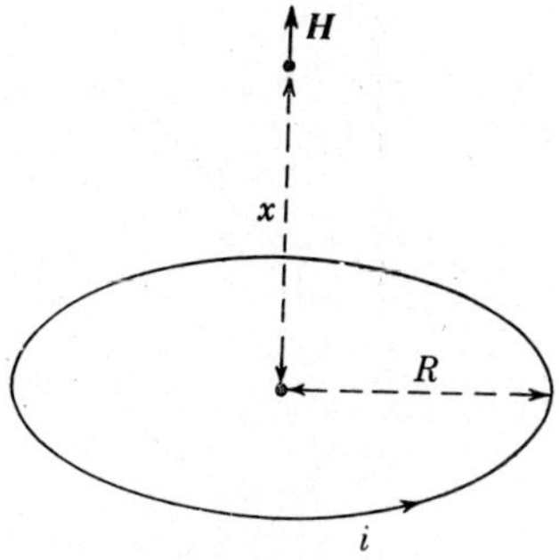

FIGURE 7

c. *On the axis of a solenoid* (Fig. 8):

$$H = \zeta\xi \frac{ni}{2} (\cos\theta_1 + \cos\theta_2) \tag{3}$$

where n = number of turns per unit length.

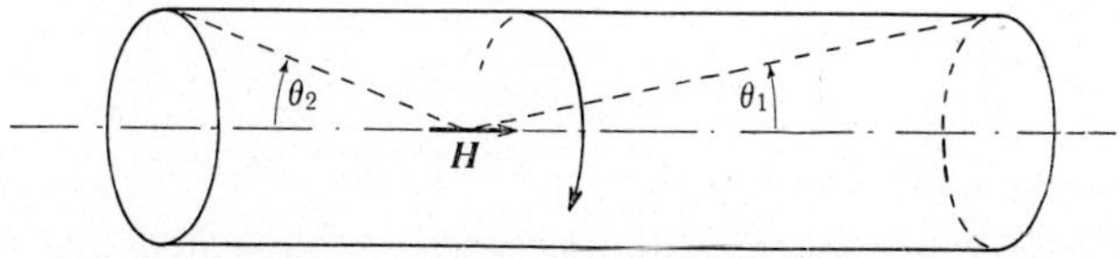

FIGURE 8

3.3. Scalar potential for magnetostatics; the magnetic dipole. For regions where $\boldsymbol{J}=0$, $\boldsymbol{H}$ is irrotational and may therefore be derived from a scalar potential function ψ.

$$\boldsymbol{H} = -\nabla\psi \tag{1}$$

The potential due to a loop of current is then

$$\text{mks} \qquad \psi = \frac{i\Omega}{4\pi}, \qquad \text{Gaussian} \qquad \psi = \frac{i\Omega}{c} \tag{2}$$

where i is the current in the loop, and Ω is the solid angle determined by the loop and the point of observation. The sign of Ω is determined as follows. Choose an origin at the center of the loop (Fig. 9). Let $\boldsymbol{r}$ be the vector from the origin to the point of observation; let $\boldsymbol{a}$ be the vector from the origin to the current element $i\boldsymbol{ds}$. Then Ω has the same sign as $\boldsymbol{a} \times i\boldsymbol{ds} \cdot \boldsymbol{r}$.

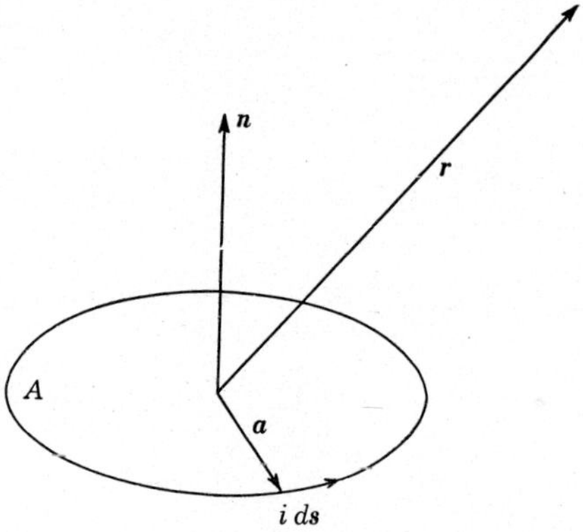

FIGURE 9

If the area A of the loop approaches zero and the current i in the loop, approaches infinity in such a way as to keep iA constant,

$$\left.\begin{aligned} &\text{mks} && \text{Gaussian} \\ &\psi \to \frac{iA}{4\pi}\cdot\frac{\cos\theta}{r^2} = \frac{iA}{4\pi}\frac{\boldsymbol{n}\cdot\boldsymbol{r}}{r^3} && \psi \to \frac{iA}{c}\,\boldsymbol{n}\cdot\nabla\left(\frac{1}{r}\right) \\ &= -\frac{iA}{4\pi}\,\boldsymbol{n}\cdot\nabla\left(\frac{1}{r}\right), && \end{aligned}\right\} \tag{3}$$

where $\boldsymbol{n}$ is the unit normal to A.

$$n = \frac{\boldsymbol{a}\times i\boldsymbol{ds}}{|\,\boldsymbol{a}\times i\boldsymbol{ds}\,|}$$

By analogy with the expression for the potential due to the electric dipole, Eq. (4) of § 2.3, iA is called the magnetic dipole moment.

The preceding expressions are readily generalized to describe an arbitrary steady-state current distribution (which can always be regarded as consisting of a collection of current loops).

mks

$$\psi = -\frac{iA}{4\pi}\boldsymbol{n}\cdot\nabla\left(\frac{1}{r}\right) = -\frac{\nabla(1/r)}{8\pi}\cdot\oint \boldsymbol{\rho}\times i\boldsymbol{ds} = -\frac{\nabla(1/r)}{8\pi}\cdot\int \boldsymbol{\rho}\times \boldsymbol{J}dv,$$

Gaussian

$$\psi = -\frac{\nabla(1/r)}{2c}\cdot\int \boldsymbol{\rho}\times \boldsymbol{J}dv \tag{4}$$

where $\boldsymbol{\rho}$ is the radius vector from the origin to the current element $\boldsymbol{J}dv = i\boldsymbol{ds}$. To find the vector potential of a magnetic dipole :

$$B = \nabla\times A = \frac{\mu}{4\pi}\xi\zeta\nabla\left[\boldsymbol{m}\cdot\nabla\left(\frac{1}{r}\right)\right]$$

$$= \frac{+\mu}{4\pi}\xi\zeta\left\{(\boldsymbol{m}\cdot\nabla)\nabla\left(\frac{1}{r}\right) + \boldsymbol{m}\times\left[\nabla\times\nabla\left(\frac{1}{r}\right)\right]\right\}$$

$$= -\frac{\mu}{4\pi}(\zeta\xi)(\boldsymbol{m}\cdot\nabla)\nabla\left(\frac{1}{r}\right) = -\frac{\mu}{4\pi}\zeta\xi\nabla\times\left[\boldsymbol{m}\times\nabla\left(\frac{1}{r}\right)\right]$$

where $\boldsymbol{m} = iA\boldsymbol{n}$, and $\zeta\xi = 1$ in mks units; $\zeta\xi = 4\pi/c$ in Gaussian units. It is seen that the vector potential of a magnetic dipole is

mks

$$\boldsymbol{A} = -\frac{\mu}{4\pi}\boldsymbol{m}\times\nabla\left(\frac{1}{r}\right) = -\frac{\mu}{4\pi}iA\boldsymbol{n}\times\nabla\left(\frac{1}{r}\right),$$

Gaussian

$$\boldsymbol{A} = \frac{\mu}{c}iA\boldsymbol{n}\times\nabla\left(\frac{1}{r}\right) \tag{5}$$

3.4. Magnetic multiples. Let $\xi\zeta = 1$ for mks units; $\xi\zeta = 4\pi/c$ for Gaussian units. The vector potential $d\boldsymbol{A}$ at the point (x,y,z) due to the current element $\boldsymbol{J}dv = i\boldsymbol{ds}$ at the point (x_1,y_1,z_1) when

$$r = \sqrt{x^2+y^2+z^2} > r_1 = \sqrt{x_1^2+y_1^2+z_1^2}$$

is

$$d\boldsymbol{A} = \frac{\mu\zeta\xi\boldsymbol{J}dv}{4\pi\sqrt{(x-x_1)^2+(y-y_1)^2+(z-z_1)^2}} = \sum_{n=0}^{\infty} d\boldsymbol{A}_n \tag{1}$$

where

$$dA_n = \frac{\mu\zeta\xi}{4\pi} J(-1)^n \left[(r_1 \cdot \nabla)_n (r_1 \cdot \nabla)_{n-1} \cdots (r_1 \cdot \nabla)_2 (r_1 \cdot \nabla)_1 \left(\frac{1}{r}\right) \right] dv$$

and

$$\nabla = i\frac{\partial}{\partial x} + j\frac{\partial}{\partial y} + k\frac{\partial}{\partial z}$$

If all the current is confined to the interior of a sphere of radius R, then for $r > R$

$$\left.\begin{aligned} A &= \sum_{n=0}^{\infty} A_n \\ &= \sum_{n=0}^{\infty} \frac{\mu\xi\zeta(-1)^n}{4\pi} \int J \left[(r_1 \cdot \nabla)_n (r_1 \cdot \nabla)_{n-1} \cdots (r_1 \cdot \nabla)_1 \left(\frac{1}{r}\right) \right] dv \end{aligned}\right\} \quad (2)$$

If the current distribution is stationary, the first term, A_0, vanishes since in that case the current distribution can be analyzed into closed current loops and for the kth such loop

$$A_0^k = \frac{\mu_0\zeta\xi}{4\pi} \oint \frac{i}{r}\, ds = \frac{\mu_0\zeta\xi}{4\pi r}\, i \oint dr_1 = 0$$

The contribution of the kth current loop to A_1 is

$$\left.\begin{aligned} A_1^k &= -\frac{\mu\xi\zeta i_k}{4\pi} \oint r_1 \cdot \nabla\left(\frac{1}{r}\right) dr_1 \\ &= -\frac{\mu\xi\zeta i_k}{4\pi} \int \frac{(r_1 \times dr_1) \times \nabla(1/r)}{2} \\ &= -\frac{\mu\xi\zeta i_k}{4\pi} A_k n_k \times \nabla\left(\frac{1}{r}\right) \end{aligned}\right\} \quad (3)$$

where A_k is the area of the kth loop and n_k is the unit normal to the loop. Thus by Eq. (5) of § 3.3,

$$A_1 = \Sigma_k A_1^k$$

is the vector potential of the magnetic dipole moment of the current distribution. Accordingly, A_n is identified with the vector potential of the magnetic 2^n pole moment of the distribution. Clearly, the magnetic monopole does not exist.

3.5. Magnetostatic boundary-value problems. In regions where $\boldsymbol{J} = 0$ the scalar magnetic potential must satisfy the following conditions:

1. $\nabla^2 \psi = 0$ at all points not on boundaries between two regions of different μ.

2. ψ is finite and continuous everywhere.

3. The normal derivatives of ψ across a surface are related by

$$\mu_2 \frac{\partial \psi_2}{\partial n} - \mu_1 \frac{\partial \psi_1}{\partial n} = 0$$

4. ψ vanishes at least as fast as $1/r^2$ as r becomes infinite, if all sources are confined to a finite region.

If $\boldsymbol{J} \neq 0$ one must use the vectors $\boldsymbol{B}$ and $\boldsymbol{H}$, which satisfy the following conditions:

1. $\nabla \times \boldsymbol{H} = \boldsymbol{J}$ (mks); $\nabla \times \boldsymbol{H} = 4\pi/c\, \boldsymbol{J}$ (Gaussian).

2. $\boldsymbol{B} = \mu_0(\boldsymbol{H} + \boldsymbol{M})$ (mks); $\boldsymbol{B} = \mu_0(\boldsymbol{H} + \boldsymbol{M})/4\pi$ (Gaussian), where $\boldsymbol{M}$ is the magnetization.

3. Across any boundary

$$\Delta(\boldsymbol{n} \times \boldsymbol{H}) = \boldsymbol{J}_s \text{ (mks)}; \qquad \Delta(\boldsymbol{n} \times \boldsymbol{H}) = 4\pi/c\, \boldsymbol{J}_s \text{ (Gaussian)}$$

$$\Delta(\boldsymbol{n} \cdot \boldsymbol{B}) = 0 \text{ (mks)}; \qquad \Delta(\boldsymbol{n} \cdot \boldsymbol{B}) = 0 \text{ (Gaussian)}$$

4. If sources are confined to a finite region, $\boldsymbol{B}$ vanishes at least as fast as $1/r^2$ as r becomes infinite.

These conditions determine the magnetic field uniquely.

In the absence of sources the solution ψ of a magnetostatic boundary value problem becomes identical with the solution φ of an electrostatic boundary value problem for the case of no charge when ϵ is replaced by μ.

As an example of a solution of a magnetostatic boundary value problem involving current, consider the field that results when an infinitely long straight wire of radius a, permeability μ_1, and with a current i is embedded in a medium of permeability μ_2, that contains an external field $\boldsymbol{B}_0$ directed transverse to the axis of the wire.

$$\left.\begin{aligned} A_z &= \xi \left\{ \frac{\mu_2}{2\pi} i \ln \frac{a}{r} - \frac{\mu_1}{4\pi} i + \left[r + \left(\frac{\mu_1 - \mu_2}{\mu_1 + \mu_2} \right) \frac{a^2}{r} \right] B_0 \sin \psi \right\}, \quad (r < a) \\ A_z &= \xi \left\{ - \frac{\mu_1 i r^2}{4\pi a^2} + \frac{2\mu_1}{\mu_2 + \mu_1} B_0 r \sin \psi \right\} \qquad (r > a) \end{aligned}\right\} \quad (1)$$

$$A_x = A_y = 0$$

where $\xi = 1$ for mks units; $\xi = 1/c$ for Gaussian units.

The demagnetization factor L_1 is defined in a manner analogous to that for the depolarization factor, Eq. (5) of § 2.5,

$$L_1 M = H_0 - H_1$$

where M is the magnetization of the body in question, H_1 the field within the body, and H_0 the uniform external field.

3.6. Inductance. The quantity $\int \boldsymbol{B} \cdot \boldsymbol{dA} = n\Phi$ for a circuit is called the total flux linkage and is generally proportional to the current giving rise to $\boldsymbol{B}$. The self-inductance of a circuit is defined by the expression

$$L = \frac{n\Phi}{i} \tag{1}$$

where i is the current in the circuit. Similarly the mutual inductance between circuit 1 and circuit 2 is defined by

$$M_{12} = \frac{(n\Phi)_{12}}{i_2} \tag{2}$$

where $(n\Phi)_{12}$ is the total flux linkage of circuit 1 caused by current i_2 in circuit 2. It can be shown that

$$M_{12} = M_{21} \tag{3}$$

The inductances of some simple circuits are listed below, where $\xi\zeta = 1$ for mks units; $\xi\zeta = 4\pi/c$ for Gaussian units.

1. Circular loop, where radius of loop $= b$, radius of wire $= a$, $\mu' =$ magnetic permeability of the wire.

$$L = b\left[\mu\left(\ln\frac{8b}{a} - 2\right) + \frac{\mu'}{4}\right]\zeta\xi \tag{4}$$

2. Solenoid, where radius $= a$, length $= l$, number of turns per unit length $= n$.

$$L = \pi a^2 \mu n^2 [\sqrt{l^2 + a^2} - a]\zeta\xi \tag{5}$$

3. Parallel wires, where radii of the wires $= a, c$; separation of the centers $= b$; permeability of the wires $= \mu =$ permeability of the external medium.

$$L = \left(1 + 2\ln\frac{b^2}{ac}\right)\frac{\mu\xi\zeta}{4\pi} \tag{6}$$

4. Coaxial cable, where inner radius $= a$, outer radius $= b$.

$$L = 2\mu \ln\left(\frac{b}{a}\right)\zeta\xi = \text{self-inductance per unit length} \tag{7}$$

5. Two closely wound coils on a ring of permeability μ, where radius of the ring $= a$, radius of the cross section of the ring $= b$, and n and m are the respective numbers of turns in the two coils.

$$M = \mu nm[a - (a^2 - b^2)^{1/2}]\zeta\xi \tag{8}$$

6. Two circular loops (Fig. 10).

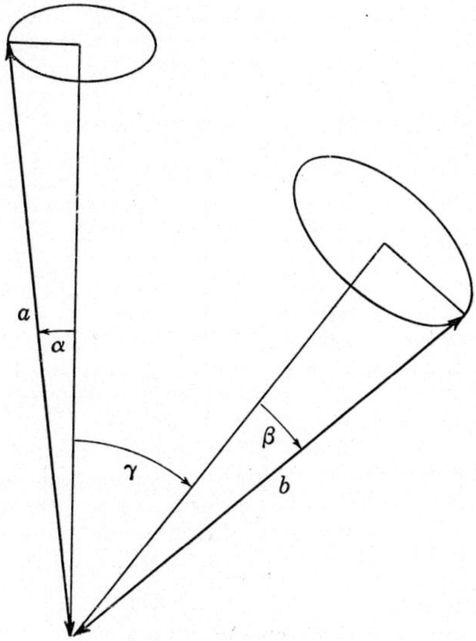

FIGURE 10

$$\left.\begin{aligned} M &= \mathrm{I}\xi\zeta\pi\mu a \sin\alpha \sin\beta \\ &\quad \sum_{n=1}^{\infty} \frac{1}{n(n+1)} \left(\frac{a}{b}\right)^n P_n{}^0(\cos\alpha)\, P_n{}^0(\cos\beta)\, P_n{}^0(\cos\gamma) \end{aligned}\right\} \tag{9}$$

3.7. Magnetostatic energy density. The work required to establish current i in a circuit of self-inductance L is

$$W = \frac{1}{2} Li^2 \tag{1}$$

If we regard this energy as being stored in the magnetic field produced by the current i, the energy density of the magnetic field is

mks	Gaussian
$\dfrac{dW}{dv} = \dfrac{1}{2}\boldsymbol{H}\cdot\boldsymbol{B}$	$\dfrac{dW}{dv} = \dfrac{1}{8\pi}\boldsymbol{H}\cdot\boldsymbol{B}$ (2)

This type of energy is the electromagnetic analogue of mechanical kinetic energy.

4. Electric Circuits

4.1. The quasi-stationary approximation. The analysis of circuits is usually based on the assumption that the electric and magnetic fields at a given moment are essentially the same as would be produced by the charge and current distribution at that moment if these distributions were fixed in time. This is called the quasi-stationary approximation and is valid where the dimensions of the circuit are small compared to c/ω, where c is the velocity of light and ω is the angular frequency of current variation.

4.2. Voltage and impedance. The difference of potential between two points of a circuit is called the difference of voltage ΔV between these points. The impedance Z between two points of a circuit is the ratio of voltage drop to current between these points :

$$Z = \frac{\Delta V}{i} \tag{1}$$

It follows that the impedance of two circuit elements connected in series is

$$Z = Z_1 + Z_2 \tag{2}$$

and the impedance of two circuit elements connected in parallel is

$$Z = \frac{1}{1/Z_1 + 1/Z_2} \tag{3}$$

4.3. Resistors and capacitors in series and parallel connection.
Resistors :

series : $$R = R_1 + R_2 + R_3 + \dots = \text{total resistance} \tag{1}$$

parallel : $$\frac{1}{R} = \frac{1}{R_1} + \frac{1}{R_2} + \dots = (\text{total resistance})^{-1} \tag{2}$$

Capacitors :

parallel : $$C = C_1 + C_2 + C_3 + \dots = \text{total capacitance} \tag{3}$$

series : $$\frac{1}{C} = \frac{1}{C_1} + \frac{1}{C_2} + \dots = (\text{total capacitance})^{-1} \tag{4}$$

4.4. Kirchhoff's rules. Direct current circuit analysis is based on Kirchhoff's rules :

a. At any branch point of a circuit, the sum of the currents entering equals the sum of the currents leaving the junction.

b. The sum of the voltage drops around any closed loop of the network equals zero.

4.5. Alternating current circuits. Consider a circuit having a source of potential causing a voltage rise E between two points of the circuit. Let R be the resistance of the circuit, C be the capacitance of the circuit, and let L be its self-inductance. Then by Faraday's law,

$$\left.\begin{aligned} \oint \mathbf{E}\cdot d\mathbf{r} = -\int dV = -L\frac{di}{dt} &= \left(\frac{q}{C} + iR - E\right) \\ \text{or} \qquad E = iR + L\frac{di}{dt} &+ \frac{1}{C}\int i\,dt \\ \frac{E}{L} = \frac{d^2}{dt^2}q + \frac{R}{L}\cdot\frac{dq}{dt} &+ \frac{1}{CL}q \end{aligned}\right\} \qquad (1)$$

The solution of this differential equation can be expressed as the sum of two parts

$$\left.\begin{aligned} q &= q_t + q_s \\ &= \text{transient solution} + \text{steady-state solution} \end{aligned}\right\} \qquad (2)$$

There are three possibilities for q_t:

a. $R^2 > 4L/C$ (overdamping)

$$q_t = \frac{(i_0 - p_1 q_0)}{(p_2 - p_1)} e^{p_2 t} + \frac{(p_2 q_0 - i_0)}{(p_2 - p_1)} e^{p_1 t} \qquad (3)$$

where

$$p_2 = -\frac{R}{2L} + \frac{1}{4L}\sqrt{R^2 - \frac{4L}{C}}$$

$$p_1 = -\frac{R}{2L} - \frac{1}{4L}\sqrt{R^2 - \frac{4L}{C}}$$

and q_0 and i_0 are the initial values of charge and current, respectively.

b. $R^2 = 4L/C$ (critical damping)

$$q_t = \left[q_0 + \left(i_0 + \frac{R}{2L}q_0\right)t\right]e^{-Rt/2L} \qquad (4)$$

c. $R^2 < 4L/C$ (underdamping)

$$q_t = \left[\left(\frac{Rq_0}{2L\omega_1} + \frac{i_0}{\omega_1}\right)\sin\omega_1 t + q_0\cos\omega_1 t\right]e^{-Rt/2L} \qquad (5)$$

where

$$\omega_1 = \frac{1}{\sqrt{LC}}\sqrt{1 - \frac{R^2C}{4L}}$$

The steady-state solution is

$$q_s = \frac{E_0 \sin(\omega t + \psi)}{L[(\omega_0{}^2 - \omega^2)^2 + (\omega_0\omega/Q)^2]^{1/2}} \qquad (6)$$

where $E = E_0 \cos \omega t$; $Q = \omega_0 L/R$; $\omega_0 = 1/\sqrt{LC}$,

or
$$q_s = \frac{E_0 e^{j\omega t}}{L\left(\omega_0^2 - \omega^2 + j\dfrac{\omega\omega_0}{Q}\right)}, \quad (\text{if } E = E_0 e^{j\omega t}) \tag{7}$$

where $j = \sqrt{-1}$.

For the case where
$$E = E_0 e^{j\omega t}$$
the impedance for the steady state is
$$Z = \frac{E}{i} = R + j\left(\omega L - \frac{1}{\omega C}\right) \tag{8}$$

The instantaneous power delivered from the voltage source is
$$p = iE = i^2 Z = \frac{E^2}{Z} \tag{9}$$

The average power is
$$p_{\text{av}} = \frac{i^2 R}{2} = \frac{E_0 i_0}{2} \cos \theta_z \tag{10}$$

where E_0 and i_0 are the amplitudes of the respective periodic functions, and
$$\theta_z = \tan^{-1} \frac{\omega L - 1/\omega C}{R} \tag{11}$$

For a given circuit the current is greatest at the circular frequency ω_0,
$$\omega_0 = \sqrt{\frac{1}{LC}} \tag{12}$$
in which case $Z = R$.

5. Electromagnetic Radiation

5.1. Poynting's theorem. From Maxwell's equations and the vector identity
$$\nabla \cdot (\boldsymbol{E} \times \boldsymbol{H}) = \boldsymbol{H} \cdot \nabla \times \boldsymbol{E} - \boldsymbol{E} \cdot \nabla \times \boldsymbol{H}$$
it can be shown that

mks
$$\nabla \cdot (\boldsymbol{E} \times \boldsymbol{H}) = -\frac{\partial}{\partial t} \cdot \frac{1}{2} (\boldsymbol{E} \cdot \boldsymbol{D} + \boldsymbol{B} \cdot \boldsymbol{H}) - \boldsymbol{E} \cdot \boldsymbol{J}$$

Gaussian
$$\nabla \cdot (\boldsymbol{E} \times \boldsymbol{H}) = -\frac{1}{c} \cdot \frac{\partial}{\partial t} \cdot \frac{1}{2} (\boldsymbol{E} \cdot \boldsymbol{D} + \boldsymbol{B} \cdot \boldsymbol{H}) - \boldsymbol{E} \cdot \boldsymbol{J} \tag{1}$$

This is called Poynting's theorem and is interpreted by identifying

$$\text{mks} \qquad \text{Gaussian}$$
$$\boldsymbol{S} = \boldsymbol{E} \times \boldsymbol{H}, \qquad \boldsymbol{S} = \frac{c}{4\pi}(\boldsymbol{E} \times \boldsymbol{H}), \quad \text{(Poynting's vector)} \tag{2}$$

with the flux density of electromagnetic energy. In addition it can be shown that

$$\text{mks} \qquad \text{Gaussian}$$
$$\boldsymbol{S} = \frac{1}{\sqrt{\epsilon\mu}}\left(\frac{\boldsymbol{E}\cdot\boldsymbol{D}}{2} + \frac{\boldsymbol{B}\cdot\boldsymbol{H}}{2}\right), \qquad \boldsymbol{S} = \frac{c}{4\pi\sqrt{\epsilon\mu}}\left(\frac{\boldsymbol{E}\cdot\boldsymbol{D}}{2} + \frac{\boldsymbol{B}\cdot\boldsymbol{H}}{2}\right) \tag{3}$$

5.2. Electromagnetic stress and momentum. Suppose we have a charge distribution $\rho(x,y,z,t)$ in a homogeneous, isotropic medium. Then the total force of electromagnetic origin on the charge contained in volume V is

$$\text{mks} \qquad \text{Gaussian}$$
$$\boldsymbol{F} = \int_V (\rho\boldsymbol{E} + \boldsymbol{J} \times \boldsymbol{B})\,dv, \qquad \boldsymbol{F} = \int_V \left(\rho\boldsymbol{E} + \frac{\boldsymbol{J} \times \boldsymbol{B}}{c}\right) dv \tag{1}$$

It is possible to reduce this equation to the following form.

$$\boldsymbol{F} = -\int_V \epsilon\mu \frac{\partial \boldsymbol{S}}{\partial t}\,dv + \zeta \iint_S (\bar{\boldsymbol{X}} \cdot d\boldsymbol{A}\boldsymbol{i} + \bar{\boldsymbol{Y}} \cdot d\boldsymbol{A}\boldsymbol{j} + \bar{\boldsymbol{Z}} \cdot d\boldsymbol{A}\boldsymbol{k}) \tag{2}$$

where $\zeta = 1$ in mks units, $\zeta = 1/4\pi$ in Gaussian units, and

$$\left.\begin{aligned}
\zeta\bar{X}_x &= \zeta\tfrac{1}{2}[\epsilon(E_x^2 - E_y^2 - E_z^2) + \mu(H_x^2 - H_y^2 - H_z^2)] = T_{11} \\
\zeta\bar{X}_y &= \zeta(\epsilon E_x E_y + \mu H_x H_y) = T_{12} \\
\zeta\bar{X}_z &= \zeta(\epsilon E_x E_z + \mu H_x H_z) = T_{13} \\
\zeta\bar{Y}_x &= \zeta(\epsilon E_x E_y + \mu H_x H_y) = T_{21} \\
\zeta\bar{Y}_y &= \zeta\tfrac{1}{2}[\epsilon(E_y^2 - E_x^2 - E_z^2) + \mu(H_y^2 - H_x^2 - H_z^2)] = T_{22} \\
&\cdots\cdots\cdots\cdots\cdots\cdots\cdots\cdots\cdots\cdots\cdots\cdots\cdots
\end{aligned}\right\} \tag{3}$$

For the case of stationary fields and charge distributions, the first term on the right of Eq. (3) vanishes, and it becomes apparent that T_{ij} is only the equilibrium electromagnetic stress tensor.

On the other hand, if the surface S is taken to be at infinity, the second term on the right of Eq. (3) vanishes, and

$$\text{mks} \qquad \text{Gaussian}$$
$$\boldsymbol{F} = -\epsilon\mu \int_V \frac{\partial \boldsymbol{S}}{\partial t}\,dv = \frac{d\boldsymbol{P}}{dt}, \qquad \boldsymbol{F} = -\frac{\epsilon\mu}{c^2}\int_V \frac{\partial \boldsymbol{S}}{\partial t}\,dv = \frac{d\boldsymbol{P}}{dt}$$

or

$$\frac{d}{dt}(\boldsymbol{P} + \boldsymbol{G}) = 0$$

mks Gaussian

where $$G = \epsilon\mu \int S dv, \qquad G = \frac{\epsilon\mu}{c^2} \int S dv \tag{4}$$

and P is the total mechanical momentum.

But since the boundaries of the system have been taken at infinity, the system must be closed. Hence its momentum must be conserved. One is thus led to identify G with the electromagnetic momentum. Accordingly, the electromagnetic momentum density is

mks Gaussian

$$g = \epsilon\mu S, \qquad g = \frac{\epsilon\mu}{c^2} S \tag{5}$$

5.3. The Hertz vector; electromagnetic waves. A completely general description of an electromagnetic field is provided by the specification of the four scalar functions that comprise the vector and scalar potentials A and φ. Very often one deals with fields that have symmetry properties rendering them susceptible to a simpler description involving less than four scalar functions. The basis for such a simplified description is provided by requiring the scalar potential or its counterpart to be some specific function of the vector potential. To see how this may best be done, perform a gauge transformation with an arbitrary function f yielding a new vector potential

$$A = A_{\text{old}} - \nabla f$$

and a new arbitrary scalar potential

$$\varphi = \varphi_{\text{old}} + \frac{\partial}{\partial t} f$$

for which Eqs. (4) and (5) of § 1.6 assume the form

$$\left.\begin{aligned} &\nabla \cdot \left(\epsilon \frac{\partial}{\partial t} A - P + \epsilon \nabla\varphi\right) = 0 \qquad \text{(mks)} \\ &\nabla \cdot \left(\frac{\epsilon}{c} \cdot \frac{\partial}{\partial t} A - 4\pi P + \epsilon \nabla\varphi\right) = 0, \quad \text{(Gaussian)} \end{aligned}\right\} \tag{1}$$

$$\left.\begin{aligned} &\frac{\partial}{\partial t}\left(\nabla \times \nabla \times \int A \frac{dt}{\mu} + \epsilon \frac{\partial}{\partial t} A - P + \epsilon \nabla\varphi\right) = 0 \qquad \text{(mks)} \\ &\frac{\partial}{\partial t}\left(\nabla \times \nabla \times \int A \frac{cdt}{\mu} + \frac{\epsilon}{c} \cdot \frac{\partial}{\partial t} A - 4\pi P + \epsilon \nabla\varphi\right) = 0, \quad \text{(Gaussian)} \end{aligned}\right\} \tag{2}$$

where $$P = \int J dt \tag{3}$$

so that $J = \partial P/\partial t$, and $\rho = -\nabla \cdot P$ by Eq. (1) of § 1.2.

When $\nabla \cdot \boldsymbol{P} = -\rho = 0$, Eqs. (1) and (2) of § 5.3 assume a simple form if f is chosen so that φ vanishes.

$$\begin{aligned} &\text{mks} && \text{Gaussian} \\ &\nabla \cdot \boldsymbol{A} = 0 && \nabla \cdot \boldsymbol{A} = 0 \\ &\nabla^2 \boldsymbol{A} - \mu\epsilon \frac{\partial^2}{\partial t^2} \boldsymbol{A} = -\mu \boldsymbol{J}, && \nabla^2 \boldsymbol{A} - \frac{\mu\epsilon}{c^2} \cdot \frac{\partial^2}{\partial t^2} \boldsymbol{A} = -\frac{4\pi\mu}{c} \boldsymbol{J} \end{aligned} \tag{4}$$

Thus the vector potential is useful for the simplified description of fields in the absence of charge.

Clearly Eqs. (1) and (2) of § 5.3 are fulfilled if it is required that

$$\begin{aligned} &\nabla \times \nabla \times \int \boldsymbol{A} dt + \epsilon\mu \frac{\partial}{\partial t} \boldsymbol{A} - \mu \boldsymbol{P} + \epsilon\mu \nabla\varphi = 0 && \text{(mks)} \\ &\nabla \times \nabla \times \int \boldsymbol{A} dt + \frac{\epsilon\mu}{c^2} \frac{\partial}{\partial t} \boldsymbol{A} - \frac{4\pi\mu}{c} \boldsymbol{P} + \frac{\epsilon\mu}{c} \nabla\varphi = 0 && \text{(Gaussian)} \end{aligned} \tag{5}$$

In this way it is possible to reduce the four equations (4) and (5) of § 1.6 to three equations. Equation (5) has a simpler form when expressed in terms of the Hertz vector $\boldsymbol{\Pi}$.

$$\begin{aligned} &\text{mks} && \text{Gaussian} \\ &\boldsymbol{\Pi} = \frac{1}{\mu} \int \boldsymbol{A} dt, && \boldsymbol{\Pi} = \frac{c}{\mu} \int \boldsymbol{A} dt \end{aligned} \tag{6}$$

In terms of the Hertz vector, Eq. (5) becomes

$$\begin{aligned} &\nabla \times \nabla \times \boldsymbol{\Pi} + \epsilon\mu \frac{\partial^2}{\partial t^2} \boldsymbol{\Pi} - \boldsymbol{P} + \epsilon \nabla\varphi = 0 && \text{(mks)} \\ &\nabla \times \nabla \times \boldsymbol{\Pi} + \frac{\epsilon\mu}{c^2} \frac{\partial^2}{\partial t^2} \boldsymbol{\Pi} - 4\pi \boldsymbol{P} + \epsilon \nabla\varphi = 0 && \text{(Gaussian)} \end{aligned} \tag{7}$$

If the gauge

$$\varphi = -\nabla \cdot \boldsymbol{\Pi}/\epsilon \tag{8}$$

is chosen, Eq. (7) reduces to a form particularly convenient when $\boldsymbol{\Pi}$ is expressed in rectangular coordinates.

$$\begin{aligned} &\text{mks} && \text{Gaussian} \\ &\nabla^2 \boldsymbol{\Pi} - \mu\epsilon \frac{\partial^2}{\partial t^2} \boldsymbol{\Pi} = -\boldsymbol{P}, && \nabla^2 - \frac{\mu\epsilon}{c^2} \cdot \frac{\partial^2}{\partial t^2} \boldsymbol{\Pi} = -4\pi \boldsymbol{P} \end{aligned} \tag{9}$$

where

$$\begin{aligned} &\boldsymbol{H} = \nabla \times \frac{\partial}{\partial t} \boldsymbol{\Pi}, && \boldsymbol{H} = \frac{1}{c} \nabla \times \frac{\partial}{\partial t} \boldsymbol{\Pi} \\ &\boldsymbol{D} = \nabla\nabla \cdot \boldsymbol{\Pi} - \epsilon\mu \frac{\partial^2}{\partial t^2} \boldsymbol{\Pi}, && \boldsymbol{D} = \nabla\nabla \cdot \boldsymbol{\Pi} - \frac{\epsilon\mu}{c^2} \cdot \frac{\partial^2}{\partial t^2} \boldsymbol{\Pi} \end{aligned} \tag{10}$$

In a region where $\boldsymbol{P}$ vanishes, Maxwell's equations are symmetrical in $\boldsymbol{E}$ and $\boldsymbol{H}$ and in $\boldsymbol{B}$ and $\boldsymbol{D}$, so that in such regions there is a second possible field represented by the Hertz vector $\boldsymbol{\Pi}_1$.

mks Gaussian

$$\left.\begin{aligned} &\boldsymbol{E} = \nabla\times\frac{\partial}{\partial t}\boldsymbol{\Pi}_1, && \boldsymbol{E} = \frac{1}{4\pi}\nabla\times\frac{\partial}{\partial t}\boldsymbol{\Pi}_1 \\ &\boldsymbol{B} = -\nabla\nabla\cdot\boldsymbol{\Pi}_1 + \epsilon\mu\frac{\partial^2}{\partial t^2}\boldsymbol{\Pi}_1, && \boldsymbol{B} = \frac{c}{4\pi}\left(-\nabla\nabla\cdot\boldsymbol{\Pi}_1 + \frac{\epsilon\mu}{c^2}\frac{\partial^2}{\partial t^2}\boldsymbol{\Pi}_1\right) \end{aligned}\right\} \quad (11)$$

where

$$\nabla^2\boldsymbol{\Pi}_1 - \mu\epsilon\frac{\partial^2}{\partial t^2}\boldsymbol{\Pi}_1 = 0, \qquad \nabla^2\boldsymbol{\Pi}_1 - \frac{\mu\epsilon}{c^2}\frac{\partial^2}{\partial t^2}\boldsymbol{\Pi}_1 = 0 \quad (12)$$

Inside an isotropic, homogeneous conductor free from external sources, we again are able to have two distinct types of solutions, each of which can be expressed in terms of a Hertz vector.

mks

$$\left.\begin{aligned} &\boldsymbol{E} = \boldsymbol{E}_1 + \boldsymbol{E}_2 = -\frac{\nabla\times\nabla\times\boldsymbol{\Pi}_2}{\epsilon} + \mu\nabla\times\frac{\partial}{\partial t}\boldsymbol{\Pi}_1 \\ &\boldsymbol{H} = \boldsymbol{H}_1 + \boldsymbol{H}_2 = \nabla\times\nabla\times\boldsymbol{\Pi}_1 + \nabla\times\frac{\partial}{\partial t}\boldsymbol{\Pi}_2 + \frac{\sigma}{\epsilon}\nabla\times\boldsymbol{\Pi}_2 \end{aligned}\right\} \quad (13)$$

$$\left.\begin{aligned} &\nabla^2\boldsymbol{\Pi}_2 - \mu\epsilon\frac{\partial^2}{\partial t^2}\boldsymbol{\Pi}_2 - \mu\sigma\frac{\partial}{\partial t}\boldsymbol{\Pi}_2 = 0 \\ &\nabla^2\boldsymbol{\Pi}_1 - \mu\epsilon\frac{\partial^2}{\partial t^2}\boldsymbol{\Pi}_1 - \mu\sigma\frac{\partial}{\partial t}\boldsymbol{\Pi}_1 = 0 \end{aligned}\right\} \quad (14)$$

Gaussian

$$\left.\begin{aligned} &\boldsymbol{E} = \boldsymbol{E}_1 + \boldsymbol{E}_2 = \frac{\mu}{c^2}\nabla\times\frac{\partial\boldsymbol{\Pi}_1}{\partial t} - \frac{1}{\epsilon}\nabla\times\nabla\times\boldsymbol{\Pi}_2 \\ &\boldsymbol{H} = \boldsymbol{H}_1 + \boldsymbol{H}_2 = \frac{1}{c}\nabla\times\nabla\times\boldsymbol{\Pi}_1 + \frac{1}{c}\nabla\times\frac{\partial}{\partial t}\boldsymbol{\Pi}_2 + \frac{4\pi\sigma}{\epsilon c}\nabla\times\boldsymbol{\Pi}_2 \end{aligned}\right\} \quad (15)$$

$$\left.\begin{aligned} &\nabla^2\boldsymbol{\Pi}_2 - \frac{\mu\epsilon}{c^2}\cdot\frac{\partial^2}{\partial t^2}\boldsymbol{\Pi}_2 - \frac{4\pi\mu\sigma}{c^2}\cdot\frac{\partial}{\partial t}\boldsymbol{\Pi}_2 = 0 \\ &\nabla^2\boldsymbol{\Pi}_1 - \frac{\mu\epsilon}{c^2}\cdot\frac{\partial^2}{\partial t^2}\boldsymbol{\Pi}_1 - \frac{4\pi\mu\sigma}{c^2}\cdot\frac{\partial}{\partial t}\boldsymbol{\Pi}_1 = 0 \end{aligned}\right\} \quad (16)$$

Since the most general separable time dependence can be represented as a sum or integral over simple harmonic terms, let

$$\boldsymbol{\Pi} = \boldsymbol{\Pi}_0 e^{-j\omega t}, \quad (j = \sqrt{-1}) \quad (17)$$

Then Eqs. (14) and (16) become the vector wave equations

mks	Gaussian	
$\nabla^2\mathbf{\Pi}_0 + \mu\epsilon\omega^2\left(1 + \frac{j\sigma}{\omega\epsilon}\right)\mathbf{\Pi}_0 = 0,$	$\nabla^2\mathbf{\Pi}_0 + \frac{\mu\epsilon}{c^2}\,\omega^2\left(1 + \frac{j4\pi\sigma}{\omega\epsilon}\right)\mathbf{\Pi}_0 = 0$	(18)
$\nabla^2\mathbf{\Pi}_0 + k^2\left(1 + \frac{j\sigma}{\omega\epsilon}\right)\mathbf{\Pi}_0 = 0,$	$\nabla^2\mathbf{\Pi}_0 + k^2\left(1 + \frac{j4\pi\sigma}{\omega\epsilon}\right)\mathbf{\Pi}_0 = 0$	(19)
$\nabla^2\mathbf{\Pi}_0 + \kappa^2\mathbf{\Pi}_0 = 0,$	$\nabla^2\mathbf{\Pi}_0 + \kappa^2\mathbf{\Pi}_0 = 0$	(20)

where

mks	Gaussian	
$k = \sqrt{\mu\epsilon}\,\omega$	$k = \sqrt{\mu\epsilon}\,\frac{\omega}{c}$	(21)
$\kappa = k\sqrt{1 + \frac{j\sigma}{\omega\epsilon}}$	$\kappa = k\sqrt{1 + \frac{j4\pi\sigma}{\omega\epsilon}}$	

For $(\sigma/\omega\epsilon) \ll 1$ this equation represents a wave traveling with phase velocity

mks	Gaussian	
$v = \frac{1}{\sqrt{\epsilon\mu}} = \frac{1}{\sqrt{\epsilon_0\mu_0}\,\sqrt{\kappa_\varepsilon\kappa_m}} = \frac{c}{n},$	$v = \frac{c}{\sqrt{\epsilon\mu}} = \frac{c}{\sqrt{\kappa_\varepsilon\kappa_m}} = \frac{c}{n}$	(22)

where c = velocity of propagation of light in free space and $n = \sqrt{\kappa_\varepsilon\kappa_m}$ is called the index of refraction.

5.4. Plane waves. To find the expression for a plane wave traveling along the x axis in a source-free region, let

$$\mathbf{\Pi}_0 = o\boldsymbol{i} + o\boldsymbol{j} + \mathbf{\Pi}(x)\boldsymbol{k}$$

Then Eqs. (13), (14), and (18) of 5.3 have the solution

mks	Gaussian	
$\boldsymbol{E}_1 = -(\mu\omega\kappa)e^{\pm j\kappa x}\boldsymbol{j},$	$\boldsymbol{E}_1 = -\frac{\mu\omega\kappa}{c^2}\,e^{\pm j\kappa x}\boldsymbol{j}$	(1)
$\boldsymbol{E}_2 = \frac{\kappa^2}{\epsilon}\,e^{\pm j\kappa x}\boldsymbol{k},$	$\boldsymbol{E}_2 = \frac{\kappa^2}{\epsilon}\,e^{\pm j\kappa x}\boldsymbol{k}$	
$\boldsymbol{H}_1 = -\kappa^2 e^{\pm j\kappa x}\boldsymbol{k},$	$\boldsymbol{H}_1 = -\frac{\kappa^2}{c}\,e^{\pm j\kappa x}\boldsymbol{k}$	
$\boldsymbol{H}_2 = -\left(\kappa\omega - j\frac{\kappa\sigma}{\epsilon}\right)e^{\pm j\kappa x}\boldsymbol{j},$	$\boldsymbol{H}_2 = -\left(\frac{\kappa\omega}{c} - j\frac{\kappa\sigma 4\pi}{\epsilon c}\right)e^{\pm j\kappa x}\boldsymbol{j}$	

The general solution is thus seen to satisfy the relations

$$\boldsymbol{E} = \boldsymbol{E}_1 + \boldsymbol{E}_2, \qquad \boldsymbol{H} = \boldsymbol{H}_1 + \boldsymbol{H}_2$$

$$\boldsymbol{E}\cdot\boldsymbol{H} = E_1H_2 + E_2H_1 = 0 \tag{2}$$

$$\boldsymbol{i}\times\boldsymbol{E} = Z\boldsymbol{H} \tag{3}$$

where

mks Gaussian

$$Z = \frac{\mu\omega}{\kappa} = \sqrt{\frac{\mu}{\epsilon + (j\sigma/\omega)}}, \qquad Z = \frac{4\pi}{c^2}\frac{\mu\omega}{\kappa} = \frac{4\pi}{c}\sqrt{\frac{\mu}{\epsilon + (j4\pi\sigma/\omega)}} \tag{4}$$

where Z is called the wave impedance.

5.5. Cylindrical waves. Let R, ψ, z be the parameters of a circular cylindrical coordinate system. To find the representation for cylindrical waves in a source-free region let the Hertz vector be

$$\boldsymbol{\Pi}_0 = o\boldsymbol{i} + o\boldsymbol{j} + \Pi(R\psi z)\boldsymbol{k}$$

Then Eq. (18) of § 5.13,

$$\nabla^2\boldsymbol{\Pi}_0 + \kappa^2\boldsymbol{\Pi}_0 = 0 \quad \text{becomes} \quad \nabla^2\Pi + \kappa^2\Pi = 0$$

which has the solutions

$$\Pi^{(n)} = e^{jn\psi}\, e^{\pm jhz} Z_n(\sqrt{\kappa^2 - h^2}\, R) \tag{1}$$

where h is a separation constant and Z_n is a solution of the nth order Bessel equation. From Eqs. (13) and (14) of § 5.3, we see that this gives two solutions:

Transverse magnetic

mks Gaussian

$$\left.\begin{aligned}
E_R &= jh\frac{\partial\Pi^{(n)}}{\partial R}, & E_R &= \frac{jh}{4\pi}\cdot\frac{\partial\Pi^{(n)}}{\partial R} \\
E_\psi &= -\frac{h}{R}n\Pi^{(n)}, & E_\psi &= -\frac{h}{4\pi R}n\Pi^{(n)} \\
E_z &= (\kappa^2 - h^2)\Pi^{(n)}, & E_z &= \frac{(\kappa^2 - h^2)\Pi^{(n)}}{4\pi} \\
H_R &= \frac{\kappa^2}{\mu\omega R}n\Pi^{(n)}, & H_R &= \frac{\kappa^2 cn\Pi^{(n)}}{4\pi\mu\omega R} \\
H_\psi &= \frac{j\kappa^2}{\mu\omega}\cdot\frac{\partial\Pi^{(n)}}{\partial R}, & H_\psi &= \frac{j\kappa^2 c}{4\pi\mu\omega}\cdot\frac{\partial\Pi^{(n)}}{\partial R} \\
H_z &= 0, & H_z &= 0
\end{aligned}\right\} \tag{2}$$

Transverse electric

$$\left.\begin{aligned}
&\text{mks} && \text{Gaussian}\\
&E_R = -\frac{\mu\omega n\Pi^{(n)}}{R}, && E_R = -\frac{\mu\omega n\Pi^{(n)}}{4\pi R}\\
&E_\varphi = -j\mu\omega\frac{\partial\Pi^{(n)}}{\partial R}, && E_\varphi = -\frac{j\mu\omega}{c^2}\frac{\partial\Pi^{(n)}}{\partial R}\\
&E_z = 0, && E_z = 0\\
&H_R = jh\frac{\partial\Pi^{(n)}}{\partial R}, && H_R = \frac{jh}{c}\frac{\partial\Pi^{(n)}}{\partial R}\\
&H_\varphi = -\frac{h}{R}n\Pi^{(n)}, && H_\varphi = -\frac{hn}{cR}\Pi^{(n)}\\
&H_z = (\kappa^2 - h^2)\Pi^{(n)}, && H_z = \frac{(\kappa^2 - h^2)\Pi^{(n)}}{c}
\end{aligned}\right\} \quad (3)$$

5.6. Spherical waves. Let r, θ, φ be the parameters of a spherical coordinate system. To find the representation for spherical electromagnetic waves in a source-free region, take the Hertz vector to be

$$\boldsymbol{\Pi}_0 = \Pi_0(r,\theta,\varphi)\boldsymbol{u}_r + o\boldsymbol{u}_\theta + o\boldsymbol{u}_\varphi$$

Then Eq. (8) of 5.3 becomes

$$\left.\begin{aligned}
&-\epsilon\frac{\partial\varphi_0}{\partial r} + \frac{1}{r^2\sin\theta}\cdot\frac{\partial}{\partial\theta}\sin\theta\frac{\partial\Pi_0}{\partial\theta} + \frac{1}{r^2\sin^2\theta}\frac{\partial^2\Pi_0}{\partial\varphi^2} + \kappa^2\Pi_0 = 0\\
&\frac{-\epsilon}{r}\cdot\frac{\partial\varphi_0}{\partial\theta} - \frac{1}{r}\frac{\partial}{\partial\theta}\left(\frac{\partial\Pi_0}{\partial r}\right) = 0\\
&\frac{-\epsilon}{r\sin\theta}\cdot\frac{\partial\varphi_0}{\partial\varphi} - \frac{1}{r\sin\theta}\frac{\partial}{\partial\varphi}\left(\frac{\partial\Pi_0}{\partial r}\right) = 0
\end{aligned}\right\} \quad (1)$$

To satisfy the last two equations we need require only that the arbitrary scalar potential φ_0 be equal to $-(1/\epsilon)(\partial\Pi_0/\partial r)$. With this substitution, the first equation reduces to the form

$$\nabla^2\left(\frac{\Pi_0}{r}\right) + \kappa^2\left(\frac{\Pi_0}{r}\right) = 0 \quad (2)$$

The general solution of this equation is

$$\left.\begin{aligned}
&\frac{\Pi_0}{r} = \frac{1}{\sqrt{\kappa r}}Z_{n+1/2}(\kappa r)P_n{}^m(\cos\theta)e^{\pm jm\varphi}\\
&\qquad (n = 0, 1, 2, 3, \ldots;\ m = 0, 1, 2, \ldots)
\end{aligned}\right\} \quad (3)$$

where $Z_{n+(1/2)}$ is a solution of the $(n + \frac{1}{2})$ order Bessel equation, and $P_n{}^m$ is the associated Legendre polynomial.

From Eq. (13) of § 5.3, we see how these solutions may be used to give two kinds of spherical waves.

Tranverse electric

mks	Gaussian	
$E_r = 0,$	$E_r = E_r$ of mks system	
$E_\theta = \dfrac{j\omega}{r \sin\theta} \cdot \dfrac{\partial \Pi_0}{\partial \varphi},$	$E_\theta = E_\theta$ of mks system	
$E_\varphi = -\dfrac{j\omega}{r} \cdot \dfrac{\partial \Pi_0}{\partial \theta},$	$E_\varphi = E_\varphi$ of mks system	
$H_r = \dfrac{1}{\mu}\left(\dfrac{\partial^2 \Pi_0}{\partial r^2} + \kappa^2 \Pi_0\right) = \dfrac{l(l+1)\Pi_0}{\mu r^2},$	$H_r = cH_r$ of mks system	(4)
$H_\theta = \dfrac{1}{\mu r} \dfrac{\partial^2 \Pi_0}{\partial r \partial \theta},$	$H_\theta = cH_\theta$ of mks system	
$H_\varphi = \dfrac{1}{\mu r \sin\theta} \dfrac{\partial^2 (\Pi_0)}{\partial r \partial \varphi},$	$H_\varphi = cH_\varphi$ of mks system	

Tranverse magnetic

mks	Gaussian	
$E_r = \dfrac{1}{\epsilon}\left(\dfrac{\partial^2 \Pi_0}{\partial r^2} + \kappa^2 \Pi_0\right) = \dfrac{l(l+1)\Pi_0}{\epsilon r^2},$	$E_r = 4\pi E_r$ of mks system	
$E_\theta = \dfrac{1}{r\epsilon} \cdot \dfrac{\partial^2 \Pi_0}{\partial r \partial \theta},$	$E_\theta = 4\pi E_\theta$ of mks system	
$E_\varphi = \dfrac{1}{\epsilon r \sin\theta} \cdot \dfrac{\partial^2 \Pi_0}{\partial r \partial \varphi},$	$E_\varphi = 4\pi E_\varphi$ of mks system	(5)
$H_r = 0,$	$H_r = (4\pi/c)H_r$ of mks system	
$H_\theta = -\dfrac{j\omega}{r \sin\theta} \cdot \dfrac{\partial \Pi_0}{\partial \varphi},$	$H_\theta = (4\pi/c)H_\theta$ of mks system	
$H_\varphi = \dfrac{j\omega}{r} \cdot \dfrac{\partial \Pi_0}{\partial \theta},$	$H_\varphi = (4\pi/c)H_\varphi$ of mks system	

where l is an integer.

5.7. Radiation of electromagnetic waves; the oscillating dipole. To find the expressions relating electromagnetic radiation in an isotropic medium to its sources we must solve the inhomogeneous vector wave equation for the Hertz vector.

$$\nabla^2\mathbf{\Pi} - \frac{1}{v^2}\cdot\frac{\partial^2\mathbf{\Pi}}{\partial t^2} = -\zeta\boldsymbol{P} \tag{1}$$

where $\zeta = 1$ for mks units; $\zeta = 4\pi$ for Gaussian units.

This is equivalent to the three inhomogeneous scalar wave equations for the rectangular components of $\boldsymbol{\pi}$ and $\boldsymbol{P}$.

$$\nabla^2\mathbf{\Pi}_i - \frac{1}{v^2}\cdot\frac{\partial^2\mathbf{\Pi}_i}{\partial t^2} = -\zeta P_i, \quad (i = 1,2,3) \tag{2}$$

A solution of this equation is

$$\left.\begin{aligned}\mathbf{\Pi}_i(x'y'z't) &= \frac{1}{4\pi}\int_V \frac{\zeta P_i^*}{r}\,dV \\ &+ \frac{1}{4\pi}\int_S\left[\frac{\nabla\Pi_i^*}{r} - \Pi_i^*\nabla\left(\frac{1}{r}\right) + \frac{1}{vr}\nabla\left(\frac{\partial\Pi_i^*}{\partial t}\right)\right]\cdot\boldsymbol{n}dS\end{aligned}\right\} \tag{3}$$

where (x',y',z') is the point of observation in volume V bounded by surface S, $r = \sqrt{(x-x')^2 + (y-y')^2 + (z-z')^2}$, $f^* = f(x,y,z,t - r/v)$, and $\boldsymbol{n}$ is the unit outward normal to surface element dS.

In an unbounded medium this becomes just

$$\mathbf{\Pi} = \frac{\zeta}{4\pi}\iiint_{\substack{\text{all}\\\text{space}}} \frac{\boldsymbol{P}(x,y,z,t - r/v)}{r}\,dxdydz \tag{4}$$

If the time dependence of $\boldsymbol{P}$ is simple harmonic

$$\boldsymbol{P} = e^{-j\omega t}\boldsymbol{P}_0(x,y,z) \tag{5}$$

then

$$\mathbf{\Pi} = \frac{\zeta e^{-j\omega t}}{4\pi}\iiint_{\substack{\text{all}\\\text{space}}} \boldsymbol{P}_0\frac{(xyz)e^{j\omega r/v}}{r}\,dxdydz \tag{6}$$

An important example is the radiation field of an oscillating electric dipole of moment $p = p_0e^{-j\omega t}$ along the z axis.

$$\begin{aligned}p &= e^{-j\omega t}\int z\rho dv = -e^{-j\omega t}\int z\nabla\cdot\boldsymbol{P}_0 dv \\ &= e^{-j\omega t}\left[\int \boldsymbol{k}\cdot\boldsymbol{P}_0 dv - \iint z\boldsymbol{P}_0\cdot\boldsymbol{n}dS\right]\end{aligned}$$

Taking the surface infinitely far from the origin

$$p = e^{-j\omega t}\int P_{0z}dv$$

And since $J_y = J_x = 0$, we must have $P_{0y} = P_{0x} = 0$ so

$$\boldsymbol{k}p = \int \boldsymbol{P}dv = \int \boldsymbol{P}_0 e^{-j\omega t} dv$$

Substituting this into Eq. (6) of 5.1, we get

$$\boldsymbol{\Pi} = \boldsymbol{k} \frac{\zeta}{4\pi} p_0 \frac{e^{-j\omega(t-r/v)}}{r}$$

Applying Eq. (10) of § 5.3 to the above Hertz vector yields the following field for the electric dipole of moment $p = p_0 e^{-j\omega t}$ along the z axis.

$$\left.\begin{aligned} E_r &= \frac{p_0 \kappa^3}{4\pi\epsilon} \zeta e^{-j(\omega t - \kappa r)} \cos\theta \left[\frac{-2j}{(\kappa r)^2} + \frac{2}{(\kappa r)^3}\right] \\ E_\theta &= \frac{p_0 \kappa^3}{4\pi\epsilon} \zeta e^{-j(\omega t - \kappa r)} \sin\theta \left[-\frac{1}{\kappa r} - \frac{j}{(\kappa r)^2} + \frac{1}{(\kappa r)^3}\right] \\ \boldsymbol{H}_\varphi &= -\frac{j\omega p_0 \kappa^2}{4\pi} \frac{\zeta}{\xi} e^{-j(\omega t - \kappa r)} \sin\theta \left[\frac{-j}{\kappa r} + \frac{1}{(\kappa r)^2}\right] \end{aligned}\right\} \quad (7)$$

where $\zeta = 1$ for mks units, $\zeta = 4\pi$ for Gaussian units; $\xi = 1$ for mks units, $\xi = 1/c$ for Gaussian units.

5.8. Huygen's principle. If ψ is a solution of the scalar equation

$$\nabla^2 \psi - \frac{1}{v^2} \ddot{\psi} = -Q \quad (1)$$

then ψ satisfies the equation

$$\left.\begin{aligned} \psi(x'y'z't) &= \frac{1}{4\pi} \int_V Q^* dV \\ &\quad + \frac{1}{4\pi} \int_S \frac{1}{r} \left[(\nabla\psi)^* - \frac{\psi^* \boldsymbol{r}}{r^2} + \frac{1}{v}\left(\frac{\partial}{\partial t}\psi\right)^* \frac{\boldsymbol{r}}{r}\right] \cdot \boldsymbol{n} dS \end{aligned}\right\} \quad (2)$$

where $\boldsymbol{r} = (x - x')\boldsymbol{i} + (y - y')\boldsymbol{j} + (z - z')\boldsymbol{k} = r \dfrac{\boldsymbol{r}}{|\boldsymbol{r}|} = r\boldsymbol{u}$

$f^* = f(x,y,z,t - r/v)$

$\boldsymbol{n}$ = unit outward normal to element of area dS

This is called Huygen's principle.

Suppose $Q = 0$ in V and ψ is the spherical wave.

$$\left.\begin{aligned} \psi &= \frac{e^{-j\omega(t - r_1/v)}}{r_1} \\ \text{where} \quad \boldsymbol{r}_1 &= (x - x_1)\boldsymbol{i} + (y - y_1)\boldsymbol{j} + (z - z_1)\boldsymbol{k} = r_1 \frac{\boldsymbol{r}_1}{|\boldsymbol{r}_1|} = r_1 \boldsymbol{u}_1 \end{aligned}\right\} \quad (3)$$

Then

$$\psi = \int_S \frac{e^{-j\omega[t-(r_1+r)/v]}}{4\pi r r_1}\left[\left(\frac{1}{r}+\frac{j\omega}{v}\right)(u \cdot n) - \left(\frac{1}{r_1}+\frac{j\omega}{v}\right)(u \cdot n)\right] dS \tag{4}$$

For light waves it is generally the case that $1/r$, $1/r_1 \ll \omega/v$, so that

$$\psi = \int_S \frac{e^{-j\omega[t-(r_1+r)/v]}}{4\pi r r_1}\frac{j\omega}{v}(u \cdot n - u_1 \cdot n)dS \tag{5}$$

5.9. Electromagnetic waves at boundaries in dielectric media. Given a plane electromagnetic wave

$$\boldsymbol{E} = \boldsymbol{E}_0 e^{-j(\omega t - \boldsymbol{k}\cdot\boldsymbol{r})} = (\boldsymbol{E}_y + \boldsymbol{E}_{xz})e^{-j(\omega t - \boldsymbol{k}\cdot\boldsymbol{r})}$$

whose propagation vector $\boldsymbol{k}$ lies in the x,z plane impinging on the boundary between two dielectrics which coincides with the x,y plane, let $n = n_1$ for $z < 0$, $n = n_2$ for $z > 0$, and let $\boldsymbol{k} \cdot \boldsymbol{u} > 0$ where $\boldsymbol{u}$ is a unit vector parallel to the z axis (Fig. 11).

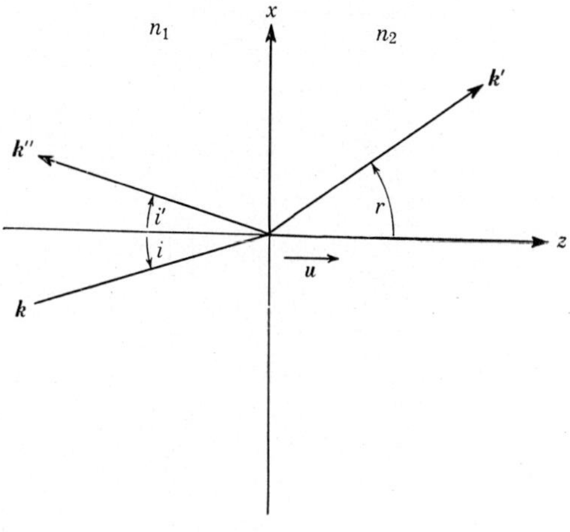

FIGURE 11

Let

$$i = \cos^{-1}\frac{\boldsymbol{k}\cdot\boldsymbol{u}}{|\boldsymbol{k}|}$$

be the angle of $\boldsymbol{k}$ with respect to $\boldsymbol{u}$. Then there can only result a refracted wave ($\boldsymbol{k}'$) a reflected wave ($\boldsymbol{k}''$) or both. The angles these waves make with the normal to the surface are related by

$$i' = i \tag{1}$$

$$n_1 \sin i = n_2 \sin r, \quad \text{(Snell's law)} \tag{2}$$

The amplitudes of the refracted and reflected waves are related to that of the incident beam by Fresnel's equations :

$$\frac{E''_y}{E_y} = \frac{\mu_1 \tan i - \mu_2 \tan r}{\mu_1 \tan i + \mu_2 \tan r} \quad \left(= \frac{\sin(i-r)}{\sin(i+r)} \text{ if } \mu_1 = \mu_2 \right) \tag{3}$$

$$\frac{E''_{xz}}{E_{xz}} = \frac{\mu_1 \sin i \cos i - \mu_2 \sin r \cos r}{\mu_1 \sin i \cos i + \mu_2 \sin r \cos r} \quad \left(= \frac{\tan(i-r)}{\tan(i+r)} \text{ if } \mu_1 = \mu_2 \right) \tag{4}$$

$$\frac{E'_y}{E_y} = \frac{2\mu_2 \sin r \cos i}{\mu_1 \sin i \cos r + \mu_2 \sin r \cos i} \quad \left(= \frac{2 \sin r \cos i}{\sin(i+r)} \text{ if } \mu_1 = \mu_2 \right) \tag{5}$$

$$\left.\begin{aligned} \frac{E'_{xz}}{E_{xz}} &= \frac{2\mu_2 \cos i \sin r}{\mu_2 \sin r \cos r + \mu_1 \sin i \cos i} \\ &\qquad \left(= \frac{2 \sin r \cos i}{\sin(i+r)\cos(i-r)} \text{ if } \mu_1 = \mu_2 \right) \end{aligned}\right\} \tag{6}$$

where E_y is the component of $\boldsymbol{E}_0$ normal to the plane of incidence (x,z plane) and E_{xz} is the component of $\boldsymbol{E}_0$ tangent to the plane of incidence.

When the angle of incidence equals

$$i_B = \tan^{-1} \frac{n_2}{n_1}, \quad \text{(Brewster's angle)} \tag{7}$$

$$\frac{E''_{xz}}{E_{xz}} = 0$$

so that the reflected light is polarized. When the angle of incidence exceeds

$$i_r = \sin^{-1} \frac{n_2}{n_1} \tag{8}$$

total reflection occurs, and the refracted wave vanishes.

For further optical formulas, see Chapters 16 and 17.

5.10. Propagation of electromagnetic radiation in wave guides. Let the z axis be the axis of the wave guide. Take the Hertz vector to be

$$\Pi_0 = o\boldsymbol{i} + o\boldsymbol{j} + \Pi_0 \boldsymbol{k} \tag{1}$$

Then Π_0 must be a solution of the scalar wave equation

$$\nabla^2 \Pi_0 + \kappa \Pi_0 = 0 \tag{2}$$

Since there are no obstacles to propagation along the z axis, one can separate out the z dependence to get

$$\Pi_0 = e^{\pm j k_1 z} u(x,y) \tag{3}$$

where u is a solution of the equation

$$\left[\frac{\partial^2}{\partial x^2}+\frac{\partial^2}{\partial y^2}+\left(\frac{2\pi}{\lambda_c}\right)^2\right]u=0 \tag{4}$$

$$\left(\frac{2\pi}{\lambda_c}\right)^2=\kappa^2-k_1{}^2=(2\pi)^2\left(\frac{1}{\lambda_0{}^2}-\frac{1}{\lambda_g{}^2}\right)$$

The expressions for the field vectors are derived from the Hertz vector by means of Eqs. (10) and (11) of § 5.3.

Transverse electric (TE)

$$\left.\begin{aligned} \boldsymbol{E}&=-j\omega\mu e^{jk_1z}\left(\boldsymbol{i}\frac{\partial u}{\partial y}-\boldsymbol{j}\frac{\partial u}{\partial x}+\boldsymbol{k}o\right)\xi^2 \\ \boldsymbol{H}&=e^{jk_1z}\left[\boldsymbol{i}jk_1\frac{\partial u}{\partial x}+\boldsymbol{j}jk_1\frac{\partial u}{\partial y}+\boldsymbol{k}(\kappa^2-k_1{}^2)u\right]\xi \end{aligned}\right\} \tag{5}$$

Transverse magnetic (TM)

$$\left.\begin{aligned} \boldsymbol{E}&=-\frac{e^{jk_1z}}{\epsilon}\left[\boldsymbol{i}jk_1\frac{\partial u}{\partial x}+\boldsymbol{j}jk_1\frac{\partial u}{\partial y}+\boldsymbol{k}(\kappa^2-k_1{}^2)u\right] \\ \boldsymbol{H}&=j\omega e^{jk_1z}\left(\boldsymbol{i}\frac{\partial u}{\partial y}-\boldsymbol{j}\frac{\partial u}{\partial x}+\boldsymbol{k}o\right)\xi \end{aligned}\right\} \tag{6}$$

where $\xi=1$ for mks units, $\xi=1/c$ for Gaussian units.

It is seen that

$$\boldsymbol{E}\cdot\boldsymbol{H}=0, \qquad \boldsymbol{H}_t=\frac{\boldsymbol{k}\times\boldsymbol{E}_t}{Z_0} \tag{7}$$

where the subscript t identifies the transverse components and

$$Z_0=\frac{\lambda_0}{\lambda_g}\sqrt{\frac{\mu}{\epsilon}}, \quad \text{(for the TM mode)} \tag{8}$$

$$Z_0=\frac{\lambda_g}{\lambda_0}\sqrt{\frac{\mu}{\epsilon}}, \quad \text{(for the TE mode)} \tag{9}$$

The function $u(x,y)$ depends on the shape of the cross section of the wave guide and on the material of its walls. If we suppose the walls to be perfect conductors,

$$E_{\text{tangent}}=B_{\text{normal}}=0$$

at the boundaries so that for TM waves

$$\left.\begin{aligned} u&=0 \\ (\nabla u)_{\tan}&=0 \end{aligned}\right\}\ \text{at the boundaries} \tag{10}$$

and for TE waves

$$(\nabla u)_{\text{normal}}=0 \quad \text{at the boundaries} \tag{11}$$

5.11. The retarded potentials; the Lienard-Wiechert potentials; the self-force of electric charge. If the gauge

$$\text{mks} \qquad\qquad \text{Gaussian}$$

$$\nabla \cdot \boldsymbol{A} = -\epsilon\mu \frac{\partial \varphi}{\partial t}, \qquad \nabla \cdot \boldsymbol{A} = -\frac{\epsilon\mu}{c} \cdot \frac{\partial \varphi}{\partial t} \tag{1}$$

is chosen, Eqs. (4) and (5) of § 1.6 take the form of inhomogeneous wave equations:

$$\text{mks} \qquad\qquad \text{Gaussian}$$

$$\nabla^2 \boldsymbol{A} - \frac{1}{v^2} \cdot \frac{\partial^2 \boldsymbol{A}}{\partial t^2} = -\mu \boldsymbol{J}, \qquad \nabla^2 \boldsymbol{A} - \frac{1}{v^2} \frac{\partial^2 \boldsymbol{A}}{\partial t^2} = -\frac{4\pi}{c} \mu \boldsymbol{J} \tag{2}$$

$$\nabla^2 \varphi - \frac{1}{v^2} \cdot \frac{\partial^2 \varphi}{\partial t^2} = -\frac{\rho}{\epsilon}, \qquad \nabla^2 \varphi - \frac{1}{v^2} \frac{\partial^2 \varphi}{\partial t^2} = -\frac{4\pi}{\epsilon} \rho$$

where $v = 1/\sqrt{\mu\epsilon}$ for the mks system, $v = c/\sqrt{\mu\epsilon}$ for the Gaussian system. We obtain the general solution of these equations by adding a special solution of the inhomogeneous wave equation to the general solution of the corresponding homogeneous wave equation. The special solution of the above equations which relates the electromagnetic field to its sources is

$$\varphi(x,y,z,t) = \frac{\zeta}{4\pi\epsilon} \iiint\limits_{\substack{\text{all}\\ \text{space}}} \frac{\rho(x_1,y_1,z_1,t - r/v)}{r} dx_1 dy_1 dz_1 \tag{4}$$

$$A(x,y,z,t) = \frac{\zeta\xi\mu}{4\pi} \iiint\limits_{\substack{\text{all}\\ \text{space}}} \frac{J(x_1,y_1,z_1,t - r/v)}{r} dx_1 dy_1 dz_1 \tag{5}$$

where r is the magnitude of the vector

$$\boldsymbol{r} = (x_1 - x)\boldsymbol{i} + (y_1 - y)\boldsymbol{j} + (z_1 - z)\boldsymbol{k}$$

The expressions above are called the retarded potentials.

When the source of the field is a point charge of magnitude q, velocity $\dot{\boldsymbol{r}} = (d/dt)\boldsymbol{r}$, and acceleration $\ddot{\boldsymbol{r}} = (d^2/dt^2)\boldsymbol{r}$; then the expressions for the retarded potentials can be integrated to give the Lienard and Wiechert potentials.

$$\varphi = \frac{\zeta}{4\pi\epsilon} \frac{q}{(r + \dot{\boldsymbol{r}} \cdot \boldsymbol{r}/c)} \Bigg|_{t-r/c} \tag{6}$$

$$\boldsymbol{A} = \frac{\zeta\xi\mu}{4\pi} \frac{q\dot{\boldsymbol{r}}}{(r + \dot{\boldsymbol{r}} \cdot \boldsymbol{r}/c)} \Bigg|_{t-r/c} \tag{7}$$

The fields resulting from these potentials are

$$E = \frac{\zeta q}{4\pi\epsilon}\left[\frac{(1-\dot{r}^2/c^2)(\boldsymbol{r}+r\dot{\boldsymbol{r}}/c)}{(r+\boldsymbol{r}\cdot\dot{\boldsymbol{r}}/c)^3} + \frac{\boldsymbol{r}}{c^2}\times\frac{(\boldsymbol{r}+r\dot{\boldsymbol{r}}/c\times\ddot{\boldsymbol{r}})}{(r+\boldsymbol{r}\cdot\dot{\boldsymbol{r}}/c^3)}\right]_{t-r/c} \tag{8}$$

$$\boldsymbol{H} = \xi\epsilon\mu\frac{(\boldsymbol{E}\times\boldsymbol{r})_{t-r/c}}{r} \tag{9}$$

The expressions above can be used to compute the interaction of a distribution of charge with its own field. For this purpose we postulate a rigid distribution of charge such that all elements of charge dq have the same velocity $\dot{\boldsymbol{r}}$ and acceleration $\ddot{\boldsymbol{r}}$. It is necessary to assume that the average linear dimension of the charge distribution r_0 is so small and the motion of the charge varies so slowly that the change of acceleration in the period of time it takes a light wave to pass the charge distribution is small compared to the acceleration itself.

$$\left|\frac{r_0}{c}\dddot{\boldsymbol{r}}\right| \ll |\ddot{\boldsymbol{r}}|$$

On the basis of this assumption the charge distribution is found to exert the force $\boldsymbol{F}$ on itself:

$$\boldsymbol{F} = \boldsymbol{F}_0 + \boldsymbol{F}_1 + \boldsymbol{F}_2 + \dots$$

where

$$\boldsymbol{F}_0 = -\frac{2}{3}\cdot\frac{\ddot{\boldsymbol{r}}}{c^2}\iint\frac{dq\,dq'}{2r}\cdot\frac{\zeta}{4\pi\epsilon} \tag{10}$$

$$\boldsymbol{F}_1 = \frac{2}{3}\cdot\frac{q^2}{c^3}\dddot{\boldsymbol{r}}\frac{\zeta}{4\pi\epsilon}, \qquad q = \int dq$$

$$\boldsymbol{F}_2 \sim \frac{\ddddot{\boldsymbol{r}}}{c^4}\iint r\,dq\,dq' \sim \frac{q^2\ddddot{\boldsymbol{r}}\,r_0}{c^4} \tag{11}$$

where $\boldsymbol{F}_0$ is the term representing the inertia of the field of the charge, $\boldsymbol{F}_1$ is independent of the form of the charge distribution and accounts for the damping resulting from the radiation of energy.

Perhaps the most important point is that this chapter has been prepared with the view of giving the reader an insight into the coherent structure of the whole subject of electromagnetic theory, rather than presenting him with an unrelated set of fundamental formulas in the field.

TABLE 1

CONVERSION TABLE FOR SYMBOLS

To convert an expression from its form in the mks system to its proper form in the Gaussian system, and vice versa, make the following substitutions

mks		Gaussian	mks		Gaussian
E	$\rightarrow$	E	J	$\rightarrow$	J
B	$\rightarrow$	B/c	φ	$\rightarrow$	φ
D	$\rightarrow$	$D/4\pi$	A	$\rightarrow$	A/c
H	$\rightarrow$	$Hc/4\pi$	$\boldsymbol{S}$	$\rightarrow$	$\boldsymbol{S}$
ϵ	$\rightarrow$	$\epsilon/4\pi$	$\boldsymbol{\Pi}$	$\rightarrow$	$\boldsymbol{\Pi}/4\pi$
μ	$\rightarrow$	$\mu 4\pi/c^2$	C	$\rightarrow$	$C/4\pi$
ρ	$\rightarrow$	ρ	L	$\rightarrow$	L/c

TABLE 2

CONVERSION TABLE FOR UNITS

	mks units	Gaussian units
time, t	1 sec	= 1 sec
length, l	1 m	= 10^2 cm
mass, m	1 kg	= 10^3 gm
force, F	1 newton	= 10^5 dynes
energy, w	1 joule	= 10^7 ergs
power, p	1 watt	= 10^7 ergs/sec
charge, q	1 coulomb	= 3×10^9 statcoulombs
electric field, E	1 v/m	= $1/3 \times 10^{-4}$ statvolt/cm
electric displacement, D	1 coulomb/m	= $4\pi \times 3 \times 10^5$ statcoulombs/cm^2
potential, φ	1 v	= $1/3 \times 10^{-2}$ statvolt
capacitance, C	1 farad	= 9×10^{11} cm
current, i	1 amp	= 3×10^9 statamperes
resistance, R	1 ohm	= $1/9 \times 10^{-11}$ statohm
magnetic field, H	1 amp/m	= $4\pi \times 10^{-3}$ oersted
magnetic induction, B	1 weber/m^2	= 10^4 gausses
magnetic flux, BdS	1 weber	= 10^8 maxwells
inductance, L	1 henry	= 10^9 abhenrys

TABLE 3

THE FUNDAMENTAL CONSTANTS

		mks		Gaussian
permitivity in vacuum, ϵ_0	=	8.854×10^{-12} farad/m	=	1
permeability in vacuum, μ_0	=	$4\pi \times 10^{-7}$ henry/m	=	1
velocity of light, c	=	2.998×10^{8} m/sec	=	2.998×10^{10} cm/sec
charge of the electron, e. .	=	1.601×10^{-19} coulomb	=	4.803×10^{-10} statcoulomb
mass of the electron, m_0. .	=	9.108×10^{-31} kg	=	9.108×10^{-28} g

TABLE 4

COORDINATES AND SYMBOLS

Unless indicated otherwise, the following systems of coordinates and symbols were used in this chapter.

Rectangular coordinates (Fig. 12), $\boldsymbol{r}_1 = \boldsymbol{i}x_1 - \boldsymbol{j}y_1 - z_1\boldsymbol{k}$:

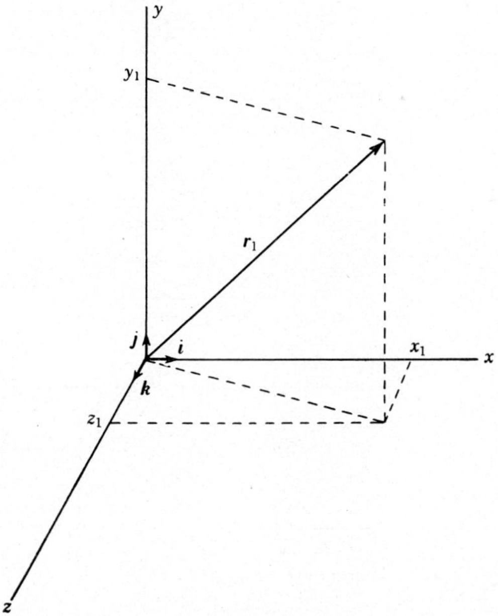

FIGURE 12

Circular cylindrical coordinates (Fig. 13):

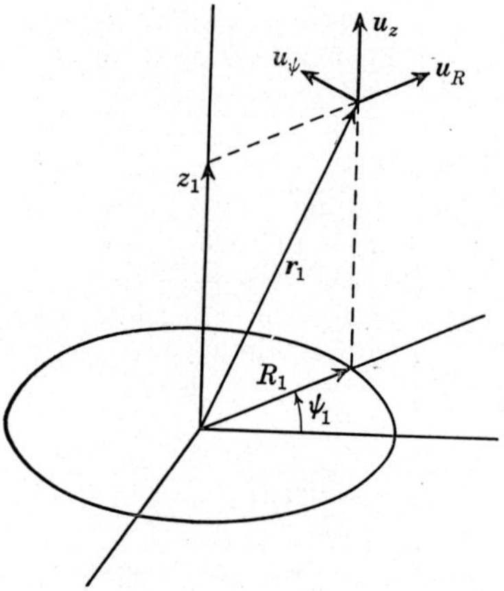

FIGURE 13

Spherical coordinates (Fig. 14):

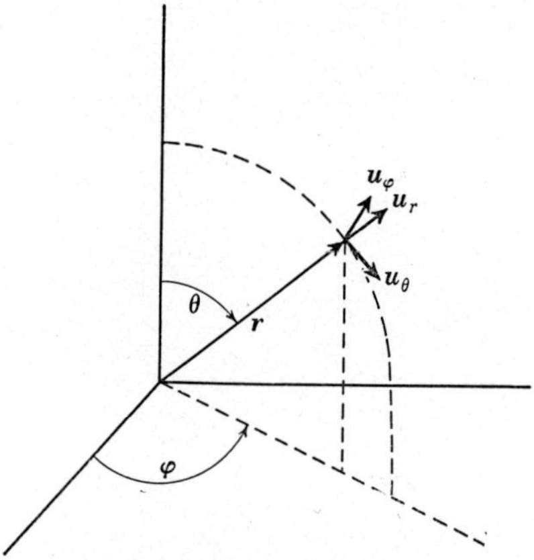

FIGURE 14

$j = \sqrt{-1}$, $\quad \zeta \begin{cases} = 1 \text{ in mks units} \\ = 4\pi \text{ in Gaussian units,} \end{cases} \quad \xi \begin{cases} = 1 \text{ in mks units} \\ = 1/c \text{ in Gaussian units} \end{cases}$

Bibliography

1. Abraham, M. and Becker, R., *The Classical Theory of Electricity and Magnetism*, Blackie & Son, Ltd., London, 1932. A standard intermediate text.
2. Becker, R., *Theorie der Elektrizität*, Band II, *Elektronentheorie*, B. G. Teubner, Berlin, 1933. The classical theory of the electron, containing much material not to be found elsewhere.
3. Born, M., *Optik*, Julius Springer, Berlin, 1933. An advanced comprehensive book based on electromagnetic theory.
4. Frank, N. H., *Introduction to Electricity and Optics*, McGraw-Hill Book Company, Inc., New York, 1950.
5. Jeans, J., *The Mathematical Theory of Electricity and Magnetism*, Cambridge University Press, London, 1948. A classical treatment of electrostatics and magnetostatics, presented without the use of vector analysis.
6. Slater, J. C., *Microwave Electronics*, D. Van Nostrand Company, Inc., New York, 1950. Contains material on transmission line theory and circuit analysis, as well as electromagnetic waves.
7. Smythe, W. R., *Static and Dynamic Electricity*, McGraw-Hill Book Company, Inc., New York, 1950. An excellent reference text for methods of solution of advanced problems.
8. Stratton, J. A., *Electromagnetic Theory*, McGraw-Hill Book Company, Inc., New York, 1941. A valuable treatise on the subject.
9. Blatt, J. M. and Weisskopf, *Theoretical Nuclear Physics*, John Wiley and Sons, New York, 1952. Appendix B provides an excellent discussion of multipole radiation.

Chapter 14

ELECTRONICS

By Emory L. Chaffee

Professor of Applied Physics
Harvard University

1. Electron Ballistics

Since the field of electronics extends over the areas of physics and engineering, many of the basic formulas in electronics dealing with specific fields will be found listed under these fields, such as atomic physics, nuclear theory, particle acceleration, conduction in gases, electron microscope, solid state, microwave spectroscopy, etc. This wide spread of the subject of electronics makes it difficult to select basic formulas not to be found duplicated elsewhere. The formulas chosen are those which are fundamental and of general application in the broad field of electronics.

1.1. Current. A stream of charged particles composed of n particles per unit length of the path, moving with a velocity $\boldsymbol{v}$ and each particle having a charge q constitutes a current $\boldsymbol{I}$.

$$\boldsymbol{I} = nq\boldsymbol{v} \tag{1}$$

The current density $\boldsymbol{J}$ is

$$\boldsymbol{J} = \rho\boldsymbol{v} \tag{2}$$

where ρ is the charge density.

1.2. Forces on electrons. An electron having a charge $-e_s$ located in an electric field $\boldsymbol{E}_s$ in esu is acted upon by a force $\boldsymbol{F}$.

$$\boldsymbol{F} = -e_s\boldsymbol{E}_s \quad \text{dynes} \qquad e_s = 4.803 \times 10^{-10} \quad \text{esu} \tag{1}$$

or

$$\boldsymbol{F} = -e_m\boldsymbol{E}_m \quad \text{dynes} \qquad e_m = 1.602 \times 10^{-20} \quad \text{emu} \tag{2}$$

where $\boldsymbol{E}_m$ is in emu.

An electron having a velocity v cm/sec in a magnetic field of flux density B in emu is acted upon by a force F.

$$\boldsymbol{F} = -e_m\boldsymbol{v} \times \boldsymbol{B} \quad \text{dynes} \qquad e_m = 1.602 \times 10^{-20} \quad \text{emu} \tag{3}$$

1.3. Energy of electron. The loss in potential energy or gain in kinetic energy U of an electron having a charge $-e_m$ while moving from point x_1 to point x_2 in an electric field E_m in emu is

$$U = -e_m \int_{x_1}^{x_2} \mathbf{E}_m \cdot \mathbf{dx} = -e_m(V_1 - V_2) \quad \text{ergs} \tag{1}$$

where V_1 and V_2 are the potentials in emu at x_1 and x_2, respectively.

The kinetic energy of an electron moving with velocity v cm/sec is

$$\left.\begin{aligned} U &= m_0c^2\left[\frac{1}{\sqrt{1-(v/c)^2}} - 1\right] \quad \text{ergs} \\ &= \frac{1}{2}m_0v^2\left[1 + \frac{3}{4}\left(\frac{v}{c}\right)^2 + \frac{5}{8}\left(\frac{v}{c}\right)^4 + \ldots\right] \quad \text{ergs} \end{aligned}\right\} \tag{2}$$

where m_0 = rest mass of the electron $= 9.106 \times 10^{-28}$ gram, and c = velocity of light $= 2.9978 \times 10^{10}$ cm/sec.

The transverse mass m_t of an electron moving with velocity v is

$$m_t = \frac{m_0}{\sqrt{1-(v/c)^2}} \tag{3}$$

The longitudinal mass m_l of an electron is

$$m_l = \frac{m_0}{[1-(v/c)^2]^{3/2}} \tag{4}$$

1.4. Electron orbit. An electron having a velocity of v cm/sec in a magnetic field of flux density B moves in a stable circular orbit of radius r cm, when $F = -m_tv^2/r$ (see § 1.2), giving for the cyclotron condition

$$\frac{m_tv}{r} = e_mB \tag{1}$$

where $m_0 = 9.108 \times 10^{-28}$ gram (see § 1.3).

$$t = 10^4\frac{2m_t}{e_m} \cdot \frac{V}{B} \quad \text{cms} \tag{2}$$

where V is the electron velocity v expressed in equivalent volts.

The periodic time T of one revolution of an electron in the cyclotron orbit is

$$T = \frac{2\pi m_t}{e_mB} \tag{3}$$

2. Space Charge

2.1. Infinite parallel planes. When space charge exists between parallel planes d centimeters apart, one being an emitter of electrons having no initial velocity, the space charge limited current is

$$\left.\begin{aligned} J &= \frac{1}{9\pi}\cdot\frac{2e_s}{m}\cdot\frac{V^{3/2}}{d^2} \quad \text{(esu)} \\ &= 2.336\times 10^{-6}\,\frac{V_b^{3/2}}{d^2} \quad \text{amp/cm}^2, \quad \text{(Child's law)} \end{aligned}\right\} \tag{1}$$

where V_b is the potential difference between the planes in volts. Relativity change in mass is neglected.

Variation of field, velocity, and space charge with distance x from emitter is

$$E_x = -\,(\text{constant})\cdot x^{1/3} \tag{2}$$

$$v_x = (\text{constant})\cdot x^{2/3} \tag{3}$$

$$\rho_x = (\text{constant})\cdot x^{-2/3} \tag{4}$$

where ρ is the space-charge density.

When initial velocity of emission is not neglected, the space-charge-limited current is

$$J = 2.336\times 10^{-6}\frac{(V_b - V_m)^{3/2}}{(d - x_m)^2}\left(1 + 2.66\,\frac{kT}{e_s(V_b - V_m)} + \dots\right) \text{amp/cm}^2 \tag{5}$$

where V_m is the potential with respect to the emitter of the potential minimum x_m cm from the emitter; k being Boltzmann's constant (1.3804×10^{-16} erg/deg), and T the absolute temperature of the emitter.

2.2. Cylindrical electrodes. The space-charge-limited current from a cylindrical central emitter of radius a cm to a concentric cylindrical anode of radius r cm, neglecting initial velocity of emission, is

$$\left.\begin{aligned} I &= \frac{2}{9}\sqrt{\frac{2e_s}{m}}\,\frac{lV^{3/2}}{\beta^2 r} \quad \text{(esu)} \\ &= 14.68\times 10^{-6}\,\frac{lV_p^{3/2}}{\beta^2 r} \quad \text{amp} \end{aligned}\right\} \tag{1}$$

where l is the length of the plate,

and

$$\beta = \log \frac{r}{a} - \frac{2}{5}\left(\log \frac{r}{a}\right)^2 + \frac{11}{120}\left(\log \frac{r}{a}\right)^3 - \frac{47}{3.300}\left(\log \frac{r}{a}\right)^4 + \dots *$$

Variation of field, velocity, and space-charge density with r is

$$E_r = (\text{constant}) \cdot (r\beta^2)^{2/3} \tag{2}$$

$$v_r = (\text{constant}) \cdot (r\beta^2)^{1/3} \tag{3}$$

$$\rho_r = (\text{constant}) \cdot (r^2\beta)^{-2/3} \tag{4}$$

3. Emission of Electrons

3.1. Thermionic emission. The saturation current density is

$$J = AT^2(1 - r)\epsilon^{-\Phi e/kT}\epsilon^{-E^{1/2}e^{3/2}/kT} \quad \text{amp/cm}^2 \tag{1}$$

where $A = 4\pi mek^2/h^3 = 120$ amp/cm² deg²
T = absolute temperature in degrees C
r = reflection coefficient of electrons at the potential barrier of the surface
Φ = electron affinity or potential barrier in esu
e = electronic charge in esu
k = Boltzmann's constant (1.3804×10^{-16} erg/deg)
E = electric field at the surface in esu
h = Planck's constant (6.625×10^{-27} erg sec)

The factor $\epsilon^{-E^{1/2}e^{3/2}/kT}$ gives the effect upon emission caused by the electric field at the surface, i.e., the " Schottky effect."

3.2. Photoelectric emission

$$\tfrac{1}{2} mv^2 = h\nu - \Phi e + U_k \quad \text{ergs} \tag{1}$$

where m = mass of the electron
v = maximum velocity of ejected electron in cm/sec
h = Planck's constant
ν = frequency of incident radiation
Φ = electron affinity or potential barrier in esu
e = charge of electron in esu
U_k = kinetic energy of electron inside metal

* For table of β^2 see Langmuir, *Phys. Rev.*, **21**, 435 (1923) and Langmuir and Blodgett, *Phys. Rev.*, **22**, 347 (1923).

4. Fluctuation Effects

4.1. Thermal noise. The mean-square voltage in frequency interval $d\nu$ across an impedance having a real component of R ohms is

$$d\bar{V}_\nu^2 = 4 \times 10^{-7} RkT\, d\nu \quad \text{volts}^2\ \text{sec} \tag{1}$$

$$d\bar{V}_\omega^2 = \frac{2}{\pi} \times 10^{-7} RkT\, d\omega \quad \text{volts}^2\ \text{sec} \tag{2}$$

where T is the temperature in degrees Kelvin and k is Boltzmann's constant, $(1.3804 \times 10^{-16}$ erg/deg), and $\omega = 2\pi\nu$.

4.2. Shot noise. The mean-square voltage across a pure resistance R ohms in the plate circuit of a diode operating under space current saturation is

$$\bar{V}^2 = \frac{eIR}{2C_{pf}} \quad \text{volts}^2 \tag{1}$$

where e is the electronic charge in coulombs, I is the average plate current in amperes, and C_{pf} is the capacitance between plate and cathode in farads.

If the impedance in the plate circuit is Z in parallel with C_{pf}, the mean-square voltage in the frequency range $2\pi\, d\nu = d\omega$ is

$$d\bar{V}_\omega^2 = \frac{eIZ_\omega^2}{\pi}\left[\left(\int_0^\infty i(\lambda)\sin\omega\lambda\, d\lambda\right)^2 + \left(\int_0^\infty i(\lambda)\cos\omega\lambda\, d\lambda\right)^2\right] d\omega \tag{2}$$

where $i(\lambda)$ is the current in Z_ω caused by unit change in C_{pf}.

Bibliography

1. Dow, W. G., *Fundamentals of Engineering Electronics*, John Wiley & Sons, Inc. New York, 1937.
2. Fink, D. F., *Engineering Electronics*, McGraw-Hill Book Company, Inc., New York, 1938.
3. Hughes, A. L. and DuBridge, L. A., *Photoelectric Phenomena*, McGraw-Hill Book Company, Inc., New York, 1932.
4. Maxfield, F. A. and Benedict, R. R., *Theory of Gaseous Conduction and Electronics*, McGraw-Hill Book Company, Inc., New York, 1941.
5. Millman, J. and Seely, S., *Electronics*, McGraw-Hill Book Company, Inc., New York, 1951.
6. M. I. T. Electrical Engineering Staff, *Applied Electronics*, John Wiley & Sons, Inc., New York, 1943.
7. Spangenberg, K. R., *Vacuum Tubes*, McGraw-Hill Book Company, Inc., New York, 1948. *Advances in Electronics*, edited by L. Marton, Academic Press, New York; Vol. I, 1948; Vol. 2, 1950; Vol. 3, 1951.

Chapter 15

SOUND AND ACOUSTICS

BY PHILIP M. MORSE

Professor of Physics
Massachusetts Institute of Technology

1. Sound and Acoustics

The science of acoustics bears a close relationship to may other fields of physics, as covered in this book of fundamental formulas. For example, hydrodynamics provides the basic equations that govern the flow of sound in an acoustic system. There are problems of dynamics and boundary values must be satisfied. Thermodynamics, statistical mechanics, and kinetic theory have a relationship in terms of the microscopic picture of acoustics. Reference to certain of these other chapters, therefore, may assist the student. The following formulas were chosen as being the most fundamental to the physical side of acoustics. The purely engineering phases, of course, properly lie outside the scope of this work, if for no other reason than the fact that many of them are empirical.

1.1. Wave equation, definitions. For a gas or fluid with negligible viscosity, where $\boldsymbol{v}(\boldsymbol{r},t)$ is the velocity of displacement of the fluid, at $\boldsymbol{r},t$, from equilibrium, P_0 is the equilibrium pressure and $p(\boldsymbol{r},t)$ the deviation from this, the equation determining the velocity potential ψ, for fluctuations of p small compared with P_0, and the relationship between ψ and other quantities is

$$c^2\nabla^2\psi = (\partial^2\psi/\partial t^2), \quad c^2 = (K/\rho) \tag{1}$$

$$\boldsymbol{v} = -\operatorname{grad}\psi, \quad p = \rho(\partial\psi/\partial t), \quad \Delta\rho = (\rho/c^2)(\partial\psi/\partial t) \tag{2}$$

where $K = \rho c^2$ is the compressional modulus of the fluid and $\Delta\rho$ is its departure from equilibrium density ρ. For a gas, vibrating rapidly enough, the departures from equilibrium are adiabatic, every change in pressure p brings about a change in temperature ΔT from the equilibrium temperature T. For a gas having ratio of specific heat $(c_p/c_v) = \gamma$, the compressional modulus and temperature change are

$$K = \rho c^2 = \gamma P_0, \quad \Delta T = (T/c^2)(\gamma - 1)(\partial\psi/\partial t) = (T/\rho c^2)(\gamma - 1)p \qquad (3)$$

1.2. Energy, intensity. The energy density of sound in the fluid is

$$\left.\begin{aligned} E &= \tfrac{1}{2}\rho v^2 + \tfrac{1}{2}(c^2/\rho)p^2 \\ &= \tfrac{1}{2}\rho(|\operatorname{grad}\psi|^2 + c^2|\partial\psi/\partial t|^2), \quad \text{(energy per unit volume)} \end{aligned}\right\} \qquad (1)$$

The power flow through the fluid, the intensity of sound

$$\boldsymbol{S} = p\boldsymbol{v} = -\rho(\partial\psi/\partial t)\operatorname{grad}\psi, \quad \text{(power per unit area)} \qquad (2)$$

When intensity can be measured directly (when *both* velocity and pressure are measured) the magnitude of $\boldsymbol{S}$ is often given in terms of the *decibel scale.*

$$\text{Intensity level} = 10 \log (\text{intensity in microwatts per sq cm}) + 100 \qquad (3)$$

An intensity of 10^{-10} microwatt per square centimeter is zero intensity level, of 1 watt per square centimeter is 160 intensity level, etc. Sound of zero intensity level at 1000 cycles per second frequency is just at the threshold of hearing for the average person. The ear is less sensitive to frequencies either higher or lower than 1000 c. For example, the threshold of hearing is at about 40 decibels for 100 c. and at about 10 decibels for 10,000 c. Above about 20,000 c. and below about 20 c. sound is not heard.

1.3. Plane wave of sound. The " standard " wave motion is the simple-harmonic, plane wave, of frequency $\nu = (\omega/2\pi) = (kc/2\pi)$, wavelength $\lambda = (2\pi/k) = (c/\nu)$ and direction parallel to the propagation vector $\boldsymbol{k}$.

$$\left.\begin{aligned} &\psi = Ae^{i(\boldsymbol{k}\cdot\boldsymbol{r}-\omega t)}, \quad p = Pe^{i(\boldsymbol{k}\cdot\boldsymbol{r}-\omega t)}, \quad \boldsymbol{v} = U_{\max}(\boldsymbol{k}/k)e^{i(\boldsymbol{k}\cdot\boldsymbol{r}-\omega t)} \\ &P_{\max} = -i\rho\omega A, \quad U_{\max} = (P_{\max}/\rho c) = ikA, \\ &\qquad\qquad (\Delta T)_{\max} = (T/\rho c^2)(\gamma - 1)P_{\max} \\ &E = (P_{\max}{}^2/2\rho c^2) = \tfrac{1}{2}\rho U_{\max}{}^2, \quad S = (P_{\max}{}^2/2\rho c) = \tfrac{1}{2}\rho c U_{\max}{}^2 = Ec \end{aligned}\right\} \qquad (1)$$

In most cases intensity is not measured directly; pressure amplitude $P_{\max}$ is measured. Sound is then measured in terms of *sound pressure level*, which is adjusted to be equal to the intensity level for a plane wave in air at standard conditions.

$$\text{Pressure level} = 20 \log (P_{\text{rms}}/2 \times 10^{-4}) = 20 \log P_{\text{rms}} + 74 \qquad (2)$$

where $P_{\text{rms}} = P_{\max}/\sqrt{2}$ is the root-mean-square pressure amplitude measured in microbars (dynes per square centimeter). Note that for any other condition except a plane wave in air at standard conditions, pressure level is *not equal* to intensity level.

1.4. Acoustical constants for various media. The pertinent sound propagation constants in cgs units for various media are as follows. Air at 760 mm mercury pressure, 20° C temperature; $\rho = 0.00121$, $c = 34{,}400$, $\rho c = 42$, $\rho c^2 = K = 1{,}420{,}000$, $\gamma = 1.40$, $P_0 = 1.013 \times 10^3$. Sea water, at 15° C temperature, 31.6 g salt per 1000 g water (standard conditions); $\rho = 1.02338$, $c = 150{,}000$, $\rho c = 1.53 \times 10^5$, $\rho c^2 = K = 2.3 \times 10^{10}$.

1.5. Vibrations of sound producers; simple oscillator. A simple oscillator has mass M grams, resistance R dyne second per centimeter, and spring compliance C centimeter per dyne. The equation of motion is

$$M(d^2x/dt^2) + R(dx/dt) + (x/C) = \text{force} \tag{1}$$

The free vibration is

$$x = Ae^{-kt} \sin (\omega_r t + \varphi) \tag{2}$$

where the damping constant $k = (R/2M)$ and the vibration frequency is $(\omega_r/2\pi)$, where $\omega_r{}^2 = (1/MC) - k^2$. The Q of the oscillator, the number of cycles for the amplitude of motion to reduce to $e^{-\pi}$ of its initial value is $Q = \sqrt{M/CR^2}$. For forced motion, if the driving force is $Fe^{-i\omega t}$, the displacement and velocity of the oscillator are $x = (F/-i\omega Z)e^{-i\omega t}$ and $(dx/dt) = (F/Z)e^{-i\omega t}$, respectively, where Z is the *mechanical impedance* of the oscillator.

$$Z = -i\omega M + R - (1/i\omega C) = j\omega M + R + (1/j\omega C), \quad (i = -j) \tag{3}$$

where M is analogous to electric inductance, and C to electric capacitance in a series RLC circuit. When M or ω is large enough for ωM to predominate, the oscillator is *mass-controlled* and $Z \simeq j\omega M$; when C or ω is small enough, the oscillator is *stiffness-controlled* and $Z \simeq (1/j\omega C)$.

1.6. Flexible string under tension. For mass ϵ gram per centimeter length, tension T dynes, the transverse displacement $y(x,t)$ of a point x on the string, from equilibrium, is given by the wave equation (neglecting friction)

$$c^2(\partial^2 y/\partial x^2) = (\partial^2 y/\partial t^2), \quad c^2 = (T/\epsilon) \tag{1}$$

where c is wave velocity. For a string clamped at $x = 0$ and $x = l$, the possible free vibrations are

$$y(x,t) = \sum_{n=1}^{\infty} A_n \sin (n\pi x/l) \cos [(n\pi ct/l) - \psi_n] \tag{2}$$

The allowed frequencies are $\nu_n = (\omega_n/2\pi) = (nc/2l)$, the nth being called

nth *harmonic* of the *fundamental frequency* $\nu_1 = (c/2l)$. The amplitudes A_n and phases φ_n are determined by the initial shape $y_0(x)$ and velocity $v_0(x)$ of the string.

$$A_n \cos \psi_n = (2/l) \int_0^l y_0(x) \sin (\pi n x/l) dx \tag{3}$$

$$A_n \sin \psi_n = (2/n\pi c) \int_0^l v_0(x) \sin (\pi n x/l) dx \tag{4}$$

For a transverse driving force $F = F_0 e^{i\omega t}$ dynes per centimeter applied uniformly along the string of length l, the steady-state driven motion of the string is

$$y(x,t) = \frac{F_0 e^{-i\omega t}}{\epsilon\omega^2} \left[\frac{\cos (\omega/c) (x - \frac{1}{2} l)}{\cos (\omega l/2c)} - 1 \right] \tag{5}$$

The mean displacement is

$$\bar{y}(t) = (F_0 e^{-i\omega t}/\epsilon\omega^2) [(2c/\omega l) \tan (\omega l/2c) - 1] \tag{6}$$

having resonances at the fundamental ω, and at all odd harmonics $\omega_3, \omega_5, \ldots$.

1.7. Circular membrane under tension. For mass σ per unit area and tension T per unit length, the transverse displacement $y(r,\varphi,t)$ from equilibrium of a circular membrane clamped at $r = a$, for free vibration, is

$$\left. \begin{aligned} y(r,\varphi,t) = \sum_{m,n} [A_{mn} \cos (m\varphi) + B_{mn} \sin (m\varphi)] J_m(\pi\beta_{mn} r/a) \cdot \\ \cdot \cos [(\pi\beta_{mn} ct/a) - \psi_{mn}] \end{aligned} \right\} \tag{1}$$

where the term $J_m(z)$ is the Bessel function of order m, and β_{mn} is the nth root of the equation $J_m(\pi\beta) = 0$. The resonance frequencies are $\nu_{mn} = (\omega_{mn}/2\pi) = (\beta_{mn} c/2a)$. The first few values of β are : $\beta_{01} = 0.7655$, $\beta_{02} = 1.7571$, $\beta_{11} = 1.2197$, $\beta_{12} = 2.2330$, $\beta_{mn} \to n + \frac{1}{2}m - \frac{1}{4}$ where $n \gg 1$.

For a transverse driving force $F = F_0 e^{-i\omega t}$ dynes per square centimeter, uniform over the membrane, the steady-state displacement, after transients have disappeared, is

$$y(r,t) = \frac{F_0 e^{-i\omega t}}{\sigma\omega^2} \left[\frac{J_0(\omega r/c)}{J_0(\omega a/c)} - 1 \right] \tag{2}$$

and the mean displacement is

$$\bar{y}(t) = (F_0 e^{-i\omega t}/\sigma\omega^2) [J_2(\omega a/c)/J_0(\omega a/c)] \tag{3}$$

Resonance occurs at $\omega = \omega_{0n} = (\pi\beta_{0n} c/a)$.

1.8. Reflection of plane sound waves, acoustic impedance. If a plane sound wave, of pressure amplitude P_{inc}, is incident on a plane surface at angle of incidence θ, a reflected wave is produced, with amplitude dependent on the reaction of the surface to the sound pressure. This reaction may be expressed in terms of a ratio z between the pressure at the surface, p at $x = 0$, to the normal velocity of the air at the surface, v_x at $x = 0$ (in many cases z is independent of θ). The pressure wave is

$$\left.\begin{aligned} p = {} & P_{\text{inc}} e^{ik(x\cos\theta + y\sin\theta - ct)} \\ & + P_{\text{inc}}\left[\frac{(z/\rho c)\cos\theta - 1}{(z/\rho c)\cos\theta + 1}\right] e^{ik(-x\cos\theta + y\sin\theta - ct)} \end{aligned}\right\} \qquad (1)$$

If S_i is the incident intensity $(P_{\text{inc}}^2/2\rho c)$, the reflected intensity is

$$S_r = S_i \left| \frac{(z/\rho c)\cos\theta - 1}{(z/\rho c)\cos\theta + 1} \right|^2 \qquad (2)$$

which is equal to S_i when z is imaginary (surface impedance a pure reactance). When z has a real part, S_r is less than S_i and the surface absorbs some of the incident power.

1.9. Sound transmission through ducts. For a pipe, with axis parallel to the x axis, of cross-sectional area $A(x)$ and length of cross-sectional perimeter $L(x)$, the inner surface of which has acoustic impedance $z_w(x)$, when the logarithmic derivatives (A'/A), (L'/L), and (z'/z) are small compared to $(1/L)$, the following wave equation is approximately valid.

$$\frac{1}{c^2}\left(\frac{\partial^2 p}{\partial t^2}\right) + \left(\frac{L}{cA}\right)\left(\frac{\rho c}{z_w}\right)\left(\frac{\partial p}{\partial t}\right) = \left(\frac{1}{A}\right)\frac{\partial}{\partial x}\left(A\frac{\partial p}{\partial x}\right), \quad (c^2 = K/\rho) \qquad (1)$$

For a simple-harmonic wave $p = P(x)e^{-i\omega t}$ where $(\omega = kc)$, this reduces to

$$\frac{1}{A}\cdot\frac{d}{dx}\left(A\frac{dP}{dx}\right) + k^2 n^2 P = 0, \quad n^2 = 1 + \left(\frac{icL}{\omega A}\right)\left(\frac{\rho c}{z_w}\right) \qquad (2)$$

When A is independent of x but (A/L) is small compared to $(c/\omega) = 2\pi\lambda$, the motion for a wave proceeding in the positive x direction is

$$p = P_{\max} e^{ik(nx - ct)} \simeq P_{\max} e^{-(L/2A)(\rho c/z_w) + ik(x - ct)} \qquad (3)$$

The reciprocal of z_w, $(1/z_w) = g - is$, is the acoustic admittance of the duct surface; the wave is attenuated if the conductance g is greater than zero; the effective phase velocity of the wave in the duct is $c/[1 + (L/2A)(\rho cs)]$, which is greater than c if s is negative (mass reactance), less than c if s is positive (stiffness reactance of wall).

The attenuation of the wave in decibels per centimeter is $(4.34L\rho cg/A)$, with L, A, etc., given in centimeters (since ρcg is dimensionless, if L and A

are given in feet, $4.34\rho cgL/A$ will be the attenuation per foot of duct). If the tube is closed at $x = l$ by material (or an abrupt change of the duct) of effective impedance $(p/v_x)_{x=l} = z_l$, there will be a reflected as well as an incident wave in the region $x < l$. The pressure and velocity at x,ϵ can be written

$$\left.\begin{aligned} p &= P_0 \sinh\,[ikn(x-l)+\psi]e^{-i\omega t} \\ v &= (nP_0/\rho c)\cosh\,[ikn(x-l)+\psi]e^{-i\omega t} \end{aligned}\right\} \quad (1)$$

where $\psi = \tanh^{-1}(nz_l/\rho c)$. The ratio of p to v at $x = 0$ is then

$$z_0 = (\rho c/n)\tanh\,[\tanh^{-1}(nz_l/\rho c) - ikn_l] \quad (2)$$

which would be proportional to the load on a diaphragm, driving the air in the tube, placed at $x = 0$.

1.10. Transmission through long horn. When z_w is large enough so that n is nearly unity, but when A varies with x, we have the case of the horn. For the conical horn $A = A_0[(x/d)+1]^2$ the solution for an outgoing wave is

$$p = P_0[(xA)+1]^{-1}e^{ik(x-ct)}, \quad z_0 = \left(\frac{p}{v}\right)_{x=0} = \frac{\rho c}{1+i(c/\omega d)} \quad (1)$$

For an exponential horn $S = S_0 e^{2x/d}$ and the solution is

$$p = P_0 e^{-x/d+ik(\tau x-ct)}, \quad z_0 = \left(\frac{p}{v}\right)_{x=0} = \rho c\tau - i\rho c(c/\omega d)\,(\omega > c/d) \quad (2)$$

where $\tau = \sqrt{1-(c/\omega d)^2}$ and $kc = \omega$. If the duct of the previous section is terminated with a conical or exponential horn at $x = l$, the z_0 of this section is to be inserted for z_l in the previous equations.

1.11. Acoustical circuits. A duct with various constrictions, openings, and divisions is analogous to an a-c electric circuit as long as the wavelength of the sound is long compared with the dimensions of the tube. The total flow of air, $A(x)v$, past any cross section, is analogous to the current, and the pressure is analogous to the voltage. The analogous impedance $Z_a = (z/A)$ may be computed in terms of the impedance of the analogous electric circuit. A constriction in the tube, consisting of a hole of area A in a baffle plate, is analogous to a series inductance of value

$$L_a = (\rho l_e/A), \quad l_e = l + 0.8\sqrt{A} \quad (1)$$

where l is the length of the constriction ($l = 0$ when the plate is of negligible thickness). A chamber of larger cross section (a tank), of volume V, is analogous to a shunt capacitance of value

$$C_a = (V/\rho c^2) \quad (2)$$

A Helmholtz resonator is a tank with a single hole, connecting to the outside, is analogous to a series LC circuit. The resonance frequency is

$$\nu_r = (1/2\pi\sqrt{L_a C_a}) = (c/2\pi)\sqrt{A/l_e V} \tag{3}$$

A muffler, consisting of a sequence of tanks, connected one to the next by constrictions, is analogous to a low-pass filter network of series inductances alternating with shunt capacitances. Frequencies above the cutoff frequency

$$\nu_c = (1/\pi\sqrt{L_a C_a}) = (c/\pi)\sqrt{A/l_e V} \tag{4}$$

are attenuated, those below ν_c are transmitted.

1.12. Radiation of sound from a vibrating cylinder. When a long cylinder of radius a oscillates with a velocity $U_0 e^{-i\omega t}$ transverse to its axis, the sound wave radiated from its surface into an infinite medium is

$$\left.\begin{aligned} P &= \left(\frac{\pi\omega^2\rho a^2 U_0}{2c}\right)(\cos\phi)\,[H_1{}^{(1)}(kr)] \\ &\to \left(\frac{\pi\omega^2\rho a^2 U_0}{2ic}\right)\sqrt{\frac{2}{i\pi kr}}\cos\phi\, e^{ik(r-ct)}, \quad (kr \gg 1) \end{aligned}\right\} \tag{1}$$

when a is small compared to $(2\pi/\lambda) = (1/k)$. Cylindrical coordinates, r, ϕ are used, ϕ being the angle between radius r and the plane of vibration of the cylinder. The intensity of the sound several wavelengths from the cylinder, and the total power radiated per unit length of cylinder are

$$S_r \simeq (\pi\omega^3\rho a^4 U_0{}^2/4c^2 r)\cos^2\phi, \quad \Pi \simeq (\pi^2\omega^3\rho a^4 U_0{}^2/4c^2) \tag{2}$$

The reaction force F of the medium back on the moving cylinder, per unit length, is proportional to its transverse velocity U; the ratio (F/U) is the radiation impedance per unit length of the vibrating cylinder.

$$Z_{\text{rad}} \simeq -i\omega(\pi a^2\rho) + (\pi^2\omega^2\rho a^4/2c^2), \quad (\omega a \ll c) \tag{3}$$

1.13. Radiation from a simple source. Any source of sound of dimensions much smaller than a wavelength of the radiated sound sends out a wave which is almost symmetric spherically if there are no reflecting objects nearby. The *source strength* Q_0 is the amplitude of the total in-and-out flow of fluid from the source, in cubic centimeters per second. The radiated wave, a distance r from the radiator is

$$p \simeq -i\omega(\rho/4\pi r)Q_0 e^{ik(r-ct)}, \quad (kc = \omega) \tag{1}$$

The corresponding intensity and total power radiated are

$$S_r \simeq (\rho\omega^2 Q_0{}^2/32\pi^2 c r^2), \quad \Pi \simeq (\rho\omega^2 Q_0{}^2/8\pi c) \tag{2}$$

1.14. Radiation from a dipole source. A sphere of radius a oscillating back and forth along the spherical coordinate axis gives rise to dipole radiation when $2\pi r$ is small compared to the wavelength. If the linear velocity of the sphere is $U_0 e^{-i\omega t}$, the radiated pressure, intensity, and power, several wavelengths from the source, are

$$\left.\begin{aligned} p &\simeq -\left(\frac{\omega^2\rho a^3 U_0}{2cr}\right)\cos\vartheta\, e^{ik(r-ct)}, \quad S_r \simeq \left(\frac{\omega^4\rho a^6 U_0^2}{8c^3}\right)\left(\frac{\cos^2\vartheta}{r^2}\right), \\ \Pi &= \left(\frac{\pi\omega^4\rho a^6 U_0^2}{6c^3}\right) \end{aligned}\right\} \tag{1}$$

The radiation impedance back on the sphere, the ratio of the net reaction force to the velocity of the sphere, is

$$Z_{\mathrm{rad}} \simeq -i\omega(\tfrac{2}{3}\pi\rho_0 a^3) + (\pi\omega^4\rho a^6/3c^3), \quad (\omega a \gg c) \tag{2}$$

1.15. Radiation from a piston in a wall. If a flat-topped piston, of circular cross section with radius a, set in a flat, rigid wall, vibrates parallel to its axis with velocity $U_0 e^{-i\omega t}$, the radiated pressure and power at a distancer ($r \gg a$) from the center of the piston, r at angle θ to the piston axis, and the total radiated power are

$$\left.\begin{aligned} p &\simeq -i\omega\rho U_0 a^2 \frac{e^{ik(r-ct)}}{r}[J_1(ka\sin\theta)/ka\sin\theta] \\ &\xrightarrow[ka\to 0]{} -i\omega\rho(\pi a^2 U_0/2\pi r)e^{ik(r-ct)} \\ S &\simeq \tfrac{1}{2}(\rho\omega^2 U_0^2 a^4/r^2)\,[J_1(ka\sin\theta)/ka\sin\theta]^2 \xrightarrow[ka\to 0]{} (\rho\omega^2/8\pi^2 cr^2)\,(\pi a^2 U_0)^2 \\ \Pi &= \tfrac{1}{2}(\pi a^2\rho c U_0^2)\,[1-(1/ka)J_1(2ka)], \quad (ka = \omega a/c = 2\pi a/\lambda) \end{aligned}\right\} \tag{1}$$

The radiation impedance, the ratio of reaction force on the piston front to the piston transverse velocity, is

$$\left.\begin{aligned} Z_{\mathrm{rad}} &= \pi a^2\rho c[R_0 - iX_0] \\ R_0 &= 1 - \left(\frac{1}{ka}\right)J_1(2ka) \to \begin{cases} \tfrac{1}{2}(ka)^2, & (ka \ll 1) \\ 1 & (ka \gg 1) \end{cases} \\ X_0 &= \frac{4}{\pi}\int_0^{1/2\pi} \sin(2ka\cos\alpha)\sin^2\alpha\, d\alpha \to \begin{cases} (8ka/3\pi), & (ka \ll 1) \\ (2/\pi ka), & (ka \gg 1) \end{cases} \end{aligned}\right\} \tag{2}$$

1.16. Scattering of sound from a cylinder. A plane wave of sound, of frequency $(\omega/2\pi)$, incident at right angles to the axis of a rigid circular cylinder of radius a is in part underflected (continuing as a plane wave) and in part scattered. For wavelengths long compared with the cylinder radius a, the intensity S_s of the wave scattered at angle φ to the direction of the incident wave and the total power scattered per unit length of cylinder are.

$$S_s \simeq (\pi\omega^3 a^4/8c^3 r)S_0(1-2\cos\phi)^2,\quad \Pi_s \simeq (3\pi^2\omega^3 a^4 S_0/4c^3),\quad (ka \ll 1) \tag{1}$$

where S_0 is the intensity of the incident plane wave. For wavelengths short compared with a, half the scattered wave interferes with the undeflected plane wave, forming the shadow of the cylinder (with diffraction at the edge of the shadow) and the other half is reflected with distribution of intensity

$$S_r \simeq (aS_0/2r)\sin(\phi/2),\quad \Pi_r \simeq 2aS_0,\quad (ka \gg 1) \tag{2}$$

The net force on the cylinder because of the wave, per unit length of cylinder, is in the direction of the incident wave of magnitude

$$F \to \begin{cases} i\omega(4\pi^2 a^2/c)P_0 e^{-i\omega t}, & (ka \ll 1) \\ \sqrt{8\pi ac/\omega}\, P_0 e^{-(\omega/c)(a-ct)i\pi/4}, & (ka \gg 1) \end{cases} \tag{3}$$

where P_0 is the pressure amplitude of the incident plane wave.

1.17. Scattering of sound from a sphere. The corresponding scattered intensity and power from a plane wave of frequency $(\omega/2\pi) = (kc/2\pi)$ incident on a rigid sphere of radius a, at distance r and angle ϑ to the incident wave are

$$S_s \simeq (\omega^4 a^6 S_0/9c^4 r^2)(1-3\cos\vartheta)^2,\quad \Pi_s \simeq (16\pi\omega^4 a^6/9c^4)S_0 \tag{1}$$

for wavelengths long compared with a, where $ka \ll 1$. For very short wavelengths half of the scattered wave produces the shadow and the other half has intensity and power scattered,

$$S_r \simeq (a^2/4r^2)S_0,\quad \Pi_r \simeq \pi a^2 S_0,\quad (ka \gg 1) \tag{2}$$

The net pressure on the sphere, caused by the incident wave is

$$p_a \simeq (1 + \tfrac{3}{2} ika\cos\vartheta)P_0 e^{i\omega t},\quad (ka \ll 1) \tag{3}$$

1.18. Room acoustics. When sound is produced in a room the average intensity eventually comes to a constant value when the power produced is just balanced by the power lost, most of which is lost by absorption at the room walls (for the acoustic frequencies; high-frequency sound is absorbed in the air). If the room walls are sufficiently irregular in shape the steady-state sound is fairly uniformly distributed in direction and position in the room. The absorbing properties of the wall, in this case, may be expressed in terms of the *absorption coefficient* α, the fraction of the incident intensity which is absorbed and not reflected. This coefficient is related to the acoustic impedance of the wall, as defined previously. If an area A_s of the wall (or ceiling or floor) has absorption coefficient α_s, the sum $(\alpha_1 A_1 + \alpha_2 A_2 + \ldots)$ over the whole surface of the room is called a, the *total absorption of the room*. If A_s is given in square feet, the units of a are called *sabines*. The mean intensity level in the room, for steady state, is

$$\text{Intensity level} \simeq 10 \log (\Pi/a) + 130 \quad \text{decibels} \tag{1}$$

if Π is the power output in watts and a is in sabines. If, after reaching steady state, the sound is turned off, the intensity decays exponentially, on the average; the time required for the intensity to diminish by 60 decibels,

$$T = (0.049V/a) \quad \text{seconds} \tag{2}$$

is called the *reverberation time* (V is the volume of the room in cubic feet). The reverberation time is a useful criterion (not the only one, however) for the acoustical properties of an auditorium. Satisfactory values lie between 0.7 second and 1.5 seconds, the higher values being more appropriate for rooms used for music, the lower for rooms used primarily for speaking. A reverberation time less than 0.5 second indicates an undue amount of absorption and a corresponding lack of room sonority.

Bibliography

1. Beranek, L. L., *Acoustic Measurements*, John Wiley & Sons, Inc., New York, 1949. A good modern text on experimental acoustics.
2. Bergmann, L., *Ultrasonics*, John Wiley & Sons, Inc., New York, 1944. A discussion of the newly developing field of very high frequency sound. Contains a good bibliography.
3. Fletcher, H., *Speech and Hearing*, D. Van Nostrand Company, Inc., New York, 1929. An excellent discussion of the physiological aspects of acoustics.
4. Knudsen, V. O. and Harris, C. M., *Acoustical Design in Architecture*, John Wiley & Sons, Inc., New York, 1950. A recent review of an important and rapidly developing application of acoustics.
5. Morse, P. M., *Vibration and Sound*, 2d ed., McGraw-Hill Book Company, Inc., New York, 1948. A text on the recent developments of the theory of wave motion and its application to acoustics.
6. Randall, R. H., *Introduction to Acoustics*, Addison-Wesley Press, Inc., Cambridge, Mass., 1951. An up-to-date and easily readable introductory text.
7. Rayleigh, J. W. S., *The Theory of Sound* (reprint), Dover Publications, New York, 1945. The classic of the science of acoustics.

Chapter 16

GEOMETRICAL OPTICS

By James G. Baker

Research Associate of Harvard College Observatory,
Optical Consultant to Perkin-Elmer Corp.

1. General Considerations

1.1. Geometrical optics and wave optics. Light energy is propagated through an optical instrument in the form of a wave motion. Nevertheless, as a consequence of several important theorems, we can, for many purposes, regard light as traversing homogeneous isotropic media in straight lines. In heterogeneous isotropic media light is propagated as a normal congruence of rays in which the direction of motion lies along the normal to the wave front at any given point. In the most general case, i.e., heterogeneous anisotropic media, the direction of motion may be inclined to the wave front. By dealing with a geometry of lines rather than of waves, one can achieve considerable simplification. From this point of view the true wave nature of light enters as a necessary correction to the results of geometrical optics.

1.2. Media. Light travels through a vacuum in straight lines at a constant velocity irrespective of color. In material media the speed of light changes to a smaller value and becomes dependent on color. In the process the frequency ν and hence the quantum energy $h\nu$ remain unchanged. The effect of a medium on light is usually characterized by the *index of refraction*, which in the most general case is a function of position, direction, and frequency.

1.3. Index of refraction. Let n be the index of refraction, c the velocity of light in vacuo, and v the velocity of light in the medium. Then

$$n = \frac{c}{v} = \frac{\nu\lambda}{v} = \frac{\lambda}{\lambda'} \quad \text{or} \quad \lambda = n\lambda \tag{1}$$

where λ' is the wavelength in the medium.

$$\lambda = n_i\lambda_i = n_{i+1}\lambda_{i+1} = \dots \text{ etc.} \tag{2}$$

for successive media; $n = 1$ for a vacuum.

1.4. Interfaces. Various kinds of physical media exist. Those of most general use are the transparent homogeneous isotropic substances, which include glass, synthetic resins, cubic crystals, etc. The most usual kinds of anisotropic media in optical applications come from uniaxial and biaxial crystals. Strain introduced mechanically or electrically may alter isotropic substances into anisotropic media.

Because of the physical nature of media, there must exist boundaries or *interfaces* between media. When this interface is a *matte* surface, the resulting reflection of light is called *diffuse*. When the interface is smooth and continuous, the resulting reflection or refraction of light is termed *regular* or sometimes *specular*.

One should note that the physical properties of material media are all a function of temperature. In detailed calculations the effect of temperature must be considered. One should also note that the usual optical instrument is immersed in air, and that the observed indices of refraction of optical glass and crystals are often referred to air under designated conditions.

1.5. Refraction and reflection. The Fresnel formulas. When a ray of light passes from one medium into another at a smooth interface, the light energy divides into two parts, one a *reflected* ray, and the other a *refracted* ray. Within a narrow region of disturbance on each side of the interface, secondary wavelets are formed in the backward direction, and a certain amount of energy is returned to the first medium as the reflected ray. The remaining energy goes into the refracted ray in the second medium. Both transmitted and reflected rays are partially polarized in a manner dependent on the *angle of incidence* and on the *angle of refraction*, which are the angles between the ray and normal in the respective media. (Cf. § 1.13.)

For light polarized in the plane of incidence (magnetic vector in the plane of incidence)

$$\frac{I}{I_0} = \frac{\sin^2(i - r)}{\sin^2(i + r)} \tag{1}$$

and for light polarized in a plane perpendicular to the plane of incidence

$$\frac{I}{I_0} = \frac{\tan^2(i - r)}{\tan^2(i + r)} \tag{2}$$

where I is the intensity of the reflected beam, and I_0 the intensity of the incident beam.

When the light is unpolarized

$$\frac{I}{I_0} = \frac{1}{2}\,\frac{\sin^2(i-r)}{\sin^2(i+r)} + \frac{1}{2}\cdot\frac{\tan^2(i-r)}{\tan^2(i+r)} \tag{3}$$

For normal incidence whether the light is polarized or unpolarized

$$\frac{I}{I_0} = \left(\frac{\boldsymbol{n}'-\boldsymbol{n}}{\boldsymbol{n}'+\boldsymbol{n}}\right)^2 \tag{4}$$

This formula may be used as an approximation for *un*polarized light up to as much as 50 degrees off the normal.

At *Brewster's angle*, defined by $i = \tan^{-1} \boldsymbol{n}'/\boldsymbol{n}$, the intensity of the reflected light vanishes for light polarized in a plane perpendicular to the plane of incidence, i.e., $\tan^2(i+r) = \infty$. For unpolarized incident light at Brewster's angle, the intensity of the reflected light, which is now 100 % polarized with its electric vector perpendicular to the plane of incidence, becomes

$$\frac{I}{I_0} = \frac{1}{2}\sin^2(i-r) = \frac{1}{2}\left(\frac{\boldsymbol{n}'^2-\boldsymbol{n}^2}{\boldsymbol{n}'^2+\boldsymbol{n}^2}\right)^2 \tag{5}$$

If the incident light is already 100 % polarized at Brewster's angle,

$$\frac{I}{I_0} = \left(\frac{\boldsymbol{n}'^2-\boldsymbol{n}^2}{\boldsymbol{n}'^2+\boldsymbol{n}^2}\right)^2 \tag{6}$$

In the latter case for $\boldsymbol{n}'/\boldsymbol{n} = 1.5$, $I \sim 15$ % of I_0. For $\boldsymbol{n}'/\boldsymbol{n} = 1.8$, $I \sim 28$ % of I_0.

1.6. Optical path and optical length. Consider a curve S through any medium, either homogeneous or heterogeneous, along which light is known to travel between points z_1 and z_2. The time of transit of the light is given by the line integral

$$t = \int_{z_1}^{z_2} \frac{ds}{v} = \frac{1}{c}\int_{z_1}^{z_2} \boldsymbol{n}\,ds \tag{1}$$

or

$$\overline{ct} = L = \int_{z_1}^{z_2} \boldsymbol{n}\,ds$$

The length L is called the *optical length* of the path, as opposed to

$$\int_{z_1}^{z_2} ds,$$

which is the *geometrical length*; L is equal to the geometrical length the light would have traveled in a vacuum in the same time interval.

In a homogeneous medium a geometrical length s has an associated optical length $L = ns$. Where light travels through a succession of discrete homogeneous media,

$$L = \sum_i n_i s_i$$

where s is the straight line distance along the path between interfaces.

1.7. Fermat's principle. Light passing through a medium follows a path for which the optical length or time of transit is an extremum, i.e., independent of first-order iefinitesimal variations of path. The time is said to have a stationary value, and usually is either a maximum or minimum.

$$\delta t = \frac{1}{c} \delta \int_{z_1}^{z_2} nds = 0 \qquad (1)$$

where n is a function of the space coordinates. Similarly,

$$\delta L = \delta \int_{z_1}^{z_2} nds = 0 \qquad (2)$$

defines the particular path between z_1 and z_2. For discrete media

$$\delta L = \delta \sum_i n_i s_i = 0 \qquad (3)$$

1.8. Cartesian surfaces and the theorem of Malus. Consider a meridian cut C of an interface. The surface C is to be so chosen that for every point on it in 3-space, $L = ns + n's' =$ constant between a given point P in the first medium of index n and P' in the second medium of index n'. This surface clearly satisfies $\delta L = 0$ and the higher order differentials are all zero. Hence any ray emitted by P_1 that strikes C will find its way through P'. Hence P' is an image point of the object point P.

For a single ray originating at P and refracted through P' by a refracting surface S, where P' is not necessarily an image point, a Cartesian surface C may be considered tangent to S at the point of intersection of the refracted ray with S. By simple construction one can then determine whether the higher order differentials of a neighboring path between P and P' are positive or negative with respect to C where they are zero. If the curve S is more convex than C toward the less dense medium, L will be found to be a maximum.

Theorem of Malus. A system of rays normal to a wave front remains normal to a wave front after any number of refractions and reflections. That is, a normal congruence remains a normal congruence.

The combined principles of Fermat and Malus lead to the conclusion that for conjugate foci

$$\sum_i n_i s_i$$

is a constant between object and image points, irrespective of the ray.

A Cartesian surface holds for a point object, point image, and a single interface, defined by $ns + n's' =$ constant. Where reflection is involved, the surface is of the second degree and is therefore a conic section. For refraction the Cartesian surface is of the fourth degree, and its meridian cut is called the Cartesian *oval*. When one point lies at infinity, the surface degenerates into a second degree surface.

1.9. Laws of reflection. Let λ, μ, ν be the direction cosines of a ray before reflection by a surface S, and λ', μ', ν' the direction cosines of the reflected ray. From the variation principle one can show that

$$\left.\begin{aligned} \lambda + \lambda' &= Jl \\ \mu + \mu' &= Jm \\ \nu + \nu' &= Jn \end{aligned}\right\} \quad (1)$$

or

$$\frac{\lambda + \lambda'}{l} = \frac{\mu + \mu'}{m} = \frac{\nu + \nu'}{n} \quad (2)$$

where l, m, n are the direction cosines of the normal to S at the point of reflection of the ray. Also

$$J = 2\Sigma\, l\lambda = 2\Sigma\, l\lambda' = 2\cos i = 2\cos i' \quad (3)$$

$$i = i'; \quad D = 2i \quad (4)$$

where D is the deviation.

$$\begin{vmatrix} \lambda & \mu & \nu \\ \lambda' & \mu' & \nu' \\ l & m & n \end{vmatrix} = 0 \quad \text{(condition of coplanarity)} \quad (5)$$

The reflected ray therefore lies in the plane of the normal and incident ray.

1.10. Laws of refraction. Let λ, μ, ν be the direction cosines of a ray before refraction by a surface S, and λ', μ', ν' the direction cosines of the refracted ray. Again from the variation principle one can show that

$$\left.\begin{aligned} n\lambda - n'\lambda' &= Jl \\ n\mu - n'\mu' &= Jm \\ n\nu - n'\nu' &= Jn \end{aligned}\right\} \quad (1)$$

or
$$\frac{n\lambda - n'\lambda'}{l} = \frac{n\mu - n'\mu'}{m} = \frac{n\nu - n'\nu'}{n} \tag{2}$$

where l, m, n are the direction cosines of the normal to S at the point of refraction. Also

$$J = n \cos i - n' \cos r \tag{3}$$

$$J^2 = n^2 + n'^2 - 2nn' \cos (i - r) \tag{4}$$

$$= n^2 + n'^2 - 2nn' \cos D \tag{5}$$

where D is the deviation.

$$\cos D = \Sigma \lambda\lambda'$$

$$\begin{vmatrix} \lambda & \mu & \nu \\ \lambda' & \mu' & \nu' \\ l & m & n \end{vmatrix} = 0, \quad \text{(condition of coplanarity)} \tag{6}$$

1.11. The fundamental laws of geometrical optics

a. The law of the rectilinear propagation of light
b. The law of mutual independence of the component parts of a light beam
c. The law of regular reflection
d. The law of regular refraction

1.12. Corollaries of the laws of reflection and refraction

a. The incident and reflected rays are equally inclined to any straight line tangent to the surface at the point of incidence.

b. The projections of the incident and reflected rays upon any plane containing the normal make equal angles with the normal.

c. $n \cos \theta = n' \cos \theta'$, where θ is the angle between the ray and any tangent line.

d. $n \sin \psi = n' \sin \psi'$, where ψ is the angle between the ray and any normal plane. (Cf. section 5.)

1.13. Internal reflection, and Snell's law.

The relation

$$n \sin i = n' \sin r \tag{1}$$

is called the optical invariant, and also *Snell's law* after its discoverer. The relationship is valid in the common plane containing the incident and refracted rays and the normal, and follows from § 1.10 above. Note (d) under § 1.12 that a similar relation exists for the oblique refractions.

Where $n'/n > 1$ and $\sin r > n/n'$, no solution exists for i. This is the case of internal reflection at the interface. The light energy remains 100 % in the same medium and obeys the laws of reflection.

1.14. Dispersion at a refraction

$$n \sin i = n' \sin r, \quad \text{(Snell's law)} \tag{1}$$

If $di = 0$ (entrant white light)

$$dr = \frac{\sin i\, dn - \sin r\, dn'}{n' \cos r} \tag{2}$$

For air-glass where $dn = 0$,

$$dr = -\tan r \frac{dn'}{n'}, \quad \text{(in the medium } n'\text{)} \tag{3}$$

For glass-air where $dn' = 0$,

$$dr = \tan r \frac{dn}{n} \tag{4}$$

where i and r are, respectively, the angles of incidence and refraction in the direction of travel of the light. Subsequent refractions determine the final effect for a system as a whole.

1.15. Deviation

a. Reflection

$$D = 2i, \quad dD = 2di, \quad \text{(for a single mirror)} \tag{1}$$

If two mirrors are separated by the angle α and the light strikes each in turn,

$$D = 2\alpha \quad \text{independent of } i \tag{2}$$

b. Refraction

$$\left.\begin{aligned} D &= i - r \\ dD &= di\left(1 - \frac{n \cos i}{n' \cos r}\right) \end{aligned}\right\} \tag{3}$$

At a glass-air surface and normal incidence,

$$dD = -(n-1)di \sim -\tfrac{1}{2}di \tag{4}$$

At a glass-air surface and $i = 30°$,

$$dD = -di \tag{5}$$

At an air-glass surface and normal incidence,

$$dD = \left(1 - \frac{1}{n}\right)di \sim \frac{1}{3}\, di \tag{6}$$

At an air-glass surface and $i = 30^{\circ}$,

$$dD = 0.4di \tag{7}$$

At an air-glass surface and $i = 90^{\circ}$,

$$dD = di \tag{8}$$

However, the final effect of a deviation depends on the subsequent refractions, as determined by magnification factors along the particular ray. The deviation increases numerically with the angle of incidence at a refraction, a fact that is a direct cause of difficulties in the design of optical systems.

2. The Characteristic Function of Hamilton (Eikonal of Bruns) *

2.1. The point characteristic, V. Here V is defined as the optical path between points x, y, z and x', y', z' in a heterogeneous medium, i.e.,

$$V = \int_{xyz}^{x'y'z'} \boldsymbol{n} ds \tag{1}$$

If both end points of the path are varied, and if $\boldsymbol{n}$ and $\boldsymbol{n}'$ are the indices of refraction in the infinitesimal neighborhood of x, y, z and x', y', z', respectively

$$\delta V = -\boldsymbol{n} \Sigma \lambda \delta x + \boldsymbol{n}' \Sigma \lambda' \delta x' \tag{2}$$

or

$$\left.\begin{aligned} \frac{\partial V}{\partial x} &= -\boldsymbol{n}\lambda, & \frac{\partial V}{\partial x'} &= \boldsymbol{n}'\lambda' \\ \frac{\partial V}{\partial y} &= -\boldsymbol{n}\mu & \frac{\partial V}{\partial y'} &= \boldsymbol{n}'\mu' \\ \frac{\partial V}{\partial z} &= -\boldsymbol{n}\nu, & \frac{\partial V}{\partial z'} &= \boldsymbol{n}'\nu' \end{aligned}\right\} \tag{3}$$

and

$$\Sigma \left(\frac{\partial V}{\partial x}\right)^2 = \boldsymbol{n}^2, \quad \Sigma \left(\frac{\partial V}{\partial x'}\right)^2 = \boldsymbol{n}'^2 \tag{4}$$

Similarly, if V is defined as the total optical path between a point x, y, z in an initial medium $\boldsymbol{n}$ and a point x', y', z' in a final medium $\boldsymbol{n}'$, the above equations continue to apply. The intermediate path may traverse a succession of heterogeneous or discrete homogeneous media, or both.

Thus V is a function of 12 quantities $(x, y, z, \lambda, \mu, \nu, x', y', z', \lambda', \mu', \nu')$

* Synge, J. L., *Geometrical Optics, an Introduction to Hamilton's Method*, Cambridge University Press, London, 1937.

not all of which are independent. Given any five, we can compute the other five from the above equations.

The importance of the use of V is that the physical instrument is now replaced by a mathematical function V, and the behavior of the instrument by the partial derivatives of V. Knowing the characteristic, one can compute the performance; knowing the performance, one can compute a characteristic containing only a set of constants to be evaluated for a given instrument of that performance. Where x, y, z is a point source, one has precise information for investigation of the character of the image when V is known.

Computation of V. Let $F_i(x_i, y_i, z_i) = 0$ be the equation of the general surface of the instrument separating various homogeneous media. Then the general optical path L becomes

$$L = ns + \sum_{1}^{N-1} n_i s_i + n's' \tag{5}$$

On application of Fermat's principle, $\delta L = 0$,

$$\sum_{i=1}^{N-1} \left(\frac{\partial L}{\partial x_i} \delta x_i + \frac{\partial L}{\partial y_i} \delta y_i + \frac{\partial L}{\partial z_i} \delta z_i \right) = 0 \tag{6}$$

Also, because variations in x_i, y_i, z_i are confined to the surface $F_i(x_i, y_i, z_i) = 0$,

$$\frac{\partial F}{\partial x_i} \delta x_i + \frac{\partial F}{\partial y_i} \delta y_l + \frac{\partial F_i}{\partial z_i} \delta z_i = 0, \quad (i = 1, 2, \ldots, N-1) \tag{7}$$

If the intermediate points are to be independent of one another, then

$$\left.\begin{aligned} \frac{\partial L}{\partial x_i} &= J_i \frac{\partial F_i}{\partial x_i} \\ \frac{\partial L}{\partial y_i} &= J_i \frac{\partial F_i}{\partial y_i} \qquad (i = 1, 2, \ldots, N-1) \\ \frac{\partial L}{\partial z_i} &= J_i \frac{\partial F_i}{\partial z_i} \end{aligned}\right\} \tag{8}$$

These $4(N-1)$ equations yield the $4(N-1)$ quantities x_i, y_i, z_i, J_i. When substituted in L, these quantities yield the relation

$$V(x,y,z,x',y',z') = L, \quad \text{(actual path)} \tag{9}$$

The course of the analytic ray is thus defined.

2.2. The mixed characteristic, W. Here W is defined as the total optical path between the point x, y, z in the initial medium $\boldsymbol{n}$ and the foot of the perpendicular dropped from the origin of coordinates onto the final ray in medium $\boldsymbol{n}'$.

$$V = W(x,y,z,\mu',\nu') + \boldsymbol{n}'(\lambda'x' + \mu'y' + \nu'z') \tag{1}$$

From application of the variational principle

$$\left.\begin{aligned} \frac{\partial W}{\partial x} &= -\boldsymbol{n}\lambda & \frac{\partial W}{\partial \mu'} &= -\boldsymbol{n}'\left(y' - \frac{\mu'}{\lambda'}x'\right) \\ \frac{\partial W}{\partial y} &= -\boldsymbol{n}\mu & \frac{\partial W}{\partial \nu'} &= -\boldsymbol{n}'\left(z' - \frac{\nu'}{\lambda'}x'\right) \\ \frac{\partial W}{\partial z} &= -\boldsymbol{n}\nu \end{aligned}\right\} \tag{2}$$

Thus, given x, y, z (source point) and μ', ν', the direction of any ray in the final medium, we can obtain at once the equation of that ray in the final medium from the partials of W.

Then W may be computed in a fashion quite similar to the method used for computing V above. Because W involves fewer unknowns, its calculation is not as difficult as that for V.

2.3. The angle characteristic, T

a. Here T is defined as the total optical path between the foot of the perpendicular dropped onto the initial ray from the origin of coordinates in the first medium $\boldsymbol{n}$ to the foot of the perpendicular dropped onto the final ray from the origin in the final medium $\boldsymbol{n}'$.

$$V = -\boldsymbol{n}\,\Sigma\,\lambda x + T(\mu,\nu,\mu',\nu') + \boldsymbol{n}'\,\Sigma\,\lambda'x' \tag{1}$$

From application of the variational principle

$$\left.\begin{aligned} \frac{\partial T}{\partial \mu} &= \boldsymbol{n}\left(y - \frac{\mu}{\lambda}x\right), & \frac{\partial T}{\partial \mu'} &= -\boldsymbol{n}'\left(y' - \frac{\mu'}{\lambda'}x'\right) \\ \frac{\partial T}{\partial \nu} &= \boldsymbol{n}\left(z - \frac{\nu}{\lambda}x\right), & \frac{\partial T}{\partial \nu'} &= -\boldsymbol{n}'\left(z' - \frac{\nu'}{\lambda'}x'\right) \end{aligned}\right\} \tag{2}$$

Thus, if μ, ν, μ', ν' are assigned, the initial and final rays are known.

The calculation of T proceeds by application of the variational principle to each pair of adjacent media, inasmuch as the final ray for medium $i-1$ becomes the initial ray for the medium i.

Thus

$$\left.\begin{aligned} &\frac{\partial}{\partial \mu_i}(T_{i-1,i} + T_{i,i+1}) = 0 \\ &\qquad\qquad\qquad (i = 1, 2, \ldots, N-1) \\ &\frac{\partial}{\partial \nu_i}(T_{i-1,i} + T_{i,i+1}) = 0 \end{aligned}\right\} \tag{3}$$

$$T = \sum_{1}^{N-1} T_{i-1,i} \tag{4}$$

for the system as a whole. The T function is not in its final form until it becomes $T(\mu, \nu, \mu', \nu')$.

b. *Translation of origin.* The value of T is dependent on the choice of origin. If T_{new} is to be calculated for a new origin, we have

$$T_{\text{new}} = T_{\text{old}} + a(\lambda' - \lambda) + b(\mu' - \mu) + c(\nu' - \nu) \tag{5}$$

where a, b, and c are the coordinates of the new origin in the old system.

c. *The value of T for a spherical surface.* Let

$$F(x,y,z) = x^2 + y^2 + z^2 - R^2 = 0 \tag{6}$$

Then

$$\left.\begin{aligned} T &= \pm R[(\boldsymbol{n}'\lambda' - \boldsymbol{n}\lambda)^2 + (\boldsymbol{n}'\mu' - \boldsymbol{n}\mu)^2 + (\boldsymbol{n}'\nu' - \boldsymbol{n}\nu)^2]^{1/2} \\ &= \pm R[\boldsymbol{n}^2 + \boldsymbol{n}'^2 - 2\boldsymbol{n}\boldsymbol{n}'(\lambda\lambda' + \mu\mu' + \nu\nu')]^{1/2} \end{aligned}\right\} \tag{7}$$

where the origin lies at the center of the sphere. A change of origin may be introduced from b. above. The choice of sign depends on the sense of curvature of R, with T reckoned positive from left to right.

d. *The value of T for a paraboloid of revolution.* Let

$$F(x, y, z) = x - \frac{1}{4F}(y^2 + z^2) = 0 \tag{8}$$

$$L = (\boldsymbol{n}\lambda - \boldsymbol{n}'\lambda')x + (\boldsymbol{n}\mu - \boldsymbol{n}'\mu')y + (\boldsymbol{n}\nu - \boldsymbol{n}'\nu')z \tag{9}$$

$$\delta L = \frac{\delta L}{\partial y}\delta y + \frac{\partial L}{\partial z}\delta z = 0 \tag{10}$$

if the variation takes place on the surface $F(x,y,z) = 0$.

$$\left.\begin{aligned} \frac{\partial L}{\partial y} &= (\boldsymbol{n}\lambda - \boldsymbol{n}'\lambda')\frac{\partial x}{\partial y} + (\boldsymbol{n}\mu - \boldsymbol{n}'\mu') = 0 \\ \frac{\partial L}{\partial z} &= (\boldsymbol{n}\lambda - \boldsymbol{n}'\lambda')\frac{\partial x}{\partial z} + (\boldsymbol{n}\nu - \boldsymbol{n}'\nu') = 0 \end{aligned}\right\} \tag{11}$$

$$\frac{\partial x}{\partial y} = \frac{1}{2F} y, \quad \frac{\partial x}{\partial z} = \frac{1}{2F} z \tag{12}$$

$$y = -2F\left(\frac{n\mu - n'\mu'}{n\lambda - n'\lambda'}\right), \quad z = -2F\left(\frac{n\nu - n'\nu'}{n\lambda - n'\lambda'}\right) \tag{13}$$

$$x = F\left[\frac{(n\mu - n'\mu')^2 + (n\nu - n'\nu')^2}{(n\lambda - n'\lambda')^2}\right] \tag{14}$$

$$T = -F\left[\frac{(n\mu - n'\mu')^2 + (n\nu - n'\nu')^2}{(n\lambda - n'\lambda')}\right] \tag{15}$$

e. *The value of T for a general ellipsoid.* Let

$$F(x,y,z) = \frac{x^2}{a^2} + \frac{y^2}{b^2} + \frac{z^2}{c^2} - 1 = 0 \tag{16}$$

$$L = \Sigma(n\lambda - n'\lambda')x \tag{17}$$

$$y = \frac{b^2}{a^2}\left(\frac{n\mu - n'\mu'}{n\lambda - n'\lambda'}\right)x, \quad z = \frac{c^2}{a^2}\left(\frac{n\nu - n'\nu'}{n\lambda - n'\lambda'}\right)x \tag{18}$$

$$x = \pm a\left[1 + \frac{b^2}{a^2}\left(\frac{n\mu - n'\mu'}{n\lambda - n'\lambda'}\right)^2 + \frac{c^2}{a^2}\left(\frac{n\nu - n'\nu'}{n\lambda - n'\lambda'}\right)^2\right] \tag{19}$$

$$T = \pm [a^2(n\lambda - n'\lambda')^2 + b^2(n\mu - n'\mu')^2 + c^2(n\nu - n'\nu')^2]^{1/2} \tag{20}$$

and similarly for other second-degree solids.

2.4. The sine condition of Abbe. An identity among the second partial derivatives of the characteristic function leads to an important general relation that must be satisfied if an elementary surface around a point source is to be imaged accurately into a corresponding elementary surface around the image point. We confine ourselves to an axial source point in an instrument with rotational symmetry.

If we have precise imagery irrespective of the initial ray, then $y' = my$ and $z' = mz$, where m is the magnification.

$$\left.\begin{aligned} \frac{\partial W}{\partial x} &= -n\lambda & \frac{\partial W}{\partial \mu'} &= -n'\left(y' - \frac{\mu'}{\lambda'}x'\right) \\ \frac{\partial W}{\partial y} &= -n\mu & \frac{\partial W}{\partial \nu'} &= -n'\left(z' - \frac{\nu'}{\lambda'}x'\right) \\ \frac{\partial W}{\partial z} &= -n\nu \end{aligned}\right\} \tag{1}$$

If we consider that all rays from the object point combine in the image point, and that the elementary surface and its image are perpendicular to the axis, W is a function $W(y, z, \mu', \nu')$ and y', z', μ, and ν become dependent variables from the above relations. We have

$$\frac{\partial^2 W}{\partial y \partial \mu'} = -n\frac{\partial \mu}{\partial \mu'} = \frac{\partial^2 W}{\partial \mu' \partial y} = -n'\frac{\partial y'}{\partial y} = -n'm \tag{2}$$

$$\frac{\partial^2 W}{\partial z \partial \nu'} = -n\frac{\partial \nu}{\partial \nu'} = \frac{\partial^2 W}{\partial \nu' \partial z} = -n'\frac{\partial z'}{\partial z} = -n'm \tag{3}$$

$$\left.\begin{aligned} \frac{\partial^2 W}{\partial y \partial \nu'} &= -n\frac{\partial \mu}{\partial \nu'} = \frac{\partial^2 W}{\partial \nu' \partial y} = -n'\frac{\partial z'}{\partial y} = 0 \\ \frac{\partial^2 W}{\partial z \partial \mu'} &= -n\frac{\partial \nu}{\partial \mu'} = \frac{\partial^2 W}{\partial \mu' \partial z} = -n'\frac{\partial y'}{\partial z} = 0 \end{aligned}\right\} \tag{4}$$

because of rotational symmetry.

Then
$$\frac{d\mu}{d\mu'} = \frac{n'}{n}m \quad \text{or} \quad n\mu = n'\mu' m \tag{6}$$

$$\frac{d\nu}{d\nu'} = \frac{n'}{n}m \quad \text{or} \quad n\nu = n'\nu' m \tag{7}$$

where the constant of integration is zero because the angles vanish together.

If θ and θ' are the respective slope angles of a ray from the object point to the image point,

$$\frac{n \sin \theta}{n' \sin \theta'} = m \tag{8}$$

which is known as the *sine condition* of Abbe. The relationship can also be derived from general principles of thermodynamics.

2.5. Clausius' equation. Consider a small line element $\overline{P_1P_2}$ inclined at an angle φ to the plane normal to the axis of a pencil at P_1 of angular half aperture θ (Fig. 1). We wish to examine the conditions that will lead to a sharp image of the line element in image space, i.e., so that P_2 will be sharply imaged.

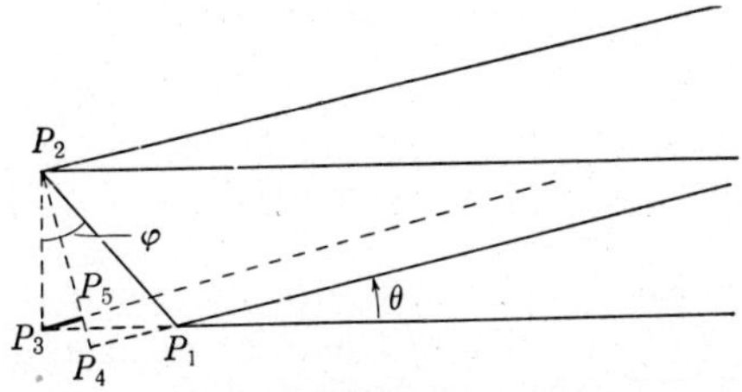

FIGURE 1

We can regard $\overline{P_2P_3}$ as a portion of a wave front proceeding to the right along the axis of the pencil. Similarly, $\overline{P_2P_4}$ can be regarded as a portion of another wave front inclined to the first at the angle θ. The two paths are related by the increment $\overline{P_3P_5}$, the optical length of which must be preserved in the final medium if the inverse construction is to produce a sharp image of the line element.

Thus

$$\boldsymbol{n}l \cos \varphi \sin \theta = \boldsymbol{n}'l' \cos \varphi' \sin \theta' \tag{1}$$

This condition was demonstrated by Clausius on the basis of energy considerations, and is useful in connection with off-axis images in rotationally symmetrical optical systems. The angle φ need not be in the plane of the paper.

2.6. Heterogeneous isotropic media. Consider a curve in the medium connecting P to P'. Let the parametric equation of the curve be

$$x = x(u), \quad y = y(u), \quad z = z(u) \tag{1}$$

The optical length is

$$L = \int_C \boldsymbol{n}(x,y,z)\,(\dot{x}^2 + \dot{y}^2 + \dot{z}^2)^{1/2}\,du \tag{2}$$

$$= \int_C w\,du, \quad (\text{where } \dot{x} = dx/du, \text{ etc.}) \tag{3}$$

where

$$w = \boldsymbol{n}(x,y,z)\,(\dot{x}^2 + \dot{y}^2 + \dot{z}^2)^{1/2} = w(x,y,z,\dot{x},\dot{y},\dot{z}) \tag{4}$$

If we hold the end points fixed but vary the curve, we have

$$\delta L = \int_u^{u'} \delta w\,du \tag{5}$$

$$= \int_u^{u'} \left(\Sigma \frac{\partial w}{\partial \dot{x}}\,\delta \dot{x} + \Sigma \frac{\partial w}{\partial x}\,\delta x \right) du \tag{6}$$

$$\delta \dot{x} = \delta \frac{dx}{du} = \frac{d}{du}\,\delta x, \quad \text{etc.} \tag{7}$$

Integration by parts gives

$$\delta L = \left[\Sigma \frac{\partial w}{\partial \dot{x}}\,\delta x \right]_u^{u'} - \int_u^{u'} \Sigma \left(\frac{d}{du}\frac{\partial w}{\partial \dot{x}} - \frac{\partial w}{\partial x} \right) \delta x\,du \tag{8}$$

Because the curves have fixed end points, the first term vanishes. If C is to be a stationary path, the value of L must be unchanged in the differential neighborhood of any point on the curve. δx, δy, and δz are completely arbitrary, and hence the coefficients must vanish under the integral all along the path. Accordingly,

$$\frac{d}{du} \cdot \frac{\partial w}{\partial \dot{x}} - \frac{\partial w}{\partial x} = 0, \quad \text{(and for } y, z\text{)} \tag{9}$$

or

$$\frac{d}{du}\left[\frac{n\dot{x}}{(\dot{x}^2 + \dot{y}^2 + \dot{z}^2)^{1/2}}\right] - \frac{\partial n}{\partial x}(\dot{x}^2 + \dot{y}^2 + \dot{z}^2)^{1/2} = 0, \quad (y, z) \tag{10}$$

If $u = s$, the arc length along C, from which $\dot{x}^2 + \dot{y}^2 + \dot{z}^2 = 1$, the above equations become

$$\frac{d}{ds}\left(n\frac{dx}{ds}\right) - \frac{\partial n}{\partial x} = 0, \quad (y, z) \tag{11}$$

2.7. Collineation. A space continuum of points, line, and planes in object space that go into conjugate points, lines, and planes in image space in one to one linear correspondence is called a *collineation.*

Let x, y, z be the coordinates of a point in object space and x', y', z' its conjugate in image space with reference to right angle conjugated coordinate systems. Then

$$\left.\begin{aligned} x' &= \frac{\alpha_1 x + \beta_1 y + \gamma_1 z + \delta_1}{\alpha x + \beta y + \gamma z + \delta} \\ y' &= \frac{\alpha_2 x + \beta_2 y + \gamma_2 z + \delta_2}{\alpha x + \beta y + \gamma z + \delta} \\ z' &= \frac{\alpha_3 x + \beta_3 y + \gamma_3 z + \delta_3}{\alpha x + \beta y + \gamma z + \delta} \end{aligned}\right\} \tag{1}$$

This system can be inverted. If the relations were not rational, there would be no one-to-one relationship of object and image space. The denominator must have the same form in order that planes in object space go into planes in image space.

$$A'x' + B'y' + C'z' + D' = 0 \tag{2}$$

$$\rightarrow \quad Ax + By + Cz + D = 0 \tag{3}$$

The inverted solution has the form

$$x = \frac{\alpha'_1 x' + \beta'_1 y' + \gamma'_1 z' + \delta'_1}{\alpha' x' + \beta' y' + \gamma' z' + \delta'}, \quad \text{etc.} \tag{4}$$

If $\alpha x + \beta y + \gamma z + \delta = 0$, then

$$x' = y' = z' = \infty \tag{5}$$

Also, if $\alpha'x' + \beta'y' + \gamma'z' + \delta' = 0$, then

$$x = y = z = \infty \tag{6}$$

In the first case, $\alpha x + \beta y + \gamma z + \delta = 0$ determines a plane conjugate to the plane at infinity in image space. This plane is called the *first* focal plane and lies in object space. The plane $\alpha'x' + \beta'y' + \gamma'z' + \delta' = 0$ is called the *second* focal plane, and lies in image space. Parallel rays in object space will meet on this focal plane in image space.

In a centered lens system we can set $z = z' = 0$ without loss of generality. The x axis becomes the optical axis. Thus for points on the axis

$$x' = \frac{\alpha_1 x + \delta_1}{\alpha x + \delta} \tag{7}$$

Intermediate images will be reducible to this form. If $\alpha = 0$, the system is called *telescopic*. In this case

$$x' = \frac{\alpha_1}{\delta} x + \frac{\delta_1}{\delta} \tag{8}$$

When $\alpha \neq 0$ but $\alpha = 1$, $x'x + \delta x' - \alpha_1 x - \delta_1 = 0$, which is of the form

$$(x + a)(x' + b) = \text{constant} \tag{9}$$

A simple change of origin produces the relation $xx' =$ constant. Evidently, x and x' are measured from the first and second focal points, respectively.

3. First Order Relationships

3.1. Conventions. Unless specified otherwise for a particular set of equations, we adopt the following conventions, all in reference to a centered rotationally symmetrical optical system.

a. Light travels from left to right.

b. An *object distance* is positive relative to a vertex when the object point lies to the left of the vertex.

c. An *image distance* is positive when the image point lies to the right of the vertex.

d. A *radius of curvature* is positive when the center of curvature lies to the right of the vertex.

e. *Slope angles* are positive when the axis must be rotated counterclockwise through less than $\pi/2$ to become coincident with the ray.

f. *Angles of incidence and refraction* are positive when the normal must be rotated counterclockwise through less than $\pi/2$ to bring it into coincidence with the ray.

g. Distances are positive above the axis.

3.2. Refraction at a single surface. The optical path between the source point and image point is simply $ns + n's'$, where s and s' are the object and image distances, respectively (Fig. 2). Any other paraxial ray from the source point must have the same total optical path to the image point in order that a focus shall exist.

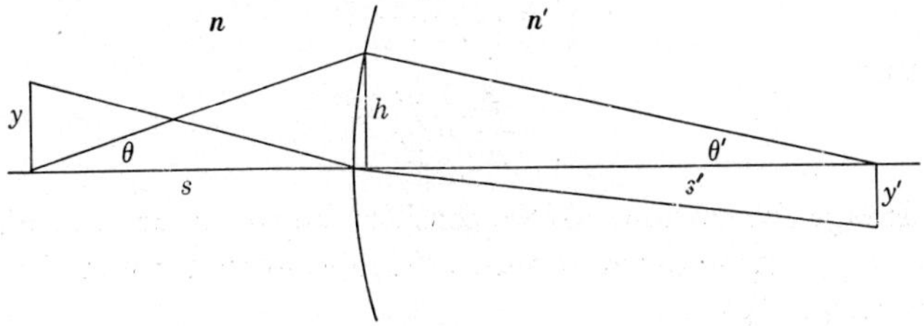

FIGURE 2

If a circle of radius s is described around the source point, and another circle of radius s' is described around the image point, one sees that the optical paths of the sagittae must be equated in the following way. (The sagitta of an arc is the depth of the arc from the chord.)

$$\sigma = \frac{1}{2} \cdot \frac{h^2}{R} \tag{1}$$

for the sagitta of a zone h and radius R. Then

$$n\left(\frac{1}{2} \cdot \frac{h^2}{s} + \frac{1}{2} \cdot \frac{h^2}{R}\right) + n'\left(-\frac{1}{2} \cdot \frac{h^2}{R} + \frac{1}{2} \cdot \frac{h^2}{s'}\right) = 0 \tag{2}$$

or

$$\frac{n}{s} + \frac{n}{R} - \frac{n'}{R} + \frac{n'}{s'} = 0 \tag{3}$$

Finally,

$$\frac{n}{s} + \frac{n'}{s'} = \frac{n' - n}{R} \tag{4}$$

It is of interest that if object and image distance are referred to the center of curvature, rather than to the vertex, we obtain an analogous formula,

$$\frac{n'}{S} + \frac{n}{S'} = \frac{n' - n}{R} \tag{5}$$

in which the indices on the left become interchanged.

3.3. Focal points and focal lengths. If $s = \infty$, we find $n'/s' = (n' - n)/R$. We define this distance s' as the *second focal length*, which then is the distance from the vertex or pole of the surface to the *second focal point*, and denote this distance by f'.

Then

$$f' = \left(\frac{n'}{n' - n}\right) R \tag{1}$$

Similarly, if $s' = \infty$, we call s the *first focal length* of the surface, which is the distance from the *first focal point* to the vertex of the surface, and denote this distance by f. Then

$$f = \left(\frac{n}{n' - n}\right) R \tag{2}$$

It follows that

$$\frac{f}{n} = \frac{f'}{n'} \tag{3}$$

3.4. Image formation. If we consider the construction in Fig. 3, the ray from b passing through C must evidently go undeviated through the image point b'. Then

$$\frac{y'}{y} = -\frac{s' - R}{s + R} = m \tag{1}$$

Also,

$$n \frac{y}{s} = -n' \frac{y'}{s'} \tag{2}$$

or

$$\frac{y'}{y} = -\frac{n}{n'} \frac{s'}{s} = m \tag{3}$$

where m is called the *lateral magnification.*

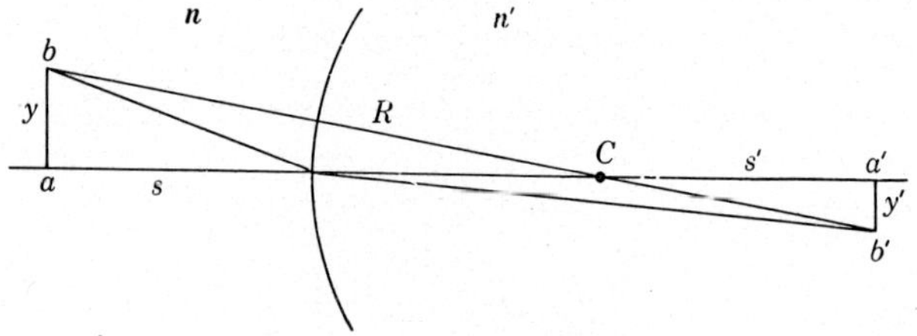

FIGURE 3

3.5. Lagrange's law (Known variously as the Helmholtz-Lagrange formula, the Smith-Helmholtz equation, or Helmholtz's equation). In the diagram

$$h = s\theta = -s'\theta' \tag{1}$$

Also,

$$ns'y = -n'sy' \tag{2}$$

or

$$n\theta y = n'\theta' y' \tag{3}$$

This relation applies to any number of successive conjugate images, and is evidently the paraxial expression of the sine condition of Abbe.

3.6. Principal planes. The principal planes are that pair of conjugate planes in which object and image are of the same size and on the same side of the optical axis. The lateral magnification for the principal planes is therefore +1. Each point of one plane images into a point on the conjugate plane in 1 to 1 correspondence. Within the accuracy of *Gaussian* optics, both points lie at the same height above the optical axis.

Consider an object $y = \overline{ab}$ (Fig. 4). A ray from b parallel to the axis strikes H at P and images at P'. This same ray passes through F', which then becomes the *second* focal point. Similarly, the ray $\overline{bF}$, if F is the *first*

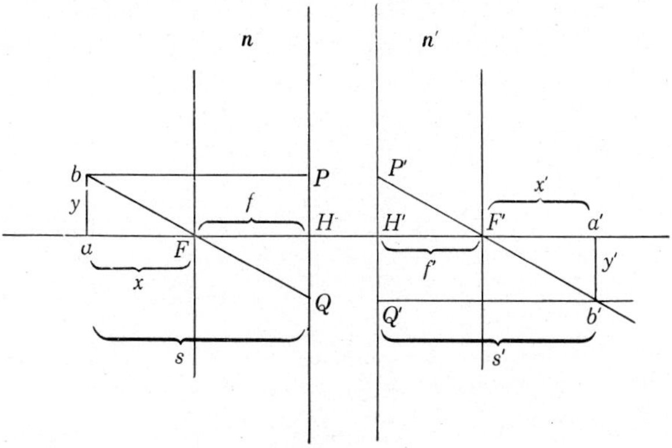

FIGURE 4

focal point, strikes the first principal plane at Q, emerges at Q', and thenceforward remains parallel to the axis. Hence the point b' where these two rays meet in image space determines the image point of b. All points of y are imaged into corresponding points of y' at a constant lateral magnification m.

$$\frac{y}{x} = -\frac{HQ}{f} = -\frac{H'Q'}{f} = -\frac{y'}{f} \tag{1}$$

$$\frac{y'}{x'} = -\frac{P'H'}{f'} = -\frac{PH}{f'} = -\frac{y}{f'} \tag{2}$$

$$m = \frac{y'}{y} = -\frac{f}{x} = -\frac{x'}{f'} \tag{3}$$

or

$$xx' = ff' \tag{4}$$

The above is called *Newton's relation*. We have

$$x = s - f, \quad x' = s' - f' \tag{5}$$

or

$$\frac{f}{s} + \frac{f'}{s'} = 1 \tag{6}$$

If Lagrange's law is applied to the principal planes, we have

$$n\theta = n'\theta' \tag{7}$$

for any ray of slope θ through H. Let θ be determined such that

$$\theta = -\frac{y}{s}, \quad \theta' = -\frac{n}{n'} \cdot \frac{y}{s} \tag{8}$$

$$s'\theta' = y' = -\frac{n}{n'} \cdot \frac{s'}{s} y \tag{9}$$

$$\frac{y'}{y} = m = -\frac{n}{n'} \cdot \frac{s'}{s} = -\frac{f}{x} = -\frac{x'}{f'} \tag{10}$$

Then

$$f = \frac{nss'}{n's + ns'}, \quad f' = \frac{n'ss'}{n's + ns'} \tag{11}$$

or

$$\frac{f}{n} = \frac{f'}{n'} \tag{12}$$

(Cf. § 3.3.) For an object at infinity, we have

$$y' = f\theta \tag{13}$$

where θ is the off-axis direction of the object point. Similarly,

$$y = -f'\theta' \tag{14}$$

for an image at infinity. The quantity f is called the *equivalent focal length* of the system in object space, or the *first focal length*, and often the *front focal length*. Similarly, the quantity f' is called the *equivalent focal length* of the system in image space, or the *second focal length*, and often the *back focal length*. (It should be noted that the terms *front* and *back* focal length are often used at the present time to describe the distance from the first focal point to the front lens vertex, and from the rear lens vertex to the second focal point. This confusion is not desirable, and the terms front and back *focal distances* are recommended instead. The terms *front focus* and *back focus* are also used.) Where initial and final media have identical indices, it is clear from the above formula that the two focal lengths are equal.

3.7. Nodal points. A ray directed toward the *first nodal point* in object space, by definition, emerges from the *second nodal point* in image space, parallel to its original direction. The nodal points are conjugate to one another. By Lagrange's law

$$n\theta y = n'\theta' y' \tag{1}$$

where y and y' are in the nodal planes.

$$\frac{y'}{y} = \frac{n}{n'} \cdot \frac{\theta}{\theta'} = \frac{n}{n'} = -\frac{f}{x} = -\frac{x'}{f'} \tag{2}$$

Therefore
$$x' = -\frac{n}{n'} f' = -f \tag{3}$$

$$x = -\frac{n'}{n} f = -f' \tag{4}$$

Note that the first nodal point lies to the right of F by a distance of f' in Fig. 4, and that the second nodal point lies to the left of F' by the distance f. Where initial and final media are identical, the nodal points and principal points coincide.

By determining the position of the second nodal point on an optical bench, one can obtain directly the first equivalent focal length of a system from which the other properties follow.

3.8. Cardinal points. The principal points, the focal points and nodal points are the more important cardinal points of an optical system. The determination of the cardinal points of a complex system can be carried out from a knowledge of the cardinal points of the elementary systems from which the complex system is constructed. However, it is usually more expedient to trace a Gaussian ray from infinity on the left to find F', and from the right to find F. To find f, we note that in a system of N surfaces

$$m = \frac{y'_N}{y_1} = (-1)^N \frac{n_0}{n_N} \cdot \frac{1}{s_1} \left(\frac{s'_1}{s_2}\right) \left(\frac{s'_2}{s_3}\right) \cdots \left(\frac{s'_{N-1}}{s_N}\right) s'_N \tag{1}$$

If we let h_i be the height of intercept above the axis at the ith surface, then by similar triangles

$$\frac{y'_N}{y_1} = -\frac{n_0}{n_N} \cdot \frac{1}{s_1} \cdot \frac{h_1}{h_2} \cdot \frac{h_2}{h_3} \cdot \ldots \cdot \frac{h_{N-1}}{h_N} s'_N \tag{2}$$

$$m = \frac{y'_N}{y_1} = -\frac{n_0}{n_N} \cdot \frac{h_1}{h_N} \cdot \frac{s'_N}{s_1} \tag{3}$$

For an infinite object distance, we have

$$y'_N = \frac{n_0}{n_N} \theta \frac{h_1}{h_N} s'_N \tag{4}$$

where θ is the slope angle or direction of the object, n_0 the index of object space, and n_N the index of image space. It is convenient to define $h_1 = 1$, in which case all other h's are called *relative heights*. Then

$$f = \frac{n_0}{n_N} \cdot \frac{s'_N}{h_N} \tag{5}$$

where f is the first focal length, or

$$f' = \frac{s'_N}{h_N} \tag{6}$$

where f' is the second focal length.

When F, F', and f' are known from the two ray traces, all other ordinary cardinal properties of the complex system follow. It is important to note that inasmuch as the paraxial ray trace beginning with s_1 refers only to an object point on the axis, the relative heights denoted by h_i are for an infinitesimally close ray starting out at the same object point. This is simply Lagrange's law again, and indeed

$$n_0\theta_1 y_1 = n_N\theta'_N y'_N \tag{7}$$

or

$$\frac{n_0 h_1 y_1}{s_1} = -\frac{n_N h_N y'_N}{s'_N} \tag{8}$$

from which

$$m = \frac{y'_N}{y_1} = -\frac{n_0}{n_N} \cdot \frac{h_1}{h_N} \cdot \frac{s'_N}{s_1} \tag{9}$$

as above. The ray trace provides the object and image distances throughout the system, and the h values can be computed by means of the relation

$$h_{i+1} = \frac{s_{i+1}}{s'_i} h_i \tag{10}$$

where $h_1 = 1$ when convenient.

3.9. The thin lens. A thin lens is defined to be one whose thickness is negligible compared to the focal length. To Gaussian accuracy we simply set the thickness equal to zero.

$$\frac{n_0}{s_1} + \frac{n_1}{s'_1} = \frac{n_1 - n_0}{R_1} \tag{1}$$

$$\frac{n_1}{s_2} + \frac{n_2}{s'_2} = \frac{n_2 - n_1}{R_2} \tag{2}$$

$$s_2 = -s'_1, \quad n_2 = n_0 = 1 \tag{3}$$

$$\frac{1}{s_1} + \frac{1}{s'_2} = (n_1 - 1)\left(\frac{1}{R_1} - \frac{1}{R_2}\right) \tag{4}$$

If $s_1 = \infty$, $s'_2 = f' = f$, and we have

$$\phi = \frac{1}{f} = (n_1 - 1)\left(\frac{1}{R_1} - \frac{1}{R_2}\right) \tag{5}$$

where ϕ is called the *power* of the lens. If now s and s' refer to object and image spaces, we have

$$\frac{1}{s} + \frac{1}{s'} = \frac{1}{f} \tag{6}$$

3.10. The thick lens. By working through the Gaussian equations above as applied to a lens of finite central thickness t, one finds that

$$\phi = \frac{1}{f} = (n_1 - 1)\left(\frac{1}{R_1} - \frac{1}{R_2}\right) + \frac{(n_1 - 1)^2}{n_1} \cdot \frac{t}{R_1 R_2} \tag{1}$$

$$\phi d = 1 - \frac{(n_1 - 1)}{n_1} \frac{t}{R_1} \tag{2}$$

where d is the distance from the second surface to the second focal point, or the back focal distance.

3.11. Separated thin lenses. Application of the elementary equations above to the case of separated thin lenses leads to the relations below. The powers of the individual thin lenses are represented by ϕ_1, ϕ_2, ϕ_3 etc. The separations are given by d_1, d_2, d_3, etc. Let d be the back focal distance, which then serves to locate the second focal point. Let ϕ be the power of the combined system of lenses, which is the reciprocal of the equivalent focal length.

a. *Two* separated thin lenses

$$\phi = \phi_1 + \phi_2 - d_1\phi_1\phi_2 = \phi_1 + h_2\phi_2 \tag{1}$$

$$\phi d = 1 - d_1\phi_1 = h_2 \tag{2}$$

b. *Three* separated thin lenses

$$\left.\begin{aligned} \phi &= \phi_1 + \phi_2 + \phi_3 - d_1\phi_1\phi_2 - (d_1 + d_2)\phi_1\phi_3 - d_2\phi_2\phi_3 + d_1d_2\phi_1\phi_2\phi_3 \\ &= \phi_1 + h_2\phi_2 + h_3\phi_3 \end{aligned}\right\} \tag{3}$$

$$\phi d = 1 - (d_1 + d_2)\phi_1 - d_2\phi_2 + d_1d_2\phi_1\phi_2 = h_3 \tag{4}$$

c. *Four* separated thin lenses

$$\left.\begin{aligned} \phi = \phi_1 &+ \phi_2 + \phi_3 + \phi_4 - d_1\phi_1\phi_2 - (d_1 + d_2)\phi_1\phi_3 - (d_1 + d_2 + d_3)\phi_1\phi_4 \\ &- d_2\phi_2\phi_3 - (d_2 + d_3)\phi_2\phi_4 + d_1d_2\phi_1\phi_2\phi_3 + d_1(d_2 + d_3)\phi_1\phi_2\phi_4 \\ &+ (d_1 + d_2)d_3\phi_1\phi_3\phi_4 + d_2d_3\phi_2\phi_3\phi_4 - d_1d_2d_3\phi_1\phi_2\phi_3\phi_4 \\ = \phi_1 &+ h_2\phi_2 + h_3\phi_3 + h_4\phi_4 \end{aligned}\right\} \tag{5}$$

$$\left.\begin{aligned} \phi d = 1 &- (d_1 + d_2 + d_3)\phi_1 - (d_2 + d_3)\phi_2 - d_3\phi_3 + d_1(d_2 + d_3)\phi_1\phi_2 \\ &+ (d_1 + d_2)d_3\phi_1\phi_3 + d_2d_3\phi_2\phi_3 - d_1d_2d_3\phi_1\phi_2\phi_3 = h_4 \end{aligned}\right\} \tag{6}$$

The corresponding expressions for five or more separated thin lenses follow readily, but serve no purpose in being reproduced here. If the above formulas are applied from right to left in order to locate the first focal point, the positions of both principal points then become established. Inasmuch as ϕ in air is the same for both first and second focal lengths, all the formulas for ϕ must possess symmetrical properties.

3.12. Chromatic aberration. The index of refraction of any material medium is a function of wavelength. Accordingly, it is important to ascertain the dependence of the Gaussian properties of an optical system on wavelength.

a. The *single* thin lens

$$\frac{1}{f} = (n-1)\left(\frac{1}{R_1} - \frac{1}{R_2}\right) \tag{1}$$

Differentiating logarithmically, we have

$$\frac{df}{f} = -\frac{dn}{n-1} = -\frac{1}{\nu} = -\frac{d\phi}{\phi} \tag{2}$$

ν is defined as $(n_D - 1)/(n_F - n_C)$, and is called the Abbe number, or the reciprocal dispersion of the glass. The negative sign indicates that the focal length is less for blue light than for red. In the case of ordinary crown glass for which $\nu \sim 60$,

$$df = -\tfrac{1}{60} f \tag{3}$$

between the red and blue focus.

b. *Two* separated thin lenses.

$$\phi = \phi_1 + \phi_2 - d_1\phi_1\phi_2 \tag{4}$$

$$\phi d = 1 - d_1\phi_1 = h_2 \tag{5}$$

Differentially, $$d\phi = d\phi_1 + d\phi_2 - d_1\phi_1\, d\phi_2 - d_1\phi_2\, d\phi_1 \tag{6}$$

$$= \frac{\phi_1}{\nu_1} + \frac{\phi_2}{\nu_2} - d_1\phi_1\phi_2\left(\frac{1}{\nu_1} + \frac{1}{\nu_2}\right) \tag{7}$$

In general, one knows ϕ and desires that $d\phi = 0$. Then ϕ_1 and ϕ_2 can be determined in terms of ϕ. If this is carried out, one finds

$$d\phi = 0 \quad \rightarrow \quad d_1 = \frac{\nu_1 f_1 + \nu_2 f_2}{\nu_1 + \nu_2} \tag{8}$$

$$\phi = \left(\frac{\nu_1}{\nu_1 + \nu_2}\right)\phi_1 + \left(\frac{\nu_2}{\nu_1 + \nu_2}\right)\phi_2 \tag{9}$$

If $\nu_1 = \nu_2$, then

$$d_1 = \tfrac{1}{2}(f_1 + f_2) \tag{10}$$

When the object distance is infinite, $y'_2 = f \tan \theta$, where θ is the field angle off-axis. If $df = 0$, then dy'_2 will be zero also. Hence achromatization of ϕ for the case of two simple lenses at the proper separation stabilizes the size of the image but not its position.

Sometimes one desires to achromatize d instead of ϕ, by selection of the proper ν_2 and ϕ_2 to go with a given ϕ_1, ν_1, and d_1.

$$dd = 0 \quad \rightarrow \quad \frac{\phi_1}{\nu_1} + h_2{}^2 \frac{\phi_2}{\nu_2} = 0 \tag{11}$$

The introduction of the h^2 shows that the color contribution of a lens to the system is weighted by the square of the relative height.

$$\phi = \phi_1 + h_2\phi_2 \tag{12}$$

which leads to

$$\phi_1 = \left(\frac{\nu_1}{\nu_1 - \nu_2/h_2}\right)\phi \tag{13}$$

$$\phi_2 = -\frac{1}{h_2}\left(\frac{\nu_2/h_2}{\nu_1 - \nu_2/h_2}\right)\phi \tag{14}$$

It is clear that when $h_2 = \nu_2/\nu_1$, the denominator is zero, and the solution loses practical significance.

In the case of 2 thin lenses, d and ϕ cannot simultaneously be stabilized for color, unless the separation vanishes. For if $d\phi$ and dd are both zero, then $d(\phi d) = 0$. But

$$d(\phi d) = -\, d_1 d\phi_1 \tag{15}$$

For the simple lens, $d\phi_1 \neq 0$ and hence the only solution is for $d_1 = 0$, $h_2 = 1$.

$$\phi_1 = \frac{\nu_1}{\nu_1 - \nu_2}\phi \tag{16}$$

$$\phi_2 = -\frac{\nu_2}{\nu_2 - \nu_2}\phi \tag{17}$$

These expressions are applicable, then, to the ordinary contact achromatized doublet.

c. *Separated doublets.* Let us consider that at least the first component can be made of two or more elements in contact. The first component can have a net power of ϕ_1 still, and when achromatized, $d\phi_1 = 0$. Then $d(\phi d) = 0$, even when $d_1 \neq 0$. But

$$d\phi = d\phi_1 + d\phi_2 - d_1\phi_1 d\phi_2 - d_1\phi_2 d\phi_1 \tag{18}$$

$$= d\phi_2(1 - d_1\phi_1) \tag{19}$$

$$= h_2 d\phi_2 \tag{20}$$

Hence, if $d\phi = 0$, $d\phi_2 = 0$ also. The result is that if two separated components yield a system stabilized for both size and position of image, the individual components must be separately achromatized.

d. *Three separated thin lenses.* In the case of three separated thin lenses we have more quantities at our disposal, and it is possible to achromatize the system for both position and size of image without achromatizing the individual elements.

If both the equivalent focal length and the back focal distance are achromatized, ϕd is also achromatized. Under § 3.11b we need only to differentiate. When we accomplish this operation, we find

$$\frac{\phi_1}{\nu_1(d_2 - d_1 d_2 \phi_1)} = \frac{-\phi_2}{\nu_2(d_1 + d_2 - d_1 d_2 \phi_2)} = \frac{(\phi d)\phi_3}{\nu_3(d_1 - d_1^2 \phi_1)} \tag{21}$$

When the above two relations are satisfied, the simple triplet will be fully achromatized.

e. *The general relations for a rotationally symmetrical system* *. The fundamental equation of Gaussian optics given in § 3.2 can be rearranged in the form

$$Q_{si} = n_{i-1}\left(\frac{1}{R_i} + \frac{1}{s_i}\right) = n_i\left(\frac{1}{R_i} - \frac{1}{s'_i}\right) \tag{22}$$

Q_{si} is called the *optical invariant.* Let

$$k_i = k_1 + \sum_1^{i-1} \frac{d_j}{n_j h_j h_{j+1}} \tag{23}$$

a relation whose significance will be more apparent below (§ 4.5). Then the respective conditions for the absence of chromatic aberration for the position and size of the image are found to be

$$\sum_{i=1}^{N} h_i^2 Q_{si}\left(\frac{dn_i}{n_i} - \frac{dn_{i-1}}{n_{i-1}}\right) = 0 \tag{24}$$

$$\sum_{i=1}^{N} k_i h_i^2 Q_{si}\left(\frac{dn_i}{n_i} - \frac{dn_{i-1}}{n_{i-1}}\right) = 0 \tag{25}$$

In these expressions dn_i is the increment in index between chosen wave lengths, such as $(n_F - n_C)$, and n_i is the mean index for the wavelength region of interest. For the above purpose k_1 is an arbitrarily chosen quantity,

* MERTÉ, W., RICHTER, R. and VON ROHR, M., *Das photographische Objektiv (Handbuch der wissenschaftlichen und angewandten Photographie*, Bd. 1), Julius Springer, Vienna, 1932, pp. 235-238.

which, however, below will be identified by the relation $k_1 = t_1(s_1 - t_1)/s_1$, where t_1 is the distance of the entrance pupil (§ 4.3f) from the front lens vertex. As before, h_i is the relative height.

3.13. Secondary spectrum. The discussions under § 3.12 refer only to the first derivative. Now, however, we must examine the higher-order variation. Consider the simple doublet, which already has been achromatized through the first order of approximation.

$$\phi = \phi_1 + \phi_2 \tag{1}$$

$$\frac{d\phi}{d\lambda} = \frac{d\phi_1}{d\lambda} + \frac{d\phi_2}{d\lambda} = 0 \tag{2}$$

$$= \frac{dn_1/d\lambda}{(n_1 - 1)}\phi_1 + \frac{dn_2/d\lambda}{(n_2 - 1)}\phi_2 \tag{3}$$

$$\left.\begin{aligned} \frac{d^2\phi}{d\lambda^2} = \frac{(dn_1/d\lambda)^2}{(n_1 - 1)^2}\phi_1 + \frac{d^2n_1/d\lambda^2}{(n_1 - 1)}\phi_1 - \frac{(dn_1/d\lambda)^2}{(n_1 - 1)^2}\phi_1 + \frac{(dn_2/d\lambda)^2}{(n_2 - 1)^2}\phi_2 \\ + \frac{d^2n_2/d\lambda^2}{(n_2 - 1)}\phi_2 - \frac{(dn_2/d\lambda)^2}{(n_2 - 1)^2}\phi_2 \end{aligned}\right\} \tag{4}$$

We find

$$\frac{d^2\phi}{d\lambda^2} = \frac{d^2n_1/d\lambda^2}{(n_1 - 1)}\phi_1 + \frac{d^2n_2/d\lambda^2}{(n_2 - 1)}\phi_2 \tag{5}$$

from which

$$\frac{(\nu_1 - \nu_2)}{\phi}\frac{d^2\phi}{d\lambda^2} = \frac{d^2n_1/d\lambda^2}{dn_1/d\lambda} - \frac{d^2n_2/d\lambda^2}{dn_2/d\lambda} = 0 \tag{6}$$

From this expression it is clear that when two glasses of widely different ν values are combined, the second derivative must bear a constant ratio to the first derivative, if the *secondary spectrum* is to be eliminated.

Customarily in glass catalogs, the first and second derivatives are replaced by their equivalents in differences, namely, by

$$(n_{A'} - n_C)/(n_C - n_F), \quad (n_g - n_h)/(n_C - n_F), \quad \text{etc.}$$

These partial dispersion ratios must then match at both ends of the spectrum if full elimination of the secondary spectrum is to be achieved.

3.14. Dispersion formulas. The function $n(\lambda)$ has been given a number of forms, some empirical and some derived from the theory of dispersion. One of the more familiar of such formulas is that given by Hartmann.

$$n = n_0 + \frac{A}{(\lambda - \lambda_0)^a} \tag{1}$$

where n_0, A, λ_0, and a are constants to be determined from observed values over a wide spectral range. The term a has been assigned the value of 1.2 for best fit, though $a = 1.0$ is far more convenient.

$$\frac{dn}{d\lambda} = -\frac{A}{(\lambda - \lambda_0)^2} \tag{2}$$

$$\frac{d^2n}{d\lambda^2} = +\frac{2A}{(\lambda - \lambda_0)^3} \tag{3}$$

The requirement that the secondary spectrum vanish is simply that

$$\lambda_{0_1} = \lambda_{0_2} \tag{4}$$

Perrin * has computed values of λ_0 for all the well-known varieties of optical glass, and has found several pairs with reduced secondary spectrum. Such pairs are characterized by quite small values of $(\nu_1 - \nu_2)$ so that the individual lens powers are rather considerable.

The Hartmann formula is inconvenient in several ways. First of all, the wavelength λ is tied up within the expression. The derivatives become more complicated functions, rather than simpler ones. Furthermore, the λ_0 has on particular utility from a physical point of view and lies in the ultraviolet.

The same objections can be applied to *Sellmeier's equation*, which is

$$n^2 = 1 + \frac{A\lambda^2}{\lambda^2 - \lambda_0^2} \tag{5}$$

Sellmeier's equation is founded in theory, and holds over quite a complete spectral range, even where there are several absorption boundaries.

The objections can be overcome by a modification of a formula due to Cauchy. The *Cauchy formula* is

$$n = A + B\frac{1}{\lambda^2} + C\frac{1}{\lambda^4} + \dots \tag{6}$$

Here the value of A is n for $\lambda = \infty$, and again of no utility. Also, the derivatives retain the wavelength, though in more explicit form than in Hartmann's formula. Let

$$n_0 = A + B\frac{1}{\lambda_0^2} + C\frac{1}{\lambda_0^4} + \dots \tag{7}$$

Then we can write

$$n = n_0 + \alpha\tilde{\omega} + \beta\tilde{\omega}^2 + \gamma\tilde{\omega}^3 + \dots \tag{8}$$

$$\tilde{\omega} = \frac{1/\lambda^2 - 1/\lambda_0^2}{1/\lambda_F^2 - 1/\lambda_C^2} \tag{9}$$

and where α, β, γ, etc., are to be determined by a least-squares solution from the observed data.

* PERRIN, F., "A Study of Harting's Criterion for Complete Achromatism," *J. Opt. Soc. Am.*, **28**, 86-93 (1938).

Use of the power series form implies that an arbitrarily close fit can be made to the observed dispersion curve, provided enough constants are used. The formula is useful in that the derivatives with respect to $\tilde{\omega}$ are simple series also. If a given lens aberration is rendered independent of $\tilde{\omega}$, it also is necessarily independent of λ. Hence, in optical formulas $\tilde{\omega}$ can be employed in simple expansions. In particular the back focal distance can be expressed

$$s'_N = s'_N(0) + a\tilde{\omega} + b\tilde{\omega}^2 + c\tilde{\omega}^3 + \ldots \tag{10}$$

The coefficient a is called the coefficient of *primary spectrum*, b the coefficient of *secondary spectrum*, c the coefficient of *tertiary spectrum*, etc. Such a formula holds for a system of almost any complexity. In combinations of ordinary glasses, one can bring a to zero in the usual process of achromization. For contact achromats

$$b = -\frac{(\beta_1/\alpha_1 - \beta_2/\alpha_2)}{\nu_1 - \nu_2} \tag{11}$$

If b is to vanish, the glass pairs must obey the requirements

$$\frac{\beta_1}{\alpha_1} = \frac{\beta_2}{\alpha_2} \tag{12}$$

and

$$(\nu_1 - \nu_2) \gg 0 \tag{13}$$

If $(\nu_1 - \nu_2)$ is too small, the curvatures are excessive.

In most ordinary combinations of glasses b is nearly constant. Its magnitude can be reduced by certain optical arrangements, such as the Petzval portrait type lens that consists of separated positive components with an attendant strongly curved field, or by more elaborate systems. A few glass pairs exist that have $b = 0$, but the powers are such as to limit the over-all aperture ratio of the system.

The particular form of $\tilde{\omega}$ is a matter of convenience. For most applications in the visual range, one can take $\lambda_0 = 5500$ angstroms, and use F at 4861 and C at 6563. Then

	$\tilde{\omega}$	$\tilde{\omega}^2$
h	1.466 754	2.151 367
G'	1.048 364	1.099 067
g	1.025 708	1.052 077
F	0.484 741	0.234 974
e	0.025 006	0.000 625
d	−0.214 239	0.045 898
D	−0.223 183	0.049 811
C	−0.515 259	0.265 492
A'	−0.843 706	0.711 840

The least-squares solution for a glass with observed values for all the designated wavelengths takes the following form.

$$A = \sum_i n_i, \quad B = \sum_i n_i\tilde{\omega}_i, \quad C = \sum n_i\tilde{\omega}_i^{\,2}$$

$$\begin{aligned} n_0 &= 0.235\,325A + 0.111\,817B - 0.244\,154C \\ \alpha &= 0.111\,817A + 0.431\,333B - 0.352\,630C \\ \beta &= -0.244\,154A - 0.352\,630B + 0.533\,273C \end{aligned}$$

Typical dispersion formulas and residuals are

BK-7: $$n = 1.518\,035 + 0.008\,163\tilde{\omega} - 0.000\,131\tilde{\omega}^2 \tag{14}$$

$$\bar{\nu} = \frac{n_0 - 1}{\alpha} = 63.46, \quad \frac{\beta}{\alpha} = -0.0160$$

F-2: $$n = 1.623\,648 + 0.017\,212\tilde{\omega} + 0.000\,784\tilde{\omega}^2 \tag{15}$$

$$\bar{\nu} = 36.23, \quad \frac{\beta}{\alpha} = +0.0455$$

	h	G′	g	F	e	d	D	C	A′
(O—C) BK-7:	6	—4	—4	—5	0	5	4	6	—7
F-2:	10	—6	—7	—7	3	4	7	5	—9

where the residuals are in units of the fifth decimal place. The magnitude of the residuals is caused partially by the extent of the wavelength range fitted in the least-squares solution. However, it is clear also from the trend of the residuals that inclusion of the $\gamma\tilde{\omega}^3$ term in the least squares solution would render the residuals as small as ± 1 in the fifth place, from 4047 to 7682.

A doublet made of BK-7 and F-2 glasses would have a secondary spectrum

$$b = \frac{0.0455 + 0.0160}{27.23} = 0.002\,259 \tag{16}$$

$$\Delta s'_N = +0.002\,259\tilde{\omega}^2 + \ldots \tag{17}$$

where $\Delta s'_N$ is in units of the focal length.

Herzberger * has introduced a new form for the dispersion formulas, derived from the near constancy for the value of b, or more strictly, from the relationship

$$\frac{\beta}{\alpha} = k_1\nu + k_2 \tag{18}$$

* Herzberger, M., "The Dispersion of Optical Glass," *J. Op. Soc. Am.*, **32**, 70-77 (1942).

This formula is given by Herzberger as

$$\mu = \mu_0 + \mu_1\lambda^2 + \frac{\mu_2}{\lambda^2 - 0.035} + \frac{\mu_3}{(\lambda^2 - 0.035)^2} \tag{19}$$

where λ is the wavelength measured in *microns*, $\mu = \boldsymbol{n} - 1$, and μ_0, μ_1, μ_2, and μ_3 are four constants depending on the material. For unusual glasses, crystals, and rare-earth glasses the linear relationship for β/α must be modified. In terms of the partial dispersions

$$P_\lambda = A_1\boldsymbol{\nu} + A_2 + A_3\rho_A + A_4\rho_h \tag{20}$$

where the A_i are universal functions of the wavelength, and ρ_A and ρ_h are constants. Each A_i has the equivalent form

$$A_i = \alpha_0 + \alpha_1\lambda^2 + \frac{\alpha_2}{\lambda^2 - 0.035} + \frac{\alpha_3}{(\lambda^2 - 0.035)^2} \tag{21}$$

The superposition of the coefficients of λ^2, etc., lead to the values of μ_0, μ_1, etc.

Herzberger shows that the $(O - C)$ residuals are mostly zero, or ± 1 in the fifth decimal place from $\lambda = 0.400$ to $\lambda = 1\mu$, almost irrespective of the material. The $\tilde{\omega}$ function above has larger residuals for the unusual materials, though with any dispersion formula an $(O - C)$ plot can always be employed as a differential correction.

The $\tilde{\omega}$ function expanded about the wavelength of best performance of a given instrument permits ready inspection of the variations of the aberrations with color. The fact that $(\tilde{\omega}_F - \tilde{\omega}_C) = 1$ gives a ready measure of the blue-red variation.

4. Oblique Refraction

4.1. First-order theory. Paraxial or first-order theory involves refraction in the immediate neighborhood of the optical axis. The equivalence of complex and simple systems through the use of the principal planes and focal points arises basically from the linear character of the refractions.

The introduction of rays that are considerably inclined to the optical axis, or more general still, of *skew* rays that do not even intersect the optical axis, brings about wide departures from the Gaussian laws. The departure may be expanded in series development around the Gaussian quantities. Because of rotational symmetry this expansion assumes only odd powers, and the successive stages of approximation are often referred to as *first-order theory*, *third-order theory*, *fifth-order theory*, etc.

The most general expansion of the problem of refraction of a light ray through an optical system involves a function of five variables, namely, μ, ν, y, z, $\tilde{\omega}$, where μ and ν are direction cosines of the ray, y and z the intercept on a reference plane normal to the axis, and $\tilde{\omega}$ is the function of the wavelength referred to in 3.14.

Explicitly, we have

$$\left.\begin{aligned} y_{i+1} &= y_{i+1}(\mu_i, \nu_i, y_i, z_i, \tilde{\omega}_i) \\ z_{i+1} &= z_{i+1}(\mu_i, \nu_i, y_i, z_i, \tilde{\omega}_i) \\ \mu_{i+1} &= \mu_{i+1}(\mu_i, \nu_i, y_i, z_i, \tilde{\omega}_i) \\ \nu_{i+1} &= \nu_{i+1}(\mu_i, \nu_i, y_i, z_i, \tilde{\omega}_i) \end{aligned}\right\} \qquad (1)$$

For rotationally symmetrical systems we must have a symmetry of expression in such a way that $y \rightleftarrows z$ and $\mu \rightleftarrows \nu$. Also, if rotational variables are used in the power series expansions, such as

$$r = \mu^2 + \nu^2, \quad s = y^2 + z^2, \quad t = \mu y + \nu z \qquad (2)$$

we must find that the several orders use r, s, t in every combination.

The explicit expansion through the third order is given below for the case where the reference plane is the tangent plane at the ith surface, where $\boldsymbol{n}_i$ is the index of refraction after the ith surface, y_i and z_i are intercepts in the tangent plane, and μ_i and ν_i are the direction cosines of the initial ray before refraction. Let $N_i = \boldsymbol{n}_{i-1}/\boldsymbol{n}_i$ and $c_i = 1/R_i$, where R_i is the radius of curvature. Here S_i is an aspheric coefficient that vanishes for a spherical surface; d_i is the vertex to vertex separation of the ith and the $(i+1)$th surface.

(3)

$\mu_{i+1} =$	$y_{i+1} =$
$[\mu_i] = N_i$	$[\mu_i] = N_i d_i$
$[y_i] = (N_i - 1)c_i$	$[y_i] = 1 + (N_i - 1)c_i d_i$
$[\mu_i^3] = 0$	$[\mu_i^3] = \frac{1}{2}N_i^3 d_i$
$[\mu_i \nu_i^2] = 0$	$[\mu_i \nu_i^2] = \frac{1}{2}N_i^3 d_i$
$[\mu_i^2 y_i] = \frac{1}{2}N_i(N_i - 1)c_i$	$[\mu_i^2 y_i] = \frac{1}{2}N_i(N_i - 1)(3N_i + 1)c_i d_i$
$[\nu_i^2 y_i] = \frac{1}{2}N_i(N_i - 1)c_i$	$[\nu_i^2 y_i] = \frac{1}{2}N_i(N_i - 1)(N_i + 1)c_i d_i$
	$[\mu_i \nu_i z_i] = N_i^2(N_i - 1)c_i d_i$
$[\mu_i y_i^2] = \frac{1}{2}(N_i - 1)(2N_i + 1)c_i^2$	$[\mu_i y_i^2] = -\frac{1}{2}(N_i - 1)c_i + \frac{1}{2}(N_i - 1)(3N_i^2 - N_i + 1)c_i^2 d_i$
$[\mu_i z_i^2] = \frac{1}{2}(N_i - 1)c_i^2$	$[\mu_i z_i^2] = -\frac{1}{2}(N_i - 1)c_i + \frac{1}{2}(N_i - 1)(3N_i^2 - N_i + 1)c_i^2 d_i$
$[\nu_i y_i z_i] = N_i(N_i - 1)c_i^2$	$[\nu_i y_i z_i] = N_i^2(N_i - 1)c_i^2 d_i$
$[y_i^3] = \frac{1}{2}(N_i - 1)S_i + \frac{1}{2}N_i(N_i - 1)c_i^3$	$[y_i^3] = \frac{1}{2}(N_i - 1)S_i d_i + \frac{1}{2}(N_i - 1)(N_i^2 - N_i + 1)c_i^3 d_i - \frac{1}{2}(N_i - 1)c_i^2$
$[y_i z_i^2] = \frac{1}{2}(N_i - 1)S_i + \frac{1}{2}N_i(N_i - 1)c_i^3$	$[y_i z_i^2] = \frac{1}{2}(N_i - 1)S_i d_i + \frac{1}{2}(N_i - 1)(N_i^2 - N_i + 1)c_i^3 d_i - \frac{1}{2}(N_i - 1)c_i^2$

Equivalent expressions for ν_{i+1} and z_{i+1} are obtained by an interchange of μ, ν and y, z. The bracketed expressions are the coefficients of the power term enclosed. The notation is useful for saving cumbersome symbols.

The explicit expressions are given here only through the third order. The fifth order has been derived, but is much too lengthy for inclusion here. In general, the explicit expressions have only a limited range of usefulness. Where a number of surfaces are involved, the insertion of successive series into one another becomes a formidable task. However, the author has solved a number of interesting problems in this way, even in the fifth order. The complexity of the procedure is compensated partly by the explicit nature of the results.

For more complex systems one must work in successive stages of approximation. Here one uses the important relations of the first order to reduce the number of corrective terms of the third order. The first order is calculated, and the numerical results used in the calculation of the third order. The results in the first and third can then be applied to the evaluation of the fifth order, a process not often attempted in this particular way.

Apart from the general development of the aberrations of an optical system, one can separate out two branches admitting of specialized treatment. The first branch involves a series expansion in all powers of the aperture but linear in the sine of the field angle. These terms are included in the sine condition of Abbe, which has already been discussed. Evaluation is most often accomplished by ray tracing, rather than by series development, at least in the fifth and higher orders. The other branch involves a series expansion in all powers of the field angle but linear in the aperture. This second branch is treated immediately below.

4.2. Oblique refraction of elementary pencils. The first-order expansion in the angular aperture of a narrow pencil of rays around a central *chief ray* or *principal ray* of finite inclination to the normal to a surface at point of contact leads to the existence of two foci along the refracted pencil. If the pencil is in a meridional section of a surface, the focus of this *tangential* fan can be determined. If the pencil is perpendicular to the meridional section, the focus of this *sagittal* fan can also be determined. In general the foci do not coincide, and only by controlled design can they be made to coincide in image space. The difference between the tangential and sagittal or radial foci along the chief ray is often called the *astigmatic difference*, and the halfway point between the two is called the *mean focus*.

If τ and σ are the respective tangential and radial object distances *along the ray* from the actual point of refraction on the surface, and if τ' and σ' are the corresponding image distances, we have

$$\frac{n_{i-1}\cos^2 i_i}{\tau_i} + \frac{n_i \cos^2 r_i}{\tau'_i} = \frac{n_i \cos r_i - n_{i-1}\cos i_i}{R_i} \tag{1}$$

$$\frac{n_{i-1}}{\sigma_i} + \frac{n_i}{\sigma'_i} = \frac{n_i \cos r_i - n_{i-1}\cos i_i}{R_i} \tag{2}$$

where i and r are the angles of incidence and refraction, respectively.

These highly important relations are a generalization of the paraxial expressions. It is clear that when i and r go to zero, the two expressions coalesce and become identical with the basic paraxial formula. The expressions may be applied to any meridional ray through a system in order to determine the foci of the particular pencil.

In the relations above the transfer equations between surfaces are

$$\tau_{i+1} = -\tau'_i + \delta_i \tag{3}$$

$$\sigma_{i+1} = -\sigma'_i + \delta_i \tag{4}$$

where

$$\delta_i = (R_{i+1} - R_i + d_i)\cos\theta'_i + R_i \cos r_i - R_{i+1}\cos i_{i+1} \tag{5}$$

Here again d_i is taken to be the axial separation between the vertices of the ith and $(i+1)$th surfaces, and θ'_i is the slope angle of the ray after refraction at the ith surface; δ_i is the separation *along* the ray.

There is another way of finding the final σ'_N in cases where τ'_N is not required. An auxiliary line connecting σ and σ' for a single surface can be shown to contain the center of curvature of the surface. This line is called the axis of sagittal symmetry, and becomes an auxiliary optical axis of the refraction. If one calls the angle between this auxiliary axis and the optical axis φ, the apparent height of the σ' focus can be multiplied throughout the system because of similar triangles, and one finds

$$\tan\varphi_N = \frac{\left(\prod_1^{N-1} a_i\right)\tan\theta_1}{1 - \left[\sum_1^{N-1} b_i \prod_1^{i-1} a_j\right]\tan\theta_1} \tag{6}$$

where θ_1 is the direction of the object relative to the optical axis, the object taken here to lie at infinity. In the above

$$a_i = \frac{K_i}{J_i}, \quad b_i = \frac{\cos\theta'_i}{J_i} \tag{7}$$

where $$J_i = K_i + \sin \theta'_i, \quad \text{and} \quad K_i = \frac{R_i \sin r_i}{R_{i+1} - R_i + d_i} \tag{8}$$

The angle φ_N is the angular subtense of σ'_N as seen from the center of curvature of the last surface. Hence,

$$(- s'_N + d'_N) \tan \theta_N = (- R_N + d'_N) \tan \varphi_N = h'_N \tag{9}$$

where s'_N is the axial intercept of the final ray in image space, relative to the vertex of R_N, in accord with the conventions of § 3.1. The coordinates d'_N and h'_N locate the position of the final σ'_N focus in image space relative to the vertex of R_N. The formula requires about half of the computing time of the first formula given for finding σ'_N. However, the second method is not applicable where any one $\sin r$ is nearly zero or zero.

4.3. The Seidel aberrations *. Ludwig von Seidel first worked out convenient expressions for the third-order aberrations of an optical system, and it has been customary to designate the five independent aberrations of the third order as the *Seidel* aberrations.

a. *Spherical aberration.* This aberration refers to the improper union, near the image point, of rays that originate from an object point. Rays outside the paraxial region intersect the optical axis progressively farther from the paraxial focus according to the angular aperture of the initial pencil. Spherical aberration ordinarily can be evaluated on the optical axis where other aberrations are zero, but is present off the axis as well.

b. *Coma.* This aberration refers to the variation of magnification of rays in a pencil outside the paraxial region. The image point of intersection of any particular ray on the focal plane will vary in height according to the ray. A comatic pattern is produced by the combined meridional and skew rays in the form of circles tangent within a pair of straight envelope lines 60 degrees inclined to one another. The apex of the pattern lies at the paraxial magnification, if not too far from the axis. The largest circle within the envelope lines arises from the extreme rays of the pencil from the object point, the pencil taken as having a circular cross section. The so-called *upper* and *lower rim rays* in the meridional plane lie farthest from the apex, and in fact intersect. Indeed, the single circle for the cross section of the pencil maps twice around for the corresponding circle in the image. Coma

* Herzberger, M., *Geometrische Optik*, Julius Springer, Berlin, 1931; also numerous papers. Merté, W., Richter, R., and von Rohr, M., *Das photographische Objektiv* (*Handbuch der wissenschaftlichen und angewandten Photographie*, Bd. 1), Julius Springer, Vienna, 1932. Whittaker, E. T., *The Theory of Optical Instruments*, Cambridge University Press, London, 1907.

is an unsymmetrical aberration. Seidel coma varies as the square of the aperture and linearly with field angle. The spherical aberration and coma together are combined within the sine condition of Abbe, which within the Seidel region simply become the third-order expansion of the sine condition in series form.

c. *Astigmatism.* This aberration refers to lack of coincidence of the τ'_N and σ'_N foci, described in §4.2. A point source images into two focal lines at right angles to one another. The tangential focus produces a tangential line, i.e., a line element perpendicular to the meridional plane. The radial or sagittal focus produces a radial line, i.e., a line element directed toward the optical axis and lying in the meridional plane. The astigmatism is measured by the separation of the focal lines, or by the diameter of the mean image for a given angular aperture of the system. The mean image is circular if the image forming pencil is of circular cross section, though in practice diffraction often produces a cross instead of a circle for the image.

d. *Curvature of field.* This aberration refers to the departure of the mean focus of an oblique pencil from a flat focal plane. The mean image in a rotationally symmetrical system lies on a surface that in the third order is spherical and tangent at its vertex to the paraxial focal plane. A flat field is simply a focal surface of infinite contact radius.

e. *Distortion.* This aberration refers to a displacement of an image point, even though sharply defined, from where it should be if the object plane were mapped at a constant magnification onto the image plane. A square reseau in an object plane ought to map into a square reseau in the conjugate image plane. If the image point is displaced outward, the distortion is called the *pincushion* type. If the image point is displaced inward, the distortion is called the *barrel* type.

f. *Stops.* A description of Seidel optics cannot be complete without introducing the concept of *stops.* The *aperture stop* limits the diameter of the bundle of rays admitted to the system. This stop may lie internally in the system. The *entrance pupil* is the image of the aperture stop in object space, and the *exit* pupil is the corresponding image in image space. If a system has a number of real stops formed by the clear apertures of the successive surfaces, the entrance pupil is the stop image in object space subtending the smallest angle as seen from the object point. Most often, the aperture stop is designed into a system, and may be simply an aperture in a metal sheet, or formed by a variable iris diaphragm.

The *principal ray* of a system passes through the center of the entrance pupil from any assigned object point. For symmetrical aberrations the principal ray remains central within the refracted pencils. For comatic aberrations, the principal ray may be shifted away from the rest of the light in the image. For these reasons the principal ray assumes particular importance in the calculation of the Seidel aberrations.

4.4. The Seidel third-order expressions. The equations of §4.2 for the τ' and σ' foci are exact for a specific pencil. If the final foci coincide, the pencil becomes stigmatic. If a variety of pencils over the aperture of a system are separately stigmatic, the optical system becomes corrected over a finite aperture.

The development is too lengthy to be reproduced here. However, through the third order the cosines of §4.2 are expanded in terms of i and r. By tracing a paraxial ray through the center of the entrance pupil, i.e., a chief ray, one can express i and r in terms of the stop location for a given surface. The astigmatic difference in image space for the ith surface becomes the astigmatic difference in object space for the $(i+1)$th surface. The equations of §4.2 can be arranged in such a way as to have the intermediate terms cancel out. Then one arrives at the following.

Zinken-Sommer's condition. Let

$$Q_{si} = n_{i-1}\left(\frac{1}{R_i} + \frac{1}{s_i}\right) = n_i\left(\frac{1}{R_i} - \frac{1}{s'_i}\right) \tag{1}$$

$$Q_{ti} = n_{i-1}\left(\frac{1}{R_i} + \frac{1}{t_i}\right) = n_i\left(\frac{1}{R_i} - \frac{1}{t'_i}\right) \tag{2}$$

where s_i refers to the object distance and t_i to the object distance of the stop from a surface. Then Zinken-Sommer's condition for the absence of astigmatism in an elementary pencil around a chosen chief ray becomes

$$\sum\left(\frac{Q_{ti}}{Q_{ti} - Q_{si}}\right)^2\left(\frac{1}{n_{i-1}s_i} + \frac{1}{ns'_i}\right) = 0 \tag{3}$$

In the original notation of Seidel there is a different choice of conventions from those adopted here. Optical conventions vary so widely that readers must always be alert to avoid error.

Zinken-Sommer's condition contain Q_{ti}, which involves the stop position at each surface. By a transformation due to Seidel, the Q_{ti} can be replaced by an equivalent involving more desirable quantities. Zinken-Sommer's condition can be written in the form

$$\sum_i \left[1 + Q_{si}h_i^2 \sum_1^{i-1} \frac{d_j}{n_j h_j h_{j+1}} + \frac{Q_{si}h_i^2}{h_1^2(Q_{t1} - Q_{s1})}\right]^2 \left(\frac{1}{n_{i-1}s_i} + \frac{1}{n_i s'_i}\right) = 0 \qquad (4)$$

This expression is still simply a condition for the elimination of astigmatism along a narrow pencil through the center of the entrance pupil, which is located at a distance of t_1 from the vertex of R_1. However, t_1 and hence Q_{t1} can be made to vary over an arbitrarily large range. If the coefficients of $1/(Q_{t1} - Q_{s1})^2$ and $1/(Q_{t1} - Q_{s1})$ vanish independently, the correction becomes independent of the stop position. The coefficient of $1/(Q_{t1} - Q_{s1})^2$ is identifiable with the condition for absence of spherical aberration, the coefficient $1/(Q_{t1} - Q_{s1})$ with the absence of coma, and the remaining constant term with astigmatism itself. Hence, Zinken-Sommer's condition in the revised form contains all in one the basic requirements for a corrected optical system through the third order of approximation.

Flatness of field. The equations of § 4.2 can be recast into a requirement that the image lie in a plane surface when the object lies in a plane. One finds

$$\sum_i \left[\left(\frac{Q_{ti}}{Q_{ti} - Q_{si}}\right)^2 \left(\frac{1}{n_{i-1}s_i} + \frac{1}{n_i s'_i}\right) + \frac{1}{R_i}\left(\frac{1}{n_{i-1}} - \frac{1}{n_i}\right)\right] = 0 \qquad (5)$$

The first part is Zinken-Sommer's condition, which in a corrected instrument can be made to vanish. In the absence of astigmatism, therefore, we have the condition for *flatness of field*,

$$P = \sum_i \frac{1}{R_i}\left(\frac{1}{n_{i-1}} - \frac{1}{n_i}\right) = 0 \qquad (6)$$

This relation is known as Petzval's condition for flatness of field, a criterion that is valid only in the absence of astigmatism. For finite values of P, a solution of the entire summation may still have a given pencil produce a mean focus on a flat image plane, but such a system cannot be satisfied simultaneously for spherical aberration, coma, and astigmatism, though any two can be zero.

For a group of thin lenses, whether separated or not,

$$P = \sum_i \frac{\phi_i}{n_i} = -\frac{1}{\rho_P} \qquad (7)$$

where ρ_P is the radius of curvature of the so-called *Petzval surface*. If the astigmatism is zero, ρ_P is the radius of curvature of the focal surface itself. In the case of the general system

$$\frac{3}{\rho_\sigma'} - \frac{1}{\rho_\tau} = \frac{2}{\rho_P} \qquad (8)$$

or

$$\underbrace{\frac{1}{2}\left(\frac{1}{\rho_{\sigma'}}+\frac{1}{\rho_{\tau'}}\right)}_{\frac{1}{\rho_f}}+\underbrace{\left(\frac{1}{\rho_{\sigma'}}-\frac{1}{\rho_{\tau'}}\right)}_{\textit{Astigmatism}}=\frac{1}{\rho_P} \tag{9}$$

where ρ_f is the radius of curvature of the mean focal surface, $\rho_{\tau'}$ of the tangential image surface, and $\rho_{\sigma'}$ of the radial or sagittal image surface. The sign of the radius follows the same conventions of § 3.1.

Distortion. The condition for the absence of distortion takes the form

$$\left.\begin{aligned}&\sum_i \frac{Q_{ti}}{h_i^2 Q_{si}(Q_{ti}-Q_{si})}\\ &\qquad\left[\frac{Q_{ti}^2}{(Q_{ti}-Q_{si})^2}\left(\frac{1}{n_{i-1}s_i}+\frac{1}{n_i s'_i}\right)+\frac{1}{R_i}\left(\frac{1}{n_{i-1}}-\frac{1}{n_i}\right)\right]=0\end{aligned}\right\} \tag{10}$$

Seidel's five third-order conditions can then be written in the condensed form :

$$\left.\begin{array}{ll}\text{spherical aberration :} & \sum\Theta_i=0\\ \text{coma :} & \sum\Theta_i U_i=0\\ \text{astigmatism :} & \sum\Theta_i U_i^2=0\\ \text{Petzval :} & \sum P_i=0\\ \text{distortion :} & \sum\{\Theta_i U_i^3+P_i U_i\}=0\end{array}\right\} \tag{11}$$

where

$$U_i=\frac{1}{Q_{si}h_i^2}\left(1+Q_{si}h_i^2\sum_1^{i-1}\frac{d_j}{n_j h_j h_{j+1}}\right) \tag{12}$$

$$\Theta=Q_{si}^2 h_i^4\left(\frac{1}{n_{i-1}s_i}+\frac{1}{n_i s'_i}\right) \tag{13}$$

The reader is referred to Merté * for evaluation of the image errors when any of the above five conditions is not satisfied.

4.5. Seidel's conditions in the Schwarzschild-Kohlschütter form+.

$$K_i=n_{i-1}\left(\frac{1}{R_i}+\frac{1}{s_i}\right)=n_i\left(\frac{1}{R_i}-\frac{1}{s'_i}\right)=Q_{si} \tag{1}$$

$$s_{i+1}=-s'_i+d_i,\quad h_1=\frac{s_1}{s_1-t_1},\quad k_1=\frac{t_1}{h_1} \tag{2}$$

* MERTÉ *et al.*, *Das photographische Objektiv*, Julius Springer, Vienna, 1932, pp. 235-238.

\+ SCHWARZSCHILD, K., *Mitteilungen der Göttingen Sternwarte*, IX-XI (1905).

$$\frac{h_{i+1}}{h_i} = \frac{s_{i+1}}{-s'_i} = \left(1 - \frac{1}{s'_i} d_i\right) \tag{3}$$

$$k_{i+1} = k_1 + \sum_{j=1}^{i} \frac{d_j}{n_j h_j h_{j+1}}, \quad (kc)_i = k_i + \frac{1}{h_i^2 K_i} \tag{4}$$

$$\bar{f}_i = \frac{1}{s_i} + \frac{1}{R_i} - \frac{1}{s'_i} \tag{5}$$

$$B_i = \frac{1}{2} h_i^4 K_i \bar{f}_i \left(\frac{1}{s_i} + \frac{1}{s'_i}\right) \tag{6}$$

$$F_i = (kc)_i B_i \tag{7}$$

$$C_i = (kc)_i^2 B_i = (kc)_i F_i \tag{8}$$

$$P_i = \frac{1}{R_i}\left(\frac{1}{n_{i-1}} - \frac{1}{n_i}\right) \tag{9}$$

$$E_i = (kc)_i \left(C_i + \tfrac{1}{2} P_i\right) \tag{10}$$

$$\left.\begin{aligned}
&\text{spherical aberration:} && B = \sum_1^N B_i \\
&\text{coma:} && F = \sum_1^N F_i \\
&\text{astigmatism:} && C = \sum_1^N C_i \\
&\text{Petzval:} && P = \sum_1^N P_i \\
&\text{distortion:} && E_i = \sum_1^N E_i
\end{aligned}\right\} \tag{11}$$

5. Ray-Tracing Equations

Apart from the approximate analysis of the performance of an optical system indicated by equations of Sec. 4., one finds it almost always necessary to trace selected rays through an optical system as a final check on its merit or for further information on its deficiencies. There are many forms of ray-tracing equations, some adapted to logarithmic computing, some to the hand calculator, and some to the automatic calculating equipment that is now making its appearance in the optical field. Typical formulations are given below.

5.1. Meridional rays *. The basic data are to be tabulated in advance in a notebook or some separate page to be used throughout the computation of any number of rays. It is necessary to tabulate only five quantities per surface otherwise, though quite often more quantities are written down to increase the information afforded by the ray.

a. Given $\sin i_i$, find $\sin r_i$ from

$$\sin r_i = N_i \sin i_i \tag{1}$$

b. Find i_i and r_i from trigonometric tables (2)

c. Find θ_i from the relation

$$\theta_i = \theta_{i-1} + r_i - i_i \tag{3}$$

d. Find $\sin \theta_i$ from tables. (4)

e. Find $\sin i_{i+1}$ from the relation

$$\sin i_{i+1} = M_i \sin r_i + L_i \sin \theta_i \tag{5}$$

Proceed to the next surface. The auxiliary quantities M_i, L_i, and N_i are calculated once and for all from the relations

$$M_i = \frac{R_i}{R_{i+1}} \tag{6}$$

$$L_i = 1 - M_i + \frac{d_i}{R_{i+1}} \tag{7}$$

$$N_i = \frac{n_{i-1}}{n_i} \tag{8}$$

* Comrie, L. J., *Proc. Phys. Soc.*, **52**, 246-252 (1940). Baker, J. G., *Design and Development of an Automatically Focusing Distortionless Telephoto, and Related Lenses for High Altitude Aerial Reconnaissance*, OSRD Report 6017, Library of Congress microfilms.

5.2. Skew rays. * The following equations have merit because of their symmetrical form, and because the same basic data can be used that have already been calculated before the meridional rays are traced. There are a number of other forms used for skew ray tracing, but space does not permit the detailed treatment that would be necessary for the formulas to be immediately applicable. The formulas below make use of square root solutions instead of the natural functions.

Given $(l_i, m_i, n_i, \bar{Y}_i, \bar{Z}_i, M_i, L_i, N_i)$ at surface i, where M, L, and N are from the separately tabulated basic data, l, m, and n are the direction cosines of the normal to the surface at point of intercept of the ray, and $\bar{Y}_i$ and $\bar{Z}_i$ are auxiliary quantities.

a. Find

$$\bar{Y}'_i = N_i \bar{Y}_i \tag{1}$$

$$\bar{Z}'_i = N_i \bar{Z}_i \tag{2}$$

b. Find

$$A_i = m_i \bar{Y}'_i + n_i \bar{Z}'_i \tag{3}$$

$$B_i = l_i^2 - (\bar{Y}'_i)^2 - (\bar{Z}'_i)^2 \tag{4}$$

$$\lambda_i = -A_i + \sqrt{A_i^2 + B_i} \tag{5}$$

$$\mu_i = \frac{1}{l_i}(m_i \lambda_i + \bar{Y}'_i) \tag{6}$$

$$\nu_i = \frac{1}{l_i}(n_i \lambda_i + \bar{Z}'_i) \tag{7}$$

c. Find

$$\bar{Y}_{i+1} = M_i \bar{Y}'_i + L_i \mu_i \tag{8}$$

$$\bar{Z}_{i+1} = M_i \bar{Z}'_i + L_i \nu_i \tag{9}$$

d. Find

$$C_{i+1} = \mu_i \bar{Y}_{i+1} + \nu_i \bar{Z}_{i+1} \tag{10}$$

$$D_{i+1} = \lambda_i^2 - \bar{Y}_{i+1}^2 - \bar{Z}_{i+1}^2 \tag{11}$$

$$l_{i+1} = C_{i+1} + \sqrt{C_{i+1}^2 + D_i} \tag{12}$$

$$m_{i+1} = \frac{1}{\lambda_i}(\mu_i l_i - \bar{Y}_{i+1}) \tag{13}$$

$$n_{i+1} = \frac{1}{\lambda_i}(\nu_i l_i - \bar{Z}_{i+1}) \tag{14}$$

* Baker, J. G., *loc. cit.*

The cycle is now complete and ready for the next surface. The usual check on the direction cosines of the ray after refraction and on the direction cosines of the normal in step d. can be applied. The starting equations at surface 1 involve finding the first l, m, and n, and the first $\bar{Y}$ and $\bar{Z}$. The ending equations at surface N involve finding the intercept of the ray with the adopted image plane from a knowledge of l_N, m_N, n_N λ_N, μ_N, and ν_N. When needed,

$$\bar{Y}_i = (l_i\mu_{i-1} - m_i\lambda_{i-1}) \tag{15}$$

$$\bar{Z}_i = (l_i\nu_{i-1} - n_i\lambda_{i-1}) \tag{16}$$

Bibliography

1. Berek, M., *Grundlagen der praktischen Optik*, Walter De Gruyter & Company, Berlin, 1930.
2. Born, M., *Optik*, Julius Springer, Berlin, 1933.
3. Boutry, G. A., *Optique instrumentale*, Masson et Cie., Paris, 1946.
4. Bouwers, A., *Achievements in Optics*, The Elesevier Press, Inc., New York, 1946.
5. Bruhat, G., *Optique (Cours de physique générale)*, Masson et Cie., Paris, 1947.
6. Caratheodory, C., *Geometrische Optik*, Julius Springer, Berlin, 1937.
7. Conrady, A. E., *Applied Optics and Optical Design*, Part 1, Oxford University Press, Oxford, 1929.
8. Cox, Arthur, *Optics*, Pitman Publishing Corp., New York, 1949.
9. Drude, Paul, *Lehrbuch der Optik*, von S. Hirzel, Leipzig, 1912.
10. Gardner, I. C., " Application of the Algebraic Aberration Equations to Optical Design," *Bureau of Standards Scientific Papers*, *500*, 1927, pp. 73-203.
11. Gleichen, A., *Theorie der modernen optischen Instrumente*, Ferdinand Enke, Stuttgart, 1911.
12. Habell, K. J. and Cox, Arthur, *Engineering Optics*, Sir Isaac Pitman & Sons, Ltd., London, 1948.
13. Hamilton, W. R., *Collected Works*, Vol. 1, Cambridge University Press, London, 1931.
14. Hardy, A. C. and Perrin, F., *Principles of Optics*, McGraw-Hill Book Company, Inc., New York, 1932.
15. Herzberger, M., *Geometrische Optik*, Julius Springer, Berlin, 1931.
16. Hopkins, H. H., *Wave Theory of Aberrations*, Clarendon Press, Oxford, 1950.
17. Jacobs, D. H., *Fundamentals of Optical Engineering*, McGraw-Hill Book Company, Inc., New York, 1943.
18. Jenkins, F. A. and White, H. E., *Fundamentals of Physical Optics*, 2d ed., McGraw-Hill Book Company, Inc., New York, 1950.
19. Johnson, B. K., *Optical Design and Lens Computation*, The Hatton Press, London, 1948.
20. Kingslake, R., *Lenses in Photography*, Garden City Books, Garden City, N. Y., 1951.

21. Kohlschütter, A., *Die Bildfehler fünfter Ordnung optischer Systeme*, Thesis, Göttingen, 1908.

22. König, A., *Geometrische Optik* (*Handbuch der experimental Physik*, Bd. 20), Akademische Verlagsgesellschaft, Leipzig, 1929.

23. Lummer, O., *Contributions to Photographic Optics* (trans. S. P. Thompson). Macmillan and Co., Ltd., London, 1900.

24. Martin, L. C., *Technical Optics*, Vols. 1, 2, Pitman Publishing Corp., New York, (1948, 1950).

25. Merté, W., Richter, R., and von Rohr, M., *Das photographische Objektiv* (*Handbuch der wissenschaftlichen und angewandten Photographie*, Bd. 1), Julius Springer, Vienna, 1932.

26. Merté, W., " Das photographische Objektiv seit dem Jahre 1929," *Handbuch der wissenschaftlichen und angewandten Photographie, Ergänzungswerk*, Springer-Verlag, Vienna, 1943.

27. Schwarzschild, K., *Untersuchung zur geometrischen Optik* (*Abhandl. kgl. Ges. Wiss. Göttingen*, Bd. 1, Nr. 4); also *Mitt. Göttingen Sternwarte*, IX-XI (1905).

28. Sears, F. W., *Principles of Physics, III, Optics*, Addison-Wesley Press, Inc., Cambridge, Mass., 1945.

29. Southall, J. P. C., *Mirrors, Prisms and Lenses*, The Macmillan Company, New York, 1918.

30. Steinheil-Voit, *Applied Optics* (trans. J. W. French), Vols. 1, 2, Blackie & Sons, Ltd., London, 1918.

31. Synge, J. L., *Geometrical Optics, an Introduction to Hamilton's Method*, Cambridge University Press, London, 1937.

32. Taylor, H. D., *A System of Applied Optics*, Macmillan and Co., Ltd., London, 1906.

33. Valasek, J., *Introduction to Theoretical and Experimental Optics*, John Wiley & Sons, Inc., New York, 1949.

34. von Rohr, M., *The Formation of Images in Optical Instruments* (translation), His Majesty's Stationery Office, London, 1920.

35. von Seidel, L., *Zur Dioptrik, Astronomischen Nachrichten*, No. 1027.

36. Whittaker, E. T., *The Theory of Optical Instruments*, Cambridge University Press, London, 1907.

Chapter 17

PHYSICAL OPTICS

FRANCIS A. JENKINS

Professor of Physics
University of California

Geometrical optics considers light as being made up of rays. Color or wavelength enters as a special parameter to distinguish one ray from another in a medium whose physical properties are not independent of wavelength. Physical optics, on the other hand, treats of properties of light in much greater detail. The interference of light, for example, can be explained only in terms of the basic vibrations. The rays enter, if at all, merely as indicating the direction of propagation of energy in the medium. Physical optics, like hydrodynamics and acoustics, depends for its solutions on certain prescribed boundary conditions, which the wave equation or its appropriate solutions must fulfil. Also, since light is electromagnetic in character, its basic properties go back to the fundamental equations of Maxwell. Relativity, and special relativity in particular, are also related to this problem, since certain properties depend upon the interpretation of matter in motion with velocities that may be a considerable fraction of the velocity of light. The formulas selected have been chosen largely from the standpoint of utility—utility, that is, for the laboratory scientist as well as for the student of theoretical phases.

The following symbols are not standard, and are not explained in the text:

a, b, d slit width, length, and separation (between centers)
A, W absorptance and radiant emittance of a surface
B, D distances from source to diffracting screen, and from diffracting screen to point of observation
E, R, E' complex amplitudes of incident, reflected, and refracted waves
e, o (as subscripts) extraordinary and ordinary components in double refraction
I intensity (flux per unit area)
l geometrical path length

m order of interference
M molecular weight
n refractive index
s, p (as subscripts) refer to light polarized perpendicular and parallel to the plane of incidence
t thickness of a plane-parallel plate
v wave velocity

α absorption coefficient, grazing angle of incidence
δ phase difference, phase change
Δ path difference (retardation)
ϵ dielectric constant
ζ angle of astronomical aberration
θ angle of diffraction
κ absorption index
μ permeability, electric or magnetic moment
ξ angle of rotation of plane of polarization
ρ reflectance of a surface
σ wave number
τ transmittance
ϕ, ϕ' angles of incidence and refraction
ψ azimuth of plane-polarized light

1. Propagation of Light in Free Space

1.1. Wave equation

$$\nabla^2 \mathbf{E} = \frac{\mu\epsilon}{C^2} \cdot \frac{\partial^2 E}{\partial t^2} = \frac{1}{v^2} \cdot \frac{\partial^2 E}{\partial t^2} \tag{1}$$

($C = 1$ in mks units; $C = c$ in Gaussian units)

The general solution is (Chap. 1, § 5.20)

$$E = f(s - vt) + g(s + vt) \tag{2}$$

For a monochromatic plane wave, the wave normal having the direction cosines l, m, and n,

$$E = E_0 e^{2\pi i\nu[t-(lx+my+nz)/v]+i\delta}, \quad (lx + my + nz = s) \tag{3}$$

or

$$E = E_0 \sin\left[2\pi\nu\left(t - \frac{lx + my + nz}{v}\right) + \delta\right] \tag{4}$$

Wave traveling in the direction $+x$, phase constant zero at origin,

$$E = E_0 \sin 2\pi\nu\left(t - \frac{x}{v}\right) \tag{5}$$

Since $\nu = 1/T$ and $v = \nu\lambda$,

$$E = E_0 \sin 2\pi\left(\frac{t}{T} - \frac{x}{\lambda}\right) \tag{6}$$

1.2. Plane-polarized wave

$$E_y = E_{0y} \sin 2\pi\nu\left(t - \frac{x}{v}\right) \tag{1}$$

$$H_z = H_{0z} \sin 2\pi\nu\left(t - \frac{x}{v}\right) \tag{2}$$

1.3. Elliptically polarized wave. Combination of the two plane-polarized waves

$$E_y = E_{0y} \sin 2\pi\nu\left(t - \frac{x}{v}\right) \quad \text{and} \quad E_z = E_{0z} \sin\left[2\pi\nu\left(t - \frac{x}{v}\right) + \delta\right] \tag{1}$$

gives, at one value of x,

$$\sin^2 \delta = \frac{E_y^2}{E_{0y}^2} - \frac{2E_yE_z}{E_{0y}E_{0z}} \cos \delta + \frac{E_z^2}{E_{0z}^2} \tag{2}$$

an ellipse in the y, z plane.

1.4. Poynting vector. The instantaneous rate of flow of energy across unit area placed normal to the direction of flow,

$$\mathbf{\Pi} = \frac{C}{4\pi}\left[\boldsymbol{E} \times \boldsymbol{H}\right] \tag{1}$$

1.5. Intensity. In vacuum, $E = H$, so

$$\Pi = \frac{C}{4\pi} E_y^2, \quad I = \frac{C}{8\pi} E_{0y}^2 \tag{1}$$

for a plane-polarized wave. For the elliptically polarized wave of § 1.3,

$$I = \frac{C}{8\pi}(E_{0y}^2 + E_{0z}^2) \tag{2}$$

For an unpolarized wave of amplitude E_0,

$$I = \frac{C}{4\pi} E_0^2 \tag{3}$$

For N such waves having random phases,

$$I = N \frac{C}{4\pi} E_0^2 \tag{4}$$

1.6. Partially polarized light. If the preferential polarization is in the y direction,

$$P = \frac{I_y - I_z}{I_y + I_z} \tag{1}$$

gives the fraction of admixed plane-polarized light (proportional polarization).

1.7. Light quanta

$$\text{energy of a photon} = h\nu, \qquad \text{velocity} = c$$

$$\text{momentum} = \frac{h\nu}{c} = \frac{h}{\lambda} \qquad \text{rest mass} = 0$$

2. Interference

2.1. Two beams of light. Difference in optical path is

$$\Delta = \Sigma\, n_i l_i - \Sigma\, n_j l_j \tag{1}$$

Phase difference is

$$\delta = \frac{2\pi}{\lambda}\Delta \tag{2}$$

$$I = E_0^2 + E'^2_0 + 2E_0 E'_0 \cos \delta \tag{3}$$

When $E_0 = E'_0$,

$$I = 4E_0^2 \cos^2 \frac{\delta}{2} \tag{4}$$

2.2. Double-source experiments. For Young's double slit, condition for maxima is

$$d \sin \theta = m\lambda \tag{1}$$

and linear separation of successive fringes is

$$y_1 = \frac{D\lambda}{d} \tag{2}$$

For Fresnel biprism

$$y_1 = \frac{(B + D)\lambda}{2B(n - 1)\alpha} \tag{3}$$

where $\alpha =$ prism angle.

For Fresnel mirrors

$$y_1 = \frac{(B + D)\lambda}{2B\alpha} \tag{4}$$

where $\alpha =$ angle between mirrors.

2.3. Fringes of equal inclination. For reflected fringes,

$$I = \frac{4\rho \sin^2 \delta/2}{(1-\rho)^2 + 4\rho \sin^2 \delta/2} \tag{1}$$

For transmitted fringes,

$$I = \frac{(1-\rho)^2}{(1-\rho)^2 + 4\rho \sin^2 \delta/2} \tag{2}$$

$$\delta = \frac{4\pi nt \cos \phi'}{\lambda} \tag{3}$$

For maxima in reflected light,

$$2nt \cos \phi' = (m + \tfrac{1}{2})\lambda \tag{4}$$

2.4. Fringes of equal thickness. At normal incidence, maxima in reflected light,

$$2nt = (m + \tfrac{1}{2})\lambda \tag{1}$$

Newton's rings

$$r_m{}^2 = \frac{r(m + \frac{1}{2})\lambda}{n} \tag{2}$$

where r_m = radius of mth bright fringe, r = radius of lens surface.

2.5. Michelson interferometer. When the interferometer is adjusted for circular fringes, maxima are

$$2t \cos \phi = m\lambda \tag{1}$$

Fringe shift (number of fringes) due to a displacement $t' - t$ of one mirror :

$$m' - m = \frac{2(t' - t)}{\lambda} \tag{2}$$

Fringe shift caused by insertion of a thin lamina of index n and thickness t :

$$m' - m = \frac{2(n - n_a)t}{\lambda} \tag{3}$$

where n_a = refractive index of air. Visibility of fringes is

$$V = \frac{I_{\text{max}} - I_{\text{min}}}{I_{\text{max}} + I_{\text{min}}} \tag{4}$$

2.6. Fabry-Perot interferometer.

$$I = \frac{\tau^2}{1 - 2\rho \cos \delta + \rho^2} = \frac{\tau^2}{(1-\rho)^2} \cdot \frac{1}{1 + \dfrac{4\rho}{(1-\rho)^2} \sin^2 \dfrac{\delta}{2}} \tag{1}$$

$$m\lambda = 2t\cos\phi \approx 2t\left(1 - \frac{r_i^2}{2f^2}\right) \tag{2}$$

where f = focal length of camera lens. Spectral range is

$$\Delta\lambda_1 = \frac{\lambda}{m} = \frac{\lambda^2}{2t}, \qquad \Delta\sigma_1 = \frac{1}{2t} \tag{3}$$

Ratio of fringe width at half maximum to fringe separation*

$$2\gamma_h = \frac{1-\rho}{\pi\rho^{1/2}} + \frac{1}{24}\left(\frac{1-\rho}{\rho^{1/2}}\right)^3 \tag{4}$$

Resolving power +

$$\frac{\lambda}{\Delta\lambda} = 3.0\,\frac{m\rho^{1/2}}{1-\rho} \tag{5}$$

Dispersion

$$\frac{d\theta}{d\lambda} = \frac{m}{2t\sin\phi} = \frac{1}{\lambda\tan\phi}, \qquad \frac{\Delta y}{\Delta\lambda} = \frac{f^2}{r\lambda} \tag{6}$$

Comparison of λ's with sliding interferometer

$$\lambda_1 - \lambda_2 = \frac{\lambda_1\lambda_2}{2d} = \frac{\lambda_{av}^2}{2d} \tag{7}$$

where d = distance one mirror is moved between coincidences.

2.7. Lummer-Gehrcke plate. Maxima

$$m\lambda = 2nt\cos\phi' = 2t\sqrt{n^2 - \sin^2\phi} \tag{1}$$

$$\Delta\lambda_1 = \frac{m\lambda^2}{m^2\lambda - 4t^2n(dn/n\lambda)} \tag{2}$$

$$\frac{d\theta}{d\lambda} = \frac{2\lambda n(dn/d\lambda) - 2(n^2 - \sin^2\phi)}{\lambda\sin 2\phi} \tag{3}$$

$$\frac{\lambda}{\Delta\lambda} = \frac{l}{\lambda\sin\phi}\left(n^2 - \sin^2\phi - \lambda n\frac{dn}{d\lambda}\right) \tag{4}$$

where l = length of the plate.

2.8. Diffraction grating

$$I = \frac{\sin^2\alpha}{\alpha^2}\cdot\frac{\sin^2 N\beta}{\sin^2\beta} \tag{1}$$

where $\alpha = (\pi a\sin\theta)/\lambda$, $\beta = (\pi d\sin\theta)/\lambda$. Principal maxima

$$m\lambda = d(\sin\phi + \sin\theta) \tag{2}$$

* Meissner, K. W., *J. Opt. Soc. Am.*, **31**, 414 (1941).
\+ Birge, R. T., Private communication.

$$\frac{}{d\lambda} = \frac{m}{d \cos \theta} \tag{3}$$

$$\frac{\lambda}{\Delta\lambda} = mN \tag{4}$$

Concave grating, radius r,

$$\cos\phi\left(\frac{\cos\phi}{r_1} - \frac{1}{r}\right) + \cos\theta\left(\frac{1}{r} - \frac{\cos\theta}{r_2}\right) = 0 \tag{5}$$

$$\frac{1}{r_1} + \frac{1}{r_3} = \frac{\cos\phi + \cos\theta}{r} \tag{6}$$

where $r_1 =$ distance of slit, $r_2 =$ distance of image (first focal line), $r_3 =$ distance of second focal line.

2.9. Echelon grating. Transmission echelon; maxima

$$m\lambda = (n-1)t - a\theta \tag{1}$$

$$\Delta\lambda_1 = \frac{\lambda}{Ct} \tag{2}$$

where $C = [(n-1)/\lambda] - dn/d\lambda$.

$$\frac{d\theta}{d\lambda} = C\frac{t}{a} \tag{3}$$

$$\frac{\lambda}{\Delta\lambda} = NCt \tag{4}$$

Reflection echelon

$$m\lambda = 2t - a\theta \tag{5}$$

The other equations are the same, with $C = 2/\lambda$.

2.10. Low-reflection coatings. Single, homogeneous layer of index n_1, deposited on glass of index n, to a thickness $t = \lambda/4n_1$:

$$\rho = \frac{n_1^2 - n}{n_1^2 + n}, \qquad \rho = 0 \text{ when } n_1 = \sqrt{n} \tag{1}$$

Two layers,* the one next to the air having index n_1 and thickness $\lambda/4n_1$, that next to the glass having index n_2 and thickness $\lambda/4n_2$:

$$\rho = \left(\frac{n_1^2 n - n_2^2}{n_1^2 n + n_2^2}\right)^2, \qquad \rho = 0 \text{ when } n_1^2 n = n_2^2 \tag{2}$$

* Vacisek, A., *J. Opt. Soc. Am.*, **37**, 623 (1947).

3. Diffraction

3.1. Fraunhofer diffraction by a rectangular aperture. For parallel light incident normally,

$$I = I_0 \frac{\sin^2 \beta}{\beta^2} \frac{\sin^2 \gamma}{\gamma^2} \tag{1}$$

where $\beta = (\pi a \sin \theta)/\lambda$, with θ measured in a plane perpendicular to b; $\gamma = (\pi b \sin \Omega)/\lambda$, with Ω measured in a plane perpendicular to a. Single slit, having $b \gg a$,

$$I = I_0 \frac{\sin^2 \beta}{\beta^2}, \qquad \beta = \frac{\pi a(\sin \phi + \sin \theta)}{\lambda} \tag{2}$$

for oblique incidence at the angle ϕ. Zeros of intensity occur at $\beta = \pi$, 2π, 3π, ...; maxima at $\tan \beta = \beta$; first zero at $\sin \theta_1 = \lambda/a$.

3.2. Chromatic resolving power of prisms and gratings

$$\frac{\lambda}{\Delta\lambda} = t \frac{dn}{d\lambda} \tag{1}$$

for prism, or prisms, with total length of base t.

$$\frac{\lambda}{\Delta\lambda} = mN = \frac{Nd(\sin \phi + \sin \theta)}{\lambda} \tag{2}$$

for grating, where Nd = total width of grating.

3.3. Fraunhofer diffraction by a circular aperture

$$I = I_0 \left(\frac{2J_1(\alpha)}{\alpha}\right)^2, \qquad \alpha = \frac{2\pi r \sin \theta}{\lambda} \tag{1}$$

where J_1 = Bessel function of order unity (Chap. 1, § 9.2).

$$\sin \theta_1 = 1.220 \frac{\lambda}{2r} \tag{2}$$

at first zero of intensity.

3.4. Resolving power of a telescope

$$\theta_1 = 1.220 \frac{\lambda}{2r} \quad \text{radians} \tag{1}$$

where r = radius of objective lens.

$$\theta_1 = \frac{14.1}{2r} \quad \text{seconds of arc} \tag{2}$$

where r is in centimeters.

3.5. Resolving power of a microscope. Smallest separation of two points resolved :

$$x = \frac{\lambda}{2n \sin \phi} = \frac{\lambda}{2(\text{numerical aperture})} \tag{1}$$

where ϕ = half-angle subtended at object by objective lens.

3.6. Fraunhofer diffraction by N equidistant slits

$$I = I_0 \frac{\sin^2 \beta}{\beta^2} \cdot \frac{\sin^2 N\gamma}{\sin^2 \gamma} \tag{1}$$

where $\beta = (\pi a \sin \theta)/\lambda$, $\gamma = (\pi d \sin \theta)/\lambda$.

$$I = I_0 \frac{\sin^2 \beta}{\beta^2} \cos^2 \gamma \tag{2}$$

for double slit.

$$d(\sin \phi + \sin \theta) = m\lambda$$

at maxima.

$$\frac{\gamma}{\beta} = \frac{d}{a} = \text{an integer} \tag{3}$$

is the condition for missing orders.

3.7. Diffraction of x rays by cristals

$$2d \sin \alpha = m\lambda, \quad \text{(Bragg's law)} \tag{1}$$

where d = separation of atomic planes, α = grazing angle of incidence and diffraction. More accurately, *

$$m\lambda = 2d\sqrt{n^2 - 1 + \sin^2 \alpha} \approx 2d\left(1 - \frac{1-n}{\lambda^2} \cdot \frac{4d^2}{m^2}\right) \sin^2 \alpha \tag{2}$$

For a cubic crystal, lattice constant c,

$$\sin \alpha = \frac{\lambda}{2c}\left[(mh)^2 + (mk)^2 + (ml)^2\right]^{1/2} \tag{3}$$

where h, k, l = Miller indexes. +

3.8. Kirchhoff's formulation of Huygens' principle

$$4\pi E_P = \iint \left\{ \cos(n, r) \frac{\partial}{\partial r}\left[\frac{E(t - r/v)}{r}\right] - \frac{1}{r} \cdot \frac{\partial}{\partial n}\left[E\left(t - \frac{r}{v}\right)\right] \right\} dS \tag{1}$$

* VALASEK, J., *Theoretical and Experimental Optics*, John Wiley & Sons, Inc., New York, 1949, p. 191.

+ *Ibid.*, p. 419.

where (n, r) is the angle between the *inward* normal to the surface element dS and the radius vector r from P to dS. For plane waves incident normally on an aperture in a screen,*

$$E_P = \frac{iE_0}{4\pi} \iint \left[\frac{2\pi}{\lambda} \cdot \frac{e^{-ikr}}{r} (1 + \cos\theta) - i \frac{e^{-ikr}}{r^2} \cos\theta \right] dS \tag{2}$$

The second term may be neglected for optical waves.

3.9. Fresnel half-period zones

$$r_m = \sqrt{mD\lambda + \frac{m^2}{4}\lambda^2} \approx \sqrt{mD\lambda} \tag{1}$$

Intensity on the axis of a circular aperture.

$$I = \frac{E_1}{2} + \frac{E_m}{2} \tag{2}$$

approaches $E_1/2$ as $m \to \infty$.

3.10. Fresnel integrals

$$x = \int_0^v \cos\frac{\pi v^2}{2}\, dv, \qquad y = \int_0^v \sin\frac{\pi v^2}{2}\, dv \tag{1}$$

where $v = l\sqrt{2B/[D\lambda(B + D)]}$, and l is the distance along the screen.

4. Emission and absorption

4.1. Kirchhoff's law of radiation

$$\frac{W}{A} = W_b \tag{1}$$

where W_b = radiant emittance of a black body at the same temperature at which W and A are measured.

4.2. Blackbody radiation laws

$$W_\nu d\nu = \frac{C_1 \nu^3}{c^4} (e^{h\nu/kT} - 1)^{-1} d\nu, \quad \text{(Planck's law)} \tag{1}$$

$$W_\lambda d\lambda = \frac{C_1}{\lambda^5} (e^{C_2/\lambda T} - 1)^{-1} d\lambda \tag{2}$$

where $C_1 = 8\pi hc$, $C_2 = hc/k_0$

* *Ibid.*, p. 185.

$$\lambda_{\max} T = \frac{C_2}{4.965}, \quad \text{(Wien's displacement law)} \tag{3}$$

$$W_b = CT^4, \quad \text{(Stefan-Boltzmann law)} \tag{4}$$

4.3. Exponential law of absorption

$$I = I_0 \tau^x = I_0 e^{-\alpha x}, \quad \text{(Bouguer's law)} \tag{1}$$

$$I = I_0 e^{-\alpha [C] x} \quad \text{(Beer's law)} \tag{2}$$

where $[C]$ = concentration of a solution.

4.4. Bohr's frequency condition

$$h\nu = E_1 - E_2, \quad \sigma = T_2 - T_1 = \frac{E_1 - E_2}{hc} \tag{1}$$

4.5. Intensities of spectral lines

$$I = N_n A_{nm} h\nu_{nm}, \quad \text{(emission lines)} \tag{1}$$

where N_n = number of atoms in initial (upper) state, and A_{nm} = spontaneous transition probability.

$$\alpha = N_m B_{nm} h\nu_{nm}, \quad \text{(absorption lines)} \tag{2}$$

where N_m = number of atoms in initial (lower) state, and B_{nm} = induced transition probability.

$$B_{nm} = \frac{c^3}{8\pi h {\nu_{nm}}^3} \cdot \frac{g_n}{g_m} A_{nm} \tag{3}$$

where g_n, g_m = statistical weights of upper and lower states.*

5. Reflection

5.1. Fresnel's equations

$$\left.\begin{aligned}
\frac{R_s}{E_s} &= -\frac{\sin(\phi - \phi')}{\sin(\phi + \phi')} \\
\frac{R_p}{E_p} &= \frac{\tan(\phi - \phi')}{\tan(\phi + \phi')} \\
\frac{E'_s}{E_s} &= \frac{2 \sin\phi' \cos\phi}{\sin(\phi + \phi')} \\
\frac{E'_p}{E_p} &= \frac{2 \sin\phi' \cos\phi}{\sin(\phi + \phi') \cos(\phi - \phi')}
\end{aligned}\right\} \tag{1}$$

* HERZBERG, G., *Atomic Spectra and Atomic Structure*, Prentice-Hall, Inc., New York, 1937, Chap. 4.

The signs conform to the convention that corresponding phases are as seen by an observer looking *against* the light, whether incident, reflected, or refracted. This leads to an apparent inconsistency in the signs of R_s/E_s and R_p/E_p at $\phi = 0$. It cannot be avoided, however, without introducing other difficulties.

5.2. Stokes' amplitude relations. Reversal of the rays makes ϕ' the angle of incidence, and ϕ the angle of refraction. Using the subscript 1 for the reversed rays,

$$\frac{R_1}{E_1} = -\frac{R}{E} \tag{1}$$

for both s and p components; also

$$\frac{E'}{E}\frac{E'_1}{E_1} = 1 - \left(\frac{R}{E}\right)^2 \tag{2}$$

5.3. Reflectance of dielectrics

$$\rho_s = \left(\frac{R_s}{E_s}\right)^2, \quad \rho_p = \left(\frac{R_p}{E_p}\right)^2 \tag{1}$$

At normal incidence ($\phi = 0$),

$$\rho = \left(\frac{n-1}{n+1}\right)^2 \tag{2}$$

for both s and p components.

5.4. Azimuth of reflected plane-polarized light

$$\tan\psi = \frac{R_p}{R_s} = -\frac{E_p}{E_s} \cdot \frac{\cos(\phi + \phi')}{\cos(\phi - \phi')} \tag{1}$$

for dielectrics; ψ = angle between R and the normal to the plane of incidence.

5.5. Transmittance of dielectrics

$$\frac{E'_s}{E_s} = 1 + \frac{R_s}{E_s}, \quad \frac{E'_p}{E_p} = \frac{1 + R_p/E_p}{n} \tag{1}$$

$$\left(\frac{R}{E}\right)^2 + n\left(\frac{E'}{E}\right)^2 \frac{\cos\phi'}{\cos\phi} = 1 \tag{2}$$

applies to both the s and p components.

$$\tau = \left(\frac{E'}{E}\right)^2 = \frac{1-\rho}{n(\cos\phi'/\cos\phi)} \tag{3}$$

5.6. Polarization by a pile of plates. For unpolarized incident light, the proportional polarization (Sec. 1.6) caused by $2m$ surfaces (m plates) is

$$P = \frac{\rho_s - \rho_p}{\rho_s + \rho_p + 2(2m-1)\rho_s\rho_p} \tag{1}$$

for reflected light

$$P = \frac{m(\rho_s - \rho_p)}{1 + (m-1)(\rho_s + \rho_p) - (2m-1)\rho_s\rho_p} \tag{2}$$

for transmitted light

$$P = \frac{m\rho_s}{1 + (m-1)\rho_s} \tag{3}$$

for light transmitted at the polarizing angle ($\rho_p = 0$).*

5.7. Phase change at total internal reflection

$$\left.\begin{aligned} \tan\frac{\delta_s}{2} &= \frac{\sqrt{n^2\sin^2\phi - 1}}{n\cos\phi} \\ \tan\frac{\delta_p}{2} &= \frac{n\sqrt{n^2\sin^2\phi - 1}}{\cos\phi} \end{aligned}\right\} \tag{1}$$

5.8. Fresnel's rhomb. The angle of incidence at each of the two internal reflections is determined by

$$\tan\frac{\delta_p - \delta_s}{2} = \frac{\cos\phi\sqrt{n^2\sin^2\phi - 1}}{n\sin^2\phi} = 45^\circ \tag{1}$$

Maximum possible phase change at a single reflection is given by

$$\tan\left(\frac{\delta_p - \delta_s}{2}\right)_{\max} = \frac{n^2-1}{2n} \tag{2}$$

This occurs at the angle of incidence ϕ_m such that

$$\sin\phi_m = \sqrt{\frac{2}{n^2+1}} \tag{3}$$

5.9. Penetration into the rare medium in total reflection

$$E' = Ce^{-(2\pi/\lambda)z\sqrt{n^2\sin^2\phi - 1}}\, e^{2\pi i\nu(t - xn\sin\phi/c)} \tag{1}$$

where the x, y plane is a totally reflecting surface, and the x, z plane is a plane of incidence.

* GEIGER, H. and SCHEEL, K. (eds.), *Handbuch der Physik*, Vol. 20, "Licht als Wellenbewegung," Julius Springer, Berlin, 1928, p. 217.

5.10. Electrical and optical constants of metals. For perpendicular incidence in the $+z$ direction,

$$I_0 e^{-4\pi\kappa_0 z/\lambda_0} = I_0 e^{-4\pi\kappa z/\lambda} \tag{1}$$

defines κ, κ_0, where $\lambda =$ wavelength in metal, $\lambda_0 =$ wavelength in vacuum.

$$\left.\begin{aligned} \epsilon' &= \epsilon - i\frac{2\sigma}{\nu} = n^2(1 - i\kappa)^2, \quad \text{(complex dielectric constant)} \\ \epsilon &= n^2(1-\kappa^2) = n^2 - \kappa_0^2 \\ \frac{\sigma}{\nu} &= n^2\kappa = n\kappa_0 \end{aligned}\right\} \tag{2}$$

5.11. Reflectance of metals *

$$\left.\begin{aligned} \rho_s &= \frac{a^2 + b^2 - 2a\cos\phi + \cos^2\phi}{a^2 + b^2 + 2a\cos\phi + \cos^2\phi} \\ \rho_p &= \rho_s\left(\frac{a^2 + b^2 - 2a\sin\phi\tan\phi + \sin^2\phi\tan^2\phi}{a^2 + b^2 + 2a\sin\phi\tan\phi + \sin^2\phi\tan^2\phi}\right) \end{aligned}\right\} \tag{1}$$

where

$$\left.\begin{aligned} a^2 &= \tfrac{1}{2}\{\sqrt{[n^2(1-\kappa^2) - \sin^2\phi]^2 + 4n^4\kappa^2} + n^2(1-\kappa^2) - \sin^2\phi\} \\ b^2 &= \tfrac{1}{2}\{\sqrt{[n^2(1-\kappa^2) - \sin^2\phi]^2 + 4n^4\kappa^2} - n^2(1-\kappa^2) + \sin^2\phi\} \end{aligned}\right\} \tag{2}$$

Useful approximate expressions are +

$$\rho_p = \frac{(n - 1/\cos\phi)^2 + n^2\kappa^2}{(n + 1/\cos\phi)^2 + n^2\kappa^2} \tag{3}$$

$$\rho_s = \frac{(n - \cos\phi)^2 + n^2\kappa^2}{(n + \cos\phi)^2 + n^2\kappa^2} \tag{4}$$

At normal incidence, the exact expressions become

$$\rho = \frac{(n-1)^2 + n^2\kappa^2}{(n+1)^2 + n^2\kappa^2} = \frac{(n-1)^2 + \kappa_0^2}{(n+1)^2 + \kappa_0^2} \tag{5}$$

* GEIGER, H. and SCHEEL, K. (eds.), *Handbuch der Physik*, Vol. 20, "Licht als Wellenbewegung," Julius Springer, Berlin, 1928, p. 242.

+ WIEN, W. and HARMS, F., *Handbuch der Experimentallphysik*, Vol. 18, "Wellenoptik und Polarisation," Akademische Verlagsgesellschaft, Leipzig, 1928, p. 164.

5.12. Phase changes and azimuth for metals

$$\tan \delta_s = -\frac{2b \cos \phi}{a^2 + b^2 - \cos^2 \phi} \tag{1}$$

where a^2 and b^2 are defined in § 5.11.

$$\tan \delta_p = \frac{2b \cos \phi(a^2 + b^2 - \sin^2 \phi)}{a^2 + b^2 - n^4(1 + \kappa^2)^2 \cos^2 \phi} \tag{2}$$

$$\tan \Delta = \frac{2b \sin \phi \tan \phi}{\sin^2 \phi \tan^2 \phi - a^2 - b^2} \tag{3}$$

where $\Delta = \delta_p - \delta_s$.

$$\tan \psi e^{i\Delta} = -\frac{E_p}{E_s} \frac{\cos(\phi + \phi')}{\cos(\phi - \phi')} \tag{4}$$

5.13. Determination of the optical constants *

$$\left.\begin{aligned} n^2 &= f^2 \tan^2 \phi \cos (\beta + \alpha) \cos (\beta - \alpha) \\ n^2\kappa^2 &= f^2 \tan^2 \phi \sin (\beta + \alpha) \sin (\beta - \alpha) \\ \kappa^2 &= \tan (\beta + \alpha) \tan (\beta - \alpha) \end{aligned}\right\} \tag{1}$$

where

$$\sin 2\alpha = \frac{\sin 2\phi \sin \Delta \sin 2\psi}{1 - \cos 2\phi \cos \Delta \sin 2\psi}$$

$$\sin \beta = \frac{\sin \phi \sin \Delta \sin 2\psi}{(1 - \cos 2\phi \cos \Delta \sin 2\psi)\,(1 - \cos \Delta \sin 2\psi)^{1/2}}$$

$$f^2 = \frac{1 - \cos 2\phi \cos \Delta \sin 2\psi}{1 - \cos \Delta \sin 2\psi}$$

Using the principal angle of incidence $\bar{\phi}$ (for which $\Delta = 90°$) and the principal azimuth $\bar{\psi}$, these simplify to

$$\left.\begin{aligned} \sin 2\bar{\alpha} &= \sin 2\bar{\phi} \sin 2\bar{\psi} \\ \sin \bar{\beta} &= \sin \bar{\phi} \sin 2\bar{\psi} \\ f^2 &= 1 \end{aligned}\right\} \tag{2}$$

The approximate equations used by Drude are

$$\left.\begin{aligned} \kappa &= \tan 2\bar{\psi} \\ n\sqrt{1 + \kappa^2} &= \sin \bar{\phi} \tan \bar{\phi} \end{aligned}\right\} \tag{3}$$

* Geiger, H. and Scheel, K. (eds.), *Handbuch der Physik*, Vol. 20, "Licht als Wellenbewegung," Julius Springer, Berlin, 1928, p. 244.

6. Scattering and dispersion

6.1. Dipole scattering *

$$E_s = \frac{8\pi N e^4}{3m^2c^4[(\nu_0/\nu)^2 - 1]^2} \tag{1}$$

where E_s = total light energy scattered per unit incident intensity; N = number of dipoles of charge e, mass m, natural frequency ν_0.

6.2. Rayleigh scattering formula

$$E_s = \frac{8\pi N e^4 \nu^4}{3m^2c^4\nu_0{}^4}, \qquad (\nu \ll \nu_0) \tag{1}$$

6.3. Thomson scattering formula

$$E_s = \frac{8\pi N e^4}{3m^2c^4}, \qquad (\nu \gg \nu_0) \tag{1}$$

6.4. Scattering by dielectric spheres. Case $r \ll \lambda$ (Rayleigh scattering):

$$E_s = 24\pi^3 N \left(\frac{n^2-1}{n^2+2}\right)^2 \frac{V^2}{\lambda^4} \tag{1}$$

where n = refractive index of the spheres relative to the surrounding medium; $V = \frac{4}{3}\pi r^3$.

$$I_s = \frac{9\pi^2 N}{2D^2}\left(\frac{n^2-1}{n^2+2}\right)^2 \frac{V^2}{\lambda^4}(1+\cos^2\theta), \quad \text{(unpolarized incident light)} \tag{2}$$

where I_s = relative intensity scattered at angle θ with incident beam; D = distance from scattering spheres to observer. +
The degree of polarization of scattered light is ×

$$P = \frac{\sin^2\theta}{1+\cos^2\theta} \tag{3}$$

Case $r \geqq \lambda$:

$$E_s = \frac{N\lambda^2}{2\pi}\sum_{k=1}^{\infty}\frac{a_k{}^2 + p_k{}^2}{2k+1} \tag{4}$$

where a_k and p_k are complex functions of $2\pi r/\lambda$. □

* VALASEK, J., *Theoretical and Experimental Optics*, John Wiley & Sons, Inc., New York, 1949, p. 332.
+ SINCLAIR, D., *J. Opt. Soc. Am.*, **37**, 476 (1947).
× BORN, M., *Optik*, Edwards Bros., Inc., Ann Arbor, Mich., 1943, p. 294.
□ MIE, G., *Ann. Physik*, **25**, 377 (1908).

6.5. Scattering by absorbing spheres *

$$E_t = \frac{N\lambda^2}{2\pi} Re \sum_{k=1}^{\infty} (-1)^k i(a_k + p_k) \qquad (1)$$

where Re = real part; E_t includes energy removed by both absorption and scattering.

6.6. Scattering and refractive index +

$$n - 1 = \frac{1}{2\pi} \sqrt{N}\, \lambda^2 \sqrt{E_s} \qquad (1)$$

6.7. Refractivity ×

$$r = \frac{n^2 - 1}{n^2 + 2} \cdot \frac{1}{\rho} \approx m_1 r_1 + m_2 r_2 + \ldots + m_s r_s, \quad \text{(specific refractivity)} \qquad (1)$$

where s = number of substances of specific refractivity r_i.

$$Mr = C_1 + \frac{C_2}{T}, \quad \text{(molecular refractivity)} \qquad (2)$$

where $C_1 = 4\pi N_0 \mu^2/9k$, μ = dipole moment of molecule, k = Boltzmann constant, N_0 = Avogadro number.

6.8. Dispersion of gases

$$\left.\begin{aligned} n^2(1 - \kappa^2) &= 1 + \sum_i \frac{\rho_i(\nu_i^2 - \nu^2)}{4\pi^2(\nu_i^2 - \nu^2)^2 + (\nu\gamma_i)^2} \\ &= 1 + \sum_i \frac{K_i \lambda^2(\lambda^2 - \lambda_i^2)}{(\lambda^2 - \lambda_i^2)^2 + g_i\lambda^2} \end{aligned}\right\} \qquad (1)$$

$$2n^2\kappa = \sum_i \frac{\rho_i \nu\gamma_i}{8\pi^3(\nu_i^2 - \nu^2)^2 + 2\pi(\nu\gamma_i)^2} = \frac{K_i\sqrt{g_i}\,\lambda^3}{(\lambda^2 - \lambda_i^2)^2 + g_i\lambda^2} \qquad (2)$$

where $\rho_i = 4\pi N_i e_i^2/m_i$, $K_i = N_i e_i^2 \lambda_i^2/\pi m_i c^2$, γ_i = damping coefficient in $E = E_0 e^{-\gamma_i t/2} e^{2\pi i \nu_i t}$ and $g_i = \lambda_i^4 \gamma_i^2/4\pi^2 c^2$.

* SINCLAIR, D., *op. cit.*, p. 476.

+ JENKINS, F. A. and WHITE, H. E., *Fundamentals of Optics*, 2d ed., McGraw-Hill Book Company, Inc., New York, 1950, p. 459.

× VALASEK, J., *Theoretical and Experimental Optics*, John Wiley & Sons, Inc., New York, 1949, p. 234.

In the immediate neighborhood of an absorption frequency ν_0,*

$$\left.\begin{aligned} n^2(1-\kappa^2) &\approx n_0{}^2 + \frac{1}{2\nu_0}\cdot\frac{\rho_0(\nu_0-\nu)}{(\nu_0-\nu)^2+(\gamma_0/4\pi)^2} \\ 2n^2\kappa &\approx \frac{\gamma_0}{8\pi\nu_0}\cdot\frac{\rho_0}{(\nu_0-\nu)^2+(\gamma_0/4\pi)^2} \end{aligned}\right\} \quad (3)$$

6.9. Dispersion of solids and liquids

$$n-1 = C + \frac{C'}{\lambda^2}, \qquad \text{(Cauchy's formula)} \qquad (1)$$

$$n^2-1 = C_1 + \frac{C_2\lambda^2}{\lambda^2-\lambda_0{}^2}, \qquad \text{(Sellmeier's formula)} \qquad (2)$$

$$\frac{n^2-1}{n^2+2} = \frac{4\pi}{3}N\alpha = \frac{Ne^2}{3\pi m}\sum_i \frac{\rho_i}{\nu_i{}^2-\nu^2} \qquad (3)$$

in transparent regions, and where α = polarizability ($\mu = \alpha E$).+

6.10. Dispersion of metals ×

$$\left.\begin{aligned} n^2(1-\kappa^2) &= 1 - \frac{4\pi\sigma}{g}\cdot\frac{1}{1+4\pi^2\nu^2/g^2} + \sum_i \frac{\rho_i(\nu_i{}^2-\nu^2)}{4\pi^2(\nu_i{}^2-\nu^2)^2+(\nu\gamma_i)^2} \\ 2n^2\kappa &= \frac{2\sigma}{\nu}\cdot\frac{1}{1+4\pi^2\nu^2/g^2} + \sum_i \frac{\rho_i\nu\gamma_i}{8\pi^3(\nu_i{}^2-\nu^2)^2+2\pi(\nu\gamma_i)^2} \end{aligned}\right\} \quad (1)$$

6.11. Quantum theory of dispersion □

$$n^2-1 = 8\pi B\sum_{l,l'} \frac{\nu_{l,l'}p^2_{l,l'}}{h(\nu^2_{l,l'}-\nu_0{}^2)}\, e^{-E_l{}^0/kT} \qquad (1)$$

$$B = \frac{N}{\sum_l e^{-E_l{}^0/kT}} \qquad (2)$$

* Born, M., *Optik*, Edwards Bros., Inc., Ann Arbor, Mich., 1943, p. 478.
+ *Ibid.*, p. 503.
× Slater, J. C. and Frank, N. H., *Introduction to Theoretical Physics*, McGraw-Hill Book Company, Inc., 1933, p. 282.
□ Van Vleck, J. H., *Theory of Electric and Magnetic Susceptibilities*, Clarendon Press, Oxford, 1932, p. 361.

7. Crystal Optics

7.1. Principal dielectric constants and refractive indices

$$\left.\begin{aligned} &D_x = \epsilon_x E_x, \quad D_y = \epsilon_y E_y, \quad D_z = \epsilon_z E_z, \quad (\epsilon_x < \epsilon_y < \epsilon_z) \\ &n_a = \frac{c}{v_a} = \sqrt{\epsilon_x}, \quad n_b = \frac{c}{v_b} = \sqrt{\epsilon_y}, \quad n_c = \frac{c}{v_c} = \sqrt{\epsilon_z} \end{aligned}\right\} \qquad (1)$$

7.2. Normal ellipsoid

$$\frac{x^2}{\epsilon_x} + \frac{y^2}{\epsilon_y} + \frac{z^2}{\epsilon_z} = 1 \qquad (1)$$

Any plane section of the ellipsoid is an ellipse, and the two normal velocities of light traveling perpendicular to this section, for which the E vibrations are parallel to the major and minor axes of the ellipse, respectively, are inversely proportional to the length of these axes.

7.3. Normal velocity surface

$$\frac{l^2}{v_n^2 - v_a^2} + \frac{m^2}{v_n^2 - v_b^2} + \frac{n^2}{v_n^2 - v_c^2} = 0 \qquad (1)$$

where v_n = velocity along the wave normal, l, m, n = direction cosines of the wave normal.

7.4. Ray velocity surface

$$\frac{v_a^2 p^2}{v_r^2 - v_a^2} + \frac{v_b^2 q^2}{v_r^2 - v_b^2} + \frac{v_c^2 r^2}{v_r^2 - v_c^2} = 0 \qquad (1)$$

where v_r = velocity along the ray, p, q, r = direction cosines of the ray.

7.5. Directions of the axes

$$\text{Optic axes: } l = \pm\sqrt{\frac{v_a^2 - v_b^2}{v_a^2 - v_c^2}}, \quad \text{Ray axes: } p = \pm\frac{v_c}{v_b}\, l \qquad (1)$$

7.6. Production and analysis of elliptically polarized light

$$\left.\begin{aligned} E'_e &= E\cos\theta, \quad I_e = E^2\cos^2\theta \\ E'_o &= E\sin\theta, \quad I_o = E^2\sin^2\theta \end{aligned}\right\} \text{(law of Malus)} \qquad (1)$$

$$\delta = \frac{2\pi}{\lambda}\, t(n_e - n_o) \qquad (2)$$

Quarter-wave plate

$$\delta = \frac{\pi}{2}, \qquad t = \frac{\lambda}{4(n_e - n_o)} \qquad (3)$$

Babinet compensator

$$\delta = \frac{2\pi}{\lambda}(t_1 - t_2)(n_e - n_o), \qquad \tan\psi = \frac{E_p}{E_s} \tag{4}$$

is the ratio of the components of the ellipse parallel and perpendicular to the optic axis of one of the wedges. The angle ψ is measured when the analyzer is set for complete extinction at the minima.

7.7. Interference of polarized light. For a thin sheet of doubly refracting material between polarizer and analyzer, with its principal section at the angle α with the plane of transmission of the polarizer,

$$I_{\perp} = E^2 \sin^2 2\alpha \sin^2 \frac{\delta}{2} \qquad \text{(analyzer crossed)} \tag{1}$$

$$I_{||} = E^2\left(1 - \sin^2 2\alpha \sin^2 \frac{\delta}{2}\right), \qquad \text{(analyzer parallel)} \tag{2}$$

7.8. Rotation of the plane of polarization

Solutions

$$\xi = [\xi]lC = [\xi]lpd \tag{1}$$

where $[\xi]$ = specific rotation, C = concentration (g/cm³), p = per cent concentration (wt %), d = density.

Crystals

$$\xi = [\xi]l \tag{2}$$

Specific rotation *

$$[\xi] = \frac{\pi}{\lambda}\left(n_r - n_l\right) = \frac{\pi G}{\lambda n^2} \tag{3}$$

where n_r, n_l = refractive indexes for right- and left-handed circular components. Dispersion of the rotation +

$$[\xi] = \sum_i \frac{K_i}{\lambda^2 - \lambda_i^2}, \qquad K_i = \frac{4\pi}{c}\frac{N_i g_i e_i^2 \lambda_i^2}{m_i} \tag{4}$$

8. Magneto-optics and Electro-optics

8.1. Normal Zeeman effect. For light linearly polarized parallel to the magnetic field,

$$\nu = \nu_0$$

* BORN, M., *Optik*, Edwards Bros., Inc., Ann Arbor, Mich., 1943, p. 418.
+ FÖRSTERLING, K., *Lehrbuch der Optik*, S. Hirzel, Leipzig, 1928, p. 198.

For light circularly polarized in the plane perpendicular to the magnetic field,

$$\left.\begin{aligned} \nu &= \nu_0 \pm \frac{eH}{4\pi mc} \\ \Delta\sigma &= \frac{\Delta\nu}{c} = 4.670 \times 10^{-5} H \end{aligned}\right\} \quad (1)$$

where H is in oersteds.

8.2. Anomalous Zeeman effect

$$\nu = \nu_0 + (M'g' - M''g'')\frac{eH}{4\pi mc} \quad (1)$$

where $M' = M''$ for light linearly polarized parallel to H, and $M' = M'' \pm 1$ for light circularly polarized perpendicular to H.

$$g = 1 + \frac{J(J+1) + S(S+1) - L(L+1)}{2J(J+1)} \quad \text{(Landé } g \text{ formula)}$$

8.3. Quadratic Zeeman effect. Due to the component of the magnetic moment perpendicular to J, *

$$\left.\begin{aligned} \nu = \nu_0 &+ (M'g' - M''g'')\frac{eH}{4\pi mc} + \frac{he^2H^2}{16\pi^2m^2c^2} \\ &\times \left\{ \frac{[f(J',M')]^2}{h\nu(J',J'+1)} + \frac{[f(J'-1,M')]^2}{h\nu(J',J'-1)} \right. \\ &\left. - \frac{[f(J'',M'')]^2}{h\nu(J'',J''+1)} - \frac{[f(J''-1,M'')]^2}{h\nu(J'',J''-1)} \right\} \end{aligned}\right\} \quad (1)$$

Due to the diamagnetic term,

$$\nu = \nu_0 + \frac{e^2H^2a_0n^4}{8mc^2} \quad (2)$$

for light linearly polarized parallel to H.

$$\nu = \nu_0 \pm \frac{eH}{4\pi mc} + \frac{e^2H^2a_0n^4}{4mc^2} \quad (3)$$

for light circularly polarized perpendicular to H. +

* Van Vleck, J. H., *Theory of Electric and Magnetic Susceptibilities*, Clarendon Press, Oxford, 1932, p. 173.

\+ Van Vleck, J. H., *op. cit.*, p. 178.

8.4. Faraday effect

$$\left.\begin{aligned} \xi &= \omega H l \\ \omega &= \frac{\pi(n_l - n_r)}{\lambda H}, \quad \text{(Verdet constant)} \\ \omega &= -\frac{e\lambda_0}{2mc^2}\cdot\frac{dn}{d\lambda}, \quad \text{(classical Becquerel formula)} \\ \omega &= \frac{\pi}{\lambda}\cdot\frac{n^2+2}{3n}Nf \end{aligned}\right\} \quad (1)$$

Here $f = f_0 + (1/kT)f_1$, where f_0 and f_1 are molecular constants.*

8.5. Cotton-Mouton effect +

$$\left.\begin{aligned} \delta &= \frac{n_o - n_e}{\lambda} l = ClH^2 \\ n_o - n_e &= H^2 N \frac{n^2+2}{6n}\left(3b + f^2 N \frac{n^2+2}{3n^2}\right) \end{aligned}\right\} \quad (1)$$

Here $b = b_0 + (1/kT)b_1 + (1/k^2T^2)b_2$, where b_0, b_1, and b_2 are molecular constants.

$$C = C_0 + \frac{1}{T}C_1 + \frac{1}{T^2}C_2, \quad \text{(Cotton-Mouton constant)}$$

8.6. Stark effect × For hydrogen and hydrogen-like orbits,

$$\sigma = \sigma_0 - \frac{3Eh}{8\pi^2 mZec}[n'(n'_\xi - n'_\eta) - n''(n''_\xi - n''_\eta)] \quad (1)$$

where n_ξ, n_η = parabolic quantum numbers.

For many-electron atoms

$$\sigma = \sigma_0 - CE^2 \quad (2)$$

8.7. Kerr electro-optic effect □

$$\left.\begin{aligned} \delta &= 2\pi BlE^2 \\ B &= \frac{n_o - n_e}{\lambda E^2}, \quad \text{(Kerr constant)} \\ B &= N\frac{n^2+2}{6n}\left(\frac{\epsilon+2}{3}\right)^2\frac{3b}{\lambda} \end{aligned}\right\} \quad (1)$$

* Born, M., *Optik*, Edwards Bros., Inc., Ann Arbor, Mich., 1943, p. 356.

+ Born, M., *Optik*, Edwards Bros., Inc., Ann Arbor, Mich., 1943, p. 362.

× Ruark, A. E., and Urey, H. C., *Atoms, Molecules, and Quanta*, McGraw-Hill Book Company, Inc., 1930, p. 153.

□ Born, M., *op. cit.*, p. 367.

9. Optics of Moving Bodies

9.1. Doppler effect

$$\nu' = \nu \frac{\sqrt{1 - v^2/c^2}}{1 - (v/c)(\cos \theta)} \tag{1}$$

where θ = angle between direction of observation and direction of motion. Reflection from a moving mirror

$$\nu' = \nu \frac{1 + (v/c) \cos \phi}{1 - (v/c) \cos \phi} \tag{2}$$

9.2. Astronomical aberration

$$\sin \zeta = \frac{|v|}{c} \tag{1}$$

9.3. Fresnel dragging coefficient

$$v = \frac{c}{n} \pm v' \left(\frac{n^2 - 1}{n^2} - \frac{\lambda}{n} \cdot \frac{dn}{d\lambda} \right) \tag{1}$$

where v = observed wave velocity of light, v' = velocity of medium, λ = wavelength in vacuum.

9.4. Michelson-Morley experiment

$$\delta = \frac{2\pi l}{\lambda} \cdot \frac{v^2}{c^2} \tag{1}$$

This is doubled when the interferometer is turned through 90°.

Bibliography

1. Born, M., *Optik*, Edwards Bros., Inc., Ann Arbor, Mich., 1943. Particularly strong on the theoretical aspects. Good treatment of scattering and dispersion.
2. Bruhat, G., *Cours d'optique*, 3d ed., Masson et Cie., Paris, 1947. An extensive textbook at the advanced undergraduate level. Considerable space devoted to spectra.
3. Ditchburn, R. W., *Light. The Student's Physics*, Interscience Publishers, New York, 1953. An advanced textbook which treats the wave and particle aspects of light in a unified manner.
4. Drude, P., *Theory of Optics*, Longmans, Green & Co., Inc., New York, 1922. The classic textbook on the electromagnetic theory of light. Uses differential equations rather than vector notation.
5. Försterling, K., *Lehrbuch der Optik*, S. Hirzel, Leipzig, 1928. Electromagnetic theory using vector notation. Devotes a large section to dispersion and spectra.

6. Gehrcke, E. (ed.), *Handbuch der physikalischen Optik* (2 vols.), Barth, Leipzig, 1926-1928. Very complete. Volume 1 (in two parts) treats wave optics; volume 2 (in three parts) treats quantum optics.
7. Geiger, H. and Scheel, K. (eds.), *Handbuch der Physik*, Vol. 20, "Licht als Wellenbewegung," Julius Springer, Berlin, 1928. An excellent reference book on classical theory. Other volumes of this handbook also deal with optics.
8. Herzberg, G., *Atomic Spectra and Atomic Structure*, Prentice-Hall, Inc., New York, 1937.
9. Jenkins, F. A. and White, H. E., *Fundamentals of Optics*, 2d ed., McGraw-Hill Book Company, Inc., New York, 1950. A textbook for advanced undergraduate courses. Many illustrations.
10. Lummer, O. (ed.), Müller-Pouillet, *Lehrbuch der Physik*, Vol. 2, "Optik" (2 parts), F. Vieweg und Sohn, Braunschweig, 1926-1929. First volume good on the experimental side; second volume on spectra and dispersion.
11. Meyer, C. F., *The Diffraction of Light, X-Rays, and Material Particles*, University of Chicago Press, Chicago, 1934. Deals with a rather limited subject matter in great detail. Emphasis is on the physical principles rather than on mathematical treatment.
12. Morgan, J., *Introduction to Geometrical and Physical Optics*, McGraw-Hill Book Co., New York, 1953. An intermediate textbook devoting about equal space to geometrical and physical optics.
13. Preston, T., *Theory of Light*, 5th ed., Macmillan and Co., Ltd., London, 1928. A very complete standard text of moderate mathematical difficulty. Well illustrated.
14. Ruark, A. E. and Urey, H. C., *Atoms, Molecules, and Quanta*, McGraw-Hill Book Company, Inc., New York, 1930.
15. Schuster, A. and Nicholson, J. W., *Theory of Optics*, 3d ed., Longmans, Green & Co., Inc., New York, 1924. Although not written from the standpoint of electromagnetic theory, a good treatment by the classical wave theory.
16. Slater, J. C. and Frank, N. H., *Introduction to Theoretical Physics*, McGraw-Hill Book Company, Inc., 1933.
17. Valasek, J., *Theoretical and Experimental Optics*, John Wiley & Sons, Inc., New York, 1949. Very up-to-date, although somewhat too brief. Many experiments are described.
18. Van Vleck, J. H., *Theory of Electric and Magnetic Susceptibilities*, Clarendon Press, Oxford, 1932.
19. Wien, W. and Harms, F., *Handbuch der Experimentallphysik*, Vol. 18, "Wellenoptik und Polarisation," Akademische Verlagsgeselschaft, Leipzig, 1928. Thorough treatment of certain special topics, including photochemistry.
20. Wood, R. W., *Physical Optics*, 3d ed., The Macmillan Company, New York, 1934. Long recognized as an outstanding account of the experimental side of the subject.

Chapter 18

ELECTRON OPTICS

By Edward G. Ramberg
RCA Laboratories Division
Radio Corporation of America

Although electron optics has certain features peculiar to itself, largely because its " lenses " and " prisms " are built to control the passage of electrons rather than light waves, a large part of the subject has close analogy to the field of light optics. In certain aspects, geometrical or ray optics are useful; in others only the application of the electron equivalent of physical optics will suffice to explain the phenomena.

The formulas here given are those that will prove most useful for description of the focusing properties and path deflections of practical electron optical systems, such as electron guns, electron microscopes, image tubes, and deflection fields. Formulas for the field distributions, focal lengths, and aberrations of characteristic electrode configurations and lenses supplement the more general formulas of electron optics. The personal experience of the author has been the primary guide for the selection—an experience gained from the computation of a wide variety of electron-optical systems, particularly in the fields of electron microscopy and television.

Symbols Employed in Formulas

A magnetic vector potential

A_z, A_r, A_θ components of magnetic vector potential in polar coordinates

$a \quad = e/(2m_0c^2)$, relativistic correction constant

$b \quad = -r'/r + 1/(2z)$ [Eq. (5.6)]

b_z, b_r components of magnetic induction

B magnetic induction along axis or in plane of symmetry

c velocity of light

$c \quad = -r'/r$, " convergence " [Eq. (5.5)]

C integration constant of electron path ($\sqrt{2em_0}\, C =$ angular momentum in zero magnetic field)

C_1, C_2, C_3 coefficients of chromatic aberration [Eq. (10.2)]
d " half-width " of refractive field; separation of electrodes
e Napierian base 2.718...
$-e$ charge of the electron
E electric field
f, f_o, f_i focal length (object-side, image-side) of complete lens field
f_n, f_{on}, f_{in} focal length (object-side, image-side) of lens field terminated by nth focal point
h_o, h_i distance of (object-side, image-side) principal plane from plane of symmetry of electron lens
i $\sqrt{-1}$
I electric current
i (subscript) referring to the image plane
k Boltzmann constant [Eq. (1.4)]
k $\sqrt{\frac{e}{8m\Phi}}B_{\max}d$, $\sqrt{\frac{3}{16}\left(\frac{\Phi'}{\Phi}\right)_{\max}}d$ = lens strength parameter of magnetic and electrostatic lenses, respectively
l length of field
m mass of the electron
m_o rest mass of the electron
M magnification
n integer, 1, 2, 3, ...
n index of refraction [Eqs. (1.1) and (1.2)]
N magnctic flux
o (subscript) referring to object plane or starting point
r distance of electron from axis of symmetry
r_a, r_i, r_o distance from axis in " aperture plane," image plane, object plane
$r_\alpha(z), r_\gamma(z)$ solutions of paraxial ray equation with initial conditions

$$r_\alpha(z_o) = 0, \quad r_\alpha'(z_o) = 1; \quad r_\gamma(z_o) = 1, \quad r_\gamma(z_a) = 0$$

$r_{\alpha a}$ $r_\alpha(z_a)$
R radius of curvature
R $= r\Phi^{1/4}$ [Eq. (5.4)]
$S_1 \ldots S_8$ coefficients of geometric aberration
t time
T absolute temperature
u object distance (from object-side principal plane to object plane)

v image distance (from image-side principal plane to image plane)

v velocity of electron [Eq. (1.2)]

w $= x + iy = re^{i\theta}$

$w_a, w_i, w_o' = x_a + iy_a,\ x_i + iy_i,\ (x_o + iy_o)e^{i\chi_i}$ = coordinates in aperture, image, and object plane, the last referred to rotated frame of reference

x coordinate parallel to axis of symmetry in two-dimensional fields

x, y, z rectangular coordinates

Y $= y\Phi^{1/4}$

z coordinate parallel to axis in axially symmetric field

z_n distance of nth (real) focal point from plane of symmetry

z_f distance of (generally virtual) focal point of complete field from plane of symmetry

α aperture angle; inclination with respect to axis

δ variation

$\Delta r_i, \Delta\Phi, \ldots$ increment of $r_i, \Phi, \ldots$

θ azimuthal angle of electron

μ permeability

π 3.1416...

χ angle between electron path and magnetic vector potential [Eq. (1.2)]

χ $= \int_{z_o}^{z} \sqrt{\frac{e}{8m\Phi}}\, B dz$

φ electric potential, so normalized that $e\varphi$ is kinetic energy of electron in question

φ^* $= \varphi + a\varphi^2 =$ " effective " electric potential

φ^{**} " equivalent potential " in presence of magnetic field [Eq. (4.1)]

Φ electric potential along axis of symmetry

$\Phi^* = \Phi + a\Phi^2 =$ " effective " axial electric potential

Superscripts :

r' first derivative of r with respect to z or x (coordinate parallel to axis of symmetry)

r'' second derivative of r with respect to z or x

$r^{(n)}$ nth derivative of r with respect to z or x

$\dot{r}$ first derivative of r with respect to t

$\ddot{r}$ second derivative of r with respect to t

$\bar{w}$ complex conjugate of w

1. General Laws of Electron Optics

1.1. Fermat's principle for electron optics

$$\delta \int_{P_1}^{P_2} n \, ds = 0 \tag{1}$$

for the path of an electron between the terminal points P_1 and P_2, where ds is an element of path and n is the refractive index for the electron.

1.2. Index of refraction of electron optics *

$$n = \frac{mv}{m_o c} - \frac{eA}{m_o c} \cos \chi = \sqrt{\frac{2e\varphi^*}{m_o c^2}} - \frac{eA}{m_o c} \cos \chi \tag{1}$$

where χ is the angle between the path of the electron and the magnetic vector potential A.

1.3. Law of Helmholtz-Lagrange for axially symmetric fields

$$\sqrt{\Phi_o}\, r_o \alpha_o = \sqrt{\Phi_i}\, r_i \alpha_i \tag{1}$$

where α_o, α_i are the apertures of the imaging pencils, which are assumed to be small, and r_i/r_o is the magnification.

1.4. Upper limit to the current density *j* in a beam cross section at potential Φ and with aperture angle α +

$$\frac{j}{j_o} = \left(\frac{e\Phi}{kT} + 1\right) \sin^2 \alpha \tag{1}$$

where j_o is the current density at the emitting cathode, T is the cathode temperature, and k is Boltzmann's constant. Φ is measured with respect to the cathode.

1.5. General lens equation

$$\frac{f_i}{v} - \frac{f_o}{u} = 1; \quad \frac{f_i}{f_o} = \sqrt{\frac{\Phi_i}{\Phi_o}}; \quad \sqrt{\frac{\Phi_o}{\Phi_i}} \frac{v}{u} = M \tag{1}$$

* GLASER, W., "Geometric-Optical Imaging by Electron Rays," *Z. Physik*, **80**, 451-464 (1933). PICHT, J., *Einführung in die Theorie der Elektronenoptik*, J. A. Barth, Leipzig, 1939.

+ LANGMUIR, D. B., "Limitations of Cathode-Ray Tubes," *Proc. IRE*, **25**, 977-991 (1937).

2. Axially Symmetric Fields

2.1. Differential equations of the axially symmetric field in free space

$$\frac{\partial^2\varphi}{\partial z^2}+\frac{1}{r}\cdot\frac{\partial}{\partial r}\left(r\frac{\partial\varphi}{\partial r}\right)=0;\quad \frac{\partial b_z}{\partial z}+\frac{1}{r}\cdot\frac{\partial}{\partial r}(rb_r)=0 \tag{1}$$

2.2. Potential distribution in axially symmetric electric field

$$\varphi(z,r)=\sum_{n=0}^{\infty}\frac{(-1)^n}{(n!)^2}\Phi^{(2n)}(z)\left(\frac{r}{2}\right)^{2n}=\Phi-\frac{1}{4}\Phi''r^2+\frac{1}{64}\Phi^{\mathrm{IV}}r^4-\ldots \tag{1}$$

2.3. Behavior of equipotential surfaces on axis

Radius of curvature :

$$R=\frac{2\Phi'}{\Phi''} \tag{1}$$

Vertex half-angle of equipotential cone at saddle point :

$$\alpha_s=\text{arc tan}\sqrt{2}=54^\circ 44' \tag{2}$$

2.4. Magnetic vector potential in axially symmetric field

$$A=A_\theta(z,r)=\frac{N}{2\pi r} \tag{1}$$

where N is the magnetic flux through a circle of radius r in the azimuthal plane defined by z.

2.5. Field distribution in axially symmetric magnetic field

$$\left.\begin{aligned}b_z(r,z)&=\frac{1}{r}\cdot\frac{\partial(rA_\theta)}{\partial r}=\sum_{n=0}^{\infty}\frac{(-1)^n}{(n!)^2}B^{(2n)}(z)\left(\frac{r}{2}\right)^{2n}\\&=B(z)-\frac{1}{4}B''(z)r^2+\ldots\\b_r(r,z)&=-\frac{\partial A_\theta}{\partial z}=\sum_{n=1}^{\infty}\frac{(-1)^n}{n!(n-1)!}B^{(2n-1)}\left(\frac{r}{2}\right)^{2n-1}\\&=-\frac{1}{2}B'(z)r+\frac{1}{16}B^{\mathrm{III}}(z)r^3-\ldots\end{aligned}\right\} \tag{1}$$

3. Specific Axially Symmetric Fields

3.1. Electric field. For a field of aperture of radius R and potential Φ_A located at $z = 0$, separating fields $-\Phi'(-\infty) = E_0$ and $-\Phi'(\infty) = E_i$,

$$\Phi(z) = \Phi_A - \frac{E_o + E_i}{2} z + \frac{R}{\pi}(E_o - E_i)\left(\frac{z}{R} \arctan \frac{z}{R} + 1\right) \qquad (1)$$

3.2. Electric field. For a field between two coaxial cylinders of equal radius R at potentials $\Phi_o(z < 0)$ and $\Phi_i(z > 0)$,

$$\left.\begin{aligned} \Phi(z) &= \frac{\Phi_i + \Phi_o}{2} + \frac{\Phi_i - \Phi_o}{\pi} \int_0^\infty \frac{\sin(kz)}{J_o(ikR)} \cdot \frac{dk}{k} \quad * \\ &\simeq \frac{\Phi_i + \Phi_o}{2} + \frac{\Phi_i - \Phi_o}{2} \tanh\left(\frac{1.315z}{R}\right) \quad + \end{aligned}\right\} \qquad (1)$$

3.3. Magnetic field. For a field of single wire loop of radius R at $z = 0$,

$$B(z) = \frac{2\pi\mu I R^2}{(z^2 + R^2)^{3/2}} \qquad (1)$$

3.4. Magnetic field. For a coil with nI ampere turns enclosed by infinitely permeable shell with narrow circular gap, and radius of inner surface of magnetic material R,

$$B(z) \simeq 2\pi\mu n I \cdot \frac{1.315}{R} \operatorname{sech}^2\left(\frac{1.315z}{R}\right) \qquad (1)$$

4. Path Equation in Axially Symmetric Field

4.1. General path equation in axially symmetric field

$$r'' = \frac{1 + r'^2}{2\varphi^{**}}\left(\frac{\partial \varphi^{**}}{\partial r} - r' \frac{\partial \varphi^{**}}{\partial z}\right) \qquad (1)$$

with

$$\varphi^{**} = \varphi^* - \left(\frac{C}{r} + \sqrt{\frac{e}{2m_o}}\, A\right)^2$$

and

$$C = \frac{r^2\theta'\sqrt{\varphi^*}}{\sqrt{r'^2 + r^2\theta'^2 + 1}} - \sqrt{\frac{e}{2m_o}}\, rA_\theta, \quad \text{(constant of integration)}$$

Here $\sqrt{2em_o}\, C$ is the angular momentum of the electron about the axis

* Morton, G. A. and Ramberg, E. G., " Electron Optics of an Image Tube," *Physics*, **7**, 451-459 (1936).

+ Bertram, S., " Determination of the Axial Potential Distribution in Axially Symmetric Electrostatic Fields," *Proc. IRE*, **13**, 496-502 (1942). Gray, F., " Electrostatic Electron Optics," *Bell System Tech. J.*, **18**, 1-31 (1939).

for zero magnetic field ($A_\theta = 0$). The azimuth of the electron is given by

$$\theta = \theta_o + \int_{z_0}^{z} \frac{\dfrac{C}{r} + \sqrt{\dfrac{e}{2m_o}}\, A_\theta}{\sqrt{\varphi^* - \left(\dfrac{C}{r} + \sqrt{\dfrac{e}{2m_o}}\, A_\theta\right)^2}} \, \frac{\sqrt{1 + r'^2}}{r} \, dz \tag{2}$$

5. Paraxial Path Equations (for $e\Phi \ll m_o c^2$)

(See § 5.7 for arbitrary electron energies.)

5.1. General paraxial path equation

$$r'' = -r' \frac{\Phi'}{2\Phi} - r\left(\frac{\Phi''}{4\Phi} + \frac{eB^2}{8m_o\Phi} - \frac{C^2}{\Phi r^4}\right) \tag{1}$$

with

$$C = r^2\left(\sqrt{\Phi}\,\theta' - \sqrt{\frac{e}{8m_o}}\, B\right)$$

5.2. Azimuth of electron

$$\theta = \theta_o + \int_{z_0}^{z} \left(\frac{C}{r^2\sqrt{\Phi}} + \sqrt{\frac{e}{8m_o\Phi}}\, B\right) dz \tag{1}$$

5.3. Paraxial path equation for path crossing axis ($C = 0$)

$$\left.\begin{aligned} r'' &= -r' \frac{\Phi'}{2\Phi} - r\left(\frac{\Phi''}{4\Phi} + \frac{eB^2}{8m_o\Phi}\right) \\ \theta &= \theta_o + \chi = \theta_o + \int_{z_0}^{z} \sqrt{\frac{e}{8m_o\Phi}}\, B\, dz \end{aligned}\right\} \tag{1}$$

5.4. Paraxial ray equation for variable $R = r\Phi^{1/4}$ (for $C = 0$) *

$$R'' = R\left[\frac{3}{16}\left(\frac{\Phi'}{\Phi}\right)^2 + \frac{eB^2}{8m_o\Phi}\right] \tag{1}$$

5.5. Paraxial ray equation in electric field for variable $c = -r'/r$ ($C = 0$)

$$c' = c^2 - \frac{\Phi'}{2\Phi}\, c + \frac{\Phi''}{4\Phi} \tag{1}$$

with

$$r = r_0 e^{-\int_{z_0}^{z} c\, dz}$$

* Picht, J., "Contributions to the Theory of Geometric Electron Optics," *Ann. Physik*, **15**, 926-964 (1932).

5.6. Paraxial ray equation in electric field for variable $b = -r'/r + 1/(2z)$ (finite at surface of flat cathode) ($C = 0$) *

$$b' = b^2 - b\left(\frac{1}{z} + \frac{\Phi'}{2\Phi}\right) + \frac{\Phi''}{4\Phi} + \frac{1}{2z}\left(\frac{\Phi'}{2\Phi} - \frac{1}{2z}\right) \tag{1}$$

with

$$r = r_0 \sqrt{\frac{z}{z_0}}\, e^{-\int_{z_0}^{z} b\, dz}$$

5.7. Paraxial ray equation in electric field for arbitrarily high voltage +

$$\left.\begin{aligned} r'' = &-r'\frac{\Phi'}{2\Phi}\frac{1+2a\Phi}{1+a\Phi} \\ &-r\left(\frac{\Phi''}{4\Phi}\frac{1+2a\Phi}{1+a\Phi} + \frac{eB^2}{8m_0(1+a\Phi)\Phi} - \frac{C^2}{r^4(1+a\Phi)\Phi}\right) \end{aligned}\right\} \tag{1}$$

with

$$C = r^2\left(\theta'\sqrt{\Phi + a\Phi^2} - \sqrt{\frac{e}{8m_0}}\, B\right)$$

6. Electron Paths in Uniform Fields $(e\Phi \ll m_0 c^2)$

6.1. Path in uniform electrostatic field $-\Phi'$ parallel to z axis. For electron with initial energy $e\Phi_0$ making an initial angle α_0 with z axis in yz plane,

$$y - y_0 = \frac{\Phi_0}{\Phi'}\left[-\sin 2\alpha_0 \pm 2 \sin \alpha_0 \sqrt{\cos^2\alpha_0 + \frac{\Phi'}{\Phi_0}(z - z_0)}\right] \tag{1}$$

6.2. Path in uniform magnetic field. For $B = B_z$ with initial energy $e\Phi_0$, initial angle α_0 with respect to z axis, and azimuth θ_0 with respect to x axis,

$$\left.\begin{aligned} x - x_0 &= R\left[\sin\left(\frac{z - z_0}{R}\tan\alpha_0 + \theta_0\right) - \sin\theta_0\right] \\ y - y_0 &= -R\left[\cos\left(\frac{z - z_0}{R}\tan\alpha_0 + \theta_0\right) - \cos\theta_0\right] \\ R &= \frac{1}{B}\sqrt{\frac{2m_0\Phi_0}{e}}\sin\alpha_0, \quad \frac{z - z_0}{R}\tan\alpha_0 = \frac{eB}{m_0}(t - t_0) \end{aligned}\right\} \tag{1}$$

* Morton, G. A. and Ramberg, E. G., "Electron Optics of an Image Tube," *Physics*, **7**, 451-459 (1936).

+ Ramberg, E. G., "Variation of Axial Aberrations of Electron Lenses with Lens Strength," *J. Appl. Phys.*, **13**, 582-594 (1942).

6.3. Path in crossed electric and magnetic field, $-\Phi' = E_y$, $B = B_z$

$$\left.\begin{aligned} x - x_o = -\frac{\Phi'}{B}t - \frac{m_o}{eB}\dot{y}_o + \frac{m_o}{eB}\sqrt{\left(\dot{x}_o + \frac{\Phi'}{B}\right)^2 + \dot{y}_o^2} \\ \times \sin\left(\frac{eB}{m_o}t + \arctan\frac{\dot{y}_o}{\Phi'/B + \dot{x}_o}\right) \end{aligned}\right\} \quad (1)$$

$$\left.\begin{aligned} y - y_o = \frac{m_o}{eB}\left(\frac{\Phi'}{B} + \dot{x}_o\right) - \frac{m_o}{eB}\sqrt{\left(\dot{x}_o + \frac{\Phi'}{B}\right)^2 + \dot{y}_o^2} \\ \times \cos\left(\frac{eB}{m_o}t + \arctan\frac{\dot{y}_o}{\Phi'/B + \dot{x}_o}\right) \end{aligned}\right\} \quad (2)$$

$$z - z_o = \dot{z}_o t$$

where $\dot{x}_o$, $\dot{y}_o$, $\dot{z}_o$ are components of initial velocity.

7. Focal Lengths of Weak Lenses * $(e\Phi \ll m_o c^2)$

7.1. General formula for focal length of a weak lens

$$\frac{1}{f_o} = \sqrt[4]{\frac{\Phi_i}{\Phi_o}}\int_{z_o}^{z_i}\left[\frac{3}{16}\left(\frac{\Phi'}{\Phi}\right)^2 + \frac{eB^2}{8m_o\Phi}\right]dz, \quad f_i = \sqrt{\frac{\Phi_i}{\Phi_o}}\,f_o \quad (1)$$

7.2. Focal length of aperture lens (§ 3.1)

$$\frac{1}{f_o} = \frac{E_o - E_i}{4\Phi_A} \quad (1)$$

7.3. Focal length of electric field between coaxial cylinders (§ 3.2)

$$\frac{1}{f_o} = \frac{1}{4}\sqrt[4]{\frac{\Phi_i}{\Phi_o}}\left(\frac{\Phi_i - \Phi_o}{\Phi_i + \Phi_o}\right)^2\frac{1.315}{R} \quad (1)$$

7.4. Focal length of magnetic field of single wire loop (§ 3.3)

$$\frac{1}{f} = \frac{3\pi^3}{16}\frac{e\mu^2}{m_o}\frac{I^2}{R}\frac{1}{\Phi} \quad (1)$$

* Rebsch, R. and Schneider, W., "Aperture Defect of Weak Electron Lenses," *Z. Physik*, **107**, 138-143 (1937).

7.5. Focal length of magnetic gap lens (§ 3.4)

$$\frac{1}{f} = \frac{2\pi^2}{3}\frac{e\mu^2}{m_o}\frac{n^2I^2 \cdot 1.315}{R\Phi} \tag{1}$$

7.6. Focal length of lens consisting of two apertures at potential Φ_o and Φ_i, separated by a distance d (radius of apertures $\ll d$) *

$$\frac{1}{f_o} = \frac{3}{8d}\left(1 - \sqrt{\frac{\Phi_o}{\Phi_i}}\right)\left(\frac{\Phi_i}{\Phi_o} - 1\right) \quad \frac{1}{f_i} = \frac{3}{8d}\left(\sqrt{\frac{\Phi_i}{\Phi_o}} - 1\right)\left(1 - \frac{\Phi_o}{\Phi_i}\right) \tag{1}$$

The position of the principal planes relative to the plane of symmetry is given by

$$h_o = -\frac{d}{2} - \frac{4d\Phi_o}{3(\Phi_i - \Phi_o)} \quad h_i = \frac{d}{2} - \frac{4d\Phi_i}{3(\Phi_i - \Phi_o)} \tag{2}$$

8. Cardinal Points of Strong Lenses ($e\Phi \ll m_oc^2$)

8.1. Strong lens. Let $r_\beta(z)$ represent a path incident parallel to the axis from $-\infty$, and let $r_\delta(z)$ represent one incident parallel to the axis from $+\infty$. Then the positions of the focal points relative to the plane of symmetry of the lens field and the focal lengths are given by the following expressions :

z_{in} = nth image-side focal point [nth point for which $r_\beta(z) = 0$, counted from the side of incidence]

z_{on} = nth object-side focal point [nth point for which $r_\delta(z) = 0$]

$f_{in} = -r_\beta(-\infty)/r_\beta'(z_{in})$ = focal length corresponding to nth image-side focal point

$f_{on} = r_\delta(\infty)/r_\delta'(z_{on})$ = focal length corresponding to nth object-side focal point

$z_{if} = (z - r_\beta/r_\beta')_{z\to\infty}$ = image-side focal point of complete field

$z_{of} = (z - r_\delta/r_\delta')_{z\to-\infty}$ = object-side focal point of complete field

$f_i = -r_\beta(-\infty)/r_\beta'(\infty)$ = image-side focal length of complete field

$f_o = r_\delta(\infty)/r_\delta'(-\infty)$ = object-side focal length of complete field

For a symmetrical magnetic or (generally) equipotential lens

$$z_n = z_{in} = -z_{on}, \quad f_n = f_{in} = f_{on}, \quad z_f = z_{if} = -z_{of}, \quad f = f_i = f_o$$

* Gans, R., "Electron Paths in Electron-Optical Systems," *Z. tech. Physik*, **18**, 41-48 (1937).

8.2. Uniform magnetic field, cut off sharply at $z = \pm d$ *

$$B = B_m, \quad |z| < d; \qquad B = 0, \quad |z| > d; \qquad k^2 = \frac{eB_m^{\ 2}}{8m_o\Phi} d^2$$

$$\left.\begin{aligned} z_n &= d\left[\frac{\pi}{2k}(2n-1) - 1\right] \\ \frac{1}{f_n} &= (-1)^{n-1}\frac{k}{d} \end{aligned}\right\} \quad [k \geq \pi/4\,(2n-1)] \qquad (1)$$

$$z_f = d\left(1 + \frac{\cot 2k}{k}\right), \quad \frac{1}{f} = \frac{k}{d}\sin 2k$$

8.3. "Bell-shaped" magnetic field.+

with

$$B = \frac{B_m}{1 + (z/d)^2}, \quad k^2 = \frac{eB_m^{\ 2}}{8m_o\Phi} d^2,$$

$$z_n = -d\cot\frac{n\pi}{\sqrt{k^2+1}}, \quad (k \geqslant \sqrt{n^2-1}) \qquad (1)$$

$$\frac{1}{f_n} = \frac{(-1)^{n-1}}{d}\sin\frac{n\pi}{\sqrt{k^2+1}}$$

$$z_f = d\sqrt{k^2+1}\cot\pi\sqrt{k^2+1}$$

$$\frac{1}{f} = -\frac{1}{d\sqrt{k^2+1}}\sin\pi\sqrt{k^2+1}$$

8.4. Electric field $\Phi = \Phi_m e^{(4/\sqrt{3})k \text{ arc tan } z/d}$ ×

$$\left.\begin{aligned} z_{in} &= -z_{on} = -d\cot\frac{n\pi}{\sqrt{k^2+1}} \\ \frac{1}{f_{in}} &= \frac{(-1)^{n-1}}{d}e^{-(k/\sqrt{3})(n\pi/\sqrt{k^2+1})}\sin\frac{n\pi}{\sqrt{k^2+1}} \\ \frac{1}{f_{on}} &= \frac{(-1)^{n-1}}{d}e^{(k/\sqrt{3})(n\pi/\sqrt{k^2+1})}\sin\frac{n\pi}{\sqrt{k^2+1}} \end{aligned}\right\} \quad (k \geqslant \sqrt{n^2-1}) \qquad (1)$$

* Lenz, F., "Computation of Optical Parameters of Magnetic Lenses of Generalized Bell-Type," *Z. angew. Physik*, **2**, 337-340 (1950).

+ Glaser, W., "Exact Calculation of Magnetic Lenses with the Field Distribution $H = H_o/[1 + (z/a)^2]$," *Z. Physik*, **117**, 285-315 (1941).

× Hutter, R. G. E., "Rigourous Treatment of the Electrostatic Immersion Lens Whose Axial Potential Distribution is Given by $\Phi(z) = \Phi_o e^{K \text{ arc tan } z}$," *J. Appl. Phys.*, **16**, 678-699 (1945).

$$z_{if} = -z_{of} = d\sqrt{k^2+1}\cot \pi\sqrt{k^2+1}$$

$$\frac{1}{f_i} = -\frac{e^{-\pi k/\sqrt{3}}}{d\sqrt{k^2+1}}\sin \pi\sqrt{k^2+1}, \quad \frac{1}{f_o} = -\frac{e^{\pi k/\sqrt{3}}}{d\sqrt{k^2+1}}\sin \pi\sqrt{k^2+1}$$

9. Electron Mirrors * $(e\Phi \ll m_o c^2)$

9.1. Paraxial ray equations

$$\dot{z} = \pm\sqrt{\frac{2e\Phi}{m_o}}, \quad \ddot{r} = -\frac{e\Phi''}{2m_o}r \tag{1}$$

9.2. Displacement of electron. For electron leaving point z_o, r_o with inclination α_o to axis after reflection by uniform retarding field $-\Phi' = \Phi_o/d$,

$$\bar{r}(z_o) = 2d\sin 2\alpha_o \tag{1}$$

9.3. Approximate formula for focal length of an electron mirror

$$\frac{1}{f} = \frac{1}{2\sqrt{\Phi_o}}\int_{z_u}^{\infty}\frac{\Phi''}{\sqrt{\Phi}}dz - \frac{1}{8\sqrt{\Phi_o}}\int_{z_u}^{\infty}\frac{\Phi''}{\sqrt{\Phi}}dz \cdot \int_{z_u}^{\infty}\frac{dz}{\sqrt{\Phi}}\int_{z}^{\infty}\frac{\Phi''}{\sqrt{\Phi}}dz \tag{1}$$

Here z_u is determined by the condition $\Phi(z_u) = 0$.

10. Aberrations $(e\Phi \ll m_o c^2)$

10.1. Geometric aberrations of the third order +

$$\left.\begin{aligned}\Delta w_i = (S_1 + iS_2)(w_o')^2\bar{w}_o' + S_3 w_o'\bar{w}_o' w_a + (S_4 + iS_5)(w_o')^2\bar{w}_a \\ + (S_6 - iS_7)\bar{w}_o' w_a^2 + 2(S_6 + iS_7)w_o' w_a \bar{w}_a + S_8 \bar{w}_a w_a^2\end{aligned}\right\} \tag{1}$$

Here $w_i = r_i e^{i\theta_i}$, $w_a = r_a e^{i\theta_a}$, $w_o' = r_o e^{i(\theta_o+\chi_i)}$ represent the coordinates of a particular electron path in the image, aperture, and object planes, respectively. The image plane is the paraxial (Gaussian) image plane, the aperture plane is any (eventually also virtual) plane parallel to the image plane, such that the space between aperture plane and image plane is field-free; Δw_i is the deviation of the actual intersection of the electron path with the image plane from that calculated by the paraxial ray equations,

* Picht, J., *Einführung in die Theorie der Elektronenoptik*, J. A. Barth, Leipzig, 1939. Recknagel, A., "The Theory of the Electron Mirror," *Z. Physik*, **104**, 381-394 (1937).

+ Glaser, W., "Theory of the Electron Microscope," *Z. Physik*, **83**, 103-122 (1933).

retaining terms of the third order in the radial coordinates. The several aberration coefficients are correlated with individual aberrations as follows: S_1, distortion; S_2, anisotropic distortion; S_3, curvature of field; S_4, astigmatism; S_5, anisotropic astigmatism; S_6, coma; S_7, anisotropic coma; S_8, aperture defect or spherical aberration.

10.2. Chromatic aberrations *

$$\Delta w_i = (C_1 + iC_2)w_o' + C_3 w_a \tag{1}$$

$$C_1 = -\frac{M\Delta\Phi}{\sqrt{\Phi_o}} \int_{z_o}^{z_i} \left[\frac{\Phi'}{2\Phi^{3/2}} r_\alpha r_\gamma' + \left(\frac{\Phi''}{4\Phi^{3/2}} + \frac{eB^2}{8m_o\Phi^{3/2}} \right) r_\alpha r_\gamma \right] dz$$

$$C_2 = -\frac{M\Delta\Phi}{2} \int_{z_o}^{z_i} \sqrt{\frac{e}{8m_o\Phi^3}}\, B\, dz$$

$$C_3 = -\frac{M\Delta\Phi}{r_{\alpha a}\sqrt{\Phi_o}} \int_{z_o}^{z_i} \left[\frac{3}{8}\frac{(\Phi')^2}{\Phi^{5/2}} + \frac{eB^2}{8m_o\Phi^{3/2}} \right] r_\alpha^2\, dz$$

Here C_1 is the coefficient of chromatic difference in magnification, C_2 is that of chromatic difference in rotation, and C_3 is that of chromatic difference in image position; Δw_i denotes the shift in the intersection of a particular electron ray with the (fixed) Gaussian image plane if the energy of the electron is increased by $e\Delta\Phi$ without changing its position or direction of motion at the object plane.

10.3. General formula for aperture defect +

$$S_8 = \frac{M}{16 r_{\alpha a}^3 \sqrt{\Phi_o}} \int_{z_o}^{z_i} \Phi^{-3/2} r_\alpha^4 \left[U + 4V\frac{r_\alpha'}{r_\alpha} + 2W\frac{r_\alpha'^2}{r_\alpha^2} \right] dz \tag{1}$$

$$U = \frac{5(\Phi'')^2}{4} + \frac{5(\Phi')^4}{24\Phi^2} + \frac{e\Phi(B')^2}{m_o} + \frac{3e^2B^4}{8m_o^2} + \frac{35e(\Phi')^2B^2}{16m_o\Phi} - \frac{3e\Phi'BB'}{m_o}$$

$$V = \frac{7(\Phi')^3}{6\Phi} - \frac{e\Phi'B^2}{2m_o}, \qquad W = -\frac{3(\Phi')^2}{4} - \frac{e\Phi B^2}{2m_o}$$

10.4. Aperture defect of weak lens ×

$$S_8 = v\left\{ \int_{z_o}^{z_i} \left[\frac{5}{64}\left(\frac{\Phi''}{\Phi}\right)^2 + \frac{e}{8m_o}\frac{(B')^2}{\Phi} \right] dz \right\} \tag{1}$$

* Wendt, G., "Chromatic Aberration of Electron-Optical Imaging Systems," *Z. Physik*, **116**, 436-443 (1940).

\+ Scherzer, O., "Calculation of Third-Order Aberrations by the Path Method," in Busch, H. and Brüche, E., *Beiträge zur Elektronenoptik*, J. A. Barth, Leipzig, 1937.

× Rebsch, R. and Schneider, W., "Aperture Defect of Weak Electron Lenses," *Z. Physik*, **107**, 138-143 (1937).

10.5. Aperture defect of bell-shaped magnetic field (§ 8.3) * (for large magnification, $|M| \gg 1$). With

$$\Delta r_i = C f_o M \alpha_o{}^3 = S_8 r_a{}^3,$$

$$\left.\begin{aligned}\frac{C f_o}{d} = \frac{n\pi}{4}\frac{k^2}{(k^2+1)^{3/2}}\csc^4\frac{n\pi}{\sqrt{k^2+1}} - \frac{1}{4}\cdot\frac{4k^2-3}{4k^2+3} \\ \times\cot\frac{n\pi}{\sqrt{k^2+1}}\csc^2\frac{n\pi}{\sqrt{k^2+1}}\end{aligned}\right\} \quad (1)$$

10.6. Aperture defect of uniform magnetic and electric field

$$\Delta r_i = -\frac{\pi}{B}\sqrt{\frac{2m_o\Phi_o}{e}}\alpha_o{}^3\sqrt{\frac{\Phi_o}{\Phi_i}} \quad (1)$$

10.7. Aperture defect of uniform electric field of length l

$$\Delta r_i = \frac{l\Phi_o}{\Phi_i - \Phi_o}\left(1 - 2\sqrt{\frac{\Phi_o}{\Phi_i}} + \frac{\Phi_o}{\Phi_i}\right)\alpha_o{}^3 \quad (1)$$

10.8. Chromatic aberration of weak unipotential electrostatic lens +

$$C_3 = -2M\frac{\Delta\Phi}{\Phi}, \quad (|M| \gg 1) \quad (1)$$

10.9. Chromatic aberration of a magnetic lens for large magnification +

$$|C_3| \leqq \left|M\frac{\Delta\Phi}{\Phi}\right| \quad (1)$$

where the equality sign applies to a weak lens.

10.10. Chromatic aberration of uniform magnetic and electric field

$$\Delta r_i = \frac{\pi}{B}\sqrt{\frac{2m_o}{e\Phi_i}}\Delta\Phi\alpha_o \quad (1)$$

10.11. Relativistic aberration of weak electrostatic unipotential

* Glaser, W., " Exact Calculation of Magnetic Lenses with the Field Distribution $H = H_o/[1 + (z/a)^2]$," *Z. Physik*, **117**, 285-315 (1941).

\+ Glaser, W., " Chromatic Aberration of Electron Lenses," *Z. Physik*, **116**, 56-67 (1940).

lens. Diffusion of axial image point as applied voltage is increased from zero to Φ_A, keeping all voltage ratios constant for $|M| \gg 1$.

$$\Delta r_i = -\frac{2}{3} a \Phi_A M f_o \alpha_o \tag{1}$$

11. Symmetrical Two-Dimensional Fields ($e\Phi \ll m_o c^2$)

$$\left.\begin{aligned} &\frac{\partial \varphi}{\partial z} = 0, \quad b_z = 0, \quad \varphi(x,y) = \varphi(x,-y) \\ &b_x(x,y) = b_x(x,-y), \quad b_y(x,y) = -b_y(x,-y) \end{aligned}\right\} \tag{1}$$

11.1. Field distributions

$$\varphi(x,y) = \sum_{n=0}^{\infty} \frac{(-1)^n}{(2n)!} \Phi^{(2n)}(x) y^{2n} = \Phi(x) - \frac{1}{2}\Phi''(x)y^2 + \frac{1}{24}\Phi^{\mathrm{IV}}(x)y^4 - \ldots \tag{2}$$

Radius of curvature of equipotentials on axis

$$R = \frac{\Phi'}{\Phi''} \tag{3}$$

Vertex half-angle of equipotential wedge at saddle point

$$\alpha_s = \text{arc tan } 1 = 45^{\circ} \tag{4}$$

$$b_x(x,y) = \sum_{n=0}^{\infty} \frac{(-1)^n}{(2n)!} B^{(2n)}(x) y^{2n} = B(x) - \frac{1}{2} B''(x) y^2 + \ldots \tag{5}$$

$$b_y(x,y) = \sum_{n=1}^{\infty} \frac{(-1)^n}{(2n-1)!} B^{(2n-1)}(x) y^{2n-1} = -B'y + \frac{1}{6} B^{\mathrm{III}} y^3 - \ldots \tag{6}$$

11.2. Paraxial path equation in electric field

$$y'' = -\frac{\Phi'}{2\Phi} y' - \frac{\Phi''}{2\Phi} y \qquad \text{or} \qquad Y'' = -\left[\frac{3}{16}\left(\frac{\Phi'}{\Phi}\right)^2 + \frac{\Phi''}{4\Phi}\right] Y \tag{1}$$

where $Y = y\Phi^{1/4}$.

11.3. Paraxial path equations in magnetic field

$$y'' = -\sqrt{\frac{e}{2m_o\Phi}}\, z'B, \quad z'' = \sqrt{\frac{e}{2m_o\Phi}}\,(yB' + y'B) \tag{1}$$

11.4. Focal length of weak electric cylinder lens

$$\frac{1}{f_o} = \frac{7}{16} \sqrt[4]{\frac{\Phi_i}{\Phi_o}} \int_{x_o}^{x_i} \left(\frac{\Phi'}{\Phi}\right)^2 dx \tag{1}$$

11.5. Focal length of weak slit lens

$$\frac{1}{f} = \frac{E_o - E_i}{2\Phi_A} \tag{1}$$

11.6. Focal length and displacement of focal point in z direction for weak magnetic cylinder lens

$$\frac{1}{f} = \frac{e}{2m_o\Phi}\int_{x_o}^{x_i} B^2\,dx, \quad z_f = y_o\sqrt{\frac{e}{2m_o\Phi}}\int_{x_o}^{x_i} B\,dx \tag{1}$$

12. Deflecting Fields * $(e\Phi \ll m_o c^2)$

$$\left.\begin{aligned} \frac{\partial\varphi}{\partial z} &\equiv 0, \quad b_z \equiv 0, \quad \varphi(x,y) - \Phi_o = \Phi_o - \varphi(x,-y), \\ b_x(x,y) &= -b_x(x,-y), \quad b_y(x,y) = b_y(x,-y) \\ E &= -\left(\frac{\partial\varphi}{\partial y}\right)_{y=0}, \quad B = b_y(x,0) \end{aligned}\right\} \tag{1}$$

12.1. Field distribution in two-dimensional deflecting fields

$$\varphi(x,y) = \Phi_o + \sum_{n=0}^{\infty}\frac{(-1)^{n+1}}{(2n+1)!}E^{(2n)}(x)y^{2n+1} = \Phi_o - Ey + \frac{1}{6}E''y^3 - \ldots \tag{1}$$

$$b_y(x,y) = \sum_{n=0}^{\infty}\frac{(-1)^n}{(2n)!}B^{(2n)}(x)y^{2n} = B - \frac{1}{2}B''y^2 + \ldots \tag{2}$$

$$b_x(x,y) = \sum_{n=0}^{\infty}\frac{(-1)^n}{(2n+1)!}B^{(2n+1)}(x)y^{2n+1} = B'y - \frac{1}{6}B^{\mathrm{III}}y^3 + \ldots \tag{3}$$

12.2. Deflection by electric field for electron incident in midplane (deflection assumed small)

$$y(x) = -\frac{1}{2\Phi_o}\int_0^x d\xi\int_0^\xi E(\zeta)d\zeta \tag{1}$$

For a uniform field of length l whose mid-point is a distance L from the screen, the deflection becomes

$$y\left(\frac{l}{2} + L\right) = -\frac{ElL}{2\Phi_o} \tag{2}$$

12.3. Deflection by magnetic field of length l

$$\sin \alpha = -\int_{o}^{x} \frac{eB}{m_0 v} dx$$

in the x,z plane with apparent point of origin of the deflected ray at

$$x_c = l - \cot \alpha_l \int_{o}^{l} \tan \alpha \, dx \tag{2}$$

For a uniform magnetic deflecting field,

$$\sin \alpha_l = -\sqrt{\frac{e}{2m_0\Phi^*}}\, Bl, \quad x_c = \frac{\tan \alpha_l/2}{\sin \alpha_l}\, l \tag{3}$$

Bibliography

1. ZWORYKIN, V. K., MORTON, G. A., RAMBERG, E. G., HILLIER, J. and VANCE, A. W., *Electron Optics and the Electron Microscope*, John Wiley & Sons, Inc., New York, (1945). The formulas given in this chapter are, with few exceptions, derived from this work.
2. BERTRAM, S., " Determination of the Axial Potential Distribution in Axially Symmetric Electrostatic Fields," *Proc. IRE*, **13**, 496-502 (1942).
3. GANS, R., " Electron Paths in Electron-Optical Systems," *Z. tech. Physik*, **18**, 41-48 (1937).
4. GLASER, W., " Geometric-Optical Imaging by Electron Rays," *Z. Physik*, **80**, 451-464 (1933).
5. GLASER, W., " Theory of the Electron Microscope," *Z. Physik*, **83**, 103-122 (1933).
6. GLASER, W., " Chromatic Aberration of Electron Lenses," *Z. Physik*, **116**, 56-67 (1940).
7. GLASER, W., " Exact Calculation of Magnetic Lenses with the Field Distribution $H = H_0/[1 + (z/a)^2]$," *Z. Physik*, **117**, 285-315 (1941).
8. GRAY, F., " Electrostatic Electron Optics," *Bell System Tech. J.*, **18**, 1-31 (1939).
9. HUTTER, R. G. E., " Rigorous Treatment of the Electrostatic Immersion Lens Whose Axial Potential Distribution Is Given by $\Phi(z) = \Phi_0 e^{K \arctan z}$," *J. Appl. Phys.*, **16**, 678-699 (1945).
10. LANGMUIR, D. B., " Limitations of Cathode-Ray Tubes," *Proc. IRE*, **25**, 977-991 (1937).
11. LENZ, F., " Computation of Optical Parameters of Magnetic Lenses of Generalized Bell-Type," *Z. angew. Physik*, **2**, 337-340 (1950).
12. MALOFF, U. and EPSTEIN, D. W., *Electron Optics in Television*, McGraw-Hill Book Company, Inc., New York, 1938. Excellent treatment of the optics of the cathode-ray tube, particularly the electrostatic electron gun.
13. MORTON, G. A. and RAMBERG, E. G., " Electron Optics of an Image Tube," *Physics*, **7**, 451-459 (1936).
14. PICHT, J., " Contributions to the Theory of Geometric Electron Optics," *Ann. Physik*, **15**, 926-964 (1932).

15. Picht, J., *Einführung in die Theorie der Elektronenoptik*, J. A. Barth, Leipzig, 1939. A primarily analytical treatment.
16. Poeverlein, H., "On Waves under Anisotropic Propagation Conditions," *Z. Naturforsch.*, **5b**, 492-499 (1950).
17. Ramberg, E. G., "Variation of Axial Aberrations of Electron Lenses with Lens Strength," *J. Appl. Phys.*, **13**, 582-594 (1942).
18. Rebsch, R. and Schneider, W., "Aperture Defect of Weak Electron Lenses," *Z. Physik*, **107**, 138-143 (1937).
19. Recknagel, A., "The Theory of the Electron Mirror," *Z. Physik*, **104**, 381-394 (1937).
20. Scherzer, O., "Calculation of Third-Order Aberrations by the Path Method," in Busch, H. and Brüche, E., *Beiträge zur Elektronenoptik*, J. A. Barth, Leipzig, 1937.
21. Wendt, G., "Chromatic Aberration of Electron-Optical Imaging Systems," *Z. Physik*, **116**, 436-443 (1940).

Chapter 19

ATOMIC SPECTRA

BY CHARLOTTE E. MOORE

In Charge of " Atomic Energy Levels " Program
National Bureau of Standards

1. The Bohr Frequency Relation

1.1. Basic combination principle

$$\bar{\nu} = \left(\frac{E_1 - E_2}{h}\right) \quad \text{sec}^{-1} \tag{1}$$

where $\bar{\nu}$ is the frequency, in vibrations per second, of the emitted spectral line; h is Planck's constant, E_1 and E_2 are the atomic energies (in ergs) involved in the transition giving rise to a spectral line.

$$\nu = \frac{\bar{\nu}}{c} = \frac{1}{\lambda} = \left(\frac{E_1}{hc} - \frac{E_2}{hc}\right) \quad \text{cm}^{-1} \tag{2}$$

where c is the velocity of light; ν is the wave number of the observed spectral line, i.e., the number of waves per cm expressed in cm^{-1};* λ is the wavelength of the observed line, expressed in cm;

$$\frac{E_1}{hc} \quad \text{and} \quad \frac{E_2}{hc}$$

are the spectroscopic energy levels. (Ref. 3, p. 1.)

2. Series Formulas

2.1. The Rydberg equation

$$\nu_n = \nu_\infty - \frac{R}{(n + \mu)^2} \tag{1}$$

where ν_n is the wave number of the observed line [called ν in Eq. (2) of

* The Joint Commission for Spectroscopy has recommended that the unit of wave number hitherto described as cm^{-1} be named *kayser* with the abbreviation K, and that the symbol σ be used for wave number instead of ν. See Trans. Joint Commission for Spectroscopy, *J. Opt. Soc. Am.*, **43**, 411 (1953).

§ 1.1]; ν_∞ is the limit of the series; R is the Rydberg constant; μ is a constant; n takes integral values only. When $\mu = 0$ and $n = 2, 3, 4, 5, \ldots, \infty$ this equation reduces to Balmer's formula for hydrogen (see below).

Rydberg's more general formula

$$\nu_n = \frac{R}{(n_1 + \mu_1)} - \frac{R}{(n_2 + \mu_2)} \tag{2}$$

If $\mu_1 = 0$, $\mu_2 = 0$, $n_1 = 2$, $n_2 = 3, 4, 5$ this reduces to the hydrogen series formula

$$\nu_n = \frac{R}{n_1^{\,2}} - \frac{R}{n_2^{\,2}} = R\left(\frac{1}{n_1^{\,2}} - \frac{1}{n_2^{\,2}}\right) \quad \text{as follows :} \tag{3}$$

Lyman series

$$\nu_n = R\left(\frac{1}{1^2} - \frac{1}{n_2^{\,2}}\right), \quad (n_2 = 2, 3, 4, \ldots) \tag{4}$$

Balmer series

$$\nu_n = R\left(\frac{1}{2^2} - \frac{1}{n_2^{\,2}}\right), \quad (n_2 = 3, 4, 5, \ldots) \tag{5}$$

Paschen series

$$\nu_n = R\left(\frac{1}{3^2} - \frac{1}{n_2^{\,2}}\right), \quad (n_2 = 4, 5, 6, \ldots) \tag{6}$$

2.2. The Ritz combination principle. From the formulas for the Lyman, Balmer, and Paschen series it may be seen that the fixed terms of the equations for the Balmer, Paschen, etc. series are the first, second, etc., running terms of the Lyman series. This is known as the Ritz combination principle as it applies to hydrogen. Predictions of new series from this principle have been verified in many spectra.

If the sharp and principal series of the alkali metals are represented, respectively, by the equations

Sharp $$\nu_n = 1\,^2P^o - n\,^2S, \quad (n = 2, 3, 4) \tag{1}$$

Principal $$\nu_n = 1\,^2S - n\,^2P^o, \quad (n = 2, 3, 4) \tag{2}$$

the series predicted by Ritz are obtained by changing the fixed terms $1\,^2P^o$, to $2\,^2P^o$, $3\,^2P^o$, etc., and $1\,^2S$ to $2\,^2S$, $3\,^2S$ etc. The resulting equations are as follows :

Combination sharp series

$$2\,^2P^o - n\,^2S, \quad (n = 3, 4, 5, \ldots) \tag{3}$$

$$3\,^2P^o - n\,^2S, \quad (n = 4, 5, 6, \ldots) \tag{4}$$

Combination principal series

$$2\,{}^2\mathrm{S} - n\,{}^2\mathrm{P}^o, \quad (n = 3, 4, 5) \tag{5}$$

$$3\,{}^2\mathrm{S} - n\,{}^2\mathrm{P}^o, \quad (n = 4, 5, 6) \tag{6}$$

Similarly, diffuse or fundamental series are predicted from the combinations ${}^2\mathrm{P}^o - {}^2\mathrm{D}$, and ${}^2\mathrm{D} - {}^2\mathrm{F}^o$, respectively. Series among terms of different multiplicities are known in many spectra. (Ref. 37, p. 15.)

2.3. The Ritz formula. By expressing the Rydberg formula for hydrogen as

$$\nu_n = R\left(\frac{1}{p^2} - \frac{1}{q^2}\right) \tag{1}$$

with p and q as functions involving the order numbers n, Ritz obtained p and q in the form of infinite series.

$$p = n_1 + a_1 + \frac{b_1}{n_1^{\,2}} + \frac{c_1}{n_1^{\,4}} + \frac{d_1}{n_1^{\,6}} + \dots \tag{2}$$

$$q = n_2 + a_2 + \frac{b_2}{n_2^{\,2}} + \frac{c_2}{n_2^{\,4}} + \frac{d_2}{n_2^{\,6}} + \dots \tag{3}$$

By using only the first two terms, the Ritz formula becomes identical with Rydberg's general formula, which is now considered only a close approximation. Two useful forms of the Rydberg-Ritz formula are

$$\nu_n = T_1 - T_n = T_1 - \frac{R}{(n + a + b/n^2)^2} \tag{4}$$

where T_n is the running term and T_1 the fixed term. Here n is an integer, T_n denotes the absolute term value, i.e., the difference between E_1/hc and E_2/hc in Eq. (2) of § 1.1, and the ionization limit of the series, and

$$T_n = \frac{R}{(n + a + bT_n)^2} \tag{5}$$

The solution of these equations gives the limit of the series.

2.4. The Hicks formula. Hicks expressed the denominator of Rydberg's equation as a series

$$n + \mu + \frac{a}{n} + \frac{b}{n^2} + \frac{c}{n^3} + \dots \tag{1}$$

The formula then becomes (Ref. 37, pp. 16-22)

$$\nu_n = \nu_\infty - \frac{R}{(n + \mu + a/n + b/n^2 + c/n^3 + \dots)^2} \tag{2}$$

Shenstone has suggested a method of solving an extended Ritz formula, and illustrated it in Cu II :

$$T_n = \frac{4R}{(n + \mu + \alpha T + \beta T_n{}^2)} \tag{3}$$

In all the series formulas, R is used for arc spectra, $4R$ for first spark spectra, $9R$ for second spark spectra, etc. Shenstone's formula is of the form of the Ritz formula given above, with one term added, and with $4R$ used because it is applied to the *first spark* spectrum of Cu.

Let x_1, x_2, x_3, x_4 be the fractional parts of the denominators when the correct limit is chosen.

$$\frac{x_1 - x_2}{T_1 - T_2},\ \frac{x_2 - x_3}{T_2 - T_3},\ \frac{x_3 - x_4}{T_3 - T_4} \tag{4}$$

and let y_1, y_2, y_3 be defined by the equation

$$\frac{y_1 - y_2}{y_2 - y_3} = \frac{T_1 - T_3}{T_2 - T_4} \tag{5}$$

T_1, T_2, etc., are running values of the limit used as approximations to derive the final value. The right-hand side of this equation depends on observed quantities only; the left depends on the limit chosen, and can be varied by varying the limit.

The constants may then be found from the intermediate equations : (Ref. 36)

$$\left.\begin{aligned} y_1 - y_2 &= \beta(T_1 - T_3) \\ y_1 &= \alpha + \beta(T_1 + T_2) \\ x_1 &= \mu + \alpha T_1 + \beta T_1{}^2 \end{aligned}\right\} \tag{6}$$

3. The Sommerfeld Fine Structure Constant for Hydrogen-like Spectra

3.1. Energy states. Energy states of an atomic system consisting of a nucleus and a single electron are given by

$$\frac{E(n,l,j)}{hc} = \mu c^2 \left[1 + \frac{\alpha^2 Z^2}{(n - j - \frac{1}{2} + \sqrt{(j + \frac{1}{2})^2 - \alpha^2 Z^2})^2}\right]^{-1/2} - \mu c^2 \tag{1}$$

where E/hc is the level value in cm^{-1}, and the term with α^2 arises from electron spin and relativity corrections.

$$\alpha = \frac{2\pi e^2}{hc} \tag{2}$$

is the Sommerfield fine-structure constant, where c is the velocity of light, h is Planck's constant, e is the electronic charge, Z is the atomic number.

$$\mu = \frac{Mm}{M + m} \tag{3}$$

is the reduced mass, M being the mass of the nucleus, and m the mass of the electron.

Each electron is characterized by the quantum numbers n, l, and j. The quantum number j gives the total angular momentum of each electron, the resultant of the orbital moment l, and the spin moment s. The unit of momentum is $h/2\pi$. n has the integral values 1, 2, etc. For energy levels, where the properties of more than one electron are considered, the vector sums of these quantities are used, i.e., J, L, S replace j, l, s, capitals denoting the vector sums of the small characters. Here $L = 0, 1, 2,$ etc., to $n - 1$; $J = L + \frac{1}{2}$, and $L - \frac{1}{2}$, but for $L + 0$, $J = \frac{1}{2}$ only. By using the first terms of the expansion, Eq. (1) becomes

$$\frac{E(n,l,j)}{hc} = \frac{RZ^2}{n^2(1 + m/M)} + \frac{R\alpha^2 Z^4}{n^3(1 + m/M)}\left(\frac{3}{4n} - \frac{1}{j + \frac{1}{2}}\right) \tag{4}$$

$$R = \frac{2\pi^2 me^4}{h^3 c} \tag{5}$$

where R is the Rydberg constant. (Ref. 3, p. 218; Refs. 6, 7, 8, 9, 10, 11; Ref. 37, pp. 117, 147.)

4. Coupling

4.1. *LS* or Russell-Saunders coupling. The terms of a spectrum are made up of groups of related energy levels. Hund has shown what terms may be expected from the different configurations which the valence electrons of the atom assume when it is excited. In addition to the total quantum number n, which tells which shell it is in, each electron is specified by the quantum numbers $l (= 0, 1, 2, 3, \ldots$ for $s, p, d, f, \ldots$ electrons) and $s (= \pm \frac{1}{2}$ which states the number of units of quantized angular momenta associated with their orbital revolutions and axial rotations). Any level ${}^rT_J$ represents quantitatively one of the resultants obtained by adding vectorially the orbital and axial angular momenta of the electrons composing a particular configuration. Thus $L = 0, 1, 2, 3$, for $S, P, D, F, \ldots$ terms; and $S = 0, \frac{1}{2}, 1, \frac{3}{2}, 2, \ldots$ for singlets, doublets, triplets, ... The inner quantum numbers, J, which represent mechanically the resultant angular momentum of the atom, are limited by the relations

$$J_{\max} = L + S$$
$$J_{\min} = L - S$$

and all intermediate values differing by unity are included. The multiplicity,

$$r = 2S + 1$$

With the orbital motions of two electrons coupled together to give a resultant L^*, and the spins of the same electron coupled together to form S^*, both L^* and S^* will in turn be coupled to form J^*. The quantum conditions imposed upon this coupling are that $J^* = \sqrt{J(J+1)}$ and that J take non-negative integral values. The g-values calculated from Eq. (3) of § 6.1 hold for LS coupling. (Ref. 37, pp. 184-186.)

jj-coupling. In this type of coupling the interaction between the spin of each electron and its own orbit is greater than the interactions between the two spins and the two orbits, respectively, i.e., L and S are no longer constants, and the formula for Landé g-values does not hold. (Refs. 17, 18; Ref. 37, p. 196.)

jl-coupling. This intermediate coupling is conspicuous in the spectra of the inert gases. Perturbations of g-values caused by configuration interaction, and various types of coupling, are well known in a number of spectra. (Refs. 15, 20, 21, 33.)

5. Line Intensities

5.1. Doublets. Lines due to $^2S - {}^2P^o$ transitions

Designation	$^2S_{0\frac{1}{2}}$
$^2P^o_{1\frac{1}{2}}$	x_1
$^2P^o_{0\frac{1}{2}}$	x_2

Here x_1 and x_2 are the observed lines. The quantum weights of the ^2P levels are $2J + 1$. For $^2P^o_{1\frac{1}{2}}$, $J = 1\frac{1}{2}$ and the quantum weight is 4. For $^2P^o_{0\frac{1}{2}}$, $J = 0\frac{1}{2}$ and the quantum weight is 2. The ratio of the intensities of the lines x_1 and x_2 is proportional to $2J + 1$, i.e., 4:2 or 2:1.

This example is oversimplified, and for multiplets of more than two lines the following sum rules must be taken into account.

1. The sum of the intensities of all lines of a multiplet which start from a common initial level is proportional to the quantum weight $(2J + 1)$ of the initial level.

2. The sum of the intensities of all lines of a multiplet which end on a common final level is proportional to the quantum weight $(2J + 1)$ of the final level.

A Fourier analysis of precessing electron orbits in conjunction with the sum rules leads to the following formulas for intensities.

For transitions $(L-1) \rightarrow L$ $\left\{ \begin{array}{c} {}^3P - {}^3D \text{ multiplets for example,} \\ \text{transitions } 1 \rightarrow 2,\ L = 2 \end{array} \right\}$.

$(J-1) \rightarrow J$:

$$I = \frac{B(L+J+S+1)(L+J+S)(L+J-S)(L+J-S-1)}{J} \qquad J = \left.\begin{array}{r} 2\rightarrow 3 \\ 1\rightarrow 2 \\ 0\rightarrow 1 \end{array}\right\} \tag{1}$$

$J \rightarrow J$:

$$I = \frac{-B(L+J+S+1)(L+J-S)(L-J+S)(L-J-S-1)(2J+1)}{J(J+1)} \qquad J = \left.\begin{array}{r} 2\rightarrow 2 \\ 1\rightarrow 1 \end{array}\right\} \tag{2}$$

$(J+1) \rightarrow J$:

$$I = \frac{B(L-J+S)(L-J+S-1)(L-J-S-1)(L-J-S-2)}{J+1} \qquad J = 1 \tag{3}$$

For transitions $L \rightarrow L$ ($D - D$ multiplets for example, $L = 2$) the equations are

$(J-1) \rightarrow J$:

$$I = \frac{-A(L+J+S+1)(L+J-S)(L-J+S+1)(L-J-S)}{J} \tag{4}$$

$J \rightarrow J$:

$$I = \frac{A[L(L+1)+J(J+1)-S(S+1)]^2(2J+1)}{J(J+1)} \tag{5}$$

$(J+1) \rightarrow J$:

$$I = \frac{-A(L+J-S+2)(L+J-S+1)(L-J+S)(L-J-S-1)}{(J+1)} \tag{6}$$

The constants A and B may be omitted, since they apply to temperature corrections and to Einstein's ν^4 correction, which will be very small for multiplets of narrow separation.

The relative theoretical intensities in a $^3P - {}^3D$ multiplet can be determined from these formulas as follows.

	$^3D_3$	$^3D_2$	$^3D_1$	*Sum*	*Ratio*
$^3P_2$	168	30	2	200	5
$^3P_1$		90	30	120	3
$^3P_0$			40	40	1
Sum	168	120	72		
Ratio	7	5	3		

$L = 1$ for a P term; $L = 2$ for a D term. $L = 2$ in Eqs. (1), (2), and (3). The subscripts 3, 2, 1 and 2, 1, 0 represent the J values, or inner quantum numbers, for ^3D and ^3P terms respectively. $S = 1$ for triplet terms, the superscript denoting the multiplicity, $2S + 1$ (3 in this case).

In Eq. (1) J has the values 3, 2, 1, giving the intensities along the main diagonals of the multiplet : 168, 90, 40. In Eq. (2) J has the values 2, 1, giving the intensities of the first satellite lines in the multiplet : 30, 30. In Eq. (3) $J = 1$, giving the intensity of the second satellite line in the multiplet : 2. (Ref. 37, pp. 120, 204-206.)

Russell gives the quantum formulas for theoretical intensities for unperturbed LS coupling, in the following form :

Ordinary multiplets (SP, PD, etc.)

$$x = \frac{(r + k - n + 1)\,(r + k - n)\,(k - n + 1)\,(k - n)}{r + k - 2n + 1} \tag{7}$$

$$y = \frac{2(r + k - 2n)\,(r + k - n)n(k - n)\,(r - n)}{(r + k - 2n + 1)\,(r + k - 2n - 1)} \tag{8}$$

$$z = \frac{(r - n)\,(r - n - 1)n(n + 1)}{r + k - 2n - 1} \tag{9}$$

$s = rk(k^2 - 1)$; x denotes the intensity of a line in the principal diagonal of the multiplet; y denotes the intensity of a line that is one of the first satellites; z denotes the intensity of a line that is one of the second satellites; s is the sum of the intensities of all the lines of the multiplet; r is the multiplicity; k has the values 2, 3, 4, 5 for the combinations SP, PP, PD, DD, etc.; n is the number of the line in the diagonal to which it belongs. The leading line of the multiplet is always x_1.

Along with these formulas he gives tables of theoretical intensities for multiplicities 2 to 11 and for term types as far as I terms. (Refs. 5, 12, 29, 30, 34, 35.)

6. Theoretical Zeeman Patterns

6.1. Landé splitting factor. An external magnetic field causes each energy level to be split up into $(2J + 1)$ sublevels. When the field is weak enough, these sublevels will be equidistant and lie symmetrically around the original position of the level without field. The distance between them is proportional to the field strength H. Since H is the same for all levels of a given atom it is convenient to express the Zeeman splitting in terms of the Lorentz unit $\boldsymbol{L}$ (in cm^{-1}).

$$\boldsymbol{L} = \frac{He}{4\pi mc^2} = \Delta\nu \tag{1}$$

Here e is the charge on the electron in electrostatic units, m is the mass of the electron, and c is the velocity of light.

Expressed (in cm^{-1}) in terms of the normal Zeeman triplet this reduces to

$$\Delta\nu = \frac{\mu}{J} m = gm \tag{2}$$

The distance between the sublevels expressed in Lorentz units is denoted by g, the Landé splitting factor. The g-factor represents the ratio of the magnetic to the mechanical moment of the state, the former expressed in Bohr magnetons, $he/4\pi mc$; the latter in units $h/2\pi$. It must be noted that m in Eq. (2) is the magnetic quantum number and must not be confused with the m used in the denominator of Eq. (1) and in the expression defining the Bohr magneton. (Ref. 37, pp. 52, 53, 157, 158; Ref. 22.)

The quantity g is expressed as a function of the quantum numbers which describe spectroscopic energy levels and terms,

$$g = 1 + \frac{J(J+1) + S(S+1) - L(L+1)}{2J(J+1)} \tag{3}$$

For details of the theory and calculation of g-values see Back, E. and Landé, A., *Zeemaneffekt und Multiplettstruktur der Spektrallinien*, Julius Springer, Berlin, 1925, p. 42; also Kiess, C. C. and Meggers, W. F., *Bur. Standards J. Research*, RP 23, 1, 641-684 (1928); Meggers, W. F., "Zeeman Effect," *Enc. Brittanica*, 1953, 4 pp.

6.2. The Paschen-Back effect. In a very strong magnetic field, the coupling between all the individual magnetic vectors may be broken down, regardless of the original coupling scheme, so that each part will quantize separately with the field H. Equation (3) of § 6.1 does not hold, owing to the Paschen-Back interaction, in which the magnetic levels are displaced from their LS-coupling positions. The displacement ϵ is given by the equation :

$$\epsilon = \frac{I^2}{\delta} \tag{1}$$

where δ is the distance between the two repelling levels, and I, the interaction factor is

$$I = \left[\frac{(J-L+S)(J+L-S)(L+S+1+J)(L+S+1-J)}{4J^2(2J-1)(2J+1)}\right]^{1/2}(J^2 - M^2)^{1/2} \tag{2}$$

Values of I and I^2 for all term combinations likely to be affected by Paschen-Back interaction have been tabulated by Catalán. (Refs. 13, 14, 15, 19, 23; Ref. 37, p. 231.)

6.3. Pauli's *g*-sum rule. This rule is that out of all the states arising from a given electron configuration the sum of the g-factors for levels with the same J-value is a constant independent of the coupling scheme. (Refs. 25, 31; Ref. 37, p. 222.)

7. Nuclear Magnetic Moments

7.1. Hyperfine structure. Approximate formulas for the calculation of nuclear magnetic moments from observed hyperfine structure separations.

For s-electrons

$$g(I) = \frac{3a}{8R\alpha^2} \cdot \frac{n_0{}^3}{Z_i Z_0{}^2} \cdot \frac{1838}{\kappa(\frac{1}{2}, Z_i)} \tag{1}$$

For non s-electrons

$$g(I) = \frac{aZ_i}{\Delta\nu} \cdot \frac{j(j+1)\,(l+\frac{1}{2})}{l(l+1)} \cdot \frac{\lambda(l,Z_i)}{\kappa(j,Z_i)} \cdot 1838 \tag{2}$$

where I is the nuclear moment in units $h/2\pi$; $g(I)$, the nuclear g-value, is the ratio of the magnetic to the mechanical moment of the nucleus, the former expressed in " proton magnetons " $eh/4\pi Mc$, where M is the mass of the proton. For a single electron a is used instead of A, where A is equal to the distance between two adjacent hyperfine levels divided by the largest of their F-values and counted positive when the larger F value belongs to the higher energy, F being the fine structure quantum number, the resultant of I and J; J the inner quantum number is the vector sum of j; L the azimuthal quantum number is the vector sum of l; and $a =$ the interval factor for hyperfine structure. R is the Rydberg constant; α is the Sommerfeld fine-structure constant; n_0 is the Rydberg denominator or effective principal quantum number; Z_0 is the effective nuclear charge of the outer region of the atom; $Z_0 = 1$ for a neutral atom, 2 for a singly ionized atom, etc.; Z_i is the average effective nuclear charge of the inner region of the atom; $Z_i = Z$ for s-electrons; $Z_i = Z - 4$ for p-electrons; $\kappa(j,Z_i)$ is the relativity correction by which the equation for the hyperfine structure must be multiplied; $\lambda(l,Z_i)$ is the relativity correction by which the equation for the multiplet separation $\Delta\nu$ must be multiplied; where $\Delta\nu$ is the spin doublet separation for fine structure. (Ref. 16.)

8. Formulas for the Refraction and Dispersion of Air for the Visible Spectrum

8.1. Meggers' and Peters' formula. Complete sets of observations made with dry air at atmospheric pressure and at temperatures of 0, 15, and 30° C are closely represented by the following dispersion formulas.

$$(n-1)_0 \times 10^7 = 2875.66 + \frac{13.412}{\lambda^2 \times 10^{-8}} + \frac{0.3777}{\lambda^4 \times 10^{-16}} \tag{1}$$

$$(n-1)_{15} \times 10^7 = 2726.43 + \frac{12.288}{\lambda^2 \times 10^{-8}} + \frac{0.3555}{\lambda^4 \times 10^{-16}} \tag{2}$$

$$(n-1)_{30} \times 10^7 = 2589.72 + \frac{12.259}{\lambda^2 \times 10^{-8}} + \frac{0.2576}{\lambda^4 \times 10^{-16}} \tag{3}$$

where $\lambda =$ wavelength in air expressed in angstroms; $(n-1) \times 10^7 =$ refractivity. (Ref. 28.)

Tabular values of $(n-1) \times 10^7$ and of $\lambda(n-1) \times 10^7$ per angstrom (2000 A to 7000 A), and per 10 A (7000 A to 10000 A) for normal pressure and 15° C, from the above formulas are given in the standard table used to convert wavelengths in air to wave numbers *in vacuo*, e.g., KAYSER, H., *Tabelle der Schwingungszahlen*, rev. ed. (prepared by Meggers, W. F.), Edwards Bros., Inc., Ann Arbor, Mich., 1944. (See also Ref. 1.)

For wave numbers of infrared spectral lines beyond 10000 A see Ref. 2.

8.2. Perard's equation. Perard's equation for CO_2-free dry air is

$$(n-1)10^6 = \left[288.02 + \frac{1.478}{\lambda^2} + \frac{0.0316}{\lambda^4}\right] \times \frac{h(1+\beta h)}{760(1+760\beta)} \cdot \frac{1}{1+0.003716\theta} \tag{1}$$

where $\lambda =$ wavelength in air (microns), $h =$ pressure (mm), $\theta =$ temperature (°C), $\beta = 2.4 \times 10^{-6}$ (which can be taken as zero without appreciable error). (Ref. 32.)

8.3. The formula of Barrell and Sears. Barrell and Sears give the following equation for the refractivity of moist, normal air.

$$\left.\begin{aligned} n_{t,p,f} - 1)10^6 = {} & \left[0.378{,}125 + \frac{0.002{,}141{,}4}{\lambda^2} + \frac{0.000{,}017{,}93}{\lambda^4}\right] \\ & \times p\,\frac{\{1 + (1.049 - 0.0157t)p \times 10^{-6}\}}{1 + 0.003{,}661t} \\ & - \left[0.0624 - \frac{0.000{,}680}{\lambda^2}\right]\frac{f}{1 + 0.003{,}661t} \end{aligned}\right\} \quad (1$$

This equation is applicable to ranges of temperature $t = 10\text{-}30^\circ$ C, and pressure $p = 720\text{-}800$ mm. The quantity $(n_{t,p,f} - 1)$ represents the refractivity of atmospheric air containing water vapor at pressure f mm, and λ is the wavelength in normal air expressed in microns. (Ref. 4.)

The formula of Kösters and Lampe is

$$(n_{t,p} - 1)10^6 = \left[268.036 + \frac{1.476}{\lambda^2} + \frac{0.01803}{\lambda^4}\right]\frac{p}{760} \cdot \frac{1 + 20\alpha}{1 + \alpha t} \qquad (2)$$

where λ refers to the wavelength *in vacuo*, α assumed to be 0.00367. Their results refer to dry, CO_2-free air for the visible spectrum (exact range not specified). The equation is intended to apply only to small departures of temperature and pressure from 20° C and 760 mm, respectively. (Ref. 24.)

From recent study of the spectrum of Hg^{198}, Meggers concludes that " the unique properties of Hg^{198} force the conclusion that a progressive scientific world will soon adopt the wavelength of green radiation (5461 A) from Hg^{198} as the ultimate standard of length." Accurately measured relative wavelengths in this spectrum tested by the combination principle, indicate that a revision of the dispersion formulas is necessary. (Refs. 26, 27.)

Barrell* has recently derived a new formula representing the arithmetical mean of data from three different laboratories, as follows :

$$(n - 1)10^6 = 272.729 + (1.4814/\lambda_s^2) + (0.02039/\lambda_s^4) \ldots$$

where λ_s = wavelength in standard air, expressed in microns.

At the 1952 meeting of the Joint International Commission for Spectroscopy, Edlén+ proposed a solution to this problem by suggesting that the

* H. Barrell, *J. Opt. Soc. Am.*, **41**, 297 (1951).
\+ B. Edlén, *J. Opt. Soc. Am.*, **43**, 339 (1953).

empirical Cauchy formulas previously used be replaced by a dispersion formula of the Sellmeier type, which has physical meaning :

$$n - 1 = \Sigma\, A_i(\sigma_i^2 - \sigma^2)^{-1}$$

where σ_i are resonance frequencies of the gas. He adopts as the formula that gives the " best representation of the observed values :"

$$(n - 1)10^8 = 6432.8 + \frac{2,949,810}{146 - \sigma^2} + \frac{25,540}{41 - \sigma^2}$$

σ being the vacuum wave number expressed in μ^{-1}. " In order to preserve the usefulness of Kayser's *Tabelle der Schwingungszahlen*," he provides a table of corrections to be applied to the wave numbers given in Kayser.

The Joint Commission for Spectroscopy* has recommended the use of the tables of Edlén for correcting wavelengths in standard air to wavelengths in vacuum.

Bibliography

1. BABCOCK, H. D., *Astrophys. J.*, **111**, 60-64 (1949).
2. BABCOCK, H. D., *Phys. Rev.*, **46**, 382 (1934).
3. BACHER, R. F. and GOUDSMIT, S., *Atomic Energy States*, McGraw-Hill Book Company, Inc., New York, 1932.
4. BARRELL, H. and SEARS, J. E., *Phil. Trans. Roy. Soc.* (London), **A238**, 1-64 (1939).
5. BATES, D. R. and DAMGAARD, A., *Phil. Trans. Roy. Soc.* (London), **A242**, 101 (1949).
6. BIRGE, R. T., *Phys. Rev.*, **58**, 658 (1940).
7. BIRGE, R. T., *Phys. Rev.*, **60**, 766-785 (1941).
8. BIRGE, R. T., *Phys. Rev.*, **79**, 193, 1005 (1950).
9. BIRGE, R. T., *Revs. Modern Phys.*, **13**, No. 4, 233-239 (1941).
10. BIRGE, R. T., *Repts. Progress in Physics*, **8**, 90 (1941).
11. BIRGE, R. T., *Am. J. Phys.*, **13**, 63-73 (1945).
12. BURGER, H. C. and DORGELO, H. B., *Z. Physik*, **23**, 258 (1924).
13. CATALÁN, M. A. and VELASCO, R., *J. Opt. Soc. Am.*, **40**, 653 (1950).
14. CATALÁN, M. A., *J. Research Natl. Bur. Standards*, RP 2278, **47**, 502 (1951).
15. CONDON, E. U. and SHORTLEY, G. H., *The Theory of Atomic Spectra*, The Macmillan Company, New York, 1935; reprinted by Bradford and Dickens, 1951.
16. GOUDSMIT, S., *Phys. Rev.*, **43**, 636 (1933).
17. GREEN, J. B. and FRIED, B., *Phys. Rev.*, **54**, 876 (1938).
18. GREEN, J. B., *Phys. Rev.*, **64**, 151 (1943).
19. GREEN, J. B. and LORING, R. A., *Phys. Rev.*, **46**, 888 (1934); **49**, 632 (1936).
20. GREEN, J. B. and LYNN, J. T., *Phys. Rev.*, **69**, 165 (1946).
21. GREEN, J. B., and PEOPLES, J. A., Jr., *Phys. Rev.*, **54**, 602 (1938).

* " Trans. Joint Comm. for Spectroscopy," *J. Opt. Soc. Am.*, **43**, 412 (1953).

22. Hund, F., *Linienspektren und periodisches System der Elemente*, Julius Springer, Berlin, 1926.
23. Kiess, C. C. and Shortley, G. H., *J. Research Natl. Bur. Standards*, RP 1961, **42**, 183 (1949).
24. Kösters, W. and Lampe, P., *Physik. Z.*, **35**, 223 (1934).
25. Laporte, O., *Handbuch der Astrophysik*, Vol. **3**, Part 2, 1930, pp. 603-723, Julius Springer, Berlin, 1930.
26. Meggers, W. F., *Sci. Monthly*, **68**, 11 (1949).
27. Meggers, W. F. and Kessler, K. G., *J. Opt. Soc. Am.*, **40**, 737 (1950).
28. Meggers, W. F. and Peters, C. G., *Sci. Papers Bur. Standards*, No. 327, **14**, 698-740 (1918).
29. Menzel, D. H. and Goldberg, L., *Astrophys. J.*, **82**, 1-25 (1935).
30. Menzel, D. H. and Goldberg, L., *Astrophys. J.*, **84**, 1-13 (1936).
31. Pauli, W., *Z. Physik*, **16**, 155 (1923).
32. Perard, A., *Trav. mém. bur. intern. poids mesures*, **19**, 78 (1934); also Peters, C. G. and Emerson, W. B., *J. Research Natl. Bur. Standards*, RP 2089, **44**, 439 (1950).
33. Racah, G., *Phys. Rev.*, **61**, 537 L (1942).
34. Russell, H. N., *Contribs. Mt. Wilson Observ.*, No. 537, 1936.
35. Russell, H. N., *Astrophys. J.*, **83**, 129 (1936).
36. Shenstone, A. G., *Phil. Trans. Roy. Soc.*, (London) **A235**, 198-199 (1936).
37. White, H. E., *Introduction to Atomic Spectra*, McGraw-Hill Book Company, Inc., New York, 1934.

Chapter 20

MOLECULAR SPECTRA

BY L. HERZBERG AND G. HERZBERG

Division of Physics
National Research Council, Canada

1. General Remarks

The motions in a molecule are determined by its Schrödinger equation (see § 1.3 of Chapter 21). The eigenvalues of the Schrödinger equation are the stationary energy values of the system. To a usually satisfactory approximation the energy can be resolved into a sum of contributions due to electronic motion, vibration, and rotation.

$$E = E_e + E_v + E_r \tag{1}$$

The observed spectra correspond to transitions between these energy levels according to the Bohr frequency condition

$$hc\nu = E' - E'' \tag{2}$$

where the $'$ and $''$ refer to the upper and lower states, respectively, and where ν is the wave number.

The transition probabilities are determined by the eigenfunctions of the Schrödinger equation by way of the matrix elements of the dipole moment (p) or other quantities considered, e.g.,

$$\int \psi' p \psi''^* d\tau$$

2. Rotation and Rotation Spectra

2.1. Diatomic and linear polyatomic molecules

a. *Moments of inertia.* The moment of inertia about an axis perpendicular to the figure axis is defined by

$$I_B = \Sigma\, m_i r_i^2 \tag{1}$$

where m_i stands for the mass of an individual nucleus, and r_i for its distance from the center of mass. The moment of inertia about the figure axis I_A is very small.

For the special case of a diatomic molecule we have

$$I_B = \mu r^2 \tag{2}$$

where

$$\mu = \frac{m_1 m_2}{m_1 + m_2}$$

is the " reduced mass," and r is the internuclear distance.

b. *Energy levels.* The rotational energy levels of the rigid diatomic or linear polyatomic molecule are given by the expression

$$\frac{E_r}{hc} = F(J) = BJ(J+1) \tag{3}$$

where E_r is the rotational energy (in ergs) and $F(J)$ is the rotational term value (in cm^{-1}). The rotational constant B is given by

$$B = \frac{h}{8\pi^2 c I_B} = \frac{27.98_{30} \times 10^{-40}}{I_B}$$

J is the rotational quantum number corresponding to the angular momentum $\boldsymbol{J}$ whose magnitude is

$$\frac{h}{2\pi}\sqrt{J(J+1)} \approx \frac{h}{2\pi} J$$

For the nonrigid diatomic or linear polyatomic molecule we have

$$\frac{E_r}{hc} = F(J) = BJ(J+1) - DJ^2(J+1)^2 + \dots \tag{4}$$

where D is a rotational constant representing the influence of the centrifugal forces. In the case of a diatomic molecule of vibrational frequency ω (in cm^{-1}), the constant D, in a first approximation, is given by

$$D = \frac{4B^3}{\omega^2}$$

In a polyatomic molecule, D depends in general on all the vibrational frequencies of the molecule.

c. *Eigenfunctions.* The rotational eigenfunctions of a diatomic or linear polyatomic molecule are the so-called surface harmonics

$$\psi_r = N_r P_J^{|M|}(\cos\vartheta) e^{iM\varphi} \tag{5}$$

where φ is the azimuth of the line connecting the mass point to the origin, taken about the z axis; ϑ is the angle between this line and the z axis; M is a second quantum number (the so-called magnetic quantum number) which takes the values $M = J,\ J-1,\ J-2,\ \dots,\ -J$, and which represents in units $h/2\pi$ the component of the angular momentum $\boldsymbol{J}$ in the direction of the z axis; $P_J^{|M|}(\cos\vartheta)$ is a function of the angle ϑ, the so-called associated Legendre function (§ 8.11 of Chapter 1); N_r is a normalization constant.

The probability of finding the system oriented in the direction (ϑ, φ) is

$$\psi_r\psi_r^* = N_r^2[P_J^{|M|}(\cos\vartheta)]^2 \tag{6}$$

that is, the probability is independent of φ.

d. *Symmetry properties.* A rotational level is called positive or negative (+ or −) depending on whether the total eigenfunction ψ remains unaltered or changes its sign by reflection of all the particles (electrons and nuclei) at the origin (inversion). In addition, if the molecule has a center of symmetry, a rotational level is symmetric (s) or antisymmetric (a) depending on whether or not the total eigenfunction ψ of the system (apart from the nuclear spin function) remains unchanged or changes sign, when all nuclei on one side of the center are simultaneously exchanged with the corresponding ones on the other side.

e. *Statistical weight.* The statistical weight g of a rotational state is dependent on two factors

$$g = g_J \times g_I \tag{7}$$

where g_J depends on the over-all rotation of the molecule and is equal to the number of possible orientations of $\boldsymbol{J}$ in a magnetic field

$$g_J = 2J + 1$$

and g_I depends on the nuclear spins, and, if the molecule has a center of symmetry, on the statistics of the nuclei.

For molecules without a center of symmetry we have

$$g_I = (2I_1 + 1)(2I_2 + 1)\ldots$$

where I_1, I_2, ... are the spins of the individual nuclei. Since in this case g_I is the same for all rotational levels, it can, for most purposes, be omitted.

If the molecule has a center of symmetry and if the number of pairs of identical nuclei following Fermi statistics is odd (while the number of pairs of identical nuclei following Bose statistics is even or odd), the statistical weight due to the nuclear spins is

$$g_I^s = \tfrac{1}{2}[(2I_X + 1)^2(2I_Y + 1)^2(2I_Z + 1)^2 - (2I_X + 1)(2I_Y + 1)(2I_Z + 1)\ldots]$$

for the symmetric rotational levels (§ 2.1d), and

$$g_I^a = \tfrac{1}{2}[(2I_X + 1)^2(2I_Y + 1)^2(2I_Z + 1)^2 + (2I_X + 1)(2I_Y + 1)(2I_Z + 1)\ldots]$$

for the antisymmetric rotational levels. If the number of pairs of identical nuclei following Fermi statistics is even, the situation is reversed. Here $X, Y, Z, \ldots$ refer to the different pairs of nuclei.

If only one pair of identical nuclei has a nonzero nuclear spin I, the ratio of the statistical weights of the symmetric to the antisymmetric rotational levels becomes simply $(I+1)/I$ or $I/(I+1)$, depending on whether the nuclei follow Bose or Fermi statistics.

f. *Thermal distribution of rotational levels.* The population N_J of the various rotational levels is given by the general formula

$$N_J = \frac{N}{Q_r} g_I (2J+1) e^{-BJ(J+1)hc/kT} \tag{8}$$

Here T is the absolute temperature and k the Boltzmann constant, B is the rotational constant, as defined in § 2.1b, g_I is the statistical weight due to the nuclear spin, as discussed in § 2.1e, and Q_r is the rotational partition function

$$Q_r = \Sigma\, g_I (2J+1) e^{-BJ(J+1)hc/kT}$$

g. *Pure rotation spectrum.* A pure rotation spectrum in the far infrared or microwave region can occur only in molecules with a permanent dipole moment, that is, in molecules without a center of symmetry. The selection rules are

$$+ \longleftrightarrow -, \quad + \not\longleftrightarrow +, \quad - \not\longleftrightarrow -$$

that is, positive levels combine only with negative levels, and

$$\Delta J = J' - J'' = 1$$

where J' and J'' are the rotational quantum numbers of the upper and lower states, respectively. Accordingly, the wave-numbers of the pure rotation spectrum are given by the formula

$$\nu = 2B(J+1) - 4D(J+1)^3 + \ldots \tag{9}$$

where $D \ll B$ (§ 2.1b) and J stands for J''.

A Raman spectrum can occur only if the polarizability of the molecule changes during the transition. This is the case for the rotation of diatomic and linear polyatomic molecules, whether or not there is a center of symmetry. The selection rules referring to the symmetry of the rotational states (§ 2.1d) are

$$+ \longleftrightarrow +, \quad - \longleftrightarrow -, \quad + \not\longleftrightarrow -$$

and

$$s \longleftrightarrow s, \quad a \longleftrightarrow a, \quad s \not\longleftrightarrow a$$

that is, positive levels combine only with positive, negative only with negative, symmetric only with symmetric, and antisymmetric only with antisymmetric levels. The selection rule for the rotational quantum number is

$$\Delta J = 0, \pm 2 \tag{10}$$

that is, besides the undisplaced line ($\Delta J = 0$) one observes two lines both with $\Delta J = J' - J'' = +2$, one with the lower state as the initial state (Stokes line) and one with the upper state as the initial state (anti-Stokes line).

The wave number shifts are given by the formula

$$|\,\Delta\nu\,| = (4B - 6D)\,(J + \tfrac{3}{2}) - 8D(J + \tfrac{3}{2})^3 \tag{11}$$

or, since always $D \ll B$, to a very good approximation

$$|\,\Delta\nu\,| = 4B(J + \tfrac{3}{2}) \tag{12}$$

where J, as always, stands for J'', the rotational quantum number of the lower state involved.

For molecules with a center of symmetry, corresponding to the alternation of statistical weights for the symmetric and antisymmetric rotational levels, an alternation of intensities will occur. If the spins of all nuclei with the possible exception of the one at the center are zero, alternate lines will be missing.

2.2. Symmetric top molecules

a. *Moments of inertia.* A symmetric top molecule is characterized by the fact that two of its principal moments of inertia are the same (I_B), and that the third (I_A) is of the same order of magnitude. The axis of the third moment of inertia is called the figure axis of the molecule. If $I_A < I_B$, we speak of a prolate symmetric top; if $I_A > I_B$, of an oblate symmetric top.

b. *Energy levels.* The rotational energy levels of a rigid symmetric top molecule are given by the expression

$$\frac{E_r}{hc} = F(J,K) = BJ(J+1) + (A-B)K^2 \tag{1}$$

Here E_r is the rotational energy (in ergs), $F(J,K)$ the rotational term value (in cm^{-1}); A and B are rotational constants given by

$$B = \frac{h}{8\pi^2 c I_B}, \quad A = \frac{h}{8\pi^2 c I_A}$$

and J and K are rotational quantum numbers. Here J corresponds to the total angular momentum $\boldsymbol{J}$, and K corresponds to the component of $\boldsymbol{J}$ in the direction of the figure axis; therefore $J = K,\ K+1,\ K+2, \ldots$. All rotational levels with $K > 0$ are doubly degenerate.

For the nonrigid symmetric top molecule, the energy formula is

$$\left.\begin{aligned} \frac{E_r}{hc} &= F(J,K) \\ &= BJ(J+1) + (A-B)K^2 - D_J J^2(J+1)^2 \\ &\qquad\qquad - D_{JK} J(J+1)K^2 - D_K K^4 + \ldots \end{aligned}\right\} \quad (2)$$

where D_J, D_{JK}, and D_K are rotational constants corresponding to D in the linear molecule (§ 2.1b).

c. *Eigenfunctions.* The rotational eigenfunctions of the symmetric top are given by

$$\psi_r = \theta_{JKM}(\vartheta) \cdot e^{iK\chi} \cdot e^{iM\varphi} \quad (3)$$

Here ϑ, φ, and χ are the so-called Eulerian angles, ϑ is the angle of the figure axis of the top with the fixed z axis, φ is the azimuthal angle about the z axis, and χ is the azimuthal angle measuring the rotation about the figure axis; J and K are rotational quantum numbers as defined in (§ 2.2b); M is the magnetic quantum number which gives the component of $\boldsymbol{J}$ in the direction of the z axis in units $h/2\pi$ and can have the values $J,\ J-1, \ldots, -J$. The function $\theta_{JKM}(\vartheta)$ depends in a somewhat complicated way on the angle ϑ; it contains the so-called Jacobi (hypergeometric) polynomials (see § 10.7 of Chapter 1).

d. *Symmetry properties.* In the nonplanar symmetric top molecule a reflection of all particles at the origin (inversion) leads to a configuration which cannot also be obtained by rotation of the molecule. Corresponding to these two configurations of the molecule, each rotational level J, K is doubly degenerate as long as the potential hill separating the two configurations is infinitely high. For a finite potential hill, a splitting occurs into two sublevels which have opposite symmetry with respect to an inversion. The eigenfunctions of these sublevels contain equal contributions from the positive and negative " original " levels (inversion doubling).

For $K > 0$ the K degeneracy exists in addition to the inversion doubling, so that each level with a given J and K (> 0) consists of four sublevels.

In the planar symmetric top molecule no inversion doubling occurs. Each rotational level J, $K(> 0)$ consists of two sublevels either both positive or both negative with respect to inversion.

For molecules which are symmetrical tops due to their symmetry, additional symmetry properties arise corresponding to the property symmetric-antisymmetric in linear molecules. Levels belonging to different species are distinguished by symbols A, E, etc.

e. *Statistical weights.* In the symmetric top molecule the statistical weight of a rotational state due to the over-all rotation is

$$g_{JK} = 2J + 1, \qquad \text{for } K = 0$$

$$g_{JK} = 2(2J + 1), \quad \text{for } K > 0$$

For molecules without symmetry the statistical weight due to the nuclear spin is

$$g_I = (2I_1 + 1)(2I_2 + 1)(2I_3 + 1) \ldots$$

In this case g_I contributes only a constant factor to the total statistical weight

$$g = g_{JK} \times g_I$$

and can usually be omitted.

If the molecule has symmetry, rotational levels of different species have different statistical weights depending on spin and statistics of the identical nuclei. If, for instance, the figure axis of the molecule is a threefold axis of rotation, in a totally symmetric vibrational and electronic state the levels with $K = 0, 3, 6, 9, \ldots (A)$ have

$$g_I = \tfrac{1}{3}(2I + 1)(4I^2 + 4I + 3)$$

while those with $K = 1, 2, 4, 5, 7, 8, \ldots (E)$ have

$$g_I = \tfrac{1}{3}(2I + 1)(4I^2 + 4I)$$

If the spin of all the identical nuclei is zero, the levels with $K = 1, 2, 4, 5, 7, 8, \ldots$ are entirely missing.

f. *Thermal distribution of rotational levels.* The population of the various rotational levels (using the same notation as in (§ 2.1f) is given by

$$N_{JK} = \frac{N}{Q_r} g_I g_{JK} e^{-[BJ(J+1)+(A-B)K^2]hc/kT} \tag{4}$$

where

$$Q_r = \sum_{J,K} g_I g_{JK} e^{-[BJ(J+1)+(A-B)K^2]hc/kT}$$

and g_{JK} and g_I are given in § 2.2e.

g. *Pure rotation spectrum.* A pure rotation spectrum in the far infrared and microwave region can occur only if the molecule has a permanent dipole moment. For the accidental symmetric top the selection rules are

$$\Delta K = 0, \pm 1; \quad \Delta J = 0, \pm 1; \quad + \longleftrightarrow -, \quad + \leftarrow\!|\!\rightarrow +, \quad - \leftarrow\!|\!\rightarrow -$$

For a molecule which is a symmetric top because of its symmetry the same selection rules hold, but $\Delta K = \pm 1$ is excluded. In addition, only states having the same species of the rotational eigenfunction combine with one another (e.g., $A \longleftrightarrow A$, $E \longleftrightarrow E$, $A \leftarrow\!|\!\rightarrow E$ for molecules with a threefold axis of symmetry).

The wave-numbers of the pure rotation lines when the molecule has an axis of symmetry are given in a first approximation by the formula

$$\nu = 2B(J+1) \tag{5}$$

or, if centrifugal stretching is taken into account,

$$\nu = 2B(J+1) - 2D_{KJ}K^2(J+1) - 4D_J(J+1)^3 \tag{6}$$

(For definition of the constants B, D_{KJ}, and D_J, see § 2.2b).

For the rotational Raman spectrum, in the case of the accidental symmetric top the selection rules are

$$\Delta J = 0, \pm 1, \pm 2; \quad \Delta K = 0, \pm 1, \pm 2$$

and

$$+ \longleftrightarrow +, \quad - \longleftrightarrow -, \quad + \leftarrow\!|\!\rightarrow -$$

If the molecule is a symmetric top because of its symmetry, the same selection rules apply except that transitions with $\Delta K \pm 1, \pm 2$ are no longer possible and, those with $\Delta J = \pm 1$ occur only for $K \neq 0$. In this case the Raman lines form two branches on either side of the undisplaced line with the displacements

$$|\Delta \nu| = F(J+2,K) - F(J,K) = 6B + 4BJ, \qquad J = 0, 1, \ldots \text{ (}S\text{-branches)}$$

and

$$|\Delta \nu| = F(J+1,K) - F(J,K) = 2B + 2BJ, \qquad J = 1, 2, \ldots \text{ (}R\text{-branches)}$$

neglecting centrifugal stretching terms.

2.3. Spherical top molecules

a. *Moment of inertia and energy levels.* A spherical top is defined as a rotating body in which all three principal moments of inertia are equal, that is,

$$I_A = I_B = I_C = I$$

The energy levels of a spherical top molecule are therefore given by (compare § 2.2b)

$$\frac{E_r}{hc} = F(J) = BJ(J+1), \quad B = \frac{h}{8\pi^2 cI} \tag{1}$$

b. *Symmetry properties and statistical weights.* In the case of a spherical top, the distinction between positive and negative rotational levels can be ignored since they always occur in close pairs, and in no case of spherical top molecules has the inversion doubling been resolved.

The statistical weight of a given rotational level due to the over-all rotation is

$$g_J = (2J+1)^2$$

and that due to the nuclear spin is

$$g_I = (2I_1+1)(2I_2+1)(2I_3+1)\ldots$$

For molecules that are spherical tops on account of their symmetry there are additional symmetry properties, e.g., A, E, and F for tetrahedral molecules. The over-all statistical weight is then a product of $(2J+1)$ times a factor that depends in a complicated way both on J and the spin of the identical nuclei (ref. 10).

c. *Pure rotation spectrum.* Molecules which are spherical tops on account of their symmetry have no pure rotation spectrum in the infrared because they have no permanent dipole moment. Accidental spherical top molecules may have a permanent dipole moment and, consequently, a pure rotation spectrum. The selection rule is

$$\Delta J = 0, \quad \pm 1$$

leading to the same wave-number formula as for linear molecules (§ 2.1g).

Molecules which are spherical tops on account of their symmetry have no pure rotational Raman spectrum, since the polarizability does not change during the rotation. In accidental spherical top molecules a rotational Raman spectrum may occur. The selection rule is

$$\Delta J = 0, \quad \pm 1, \quad \pm 2$$

The Raman displacements are the same as those of a symmetric top molecule (§ 2.2h).

2.4. Asymmetric top molecules

a. *Moments of inertia.* The asymmetric top molecule is defined as one in which all three principal moments of inertia are different from each other.

$$I_A \neq I_B \neq I_C \quad (I_A < I_B < I_C)$$

b. *Energy levels.* The energy levels of the asymmetric top are represented by the formula

$$F(J_\tau) = \tfrac{1}{2}(B + C)J(J + 1) + [A - \tfrac{1}{2}(B + C)]W_\tau \qquad (1)$$

Here $A = h/8\pi^2cI_A$, $B = h/8\pi^2cI_B$, $C = h/8\pi^2cI_C$. The symbol τ numbers the $2J + 1$ levels of a given J in the order of their energy, i.e.,

$$\tau = -J, -J + 1, \ \ldots, \ +J$$

and W_τ are the roots of algebraic equations containing A, B, and C. For the lowest values of J one has

$J = 0:$ $W_0 = 0$

$J = 1:$ $W_\tau = 0$
$W_\tau^2 - 2W_\tau + (1 - b^2) = 0$

$J = 2:$ $W_\tau - 1 + 3b = 0$
$W_\tau - 1 - 3b = 0$
$W_\tau - 4 = 0$
$W_\tau^2 - 4W_\tau - 12b^2 = 0$

$J = 3:$ $W_\tau - 4 = 0$
$W_\tau^2 - 4W_\tau - 60b^2 = 0$
$W_\tau^2 - (10 - 6b)W_\tau + (9 - 54b - 15b^2) = 0$
$W_\tau^2 - (10 + 6b)W_\tau + (9 + 54b - 15b^2) = 0$

$J = 4:$ $W_\tau^2 - 10(1 - b)W_\tau + (9 - 90b - 63b^2) = 0$
$W_\tau^2 - 10(1 + b)W_\tau + (9 + 90b - 63b^2) = 0$
$W_\tau^2 - 20W_\tau + (64 - 28b^2) = 0$
$W_\tau^3 - 20W_\tau^2 + (64 - 208b^2)W_\tau + 2880b^2 = 0$

Here b stands for

$$b = \frac{C - B}{2[A - \frac{1}{2}(B + C)]}$$

For higher values of J see (Refs. 7, 12, 14, 18).

The average of the levels with a certain J follows accurately (neglecting centrifugal stretching) the formula for the simple rotator with an average rotational constant, that is,

$$\frac{\Sigma_J F(J_\tau)}{2J + 1} = \frac{1}{3}(A + B + C)J(J + 1) \qquad (2)$$

When two of the three principal moments of inertia are nearly equal, the formulas for the symmetric top can be applied (see § 2.2*b*) if the average of the two corresponding rotational constants (B and C or A and B) is used in place of B.

c. *Symmetry properties.* Apart from the symmetry property positive-negative with respect to inversion, which is unimportant for asymmetric top molecules, the rotational levels are distinguished by the behavior of their eigenfunctions with respect to rotations by 180° about the axes of largest and smallest moment of inertia (C_2^c and C_2^a). There are thus four different types (species) of rotational levels, briefly described by $++$, $+-$, $-+$, and $--$, where the first sign refers to the behavior of the rotational eigenfunction with respect to C_2^c, the second to the behavior with respect to C_2^a.

The highest level (J_{+J}) of each set with a given J is always $+$ with respect to C_2^c, the two next are $-$, the two next $+$, and so on. The lowest level (J_{-J}) of each set with a given J is always $+$ with respect to C_2^a, the two next $-$, the two next $+$, and so on.

If an asymmetric top molecule has elements of symmetry, the eigenfunctions have additional symmetry properties corresponding to the exchange of identical nuclei, e.g., A and B (similar to *a* and *s* of linear molecules) for molecules with one twofold axis and A, B_1, B_2, B_3 for molecules with three twofold axes.

d. *Statistical weights.* For the asymmetric top molecule the statistical weight of a rotational level J_τ due to the over-all rotation of the molecule is

$$g_J = 2J + 1$$

If the molecule has no axis of symmetry, the statistical weight due to the nuclear spins is

$$g_I = (2I_1 + 1)(2I_2 + 1)(2I_3 + 1)\ldots$$

If the molecule has one twofold axis of symmetry, the dependence of the statistical weights of the symmetric and antisymmetric rotational levels on the spins and statistics of the identical nuclei is the same as in linear molecules (§ 2.1e). If there are three axes of symmetry, more complex relations hold (Ref. 10).

e. *Pure rotation spectrum.* Asymmetric top molecules in general have a permanent dipole moment, and therefore have a pure rotation spectrum in the far infrared or microwave region. The selection rule for J is

$$\Delta J = 0, \pm 1$$

If the molecule has no symmetry the only further restriction is that levels of the same species do not combine with each other

$$++ \nleftrightarrow ++, \quad +- \nleftrightarrow +-, \quad -+ \nleftrightarrow -+, \quad -- \nleftrightarrow --$$

If the molecule has an axis of symmetry, only those rotational levels can combine with one another whose eigenfunctions have the same behavior with respect to a rotation by 180° about this axis, and opposite behavior with respect to similar rotations about the other two axes. Thus if the dipole moment lies in the axis of least moment of inertia (*a* axis) only the transitions

$$++ \longleftrightarrow -+ \quad \text{and} \quad +- \longleftrightarrow --$$

can take place. If the dipole moment lies in the axis of intermediate moment of inertia (*b* axis) only the transitions

$$++ \longleftrightarrow -- \quad \text{and} \quad +- \longleftrightarrow -+$$

can take place. If the dipole moment lies in the axis of largest moment of inertia (*c* axis), only the transitions

$$++ \longleftrightarrow +- \quad \text{and} \quad -+ \longleftrightarrow --$$

can take place.

f. *Raman spectrum.* The polarizability of an asymmetric top molecule in general changes during the rotation, and therefore as a rule a rotational Raman spectrum will occur. The selection rule for J is

$$\Delta J = 0, \pm 1, \pm 2$$

If the molecule has no symmetry, transitions between levels of any of the symmetry types ($++$, $+-$, $-+$, $--$) can occur. If the molecule has at least one twofold axis of symmetry, only levels of the same species can combine with each other, that is

$$++ \longleftrightarrow ++, \quad +- \longleftrightarrow +-, \quad -+ \longleftrightarrow -+, \quad -- \longleftrightarrow --$$

2.5. Effect of external fields

a. *Zeeman effect.* In an external magnetic field of intensity H, a state of angular momentum $\boldsymbol{J}$ is split into $2J + 1$ components of energy

$$W = W_0 - \bar{\mu}_H H \tag{1}$$

where W_0 is the energy without field and $\bar{\mu}_H$ the mean value of the component of the magnetic moment of the molecule in the field direction. If the magnetic moment is due to the orbital motion of the electrons (orbital angular momentum $= \Lambda h/2\pi$ (see § 5.1), one has

$$\bar{\mu}_H = \frac{\Lambda^2}{J(J+1)} M\mu_0$$

where

$$M = J, J-1, \ldots, -J$$

is the quantum number of the component of $\boldsymbol{J}$ in the field direction, and where

$$\mu_0 = \frac{e}{2mc} \cdot \frac{h}{2\pi}$$

is the Bohr magneton. If the magnetic moment is due to the electron spin only ($S \neq 0, \Lambda = 0$) one has

$$\bar{\mu}_H = 2M_S\mu_0$$

where

$$M_S = S, \quad S-1, \quad \ldots, \quad -S$$

If both orbital motion and electron spin are contributing to $\bar{\mu}_H$ more complicated formulas hold (Ref. 9). If the orbital and the spin angular momentum of the electrons is zero ($\Lambda = 0$, $S = 0$) as is usual for the electronic ground states of molecules, one has

$$\bar{\mu}_H = g_r M \mu_{0n}$$

where

$$\mu_{0n} = \frac{e}{2m_p c} \cdot \frac{h}{2\pi}$$

is the nuclear magneton ($m_p =$ mass of proton) and where g_r is a number of order 1 characteristic of the particular molecular state.

The selection rule for the quantum number M is

$$\Delta M = 0, \quad \pm 1 \qquad (M = 0 \leftarrow\!\!|\!\!\rightarrow M = 0 \text{ for } \Delta J = 0)$$

where $\Delta M = 0$ applies when the field is parallel to the electric vector of the incident radiation, $\Delta M = \pm 1$ when it is perpendicular to this vector. From these formulas it follows that for $\Lambda = 0$, $S = 0$ in a magnetic field the lines of the rotation spectrum split into three components whose spacing is (in cm^{-1})

$$\Delta\nu = \frac{g_r \mu_{0n}}{hc} H \tag{2}$$

Transitions between the Zeeman levels without change of rotational level may occur as magnetic dipole radiations. Their wave number is

$$\nu = \frac{g_r \mu_{0n} H}{hc} \tag{3}$$

b. *Stark effect.* In an electric field (of intensity E) the values of M are the same as in a magnetic field (§ 2.5a) but levels with the same $|M|$ coincide. Thus there is a splitting into only $J+1$ or $J+\frac{1}{2}$ component levels (depending on whether J is integral or half integral). The energies of these levels are given by

$$W = W_0 - \bar{\mu}_E E \tag{4}$$

where $\bar{\mu}_E$ is the mean component of the *electric* dipole moment in the field direction. For molecules without permanent dipole moment

$$\bar{\mu}_E = a_{J|M|} E$$

For linear or symmetric top molecules with a permanent dipole moment μ,

$$\bar{\mu}_E = +\frac{\mu M k}{J(J+1)} - \frac{4\pi^2 I_0 \mu^2 E}{h^2}\left\{\frac{(J^2-M^2)(J^2-K^2)}{J^3(2J-1)(2J+1)} - \frac{[(J+1)^2-M^2][(J+1)^2-K^2]}{(J+1)^3(2J+1)(2J+3)}\right\}$$

Here $k = \pm K$. For diatomic molecules K must be replaced by Λ, for linear polyatomic molecules by l (see Ref. 10). If K (or Λ or l) is zero the preceding equation simplifies to

$$\bar{\mu}_E = -\frac{4\pi^2 I_0 \mu^2 E}{h^2}\left[\frac{J(J+1)-3M^2}{J(J+1)(2J-1)(2J+3)}\right]$$

that is, only a quadratic, no linear Stark effect occurs.

The same selection rule applies for M as in the case of the Zeeman effect. But the line splittings in the rotation spectrum are not as simple.

2.6. Hyperfine structure (influence of nuclear spin).

If one of the nuclei of the molecule has a nonzero spin $\boldsymbol{I}$, the total angular momentum $\boldsymbol{F}$ will be the vector sum of $\boldsymbol{J}$ and $\boldsymbol{I}$. The corresponding quantum numbers are

$$F = J+I, \quad J+I-1, \quad \ldots, \quad |J-I|$$

For $J > I$ there is thus a splitting into $2I+1$ hyperfine structure components. The magnitude of the splitting depends on the interaction of the nuclear spin with the rest of the molecule.

For purely magnetic interaction the energies of the component levels are given (Ref. 8) by

$$W = W_0 + \left(\frac{aK^2}{J(J+1)} + b\right)[F(F+1) - J(J+1) - I(I+1)] \tag{1}$$

where a and b are constants depending on the nuclear magnetic moment and the magnetic moment due to rotation (§ 2.5a). According to this formula the separation of successive levels is proportional to $F + 1$ (" interval rule ").

If the nucleus of spin $I \neq 0$ has an electric quadrupole moment, a hyperfine structure splitting arises on account of the electrostatic interaction with the electric field produced by the other nuclei and the electrons at the position of the nucleus considered. This interaction energy is usually much larger than the magnetic interaction energy. For diatomic, linear polyatomic, and symmetric top molecules, the energy levels are given to a first, good approximation by

$$W = W_0 + e^2qQ\left(\frac{3K^2}{J(J+1)} - 1\right)\frac{\frac{3}{8}G(G+1) - \frac{1}{2}I(I+1)J(J+1)}{I(2I-1)(2J-1)(2J+3)} \tag{2}$$

where Q is the quadrupole moment of the nucleus in cm^2, eq is the average inhomogeneity of the electrostatic field at the position of the nucleus in the direction of the z axis

$$eq = \left(\frac{\partial^2 V}{\partial z^2}\right)_{\text{average}} = \int \frac{3z^2 - r^2}{r^5}\, de$$

and where

$$G = F(F+1) - I(I+1) - J(J+1)$$

Higher approximations and the case of molecules with two nuclei having a nonzero quadrupole moment have been considered by Bardeen and Townes (Ref. 1).

Transitions between the hyperfine structure levels follow the selection rules

$$\Delta F = 0, \quad \pm 1; \quad F = 0 \leftarrow\!\!|\!\!\rightarrow F = 0$$

For more details see Gordy (Ref. 6).

In a magnetic field each component level of the hyperfine structure splits into $2F + 1$ components distinguished by

$$M_F = F, \quad F - 1, \quad \ldots, \quad -F$$

The energy in the field is obtained from the first equation in (§ 2.5a) by substituting

$$\bar{\mu}_H = g_F M_F \mu_{0n}$$

where (Ref. 11),

$$g_F = \frac{[F(F+1)+J(J+1)-I(I+1)]g_r + [F(F+1)+I(I+1)-J(J+1)]g_I}{2F(F+1)}$$

and g_r and g_I are rotational and nuclear g-factors (for g_r see § 2.5a). The selection rule for M_F is

$$\Delta M_F = 0, \pm 1$$

3. Vibration and Vibration Spectra

3.1. Diatomic molecules

a. *Energy levels.* The vibrational energy levels of a diatomic molecule can be represented by the formula

$$G(v) = \omega_e(v + \tfrac{1}{2}) - \omega_e x_e(v + \tfrac{1}{2})^2 + \omega_e y_e(v + \tfrac{1}{2})^3 + \omega_e z_e(v + \tfrac{1}{2})^4 + \dots \quad (1)$$

where v is the vibrational quantum number which assumes the values 0, 1, 2, ..., and where ω_e is, apart from a factor c, the vibrational frequency for infinitesimal amplitude. One has in general $\omega_e z_e \ll \omega_e y_e \ll \omega_e x_e \ll \omega_e$ and frequently $\omega_e z_e \approx 0$ and $\omega_e y_e \approx 0$. The frequency ω_e is related to the force constant k_e in the equilibrium position by the relation

$$\omega_e = \frac{\nu_{\text{osc}}}{c} = \frac{1}{2\pi c}\sqrt{\frac{k_e}{\mu}}$$

or

$$k_e = 4\pi^2\mu c^2\omega_e{}^2 = 5.8883 \times 10^{-2}\mu_A\omega_e{}^2 \quad \text{dyne/cm}$$

where μ and $\mu_A (= \mu N_A)$ stand for the reduced mass in grams and in atomic weight units ($O^{16} = 16$), respectively.

The zero-point vibrational energy of a diatomic molecule is

$$G(0) = \tfrac{1}{2}\omega_e - \tfrac{1}{4}\omega_e x_e + \tfrac{1}{8}\omega_e y_e + \tfrac{1}{16}\omega_e z_e + \dots \quad (2)$$

If the vibrational energy is measured relative to the lowest level the vibrational formula may be written

$$G_0(v) = \omega_0 v - \omega_0 x_0 v^2 + \omega_0 y_0 v^3 + \omega_0 z_0 v^4 \dots \quad (3)$$

If higher powers of $(v + \tfrac{1}{2})$ are negligible, the vibrational constants ω_e, $\omega_e x_e$, etc. are related to the constants ω_0, $\omega_0 x_0$, etc. by the formulas

$$\left.\begin{aligned} \omega_e z_e &= \omega_0 z_0 \\ \omega_e y_e &= \omega_0 y_0 - 2\omega_0 z_0 \\ \omega_e x_e &= \omega_0 x_0 + \tfrac{3}{2}\omega_0 y_0 - \tfrac{3}{2}\omega_0 z_0 \\ \omega_e &= \omega_0 + \omega_0 x_0 + \tfrac{3}{4}\omega_0 y_0 - \tfrac{1}{2}\omega_0 z_0 \end{aligned}\right\} \quad (4)$$

The separation of successive vibrational levels is

$$\left.\begin{aligned} \Delta G_{v+\frac{1}{2}} &= G(v + 1) - G(v) = G_0(v + 1) - G_0(v) \\ &= (\omega_e - \omega_e x_e + \omega_e y_e + \omega_e z_e) - (2\omega_e x_e - 3\omega_e y_e - 4\omega_e z_e)(v + \tfrac{1}{2}) \\ &\quad + (3\omega_e y_e + 6\omega_e z_e)(v + \tfrac{1}{2})^2 + 4\omega_e z_e(v + \tfrac{1}{2})^3 \\ &= (\omega_0 - \omega_0 x_0 + \omega_0 y_0 + \omega_0 z_0) - (2\omega_0 x_0 - 3\omega_0 y_0 - 4\omega_0 z_0)v \\ &\quad + (3\omega_0 y_0 + 6\omega_0 z_0)v^2 + 4\omega_0 z_0 v^3 \end{aligned}\right\} \quad (5)$$

b. *Potential functions and dissociation energy.* For a harmonic oscillator the potential energy is given by

$$V = \tfrac{1}{2}kx^2 \tag{6}$$

where k is the force constant (§ 3.1a) and $x = r - r_e$ is the displacement from the equilibrium position (r_e). If anharmonicity is taken into account the potential energy may be represented by a power series

$$V = \tfrac{1}{2}kx^2(1 + a_1x + a_2x^2 + \ldots) \tag{7}$$

or, if large internuclear distances are considered, by a Morse function

$$V(r - r_e) = D_e[1 - e^{-\beta(r-r_e)}]^2 \tag{8}$$

Here D_e is the dissociation energy referred to the minimum of the potential energy and

$$\beta = \sqrt{\frac{2\pi^2 c\mu}{D_e h}}\,\omega_e = 1.2177 \times 10^7 \omega_e \sqrt{\frac{\mu_A}{D_e}}$$

where μ_A is in atomic weight units ($O^{16} = 16$) and D_e is in cm^{-1}.

The dissociation energies D_e and D_0 are the energies required to dissociate the molecule from the minimum and from the lowest vibrational level, respectively. Therefore

$$D_e = D_0 + G(0)$$

Quite generally D_0 is given by

$$D_0 = \sum_v \Delta G_{v+\frac{1}{2}}$$

If the Morse function is a good approximation, the cubic and quartic terms in the energy expression vanish ($\omega_e y_e = \omega_e z_e \approx 0$) and

$$D_0 = \frac{\omega_0^{\ 2}}{4\omega_0 x_0}, \quad D_e = \frac{\omega_e^{\ 2}}{4\omega_e x_e}$$

This approximation is frequently very poor.

c. *Eigenfunctions.* As long as the anharmonicity of the vibration is small, the vibrational eigenfunctions are approximated by the harmonic oscillator eigenfunctions. These are the Hermite orthogonal functions

$$\psi_v(x) = N_v e^{-\frac{1}{2}\alpha x^2} H_v(\sqrt{\alpha}x) \tag{9}$$

where N_v is a normalization factor, $H_v(\sqrt{\alpha}x)$ the Hermite polynomial of the vth degree (see § 12.1 of Chapter 1), and

$$\alpha = \frac{4\pi^2\mu\nu_{\text{osc}}}{h} = \frac{2\pi\sqrt{\mu k}}{h}$$

For the anharmonic oscillator eigenfunctions see Refs. 3 and 5.

17

d. *Selection rules and spectrum.* An infrared vibration spectrum can occur only if the molecule has no center of symmetry, that is, if it does not consist of two like nuclei. A vibrational Raman spectrum occurs for both symmetrical and asymmetrical molecules. For the harmonic oscillator the selection rule for the vibrational quantum number is (both in the Raman effect and the infrared)

$$\Delta v = \pm 1$$

For the anharmonic oscillator no strict selection rule exists, but transitions with $\Delta v = 1$ are much stronger than those with $\Delta v = 2$, those with $\Delta v = 2$ much stronger than those with $\Delta v = 3$, and so on.

Absorption of light by the molecule in the ground state produces a series of bands whose wave numbers correspond to the energies of successive vibrational levels

$$\left.\begin{aligned} \nu_{\text{abs}} &= G(v) - G(0) \\ &= \omega_e[(v + \tfrac{1}{2}) - \tfrac{1}{2}] - \omega_e x_e[(v + \tfrac{1}{2})^2 - \tfrac{1}{4}] + \omega_e y_e[(v + \tfrac{1}{2})^3 - \tfrac{1}{8}] + \dots \\ &= G_0(v) = \omega_0 v - \omega_0 x_0 v^2 + \omega_0 y_0 v^3 + \dots \end{aligned}\right\} \quad (10)$$

The same formula holds for the displacements observed in the Raman spectrum.

e. *Isotope effect.* The vibrational constants of an isotopic molecule [designated by the superscript (i)] are related to those of the " normal " molecule by the formulas

$$\omega_e^{(i)} = \rho\omega_e, \quad \omega_e^{(i)} x_e^{(i)} = \rho^2 \omega_e x_e, \quad \omega_e^{(i)} y_e^{(i)} = \rho^3 \omega_e y_e, \quad \dots \quad (11)$$

where

$$\rho = \sqrt{\frac{\mu}{\mu^{(i)}}}$$

and μ and $\mu^{(i)}$ are the reduced masses (see § 2.1a) of the " normal " and the isotopic molecules, respectively. The vibrational absorption bands of an isotopic molecule are given by the formula (see § 3.1d).

$$\left.\begin{aligned} \nu_{\text{abs}}^{(i)} = \rho\omega_e[(v + \tfrac{1}{2}) - \tfrac{1}{2}] - \rho^2\omega_e x_e[(v + \tfrac{1}{2})^2 - \tfrac{1}{4}] \\ + \rho^3 \omega_e y_e[(v + \tfrac{1}{2})^3 - \tfrac{1}{8}] + \dots \end{aligned}\right\} \quad (12)$$

The vibrational isotope shift is therefore

$$\left.\begin{aligned} \Delta\nu &= \nu_{\text{abs}} - \nu_{\text{abs}}^{(i)} \\ &= \omega_e(1 - \rho)v - \omega_e x_e(1 - \rho^2)(v^2 + v) \\ &\qquad + \omega_e y_e(1 - \rho^3)(v^3 + \tfrac{3}{2}v^2 + \tfrac{3}{4}v) + \dots \end{aligned}\right\} \quad (13)$$

If ρ is close to one, the vibrational isotope shift is approximately given by the expression

$$\Delta\nu = (1-\rho)v\Delta G_{v+\frac{1}{2}} \tag{14}$$

3.2. Polyatomic molecules

a. *Normal vibrations and normal coordinates.* The potential and kinetic energies of a system of N particles of masses m_i for small displacements from the equilibrium position are given by

$$V = \tfrac{1}{2}\sum_{ij} k_{ij}q_iq_j \tag{1}$$

and

$$T = \tfrac{1}{2}\sum_{ij} b_{ij}\dot{q}_i\dot{q}_j \tag{2}$$

where the q_i may either be $3N$ Cartesian displacement coordinates or, for nonlinear molecules, $3N-6$, for linear molecules, $3N-5$ internal displacement coordinates such as changes of internuclear distances. The $k_{ij}\,(=k_{ji})$ are force constants, the $b_{ij}\,(=b_{ji})$ are constants depending on the masses and geometrical parameters of the molecule. By the linear transformation

$$q_i = c_{i1}\xi_1 + c_{i2}\xi_2 + c_{i3}\xi_3 + \dots$$

new coordinates ξ_i, so-called normal coordinates, can be formed such that both V and T are sums of squares.

$$V = \tfrac{1}{2}(\lambda_1\xi_1^2 + \lambda_2\xi_2^2 + \lambda_3\xi_3^2 + \dots) \tag{3}$$

$$T = \tfrac{1}{2}(\dot{\xi}_1^2 + \dot{\xi}_2^2 + \dot{\xi}_3^2 + \dots) \tag{4}$$

that is, the motion in the molecule in this approximation may be considered as a superposition of $3N$ or $3N-6$ or $3N-5$ independent harmonic oscillators described by the normal coordinates ξ_i such that

$$\xi_i = \xi_i^0 \cos(2\pi\nu_i t + \varphi_i)$$

In each such normal vibration all nuclei in the molecule carry out simple harmonic motions about their respective equilibrium positions with one and the same frequency ν_i which is related to λ_i by

$$\lambda_i = 4\pi^2\nu_i^2 \tag{5}$$

The λ_i, that is, the frequencies of the different normal vibrations, are determined by the secular equation :

$$\begin{vmatrix} k_{11}-b_{11}\lambda & k_{12}-b_{12}\lambda & k_{13}-b_{13}\lambda & \cdots \\ k_{21}-b_{21}\lambda & k_{22}-b_{22}\lambda & k_{23}-b_{23}\lambda & \cdots \\ k_{31}-b_{31}\lambda & k_{32}-b_{32}\lambda & k_{33}-b_{33}\lambda & \cdots \\ \cdots\ \cdots\ \cdots & \cdots\ \cdots\ \cdots & \cdots\ \cdots\ \cdots & \cdots \end{vmatrix} = 0 \qquad (6)$$

If Cartesian coordinates are used, six or five of the λ_i are found to be zero depending on whether the molecule is nonlinear or linear, respectively. These zero roots correspond to the nongenuine normal vibrations (null vibrations) : the translations and rotations. When two or three λ_i are equal, we have doubly or triply degenerate normal vibrations.

The form of a given normal vibration ξ_j can be obtained from the transformation equations by putting all other ξ_i equal to zero. The coefficients c_{ij} are the minors of the above determinant.

Special cases. The general relation between the force constants and the frequencies of the normal vibrations is given by the determinantal equation (6) above. In the most general case there are $\frac{1}{2}n(n+1)$ force constants, $(n = 3N - 6$ or $3N - 5)$ while there are only n normal frequencies.

If the molecule has symmetry the normal vibrations also have certain symmetry properties. For a given molecular symmetry there are a number of symmetry types (or species) of the normal vibrations. For example, if the molecule has a single plane of symmetry there are two species of normal vibrations, those that are symmetric with respect to that plane and those that are antisymmetric with respect to it. They are designated A' and A'', respectively. For a molecule with two mutually perpendicular planes of symmetry there are four species which may be characterized by $++$, $--$, $+-$, $-+$ where the two signs indicate the behavior with respect to the two planes. These four species are designated A_1, A_2, B_1, and B_2, respectively. For other cases see Ref. 10.

In the case of a symmetrical molecule, if the original coordinates are appropriately chosen (symmetry coordinates) the secular determinant can be factored into as many smaller determinants as there are different species. The degree of each of these subdeterminants, that is, the number f_j of vibrations of the particular species j can be readily obtained from the number of the various atoms in the molecule. The number of force constants belonging to each species is $\frac{1}{2}f_j(f_j + 1)$ and therefore the total number of force constants is $\Sigma\,\frac{1}{2}f_j(f_j + 1)$ which is smaller, often much smaller, than $\frac{1}{2}n(n + 1)$. But even then the number of force constants is in general larger than the number of normal frequencies.

In order to reduce the number of unknown force constants, often simplifying assumptions are made about the restoring forces in the molecule. The assumption most often used is that of valence forces, that is, of a strong restoring force in the line of every valence bond and a weaker one opposing a change of the angle between two valence bonds connecting one atom with two others.

Thus, if in nonlinear symmetric XY_2 molecules k_1 is the force constant of the XY bond and k_δ the force constant of the Y-X-Y angle, the following simple relations between the frequencies and force constants are obtained by solving the corresponding secular equations :

$$\left.\begin{aligned} 4\pi^2(\nu_1^2+\nu_2^2) &= \left(1+\frac{2m_Y}{m_X}\cos^2\alpha\right)\frac{k_1}{m_Y}+\frac{2}{m_Y}\left(1+\frac{2m_Y}{m_X}\sin^2\alpha\right)\frac{k_\delta}{l^2} \\ 16\pi^4\nu_1^2\nu_2^2 &= 2\left(1+\frac{2m_Y}{m_X}\right)\frac{k_1}{m_Y^2}\cdot\frac{k_\delta}{l^2} \\ 4\pi^2\nu_3^2 &= \left(1+\frac{2m_Y}{m_X}\sin^2\alpha\right)\frac{k_1}{m_Y} \end{aligned}\right\} \tag{7}$$

Here m_X and m_Y are the masses of the atoms X and Y, α is half the Y-X-Y angle, and l is the XY distance.

For linear symmetric XY_2, one finds

$$\left.\begin{aligned} 4\pi^2\nu_1^2 &= \frac{k_1}{m_Y} \\ 4\pi^2\nu_2^2 &= \frac{2}{m_Y}\left(1+\frac{2m_Y}{m_X}\right)\frac{k_\delta}{l^2} \\ 4\pi^2\nu_3^2 &= \left(1+\frac{2m_Y}{m_X}\right)\frac{k_1}{m_Y} \end{aligned}\right\} \tag{8}$$

For linear XYZ molecules, if k_1 and k_2 are the force constants, l_1 and l_2 the lengths of the XY and YZ bonds, one finds

$$\left.\begin{aligned} 4\pi^2(\nu_1^2+\nu_3^2) &= k_1\left(\frac{1}{m_X}+\frac{1}{m_Y}\right)+k_2\left(\frac{1}{m_Y}+\frac{1}{m_Z}\right) \\ 16\pi^4\nu_1^2\nu_3^2 &= \frac{m_X+m_Y+m_Z}{m_Xm_Ym_Z}k_1k_2 \\ 4\pi^2\nu_2^2 &= \frac{1}{l_1^2l_2^2}\left(\frac{l_1^2}{m_Z}+\frac{l_2^2}{m_X}+\frac{(l_1+l_2)^2}{m_Y}\right)k_\delta \end{aligned}\right\} \tag{9}$$

b. *Energy levels.* In the approximation in which the normal vibrations are well defined, that is, when the potential energy contains only quadratic terms the vibrational energy is simply

$$G(v_1,v_2,v_3,\ldots) = \Sigma\, \omega_i(v_i + \tfrac{1}{2}) \tag{10}$$

where v_i is the vibrational quantum number of the ith normal vibration and $\omega_i = \nu_i/c$. If the potential energy contains higher powers, that is

$$2V = \sum_i \sum_j k_{ij}q_iq_j + \sum\sum\sum f_{ijk}q_iq_jq_k + \sum\sum\sum\sum g_{ijkl}q_iq_jq_kq_l + \ldots$$

and if there are no degenerate vibrations, the vibrational energy becomes

$$G(v_1,v_2,v_3,\ldots) = \sum_i \omega_i(v_i + \tfrac{1}{2}) + \sum_i \sum_{k \geq i} x_{ik}(v_i + \tfrac{1}{2})\,(v_k + \tfrac{1}{2}) + \ldots \tag{11}$$

Here the anharmonicity constants x_{ik} are small compared to the ω_i if the deviations from a quadratic potential are small ; the ω_i are now the (classical) vibrational frequencies in cm^{-1} for infinitesimal amplitudes (so-called zero-order frequencies).

The zero-point vibrational energy is

$$G(0,0,\ldots) = \frac{1}{2}\sum_i \omega_i + \frac{1}{4}\sum_i \sum_{k \geq i} x_{ik} \tag{12}$$

Referred to this lowest energy level the vibrational energy may also be written

$$G_0(v_1,v_2,\ldots) = \sum_i \omega_i^0\, v_i + \sum_i \sum_{k \geq i} x_{ik}^0\, v_iv_k + \ldots \tag{13}$$

where
$$\omega_i^0 = \omega_i + x_{ii} + \frac{1}{2}\sum_{k \neq i} x_{ik} + \ldots$$

The wave numbers of the 1-0 bands, the so-called fundamentals, are given by

$$\nu_i = \omega_i^0 + x_{ii}^0 = \omega_i + 2x_{ii} + \frac{1}{2}\sum_{k \neq i} x_{ik} + \ldots$$

where $x_{ik} = x_{ki}$, and, if higher powers are neglected, $x_{ik}^0 = x_{ik}$.

If degenerate normal vibrations are present the previous energy formula has to be replaced by

$$\left.\begin{aligned} G(v_1,v_2,\ldots) = \sum_i \omega_i\left(v_i + \frac{d_i}{2}\right) + \sum_i \sum_{k \geq i} x_{ik}\left(v_i + \frac{d_i}{2}\right)\left(v_k + \frac{d_k}{2}\right) \\ + \sum_i \sum_{k \geq i} g_{ik}l_il_k + \ldots \end{aligned}\right\} \tag{14}$$

In this equation d_i is the degree of degeneracy ; the l_i are integral numbers which assume the values

$$l_i = v_i, \quad v_i - 2, \quad v_i - 4, \quad \ldots \quad 1 \text{ or } 0$$

and the g_{ik} are constants of the order of the x_{ik} (not to be confused with the potential constants g_{ijkl}).

The zero-point energy in the presence of degenerate vibrations is

$$G(0,0,\ldots) = \sum_i \omega_i \frac{d_i}{2} + \sum_i \sum_{k \geq i} x_{ik} \frac{d_i d_k}{4} \ldots \tag{15}$$

The vibrational energy referred to the lowest vibrational energy level is

$$G_0(v_1,v_2,\ldots) = \sum_i \omega_i^0 \, v_i + \sum_i \sum_{k \geq i} x_{ik}^0 \, v_i v_k + \sum_i \sum_{k \geq i} g_{ik} l_i l_k + \ldots \tag{16}$$

where $$\omega_i^0 = \omega_i + x_{ii} d_i + \frac{1}{2} \sum_{k \neq i} x_{ik} d_k + \ldots$$

and where $x_{ik}^0 = x_{ik}$, if higher powers are neglected. The fundamentals are

$$\nu_i = \omega_i^0 + x_{ii} + g_{ii} = \omega_i + x_{ii}(1 + d_i) + \frac{1}{2} \sum_{k \neq i} x_{ik} d_k + g_{ii}$$

where, as previously, $x_{ik} = x_{ki}$.

c. *Eigenfunctions.* The total vibrational eigenfunction of a polyatomic molecule is, to a first approximation, the product of $3N - 6$, or, in the case of a linear molecule, $3N - 5$, harmonic oscillator functions (§ 3.1c).

$$\psi_v = \Pi \psi_i(\xi_i) = \Pi N_{v_i} e^{-\frac{1}{2}\alpha_i \xi_i^2} H_{v_i}(\sqrt{\alpha_i} \xi_i) \tag{17}$$

where $\alpha_i = 2\pi c \omega_i / h$.

d. *Selection rules, vibration spectra.* In the harmonic oscillator approximation, the only allowed transitions are those in which one vibration changes its vibrational quantum by one unit, i.e.,

$$\Delta v_i = \pm 1, \quad \Delta v_k = 0$$

If the anharmonicity of the vibrations is taken into account also transitions in which v_i changes by several units or in which several v_i change will occur. But they are in general less intense than the fundamentals.

If the molecule has symmetry, certain rigorous selection rules for vibrational transitions hold irrespective of the degree of anharmonicity. Quite generally a vibrational transition $v' \longleftrightarrow v''$ is allowed in the infrared when there is at least one component of the dipole moment M that has the same species (i.e., the same behavior with respect to the symmetry operations permitted by the symmetry of the molecule) as the product $\psi_v'\psi_v''$. A vibrational transition $v' \longleftrightarrow v''$ is allowed in the Raman effect if at least one component of the polarizability tensor has the same species as the product $\psi_v'\psi_v''$.

As a result, for example, for molecules with a center of symmetry, transitions that are allowed in the infrared are forbidden in the Raman spectrum, and those allowed in the Raman spectrum are forbidden in the infrared.

A table of the species of the components of the dipole moment and of the polarizability for the more important point groups is given in Ref. 10.

For molecules for which the inversion doubling (§ 2.2d) is not negligible the additional selection rule has to be taken into account that in the infrared only sublevels of opposite parity can combine with one another ($+ \longleftrightarrow -$), whereas in the Raman effect only sublevels of the same parity can combine with one another ($+ \longleftrightarrow +$, $- \longleftrightarrow -$).

c. *Isotope effect.* For two isotopic molecules the product of the $\omega^{(i)}/\omega$ values for all vibrations of a given symmetry type is independent of the potential constants and depends only on the masses of the atoms and the geometrical structure of the molecule according to the following formula (Teller-Redlich product rule):

$$\left.\begin{aligned} &\frac{\omega_1^{(i)}\omega_2^{(i)}}{\omega_1\ \omega_2}\cdots\frac{\omega_f^{(i)}}{\omega_f} \\ &= \sqrt{\left(\frac{m_1}{m_1^{(i)}}\right)^{\alpha}\left(\frac{m_2}{m_2^{(i)}}\right)^{\beta}\cdots\left(\frac{M^{(i)}}{M}\right)^{t}\left(\frac{I_x^{(i)}}{I_x}\right)^{\delta x}\left(\frac{I_y^{(i)}}{I_y}\right)^{\delta y}\left(\frac{I_z^{(i)}}{I_z}\right)^{\delta z}} \end{aligned}\right\} \quad (18)$$

Here quantities with the superscript (i) refer to one of the isotopic molecules, quantities without superscript to the other; $\omega_1, \omega_2, \ldots, \omega_f$ are the zero order frequencies of the f (genuine) vibrations of the symmetry type considered; $m_1, m_2, \ldots$ are the masses of the representative atoms of the various sets (each set consisting of those identical atoms that are transformed into one another by the symmetry operations permitted by the molecule); $\alpha, \beta, \ldots$ are the numbers of vibrations (inlusive of nongenuine vibrations) that each set contributes to the symmetry type considered; M is the total mass of the molecule; t is the number of translations of the symmetry type considered; I_x, I_y, I_z are the moments of inertia about the x, y, and z axes; $\delta x, \delta y, \delta z$ are 1 or 0 depending on whether or not the rotation about the x, y, or z axis is a nongenuine vibration of the symmetry type considered. Both on the left and right hand side (in $\alpha, \beta, \ldots, t, \delta x, \delta y, \delta z$) a degenerate vibration is counted only once.

4. Interaction of Rotation and Vibration: Rotation-Vibration Spectra

4.1. Diatomic molecules

a. *Energy levels.* The interaction of rotation and vibration causes the rotational energy of a vibrating molecule to be somewhat different from that of a nonvibrating molecule. One has for the term values of the rotating vibrator

$$T = G(v) + F_v(J) \tag{1}$$

where $G(v)$ is given by the previous formula (§ 3.1a) and where

$$F_v(J) = B_v J(J+1) - D_v J^2(J+1)^2 + \ldots$$

Here

$$B_v = B_e - \alpha_e(v + \tfrac{1}{2}) + \ldots$$

and

$$D_v = D_e + \beta_e(v + \tfrac{1}{2}) + \ldots$$

The constants B_e and D_e refer to the equilibrium position and are defined by formulas entirely similar to those previously given for B and D (§ 2.1b). The constants α_e and β_e are small compared to B_e and D_e, respectively, and are determined by the form of the potential function.

b. *Selection rules and spectrum.* For rotation-vibration spectra the same selection rules apply as for the pure rotation and the pure vibration spectrum separately. Therefore the vibrational quantum number can change by

$$\Delta v = \pm 1, \quad \pm 2, \quad \ldots$$

with $\Delta v = \pm 1$ giving by far the strongest transitions. The selection rules for the rotational quantum number, assuming that there is no electronic angular momentum about the internuclear axis, are, in the case of infrared transitions

$$\Delta J = J' - J'' = \pm 1$$

and in the case of Raman transitions

$$\Delta J = J' - J'' = 0, \pm 2$$

Hence in the infrared a rotation-vibration band consists of two branches, an R branch ($\Delta J = +1$) and a P branch ($\Delta J = -1$) which are given by (neglecting small terms in D' and D'')

$$\nu_R = \nu_0 + 2B_v' + (3B_v' - B_v'')J + (B_v' - B_v'')J^2 \qquad (J = 0, 1, \ldots)$$

$$\nu_P = \nu_0 - (B_v' + B_v'')J + (B_v' - B_v'')J^2 \qquad (J = 1, 2, \ldots)$$

Here ν_0, the vibrational energy difference between the two states (band origin), is given by ν_{abs} in § 3.1d ; J is the rotational quantum number J'' of the lower state.

In the Raman effect a rotation-vibration band consists of three branches, an S branch ($\Delta J = +2$), an O branch ($\Delta J = -2$), and a Q branch ($\Delta J = 0$). Formulas for these branches may be found in Ref. 9.

c. *Combination differences and combination sums.* The combination differences

$$R(J-1) - P(J+1) = F_v''(J+1) - F_v''(J-1) = \Delta_2 F''(J)$$
$$= (4B_v'' - 6D_v'')(J+\tfrac{1}{2}) - 8D_v''(J+\tfrac{1}{2})^3$$
$$R(J) - P(J) = F_v'(J+1) - F_v'(J-1) = \Delta_2 F'(J)$$
$$= (4B_v' - 6D_v')(J+\tfrac{1}{2}) - 8D_v'(J+\tfrac{1}{2})^3$$

are used to separate the rotational energy levels of the upper and lower vibrational states and to determine the rotational constants.

The combination sums

$$R(J-1) + P(J) = 2\nu_0 + 2(B_v' - B_v'')J^2 - 2(D_v' - D_v'')J^2(J^2+1)$$

are used to determine the band origins (zero lines) and the differences $(B_v' - B_v'')$ and $(D_v' - D_v'')$ of the rotational constants.

Similar combination relations apply to the S and O branches observed in the Raman effect.

4.2. Linear polyatomic molecules

a. *Energy levels.* The rotational term values of a vibrating linear polyatomic molecule are given by the same formula as those of diatomic molecules (§ 4.1) except that B_v depends now on the vibrational quantum numbers of all the vibrations. We have

$$B_{[v]} = B_{v_1 v_2 v_3} \cdots = B_e - \Sigma\alpha_i\left(v_i + \frac{d_i}{2}\right) \tag{1}$$

where the α_i are small constants similar to α_e for diatomic molecules and where d_i is the degeneracy of the vibration i. Here B_e is the rotational constant for the equilibrium position and is given by

$$B_e = \frac{h}{8\pi^2 c I_e}$$

where I_e is the moment of inertia in the equilibrium position. The rotational constant $B_{000\cdots}$, obtainable from the pure rotation spectrum, for the lowest vibrational level is given by

$$B_{[0]} = B_{000}\cdots = B_e - \sum \alpha_i \frac{d_i}{2}$$

Vibrational levels with $l = 1, 2, \ldots$, (Π, Δ, ... vibrational levels) are doubly degenerate (§ 3.2a). With increasing rotation a splitting of this degeneracy arises (l-type doubling). As a result there are two rotational term series with slightly different rotational constants, B_v^c and B_v^d. The splitting is given by

$$\Delta\nu = q_i J(J+1) = (B_v^c - B_v^d) J(J+1) \tag{2}$$

The splitting constant q_i for a given perpendicular vibration ν_i is of the same order as α_i. For detailed formulas see Ref. 15. The two levels of a given J have opposite parity (+, −).

b. *Selection rules and spectrum.* The selection rules for rotation-vibration spectra of linear polyatomic molecules are the same as for diatomic molecules (§ 4.1b) if the quantum number l of the vibrational angular momentum is zero in both the upper and lower states, i.e., if $l' = l'' = 0$. In this case the same two branches occur.

If l' or l'' or both are different from zero, in addition to the transitions discussed in § 4.1b, in the infrared, transitions with $\Delta J = 0$ occur; in the Raman effect, transitions with $\Delta J = \pm 1$ occur. That is, the selection rules are

$$\Delta J = 0, \pm 1 \qquad \text{(infrared)}$$

$$\Delta J = 0, \pm 1, \pm 2 \quad \text{(Raman effect)}$$

At the same time the symmetry selection rules

$$+ \longleftrightarrow -, \quad s \leftarrow\!\!|\!\!\rightarrow a \qquad \text{(infrared)}$$

$$+ \longleftrightarrow +, \quad - \longleftrightarrow -, \quad S \leftarrow\!\!|\!\!\rightarrow \qquad \text{(Raman effect)}$$

must be obeyed.

The additional possibility $\Delta J = 0$ in the infrared gives rise to a Q branch whose formula is

$$\nu_Q = \nu_0 + (B' - B'')J + (B' - B'')J^2 \tag{3}$$

In the Raman spectrum in such cases P and R branches in addition to the S, O, and Q branches can occur.

According to the preceding selection rules, when l_i is different from zero a transition between the two components of an l-type doublet can occur. Such transitions occur in the microwave region and are represented by the formula

$$\nu = q_i J(J+1) \tag{4}$$

4.3. Symmetric top molecules

a. *Energy levels.* As for linear molecules, the term values of a vibrating symmetric top molecule can be represented as the sum of vibrational and rotational term values

$$T = G(v_1,v_2,v_3,\ldots) + F_{[v]}(J,K) \tag{1}$$

In the case of a nondegenerate vibrational level and neglecting the effect of centrifugal forces, the rotational term values are given by

$$F_{[v]}(J,K) = B_{[v]}J(J+1) + (A_{[v]} - B_{[v]})K^2 \tag{2}$$

where $[v]$ stands for the set of vibrational quantum numbers v_1, v_2, v_3, ... and where

$$B_{[v]} = B_e - \sum \alpha_i^B\left(v_i + \frac{d_i}{2}\right) + \ldots$$

$$A_{[v]} = A_e - \sum \alpha_i^A\left(v_i + \frac{d_i}{2}\right) + \ldots$$

The α_i^B and α_i^A are constants similar to α_e of diatomic molecules and

$$B_e = \frac{h}{8\pi^2 c I_B{}^e} \quad \text{and} \quad A_e = \frac{h}{8\pi^2 c I_A{}^e}$$

are the rotational constants corresponding to the equilibrium position.

In a degenerate vibrational level the Coriolis interaction of the degenerate components causes an additional term

$$-2A_{[v]} \sum_i (\pm\zeta_i l_i)K \tag{3}$$

which has to be added to the previous expression for $F_{[v]}(J,K)$. Here ζ_i is a constant, $0 \leq \zeta_i \leq 1$, measuring the magnitude of the vibrational angular momentum of the degenerate vibration ν_i in units $h/2\pi$ and $l_i = v_i$, $v_i - 2$, ..., 1 or 0 is the azimuthal quantum number of the degenerate vibration. For a state in which only one degenerate vibration is singly excited ($l_i = 1$) the additional term is

$$\mp 2A_{[v]}\zeta_i K$$

leading to an increasing splitting of the degeneracy with increasing K.

The individual ζ_i are complicated functions of the potential constants and other parameters of the molecule. But the sums of the ζ_i of all vibrations of a given species are independent of the potential constants. For example, for axial XY_3 molecules (pyramidal or planar)

$$\zeta_3 + \zeta_4 = \frac{I_A}{2I_B} - 1 = \frac{B}{2A} - 1$$

for axial XYZ_3 molecules

$$\zeta_4 + \zeta_5 + \zeta_6 = \frac{I_A}{2I_B} = \frac{B}{2A}$$

for axial $WXYZ_3$ molecules

$$\zeta_5 + \zeta_6 + \zeta_7 + \zeta_8 = \frac{I_A}{2I_B} + 1 = \frac{B}{2A} + 1$$

For X_2Y_6 molecules of point group D_{3h} or D_{3d}

$$\zeta_7 + \zeta_8 + \zeta_9 = 0, \quad \text{and} \quad \zeta_{10} + \zeta_{11} + \zeta_{12} = \frac{I_A}{2I_B} = \frac{B}{2A}$$

b. *Selection rules and spectrum.*

Infrared. The selection rules for the vibrational quantum numbers are the same as for the pure vibration spectrum. If the molecule is a symmetric top on account of its symmetry, the (vibrational) transition moment can be only either parallel or perpendicular to the figure axis. For an accidental symmetric top any orientation with regard to the figure axis is possible.

If the transition is parallel to the figure axis (|| band), the selection rules for the rotational quantum numbers are

$$\Delta K = 0, \quad \Delta J = 0, \pm 1 \qquad (\Delta J = 0 \text{ forbidden for } K = 0)$$

and if the transition moment is perpendicular to the figure axis ($\perp$ band)

$$\Delta K = \pm 1, \quad \Delta J = 0, \pm 1$$

If the transition moment has a general direction with respect to the figure axis, changes of the rotational quantum numbers allowed by either set of selection rules may occur, i.e., the resulting band has both a || and a $\perp$ component (hybrid band).

Both || and $\perp$ bands consist of a number of subbands corresponding to the different values of K. Each subband consists of a P, a Q and an R branch corresponding to $\Delta J = -1, 0,$ and $+1$, respectively, similar to the bands of linear molecules.

The zero lines of the subbands of a || band or of the || component of a hybrid band are given by

$$\nu_0^{\text{sub}} = \nu_0 + [(A_{[v]}' - A_{[v]}'') - (B_{[v]}' - B_{[v]}'')]K^2 \tag{4}$$

those of a $\perp$ band or of the $\perp$ component of a hybrid band are given by

$$\left.\begin{aligned} \nu_0^{\text{sub}} = \nu_0 &+ (A_{[v]}' - B_{[v]}') \pm 2(A_{[v]}' - B_{[v]}')K \\ &+ [(A_{[v]}' - B_{[v]}') - (A_{[v]}'' - B_{[v]}'')]K^2 \end{aligned}\right\} \tag{5}$$

Here it is assumed that both states involved are nondegenerate or, if degenerate, of such a nature that the effect of Coriolis forces can be neglected. If this is not the case the term $-2A_{[v]}\,\Sigma\,(\pm\,\zeta_i l_i)K$ has to be added to the energy formula, and the subband formulas are correspondingly changed. For example, if the upper state is degenerate with $\zeta_i \neq 0,\ l_i = 1$, and the lower state nondegenerate, the subbands of the resulting $\perp$ band are given by

$$\left.\begin{aligned}\nu_0^{\text{sub}} = \nu_0 + [A_{[v]}'(1-2\zeta_i) - B_{[v]}'] \pm 2[A_{[v]}'(1-\zeta_i) - B_{[v]}']K \\ + [(A_{[v]}' - B_{[v]}') - (A_v'' - B_v'')]K^2\end{aligned}\right\} \quad (6)$$

where the upper sign holds for $\Delta K = +1$ and the lower for $\Delta K = -1$. Neglecting the dependence of A and B on the v_i, the spacing of the subbands is $2[A(1-\zeta_i) - B]$ instead of $2(A - B)$ for a nondegenerate upper state.

The intensities of the lines in absorption are given by the expression

$$I(J,K) = CA_{KJ}\nu g_{KJ} e^{-F(K,J)hc/kT} \quad (7)$$

where the statistical weight factors g_{KJ} are the same as those given in § 2.2e and the intensity factors A_{KJ} are

$$\left.\begin{aligned}\Delta J = +1:\quad A_{KJ} &= \frac{(J+1)^2 - K^2}{(J+1)(2J+1)} \\ \Delta J = 0:\quad A_{KJ} &= \frac{K^2}{J(J+1)} \\ \Delta J = -1:\quad A_{KJ} &= \frac{J^2 - K^2}{J(2J+1)}\end{aligned}\right\} \quad (\Delta K = 0) \quad (8)$$

$$\left.\begin{aligned}\Delta J = +1:\quad A_{KJ} &= \frac{(J+2\pm K)(J+1\pm K)}{(J+1)(2J+1)} \\ \Delta J = 0:\quad A_{KJ} &= \frac{(J+1\pm K)(J\mp K)}{J(J+1)} \\ \Delta J = -1:\quad A_{KJ} &= \frac{(J-1\mp K)(J\mp K)}{J(2J+1)}\end{aligned}\right\} \quad (\Delta K = \pm 1) \quad (9)$$

Here K and J refer to the rotational quantum numbers of the lower state. For $K = 0$, $\Delta K = +1$ the values given by the formulas have to be multiplied by 2.

Raman effect. The vibrational selection rules are again the same as for the pure vibration spectrum (§ 3.2d). In the most general case of an accidental symmetric top with arbitrary orientation of the polarizability ellipsoid with respect to the momental ellipsoid the selection rules for the rotational quantum numbers are

$$\Delta K = 0, \pm 1, \pm 2\,; \quad \Delta J = 0, \pm 1, \pm 2 \qquad (J' + J'' \geq 2)$$

If the molecule has symmetry and if therefore the figure axis coincides with one of the symmetry axes, only certain components of the matrix elements of the polarizability α are different from zero and only certain of the above transitions can occur.

For vibrational transitions for which only $[\alpha_{zz}]^{nm}$ or $[\alpha_{xx} + \alpha_{yy}]^{nm}$ or both are different from zero, only $\Delta K = 0$ occurs. Here it is assumed that the z axis is the figure axis ; $[\alpha_{zz}]^{nm}$ stands for the integral $\int \alpha_{zz}\psi_n\psi_m{}^* dt$, and similarly in other cases. For axial molecules $\Delta K = 0$ applies to all transitions for which $\psi_n\psi_m{}^*$ is totally symmetric. For vibrational transitions for which only $[\alpha_{xz}]^{nm}$ or $[\alpha_{yz}]^{nm}$ or both are different from zero, only $\Delta K = \pm 1$ applies, and for vibrational transitions for which only $[\alpha_{xx} - \alpha_{yy}]^{nm}$ or $[\alpha_{xy}]^{nm}$ or both are different from zero, $\Delta K = \pm 2$ applies.

Inversion spectrum. The inversion doubling which occurs for all non-planar molecules (§ 2.2d) is usually negligibly small. But for molecules like NH_3 for which the two configurations obtained by inversion are separated by only a comparatively small potential barrier, an appreciable doubling arises. The rotational constants in the two component levels are slightly different, that is, one has

$$\left.\begin{aligned} F_{[v]}{}^s(J,K) &= B_{[v]}{}^s J(J+1) + (A_{[v]}{}^s - B_{[v]}{}^s)K^2 + \ldots \\ F_{[v]}{}^a(J,K) &= B_{[v]}{}^a J(J+1) + (A_{[v]}{}^a - B_{[v]}{}^a)K^2 + \ldots \end{aligned}\right\} \qquad (10)$$

where the superscripts s and a refer to the levels whose vibrational eigenfunctions are symmetric and antisymmetric with respect to the inversion. Transitions from one set of levels to the other occur in the microwave region, the selection rules being

$$\Delta J = 0, \quad \Delta K = 0, \quad K \neq 0$$

The resulting lines are therefore given by the formula

$$\left.\begin{aligned} \nu = \nu_0 &+ (B_{[v]}{}^s - B_{[v]}{}^a)J(J+1) \\ &+ [(A_{[v]}{}^s - A_{[v]}{}^a) - (B_{[v]}{}^s - B_{[v]}{}^a)]K^2 + \ldots \end{aligned}\right\} \qquad (11)$$

where ν_0 is the inversion splitting for zero rotation. Slight deviations of the observed microwave spectra from this formula can be accounted for by adding higher (quartic) terms to it.

4.4. Spherical top molecules

a. *Energy levels.*—The energy of a vibrating spherical top is the sum of the vibrational energy $G(v_1, v_2, v_3, \ldots)$ and the rotational energy

$$F_{[v]}(J) = B_{[v]}J(J+1) + \ldots \tag{1}$$

where
$$B_{[v]} = B_e - \sum \alpha_i^B\left(v_i + \frac{d_i}{2}\right) + \ldots$$

For a molecule that is a spherical top on account of its symmetry (e.g., CH_4) doubly and triply degenerate vibrational levels occur. In the case of the latter (but not of the former) the Coriolis interaction produces a splitting into three sets of levels given by

$$\left.\begin{aligned} F_{[v]}^{+}(J) &= B_{[v]}J(J+1) + 2B_{[v]}\zeta_i(J+1) \\ F_{[v]}^{0}(J) &= B_{[v]}J(J+1) \\ F_{[v]}^{-}(J) &= B_{[v]}J(J+1) - 2B_{[v]}\zeta_i J \end{aligned}\right\} \tag{2}$$

where ζ_i is a constant giving the vibrational angular momentum in units $h/2\pi$ (compare § 4.3a).

b. *Selection rules and spectrum.* For the accidental spherical top the selection rules for J are the same as for the symmetric top, both in the infrared and the Raman effect (§ 4.3b). For a molecule that is a spherical top on account of its symmetry, additional rules apply.

In the infrared the most common vibrational transitions are $F_2 - A_1$. Of the three components of the upper state the F^+ levels combine with the lower state only with $\Delta J = -1$, the F_0 levels only with $\Delta J = 0$ and the F^- levels only with $\Delta J = +1$. Therefore $F_2 - A_1$ bands have only three branches represented by the formulas

$$\left.\begin{aligned} R(J) &= \nu_0 + 2B_{[v]}' - 2B_{[v]}'\zeta_i + (3B_{[v]}' - B_{[v]}'' - 2B_{[v]}'\zeta_i)J \\ &\qquad + (B_{[v]}' - B_{[v]}'')J^2 \\ Q(J) &= \nu_0 + (B_{[v]}' - B_{[v]}'')J + (B_{[v]}' - B_{[v]}'')J^2 \\ P(J) &= \nu_0 - (B_{[v]}' + B_{[v]}'' - 2B_{[v]}'\zeta_i)J + (B_{[v]}' - B_{[v]}'')J^2 \end{aligned}\right\} \tag{3}$$

In the Raman effect, for $A_1 - A_1$ vibrational transitions only $\Delta J = 0$ occurs, that is, only a Q branch. But in $F_2 - A_1$ vibrational transitions all five ΔJ values are possible for each of the three sublevels of the F_2 state; the resulting bands therefore consist of fifteen branches.

4.5. Asymmetric top molecules

a. *Energy levels.* To a good approximation the rotational energy levels of a vibrating asymmetric top molecule are obtained from those of the non-vibrating asymmetric top molecule (§ 2.4b) by substituting effective values of the various rotational constants corresponding to the vibrational level considered, that is

$$F_{[v]}(J_\tau) = \tfrac{1}{2}(B_{[v]} + C_{[v]})J(J+1) + [A_{[v]} - \tfrac{1}{2}(B_{[v]} + C_{[v]})]W_\tau^{[v]} \tag{1}$$

where

$$A_{[v]} = A_e - \Sigma\, \alpha_i^A(v_i + \tfrac{1}{2})$$
$$B_{[v]} = B_e - \Sigma\, \alpha_i^B(v_i + \tfrac{1}{2})$$
$$C_{[v]} = C_e - \Sigma\, \alpha_i^C(v_i + \tfrac{1}{2})$$

and where the quantities $W_\tau^{[v]}$ are given by equations similar to those in (§ 2.4b), except that the constants A, B, C are to be replaced by $A_{[v]}$, $B_{[v]}$, and $C_{[v]}$.

b. *Selection rules and spectrum.* The selection rules for the rotation-vibration spectra of asymmetric top molecules are the same as those for the vibration and the rotation spectra separately, except that it is now the direction of the *change* of dipole moment and *change* of polarizability that determines the infrared and Raman transitions respectively. The fine structure of the bands is always very complicated and cannot be represented by simple formulas, except if the molecule approaches the limiting case of a symmetric top ($A \simeq B$ or $C \simeq B$). For more details see Ref. 10.

4.6. Molecules with internal rotation

a. *Energy levels*

Free rotation. When one part of a symmetric top molecule can rotate freely relative to the other about the figure axis, the following term has to be added to the ordinary rotational energy $F(J,K)$

$$F_t(k_1,k) = \frac{A_1A_2}{A}\left(k_1 - k\frac{A}{A_1}\right)^2 \tag{1}$$

Here A_1 and A_2 are the rotational constants corresponding to the partial moments of inertia $I_A^{(1)}$ and $I_A^{(2)}$; $k(=\pm K)$ is the quantum number of the component of the total angular momentum $\boldsymbol{J}$ about the top axis ; k_1 is the quantum number of the angular momentum of part 1 [moment of inertia $I_A^{(1)}$] of the molecule and assumes the values

$$k_1 = 0, \quad \pm 1, \quad \pm 2, \quad \ldots$$

For molecules with $I_{A_1} = I_{A_2}$ or $\dfrac{A}{A_1} = \frac{1}{2}$ the term F_t simplifies to

$$F_t(k_1,k) = A(2k_1 - k)^2 = A(k_1 - k_2)^2 = AK_i^2 \qquad (2)$$

where $K_i = | k_1 - k_2 |$ is the quantum number of internal rotation.

Hindered rotation. The limiting case of hindered rotation is that of torsional oscillation in a periodic potential field with n potential minima

$$V(\chi) = V\left(\chi \pm \frac{2\pi}{n}\right) \qquad (3)$$

If a cosine form is assumed for the hindering potential

$$V = \tfrac{1}{2}V_0(1 - \cos n\chi)$$

the energy levels in the neighborhood of the minima for large V_0 are those of a harmonic oscillator :

$$G(v_t) = \omega_t(v_t + \tfrac{1}{2}) \qquad (4)$$

where the torsional frequency ω_t is given by

$$\omega_t = n\sqrt{\frac{V_0 A_1 A_2}{A}}$$

or, for a molecule with two equal parts

$$\omega_t = 2n\sqrt{V_0 A}$$

For small values of V_0 the vibrational motion of the molecule becomes a hindered rotation. The energy levels corresponding to this intermediate case can be found qualitatively by interpolation between those of the two limiting cases, free rotation and torsional oscillation (Ref. 10). Quantitative discussions of this intermediate case have been given in Refs. 4, 13, 16, and 17.

b. *Infrared spectrum.* For symmetrical molecules there is no pure rotation spectrum corresponding to free rotation. For the vibration-rotation spectrum the selection rules for the quantum number K_i of the internal rotation are $\Delta K_i = 0$ for $\Delta K = 0$ and $\Delta K_i = \pm 1$ for $\Delta K = \pm 1$. As a consequence the $||$ bands of a symmetric top molecule are not affected by the presence of internal rotation, while in the $\perp$ bands each of the line-like Q branches is split into a number of nearly equidistant " lines " of spacing $2B$.

In slightly asymmetric molecules the internal rotation is infrared active.

For the pure internal rotation spectrum the selection rules are

$$\Delta J = 0, \pm 1, \quad \Delta K = \pm 1, \quad \Delta K_1 = \pm 1, \quad \Delta K_2 = 0$$

where $K_1 = |k_1|$, and $K_2 = |k_2|$. Therefore the Q " lines " of the free internal rotation spectrum form the double series

$$\nu = A_1 - B \mp 2BK \pm 2A_1K_1 \tag{5}$$

where the upper signs hold for positive ΔK and ΔK_1, the lower signs for negative ΔK and ΔK_1.

For the rotation-vibration spectrum we have in the case of $\parallel$ bands ($\Delta K = 0$) the selection rule

$$\Delta K_1 = 0, \quad \Delta K_2 = 0$$

and in the case of $\perp$ bands ($\Delta K = \pm 1$)

$$\Delta K_1 = \pm 1, \quad \Delta K_2 = 0 \quad \text{or} \quad \Delta K_1 = 0, \quad \Delta K_2 = \pm 1$$

depending on whether the dipole moment of the vibrational transition is in part 1 or part 2 of the molecule. The structure of the $\parallel$ bands is therefore not affected by the presence of internal rotation, while in the $\perp$ bands each subband corresponding to a given K and ΔK is resolved into a number of sub-subbands corresponding to the different K_1 values and $\Delta K_1 = \pm 1$ or to the different K_2 values and $\Delta K_2 = \pm 1$ depending on whether the oscillating dipole moment is in part 1 or part 2. For $\Delta K_1 = \pm 1$ the spacing of the sub-subbands is $2A_1$, for $\Delta K_2 = \pm 1$ it is $2A_2$.

5. Electronic States and Electronic Transitions

5.1. Total energy and electronic energy. The energy of a molecule may be written as the sum of electronic, vibrational, and rotational energy (Section 1):

$$E = E_e + E_v + E_r$$

or in wave number units (term values)

$$T = T_e + G + F$$

The total eigenfunction can be expressed as

$$\psi = \psi_e \psi_v \psi_r \tag{1}$$

where ψ_e is the electronic eigenfunction, ψ_v the vibrational eigenfunction, and ψ_r the rotational eigenfunction.

The different electronic states of a molecule are characterized by certain quantum numbers and symmetry properties of their eigenfunctions. For diatomic and linear polyatomic molecules the orbital angular momentum $\boldsymbol{\Lambda}$ about the internuclear axis is defined and has the magnitude $\Lambda h/2\pi$, where Λ is the corresponding quantum number which can assume only integral values. Depending on whether $\Lambda = 0, 1, 2, \ldots$, we distinguish $\Sigma, \Pi, \Delta, \ldots$ states. For nonlinear molecules different types (species) of electronic states arise depending on the symmetry properties of the nuclear frame. For example, for molecules with two mutually perpendicular planes of symmetry there are four types of electronic states, A_1, A_2, B_1, and B_2 (see § 3.2a). These species are precisely the same as those of the vibrational levels (see the tables in Ref. 10).

Each electronic state has a multiplicity $(2S + 1)$ depending on the value of the quantum number S of the resultant electron spin of the molecule.

No general formulas for the energies of the electronic states of a molecule can be given except for those states in which one electron is excited to orbitals of increasing principal quantum number n. In this case one has to a good approximation

$$T_e = A - \frac{R}{(n - a)^2} \tag{2}$$

where A is the ionization potential, R the Rydberg constant, and a the Rydberg correction.

5.2. Interaction of rotation and electronic motion in diatomic and linear polyatomic molecules

a. *Multiplet splitting.* The total angular momentum $\boldsymbol{J}$ is the vector sum of the angular momentum of the nuclear frame, the electronic orbital angular momentum $\boldsymbol{\Lambda}$, and the electron spin $\boldsymbol{S}$. The total angular momentum apart from spin is designated $\boldsymbol{K}$.* For the corresponding quantum numbers we have

$$J = K + S, \quad K + S - 1, \quad \ldots, \quad |K - S|$$

The interaction of rotation and electron spin (which increases with increasing rotation) causes a variation of the multiplet splitting with K or J.

* In a recent report, the Joint Commission for Spectroscopy [*J. Opt. Soc. Am.*, **43**, 416 (1953)] recommends N in place of K as a designation of angular momentum apart from spin and of the corresponding quantum number.

The following formulas give the rotational term values for some important cases referring to diatomic and linear polyatomic molecules :

$^2\Sigma$ states ($\Lambda = 0,\ S = \frac{1}{2}$)

$$\left.\begin{aligned} F_1(K) &= B_v K(K+1) + \tfrac{1}{2}\gamma K \\ F_2(K) &= B_v K(K+1) - \tfrac{1}{2}\gamma(K+1) \end{aligned}\right\} \qquad (1)$$

Here $F_1(K)$ and $F_2(K)$ refer to the levels with $J = K + \frac{1}{2}$ and $J = K - \frac{1}{2}$, respectively, and γ is a small coupling constant ($\gamma \ll B_v$).

$^3\Sigma$ states ($\Lambda = 0,\ S = 1$) (Schlapp's formula)

$$\left.\begin{aligned} F_1(K) &= B_v K(K+1) + (2K+3)\,B_v - \lambda \\ &\qquad - \sqrt{(2K+3)^2 B_v^{\,2} + \lambda^2 - 2\lambda\omega_v} + \gamma(K+1) \\ F_2(K) &= B_v K(K+1) \\ F_3(K) &= B_v K(K+1) - (2K-1)B_v - \lambda \\ &\qquad + \sqrt{(2K-1)^2 B_v^{\,2} + \lambda^2 - 2\lambda B_v} - \gamma K \end{aligned}\right\} \qquad (2)$$

Here $F_1(K)$, $F_2(K)$, $F_3(K)$ refer to the levels with $J = K + 1$, $J = K$, and $J = K - 1$, respectively, and λ and γ are small coupling constants.

$^2\Pi$, $^2\Delta$, ... states ($\Lambda = 1, 2, \ldots, S = \frac{1}{2}$) (Hill and Van Vleck's formula)

$$\left.\begin{aligned} F_1(J) &= B_v[(J+\tfrac{1}{2})^2 - \Lambda^2 - \tfrac{1}{2}\sqrt{4(J+\tfrac{1}{2})^2 + Y(Y-4)\Lambda^2}] - D_v J^4 \\ F_2(J) &= B_v[(J+\tfrac{1}{2})^2 - \Lambda^2 + \tfrac{1}{2}\sqrt{4(J+\tfrac{1}{2})^2 + Y(Y-4)\Lambda^2}] \\ &\qquad - D_v(J+1)^4 \end{aligned}\right\} \qquad (3)$$

Here $Y = A/B_v$, where the coupling constant A is a measure of the strength of the coupling between the spin $\boldsymbol{S}$ and the orbital angular momentum $\boldsymbol{\Lambda}$; $F_1(J)$ is the term series that forms for large rotation the levels with $J = K + \frac{1}{2}$, while $F_2(J)$ forms for large rotation the levels with $J = K - \frac{1}{2}$.

b. *Lambda-type doubling*. The Π, Δ, ... states of diatomic and linear polyatomic molecules are doubly degenerate if the molecule is not rotating. In the rotating molecule the interaction of rotation and electronic motion causes a splitting of this degeneracy which in general increases with increasing rotation (Λ-type doubling). The rotational levels of the two term series, distinguished by superscripts c and d, are in the case of a $^1\Pi$ state

$$F_c(J) = B_v^{\,c} J(J+1) + \ldots, \quad F_d(J) = B_v^{\,d} J(J+1) + \ldots$$

that is, the splitting is given by

$$\Delta\nu_{cd} = (B_v^c - B_v^d)J(J+1) = qJ(J+1) \tag{4}$$

where the splitting constant q depends on the position of nearby Σ states. For Δ states the splitting is usually negligibly small.

5.3. Selection rules and spectrum. A transition between the electronic states i and k is allowed as dipole radiation if there is at least one component of the dipole moment M_x, M_y, or M_z which has the same symmetry properties as the product of the electronic eigenfunctions $\psi_e^i\psi_e^{k*}$. The electronic selection rules therefore are of the same form as the vibrational selection rules. The symmetry of the products $\psi_e^i\psi_e^{k*}$ can be determined from tables given in Ref. 19 or in Ref. 10, though the latter were originally prepared for vibrational transitions.

For diatomic and linear polyatomic molecules the selection rule

$$\Delta\Lambda = 0, \pm 1$$

results from the above general rule.

a. *Vibrational structure.* The totality of vibrational transitions for a given electronic transition is a band system. The wave numbers of the bands of a band system are represented by the formula

$$\nu = \nu_e + G'(v_1', v_2', \ldots) - G''(v_1'', v_2'', \ldots) \tag{1}$$

or in the case of diatomic molecules

$$\left.\begin{aligned} \nu = \nu_e + \omega_e'(v' + \tfrac{1}{2}) - \omega_e'x_e'(v' + \tfrac{1}{2})^2 + \\ \ldots - [\omega_e''(v'' + \tfrac{1}{2}) - \omega_e''x_e''(v'' + \tfrac{1}{2})^2 + \ldots] \end{aligned}\right\} \tag{2}$$

where $\nu_e = T_e' - T_e''$ is the origin of the band system.

Which vibrational transitions are possible and what intensities they have is determined by the integral

$$\int \psi_v' \psi_v'' d\tau_v$$

To a good approximation the relative intensities of the various vibrational transitions are proportional to the square of this integral. Only those vibrational transitions are possible for which the product $\psi_v'\psi_v''$ is symmetric with respect to all symmetry operations permitted by the symmetry of the molecule.

b. *Rotational structure.* The rotational structure of the individual vibrational transitions (bands) of an electronic transition is essentially the same as that of rotation-vibration bands (Section 4) as long as there is no spin splitting. If spin splitting is present, additional selection rules apply; for example, for diatomic and linear polyatomic molecules, if $\boldsymbol{K}$ the angular momentum apart from spin is defined, one has

$$\Delta K = 0, \pm 1$$

For $\Sigma - \Sigma$ transitions $\Delta K = 0$ does not occur. For details about the formulas for the branches in such cases see Ref. 9.

c. *Microwave spectra.* Transitions between individual multiplet components of a given electronic state can occur as magnetic dipole radiation. They give rise to absorption lines (bands) in the microwave region. For example, for a $^3\Sigma$ state the wave numbers of the transitions between the triplet components of a given K are

$$\nu = F_2(K) - F_1(K) \quad \text{and} \quad \nu = F_2(K) - F_3(K) \tag{3}$$

where the $F_i(K)$ are given in § 5.2a.

Transitions between the Λ doublet components of Π, Δ, ... states are possible as dipole radiation and are likely to be observed in the microwave region. The formula for such lines would be

$$\nu = F_c(J) - F_d(J) = qJ(J+1) \tag{4}$$

where q is the Λ doubling constant (§ 5.2b).

Bibliography

1. Bardeen, J. and Townes, C. H., *Phys. Rev.*, **73**, 97, 627, 1204 (1948).
2. Benedict, W. S., *Phys. Rev.*, **75**, 1317A (1949); *J. Research Natl. Bur. Standards*, **46**, 246 (1951).
3. Coolidge, A. S., James, H. M., and Present, R. D., *J. Chem. Phys.*, **4**, 193 (1936).
4. Crawford, B. L., *J. Chem. Phys.*, **8**, 273 (1940).
5. Dunham, J. L., *Phys. Rev.*, **34**, 438 (1929).
6. Gordy, W., *Revs. Modern Phys.*, **20**, 668 (1948).
7. Hainer, R. M., Cross, P. C. and King, G. W., *J. Chem. Phys.*, **17**, 826 (1949).
8. Henderson, R. S., *Phys. Rev.*, **74**, 107, 626 (1948).
9. Herzberg, G., *Molecular Spectra and Molecular Structure*, Vol. 1, *Spectra of Diatomic Molecules*, 2d ed., D. Van Nostrand Company, Inc., New York, 1950.
10. Herzberg, G., *Molecular Spectra and Molecular Structure*, Vol. 2, *Infrared and Raman Spectra of Polyatomic Molecules*, D. Van Nostrand Company, Inc., New York, 1945.
11. Jen, C. K., *Phys. Rev.*, **74**, 1396 (1948).
12. King, G. W., *J. Chem. Phys.*, **15**, 820 (1947).
13. Koehler, J. S. and Dennison, D. M., *Phys. Rev.*, **57**, 1006 (1940).

14. Nielsen, H. H., *Phys. Rev.*, **38**, 1432 (1931).
15. Nielsen, H. H., *Phys. Rev.*, **77**, 130 (1950).
16. Pitzer, K. S. and Gwinn, W. D., *J. Chem. Phys.*, **10**, 428 (1942).
17. Price, D., *J. Chem. Phys.*, **9**, 807 (1941).
18. Randall, H. M., Dennison, D. M., Ginsburg, N. and Weber, L. R., *Phys. Rev.*, **52**, 160 (1937).
19. Sponer, H. and Teller, E., *Revs. Modern Phys.*, **13**, 75 (1941).

Chapter 21

QUANTUM MECHANICS

BY L. I. SCHIFF

Professor of Physics
Stanford University

The collection of formulas given below has been assembled on the premise that the reader already has some familiarity with the subject matter of quantum mechanics. The collection is intended to be complete, except that selection rules are omitted here since they are included in Chapter 19. The formalism of quantized field theory is so abstruse that no attempt was made to condense it into formulas for this book.

1. Equations of Quantum Mechanics

1.1. Old quantum theory. The energy E, circular frequency ν, and angular frequency ω of a light quantum are related by

$$E = h\nu = \hbar\omega, \quad \hbar = h/2\pi \tag{1}$$

where h is Planck's constant. Since $E = pc$, where p is the momentum and c the speed of light, we also have

$$p = h/\lambda = \hbar k \tag{2}$$

where λ is the wavelength and $k = 2\pi/\lambda$ is the wave number.

The Planck distribution formula for the electromagnetic energy density per unit angular frequency range within a cavity at temperature T is

$$\frac{\hbar\omega^3}{\pi^2 c^3(e^{\hbar\omega/kT} - 1)} \tag{3}$$

where k is Boltzmann's constant.

The Bohr-Wilson-Sommerfeld quantization rule for a cyclic variable q and its canonical momentum p is

$$\oint p\,dq = nh \tag{4}$$

where the integral is over one cycle and n is a positive integer, called the quantum number.

If a quantum of wavelength λ is scattered by an electron of mass m through an angle θ, the wavelength λ' after scattering is (Compton effect)

$$\lambda' = \lambda + \frac{h}{mc}(1 - \cos\theta) \tag{5}$$

1.2. Uncertainty principle. A coordinate q and its canonically conjugate momentum p cannot both be measured precisely; the uncertainties in their values are related by the Heisenberg uncertainty principle

$$\Delta q \cdot \Delta p \gtrsim \hbar \tag{1}$$

The same relation holds between an angular coordinate ϕ and the component of angular momentum J perpendicular to the plane of ϕ, and between the time t of observation and the energy E of the system observed.

$$\Delta\phi \cdot \Delta J \gtrsim \hbar, \quad \Delta t \cdot \Delta E \gtrsim \hbar \tag{2}$$

Expressed in terms of a space wave packet of wave number k, or a time wave packet of angular frequency ω

$$\Delta x \cdot \Delta k \gtrsim 1, \quad \Delta t \cdot \Delta\omega \gtrsim 1 \tag{3}$$

For an electron, $E = p^2/2m = \hbar\omega$, the de Broglie relation is $p = \hbar k$, and the group velocity of the packet is

$$v_g = \frac{d\omega}{dk} = \frac{p}{m} \tag{4}$$

1.3. Schrödinger wave equation. The classical relation that the total energy E is the sum of the kinetic energy $\mathbf{p}^2/2\mu$ and the potential energy $V(\mathbf{r},t)$ of a particle of mass μ, can be transcribed into quantum mechanics by substituting

$$E \to i\hbar\frac{\partial}{\partial t}, \quad \mathbf{p} \to -i\hbar\,\mathbf{grad}$$

and operating on a wave function $\psi(\mathbf{r},t)$ to yield the Schrödinger equation,

$$i\hbar\frac{\partial\psi}{\partial t} = -\frac{\hbar^2}{2\mu}\nabla^2\psi + V(\mathbf{r},t)\psi \tag{1}$$

More generally,

$$i\hbar\frac{\partial\psi}{\partial t} = H\psi \tag{2}$$

where H is the Hamiltonian of the system with $\mathbf{p}$ replaced by $-i\hbar\,\mathbf{grad}$. The wave function is normalized if $\int\bar{\psi}\psi\,d\tau = \int|\psi|^2\,d\tau = 1$, where the integral is over all space $(d\tau = dx\,dy\,dz)$, and $\bar{\psi}$ is the complex conjugate of ψ.

The probability density P and the probability current density $\mathbf{S}$ are

$$P(\mathbf{r},t) = |\psi(\mathbf{r},t)|^2, \quad \mathbf{S}(\mathbf{r},t) = \frac{\hbar}{2i\mu}(\bar{\psi}\,\mathbf{grad}\,\psi - \psi\,\mathbf{grad}\,\bar{\psi}) \tag{3}$$

and obey the continuity equation

$$\frac{\partial P}{\partial t} + \operatorname{div} \boldsymbol{S} = 0 \tag{4}$$

If F is a function or an operator expressed in terms of $\boldsymbol{r}$ and t, its average or expectation value for the state ψ is

$$\langle F \rangle = \int \bar{\psi} F \psi \, d\tau \tag{5}$$

The uncertainty Δx can be defined as the root-mean-square deviation of x from its expectation value,

$$(\Delta x)^2 = \langle (x - \langle x \rangle)^2 \rangle = \langle x^2 \rangle - \langle x \rangle^2 \tag{6}$$

in which case a typical uncertainty relation becomes

$$\Delta x \cdot \Delta p_x \geqq \tfrac{1}{2}\hbar \tag{7}$$

For the minimum value of uncertainty product, the wave packet ψ has the instantaneous x dependence

$$\psi(x) = [2\pi(\Delta x)^2]^{-1/4} \exp \left[-\frac{(x - \langle x \rangle)^2}{4(\Delta x)^2} + \frac{ix\langle p_x \rangle}{\hbar} \right] \tag{8}$$

Ehrenfest's theorem states that the expectation values computed for a wave packet that satisfies the Schrödinger equation, obey the classical equations of motion; for example,

$$\frac{d}{dt}\langle \boldsymbol{r} \rangle = \frac{1}{\mu}\langle \boldsymbol{p} \rangle, \quad \frac{d}{dt}\langle \boldsymbol{p} \rangle = \langle - \mathbf{grad}\, V \rangle \tag{9}$$

The Fourier transform of $\psi(\boldsymbol{r},t)$ can be used to specify the momentum probability density, which is so defined that $P(\boldsymbol{k},t)\, dk_x\, dk_y\, dk_z$ is the probability that the momentum components lie between $\hbar k_x$ and $\hbar(k_x + dk_x)$, etc. Here $(d\tau_k = dk_x\, dk_y\, dk_z)$:

$$\left.\begin{aligned} \psi(\boldsymbol{r},t) &= (8\pi^3)^{-1/2} \int \phi(\boldsymbol{k},t) e^{i\boldsymbol{k}\cdot\boldsymbol{r}} d\tau_k \\ \phi(\boldsymbol{k},t) &= (8\pi^3)^{-1/2} \int \psi(\boldsymbol{r},t) e^{-i\boldsymbol{k}\cdot\boldsymbol{r}} d\tau \\ P(\boldsymbol{k},t) &= |\phi(\boldsymbol{k},t)|^2 \end{aligned}\right\} \tag{10}$$

An operator Ω has the eigenfunction u_n corresponding to the eigenvalue ω_n if

$$\Omega u_n = \omega_n u_n \tag{11}$$

The numbers ω_n are then the only possible results of precise measurement of the dynamical variable represented by the operator Ω.

Energy eigenfunctions exist if V is independent of t.

$$\psi(\boldsymbol{r},t) = u(\boldsymbol{r})e^{-iEt/\hbar}, \quad -\frac{\hbar^2}{2\mu}\nabla^2 u + Vu = Eu \tag{12}$$

Wherever V is finite (whether or not continuous), u and **grad** u must be finite and continuous; u must remain finite or vanish as $r \to \infty$. If $V \to \infty$ as $r \to \infty$, well-behaved solutions exist only for discrete values of E. If $V \to V_0$ as $r \to \infty$, well-behaved solutions exist for all values of E greater than V_0; if they exist for $E < V_0$ it is only for discrete values of E. Energy eigenfunctions that correspond to different energy eigenvalues are orthogonal.

$$\int \bar{u}_E(\boldsymbol{r})u_{E'}(\boldsymbol{r})d\tau = 0, \quad \text{if} \quad E \neq E' \tag{13}$$

Whenever $V(\boldsymbol{r})$ is unchanged by reflection of x, y, z in the origin [so that $V(-\boldsymbol{r}) = V(\boldsymbol{r})$], linear combinations of the energy eigenfunctions can be found that have a definite parity; that is, either $u(-\boldsymbol{r}) = u(\boldsymbol{r})$ (even parity), or $u(-\boldsymbol{r}) = -u(\boldsymbol{r})$ (odd parity). If an energy level is nondegenerate (only one linearly independent eigenfunction), then that function is either even or odd.

Discrete energy eigenfunctions are normalized by setting $\int |u_E(\boldsymbol{r})|^2 d\tau = 1$, since u_E falls off rapidly as $r \to \infty$, and we have a localized or bound state. Continuous energy eigenfunctions ($E > V_0$) cannot be normalized in this way since $|u_E| \to$ constant as $r \to \infty$ and the integral is infinite. We can normalize in a large cubical box of volume L^3 by imposing periodic boundary conditions at the walls, in which case the continuous energy levels become discrete with very close spacing. For example, the box-normalized momentum eigenfunctions are

$$u_k(\boldsymbol{r}) = L^{-3/2} \exp(i\boldsymbol{k} \cdot \boldsymbol{r}), \quad \text{where} \quad k_x = 2\pi n_x/L, \text{ etc.}$$

and n_x, n_y, n_z are positive or negative integers or zero. Then

$$\int \bar{u}_k(\boldsymbol{r})u_l(\boldsymbol{r})d\tau = \delta_{k_x l_x}\delta_{k_y l_y}\delta_{k_z l_z} \tag{14}$$

where $\delta_{nm} = 1$ if $n = m$ and zero otherwise (Kroneker δ symbol.) Alternatively, we can normalize in an infinite region by using the Dirac δ function, defined by

$$\delta(x) = 0 \quad \text{if} \quad x \neq 0, \qquad \int_{-\infty}^{\infty} \delta(x)dx = 1 \tag{15}$$

or by

$$\delta(x) = \frac{1}{2\pi}\int_{-\infty}^{\infty} e^{ikx}dk \tag{16}$$

Then $u_k(\boldsymbol{r}) = (8\pi^3)^{-1/2} \exp(i\boldsymbol{k} \cdot \boldsymbol{r})$, and

$$\int \bar{u}_k(\boldsymbol{r}) u_l(\boldsymbol{r}) d\tau = \delta(k_x - l_x)\delta(k_y - l_y)\delta(k_z - l_z) \tag{17}$$

For both normalizations, the momentum eigenfunctions have the closure property

$$\left.\begin{aligned} \sum_k \bar{u}_k(\boldsymbol{r}) u_k(\boldsymbol{r}') = \delta(x - x')\delta(y - y')\delta(z - z') \\ \text{(box normalization)} \end{aligned}\right\} \tag{18}$$

$$\left.\begin{aligned} \int \bar{u}_k(\boldsymbol{r}) u_k(\boldsymbol{r}') d\tau_k = \delta(x - x')\delta(y - y')\delta(z - z') \\ (\delta \text{ function normalization}) \end{aligned}\right\} \tag{19}$$

Complete sets of eigenfunctions of other operators have properties analogous to the above properties of the momentum eigenfunctions.

The δ function has the additional properties

$$\left.\begin{aligned} \delta(x) = \delta(-x), \quad \delta'(x) = -\delta'(-x), \quad x\delta(x) = 0, \quad x\delta'(x) = -\delta(x) \\ \delta(ax) = a^{-1}\delta(x), \qquad (a > 0) \\ \delta(x^2 - a^2) = (2a)^{-1}[\delta(x - a) + \delta(x + a)], \qquad (a > 0) \\ \int \delta(a - x)\delta(x - b)dx = \delta(a - b) \\ f(x)\delta(x - a) = f(a)\delta(x - a) \end{aligned}\right\} \tag{20}$$

In each case, a subsequent integration over the argument of the δ functions is implied; a prime denotes differentiation with respect to the argument.

1.4. Special solutions of the Schrödinger equation for bound states. The linear harmonic oscillator is described by the equation

$$-\frac{\hbar^2}{2\mu}\frac{d^2u}{dx^2} + \tfrac{1}{2}kx^2u = Eu \tag{1}$$

and has all discrete energy eigenvalues since $V \to \infty$ as $x \to \pm\infty$. The energy levels are $E_n = (n + \frac{1}{2})\hbar\omega$, where $\omega = (k/\mu)^{1/2}$ is the angular frequency of the corresponding classical oscillator. The normalized wave functions are

$$u_n(x) = \left(\frac{\alpha}{\pi^{1/2}2^n n!}\right)^{1/2} H_n(\alpha x) e^{-\alpha^2x^2/2}, \quad \alpha = \left(\frac{\mu k}{\hbar^2}\right)^{1/4} \tag{2}$$

H_n is a Hermite polynomial (§ 12.1 of Chapter 1).

In three dimensions, the spherical coordinates of a point are related to the rectangular coordinates of that point by $x = r \sin\theta \cos\phi$, $y = r \sin\theta \sin\phi$,

$z = r\cos\theta$. Whenever the potential energy $V(r)$ is spherically symmetric, the angular dependence of the wave function can be separated out.

$$-\frac{\hbar^2}{2\mu}\nabla^2 u + V(r)u = Eu$$

$$u(r,\theta,\phi) = R_l(r)Y_{lm}(\theta,\phi)$$

$$l = 0, 1, 2, \ldots, \quad m = -l, -l+1, \ldots, l-1, l$$

$$Y_{lm}(\theta,\phi) = \left[\frac{2l+1}{4\pi}\frac{(l-|m|)!}{(l+|m|)!}\right]^{1/2} P_l^{|m|}(\cos\theta)e^{im\phi} \tag{3}$$

$P_l^{|m|}(\cos\theta)$ is an associated Legendre function (§ 8.11 of Chapter 1). Here $Y_{lm}(\theta,\phi)$ is a tesseral harmonic, and is the normalized angular momentum eigenfunction.

The angular momentum operator is

$$\left.\begin{aligned}
\boldsymbol{M} &= \boldsymbol{r}\times\boldsymbol{p} = -i\hbar\boldsymbol{r}\times\mathbf{grad}\\
M_x &= yp_z - zp_y = -i\hbar\left(y\frac{\partial}{\partial z} - z\frac{\partial}{\partial y}\right)\\
&= i\hbar\left(\sin\phi\frac{\partial}{\partial\theta} + \cot\theta\cos\phi\frac{\partial}{\partial\phi}\right)\\
M_y &= zp_x - xp_z = -i\hbar\left(z\frac{\partial}{\partial x} - x\frac{\partial}{\partial z}\right)\\
&= i\hbar\left(-\cos\phi\frac{\partial}{\partial\theta} + \cot\theta\sin\phi\frac{\partial}{\partial\phi}\right)\\
M_z &= xp_y - yp_x = -i\hbar\left(x\frac{\partial}{\partial y} - y\frac{\partial}{\partial x}\right) = -i\hbar\frac{\partial}{\partial\phi}\\
\boldsymbol{M}^2 &= M_x^2 + M_y^2 + M_z^2\\
&= -\hbar^2\left[\frac{1}{\sin\theta}\frac{\partial}{\partial\theta}\left(\sin\theta\frac{\partial}{\partial\theta}\right) + \frac{1}{\sin^2\theta}\frac{\partial^2}{\partial\phi^2}\right]
\end{aligned}\right\} \tag{4}$$

The functions $Y_{lm}(\theta,\phi)$ satisfy the equations

$$\left.\begin{aligned}
&\boldsymbol{M}^2 Y_{lm}(\theta,\phi) = \hbar^2 l(l+1)Y_{lm}(\theta,\phi)\\
&M_z Y_{lm}(\theta,\phi) = \hbar m Y_{lm}(\theta,\phi)\\
&\int_0^\pi\int_0^{2\pi}\bar{Y}_{lm}(\theta,\phi)Y_{l'm'}(\theta,\phi)\sin\theta\,d\theta\,d\phi = \delta_{ll'}\delta_{mm'}
\end{aligned}\right\} \tag{5}$$

so that they form an orthonormal (orthogonal and normalized) set of eigenfunctions of $\boldsymbol{M}^2$ and M_z. Here l is the azimuthal or orbital angular momentum quantum number, and m is the magnetic quantum number.

The radial function satisfies the equation

$$-\frac{\hbar^2}{2\mu}\cdot\frac{1}{r^2}\cdot\frac{d}{dr}\left(r^2\frac{dR_l}{dr}\right)+\left[V(r)+\frac{\hbar^2 l(l+1)}{2mr^2}\right]R_l = ER_l \tag{6}$$

and may have discrete negative energy eigenvalues that correspond to bound states.

For $V(r)$ in the form of a square well,

$$V(r) = -V_0 < 0 \quad \text{for } r < a, \qquad V(r) = 0 \quad \text{for } r > a \tag{7}$$

there is at least one bound state if $V_0 a^2 > \pi^2\hbar^2/8\mu$, and none otherwise. The radial functions can be expressed in terms of Bessel functions of order $\pm(l+\frac{1}{2})$. (See Sec. 9 of Chapter 1.) For $r < a$,

$$R_l(r) = Aj_l(\alpha r), \quad \frac{\hbar^2\alpha^2}{2\mu} = V_0 + E, \quad j_l(\rho) = \left(\frac{\pi}{2\rho}\right)^{1/2} J_{l+1/2}(\rho) \tag{8}$$

For $r > a$ and $E < 0$,

$$\left.\begin{aligned} R_l(r) &= Bh_l^{(1)}(i\beta r), \quad \frac{\hbar^2\beta^2}{2\mu} = -E \\ h_l^{(1)}(\rho) &= j_l(\rho) + in_l(\rho), \quad h_l^{(2)}(\rho) = j_l(\rho) - in_l(\rho) \\ n_l(\rho) &= (-1)^{l+1}\left(\frac{\pi}{2\rho}\right)^{1/2} J_{-l-1/2}(\rho) \end{aligned}\right\} \tag{9}$$

The constants A and B and the energy level E are determined by the requirements that R_l and dR_l/dr be continuous at $r = a$, and by the normalization requirement

$$\int_0^\infty R_l^2 r^2 dr = 1$$

For an attractive Coulomb potential $V(r) = -Ze^2/r$, the radial equation has an infinite number of discrete energy eigenvalues.

$$E_n = -\frac{\mu Z^2 e^4}{2\hbar^2 n^2}, \quad (n = 1, 2, 3, \ldots) \tag{10}$$

With $Z = 1$, this is the Bohr formula for the energy levels of the hydrogen atom, obtained from the old quantum theory. For each value of the total quantum number n there are linearly independent solutions with the same energy for $l = 0, 1, \ldots, n-1$; since for each value of l the magnetic quantum number can lie between $-l$ and $+l$, there are altogether n^2 linearly independent solutions with the same energy E_n. The nth level is said to be n^2-fold degenerate. The normalized energy eigenfunctions are

$$\left.\begin{aligned} u_{nlm}(r,\theta,\phi) &= R_{nl}(r)Y_{lm}(\theta,\phi) \\ R_{nl}(r) &= \left(\frac{2Z}{na_0}\right)^{3/2} \left\{\frac{(n-l-1)!}{2n[(n+l)!]^3}\right\}^{1/2} e^{-\varrho/2}\, \rho^l L_{n+l}^{2l+1}(\rho) \end{aligned}\right\} \tag{11}$$

where $a_0 = \hbar^2/\mu e^2$, $\rho = 2Zr/na_0$, and L is an associated Laguerre polynomial (§ 11.5 of Chapter 1). The Coulomb wave functions can also be expressed in terms of parabolic coordinates $\xi = r(1 - \cos\theta)$, $\eta = r(1 + \cos\theta)$, $\phi = \phi$. The unnormalized energy eigenfunctions are

$$u_{n_1 n_2 m}(\xi,\eta,\phi) = e^{-\alpha(\xi+\eta)/2}\,(\xi\eta)^{|m|/2}\,L_{n_1+|m|}^{|m|}(\alpha\xi)L_{n_2+|m|}^{|m|}(\alpha\eta)e^{im\phi} \tag{12}$$

$$\alpha = \frac{\mu Z e^2}{\hbar^2(n_1 + n_2 + |m| + 1)} \tag{13}$$

where the L's are again associated Laguerre polynomials and the total quantum number (which determines the energy) is $n = n_1 + n_2 + |m| + 1$.

If the particle of mass μ does not move in a stationary (infinitely massive) force field, but in the field of another particle of finite mass M, we must replace μ by the reduced mass $\mu M/(\mu + M)$ in all equations of this section and the last.

1.5. Solutions of the Schrödinger equation for collision problems. Let a group of n stationary particles of mass m_2 be bombarded with a parallel flux of N particles of mass m_1 per unit area and time; then the number of m_1 particles that are scattered per unit time into a small solid angle $\Delta\omega_0$ about a direction that makes polar angles θ_0, ϕ_0 with respect to the bombarding direction is $nN\sigma_0(\theta_0\phi_0)\Delta\omega_0$, where $\sigma_0(\theta_0,\phi_0)$ is the differential scattering cross section in the laboratory system. Its integral over all angles is the total cross section σ_0 in the laboratory system. In the center-of-mass coordinate system, in which the center of mass of the colliding particles is at rest, the differential and total cross sections are $\sigma(\theta,\phi)$ and σ, respectively. The relations between the two coordinate systems are

$$\left.\begin{aligned} \tan\theta_0 &= \frac{\sin\theta}{\gamma + \cos\theta}, \quad \phi_0 = \phi, \quad \gamma = \frac{m_1}{m_2} \\ \sigma_0(\theta_0,\phi_0) &= \frac{(1 + \gamma^2 + 2\gamma\cos\theta)^{3/2}}{|1 + \gamma\cos\theta|}\sigma(\theta,\phi) \\ \sigma_0 &= \sigma \end{aligned}\right\} \tag{1}$$

If $\gamma > 1$, θ_0 cannot exceed that angle less than 90° whose sine is equal to $1/\gamma$.

If the kinetic energy of particle m_1 in the laboratory system is $E_0 = \frac{1}{2}m_1v^2$, the energy associated with the relative motion in the center-of-mass system is $E = m_2E_0/(m_1 + m_2)$, and the energy associated with the motion of the center of mass is $m_1E_0/(m_1 + m_2)$. Here v is the speed of m_1 in the laboratory system, and is also the relative speed of m_1 with respect to m_2 in the center-of-mass system. If the collision process is a reaction in which particles of masses m_3 and m_4 emerge ($m_1 + m_2 = m_3 + m_4$), an energy Q is released (so that the relative energy in the center-of-mass system after the reaction is $E + Q$), and the particle m_3 is observed, then the relations between laboratory and center-of-mass coordinate systems are as given above except that now

$$\gamma = + \{(m_1m_3/m_2m_4)[E/(E + Q)]\}^{1/2}.$$

The differential cross section in the center-of-mass system can be expressed in terms of phase shifts δ_l when the potential is spherically symmetric. The reduced mass is $\mu = m_1m_2/(m_1 + m_2)$, and $E = \frac{1}{2}\mu v^2 > 0$; then for r so large that $V(r)$ can be neglected, the radial wave function can be written

$$R_l(r) = A_l[\cos \delta_l j_l(kr) - \sin \delta_l n_l(kr)], \quad \frac{\hbar^2k^2}{2\mu} = E \tag{2}$$

and asymptotically

$$R_l(r) \xrightarrow[r\to\infty]{} (kr)^{-1}A_l \sin(kr - \tfrac{1}{2}l\pi + \delta_l) \tag{3}$$

The complete wave function has the asymptotic form

$$\left.\begin{aligned} u(r,\theta) &\xrightarrow[r\to\infty]{} A\left(e^{ikr\cos\theta} + f(\theta)\frac{e^{ikr}}{r}\right) \\ f(\theta) &= k^{-1}\sum_{l=0}^{\infty}(2l + 1)e^{i\delta_l}\sin \delta_l P_l(\cos \theta) \end{aligned}\right\} \tag{4}$$

and the differential and total cross sections are

$$\left.\begin{aligned} \sigma(\theta) &= |f(\theta)|^2 = \frac{1}{k^2}\left|\sum_{l=0}^{\infty}(2l + 1)e^{i\delta_l}\sin \delta_l P_l(\cos \theta)\right|^2 \\ \sigma &= \frac{4\pi}{k^2}\sum_{l=0}^{\infty}(2l + 1)\sin^2 \delta_l \end{aligned}\right\} \tag{5}$$

Because of the spherical symmetry of V, $\sigma(\theta)$ and the scattered amplitude $f(\theta)$ do not depend on ϕ.

For a perfectly rigid sphere of radius a [$V(r) = +\infty$ for $r < a$, $V(r) = 0$ for $r > a$], the scattering for very low energies ($ka \ll 1$) is spherically symmetric with $\sigma = 4\pi a^2$. For very high energies ($ka \gg 1$), half of the scattering is spherically symmetric and the other half is concentrated in a sharp forward maximum whose angular width is of order $1/ka$ radians (diffraction peak); each contributes πa^2 to the total cross section, so that $\sigma = 2\pi a^2$.

In the collision of particles of charges ze and Ze, the interaction is the Coulomb potential energy $V(r) = zZe^2/r$. The scattered amplitude and differential cross section in the center-of-mass coordinate system are

$$\left.\begin{aligned} f_c(\theta) &= \frac{n}{2k} \operatorname{cosec}^2 \tfrac{1}{2}\theta e^{-in \ln(\sin^2\theta/2) + i\pi + 2i\eta_0} \\ \sigma_c(\theta) &= |f_c(\theta)|^2 = \left(\frac{zZe^2}{2\mu v^2}\right)^2 \operatorname{cosec}^4 \tfrac{1}{2}\theta, \quad n = \frac{zZe^2}{\hbar v} \end{aligned}\right\} \tag{6}$$

where $\eta_0 = \arg \Gamma(1 + in)$ (see 13 of Chapter 1). Here $\sigma_c(\theta)$ is just the Rutherford formula derived from classical dynamics. The total cross section is infinite. If $V(r)$ deviates from the Coulomb form only for short distances, the asymptotic form of the radial wave function can be written

$$R_l(r) \xrightarrow[r\to\infty]{} (kr)^{-1} A_l \sin(kr - \tfrac{1}{2}l\pi - n \ln 2kr + \eta_l + \delta_l) \tag{7}$$

where $n_l = \arg \Gamma(l + 1 + in)$. The scattered amplitude is then

$$f(\theta) = f_c(\theta) + k^{-1} \sum_{l=0}^{\infty} (2l + 1) e^{i(2\eta_l + \delta_l)} \sin \delta_l P_l(\cos\theta) \tag{8}$$

and the differential cross section is $\sigma(\theta) = |f(\theta)|^2$. Here σ is again infinite.

1.6. Perturbation methods. If the Hamiltonian H is independent of the time, the Schrödinger wave equation $i\hbar(\partial\psi/\partial t) = H\psi$ has stationary solutions $\psi = u \exp(-iEt/\hbar)$, where u is independent of time and satisfies the equation $Hu = Eu$. Suppose that this equation cannot be solved, but that the corresponding equation with H_0 can be solved, where $H = H_0 + H'$: $H_0 u_n = E_n u_n$. Then if H' is small compared with H_0, an approximate (perturbation) solution can be obtained that expresses u and E in terms of the normalized u_n, E_n, and H'. Define the matrix element

$$H'_{nm} = \int \bar{u}_n H' u_m d\tau \tag{1}$$

If a particular unperturbed state u_m is discrete and nondegenerate (although other states may be degenerate) the perturbed energy level and state lying close to E_m and u_m are given, through terms of second order in H', by

$$\left.\begin{aligned} E &\cong E_m + H'_{mm} + \sum_n{}' \frac{|H'_{nm}|^2}{E_m - E_n} \\ u &\cong u_m + \sum_n{}' \frac{H'_{nm}u_n}{E_m - E_n} + \sum_n{}' \Big\{ -\tfrac{1}{2}\cdot\frac{|H'_{nm}|^2 u_m}{(E_m - E_n)^2} \\ &\quad + \left[-\frac{H'_{nm}H'_{mm}}{(E_m - E_n)^2} + \sum_k{}' \frac{H'_{nk}H'_{km}}{(E_m - E_n)(E_m - E_k)} \right] u_n \Big\} \end{aligned}\right\} \qquad (2)$$

The prime on the summation over n or k means that the term $n = m$ or $k = m$ is to be omitted from the sum; if some of the states are continuously distributed, the sums are to be replaced by integrals over those states. If the unperturbed state m is degenerate, the calculation is more complicated, and involves first finding linear combinations of the unperturbed degenerate states that are approximate eigenfunctions of the complete Hamiltonian H with unequal eigenvalues.

The Born approximation is an application of perturbation theory to a collision problem, in which the unperturbed states are continuously distributed in energy and degenerate. Let $H = -(\hbar^2/2\mu)\nabla^2 + V(\boldsymbol{r})$, where V is not necessarily spherically symmetric, and regard V as the perturbation. Then an approximate expression for the scattered amplitude, valid to first order in V, is

$$\left.\begin{aligned} f(\theta,\phi) &\cong -\frac{\mu}{2\pi\hbar}\int V(\boldsymbol{r})e^{i\boldsymbol{K}\cdot\boldsymbol{r}}d\tau \\ \boldsymbol{K} &= \boldsymbol{k}_0 - \boldsymbol{k} \end{aligned}\right\} \qquad (3)$$

where $\boldsymbol{k}_0$ is a vector along the bombarding direction, and $\boldsymbol{k}$ a vector along the direction of observation, both of magnitude $k = (2\mu E/\hbar^2)^{1/2}$; θ and ϕ are the polar angles of $\boldsymbol{k}$ with respect to $\boldsymbol{k}_0$. If V is spherically symmetric, f depends only on θ, and

$$f(\theta) \cong -\frac{2\mu}{\hbar^2 K}\int_0^\infty r\sin Kr V(r)dr, \quad K = 2k\sin\tfrac{1}{2}\theta \qquad (4)$$

In both cases, the differential scattering cross section is $|f|^2$. The phase shifts can also be calculated to first order in V by the Born approximation, when V is spherically symmetric.

$$\delta_l \cong -\frac{2\mu k}{\hbar^2}\int_0^\infty r^2 j_l^2(kr)V(r)dr \qquad (5)$$

A convenient criterion for the validity of the Born approximation is

$$\frac{\mu}{2\pi\hbar^2}\left|\int \frac{1}{r}\, e^{i(kr+\mathbf{k}_0\cdot\mathbf{r})}V(\mathbf{r})d\tau\right| \ll 1 \tag{6}$$

If V is spherically symmetric, this validity criterion becomes

$$\frac{\mu}{\hbar^2 k}\left|\int_0^\infty (e^{2ikr}-1)V(r)dr\right| \ll 1 \tag{7}$$

Perturbation theory may also be used to calculate the probability for a transition between stationary states u_n of an unperturbed Hamiltonian $H_0\,(H_0 u_n = E_n u_n)$, that are caused by a time-dependent perturbation H'. If H' is a transient disturbance, the first-order probability that the system has made a transition from any state m to any state n after a long time is

$$\frac{1}{\hbar^2}\left|\int_{-\infty}^{\infty} H'_{nm} e^{i(E_n-E_m)t/\hbar}dt\right|^2 \tag{8}$$

If H' is independent of time except for being turned on at some instant, the first-order probability per unit time that the system will make a transition from any state m to a state n that has the same energy is

$$w = \frac{2\pi}{\hbar}\,\rho(n)\,|\,H'_{nm}\,|^2 \tag{9}$$

where $\rho(n)dE_n$ is the number of final states with energies between E_n and $E_n + dE_n$. In this latter case, if $H'_{nm} = 0$, it may be replaced in the formula by the second-order matrix element

$$\sum_k \frac{H'_{nk}H'_{km}}{E_m - E_k} \tag{10}$$

If any of the states k are continuously distributed, the sum is to be replaced by an integral over those states.

1.7. Other approximation methods. Let E_0 be the smallest energy eigenvalue of a Hamiltonian $H\,(Hu_0 = E_0 u_0)$. Then

$$E_0 \leqq E = \frac{\int \bar{u}Hu\,d\tau}{\int |\,u\,|^2 d\tau} \tag{1}$$

for any function u. The equal sign holds if and only if $u = u_0$. This is the variation method, and u is the trial function, which usually contains parameters that can be varied to minimize the variational energy E. If u differs from u_0 by a first-order infinitesimal, then E exceeds E_0 only by a second-order infinitesimal. If the trial function is chosen in the form

$$u - \frac{u_0 \int \bar{u}_0 u\,d\tau}{\int |\,u_0\,|^2 d\tau} \tag{2}$$

the variational energy will provide an upper limit on the next to the smallest energy eigenvalue.

The WKB (Wentzel-Kramers-Brillouin) approximation can be used to obtain approximate solutions of the one-dimensional time-independent wave equation

$$\frac{d^2u}{dx^2} + k^2(x)u = 0, \quad k^2 = \frac{2\mu}{\hbar^2}[E - V(x)] \tag{3}$$

when the potential changes slowly enough so that $dk/dx \ll k^2$. If k is real ($V < E$), the two linearly independent solutions are

$$A_1 k^{-1/2} \exp\left[i\int_{a_1}^{x} k(x)dx\right], \quad A_2 k^{-1/2} \exp\left[-i\int_{a_2}^{x} k(x)dx\right] \tag{4}$$

If $\kappa = ik$ is real ($V > E$), the solutions are

$$B_1 \kappa^{-1/2} \exp\left[\int_{b_1}^{x} \kappa(x)dx\right], \quad B_2 \kappa^{-1/2} \exp\left[-\int_{b_2}^{x} \kappa(x)dx\right] \tag{5}$$

Near the turning points of the corresponding classical motion (where $V = E$), $dk/dx \gg k^2$, and the above approximate solutions are not valid. They can be connected to each other across a turning point (taken to be at $x = 0$ with $V > E$ for $x < 0$ and $V < E$ for $x > 0$) by means of the following formulas.

$$\left.\begin{aligned} \tfrac{1}{2}\kappa^{-1/2} \exp\left(-\int_{x}^{0} \kappa dx\right) &\to k^{-1/2} \cos\left(\int_{0}^{x} k dx - \tfrac{1}{4}\pi\right) \\ \sin\eta\,\kappa^{-1/2} \exp\left(\int_{x}^{0} \kappa dx\right) &\leftarrow k^{-1/2} \cos\left(\int_{0}^{x} k dx - \tfrac{1}{4}\pi + \eta\right) \end{aligned}\right\} \tag{6}$$

where η is appreciably different from zero or an integer multiple of π. Without more careful consideration, the connections can be made only in the directions indicated by the arrows; for example, in the first formula, the expression on the left goes into that on the right, but the reverse is not necessarily true.

If x_1 and x_2 are two turning points of a potential well, so that $V < E$ for $x_1 < x < x_2$, the WKB approximation states that the energy levels are given by the formula

$$\int_{x_1}^{x_2} k(x)dx = (n + \tfrac{1}{2})\pi, \quad (n = 0, 1, 2, \ldots) \tag{7}$$

This is the same as the Bohr-Wilson-Sommerfeld quantization rule (see § 1.1) except than n is now replaced by $n + \frac{1}{2}$.

The time-dependent Schrödinger wave equation

$$i\hbar \frac{\partial \psi}{\partial t} = H(t)\psi \tag{8}$$

can be solved approximately if H depends on t, provided it has a simple enough form and changes slowly enough with time. The adiabatic approximation shows that the system stays in a particular state $u_m(t)$ for a long time, where

$$H(t)u_m(t) = E_m(t)u_m(t) \tag{9}$$

provided that

$$\hbar \frac{\partial H}{\partial t} \ll (E_n - E_m)^2 \tag{10}$$

for all other states n.

On the other hand, if $H(t)$ changes very rapidly from one constant form to another, the wave function ψ is approximately the same just before and just after the change in H. The sudden approximation shows that if the change in H takes place in a short time τ, the wave function is unchanged if $\hbar/\tau$ is large in comparison with the energy differences between the initial state of the original Hamiltonian and those final states of the altered Hamiltonian that are most prominent in the expansion of ψ.

1.8. Matrices in quantum mechanics. Hermitian and unitary matrices (see § 7.11 of Chapter 1), often with infinite numbers of rows and columns, play an important role in quantum mechanics. Every dynamical variable can be represented by an operator, or by an infinite number of Hermitian matrices, one for every complete orthonormal set of eigenfunctions of that or any other operator. For example, suppose that we have two dynamical variables represented by operators Ω and Ω', with orthonormal eigenfunction sets u_n and v_s.

$$\Omega u_n = \omega_n u_n, \quad \Omega' v_s = \omega'_s v_s$$

Then four matrices that have the following elements can be calculated.

$$\left.\begin{aligned} &\int \bar{u}_m \Omega u_n d\tau = \omega_n \delta_{mn}, \quad \int \bar{u}_m \Omega' u_n d\tau = \Omega'_{mn} \\ &\int \bar{v}_r \Omega v_s d\tau = \Omega_{rs}, \quad\quad \int \bar{v}_r \Omega' v_s d\tau = \omega'_s \delta_{rs} \end{aligned}\right\} \tag{1}$$

The first and third of these are different representations of Ω, and the second and fourth are different representations of Ω'. The first and fourth are diagonal matrix representations, in which case the diagonal elements are the eigenvalues of the operators. If these eigenvalues are real, as they are for physically meaningful variables, the operators and matrices (whether or not diagonal) are Hermitian. A matrix element Ω_{rs} is sometimes written $(r \mid \Omega \mid s)$.

A transformation from the nondiagonal to the diagonal representation of Ω can be effected by means of the unitary matrix $U_{mr} = \int \bar{u}_m v_r d\tau$.

$$\sum_r \sum_s U_{mr} \Omega_{rs} (U^{-1})_{sn} = \omega_n \delta_{mn} \tag{2}$$

The unitary property of U means that

$$(U^{-1})_{sn} = (\tilde{U})_{sn} = \bar{U}_{ns} \tag{3}$$

where U^{-1} is the reciprocal of U, $\tilde{U}$ is the Hermitian conjugate of U, $\bar{U}_{ns}$ is the complex conjugate of the matrix element U_{ns}.

Heisenberg's form of the equations of motion of quantum mechanics expresses the change in dynamical variables with time without explicit use of wave functions, and hence are valid in any matrix representation. If H is the Hamiltonian, the equation of motion for any dynamical variable Ω is

$$\frac{d\Omega}{dt} = \frac{\partial \Omega}{\partial t} + \frac{1}{i\hbar}(\Omega H - H\Omega) \tag{4}$$

Here the term $d\Omega/dt$ indicates the time derivative of a typical matrix element of Ω, the term $\partial\Omega/\partial t$ indicates the corresponding matrix element of the partial derivative of Ω with respect to t (which is zero if Ω does not depend explicitly on the time), and the parenthesis is calculated according to the rules for matrix multiplication. If Ω does not depend explicitly on the time, and if it commutes with the Hamiltonian ($\Omega H = H\Omega$), then $d\Omega/dt = 0$ and Ω is a constant of the motion.

In general, to quantize a classical system replace Poisson brackets (see § 1.6 of Chapter 2) by commutator brackets in the following way.

$$\{A,B\} = \sum_i \left(\frac{\partial A}{\partial q_i} \frac{\partial B}{\partial p_i} - \frac{\partial B}{\partial q_i} \frac{\partial A}{\partial p_i} \right) \rightarrow \frac{1}{i\hbar}[A,B] = \frac{1}{i\hbar}(AB - BA)$$

Thus for canonical coordinates and momenta q_i, p_i, we get the quantum conditions

$$[q_i,p_j] = i\hbar\delta_{ij}, \quad [q_i,q_j] = 0, \quad [p_i,p_j] = 0 \tag{5}$$

A particular representation for these quantum conditions is that used in (1.3) to write down the Schrödinger wave equation

$$q_i = q_i, \quad p_i = -i\hbar \frac{\partial}{\partial q_i} \tag{6}$$

1.9. Many-particle systems. The Schrödinger wave function for many particles depends on the coordinates of all the particles, and the Hamiltonian is the sum of their kinetic, potential, and interaction energies. If the particles are identical, the wave function must be either symmetrical or antisymmetrical with respect to an interchange of all the coordinates of any two particles (including in the interchange both space and spin coordinates). Particles that obey Einstein-Bose statistics are described by symmetrical wave functions, and particles that obey Fermi-Dirac statistics, or (equivalently) the Pauli exclusion principle, are described by antisymmetrical wave functions.

In the special case in which the particle interaction energies can be neglected, the wave function can be written as a sum of products of one-particle wave functions like

$$v_\alpha(1)v_\beta(2) \dots v_\nu(n) \tag{1}$$

where $v_\alpha(1)$ denotes that particle 1 is in the state α with energy E_α. The total energy is then $E_\alpha + E_\beta + \dots + E_\nu$. A symmetrical wave function is the sum of all distinct terms that arise from permuting the numbers 1, ..., n among the functions. An antisymmetrical wave function can be written as a determinant

$$\begin{vmatrix} v_\alpha(1) & v_\alpha(2) & \dots & v_\alpha(n) \\ v_\beta(1) & v_\beta(2) & \dots & v_\beta(n) \\ \dots & \dots & \dots & \dots \\ v_\nu(1) & v_\nu(2) & \dots & v_\nu(n) \end{vmatrix} \tag{2}$$

and vanishes if any two of the states α, β, ... ν are the same.

1.10. Spin angular momentum. A particle, like an electron, proton, or neutron, that has spin angular momentum $\frac{1}{2}\hbar$, can be described non-relativistically by a two-component wave function. The spin angular momentum operator $\boldsymbol{S} = \frac{1}{2}\hbar\boldsymbol{\sigma}$ operates on these two-component functions, and can be expressed in terms of the two-row, two-column Pauli spin matrices.

$$\sigma_x = \begin{pmatrix} 0 & 1 \\ 1 & 0 \end{pmatrix}, \quad \sigma_y = \begin{pmatrix} 0 & -i \\ i & 0 \end{pmatrix}, \quad \sigma_z = \begin{pmatrix} 1 & 0 \\ 0 & -1 \end{pmatrix} \tag{1}$$

The two spin states may be chosen to be eigenfunctions of S_z as well as of $\boldsymbol{S}^2$, in which case they may be written

$$u_{1/2}(\boldsymbol{r}) = \begin{pmatrix} 1 \\ 0 \end{pmatrix} v(\boldsymbol{r}), \quad u_{-1/2}(\boldsymbol{r}) = \begin{pmatrix} 0 \\ 1 \end{pmatrix} w(\boldsymbol{r}) \tag{2}$$

It then follows that

$$\left.\begin{aligned} S_z u_{1/2} &= \tfrac{1}{2}\hbar u_{1/2}, \quad S_z u_{-1/2} = -\tfrac{1}{2}\hbar u_{-1/2} \\ \boldsymbol{S}^2 u_{1/2} &= \tfrac{3}{4}\hbar^2 u_{1/2}, \quad \boldsymbol{S}^2 u_{-1/2} = \tfrac{3}{4}\hbar^2 u_{-1/2} \end{aligned}\right\} \tag{3}$$

For a particle of spin s, which can be one of the numbers $0, \tfrac{1}{2}, 1, \tfrac{3}{2}, \ldots$, the spin matrix has $2s + 1$ rows and columns, and the wave functions have $2s + 1$ components. These wave functions may be chosen to be eigenfunctions of S_z with eigenvalues $s\hbar, (s - 1)\hbar, \ldots -s\hbar$, and all are eigenfunctions of $\boldsymbol{S}^2$ with eigenvalue $s(s + 1)\hbar^2$.

If $s = 0, 1, 2, \ldots$, the particles obey Einstein-Bose statistics; if $s = \tfrac{1}{2}, \tfrac{3}{2}, \tfrac{5}{2}, \ldots$, they obey Fermi-Dirac statistics. In both cases the differential scattering cross section for a collision of two identical particles in the center-of-mass coordinate system may be written in terms of the scattered amplitude $f(\theta)$ as

$$\sigma(\theta) = | f(\theta) |^2 + | f(\pi - \theta) |^2 + \frac{(-1)^{2s}}{2s + 1} 2\mathrm{Re}[f(\theta)\bar{f}(\pi - \theta)] \tag{4}$$

where Re denotes the real part of what follows.

1.11. Some radiation formulas. Interaction of a particle of charge e with radiation may be taken into account by replacing $\boldsymbol{p}$ or $-i\hbar$ **grad** with $\boldsymbol{p} - (e/c)\boldsymbol{A}$ or $-i\hbar$ **grad** $- (e/c)\boldsymbol{A}$ in the Schrödinger equation, where $\boldsymbol{A}$ is the radiation vector potential (see § 3.3 of Chapter 10).

When a one-electron atom in state n is irradiated by electromagnetic waves that are continuously distributed in frequency (with random phases) in the neighborhood of the angular frequency $| E_n - E_k |/\hbar = \omega$, transitions will be induced from the state n to the state k (corresponding to either absorption or emission of energy) at the rate

$$\frac{4\pi^2 e^2}{m^2 c \omega^2} I(\omega) \left| \int \bar{u}_k e^{i\boldsymbol{k}\cdot\boldsymbol{r}} \operatorname{grad}_{pol} u_n d\tau \right|^2 \tag{1}$$

per unit time. Here e and m are the charge and mass of the electron, $I(\omega)$ is the intensity of the incident radiation per unit angular frequency range, $\boldsymbol{k}$ is the propagation vector of the incident radiation, and the component of the gradient along the polarization vector of the incident radiation is taken.

For allowed or electric-dipole transitions, this formula becomes

$$\frac{4\pi^2 e^2}{3\hbar^2 c} I(\omega) | (\boldsymbol{r})_{kn} |^2 \tag{2}$$

where the last factor is equal to the sum of the squares of the magnitudes of the matrix elements of x, y, and z. The rate of spontaneous radiative electric-dipole transitions per unit time is

$$\frac{4e^2\omega^3}{3\hbar c^3} \mid (\boldsymbol{r})_{kn} \mid^2 \tag{3}$$

Forbidden transitions (electric quadrupole, magnetic dipole, etc.) generally have a rate smaller than allowed transitions by a factor of order $(ka)^2$ or less, where a is a typical linear dimension of the atomic system.

In simple cases, the intensity radiated per unit frequency range is proportional to

$$[(\omega - \omega_0)^2 + \tfrac{1}{4}w^2]^{-1} \tag{4}$$

where ω_0 is the center of the emitted line and the line breadth is proportional to w, the spontaneous transition probability per unit time.

1.12. Relativistic wave equations. A scalar particle (spin 0) of mass m is described relativistically by the Schrödinger relativistic wave equation

$$E^2\psi = c^2\boldsymbol{p}^2\psi + m^2c^4\psi \tag{1}$$

or

$$-\hbar^2\frac{\partial^2\psi}{\partial t^2} = -\hbar^2c^2\nabla^2\psi + m^2c^2\psi \tag{2}$$

If the particle has charge e, the electric charge and current densities are

$$\left.\begin{aligned} P &= \frac{ie\hbar}{2mc^2}\left(\bar{\psi}\frac{\partial\psi}{\partial t} - \psi\frac{\partial\bar{\psi}}{\partial t}\right) \\ \boldsymbol{S} &= \frac{e\hbar}{2im}(\bar{\psi}\,\mathbf{grad}\,\psi - \psi\,\mathbf{grad}\,\bar{\psi}) \end{aligned}\right\} \tag{3}$$

and satisfy the conservation law

$$\frac{\partial P}{\partial t} + \operatorname{div}\boldsymbol{S} = 0 \tag{4}$$

When electromagnetic fields described by the potentials $\boldsymbol{A}$, ϕ (see § 3.3 of Chapter 10) are present, the substitutions $E \to E - e\phi$ and $\boldsymbol{p} \to \boldsymbol{p} - (e/c)\boldsymbol{A}$ can be made in the wave equation above. The energy levels in a Coulomb field ($\boldsymbol{A} = 0$, $e\phi = -Ze^2/r$), including the rest energy mc^2, are given by

$$\left.\begin{aligned} &E = mc^2\left[1 + \frac{\alpha^2}{\{n - l - \frac{1}{2} + [(l + \frac{1}{2})^2 - \alpha^2]^{1/2}\}^2}\right]^{-1/2}, \quad \alpha = \frac{Ze^2}{\hbar c} \\ &\qquad (l = 0, 1, \ldots, n-1; \quad n = 1, 2, 3, \ldots) \end{aligned}\right\} \tag{5}$$

This formula disagrees with the Sommerfeld fine-structure formula, derived on the basis of the old quantum theory, and also disagrees with experiment.

An electron (spin $\frac{1}{2}\hbar$) is described relativistically by Dirac's relativistic wave equation

$$E\psi + c(\boldsymbol{\alpha} \cdot \boldsymbol{p})\psi + mc^2\beta\psi = 0 \tag{6}$$

or

$$i\hbar \frac{\partial \psi}{\partial t} - i\hbar c\boldsymbol{\alpha} \cdot \mathbf{grad}\, \psi + mc^2\beta\psi = 0 \tag{7}$$

where

$$\left.\begin{aligned} \alpha_x^2 = \alpha_y^2 = \alpha_z^2 = \beta^2 = 1 \\ \alpha_x\alpha_y + \alpha_y\alpha_x = \alpha_y\alpha_z + \alpha_z\alpha_y = \alpha_z\alpha_x + \alpha_x\alpha_z = 0 \\ \alpha_x\beta + \beta\alpha_x = \alpha_y\beta + \beta\alpha_y = \alpha_z\beta + \beta\alpha_z = 0 \end{aligned}\right\} \tag{8}$$

Here β and $\boldsymbol{\alpha}$ can be expressed as four-row, four-column matrices

$$\left.\begin{aligned} \beta = \begin{bmatrix} 1 & 0 & 0 & 0 \\ 0 & 1 & 0 & 0 \\ 0 & 0 & -1 & 0 \\ 0 & 0 & 0 & -1 \end{bmatrix} \qquad \alpha_x = \begin{bmatrix} 0 & 0 & 0 & 1 \\ 0 & 0 & 1 & 0 \\ 0 & 1 & 0 & 0 \\ 1 & 0 & 0 & 0 \end{bmatrix} \\ \alpha_y = \begin{bmatrix} 0 & 0 & 0 & -i \\ 0 & 0 & i & 0 \\ 0 & -i & 0 & 0 \\ i & 0 & 0 & 0 \end{bmatrix} \qquad \alpha_z = \begin{bmatrix} 0 & 0 & 1 & 0 \\ 0 & 0 & 0 & -1 \\ 1 & 0 & 0 & 0 \\ 0 & -1 & 0 & 0 \end{bmatrix} \end{aligned}\right\} \tag{9}$$

The wave function has four components.

$$\psi(\boldsymbol{r},t) = \begin{bmatrix} \psi_1(\boldsymbol{r},t) \\ \psi_2(\boldsymbol{r},t) \\ \psi_3(\boldsymbol{r},t) \\ \psi_4(\boldsymbol{r},t) \end{bmatrix} \tag{10}$$

The electric charge and current densities are

$$P = e\tilde{\psi}\psi, \quad \boldsymbol{S} = -ce\tilde{\psi}\boldsymbol{\alpha}\psi \tag{11}$$

where $\tilde{\psi}$ is the Hermitian conjugate matrix to ψ; P and $\boldsymbol{S}$ satisfy the usual conservation law.

Electromagnetic fields can be included by making the substitutions $E \to E - e\phi$ and $\boldsymbol{p} \to \boldsymbol{p} - (e/c)\boldsymbol{A}$. In the nonrelativistic limit with $\phi = 0$ and $\boldsymbol{A}$ constant in time, the Schrödinger wave equation is obtained with an extra term in the Hamiltonian $-(e\hbar/2mc)\boldsymbol{\sigma} \cdot \boldsymbol{H}$; this is the energy of the electron's magnetic moment of magnitude $e\hbar/2mc$ in a magnetic field $\boldsymbol{H}$. In this limit, the σ's are the Pauli spin matrices, and the wave function has two components.

In a central field $[\boldsymbol{A} = 0,\ e\phi = V(r)]$, the nonrelativistic limit gives the Schrödinger wave equation with an extra term that is the spin-orbit energy

$$\frac{1}{2mc^2r}\cdot\frac{dV}{dr}\,\boldsymbol{S}\cdot\boldsymbol{M} \tag{12}$$

added to the Hamiltonian. Here the wave function has two components, $\boldsymbol{S} = \frac{1}{2}\hbar\boldsymbol{\sigma}$ is the spin angular momentum, and $\boldsymbol{M} = \boldsymbol{r} \times \boldsymbol{p}$ is the orbital angular momentum.

The relativistic energy levels in a Coulomb field $(\boldsymbol{A} = 0,\ e\phi = -Ze^2/r)$, including the rest energy mc^2, are given by

$$E = mc^2\left\{1 + \frac{\alpha^2}{[n - k + (k^2 - \alpha^2)^{1/2}]^2}\right\}^{-1/2}, \quad \begin{matrix}(k = 1, 2, \ldots, n)\\(n = 1, 2, \ldots)\end{matrix} \tag{13}$$

where $\alpha = Ze^2/\hbar c$. This formula is the same as the Sommerfeld fine-structure formula, and is in good agreement with experiment.

Bibliography

1. BOHM, D., *Quantum Theory*, Prentice-Hall, Inc., New York, 1951. A good general book on nonrelativistic quantum mechanics that emphasizes the physical basis of the subject.
2. DIRAC, P. A. M., *The Principles of Quantum Mechanics*, 3d ed., Oxford University Press, New York, 1947. A coherent, fundamental treatment of the subject by one who played a major role in its development.
3. HEISENBERG, W., *The Physical Principles of the Quantum Theory*, University of Chicago Press, Chicago, 1930. A qualitative discussion emphasizing physical points of view, by the discoverer of quantum mechanics; appendices give a very condensed outline of the mathematical formalism.
4. PAULING, F. and WILSON, E. B. Jr., *Introduction to Quantum Mechanics*, McGraw-Hill Book Company, Inc., New York, 1935. An excellent and widely used general textbook that stresses applications to atoms and molecules.
5. ROJANSKY, V., *Introductory Quantum Mechanics*, Prentice-Hall, Inc., New York, 1938. A good introductory textbook that works out several of the more elementary problems in considerable mathematical detail.
6. SCHIFF, L. I., *Quantum Mechanics*, McGraw-Hill Book Company, Inc., New York, 1949. A concise treatment of all aspects of quantum mechanics, including quantized field theory, with a few simple applications to atoms, molecules, and atomic nuclei.

Chapter 22

NUCLEAR THEORY

BY M. E. ROSE

Oak Ridge National Laboratory

Nuclear physics is still in a state of rapid change, and with the passage of time new developments and shifts of emphasis are inevitable. The material selected for presentation in this chapter was chosen so as to provide a comprehensive survey of the field. However, the choice of material is also conditioned by the criteria that the formal aspect of the topics treated be fairly well-developed and of reasonable expectation value of relative permanence at the time of writing. The omission of some subject matter in the field of nuclear physics may be understood in this light.

1. Table of Symbols

The numbers in **boldface** in parentheses preceding the various groups of symbols that follow indicate the section where particular symbols are introduced. (***Bold-face italic*** type is used for vectors and vector operators.)

(2.1)

$N =$ number of neutrons in nucleus.

$Z =$ number of protons in nucleus.

$A = N + Z$, mass number.

$M_Z^A =$ mass of neutral atom.

${}_ZM^A =$ mass of nucleus; ${}_1M^1 = M_p$, ${}_0M^1 = M_n$, proton and neutron masses, respectively.

$m =$ (rest) mass of electron.

$\Delta_Z^A = M_Z^A - A$, mass excess.

$\mathcal{P}_Z^A = (M_Z^A - A)/A$, packing-fraction.

$\epsilon_Z^A =$ binding energy.

$e =$ proton charge (in esu).

$R =$ nuclear radius.

β_+, (β_-) refers to positive (negative) electrons emitted by nucleus.

ϵ_e = binding energy of orbital electron.
c = vacuum velocity of light.

(2.2)

$\sigma_k{}^{(j)}$ = kth component of the Pauli spin vector for the jth nucleon.
$\boldsymbol{s}^{(j)} = \frac{1}{2}\boldsymbol{\sigma}^{(j)}$, $\hbar \boldsymbol{s}^{(j)}$ is the spin operator for the jth nucleon.
$\hbar$ = Dirac action constant.

$\boldsymbol{S} = \sum_j \boldsymbol{s}^j$; eigenvalue of $\boldsymbol{S}^2 = S(S+1)$.

$\boldsymbol{L}$ = orbital angular momentum operator divided by $\hbar$ [Eq. (2.3)]; eigenvalues of $\boldsymbol{L}^2 = L(L+1)$, $L = 0, 1, 2, \ldots$
$\boldsymbol{\nabla}_j$ = gradient operator in configuration space of jth nucleon.
$\boldsymbol{J}$ = total angular momentum operator divided by $\hbar$ [Eq. (2.4)]; eigenvalues of $\boldsymbol{J}^2 = J(J+1)$.
m_J = eigenvalue of J_3.
Ψ = nuclear wave function (sometimes written with appropriate quantum numbers as index).
H = nuclear Hamiltonian, eigenvalue $E = -\epsilon_Z^A$, ($E = 0$ for nucleons at rest and at infinite separation).
∇_j^2 = Laplacian operator in space of jth nucleon.
$\mathcal{V}$ = nuclear interaction operator.
$\langle O \rangle = (\Psi, O\Psi)$, expectation value of the operator O where the inner product is taken in configuration and spin space of all the nucleons and $(\Psi,\Psi) = 1$.
$\mu_0 = e\hbar/2M_pc$, nuclear magneton.
μ_n = neutron magnetic moment in units μ_0, $\mu_n = -1.9135$.
μ_p = proton magnetic moment in units μ_0, $\mu_p = 2.7926$.

(2.3)

P_K = exchange operator in two-nucleon interactions, $K = M, H, B$.
$m_s^{(j)}$ = eigenvalue of $s_3^{(j)}$.
$\boldsymbol{\tau}^j$ = isotopic spin (matrix) vector for jth nucleon.
$m_\tau^{(j)}$ = eigenvalue of $\tau_3^{(j)}$.
r = distance between two nucleons.
V^0 = scale parameter in two nucleon interactions determining strength of interaction.
b = range parameter in two-nucleon interaction.

(2.4)

$\eta = \sqrt{M\epsilon}/\hbar$.

$\Psi_S = {}^3S_1$ part of deuteron wave function, $S^2\Psi_S = 2\Psi_S$, $L^2\Psi_S = 0$, $J^2\Psi_S = 2\Psi_S$.

$\Psi_D = {}^3D_1$ part of deuteron wave function, $S^2\Psi_D = 2\Psi_D$, $L^2\Psi_D = 6\Psi_D$, $J^2\Psi_D = 2\Psi_D$.

$\hbar\omega$ = energy of electromagnetic radiation.

σ_e, σ_m = total cross sections for photoelectric and photomagnetic disintegration of deuteron, respectively.

$\sigma_e(\vartheta)$, $\sigma_m(\vartheta)$ = cross sections per unit solid angle for disintegration with angle ϑ between photon and relative direction of motion of nucleons.

ϵ' = negative binding energy of ${}^1S$ state of deuteron, $\epsilon' \cong 75$ kev.

(2.5)

A particle of mass M_1 is scattered by a target nucleus of mass M_2.

Laboratory (L) system :

$\bar{E}_n$, $\bar{E}'_n$ kinetic energy of M_n before and after scattering.

Θ, scattering angle of M_1, azimuth ϕ.

$d\Omega_\Theta = \sin\Theta \, d\Theta \, d\phi$.

$\sigma_0(\Theta)$ = scattering cross section per unit solid angle.

Center of mass (C) system :

E = sum of kinetic energies of both particles.

θ = scattering angle of M_1, azimuth φ.

$d\Omega = \sin\theta \, d\theta \, d\varphi$.

$M_r = M_1M_2/(M_1 + M_2)$, reduced mass.

$k = \sqrt{2M_rE/\hbar^2}$, wave number at $r = \infty$.

v = relative velocity at $r = \infty$.

δ_l = nuclear phase shift of partial wave with orbital angular momentum $l\hbar$.

P_l = Legendre polynomial (argument $\cos\theta$).

δ_r = real part of s-phase shift ($l = 0$).

$\frac{1}{2}\Delta$ = imaginary part of s-phase shift.

Z_1, Z_2 = atomic numbers for scattered and target nuclei.

$\alpha = e^2/\hbar v$.

(2.6)

$\bar{E}_n$, E_n = energy of particle of mass M_n in L, C systems, respectively.

$Q = (M_1 + M_2 - M_3 - M_4)c^2$ is energy release in transmutation, (Q-value).

Θ_n, θ_n angle between outgoing direction of M_n and incident beam, in (L), (C) systems, respectively.
$H^{(1,2)}_{l+\frac{1}{2}}(x)$ = Hankel functions of first, second kind and order $l+\frac{1}{2}$.
$\kappa = Z_P Z_A \alpha$ or $Z_Q Z_B \alpha$; Z_P or $Z_Q = 0$ for neutrons and photons.
$\zeta_l(r) = kr - \frac{1}{2}l\pi - \kappa \ln kr + \arg[(l+i\kappa)!]$.
$J_{\pm(l+1/2)}(x)$ = Bessel function of order $\pm(l+\frac{1}{2})$.

(2.7)

W = electron (or positron) energy (including rest energy) in units mc^2.
$p = \sqrt{W^2-1}$, β-particle momentum in units mc.
$W_0 = (\Delta M)_\pm/m$, maximum W.
G_F = Fermi coupling constant for β-decay, $G^2 \sim 10^{-2}$ sec^{-1}.
$d\Omega_\nu$ = differential solid angle for neutrino.
Ψ_e = wave function of $\beta_\pm$-particle.
Ψ_ν = wave function of neutrino.
Ψ_f, Ψ_i = nuclear wave functions for final and initial states, respectively.
$y = e^2 ZW/\hbar cp$.
$\gamma = (1 - e^4Z^2/\hbar^2c^2)^{1/2}$.

2. Nuclear Theory

2.1. Nuclear masses and stability. a. *Energy relations.* Neglecting the binding of the orbital electrons

$$ {}_Z M^A = M^A_Z - Zm \tag{1}$$

Numerical values are defined by $M^{16}_8 \equiv 16.0$ and 1 mass unit = 931 Mev = 10^3 mmu. The binding energy of the nucleus is

$$\left.\begin{aligned} \epsilon^A_Z &= ZM^1_1 + NM^1_0 - M^A_Z = Z\Delta^1_1 + N\Delta^1_0 - \Delta^A_Z \\ &\approx A[\tfrac{1}{2}(\mathcal{P}^1_1 + \mathcal{P}^1_0) - \mathcal{P}^A_Z] \end{aligned}\right\} \tag{2}$$

Semi-empirical formula for binding energy (incompressible nucleus) *

$$\epsilon^A_Z = u_v A - u_s A^{2/3} - u_\tau \frac{(N-Z)^2}{A} - \frac{3}{5} u_c \frac{Z(Z-1)}{A^{1/3}} \tag{3}$$

* Weizsacker, C. V., *Z. Physik*, **96**, 431 (1935); Bethe, H. A. and Bacher, R., *Revs. Modern Phys.*, 8, 82 (1936). Feenberg, E., *Revs. Modern Phys.*, **19**, 239 (1947) gives the small correction arising from nuclear compressibility.

where

$$u_v = 15.1 \text{ mmu} = 14.1 \text{ Mev}, \quad u_s = 14.1 \text{ mmu} = 13.1 \text{ Mev},$$
$$u_\tau = 19.4 \text{ mmu} = 18.1 \text{ Mev}, \quad u_c = e^2/r_0 = 0.157 \text{ mmu} = 0.146 \text{ Mev}.$$

The result [Eq. (3)] corresponds to a nuclear radius R given (in cm) by

$$R = r_0 A^{1/3} = 1.47 \times 10^{-13} A^{1/3} \tag{4}$$

b. *Stability conditions.* A necessary and sufficient condition for stability against nuclear particle emission is

$$M_A^Z < \Sigma\, M_{A'}^{Z'} \tag{5}$$

where the sum is taken over all possible combinations for which

$$\Sigma\, A' = A, \quad \Sigma\, Z' = Z \tag{6}$$

Therefore Eq. (5) includes the condition $\epsilon_Z^A > 0$.

For $\beta_\pm$ decay and capture of orbital electrons the stability conditions are (assuming zero neutrino rest mass)

$$(\Delta M)_- = M_Z^A - M_{Z+1}^A < 0, \qquad \text{(for } \beta_- \text{ decay)} \tag{7}$$

$$(\Delta M)_+ = M_Z^A - M_{Z-1}^A - 2m < 0, \qquad \text{(for } \beta_+ \text{ decay)} \tag{8}$$

$$(\Delta M)_\nu = M_Z^A - M_{Z-1}^A - \epsilon_e/c^2 < 0, \quad \text{(for orbital electron capture)} \tag{9}$$

Only the very small difference of electronic binding energies of the parent and daughter nuclei is neglected. When these conditions are not fulfilled $(\Delta M)_\pm c^2$ is the total energy (including rest energy of the $\beta_\pm$ particle) liberated in the decay process and $(\Delta M)_\nu c^2$ is the neutrino energy.

The decay constant λ for a disintegration process is defined by

$$\lambda = -d \ln N/dt \tag{10}$$

where N is the number of decaying nuclei at time t. The mean life and half-life are, respectively,

$$T = 1/\lambda, \quad T_{1/2} = (\ln 2)/\lambda \tag{11}$$

2.2. Stationary state properties. The spin properties of particles with spin $\frac{1}{2}\hbar$ (nucleons) are described in terms of the Pauli spin matrices. In the spin space of each nucleon the matrix-vector $\boldsymbol{\sigma}$ has components

$$\sigma_1 = \begin{pmatrix} 0 & 1 \\ 1 & 0 \end{pmatrix} \quad \sigma_2 = \begin{pmatrix} 0 & -i \\ i & 0 \end{pmatrix} \quad \sigma_3 = \begin{pmatrix} 1 & 0 \\ 0 & -1 \end{pmatrix} \tag{1}$$

The spin operator $\hbar \boldsymbol{s} = \frac{1}{2}\hbar\boldsymbol{\sigma}$. For a complex nucleus $\boldsymbol{s}$ is replaced by

$$\boldsymbol{S} = \tfrac{1}{2}\sum_{j=1}^{A} \boldsymbol{\sigma}^{(j)} \tag{2}$$

where $\boldsymbol{\sigma}^{(j)}$ refers to the jth nucleon and a direct product with unit matrices in the space of the other nucleons is implied in each term of Eq. (2). The spin quantum number $S = n/2$, $n \leqslant A$ and n even (odd) for A even (odd). For a single nucleon $S = s = \frac{1}{2}$.

The orbital angular momentum operator is $\hbar \boldsymbol{L}$

$$\boldsymbol{L} = -i\sum_{j=1}^{A} (\boldsymbol{r}_j \times \boldsymbol{\nabla}_j) \tag{3}$$

where the summand is a direct product of A unit matrices.

The total angular momentum operator is $\hbar \boldsymbol{J}$

$$\boldsymbol{J} = \boldsymbol{S} + \boldsymbol{L} \tag{4}$$

For any nuclear state $\boldsymbol{J}^2$ is diagonal, with eigenvalues $J(J+1)$, and $J = n/2$, $(-)^n = (-)^A$. Along the quantization axis the component of total angular momentum is $m_J\hbar$

$$m_J = -J, \quad -J+1, \quad \ldots, \quad J-1, \quad J \tag{5}$$

A nuclear wave function $\Psi_{J,m_J}(\boldsymbol{r}_1, \boldsymbol{r}_2, \ldots, \boldsymbol{r}_A)$ is a simultaneous eigenfunction of J^2, J_3 with the eigenvalues $J(J+1)$ and m_J, and of a Hamiltonian operator with eigenvalue E.

$$H\Psi = \left(-\sum_{j=1}^{A} \frac{\hbar^2}{2M_j} \nabla_j^2 + \mathcal{V}\right)\Psi = E\Psi \tag{6}$$

where $\mathcal{V}$ is the total interaction operator (§ 2.3); Ψ is also an eigenfunction of the *parity* operator (inversion through the origin, center of mass)

$$\Psi(-\boldsymbol{r}_1, -\boldsymbol{r}_2, \ldots, -\boldsymbol{r}_A) = \pm\Psi(\boldsymbol{r}_1, \boldsymbol{r}_2, \ldots, \boldsymbol{r}_A) \tag{7}$$

the $+$ and $-$ sign belonging to states of even and odd *parity*, respectively. For interacting nucleons H, $\boldsymbol{J}^2$, J_3, and parity are conserved (diagonal) but in general $\boldsymbol{S}^2$ and $\boldsymbol{L}^2$ are not. In special case where the latter are conserved the quantum numbers S and L are introduced.

The magnetic dipole moment (neglecting small contributions from exchange currents) is

$$\mu = \mu_0 \left\langle \sum_{j=1}^{Z} \left[\mu_p \sigma_3^{(j)} - i\left(x_j \frac{\partial}{\partial y_j} - y_j \frac{\partial}{\partial x_j}\right)\right] + \mu_n \sum_{J=Z+1}^{A} \sigma_3^{(j)} \right\rangle_{m_J=J} \tag{8}$$

The electric quadrupole moment is

$$q = \left\langle \sum_{j=1}^{Z} (3z_j^2 - r_j^2) \right\rangle_{m_J = J} \tag{9}$$

where the sum is over protons only. For $J < 1$, $q = 0$.

2.3. Nuclear interactions.* *Restriction:* only velocity-independent interactions are considered; interactions are in the two-particle system (neglect difference in mass of neutron and proton).

a. *Central interactions.* Aside from the Coulomb interaction between protons $\mathcal{V}(\boldsymbol{r})$ is, in general, a linear combination of the following four fundamental interactions: (1) $V_W(r)$ ordinary (or Wigner) interaction, (2) $V_M(r)P_M$ space exchange (or Majorana) interaction, (3) $V_H(r)P_H$ space-spin exchange (or Heisenberg) interaction, (4) $V_B(r)P_B$ spin exchange (or Bartlett) interaction. If $\Psi(\boldsymbol{r}_1, m_s^{(1)}; \boldsymbol{r}_2 m_s^{(2)})$ is the two-nucleon wave function, the exchange operators are defined by

$$\left.\begin{aligned} P_M\Psi[\boldsymbol{r}_1, m_s^{(1)}; \boldsymbol{r}_2, m_s^{(2)}] &= \Psi[\boldsymbol{r}_2, m_s^{(1)}; \boldsymbol{r}_1, m_s^{(2)}] \\ P_H\Psi[\boldsymbol{r}_1, m_s^{(1)}; \boldsymbol{r}_2, m_s^{(2)}] &= \Psi[\boldsymbol{r}_2, m_s^{(2)}; \boldsymbol{r}_1, m_s^{(1)}] \\ P_B\Psi[\boldsymbol{r}_1, m_s^{(1)}; \boldsymbol{r}_2, m_s^{(2)}] &= \Psi[\boldsymbol{r}_1, m_s^{(2)}; \boldsymbol{r}_2, m_s^{(1)}] \end{aligned}\right\} \tag{1}$$

The P-operators commute, and any one is the product of the other pair. For these interactions $\boldsymbol{L}^2$ and $\boldsymbol{S}^2$ are conserved. Then $S = 0, 1$,

$$P_M\Psi = (-)^L\Psi; \quad P_B\Psi = (-)^{S+1}\Psi \tag{2}$$

and for identical particles $S + L$ is an even integer.

Isotopic spin formalism. All nucleons are treated as (charge) substates of a single particle (Fermion). The isotopic spin matrices $\tau_1^{(j)}$, $\tau_2^{(j)}$, $\tau_3^{(j)}$ are introduced (one matrix vector for each nucleon) just as in Eq. (1) of § 2.2 except that $\tau_i^{(j)}$ operates on the isotopic spin coordinate $m_\tau^{(j)} (= \pm 1)$ which is adjoined to $\boldsymbol{r}^{(j)}$ and $m_s^{(j)}$ as arguments in Ψ; $m_\tau = 1$ (neutron), $m_\tau = -1$ (proton). (Exclusion principle for two particles.)

$$\Psi(\boldsymbol{r}_1, m_s^{(1)}, m_\tau^{(1)}; \boldsymbol{r}_2, m_s^{(2)}\ m_\tau^{(2)}) = -\Psi(\boldsymbol{r}_2, m_s^{(2)}, m_\tau^{(2)}; \boldsymbol{r}_1, m_s^{(1)}, m_\tau^{(1)}) \tag{3}$$

* Rosenfeld, L., *Nuclear Forces*, 2 vols., Interscience Publishers, Inc., New York, 1948.

Requirement of invariance under the rotation-reflection group in spin, isotopic-spin and configurational space admits the following central operators : 1, $\boldsymbol{\tau}^{(1)} \cdot \boldsymbol{\tau}^{(2)}$, $\boldsymbol{\sigma}^{(1)} \cdot \boldsymbol{\sigma}^{(2)}$, $\boldsymbol{\tau}^{(1)} \cdot \boldsymbol{\tau}^{(2)} \boldsymbol{\sigma}^{(1)} \cdot \boldsymbol{\sigma}^{(2)}$ which are related to the foregoing operators by

$$\left.\begin{aligned} \tfrac{1}{2}(1 + \boldsymbol{\sigma}^{(1)} \cdot \boldsymbol{\sigma}^{(2)}) &= P_B \\ \tfrac{1}{2}(1 + \boldsymbol{\tau}^{(1)} \cdot \boldsymbol{\tau}^{(2)}) &= - P_H \end{aligned}\right\} \tag{4}$$

b. *Noncentral interaction.* Invariance requirements admit the additional (tensor) operator

$$S_{12} = \frac{3(\boldsymbol{\sigma}^{(1)} \cdot \boldsymbol{r})\,(\boldsymbol{\sigma}^{(2)} \cdot \boldsymbol{r})}{r^2} - \boldsymbol{\sigma}^{(1)} \cdot \boldsymbol{\sigma}^{(2)} \tag{5}$$

and the product $\boldsymbol{\tau}^{(1)} \cdot \boldsymbol{\tau}^{(2)} S_{12}$. The following interaction models have been used * :

$$\text{I.}\quad \mathcal{V} = \boldsymbol{\tau}^{(1)} \cdot \boldsymbol{\tau}^{(2)} [V_0(r) + V_1(r) \boldsymbol{\sigma}^{(1)} \cdot \boldsymbol{\sigma}^{(2)} + V_2(r) S_{12}] \tag{6}$$

$$\text{II.}\quad \mathcal{V} = \tfrac{1}{2}(1 + \boldsymbol{\tau}^{(1)} \cdot \boldsymbol{\tau}^{(2)})\,[V_0'(r) + V_1'(r) \boldsymbol{\sigma}^{(1)} \cdot \boldsymbol{\sigma}^{(2)} + V_2'(r) S_{12}] \tag{7}$$

$$\text{III.}\quad \mathcal{V} = V_0''(r) + V_1''(r) \boldsymbol{\sigma}^{(1)} \cdot \boldsymbol{\sigma}^{(2)} + V_2''(r) S_{12} \tag{8}$$

which are sometimes referred to as " symmetrical," " charged," and " neutral " (meson field theories) interactions, respectively. If $\mathcal{V}_0$ and $\mathcal{V}_e$ refer to the (neutron-proton) interactions in the states of odd and even L, respectively,

$$\mathcal{V}_0 = - 3^{1-2S} \mathcal{V}_e, \quad \text{(for I)} \tag{9}$$

$$\mathcal{V}_0 = - \mathcal{V}_e \qquad \text{(for II)} \tag{10}$$

$$\mathcal{V}_0 = \mathcal{V}_e \qquad \text{(for III)} \tag{11}$$

with $S = 0, 1 : [\boldsymbol{\sigma}^{(1)} \cdot \boldsymbol{\sigma}^{(2)} = 2S(S+1) - 3]$.

For interactions in nuclei with more than two constituents the restriction to two-body interactions is customarily made so that

$$\mathcal{V} = \sum_{i > j} \left[\mathcal{V}_{ij} + \frac{1}{4} \cdot \frac{e^2}{|r_i - r_j|} (1 - \tau_3^{(i)})\,(1 - \tau_3^{(j)}) \right] \tag{12}$$

where $\mathcal{V}_{ij}$ is the specific nuclear interaction between nucleons i and j described above.

* Rarita, W. and Schwinger, J., *Phys. Rev.*, **59**, 436, 556 (1941).

In all cases the functions V_0, V_1, etc. are defined in terms of two parameters : a depth parameter V^0 which fixes the scale of the interaction, and a range b such that for $r > b$, $V \ll V^0$. For example,

$$V = -V^0 g(r/b); \quad V^0 > 0 \tag{13}$$

Square well, $g_S(x) = 1$ for $x < 1$, $g = 0$ for $x > 1$; Yukawa well, $g_Y(x) = e^{-x}/x$; exponential well, $g_E(x) = e^{-x}$; Gaussian well, $g_G(x) = e^{-x^2}$.

2.4. Properties of the deuteron. a. *Ground state properties.* Fundamental data are : $J = 1$, $\mu/\mu_0 = 0.85761$, $q = 2.766 \times 10^{-27}$ cm^2, and $\epsilon_1^2 \equiv \epsilon = 2.228$ Mev, parity even. (For central interactions $L = 0$, $S = 1$.) Take $M_p = M_n = M$. For each well shape the assigned value of ϵ fixes a relation between V^0 and b. For a square well $[\mathcal{V} = -V^0 g_S(r/b)]$,

$$\sqrt{\frac{M}{\hbar^2}(V - \epsilon)} \cot b \sqrt{\frac{M}{\hbar^2}(V^0 - \epsilon)} = -\eta \equiv -\sqrt{\frac{M\epsilon}{\hbar^2}} \tag{1}$$

With tensor forces, $\boldsymbol{L}^2$ is not conserved but $\boldsymbol{S}^2$ is. For the ground state $^3(S = 1)$,

$$\Psi = \Psi_S + \Psi_D \tag{2}$$

b. *Interaction with electromagnetic radiation* (No tensor forces considered). For photon wavelengths $\gg b$ the total cross section for *photoelectric disintegration* of the deuteron is [with neglect of nuclear force in the final (^3P) state]

$$\sigma_e = \frac{8\pi}{3} \cdot \frac{e^2\hbar}{Mc} \cdot \frac{\epsilon^{1/2}(\hbar\omega - \epsilon)^{3/2}}{(1 - \eta\rho)\,(\hbar\omega)^3} \tag{3}$$

and ρ is an effective range,

$$\rho = 2\int_0^\infty [e^{-2\eta r} - u^2(r)]dr \tag{4}$$

$u = r\Psi_S$ normalized to $e^{-\eta r}$ at $r = \infty$. The angular distribution is given by

$$\sigma_e(\vartheta) = \frac{3}{8\pi}\sigma_e \sin^2\vartheta \tag{5}$$

The *photomagnetic disintegration* cross section is

$$\sigma_m = \frac{2\pi}{3} \frac{(\mu_p - \mu_n)^2}{1 - \eta\rho} \frac{e^2\hbar}{M^2c^3} \cdot \frac{\sqrt{|\epsilon'|}(\hbar\omega - \epsilon)(\sqrt{\epsilon} + \sqrt{|\epsilon'|})^2}{\hbar\omega(\hbar\omega - \epsilon + |\epsilon'|)} \tag{6}$$

The angular distribution is isotropic

$$\sigma_m(\vartheta) = \sigma_m/4\pi \tag{7}$$

The total photodisintegrations cross section is then

$$\sigma = \sigma_m + \sigma_e \tag{8}$$

and for the angular distribution

$$\sigma(\vartheta) = \frac{\sigma_e}{4\pi}\left(\frac{\sigma_m}{\sigma_e} + \frac{3}{2}\sin^2\vartheta\right) \tag{9}$$

The cross section for capture of neutrons of energy $\bar{E}_1$ by protons ($^1S \rightarrow {}^3S$ transition) is

$$\sigma_c = \pi\,\frac{(\mu_p - \mu_n)^2}{1-\eta\rho}\cdot\frac{e^2\hbar}{M^3c^5}\sqrt{\frac{2\epsilon}{\bar{E}_1}}\,\frac{(\sqrt{\epsilon}+\sqrt{|\,\epsilon'\,|})^2(\epsilon+\frac{1}{2}\bar{E}_1)}{|\,\epsilon'\,|+\frac{1}{2}\bar{E}_1} \tag{10}$$

2.5. Potential scattering. a. *Transformation between laboratory (L) and center of mass (C) reference systems*

$$E = \frac{M_2}{M_1+M_2}\,\bar{E}_1 \tag{1}$$

$$\tan\Theta = \frac{M_2\sin\theta}{M_1+M_2\cos\theta},\quad \phi=\varphi \tag{2}$$

For $M_1 \geqslant M_2$, $\Theta \leqslant \arcsin M_2/M_1 \leqslant \pi/2$. (See also § 2.6a.)

$$d\Omega_\Theta = d\Omega M_2^2\,\frac{M_2+M_1\cos\theta}{(M_2^2+M_1^2+2M_1M_2\cos\theta)^{3/2}} \tag{3}$$

$$\bar{E}_1' = \frac{\bar{E}_1}{(M_1+M_2)^2}\,(M_2^2+M_1^2+2M_1M_2\cos\theta) \tag{4}$$

$$\bar{E}_2' = \frac{2\bar{E}_1M_1M_2}{(M_1+M_2)^2}\,(1-\cos\theta) \tag{5}$$

b. *Method of phase shifts.* In the following only central interactions will be considered. Therefore $\boldsymbol{L}^2$ and $\boldsymbol{S}^2$ are conserved. In the C system, the scattering cross section per unit solid angle (for target and scattered nuclei not identical) is

$$\sigma(\theta,\varphi) = |\,f(\theta,\varphi)\,|^2 = \sigma_0(\Theta,\phi)\,d\Omega_\Theta/d\Omega \tag{6}$$

where the scattering amplitude $f(\theta,\varphi)$ is defined by the asymptotic ($r \rightarrow \infty$) form of the solution of the wave equation

$$\left[\nabla^2 + \frac{2M_r}{\hbar^2}(E-\mathcal{V})\right]\Psi = 0 \tag{7}$$

which is

$$\Psi_\infty = e^{ikz} + f(\theta,\varphi)\,\frac{e^{ikr}}{r} \tag{8}$$

Here the z axis has been taken along the direction of the incident beam, and the scattered particle is observed without regard to its spin state. When there is no preferred direction in the plane normal to the incident beam (scattering of unpolarized particles) $\partial \mid f \mid / \partial \varphi = 0$.

The solution of Eq. (7) which has the required asymptotic form is a sum of partial waves each one of which is an eigenfunction of $\boldsymbol{L}^2$ with eigenvalue $l(l+1)$.

$$\Psi = \sum_{l=0}^{\infty} e^{i(\delta_l + l\pi/2)}(2l+1)\,\frac{F_l(kr)}{kr}\,P_l(\cos\theta) \tag{9}$$

where F_l is the solution of

$$\frac{d^2F_l}{dr} + \left(k^2 - \frac{2M_r}{\hbar^2}\,\mathcal{V} - \frac{l(l+1)}{r^2}\right)F = 0 \tag{10}$$

normalized to

$$F_l(\infty) = \sin\left(kr - \frac{l\pi}{2} + \delta_l\right) \tag{11}$$

Then

$$f(\theta) = \frac{1}{2ik}\sum_{l=0}^{\infty}(2l+1)\,(e^{2i\delta_l} - 1)P_l(\cos\theta) \tag{12}$$

The total cross section (in either reference frame) is

$$\sigma = \sigma_0 = \int \mid f(\theta) \mid^2 d\Omega = \frac{4\pi}{k^2}\sum_{l=0}^{\infty}(2l+1)\sin^2\delta_l \tag{13}$$

For s-scattering of neutrons. For $kR \ll 1$, $\delta_l \sim (kR)^{l+1}$ and $f(\theta) \cong \delta_0/k$,

$$\sigma = \frac{4\pi}{k^2}\sin^2\delta_0, \quad \sigma(\theta) = \frac{\sigma}{4\pi} \tag{14}$$

For scattering with absorption the phase δ_0 is complex

$$2\delta_0 = 2\delta_r + i\Delta, \quad (\delta_r, \Delta \text{ real}) \tag{15}$$

The s-scattering and absorption cross sections are then

$$\sigma_{sc} = \frac{\pi}{k^2}\,[(1 - e^{-\Delta})^2 + 4e^{-\Delta}\sin^2\delta_r] \tag{16}$$

$$\sigma_a = \frac{\pi}{k^2}\,(1 - e^{-2\Delta}) \tag{17}$$

and the total cross section is

$$\sigma_t = \sigma_{sc} + \sigma_a = \frac{2\pi}{k^2}\,[2e^{-\Delta}\sin^2\delta_r + 1 - e^{-\Delta}] \tag{18}$$

For very fast neutrons ($kR \gg 1$) all phase shifts $\delta_l(l \lesssim kR)$ contribute and σ_t, the total cross section, is given by

$$\tfrac{1}{2}\sigma_t = \sigma_{sc} = \sigma_a = \pi R^2 \tag{19}$$

c. *Scattering length.* For zero energy neutrons $r\Psi$ is a linear function of r outside the range of the nuclear forces. The extrapolation of this linear function $r\Psi_{\text{ext}}$ gives the scattering length a according to

$$\Psi_{\text{ext}}(a) = 0, \quad (a \gtrless 0) \tag{20}$$

For incident s-neutrons scattered by a nucleus of total angular momentum (spin) $= I\hbar$, the value of a will depend on the relative spin orientation of neutron and nucleus, i.e., on the total angular momentum $J = I \pm \frac{1}{2}$ of the combined system. There will be two scattering lengths $a_{I\pm\frac{1}{2}}$ in this case. In general the phase shifts may be expressed as a power series in k by means of the following *

$$k \cot \delta_J = -\frac{1}{a_J} + \tfrac{1}{2}k^2 r_e(J) + \ldots \tag{21}$$

where $r_e(J)$ is the effective range,

$$r_e(J) = 2\int_0^\infty \left[\left(1 - \frac{r}{a_J}\right)^2 - u_0^2\right] dr \tag{22}$$

and $u_0 = r\Psi$ (for $E = 0$) normalized to $u_0 = 1 - r/a_J$ at $r = \infty$. In terms of a_J the scattering cross section for slow neutrons is to zeroth order in k,

$$\sigma = 4\pi\left(\frac{I+1}{2I+1}\,a^2_{I+\frac{1}{2}} + \frac{I}{2I+1}\,a^2_{I-\frac{1}{2}}\right) \tag{23}$$

When neutrons are scattered by a crystal the total scattering is composed of two parts, coherent and incoherent scattering

$$\sigma_{\text{coh}} = 4\pi\left(\frac{I+1}{2I+1}\,a_{I+\frac{1}{2}} + \frac{I}{2I+1}\,a_{I-\frac{1}{2}}\right)^2 \tag{24}$$

$$\sigma_{\text{inc}} = 4\pi\,\frac{I(I+1)}{(2I+1)^2}\,(a_{I+\frac{1}{2}} - a_{I-\frac{1}{2}})^2 \tag{25}$$

For neutron-proton scattering ($I = \frac{1}{2}$),

$$\sigma_{n-p} = \frac{\pi\hbar^2}{M}\left(\frac{3}{\epsilon + \frac{1}{2}\bar{E}_1} + \frac{1}{|\epsilon'| + \frac{1}{2}\bar{E}_1}\right) \tag{26}$$

* Bethe, H. A., *Phys. Rev.*, **76**, 38 (1949). Blatt, J. M. and Jackson, J. D., *Phys. Rev.*, **76**, 18 (1949).

which is independent of the well shape to a high degree of approximation. Equation (26) is applicable for $E_0 <$ about 10 Mev, but below about 1 ev molecular binding and crystal diffraction effects have to be considered. Also in neutron diffraction the scattering lengths a_J in Eqs. (24) and (25) must be multiplied by the Debye-Waller temperature factor and by a factor $1 + M_n/M_Z^A$).

d. *Scattering of charged particles.* If the two particles participating in the collision are not identical the results of Eqs. (6) and (12) are used with δ_l replaced by

$$\bar{\delta}_l = \delta_l + \arg\left[\left(l + \frac{ie^2 Z_1 Z_2}{\hbar v}\right)!\right] \tag{27}$$

where δ_l are the nuclear phase shifts, and the additional term is the phase shift due to the Coulomb interaction.

For the collision of (unpolarized) identical particles of spin $I\hbar$

$$\sigma(\theta) = \frac{I}{2I+1} \,|\, f(\theta) \pm f(\pi - \theta) \,|^2 + \frac{I+1}{2I+1} \,|\, f(\theta) \mp f(\pi - \theta) \,|^2 \tag{28}$$

where the upper signs apply for Fermi statistics and the lower for Bose statistics and Eq. (12) together with (27) is to be used. For proton-proton scattering only s-wave nuclear scattering is important, and only the first term of Eq. (28) contributes to the nuclear part of the scattering. In the (L) system

$$\left.\begin{aligned} \sigma_0(\Theta) = \frac{e^4}{\bar{E}_1^2} \cos\Theta \Bigg[& \frac{1}{\sin^4\Theta} + \frac{1}{\cos^4\Theta} - \frac{\cos\alpha \ln\tan^2\Theta}{\sin^2\Theta\cos^2\Theta} \\ & - \frac{2}{\alpha}\sin\delta_0 \left(\frac{\cos(\delta_0 + \alpha\ln\sin^2\Theta)}{\sin^2\Theta} + \frac{\cos(\delta_0 + \alpha\ln\cos^2\Theta)}{\cos^2\Theta} \right) \\ & + \frac{4}{\alpha^2}\sin^2\delta_0 \Bigg] \end{aligned}\right\} \tag{29}$$

For the scattering of α-particles in He^4 in the (L) system

$$\left.\begin{aligned} \sigma_0(\Theta) = \left(\frac{4e^2}{\bar{E}_1}\right)^2 \cos\Theta \Bigg| & \frac{e^{-4i\alpha \ln\sin^2\Theta}}{\sin^2\Theta} + \frac{e^{-4i\alpha\ln\cos^2\Theta}}{\cos^2\Theta} \\ & + \frac{i}{2\alpha} \sum_{l\ \mathrm{even}} (2l+1)(e^{2i\delta_l} - 1) \frac{(1+4i\alpha)^2 \ldots (l+4i\alpha)^2}{(1+16\alpha^2)\ldots(l^2+16\alpha^2)} \\ & \times P_l(\cos 2\Theta) \Bigg|^2 \end{aligned}\right\} \tag{30}$$

and, in general, only $l \lesssim kR$ need be considered.

2.6. Resonance reactions.* a. *Energy relations for the reaction* $M_1 + M_2 \rightarrow M_3 + M_4, \quad (\bar{E}_2 = 0)$

$$E_3 = \frac{Q + M_2\bar{E}_1/(M_1 + M_2)}{1 + M_3/M_4} = \frac{M_4}{M_3} E_4 \tag{1}$$

$$(\bar{E}_1)_t = -\left(Q1 + \frac{M_1}{M_2}\right), \quad \text{(threshold energy)} \tag{2}$$

$$\tan \Theta_3 = \frac{\tan \theta_3}{1 + \sqrt{(M_1M_3/M_2M_4)}\{\bar{E}_1/[\bar{E}_1 - (\bar{E}_1)_t]\}\sec \theta_3} \tag{3}$$

$$\sin(\theta_3 - \Theta_3) = \sqrt{\frac{M_1M_3}{M_2M_4}\,\frac{\bar{E}_1}{\bar{E}_1 - (\bar{E}_1)_t}}\,\sin \Theta_3 \tag{4}$$

$$\left.\begin{aligned}\bar{E}_3 &= \frac{1}{(M_3 + M_4)^2}\\ &\left\{\sqrt{M_1M_3\bar{E}_1}\,\xi_3 + \sqrt{\bar{E}_1M_1M_3\xi_3^2 + (M_3 + M_4)[QM_4 + (M_4 - M_1)\bar{E}_1]}\right\}^2\end{aligned}\right\} \tag{5}$$

where $\xi_3 = \cos \theta_3$. A corresponding result holds for $\bar{E}_4$ by interchanging indexes 3, 4. Alternatively

$$\bar{E}_4 = \bar{E}_1 - \bar{E}_3 + Q \tag{6}$$

For photon emission no distinction need be made between C and L systems in practical cases ($\hbar\omega \ll M_nc^2$).

b. *Scattering and reaction cross sections.* Consider the nuclear transmutation symbolized by

$$P + A \rightarrow C \rightarrow B + Q \tag{7}$$

where P is the projectile nucleus, A the target nucleus, C the compound nucleus, B the residual nucleus, and Q the observed outgoing particle; P and/or Q may also refer to photons. The total angular momenta (units $\hbar$) are s, I, J, I', s', respectively. The orbital angular momenta for the $P - A$ and $B - Q$ relative motion are l and l' (units $\hbar$), respectively.

$$\mathfrak{S} = \boldsymbol{I} + \boldsymbol{s}, \quad \mathfrak{S}' = \boldsymbol{I}' + \boldsymbol{s}' \tag{8}$$

* Bethe, H. A., *Revs. Modern Phys.*, **9**, 69 (1937); Livingston, M. S. and Bethe, H. A., *Revs. Modern Phys.*, **9**, 245 (1937); Blatt, J. M. and Weisskopf, V. F., "The Theory of Nuclear Reactions," *ONR Technical Report 42.*

are referred to as total intrinsic spins for the breakup of the compound state into particle with the specified angular momenta I, s and I', s', respectively. All particles are considered to be unpolarized. The mean life of a specified compound state (n) for breakup into $P + A$ or $B + Q$ is

$$\left. \begin{aligned} T^{(n)}_{P,l,\mathfrak{S}} &= \frac{\hbar}{\Gamma^{(n)}_{P,l,\mathfrak{S}}} \\ T^{(n)}_{Q,l',\mathfrak{S}'} &= \frac{\hbar}{\Gamma^{(n)}_{Q,l',\mathfrak{S}'}} \end{aligned} \right\} \tag{9}$$

where $\Gamma_{P,l,\mathfrak{S}}$ etc. are partial widths of the specified state (n). The total width of this state of the compound nucleus is

$$\Gamma^{(n)} = \sum_{P,l,\mathfrak{S}} \Gamma^{(n)}_{P,l,\mathfrak{S}} \tag{10}$$

and E_n is the resonance energy of the state.

The resonance elastic scattering cross section for P scattered by A, with C-system energy E ($= \hbar ck$ for photons), is approximately [see Eqs. (15) and (16)]

$$\sigma^{(J)}_{sc} = \frac{\pi}{k^2} \cdot \frac{2J+1}{(2I+1)(2s+1)} \mathcal{S} \left| \frac{\Gamma^{(n)}_{P,l,\mathfrak{S}}}{E - E_n + (i/2)\Gamma^{(n)}} + \mathcal{A}_l \right|^2 \tag{11}$$

where

$$\mathcal{S} = \sum_{\mathfrak{S}=|I-s|}^{I+s} \; \sum_{l=|J-\mathfrak{S}|}^{J+\mathfrak{S}} \tag{12}$$

Here l is even (odd) if the parity of (n) is even (odd); $\mathcal{A}_l$ gives the contribution of the potential scattering. For neutrons

$$\mathcal{A}_l = -\frac{H^{(1)}_{l+\frac{1}{2}}(kR)}{H^{(2)}_{l+\frac{1}{2}}(kR)} - 1 \approx \frac{2i(2l+1)(kR)^{2l+1}}{[1 \cdot 3 \cdot 5 \ldots (2l+1)]^2} \tag{13}$$

The last result applies for $kR \ll 1$. For charged particles

$$\left. \begin{aligned} \mathcal{A}_l &\approx \mathcal{A}_0 \frac{(2kR)^{2l}}{(2l)!(2l+1)!} \prod_{\nu=1}^{l} (\nu^2 + \kappa^2) \\ \mathcal{A}_0 &\approx 2ikR \frac{2\pi\kappa}{e^{2\pi\kappa} - 1} \end{aligned} \right\} \tag{14}$$

and again $kR \ll 1$. In addition to Eq. (11) there is a contribution (usually small) to $\sigma_{sc}^{(J)}$ in which the orbital angular momentum and/or the total intrinsic spin changes. This is

$$\delta\sigma_{sc}^{(J)} = \frac{\pi}{k^2} \frac{2J+1}{(2I+1)(2s+1)} \cdot \mathcal{S}\mathcal{S}' \frac{\Gamma^{(n)}_{Pl\mathfrak{S}} \Gamma^{(n)}_{Pl'\mathfrak{S}'}(1 - \delta_{ll'}\delta_{\mathfrak{S}\mathfrak{S}'})}{(E - E_n)^2 + [\frac{1}{2}\Gamma^{(n)}]^2} \tag{15}$$

$$\mathcal{S}' = \sum_{\mathfrak{S}'=|I'-s'|}^{I'+s'} \sum_{l'=|J-\mathfrak{S}'|}^{J+\mathfrak{S}'}$$

except that for $l = l' = 0$ only $\mathfrak{S} = \mathfrak{S}'$ is allowed. The other states of the compound nucleus contribute a background (nonresonance) scattering so that the total elastic cross section is

$$\sigma_{sc} = \sum_{J,\ \text{parity}} (\sigma_{sc}^{(J)} + \delta\sigma_{sc}^{(J)}) \tag{16}$$

The absorption cross section (including inelastic scattering of P) is, *near resonance*,

$$\sigma_a = \frac{\pi}{k^2} \cdot \frac{2J+1}{(2I+1)(2s+1)} \cdot \frac{\Gamma^{(n)}_P \Gamma^{(n)}_Q}{(E - E_n)^2 + [\frac{1}{2}\Gamma^{(n)}]^2} \tag{17}$$

$$\Gamma_P^{(n)} = \mathcal{S}\Gamma^{(n)}_{Pl\mathfrak{S}}, \quad \Gamma_Q^{(n)} = \mathcal{S}'\Gamma^{(n)}_{Ql'\mathfrak{S}'} \tag{18}$$

and the selection rules are

$$\left.\begin{aligned} (-)^l &= (-)^{l'} && \text{(if parity of } A = \text{parity of } B) \\ (-)^l &= (-)^{l'+1}, && \text{(if parity of } A \neq \text{parity of } B) \end{aligned}\right\} \tag{19}$$

For photon absorption (or emission) $2s + 1$ (or $2s' + 1) = 2$.

Selection rules for photon emission. The entries below give the type of multipole field emitted with greatest intensity. Multipole fields of higher order can always be neglected. Here $I'\hbar$ is the angular momentum of the final state in the transition and $\mathcal{L} = |J - I'|$.

Parity	Even	Odd
changes	electric $2^{\mathcal{L}}$ pole magnetic $2^{\mathcal{L}+1}$ pole	electric $2^{\mathcal{L}+1}$ pole magnetic $2^{\mathcal{L}}$ pole
does not change	electric $2^{\mathcal{L}+1}$ pole magnetic $2^{\mathcal{L}}$ pole	electric $2^{\mathcal{L}}$ pole magnetic $2^{\mathcal{L}+1}$ pole

and $J = 0$, $I' = 0$ is absolutely forbidden for single quantum emission. *

* Internal conversion coefficients are given conveniently only in numerical form, see *Phys. Rev.*, **83**, 79 (1951).

The energy and l-dependence of the partial widths is given by

$$\Gamma^{(n)} = \chi_l(E)\Gamma_0^{(n)} \cong \chi_l(E)\sqrt{\frac{E}{E_n}}\,\Gamma_0^{(n)}(E_n) \tag{20}$$

where superfluous indices have been suppressed. The barrier penetrability χ_l is

$$\chi_l = \frac{1}{F_l^2(R) + G_l^2(R)} \tag{21}$$

where F_l and G_l are the real solutions of Eq. (10) *without specific nuclear interactions* and with the normalization at $r = \infty$

$$G_l(\infty) + iF_l(\infty) = e^{i\zeta_l(r)} \tag{22}$$

For neutrons * ($Z_Q = 0$, $\kappa = 0$)

$$\left.\begin{aligned} G_l(R) &= \sqrt{\frac{\pi kR}{2}}\,J_{-l-\frac{1}{2}}(kR) \\ F_l(R) &= \sqrt{\frac{\pi kR}{2}}\,J_{l+\frac{1}{2}}(kR) \end{aligned}\right\} \tag{23}$$

and for $kR \ll 1$, $G_l \gg F_l$ and

$$\chi_l = \frac{(kR)^{2l}}{[1 \cdot 3 \cdot 5 \ldots (2l-1)]^2} \tag{24}$$

For charged particles + and $kR \ll 1$

$$\left.\begin{aligned} \chi_l &\approx \chi_0 \frac{2^{2l}}{(2l)!^2}(kR)^{2l}\prod_{\nu=1}^{l}(\nu^2 + \kappa^2) \\ \chi_0 &\approx [2\pi\kappa/(e^{2\pi\kappa} - 1)]e^{4\sqrt{2\kappa kR}} \end{aligned}\right\} \tag{25}$$

2.7. Beta decay. The probability per unit time for the emission of a β particle with energy between W and $W + dW$ is ×

$$P_\beta(W)dW = \frac{1}{2\pi^3}\langle|H_\beta|^2\rangle_{\text{av}}\, pW(W_0 - W)^2 dW \tag{1}$$

where H_β is the Hamiltonian for β decay

$$\langle|H_\beta|^2\rangle_{\text{av}} = \frac{G_F^2}{2p^2}\int d\Omega_\nu \sum_e \left|\int dv_N \sum_j H_j\right|^2 \tag{2}$$

* Cf. Wigner, E. P. and Eisenbud, L., *Phys. Rev.*, **72**, 29 (1947).
\+ Cf. Yost, F. L., Wheeler, J. A. and Breit, G., *Phys. Rev.*, **49**, 174 (1935).
× Konopinski, E. J., *Revs. Modern Phys.*, **15**, 209 (1943).

In Eq. (2) $\sum_e$ is a sum over all eigenvalues of diagonal operators specifying the angular momentum direction of motion of the β particle, $\int dv_N$ implies an integration over the space and spin coordinates of all nucleons, and $\sum_j$ is sum over neutrons (protons) for $\beta_-(\beta_+)$ emission. The relativistic invariant H_j is formed by contractions of five possible covariants. In the spin space of the light particles (β particle and neutrino) and each of the nucleons the following 4 by 4 matrices are defined

$$\boldsymbol{\alpha} = \begin{pmatrix} 0 & \boldsymbol{\sigma} \\ \boldsymbol{\sigma} & 0 \end{pmatrix}, \quad \beta = \begin{pmatrix} 1 & 0 \\ 0 & -1 \end{pmatrix} \tag{3}$$

$$\bar{\sigma} = -\frac{i}{2}(\boldsymbol{\alpha} \times \boldsymbol{\alpha}), \quad \gamma_5 = i\alpha_1\alpha_2\alpha_3 \tag{4}$$

wherein each element in Eq. (3) is a 2 by 2 matrix [see Eq. (2) of § 2.2]. Then H_j is, in general, a linear combination of the five invariants

$$H_s = (\Psi_f^* \beta \tau_1^{(j)} \Psi_i)(\psi_e^* \beta \psi_\nu) \tag{5}$$

$$H_v = (\Psi_f^* \tau_1^{(j)} \Psi_i)(\psi_e^* \psi_\nu) - (\Psi_f^* \boldsymbol{\alpha} \tau_1^{(j)} \Psi_i) \cdot (\psi_e^* \boldsymbol{\alpha} \psi_\nu) \tag{6}$$

$$H_T = (\Psi_f^* \beta \bar{\boldsymbol{\sigma}} \tau_1^{(j)} \Psi_i) \cdot (\psi_e^* \beta \bar{\boldsymbol{\sigma}} \psi_\nu) + (\Psi_f^* \beta \boldsymbol{\alpha} \tau_1^{(j)} \Psi_i) \cdot (\psi_e^* \beta \boldsymbol{\alpha} \psi_\nu) \tag{7}$$

$$H_A = (\Psi_f^* \bar{\boldsymbol{\sigma}} \tau_1^{(j)} \Psi_i) \cdot (\psi_e^* \bar{\boldsymbol{\sigma}} \psi_\nu) - (\Psi_f^* \gamma_5 \tau_1^{(j)} \Psi_i)(\psi_e^* \gamma_5 \psi_\nu) \tag{8}$$

$$H_P = (\Psi_f^* \beta \gamma_5 \tau_1^{(j)} \Psi_i)(\psi_e^* \beta \gamma_5 \psi_\nu) \tag{9}$$

The index S, V, T, A, P indicate that the invariants have been formed by contraction of scalar, polar vector, tensor, axial vector, and pseudoscalar covariants. All quantities in H_j are evaluated at the position of the jth nucleon.

Allowed transition. The selection rules are *

	Nuclear spin change	Parity
Scalar	0	no change
Polar vector	0	no change
Tensor	0, ±1 (no 0→0)	no change
Axial vector	0, ±1 (no 0→0)	no change
Pseudoscalar	0	change

* See GREULING, E., *Phys. Rev.*, **61**, 568 (1942) for forbidden transitions.

The decay constant is

$$\lambda_\beta = \int_1^{W_0} P(W)dW \tag{10}$$

For each of the five interactions [Eqs. (5), (6), (7), (8), (9)] the spectrum shape is the same.

$$P_{\beta^\pm}(W) = \frac{G_F^2}{2\pi^3} |\mathcal{M}|^2 pW(W_0 - W)^2 F(\mp Z, W)dW \tag{11}$$

The constant $\mathcal{M}$ is

$$\mathcal{M} = \int dv_N \sum_j \Psi_f^* \mathcal{O}\tau_1^{(j)} \Psi_i$$

where $\mathcal{O} = \beta, 1, \beta\bar{\sigma}, \bar{\sigma}$ and $\beta\gamma_5$ acting on the nucleon spin for the five invariants (5, 6, 7, 8, 9) respectively. The effect of the (unscreened) Coulomb field acting on the electron is represented by the Fermi function

$$F(Z,W) = \frac{2(1+\gamma)(2pR)^{2\gamma-2} |(\gamma - 1 + iy)!|^2 e^{\pi y}}{(2\gamma)!^2} \tag{12}$$

where Z and R refer to the final nucleus. The probability per unit energy interval for a decay process with angle ϑ between β particle and neutrino is

$$P_{\beta^\pm}\left(1 + \frac{np}{W}\cos\vartheta\right) \tag{13}$$

with $n = -1$ for S and P, $n = 1$ (for V), $n = \frac{1}{3}$ (for T) and $n = -\frac{1}{3}$ (for A).

The decay constant for capture of K-shell electrons is

$$\lambda_K = \frac{G_F^2}{\pi^2} |\mathcal{M}|^2 (2R)^{2\gamma-2} \left(\frac{e^2 Z}{\hbar c}\right)^{2\gamma+1} \frac{1+\gamma}{(2\gamma)!} (W_0 + 1 - \epsilon_K)^2 \tag{14}$$

and $\epsilon_K \cong 1 - \gamma$ is the K-shell electron binding energy in units mc^2.

Bibliography

1. Bethe, H. A. and Bacher, R., *Revs. Modern Phys.*, **8**, 82 (1936).
2. Bethe, H. A., *Revs. Modern Phys.*, **9**, 69 (1937).
3. Bethe, H. A., *Elementary Nuclear Theory*, John Wiley & Sons, Inc., New York, 1947.
4. Blatt, J. M. and Weisskopf, V. F., "The Theory of Nuclear Reactions," *ONR Technical Report 42*.
5. Fermi, E., *Nuclear Physics*, University of Chicago Press, Chicago, 1950.
6. Gamow, G. and Critchfield, C. L., *Atomic Nucleus and Nuclear Energy Sources*, Oxford University Press, New York, 1949.
7. Livingston, M. S. and Bethe, H. A., *Revs. Modern Phys.*, **9**, 245 (1937).
8. Rosenfeld, L., *Nuclear Forces*, 2 vols., Interscience Publishers, Inc., New York, 1948.

Chapter 23

COSMIC RAYS AND HIGH-ENERGY PHENOMENA

BY ROBERT W. WILLIAMS

Associate Professor of Physics
Massachusetts Institute of Technology

The following formulas have been chosen because they represent the reliable tools of the worker in high-energy physics. While the results of calculations based on meson theories have had a great heuristic value, they are not quantitatively reliable and are being continuously revised. The present chapter is therefore restricted to the " classical " and presumably nearly permanent aspects of high-energy physics. The formulas have been chosen to guide the student of the subject as well as to provide useful information for the advanced research worker.

1. Electromagnetic Interactions

1.1. Definitions and some natural constants.

$\sigma(E,\Theta)$ = the cross section in cm^2 of an *atom* for an interaction involving a final energy $< E$ and a final zenith angle $< \Theta$ (all processes considered have azimuthal symmetry). Thus $(\partial\sigma/\partial E)dE$ is the cross section for a process involving a final energy between E and $E + dE$; $(\partial\sigma/\partial\omega)d\omega$ is the cross section for a process whose final state involves a particle lying in the solid angle $d\omega$ at the angle Θ, where $\omega = 2\pi(1 - \cos\Theta)$.

E = kinetic energy. $E = mc^2/\sqrt{1-\beta^2} - mc^2$
m = rest mass
U = total energy. $U = E + mc^2$
p = momentum. $(pc)^2 + (mc^2)^2 = U^2$; $\mathbf{p} = m\mathbf{v}/\sqrt{1-\beta^2}$
β = velocity relative to the velocity of light. $\beta = |\,pc\,|/U$
m_ec^2 = rest energy of the electron, 0.51098 Mev
m_pc^2 = rest energy of the proton, 938.2 Mev
$m_\pi c^2$ = rest energy of the π meson, 139.4 Mev for $\pi^\pm$, 135 Mev for π^0
$m_\mu c^2$ = rest energy of the μ-meson, 105.7 Mev

$\alpha =$ Fine-structure constant, $e^2/\hbar c = 1/137.038$.
$r_e =$ classical radius of the electron, $e^2/m_e c^2 = 2.8178 \times 10^{-13}$ cm
$Z, A =$ atomic number and atomic weight of the material in which the interactions take place
$z =$ atomic number of the bombarding particle
$N, e, c, \hbar$ have their usual significance (Avogadro number, electronic charge, velocity of light, Planck's constant). Values may be found in Chapter 4. Note that e always represents a positive magnitude
$x =$ thickness of matter in g cm^{-2}, given by $l\rho$, the product of distance and density. The probability for the occurrence of a process with cross section σ in thickness dx is $(\sigma N/A)dx$
$X_0 =$ the radiation length (§ 1.7) expressed in g cm^{-2}
$t =$ thickness of matter in radiation lengths, $t = x/X_0$

The sign of the charge of electrons is distinguished, where necessary, by the terms positon and negaton.

1.2. Cross sections for the collision of charged particles with atomic electrons, considered as free *(knock-on probabilities)*. Let E be the energy of the bombarding particle of mass m; let E' be the energy acquired by an atomic electron. If

$$\left.\begin{aligned} E' \ll E'_{\max} &= \frac{2m_e p^2 c^4}{m_e{}^2 c^4 + m^2 c^4 + 2m_e c^2 (p^2 c^2 + m^2 c^4)^{1/2}} \\ \frac{\partial \sigma_{\text{col}}}{\partial E'}\, dE' &= \frac{2Zz^2 \pi r_e{}^2}{\beta^2} \cdot \frac{m_e c^2 dE'}{(E')^2} \end{aligned}\right\} \qquad (1)$$

is valid for all particles (Rutherford formula).

At larger E', spin of bombarding particle becomes important and we have

Particles of mass m and spin O :

$$\frac{\partial \sigma}{\partial E'} = \left(\frac{\partial \sigma}{\partial E'}\right)_{\text{Rutherford}} \left(1 - \beta^2 \frac{E'}{E'_{\max}}\right) \qquad (2)$$

Particles (not electrons) of mass m, spin 1/2 :

$$\frac{\partial \sigma}{\partial E'} = \left(\frac{\partial \sigma}{\partial E'}\right)_{\text{Rutherford}} \left[1 - \beta^2 \frac{E'}{E'_{\max}} + \frac{1}{2}\left(\frac{E'}{E + mc^2}\right)^2\right] \qquad (3)$$

Positons with $E \gg m_e c^2$:

$$\frac{\partial \sigma}{\partial E'} = \left(\frac{\partial \sigma}{\partial E'}\right)_{\text{Rutherford}} \left[1 - \frac{E'}{E} + \left(\frac{E'}{E}\right)^2\right]^2 \qquad (4)$$

Negatons (negative electrons) with $E \gg m_e c^2$:

$$\frac{\partial\sigma}{\partial E'} = \left(\frac{\partial\sigma}{\partial E'}\right)_{\text{Rutherford}} \frac{E^2}{(E-E')^2}\left[1 - \frac{E'}{E} + \left(\frac{E'}{E}\right)^2\right]^2 \tag{5}$$

This is the cross section for leaving *either* negaton in the energy state E', so that $E' \leqslant E/2$.

1.3. Energy loss by collision with atomic electrons *(ionization loss)*. Let $k_{\text{col}}(E) = -(dE/dx)_{\text{col}}$ be the energy per g cm^{-2} in collisions with atomic electrons (the effect of atomic binding is included, but the particle's velocity is assumed to be large compared with that of the K electrons).

Heavy particles $(m > m_e)$:

$$k_{\text{col}}(E) = \frac{4Nz^2(Z/A)\pi r_e^2 m_e c^2}{\beta^2}\left[\ln \frac{2m_e c^2\beta^2}{(1-\beta^2)I(Z)} - \beta^2\right] \tag{1}$$

Electrons with $\beta \approx 1$:

$$k_{\text{col}} = 4N\frac{Z}{A}\pi r_e^2 m_e c^2\left[\ln \frac{\pi m_e c^2}{(1-\beta^2)^{3/4}I(Z)} - \frac{a}{2}\right] \tag{2}$$

where $a = 2.9$ for negatons, 3.6 for positons. The average ionization potential, $I(Z)$, may be approximated by $I(Z) = (12.5Z)$ ev.

The energy loss considering only collisions in which the energy transferred is less than η is

$$k_{\text{col}(<\eta)}(E) = \frac{2Nz^2(Z/A)\pi r_e^2 m_e c^2}{\beta^2}\left[\ln \frac{2m_e c^2\beta^2\eta}{(1-\beta^2)I^2(Z)} - \beta^2\right] \tag{3}$$

This formula holds for both electrons and heavy particles if η is not too large ($\sim 10^5$ ev for electrons).

The actual collision loss, in condensed materials, of particles with $\beta \approx 1$ will be reduced somewhat by the "density effect," which has not been formulated concisely. Calculations for certain materials will be found in Refs. 5 and 29.

1.4. Range of heavy particles. When collision loss (§ 1.3) represents the only important type of energy loss, all particles of a given energy travel approximately the same distance in matter before being stopped. This distance is the range (or mean range)

$$R(E) = \int_{E_{\text{exp}}}^{E} \frac{dE'}{k_{\text{col}}(E')} + R_{\text{exp}}$$

where R_{exp} is the observed range for a known energy E_{exp}.

Since for a given material $k_{col} = z^2 f(\beta)$, and $\beta = g(E/m)$, we have

$$R = \frac{m}{z^2} F_1\left(\frac{E}{m}\right) = \frac{m}{z^2} F_2\left(\frac{p}{m}\right) \tag{1}$$

Numerical values for z^2R/m as functions of E/m or p/m are given, for example, in Refs. 24 and 29. A useful approximation for $E < mc^2$ (it is high by 15 per cent at $E = mc^2$) is

$$R = 43\left(\frac{mc^2}{100\text{ Mev}}\right)\left(\frac{E}{mc^2}\right)^{1.75}, \quad (\text{g cm}^{-2}\text{ in air}) \tag{2}$$

$$R = 80\left(\frac{mc^2}{100\text{ Mev}}\right)\left(\frac{E}{mc^2}\right)^{1.75}, \quad (\text{g cm}^{-2}\text{ in lead}) \tag{3}$$

1.5. Specific ionization. The total number of ion pairs produced in matter per g cm^{-2} by a charged particle and its secondaries is the *total specific ionization*, $j_T(E)$. For a given material it is found experimentally (at least for gases) that $j_T(E)$ is proportional to $k_{col}(E)$; that is, $j(E) = k_{col}(E)/V_0$. For air, V_0 has the value 35 ev/ion pair. Its value for other substances may be found in Ref. 23.

The primary specific ionization, j_p, is the average number of collisions per g cm^{-2} that result in the ejection of an electron from an atom. It is given by Bethe (Ref. 1) as

$$j_p = \frac{2Nz^2(Z/A)\pi r_e^2 m_e c^2}{\beta^2} \cdot \frac{r}{I_0}\left[\ln \frac{2m_e c^2\beta^2}{(1-\beta^2)I_0} + s - \beta^2\right] \tag{1}$$

where for hydrogen $r = 0.285$, $s = 3.04$, and I_0 is the Rydberg energy. Calculations are not available for other gases, but experimentally j_p is usually about one-third of j_T.

1.6. Cross sections for emission of radiation by charged particles.

a. *Electrons.* We consider the cross section for emission of a photon of energy E' when an electron of kinetic energy E, total energy U collides with an atom. The result depends on the degree to which the atomic electrons screen the electrostatic field of the nucleus. The parameter

$$\gamma = 100\frac{m_e c^2}{U} \cdot \frac{E'/U}{1 - E'/U} Z^{-1/3}$$

determines the magnitude of this effect; if $\gamma \gg 1$, screening can be neglected; if $\gamma \ll 1$, screening may be considered "complete." For $U \gg 137\ m_e c^2 Z^{-1/3}$ the latter may be considered always to be the case.

Write the cross section, assuming $U \gg m_e c^2$, as

$$\frac{\partial \sigma_{\text{rad}}}{\partial E'} dE' = 4\alpha Z(Z+1) r_e^2 \frac{dE'}{E'} F(U,v) \tag{1}$$

where $v = E'/U$, and $F(U,v)$ is given by:

For no screening, $\gamma \gg 1$,

$$F(U,v) = \left[1 + (1-v)^2 - \frac{2}{3}(1-v)\right]\left[\ln\left(\frac{2U}{m_e c^2}\cdot\frac{1-v}{v}\right) - \frac{1}{2}\right] \tag{2}$$

For complete screening, $\gamma \approx 0$,

$$F(U,v) = \left\{\left[1 + (1-v)^2 - \frac{2}{3}(1-v)\right]\ln(183Z^{-1/3}) + \frac{1}{9}(1-v)\right\} \tag{3}$$

Expressions for the intermediate cases may be found in Ref. 20.

The factor $Z(Z+1)$ (instead of the conventional Z^2) takes account of radiative transitions of the atomic electrons in an approximate way; no satisfactory calculation is available.

These cross sections are calculated in the Born approximation; experiments at 62 Mev show that they are too large for high Z materials, about 10 per cent for lead. For simplicity we shall use the same correction term as that which has been accurately determined in the case of pair production, $[1 + 0.12(Z/82)^2]$. These cross sections should therefore be *divided* by $[1 + 0.12(Z/82)^2]$.

The divergence of the cross section as $E' \to 0$ correspond physically to the fact that an infinite number of extremely low-energy quanta are emitted in every collision. The energy loss remains finite (§ 1.7).

The root mean square of the angle Θ at which the photon of energy E' is emitted is approximately

$$\sqrt{\langle\Theta^2\rangle_{\text{av}}} \sim 0.65 \frac{m_e c^2}{U} \ln \frac{U}{m_e c^2}$$

b. *Heavy particles.* We give the result for mass m, spin $\frac{1}{2}$, and normal magnetic moment. (Other cases are considered in Ref. 20.)

$$\frac{\partial \sigma_{\text{rad}}}{\sigma E'} dE' = 4\alpha Z^2 r_e^2 \left(\frac{m_e}{m}\right)^2 \frac{dE'}{E'} F(U,v) \tag{4}$$

where

$$F(U,v) = \left[1 + (1-v)^2 - \frac{2}{3}(1-v)\right]\left[\ln\left(\frac{2U}{mc^2}\cdot\frac{\hbar}{mc(0.49 r_e A^{1/3})}\cdot\frac{1-v}{v}\right) - \frac{1}{2}\right]$$

The effect of the nuclear radius has been included; the effect of the atomic electrons has not.

1.7. Energy loss of electrons by radiation. The average radiation loss of electrons per g cm^{-2} is

$$-\left(\frac{dE}{dx}\right)_{\text{rad}} = k_{\text{rad}}(E) = \int_0^E E' \frac{N}{A} \frac{\partial \sigma_{\text{rad}}}{\partial E'} dE' \tag{1}$$

(The amount of energy transferred to the nucleus can be neglected). When $E \gg 137 m_e c^2 Z^{-1/3}$ (complete screening) we have

$$k_{\text{rad}}(E) = 4\alpha Z(Z+1) \frac{N}{A} r_e^2 E \left[\ln(183 Z^{-1/3}) + \frac{1}{18}\right] \left[1 + 0.12\left(\frac{Z}{82}\right)^2\right]^{-1} \tag{2}$$

Radiation loss increases with energy in a linear fashion (even slightly faster in the region of incomplete screening) and exceeds collision loss at approximately the *critical energy*, ϵ, of shower theory (§ 2.1).

In dealing with radiation phenomena it is convenient to measure thickness in terms of the *radiation length*, X_0 g cm^{-2}, defined by

$$\frac{1}{X_0} = 4\alpha Z(Z+1) \frac{N}{A} r_e^2 [\ln(183 Z^{-1/3})] \left[1 + 0.12\left(\frac{Z}{82}\right)^2\right]^{-1} \tag{3}$$

Table 1 gives some numerical values for X_0 and ϵ.

TABLE 1

VALUES FOR THE RADIATION LENGTH X_0, AND CRITICAL ENERGY, ϵ, FOR VARIOUS SUBSTANCES

Substance	Z	A	X_0 g cm^{-2}	ϵ Mev: Formula of Sect. 1.3	ϵ Mev: With density effect correction
Carbon	6	12	44.6	102	76
Nitrogen	7	14	39.4	88.7	
Oxygen	8	16	35.3	77.7	
Aluminium	13	27	24.5	48.8	
Argon	18	39.9	19.8	35.2	
Iron	26	55.84	14.1	24.3	21
Copper	29	63.57	13.1	21.8	
Lead	82	207.2	6.5	7.8	7.6
Air	7.37	14.78	37.7	84.2	
Water	7.23	14.3	37.1	83.8	65

The probability of radiating in a thickness dt radiation lengths

$$(t = x/X_0) \quad \text{is} \quad \frac{N}{A} \cdot \frac{\partial \sigma_{\text{rad}}}{\partial E'} dE' X_0 dt$$

and does not depend strongly on atomic number. In the limit of $E \gg 137 m_e c^2 Z^{-1/3}$ it is independent of atomic number. A crude high-energy approximation often used for this probability is $(dE'/E')dt$. Similarly, the fractional energy loss per radiation length,

$$-\frac{1}{E}\left(\frac{dE}{dt}\right)_{\text{rad}} = \frac{1}{E} k_{\text{rad}}(E) X_0 \tag{4}$$

is nearly independent of Z, and at high energies becomes

$$-\frac{1}{E}\left(\frac{dE}{dt}\right)_{\text{rad}} = 1 + b$$

where without appreciable error we may take $b = 0.014$ for all elements.

Radiation is not an important source of energy loss of particles heavier than electrons, with the exception of μ-mesons of $E > 10^{11}$ ev.

Fluctuations in the radiation loss of electrons are very large. Neglecting collision loss, the probability that an electron of total energy U_0 will have energy U in dU after t radiation lengths is approximately

$$w(U_0, U, t) dU = \frac{dU}{U_0}\left[\ln \frac{U_0}{U}\right]^{(t/\ln 2)-1}\left[\Gamma\left(\frac{t}{\ln 2}\right)\right]^{-1} \tag{5}$$

(for Γ see § 13.1 of Chapter 1).

1.8. Cross sections for scattering of charged particles. Classically the nonrelativistic cross section for scattering of a particle of charge ze by a fixed point charge Ze is

$$\frac{\partial \sigma}{\partial \omega} d\omega = \frac{1}{4} z^2 Z^2 r_e^{\,2} \left(\frac{m_e c}{\beta p}\right)^2 \frac{d\omega}{\sin^4 (\Theta/2)} \tag{1}$$

the *Rutherford scattering law.* Quantum mechanics gives the same result : (1) exactly for the nonrelativistic region ($\beta^2 \ll 1$, spin effects unimportant); (2) in the Born approximation ($Z\alpha/\beta \ll 1$) for (relativistic) *particles of spin O.*

For *particles of spin* $\frac{1}{2}$ and normal magnetic moment,

$$\frac{\partial \sigma}{\partial \omega} = \left(\frac{\partial \sigma}{\partial \omega}\right)_{\text{Rutherford}}\left[1 - \beta^2 \sin^2 \frac{\Theta}{2} + Z\pi\alpha\beta \sin \frac{\Theta}{2}\left(1 - \sin \frac{\Theta}{2}\right) + \ldots\right] \tag{2}$$

The third term in the square brackets is a correction to the Born approximation. Still higher corrections are needed for $Z \gtrsim 50$ (see Ref. 12).

The correction for radiative effects is usually less than 5 per cent, even for electrons (Ref. 25).

The cross section for scattering by real atoms is reduced in the limits of small and large angles : at small angles the screening by atomic electrons becomes important at $\Theta \sim \Theta_1 = \alpha Z^{1/3}(m_e c/p)$ and the angular dependence of the cross section is

$$\sim \frac{d\omega}{[(\Theta/2)^2 + (\Theta_1/2)^2]^2}$$

For an accurate treatment see Ref. 14. At large angles the nuclear size becomes important for

$$\Theta \sim \Theta_2 = 280 A^{-1/3} \frac{m_e c}{p} \tag{3}$$

1.9. Scattering of charged particles in matter. The probability that a particle be scattered through an angle Θ in traversing a thickness of material x can be found (in numerical form) in Refs. 26 and 15; the latter is more accurate for high-Z materials because of corrections to the Born approximation.

A convenient approximation is given by Williams' (Ref. 30) calculation of small-angle multiple scattering, neglecting single processes in which a large angular deflection occurs. For a thickness x small enough so that energy loss can be neglected, the mean square angle of scattering can be expressed as

$$\langle\Theta^2\rangle_{\text{av}} = \left(\frac{E_s}{\beta c p}\right)^2 \frac{x}{X_0} \tag{1}$$

where $E_s = (4\pi/\alpha)^{1/2} m_e c^2 = 21 \times 10^6$ ev.

For the projected angle ϑ made by the projection of the particle's track on a plane containing the initial trajectory one has, for small angles,

$$\langle\vartheta^2\rangle_{\text{av}} = \tfrac{1}{2}\langle\Theta^2\rangle_{\text{av}} \tag{2}$$

The distribution in ϑ can be approximated by a Gaussian,

$$P(\vartheta)d\vartheta = \frac{1}{\sqrt{2\pi\langle\vartheta^2\rangle_{\text{av}}}} e^{-\vartheta^2/2\langle\vartheta^2\rangle_{\text{av}}} d\vartheta \tag{3}$$

for small ϑ. At larger angles, the probability that the deflection occur in a single collision will be larger than the value of this Gaussian, and one can estimate $P(\vartheta)$ from the probability for *single* scattering alone, obtained from the space-angle cross section of § 1.8.

An accurate expression for the *mean* absolute projected angle of scattering in a thickness x, neglecting energy loss but considering the complete scattering probability function and using corrected cross sections (i.e., not merely Born approximation) is (Ref. 4)

$$\left.\begin{aligned}\langle\vartheta\rangle_{\text{av}} &= 2z\left(Z^2\frac{N}{A}r_e^2x\right)^{1/2}\left(\frac{m_ec}{\beta p}\right)\\ &\cdot\left[1.45+0.8\sqrt{\ln\left(0.2\pi Z^{-2/3}\frac{N}{A}r_e^2\frac{x}{\alpha}\frac{1}{(0.3\beta^2/\alpha^2zZ^2)}\right)}\right]\end{aligned}\right\} \quad (4)$$

1.10. Compton effect. A photon of energy E scattered through an angle Θ by a free electron initially at rest will have an energy

$$E' = \frac{E}{1+(E/m_ec^2)(1-\cos\Theta)}$$

The cross section for this process is the *Klein-Nishina* formula (Ref. 10)

$$\frac{\partial\sigma_{\text{Comp}}}{\partial E'}dE' = Z\pi r_e^2\frac{m_ec^2}{E}\cdot\frac{dE'}{E'}\left[1+\left(\frac{E'}{E}\right)^2-\frac{E'}{E}\sin^2\Theta\right] \quad (1)$$

As usual we have written the cross section *per atom*; sin Θ is written in place of the explicit function of E' and E for algebraic simplicity; the term containing it is negligible when $E \gg m_ec^2$.

The effect of the binding of the atomic electrons is unimportant when the recoil energy of the electron is large compared to its binding energy; this is nearly always the case if $E > m_ec^2$.

1.11. Pair production. The materialization of a photon of energy E as a pair of electrons of energies E' (positon) and E'' (negaton) occurs with very little energy transfer to the nucleus, so that to good approximation

$$E' + E'' + 2m_ec^2 = E \quad (1)$$

Letting $v = (E' + m_ec^2)/E$ be the fractional energy of the positon (or negaton —the formulas are symmetrical for $E \gg m_ec^2$) we have

$$\gamma = 100\frac{m\ c^2}{E}\cdot\frac{1}{v(1-v)}Z^{-1/3} \quad (2)$$

as the quantity which determines the influence of screening by the atomic electrons.

Write the cross section, assuming $E \gg m_ec^2$, as

$$\frac{\partial\sigma_{\text{pair}}}{\partial E'}dE' = 4\alpha Z(Z+1)r_e^2\frac{dE'}{E}G(E,v) \quad (3)$$

where $G(E,v)$ is given in the two limiting cases by :

For no screening, $\gamma \gg 1$,

$$G(E,v) = \left[v^2 + (1-v)^2 + \frac{2}{3}v(1-v)\right]\left[\ln\left(\frac{2E}{m_ec^2}v(1-v)\right) - \frac{1}{2}\right]$$

For complete screening, $\gamma \approx 0$,

$$G(E,v) = [v^2 + (1-v)^2 + \tfrac{2}{3}v(1-v)] \ln (183Z^{-1/3}) - \tfrac{1}{9}v(1-v)$$

Expressions for the intermediate cases may be found in Ref. 20.

As in § 1.6, the factor $Z(Z+1)$ instead of the conventional Z^2 must be considered merely as an improved approximation.

Again as in § 1.6, experiments show these cross sections to be too high for high-Z materials; they should be *divided* by the empirical correction term $[1 + 0.12(Z/82)^2]$.

The total cross section for pair production in the high-energy limit

$$\sigma_{\text{pair}} = 4\alpha Z(Z+1)r_e^2[\tfrac{7}{9} \ln (183Z^{-1/3}) - \tfrac{1}{54}] \tag{4}$$

The probability for pair production in a thickness dt radiation lengths does not depend strongly on atomic number. In the high-energy limit $E \gg 137m_ec^2Z^{-1/3}$ it becomes

$$\frac{N}{A}\sigma_{\text{pair}}X_0 dt = \left(\frac{7}{9} - \frac{b}{3}\right)dt \tag{5}$$

where without appreciable error we may take $b = 0.014$.

The root-mean-square angle between the direction of one of the electrons with energy E' and the original direction of the photon is approximately

$$\sqrt{\langle\Theta^2\rangle_{\text{av}}} \approx 0.47\frac{m_ec^2}{E'}\ln\frac{E}{m_ec^2}$$

2. Shower Theory

2.1. Definitions

X_0 is the radiation length (§ 1.6 and Table 1).

t specifies distance into the material, measured in radiation lengths.

$\pi^{(\pi)}(E_0,E,t)dE$, called a differential spectrum, is the average number of *electrons* with energy in dE at E that cross a plane at distance t beyond the start of a shower initiated by an *electron* of energy E_0. No distinction is made between positons and negatons.

$\pi^{(\gamma)}(E_0,E,t)dE$ is the same quantity for a shower initiated by a *photon* of energy E_0.

$\gamma^{(\pi)}(E_0,E,t)dE$ is, analogously, the average number of *photons* in a shower initiated by an *electron* of energy E_0.

$\gamma^{(\gamma)}(E_0,E,t)dE$ is the same quantity for a shower initiated by a *photon* of energy E_0.

The integral spectra are designated by capital letters :

$$\Pi^{(\pi)}(E_0,E,t) = \int_E^\infty \pi(E_0,E',t)dE', \quad \text{etc.}$$

$P_0(E_0E) = \int_0^\infty \Pi(E_0,E,t)dt$ is the integral electron track length, essentially an energy spectrum averaged over the shower.

$G_0(E_0,E) = \int_0^\infty \Gamma(E_0,E,t)dt$ is the integral photon track length.

ϵ, the critical energy, is defined by the equation $\epsilon = k_{\mathrm{col}(<\eta)}(\epsilon)X_0$ (§ 1.3 and § 1.7). Table 1 contains some numerical values calculated for $\eta = 5 \times 10^6$ ev. This is the limiting energy below which electrons are considered "lost." It is at approximately the critical energy that energy loss by radiation (for electrons) becomes predominant.

$E_s = 21$ Mev is the scattering energy (§ 1.9).

2.2. Track lengths

Tamm and Belenky solution

$$P_0^{(\pi)}(E_0,E) = \frac{E_0}{\epsilon} e^x \left[e^{-x} + xE_i(-x) - \frac{x}{x_0} e^{-x_0} - xE_i(-x_0) \right] \tag{1}$$

where $x = (1/0.437)\,(E/\epsilon)$, $x_0 = (1/0.437)\,(E_0/\epsilon)$, and

$$E_i(-x) = -\int_x^\infty (e^{-s}/s)ds$$

is the exponential integral tabulated, for example, in Ref. 8. This expression is derived under the following assumptions (" Approximation B " of Rossi and Greisen, Ref. 20) : asymptotic (complete screening) cross sections (§ 1.6 and § 1.11), continuous collision loss with $k_{\mathrm{col}}(E) = \epsilon/X_0$, and neglect of Compton effect. However, exact numerical calculations (Refs. 18 and 21) have indicated that it is quite accurate (less than 10 per cent error) at least for low-atomic-number materials and $E > \frac{1}{10}\epsilon$; and $P_0^{(\gamma)}(E_0,E)$ differs significantly from $P_0^{(\pi)}(E_0,E)$ only when $E \sim E_0$.

Numerical results on $G_0(E_0,E)$ can be found in Ref. 18.

If the restriction $E \gg \epsilon$ is made, collision loss may be neglected entirely (" Approximation A " of Ref. 20), and with the further restriction $E \ll E_0$, the integral track lengths become

$$\left.\begin{aligned} P_0^{(\pi)}(E_0,E) &= P_0^{(\gamma)}(E_0,E) = 0.437\,\frac{E_0}{E} \\ \Gamma_0^{(\pi)}(E_0,E) &= \Gamma_0^{(\gamma)}(E_0,E) = 0.572\,\frac{E_0}{E} \end{aligned}\right\} \tag{2}$$

2.3. Integral spectrum. With the assumption of asymptotic cross sections and neglect of collision loss and Compton effect ("Approximation A"), solutions for the spectra valid for $\epsilon \ll E \ll E_0$ and $t \gg 1$ are given in Ref. 20. An approximate analytic expression for this range of validity has been given by Heisenberg (Ref. 6).

$$\left.\begin{aligned}\Pi_A{}^{(\pi)}(E_0,E,t) = \Pi_A{}^{(\gamma)}(E_0,E,t) &= \left[\frac{\ln E_0/E - 0.56}{t(t-1.4)}\right]^{1/2}\\ &\cdot \exp\left\{-t + 2\left[(t-1.4)\left(\ln\frac{E_0}{E} - 0.56\right)\right]^{1/2}\right\}\end{aligned}\right\} \quad (1)$$

Inclusion of a continuous collision loss as in (§ 2.2) allows an approximate solution for the "total" number of electrons in the shower. (Only electrons arising from pair production are counted—the knock-on electrons are lumped with the collision loss.) We write it as a factor times the Approximation A solution with $E = \epsilon$.

$$\Pi^{(\pi)}(E_0,0,t) = K\left(\frac{E_0}{\epsilon},t\right)\Pi_A{}^{(\pi)}(E_0,\epsilon,t) \quad (2)$$

The factor K is given in Ref. 20. It has the value 2.3 at the shower maximum, and may be expressed in rough approximation by

$$K = 1 + 1.3\left(t/\ln\frac{E_0}{\epsilon}\right)^{1/2} \quad (3)$$

2.4. Properties of the shower maxima. If T is the value of t for which the functions Π, etc., have a maximum for a fixed value of E, then in the range $\epsilon \ll E \ll E_0$ we have

$$T(E_0,E) = 1.01\left(\ln\frac{E_0}{E} - n\right) \quad (1)$$

$$\left.\begin{aligned}\pi_{\max}(E_0,E)\,dE\\ \gamma_{\max}(E_0,E)\,dE\end{aligned}\right\} = \frac{l}{[\ln(E_0/E) - m]^{1/2}} \cdot \frac{E_0}{E^2}\,dE \quad (2)$$

$$\Pi_{\max}(E,E) = \frac{l}{[\ln(E_0/E) - m]^{1/2}} \cdot \frac{E_0}{E} \quad (3)$$

where l, m, and n are given in Table 2.

For $E \sim 0$, we have $T(E_0,0) = T(E_0,\epsilon)$ (see above) and

$$\Pi_{\max}{}^{(\pi)}(E_0,0,t) = \frac{0.31}{[\ln(E_0/E) - 0.18]^{1/2}} \cdot \frac{E_0}{\epsilon}$$

TABLE 2

Function \ Primary particle	Electron			Photon		
	l	m	n	l	m	n
π	0.137	0	0	0.137	-0.18	-0.5
γ	0.180	0.18	0.5	0.180	0	0
Π	0.137	0.37	1	0.137	0.18	0.5

2.5. Stationary solutions. If at $t = 0$ a beam of electrons and/or photons is incident with an energy distribution in the form of a power law, $dN = \text{const}(dE_0/E_0^{s+1})$, this distribution in energy will retain its form as long as $E \gg \epsilon$, yielding solutions of the form $\pi(E,t)dE$ or

$$\gamma(E,t)dE = [a(s)e^{\lambda_1(s)t} + b(s)e^{\lambda_2(s)t}]\frac{dE}{E^{s+1}}$$

For large t the total number of particles decreases exponentially with t if $s > 1$, increases if $s < 1$. Details will be found in Ref. 20.

2.6. Lateral and angular spread of showers. The only explicit calculation of lateral and angular distribution of shower particles is due to Moliere (Ref. 13), where results are given in graphical form. The lateral distribution function gives the fraction dF of all shower particles which are at distances between r and $r + dr$ from the shower axis, averaged over the shower. An analytic approximation for Moliere's calculation of this fraction, adequate for $r/r_1 \lesssim 1$, is

$$dF = 2.85\left(1 + 4\frac{r}{r_1}\right)\exp\left[-4\left(\frac{r}{r_1}\right)^{2/3}\right]\frac{dr}{r_1} \tag{1}$$

where $r_1 = (E_s/\epsilon)X_0$, and $E_s = 21$ Mev (see § 1.9).

The mean-square lateral spread and mean-square angular spread for shower particles, averaged over the shower, are given for all energies in Ref. 19. Their values for particles of energy $E \gg \epsilon$ are

	electrons	*photons*
$\langle r^2\rangle_{\text{av}}$	$0.64\left(\frac{E_s}{E}\right)^2 X_0^2$	$1.13\left(\frac{E_s}{E}\right)^2 X_0^2$
$\langle\Theta^2\rangle_{\text{av}}$	$0.55\left(\frac{E_s}{E}\right)^2$	$0.18\left(\frac{E_s}{E}\right)^2$

These results are valid only for $E \ll E_0$; they therefore apply equally to showers initiated by either electrons or photons.

3. Nuclear Interactions

3.1. Nuclear radius and transparency. The geometrical cross section of a nucleus of mass number A is

$$\sigma_g = \pi r_n^2 = \pi r_0^2 A^{2/3}, \quad (r_0 \approx 1.38 \times 10^{-13}\,\text{cm}) \tag{1}$$

If the average cross section for a nucleon-nucleon interaction of a given type is $\bar{\sigma}$, the assumption that the particles in the nucleus are independent leads to the following cross section for this type of collision of the particle with a nucleus, if $\sqrt{\bar{\sigma}/\pi}$ is small compared with r_n

$$\sigma_i = \left[1 - t\left(\frac{l_c}{r_n}\right)\right] \pi r_n^2 \tag{2}$$

where $l_c = \frac{4}{3}(\pi r_n^3/A\bar{\sigma})$, and the transparency

$$t\left(\frac{l_c}{r_n}\right) = \frac{l_c^2}{2r_n^2}\left[1 - e^{-2r_n/l_c} - 2\,\frac{r_n}{l_c}\,e^{-2r_n/l_c}\right] \tag{3}$$

3.2. Altitude variation of nuclear interactions: Gross transformation. An isotropic flux of particles of intensity per unit solid angle J_0 is incident on a semi-infinite slab (e.g., the atmosphere). If the particles are absorbed exponentially with a mean free path L, the intensity at a depth x, integrated over angle, is

$$\int_0^{\pi/2} J(x,\vartheta)\,d\omega = 2\pi\,\frac{x}{L}\,J_0\left[e^{-x/L} + \frac{x}{L}\,E_i\left(-\frac{x}{L}\right)\right] \tag{1}$$

see § 2.2 for $E_i(-t)$.

4. Meson Production

4.1. Threshold energies. A nucleus (or other system) of mass M_i, initially at rest, is bombarded by a particle of mass m. All masses are " rest masses " (§ 1.1). In order to create a new particle of mass μ, the bombarding particle must have at least a kinetic energy

$$E = \frac{[(\mu + \Sigma\, M_f)^2 - (m + M_i)^2]c^2}{2M_i} \tag{1}$$

where ΣM_f is the sum of all masses present (except μ) after the collision.

4.2. Relativity transformations. The maximum energy in the center-of-mass system, when a particle of energy E bombards a particle initially at rest, is the quantity μc^2 in the equation of (§ 4.1) (it is assumed that the projectile and target particles are left at rest in the center-of-mass system).

The velocity of the center of mass, in this collision, is

$$\beta_c c = \frac{c\sqrt{E^2 + 2mc^2E}}{E + (m + M_i)c^2} \tag{2}$$

Let Θ be the angle between this velocity and the trajectory of an ejected meson in the laboratory system, Θ^* and $\beta^* c$ the corresponding angle and the velocity of the meson in the center-of-mass system; then

$$\tan \Theta = \frac{\sin \Theta^*}{\cos \Theta^* + \beta_c/\beta^*} \cdot \sqrt{1 - \beta_c^2} \tag{3}$$

In the extreme relativistic approximation $\sqrt{1-\beta_c^2} \ll 1$ and $\sqrt{1-\beta^{*2}} \ll 1$ this becomes

$$\tan \Theta = \sqrt{1 - \beta_c^2} \tan \frac{\Theta^*}{2} \tag{4}$$

If the angular distribution of mesons in the center-of-mass system is $F(\Theta^*)d\omega^*$, the corresponding angular distribution in the laboratory system (with the additional restriction $\Theta \ll 1$) is

$$G(\Theta)d\omega = F[\Theta^*(\Theta)] \frac{4(1 - \beta_c^2)}{(1 - \beta_c^2 + \Theta^2)^2} d\omega \tag{5}$$

General formulas for the transformation of both angular and energy distributions are given in Ref. 3.

5. Meson Decay

5.1. Distance of flight. If τ is the mean life of the meson at rest, the mean distance traversed before decay, when the meson has constant momentum p, is $L = p\tau/m$.

In a real medium p is a function of the thickness traversed, x g cm^{-2}. The density of the material, ρ, may be a function of x (e.g., x/ρ = constant in an isothermal static atmosphere). The probability that the meson has not decayed before reaching x_2, if it existed at x_1, is

$$w(x_1,x_2) = \exp\left[-\int_{x_1}^{x_2} \frac{m\,dx}{\tau\rho(x)p(x)}\right] \tag{1}$$

5.2. Energy distribution of decay products. Let a particle of mass m_1 disintegrate into particles of masses m_2 and m_3. Then the total energy of one of the products, U_2^* (the star designates the center-of-mass system) is

$$U_2^* = \left(\frac{m_1^2 + m_2^2 - m_3^2}{2m_1}\right)c^2 \tag{1}$$

If the original particle had total energy U_1 and momentum of magnitude p_1 (as seen from the laboratory system) the differential energy distribution of a product particle has the constant value

$$\left.\begin{aligned} F(U_2)dU_2 &= \frac{1}{2}\frac{m_1}{p_1 p_2^*}dU_2 \\ \text{for} \quad \frac{U_1 U_2^*}{m_1 c^2} - \frac{p_1 p_2^*}{m_1} &< U_2 < \frac{U_1 U_2^*}{m_1 c^2} + \frac{p_1 p_2^*}{m_1} \end{aligned}\right\} \tag{2}$$

and is zero otherwise.

If the original particle disintegrates into more than two particles, and U_2^* designates the total energy of one of them in the center-of-mass system, then

$$U_{2\,\max}^* = \left(\frac{m_1^2 + m_2^2 - (m_3 + m_4 + \dots)^2}{2m_1}\right)c^2 \tag{3}$$

and

$$\langle U_2 \rangle_{\text{av}} = \frac{U_1}{m_1 c^2}\langle U_2^* \rangle_{\text{av}} \tag{4}$$

5.3. Angular distribution in two-photon decay. The equations of § 5.2 may be applied to a simple case of physical interest, the neutral π-meson (mass m_1) which decays into two gamma rays. If (in the laboratory system) the gamma rays have energies E_2 and E_3, and the angle included between their trajectories is ϕ, then $\sin(\phi/2) = m_1 c^2/2\sqrt{E_2 E_3}$. The distribution in the angle ϕ, in terms of $U_1 = E_2 + E_3$, and p_1, is

$$f(\phi)d\phi = \frac{m_1 c}{p_1} \cdot \frac{\cos(\phi/2)d\phi}{[4\sin^2(\phi/2)]\,[(U_1/m_1 c^2)^2 \sin^2(\phi/2) - 1]^{1/2}} \tag{1}$$

The distribution function goes to infinity at the minimum angle,

$$\phi_{\min} = 2\sin^{-1}(m_1 c^2/U_1)$$

6. Geomagnetic Effects

6.1. Motion in static magnetic fields. The equation of motion in a static magnetic field for a particle of charge ze, mass m is $(d\boldsymbol{p}/dt) = (ze/c)\boldsymbol{v} \times \boldsymbol{B}$, where $\boldsymbol{p} = m\boldsymbol{v}/\sqrt{1-\beta^2}$ is the momentum of the particle, sometimes called the kinetic momentum to distinguish it from the variable $[mv_x/\sqrt{1-\beta^2} + (ze/c)A_x]$ which is canonically conjugate to the coordinate x. Since ds/dt, the magnitude of $\boldsymbol{v}$, is constant, we have as the equation for the trajectory

$$\frac{d\boldsymbol{t}}{ds} = \frac{ze}{pc}\,\boldsymbol{t} \times \boldsymbol{B} \tag{1}$$

where $\boldsymbol{t}$ is the unit tangent vector defined in § 6.9 of Chapter 1.

If $\boldsymbol{B}$ is uniform, the path is a helix, the angle α between $\boldsymbol{p}$ and $\boldsymbol{B}$ is constant, and the radius of the projection of the path on a plane perpendicular to $\boldsymbol{B}$ is $R = (pc \sin\alpha/zeB)$. If B is measured in gausses, R in cm, and pc/ze in volts, $(pc \sin\alpha/ze) = 300\ BR$. The quantity pc/ze is called the magnetic rigidity of the particle; for $z = 1$ it is numerically equal, when expressed in volts, to the momentum in units of ev/c.

6.2. Flux of particles in static magnetic fields. Let the directional intensity of a flux of noninteracting charged particles be $I(\boldsymbol{r},\boldsymbol{p})dp\,d\omega\,d\sigma$ = the number of particles, observed at point $\boldsymbol{r}$, having momentum $\boldsymbol{p}$ in $dp\,d\omega$, crossing area $d\sigma$ perpendicular to $\boldsymbol{p}$. Then $I(\boldsymbol{r},\boldsymbol{p})$ is constant along any particle trajectory. If one assumes that the flux of particles at great distances from the earth is isotropic, the problem of the influence of the earth's magnetic field on cosmic-ray intensities at the earth's surface is therefore reduced to the investigation of classes of allowed trajectories.

6.3. Limiting momenta on the earth's surface. Let the earth's magnetic field be represented by a dipole of moment M, the earth's radius by r_0, and an observation point on the earth's surface by the geomagnetic latitude λ. A particle of rigidity pc/ze can arrive (from outer space) at any point, in any direction, if $pc/ze > M/r_0^2 \approx 60 \times 10^9$ volts. The particle cannot arrive at all, at a particular point, if

$$\frac{pc}{ze} < \frac{\mathrm{M}}{r_0^2} \cdot \frac{\cos^4\lambda}{[(1+\cos^3\lambda)^{1/2}+1]^2}$$

Let the angle between the direction of arrival of the particle and the tangent to the circle of latitude be ϑ, and let $\vartheta = 0$ correspond to arrival from the *west* for *positive* particles. (Then for *negative* particles ϑ must be redefined so that $\vartheta = 0$ corresponds to arrival from the *east*. Note that z and e are positive magnitudes, so that no question of sign arises in the equations).

If we observe in the direction ϑ, at latitude λ, no particle can arrive from outer space if

$$\frac{pc}{ze} < \frac{M}{r_0^2} \cdot \frac{\cos^4 \lambda}{[(1 + \cos\vartheta \cos^3 \lambda)^{1/2} + 1]^2}$$

Thus more positive particles will come from the west than from the east.

The cone of semivertex angle ϑ, for a fixed pc/ze, is called the Störmer cone. The equation is correct for any dipole field if r_0 is the distance to the point of observation.

Not all momenta above the limit set by this equation are allowed, when one considers observations on the real earth. For a certain range of momenta above this lower limit the trajectories are so tortuous that certain classes of them intersect the earth (at some other point) before arriving at the observation point. This " shadow effect " of the earth is unimportant at higher latitudes (say, $|\lambda| > 40°$), except for some nearly horizontal directions of approach. Near the equator the shadow effect is very small in the vertical direction, and raises the lower limit, at 45° zenith angle, by a few per cent for east and west azimuths, and perhaps 15 per cent for north and south azimuths. Intermediate latitudes are particularly complex; details and further references will be found in Ref. 28.

Bibliography

1. Bethe, H. A., in *Handbuch der Physik*, Vol. 24/1, Julius Springer, Berlin, 1933.
2. Blatt, J. M., *Phys. Rev.*, **75**, 1584 (1949).
3. Bradt, H. L., Kaplon, M. F. and Peters, B., *Helv. Phys. Acta*, **23**, 24 (1950).
4. Goldschmidt-Clermont, Y., *Nuovo cim.*, **7**, 1 (1950).
5. Halpern, O. and Hall, H., *Phys. Rev.*, **73**, 477 (1948).
6. Heisenberg, W. (ed.), *Cosmic Radiation*, Dover Publications, New York, 1946. Contains several brief theoretical papers of interest.
7. Heitler, W., *Quantum Theory of Radiation*, 2d ed., Oxford University Press, Oxford, 1944. Contains derivations of the electromagnetic cross sections.
8. Jahnke, E. and Emde, F., *Tables of Functions*, Dover Publications, New York, 1945.
9. Janossy, L., *Cosmic Rays*, 2d ed., Oxford University Press, Oxford, 1950. A large treatise containing much useful material.
10. Klein, O. and Nishina, Y., *Z. Physik*, **52**, 853 (1929).
11. Leprince-Ringuet, L., *Cosmic Rays*, Prentice-Hall, Inc., New York, 1950. A beautifully illustrated semipopular work that includes some of the recent researches on artificial mesons.
12. McKinley, W. A. and Feshbach, H., *Phys. Rev.*, **74**, 1759 (1948).
13. Moliere, G., in *Cosmic Radiation* (ed. Heisenberg, W.), Dover Publications, New York, 1946.
14. Moliere, G., *Z. Naturforsch.*, **2a**, 133 (1947).

15. MOLIERE, G., *Z. Naturforsch.*, **3a**, 78 (1948).
16. MONTGOMERY, D. J. F., *Cosmic Ray Physics*, Princeton University Press, Princeton, 1949. A rather brief survey of cosmic ray research through 1948.
17. MOTT, N. F. and MASSEY, H. S. W., *Theory of Atomic Collisions*, 2d ed., Oxford University Pres, Oxford, 1949. Contains derivations of the electromagnetic cross sections.
18. RICHARDS, J. A. and NORDHEIM, L. W., *Phys. Rev.*, **74**, 1106 (1948).
19. ROBERG, J. and NORDHEIM, L. W., *Phys. Rev.*, **75**, 444 (1949).
20. ROSSI, B. and GREISEN, K., *Revs. Modern Phys.*, **13**, 240 (1941). Electromagnetic interactions, and especially shower theory, are treated in detail.
21. ROSSI, B. and KLAPMAN, S. J., *Phys. Rev.*, **61**, 414 (1942).
22. ROSSI, B., *High-Energy Particles*, Prentice-Hall, Inc., New York, 1952. The authoritative work in this field. Much of the material of the present chapter was taken, with the kind permission of the author, from a pre-publication manuscript of this book.
23. ROSSI, B. and STAUB, H., *Ionization Chambers and Counters*, McGraw-Hill Book Company, Inc., New York, 1949.
24. SMITH, J. H., *Phys. Rev.*, **71**, 32 (1947).
25. SCHWINGER, J., *Phys. Rev.*, **75**, 898 (1949).
26. SNYDER, H. S. and SCOTT, W. T., *Phys. Rev.*, **76**, 220 (1949).
27. VALLARTA, M. S., *Outline of the Theory of the Allowed Core*, University of Toronto Press, Toronto, 1938. Geomagnetic effects are discussed in detail.
28. VALLARTA, M. S., *Phys. Rev.*, **74**, 1837 (1948).
29. WICK, G. C., *Nuovo cim.*, **1**, 302 (1943).
30. WILLIAMS, E. J., *Proc. Roy. Soc.* (London), A**169**, 531 (1939).
31. WILSON, J. G. (ed.), *Progress in Cosmic Ray Physics*, Interscience Publishers, Inc., New York, 1952. A series of reviews, by specialists, of some of the most active fields of cosmic ray research.

Chapter 24

PARTICLE ACCELERATORS

By Leslie L. Foldy

Associate Professor of Physics
Case Institute of Technology

1. General Description and Classification of High-Energy Particle Accelerators

1.1. General description. High-energy particle accelerators are devices employed to accelerate atomic or subatomic particles (electrons, protons, deuterons, alpha particles, etc.) to high energies. " High energies " is generally interpreted to mean energies greater than a few hundred kilovolts. Existing accelerators of various types are adapted to accelerate particles to energies in the range from a few hundred kilovolts to about 400 million volts, but higher energy accelerators are under construction. The high-energy particles produced are employed principally to study the properties of nuclei of atoms and nuclear transformations or reactions, and also to study the properties of the fundamental particles themselves. They are also used in medical applications.

1.2. Classification according to particle accelerated. Accelerators may be first classified according to the type of particle they have been designed to accelerate. The two principal types according to this classification are electron accelerators employed to accelerate electrons, and which, by allowing the electrons to strike a target, can also be used as a source of high-energy x rays; and heavy-particle accelerators employed to accelerate protons, deuterons, alpha particles, and in some cases nuclei of heavier atoms. Because of the great difference in mass between the electron and the heavier particles, there are (except in the case of electrostatic accelerators) great differences in the problems to be met in the two cases; consequently electron accelerators differ considerably from heavy-particle accelerators both in design and often in principle of operation. Usually the same principle of operation can be used for the acceleration of protons, deuterons, and alpha particles, and some machines can easily be adapted to accelerate any of these particles.

The principal types of electron accelerators employed at present are Cockcroft-Walton machines, electrostatic generators, linear electron accelerators, betatrons, and synchrotrons. The principal types of heavy-particle accelerators employed at present are Cockcroft-Walton machines, electrostatic generators, linear accelerators for heavy particles, cyclotrons, and synchrocyclotrons. Under construction at the present time are heavy-particle accelerators for the very high-energy range employing combinations of the cyclotron, betatron, and synchrotron principles. The principal differences in design and principle of operation of electron and heavy-particle accelerators stem from the fact that the electron mass varies greatly during the acceleration process because of relativistic effects, while the mass of heavy particles varies only by a relatively small amount during acceleration in present-day machines.

1.3. Classification according to particle trajectories. Accelerators may also be classified according to the spatial region occupied by the trajectories of the particles being accelerated. Two broad classifications occur : linear accelerators in which the trajectories are essentially straight lines, and circular accelerators in which the trajectories are confined to a circular region. To the first class belong Cockcroft-Walton machines, electrostatic generators, and number of different types of so-called linear accelerators. Circular accelerators may further be divided into accelerators in which the trajectories are essentially spirals extending from the center to the edge of a circular region (of which cyclotrons and synchrocyclotrons are examples), and accelerators in which the trajectories are confined to an annular region of relatively small radial breadth (of which the betatron and synchrotron are the principal examples).

1.4. Designation of accelerators. Accelerators are usually designated by the maximum energy to which they are designed to accelerate particles. In the case of cyclotrons and synchrocyclotrons, which can be used for different heavy particles and for which the maximum energies depend on the particle being accelerated, the machine is often designated in terms of the diameter of the pole piece of the magnet employed to confine the particle trajectories in the acceleration region.

1.5. Basic components. Almost all high-energy accelerators have certain basic features and components in common although the physical form of these may vary greatly from one type of accelerator to another. These basic components are :

a. An acceleration chamber within which the trajectories of the accelerated particles are confined. In linear accelerators, the chamber defines a linear region along which the particles travel in essentially straight lines. In circular accelerators the chamber defines a disk-shaped or annular region depending on whether the trajectories are essentially spirals or circles. In all accelerators the acceleration chamber must be evacuated to a high vacuum in order to prevent undue scattering of the accelerated particles by molecules of gas.

b. In a circular accelerator a magnetic field must be employed to cause the accelerated particles to move in circles. In some accelerators the magnetic guide field is a static field, in others it varies with time.

c. A means of supplying energy to the particles in order to accelerate them must be provided. In all machines the acceleration is performed by electric fields, but the manner in which the electric fields are provided varies greatly. It may consist of an electrostatic or quasi-electrostatic field (Cockcroft-Walton machines and electrostatic generators), an electric field produced by magnetic induction (betatron), the electric field in a standing or traveling electromagnetic wave (linear accelerators), or the acceleration may occur by having the particle pass at appropriate times through a gap across which an alternating voltage is established (cyclotron, synchrocyclotron, and synchrotron). In some machines (Cockcroft-Walton, electrostatic generator, betatron, and traveling wave linear accelerators) the particles may be continuously accelerated; in others (cyclotron, synchrocyclotron, synchrotron, and standing wave linear accelerators) the acceleration process may take place in steps by a series of impulses.

d. In some machines, some "focusing" of the beam of accelerated particles must be provided in order that motion of the particles along the desired trajectories shall be stable. In circular machines some focusing can easily be provided by an appropriate radial variation of the magnetic guiding field. In linear accelerators the problem of providing focusing may be much more critical.

e. Other components generally required, but which we shall not discuss, are electron guns or ion sources to supply the particles to be accelerated, vacuum pumps and associated equipment, electronic equipment to provide the radio frequency accelerating fields where these are necessary, etc.

2. Dynamic Relations for Accelerated Particles

2.1. Fundamental relativistic relations. If the mass of a particle at rest is m_0 and if c represents the velocity of light, then when the particle is moving with a velocity v

Momentum :	$p = m_0v/(1 - v^2/c^2)^{1/2}$	(1)
Total energy :	$E = m_0c^2/(1 - v^2/c^2)^{1/2}$	(2)
Kinetic energy :	$T = E - m_0c^2$	(3)
Relativistic mass :	$m = m_0/(1 - v^2/c^2)^{1/2}$	(4)
Rest energy :	$E_0 = m_0c^2$	(5)

2.2. Derived relations. The relations in 2.1 lead to the following derived relations.

$$E = mc^2 = (m_0^2c^4 + c^2p^2)^{1/2} \quad (1)$$

$$p = [(E/c)^2 - m_0^2c^2]^{1/2} \quad (2)$$

$$v = c^2p/E = c[1 - (m_0c^2/E)^2]^{1/2} = p/[m_0^2 + (p/c)^2]^{1/2} \quad (3)$$

$$m = E/c^2 = [m_0^2 + (p/c)^2]^{1/2} \quad (4)$$

2.3. Nonrelativistic relations. When $v \ll c$ or $p \ll m_0c$, the relations in 2.1 and 2.2 take the forms

$$p = m_0v \quad (1)$$

$$E = m_0c^2 + \tfrac{1}{2}m_0v^2 = m_0c^2 + p^2/2m_0 \quad (2)$$

$$T = \tfrac{1}{2}m_0v^2 = p^2/2m_0 \quad (3)$$

2.4. Units. The above equations hold when all quantities are measured in absolute units (e.g., m_0 and m in grams, E and T in ergs, v and c in cm/sec, p in gm-cm/sec). The velocity of light $c = 2.998 \times 10^{10}$ cm/sec.

The energies of accelerated particles are often expressed in "million-electron-volts" (Mev). The energy unit 1 Mev is defined as the energy gained by a particle bearing one elementary charge ($e - 4.802 \times 10^{-10}$ esu) in falling through a potential difference of one million volts.

$$(1 \text{ Mev} = 1.602 \times 10^{-6} \text{ erg})$$

In all the equations which follow, the quantity e is presumed to be measured in electrostatic units. Furthermore, all electric field strengths and potential differences are to be measured in absolute electrostatic units and all magnetic field strengths in absolute electromagnetic units (gausses or oersteds).

3. Magnetic Guiding Fields

3.1. Specification of magnetic guiding fields. Magnetic guiding fields, whether static or time-dependent, generally have cylindrical symmetry, so that polar coordinates (r,ϑ,z) are used to specify the field with the z axis chosen along the axis of symmetry. Ideally, in the regions in which the accelerated particles move, the fields have the following properties.

a. There exists a median plane normal to the axis of the field in which the magnetic field has only a z component. In this median plane which is generally taken to be the plane $z = 0$, H_z is a function only of r and possibly of the time t.

b. The magnetic field has no azimuthal component H_ϑ.

c. The magnetic field is symmetrical about the median plane.

$$H_z(r,z;t) = H_z(r,-z;t), \quad H_r(r,z;t) = -H_r(r,-z;t) \tag{1}$$

d. If the active region of the field includes points on the axis ($r = 0$), then H_z can be written as a power series.

$$H_z(r,z;t) = H_0 \sum_{l=0}^{\infty} \sum_{m=0}^{\infty} h_{lm} r^l z^{2m} = H_0(1 + h_{01}z^2 + h_{20}r^2 + h_{21}r^2z^2 + \ldots) \tag{2}$$

From Maxwell's equations it follows that H_r can be written as

$$\left.\begin{aligned} H_r(r,z;t) &= -H_0 \sum_{l=0}^{\infty} \sum_{m=1}^{\infty} \frac{2mh_{lm}}{l+2} r^{l+1} z^{2m-1} \\ &= -H_0(h_{01}rz + \tfrac{1}{2}h_{21}r^3z + \ldots) \end{aligned}\right\} \tag{3}$$

The following relations hold among the coefficients.

$$h_{00} = 1, \quad h_{1m} = 0 \tag{4}$$

While in the general case the coefficients h_{lm} may be time-dependent, usually they are essentially constant, and only H_0 is a function of the time.

e. The field described by the equations in (d.) can be derived from a vector potential $\boldsymbol{A}$ ($\boldsymbol{H} = \textbf{curl}\ \boldsymbol{A}$) having only an azimuthal component ($A_r = A_z = 0$) given by

$$A_\vartheta = H_0 \sum_{l=0}^{\infty} \sum_{m=0}^{\infty} \frac{h_{lm}}{l+z} r^{l+1} z^{2m} \tag{5}$$

f. The *field exponent* $n(r;t)$ is defined by the equation

$$n(r;t) = \frac{r}{H_z(r,0;t)} \cdot \frac{\partial H_z(r,0;t)}{\partial r} = \frac{\partial \ln H_z(r,0;t)}{\partial \ln r} \tag{6}$$

and plays an important role in determining the stability of particle motion (see below).

It is often convenient, especially when the active region of the magnetic field does not include points on the axis (annular field) to specify the variation of the field in the median plane over a small annular region about a radius r_0 in the form

$$H_z(r,0;t) = H_z(r_0,0;t)\left(\frac{r}{r_0}\right)^{n(r_0;t)} \tag{7}$$

For the field specified in (d.), the field exponent is given by the expression

$$n(r;t) = \frac{\sum_{l=z}^{\infty} l h_{l0} r^l}{\sum_{l=0}^{\infty} h_{l0} r^l} = \frac{2h_{20}r^2 + 3h_{30}r^3 + \ldots}{h_{00} + h_{20}r + h_{30}r^3 + \ldots} \tag{8}$$

3.2. Force on a charged particle in a magnetic field. A charged particle with charge Ze moving with a velocity v in a static magnetic field H is subjected to a force at right angles to both the field and the direction of motion given by

$$\boldsymbol{F} = \frac{Ze}{c}\, \boldsymbol{v} \times \boldsymbol{H} \tag{1}$$

If the magnetic field is changing with time, the associated induced electric field will give rise to an additional force having a component in the direction of motion of the particle.

The radius of curvature ρ of the orbit of a charged particle of momentum p moving perpendicularly to a magnetic field is given by

$$\rho = \frac{cp}{|Z|\, eH} \tag{2}$$

3.3. Equations of motion of a charged particle in a magnetic guiding field. If r, ϑ, and z represent the cylindrical coordinates of a particle of charge Ze moving in a magnetic guiding field of the type described in Sec. 3.1 and $A_\vartheta(r,z;t)$ represents the vector potential from which the magnetic field is derived, then the equations of motion of the particle are given by

$$\frac{d}{dt}\left[\frac{m_0\dot{r}}{\sqrt{1-v^2/c^2}}\right] + Ze\dot{\vartheta}A_\vartheta(r,z;t) + \frac{Zer\dot{\vartheta}\partial A_\vartheta(r,z;t)}{\partial r} = f_r \tag{1}$$

$$\frac{d}{dt}\left[\frac{m_0 r^2\dot{\vartheta}}{\sqrt{1-v^2/c^2}} - ZerA_\vartheta(r,z;t)\right] = f_\vartheta \tag{2}$$

$$\frac{d}{dt}\left[\frac{m_0\dot{z}}{\sqrt{1-v^2/c^2}}\right] + \frac{Zer\dot{\vartheta}\partial A_\vartheta(r,z;t)}{\partial z} = f_z \tag{3}$$

where dots denote time differentiation, f_r, f_ϑ, and f_z represent the radial, azimuthal, and vertical components of any forces acting on the particle other than those due to the field A_ϑ, and

$$v^2 = \dot{r}^2 + r^2\dot{\vartheta}^2 + \dot{z}^2 \tag{4}$$

3.4. Equilibrium orbit. A charged particle (charge Ze) with momentum p and energy E moving in a static cylindrical guide field of the type described in § 3.1 has as a possible orbit, a motion in a circle concentric with the axis of the field and lying in the median plane. The radius of this circular orbit is determined by the solution for r_e of the following equation.

$$cp = |Z|\, er_e H_z(r_e,0) \tag{1}$$

This orbit is called the *equilibrium orbit* for the particle, and the radius r_e is called the *equilibrium radius*.

The angular frequency of revolution of the particle in its equilibrium orbit (the so-called " *cyclotron frequency* ") is given by

$$\omega_e = \frac{|Z|\, eH_e}{mc} = \frac{|Z|\, ecH_e}{E} \tag{2}$$

where $H_e = H_z(r_e,0)$.

The period of revolution in this orbit is therefore given by

$$T_e = \frac{2\pi E}{|Z|\, ecH_e}$$

If the momentum of the particle and the magnetic field vary sufficiently slowly with time (adiabatically), the equilibrium orbit radius and cyclotron frequency are defined at each instant by the above equations and may be considered also to vary adiabatically with the time. The physical importance of the equilibrium orbit lies in the fact that in all circular accelerators, the acceleration process involves an approximately adiabatic variation of the parameters, defining the equilibrium orbit, and the general motion of an accelerated particle can be described in terms of oscillations about an adiabatically varying equilibrium orbit.

3.5. Stability of motion in the equilibrium orbit. Motion of a particle in its equilibrium orbit is stable against small disturbances of this motion if and only if

$$0 < n(r_e,t) < 1 \tag{1}$$

where $n(r_e)$ is the field exponent defined in (§ 3.1f) evaluated at the equilibrium radius.

3.6. Oscillations about the equilibrium orbit. Small disturbances of the motion of a particle in its equilibrium orbit, or a small non-adiabatic variation of the parameters defining this orbit, will give rise to small vertical (z) and radial (r) oscillations of the particle about the equilibrium orbit. The angular frequency of free oscillations of this character are given by the equations

$$\omega_r = [1 - n(r_e;t)]^{1/2}\omega_e \tag{1}$$

$$\omega_z = [n(r_e,t)]^{1/2}\omega_e \tag{2}$$

3.7. Coupling of oscillations about the equilibrium orbit. The presence of high-order nonlinear terms in the equations of motion describing radial and vertical oscillations leads to coupling of these oscillations with each other and with the rotational motion. For certain values of the field exponent n, leading to commensurability of harmonics of the frequencies of oscillation and of the frequency of rotation (cyclotron frequency), resonance may occur between oscillations, leading to increases in the amplitude of a mode of oscillation to a degree where the particles may strike the walls of the accelerating chamber. The principal case where such resonance may occur (corresponding to n values which are generally to be avoided) are :

(*a*) If $\sqrt{n/(1-n)}$ or $\sqrt{(1-n)/n}$ is an integer N (or lies close to an integer), resonance between radial and vertical oscillations may take place.

(*b*) If $1/\sqrt{n}$ or $1/\sqrt{1-n}$ is an integer N, resonance between rotational motion and radial and vertical oscillations, respectively, may take place. This can be especially serious if the acceleration process takes place impulsively with a frequency which is a harmonic of the rotation frequency (as is often actually the case) or if azimuthal inhomogeneities are present in the magnetic guide field.

If n varies with time, the seriousness of these resonances will depend on N and on how long a time n spends in the neighborhood of a critical value defined in (a) and (b) alone. Resonances are more serious, the smaller the value of N.

3.8. Damping of radial and vertical oscillations. If the parameters defining the equilibrium orbit are varied adiabatically, the amplitude of the free radial and vertical oscillations about the equilibrium orbit will be damped (either positively or negatively). The principle of adiabatic invariance of the action applied to these oscillations leads to the result that the amplitude of free vertical oscillations will vary as $\omega_z^{-1/2}$ as ω_e varies adiabatically, and the amplitude of free radial oscillations will vary as $\omega_r^{-1/2}$ as W_e varies adiabatically. In case n does not vary with time, the amplitudes of both oscillations will vary as $(E/H_e)^{1/2}$.

4. Particle Acceleration

The agency for accelerating particles in all types of accelerators consists of properly applied electric fields. The electric fields employed may be either static, quasi-static, or time-varying. Acceleration processes may be divided into two classes according to whether the particle is continuously accelerated or whether the accelerating takes place in discrete steps of an impulsive character. The former is employed in linear accelerators of the Cockcroft-Walton, Van de Graaff, and traveling-wave types, and in the betatron, while the latter is employed in the cyclotron, synchrocyclotron, synchrotron, and their variants, as well as in linear accelerators employing drift tubes.

4.1. Electrostatic and quasi-electrostatic acceleration. In the Van de Graaff accelerator, the charged particles are accelerated by falling through an electrostatic potential difference of magnitude corresponding to the final energy of the particles. This method requires the establishment over some linear region of very high potential differences. The same type of acceleration process is used in Cockcroft-Walton machines except that the potential difference is an alternating one of such low frequency that the particles undergo the complete acceleration process before the potential has changed sign. The practical difficulties of establishing and maintaining large potential differences limits present application of these methods to energies up to about 5 Mev.

4.2. Induction acceleration. In this type of acceleration, which is used in the betatron, the electric fields are azimuthal and are produced by electromagnetic induction by varying the magnetic flux through the area spanned by the orbit of the accelerated particles. If the particle orbit is a circle, the gain in energy of the particle per revolution (in electron volts) is given by the electromotive force about the particle orbit. The particles make many revolutions during the acceleration cycle, so that the electromotive force around the orbit is generally a small fraction of the final energy of the accelerated particles. Hence while the acceleration process is continuous the electromotive forces present at any instant of time are much smaller than the corresponding potential differences in electrostatic acceleration to the same final energy. The energy gain of the accelerated particle per revolution in a betatron is given by

$$\Delta E = 2\pi r_e \, | Z | \, e dF_e/dt$$

where F_e is the magnetic flux through a circle of radius r_e concentric with the field and lying in the median plane.

4.3. Traveling wave acceleration. In this type of acceleration, the electric field employed for acceleration consists of the longitudinal electric field of an electromagnetic wave traveling through a wave guide. Acceleration takes place by having the particles travel in groups down the wave guide with a velocity closely equal to that of the wave. By having the groups of particles enter the wave guide at the proper phase of the electromagnetic field, the particles will be continuously accelerated down the guide by the co-moving electric field. Since the particle velocity is always less than that of light and increases during the accelerating process, it is necessary to " load " the wave guide with irises or other structures to reduce the phase velocity of the electromagnetic field to a value smaller than the velocity of light. By variation of the loading along the guide, the phase velocity of the wave may be varied to keep pace with the change in velocity of the particles.

Since at any instant, both accelerating and decelerating regions of the traveling electromagnetic field are accessible to the particles being accelerated, it is necessary that certain " phase stability " conditions be met in order that the particles be eventually accelerated to high energies, or the acceleration process must be terminated before the particles enter decelerating phases. The phase stability conditions require that if a particle finds itself in a region of phase unfavorable to its continued acceleration, its subsequent acceleration or deceleration be such as to return it to a favorable phase relative to the electromagnetic field.

4.4. Impulsive acceleration. When acceleration of particles is obtained by allowing them to pass once or repeatedly through one or more regions in which alternating electric fields are established, one has a process of impulsive acceleration. This type of acceleration is used both in circular accelerators and in linear accelerators. As in traveling wave acceleration, it is possible for the particles to pass through the alternating fields at such times as to be decelerated rather than accelerated. Again certain conditions of "phase stability" must be met in order that particles be eventually accelerated to high energies, or the acceleration process must be terminated before the particles reach decelerating phases. In general, all employed types of impulsive acceleration can, to a good approximation for theoretical study of the phase stability problem, be replaced by an equivalent traveling wave acceleration in which the successive impulsive accelerations are smoothed out into an equivalent continuous acceleration.

5. Phase Stability and Phase Oscillations

5.1. Phase stability. As mentioned in the previous section, the successful operation of accelerators employing traveling-wave or impulsive acceleration requires a condition of phase stability to be met. The exact formulation of this condition depends generally on the detailed construction of the accelerator concerned, but provided certain quantities are appropriately defined in each case, the pertinent equations may be made to take analogous forms.

The first of these quantities is thc phase of the particle relative to alternating electric field. In all cases we shall define the phase ϕ as the phase of the electric field at the time which the particle traverses it relative to the last time that the electric field has passed through the value zero from a *decelerating* to an *accelerating* value at that point.

The second quantity is the effective amplitude $\mathcal{E}$ of the accelerating electric field. For a traveling wave accelerator we shall define it as the amplitude of the electric field component in the direction of motion of the particle of the traveling electromagnetic wave. For impulsive acceleration, we shall define it as the corresponding amplitude of the equivalent traveling wave, where the equivalent traveling wave is one leading to the same average acceleration of the particle over several impulsive accelerations.

It is further helpful to define what is meant by *synchronous motion* of the particle. In a circular accelerator, this is defined to be motion in which the angular velocity of the particle is effectively at each instant equal to the angular frequency of the accelerating alternating electric field. In a linear accelerator, this is defined to be a motion in which the linear velocity of the particle is effectively at each point equal to the phase velocity of the accelerating traveling wave or the phase velocity of the equivalent accelerating traveling wave at that point.

5.2. Phase oscillations in circular accelerators. When alternating electric fields are employed in circular accelerators, the motion of an accelerated particle may be most easily described in terms of the deviation of its motion from a special synchronous motion in which the frequency of revolution of the particle is at each instant equal to the frequency of the applied electric fields. Let

$\omega_s(t)$ = the angular frequency of the applied electric fields at time t (1)

$r_s(t)$ = the value of the equilibrium radius $r_e(t)$ for which $\omega_e(t) = \omega_s(t)$ at each instant t (2)

$$H_s(t) = H_z(r_s, 0; t) \tag{3}$$

$$E_s(t) = |Z| \, ecH_s/\omega_s \tag{4}$$

$$\vartheta_s(t) = \int_0^t \omega_s(t) dt \tag{5}$$

$$\Delta E_s = \frac{2\pi}{\omega_s} \cdot \frac{dE_s}{dt} \tag{6}$$

$$\mathcal{E} = V/2\pi r_s \tag{7}$$

$L_s = \dfrac{4\pi}{3} \dfrac{|Z|^2 e^2}{r_s^2} \left(\dfrac{E_s}{m_0 c^2} \right)^4$ = energy loss of particle per revolution due to radiation (8)

ϵ_s = tangential component of induced electric field at the synchronous radius $r_s(t)$ due to changing magnetic flux (9)

Then the synchronous phase $\phi_s(t)$ is defined by the equation

$$|Z| \, eV \sin \phi_s = \Delta E_s + L_s - 2\pi r_s |Z| \, e\epsilon_s \tag{10}$$

When the accelerating particle is not following the synchronous orbit, (but follows an adiabatically varying equilibrium orbit) let its energy at time t be $E_e(t)$ and the corresponding equilibrium radius be $r_e(t)$; also let

$$H_e(t) = H_z(r_e, 0; t) \tag{11}$$

$$\omega_e(t) = |Z| \, ecH_e/E_e \tag{12}$$

If the azimuth of the particle at time t is $\vartheta_e(t)$, then

$$\omega_e(t) = d\vartheta_e/dt \tag{13}$$

The phase $\phi(t)$ of the particle is then defined by

$$\phi = \vartheta_e - \vartheta_s + \alpha \tag{14}$$

where α is a constant. The constant α may always be so chosen that the energy gain per revolution of the particle due to the alternating electric fields can be written as

$$|Z|\, eV \sin\phi \tag{15}$$

where $|Z|\, eV$ is the maximum energy gain per revolution.

Then the following relations hold.

$$\frac{d\phi}{dt} = \omega_e - \omega_s \tag{16}$$

$$\frac{d}{dt}\left[\frac{E_s}{\omega_s^2 K_s}\frac{d\phi}{dt}\right] + \frac{L'_s c^2}{2\pi(1-n_s)r_s\omega_s^3}\frac{d\phi}{dt} + \frac{|Z|\, eV}{2\pi}\sin\phi = \frac{|Z|\, eV}{2\pi}\sin\phi_s \tag{17}$$

where

$$L'_s = \partial L_s/\partial r_s, \quad n_s = n(r_s; t), \quad K_s = 1 + \frac{n_s}{1-n_s}\cdot\frac{c^2}{r_s^2\omega_s^2} \tag{18}$$

Equation (17) is the fundamental equation governing the variation of the phase of the particle with time. Once the phase of the particle is known, its equilibrium angular frequency is determined by Eq. (16); its equilibrium energy is given by

$$E_e(t) = E_s(t)\left[1 - \frac{1}{K_s\omega_s}\frac{d\phi}{dt}\right] \tag{19}$$

and its equilibrium radius can then be determined from Eq. (12).

A first integral of Eq. (17) can be easily obtained when the slow variation of $E_s/\omega_s^2 K_s$, ϕ_s, and possibly V with time is neglected together with the radiation loss term. The first integral is then

$$\left(\frac{d\phi}{dt}\right)^2 = \frac{|Z|\, eV\omega_s^2 K_s}{\pi E_s}[U(\phi_m) - U(\phi)] \tag{20}$$

where $$U(\phi) = -[\cos\phi + \phi\sin\phi_s]$$

and ϕ_m is a constant of integration determined by the initial conditions for the motion and representing the maximum value of the phase of the particle.

The condition for phase-stable motion (motion in which the phase of the particle performs stable oscillations about the synchronous phase, the equilibrium energy of the particle performs stable oscillations about the synchronous energy, and the equilibrium radius performs stable oscillations about the synchronous radius) is

$$\phi_s \leqslant \phi_m < \pi - \phi_s \tag{21}$$

The corresponding initial conditions are that the initial phase ϕ_0 and the initial $(d\phi/dt)_0$ lie within closed curve in the $(\phi, d\phi/dt)$ plane obtained by plotting Eq. (20) with ϕ_m equal to $\pi - \phi_s$.

The frequency of small phase oscillations about the synchronous orbit is given by

$$\omega_\phi = \left[\frac{|Z| \, eVK_s \cos\phi_s}{2\pi E_s}\right]^{1/2} \omega_s \tag{22}$$

When E_s, ω_s, V, and K_s vary adiabatically, the corresponding variations in the amplitude of small oscillation of ϕ, E_e, and r_e are given by

$$(\phi - \phi_s)_{\max} \propto [K_s\omega_s^2/VE_s \cos\phi_s]^{1/4} \tag{23}$$

$$(E_e - E_s)_{\max} \propto [VE_s\omega_s^2 \cos\phi_s/K_s]^{1/4} \tag{24}$$

$$(r_e - r_s)_{\max} \propto \left[\frac{1}{\omega_s r_s(1 - n_s)}(V \cos\phi_s/E_s^3 K_s \omega_s^2)\right]^{1/4} \tag{25}$$

Radiation losses by the accelerated particle can lead to further damping of the oscillations.

5.3. Phase motion in linear accelerators. The motion of an accelerated particle in a linear accelerator employing traveling wave acceleration or its equivalent is most easily described in terms of the deviation of the motion from a special synchronous motion in which the velocity of the particle is at each point equal to the phase velocity of the traveling wave at that point. Let

$v_s(x) =$ phase velocity of the traveling wave at a distance x along the accelerator (1)

$\omega =$ angular frequency of the traveling wave (2)

$$t_s(x) = \int_0^x dx/v_s(x) \tag{3}$$

$$E_s(x) = m_0c^2[1 - v_s^2/c^2]^{-1/2} \tag{4}$$

and define ϕ_s by $|Z| \, e\mathcal{E} \sin\phi_s = dE_s/dx$ (5)

For an accelerating particle not following the synchronous motion, let

$$t(x) = \text{time at which particle reaches the point } x \tag{6}$$

$$v(x) = 1/[dt(x)/dx] \tag{7}$$

$$E(x) = m_0c^2[1 - v^2/c^2]^{-1/2} \tag{8}$$

$$\phi(x) = \omega[t(x) - t_s(x)] + \alpha \tag{9}$$

where the constant α can always be chosen so that

$$dE/dx = |Z| e\mathcal{E} \sin\phi \tag{10}$$

with $\mathcal{E} =$ electric field amplitude of the (equivalent) traveling wave. Then

$$\frac{d\phi}{dx} = \omega\left[\frac{1}{v} - \frac{1}{v_s}\right] \tag{11}$$

and

$$E(x) = m_0 \left[1 - \left(\frac{c}{v_s} + \frac{c}{\omega}\frac{d\phi}{dx}\right)^{-2}\right]^{-1/2} \tag{12}$$

The fundamental equation governing the motion of the phase is

$$\left.\begin{aligned}\frac{d}{dx}\left\{ m_0c^2\left[1 - \left(\frac{c}{v_s} + \frac{c}{\omega}\frac{d\phi}{dx}\right)^{-2}\right]^{-1/2} - m_0c^2\left(1 - \frac{v_s^2}{c^2}\right)^{-1/2}\right\} \\ = |Z| e\mathcal{E}\sin\phi - |Z| e\mathcal{E}\sin\phi_s\end{aligned}\right\} \tag{13}$$

Special cases

Case I. $v_s \ll c$ (heavy-particle accelerators). In this case the phase equation reduces to

$$\frac{d}{dx}\left[\left(\frac{v_s}{c}\right)^3\left(\frac{E_s}{m_0c}\right)^2\frac{cE_s}{\omega}\cdot\frac{d\phi}{dx}\right] + |Z| e\mathcal{E}\sin\phi = |Z| e\mathcal{E}\sin\phi_s \tag{14}$$

In case the slow variation of v_s, E_s, and (possibly) $\mathcal{E}$ with x is neglected, a first integral of this equation is

$$\left(\frac{d\phi}{dx}\right)^2 = \frac{2|Z| e\mathcal{E}\omega}{cE_s(v_s/c)^3(E_s/m_0c^2)^2}[U(\phi_m) - U(\phi)] \tag{15}$$

where U and ϕ_m have the same meaning as in § 5.2.

The condition for phase-stable motion is again

$$\phi_s \leqslant \phi_m < \pi - \phi_s \tag{16}$$

and the corresponding initial conditions are the same again as in § 5.2. The frequency of small phase oscillations about the synchronous orbit is given by

$$\omega_\phi = \left[\frac{c^2 |Z| e\mathcal{E}\cos\phi_s}{\omega E_s v_s(E_s/m_0c^2)^2}\right]^{1/2}\omega \tag{17}$$

When v_s, E_s, and $\mathcal{E}$ vary adiabatically, the corresponding variation in the amplitude of oscillation of ϕ is given by

$$(\phi - \phi_s)_{\max} \propto (v_s^2 E_s^3 \, \mathcal{E} \cos \phi_s)^{-1/4} \tag{18}$$

Case II. $v_s = c$, $(c - v) \ll c$. In this case $\phi_s = 0$ and the phase equation reduces to

$$m_0 c^2 \left(\frac{\omega}{2c}\right)^{1/2} \left(\frac{d\phi}{dx}\right)^{-3/2} \frac{d^2\phi}{dx^2} + 2 \mid Z \mid e\mathcal{E} \sin \phi = 0 \tag{19}$$

If $\mathcal{E}$ does not vary along the accelerator, a first integral of this equation is

$$m_0 c^2 \left(\frac{\omega}{2c}\right)^{1/2} \left[\left(\frac{d\phi}{dx}\right)^{1/2} - \left(\frac{d\phi}{dx}\right)_0^{1/2}\right] = \mid Z \mid e\mathcal{E}(\cos \phi - \cos \phi_0) \tag{20}$$

where $(d\phi/dx)_0$ and ϕ_0 are the initial values of $d\phi/dx$ and ϕ, respectively.

Expressed in terms of energies the first integral is

$$E = E_0 \left[1 + \frac{2 \mid Z \mid c\mathcal{E}E_0}{m_0{}^2 c^3 \omega} (\cos \phi - \cos \phi_0)\right]^{-1} \tag{21}$$

where E_0 is the initial energy.

6. Injection and Focusing

The considerations involved in providing appropriate particle injection and adequate focusing vary so greatly among different types of accelerators that no adequate summary in a brief space is possible. Reference should be made to the literature for information on these questions.

7. Additional Remarks about Special Accelerators

7.1. The conventional cyclotron. This is a circular accelerator for heavy particles with spiral particle trajectories, employing a time constant magnetic field and impulsive acceleration at constant frequency. The phase-stability principle is not employed but the acceleration process is terminated before decelerating phases are reached. This limits attainable energies except by the use of excessive accelerating voltages. The starting phase of the particles is effectively 90°. The output is practically continuous.

7.2. The betatron. This is a circular accelerator for electrons with particle trajectories confined to an annular region and employing induction acceleration only. The same time-varying magnetic field is commonly employed to provide both the magnetic guiding field and the induction acceleration. To maintain the equilibrium radius constant, the following well-known "*two-to-one*" *condition* must be met.

$$\frac{dF_e}{dt} = 2\pi r_e^2 \frac{dH_e}{dt} \tag{1}$$

where F_e is the magnetic flux through the equilibrium orbit and H_e is the magnetic field at the equilibrium radius r_e. The attainable energies are limited by energy loss of the accelerating electrons due to radiation. The betatron is most commonly used to produce a pulsed output of x rays.

7.3. The synchrotron. This is a circular accelerator, at present employed for accelerating electrons (although construction of proton synchrotrons is underway) with particle trajectories confined to an annular region and employing a combination of induction and impulsive electric acceleration. A time-varying magnetic field is used, together with constant or time-varying radio frequency accelerating electric fields. The principle of phase stability is employed, allowing very high energies to be attained, although the ultimate attainable electron energies will probably be limited by inability to compensate radiation losses. The synchrotron is at present mainly used for the production of a pulsed output of high energy x rays.

7.4. The synchrocyclotron or frequency modulated cyclotron. This is a circular accelerator for heavy particles with spiral (synchronous) particle trajectories employing varying frequency impulsive electric acceleration in a time constant magnetic guide field. The principle of phase stability is employed to attain high energies limited at present only by practical considerations. The output is pulsed and has an average value considerably smaller than that of a conventional cyclotron. The accelerated particles are also much more difficult to remove from the machine than in the conventional cyclotron.

7.5. Linear accelerators. Linear accelerators employing impulsive electric or traveling-wave acceleration are employed for accelerating both electrons and heavy particles. Individual designs vary considerably. Present attainable energies for linear heavy particle accelerators are limited by electric defocusing or by the devices (grids) employed to avoid the defocusing.

Bibliography

General

The Acceleration of Particles to High Energies (based on a session arranged by the Electronic Group at the Institute of Physics Convention, May 1949), *Physics in Industry Series,* Institute of Physics, London, 1950. This volume contains extensive lists of further references.

HALLIDAY, D., *Introductory Nuclear Physics,* John Wiley & Sons, Inc., New York, 1950, Chap. 7. The chapter contains a general, and in some cases detailed description of various types of particle accelerators, including design features.

The Cyclotron

LIVINGSTON, M. S., *J. Appl. Phys.,* **15**, 2, 128 (1944).

MANN, W. B., *The Cyclotron,* 3d ed., Methuen & Co., Ltd., London, 1948.

The Synchrocyclotron

BOHM, D. and FOLDY, L. L., *Phys. Rev.,* **72**, 649 (1947).

PICKAVANCE, T. G., *Progress in Nuclear Physics,* Butterworth's Scientific Publications, Ltd., London, 1950.

The Betatron

KERST, D. W. and SERBER, R., *Phys. Rev.,* **60**, 53 (1941).

The Synchrotron

BOHM, D. and FOLDY, L. L., *Phys. Rev.,* **70**, 249 (1946).

OLIPHANT, M. L., GOODEN, J. S. and HIDE, G. S., *Proc. Phys. Soc.* (London), **59**, 666, 677 (1947).

Electrostatic Generators

VAN DE GRAAFF, R. J., TRUMP, J. G. and BUECHNER, W. W., *Reports on Progress in Physics,* **11**, 1 (1946-1947).

Linear Accelerators

FRY, D. W. and WALKINSHAW, W., *Reports on Progress in Physics,* **12**, 102 (1948-1949).

SLATER, J. C., *Revs. Modern Phys.,* **20**, 473 (1948).

Chapter 25

SOLID STATE

By Conyers Herring
Bell Telephone Laboratories

Introduction

This chapter attempts to cover the fields that are of most interest in connection with contemporary basic research in solid-state physics, omitting, however, fields such as electron emission, optics, and ferromagnetism, which fall naturally in the domain of other chapters of the book. Since a major part of our theoretical knowledge of solid state physics is based on approximate models, the choice of formulas for inclusion had to be based on the author's guesses of the durability of present concepts and of their utility to research workers while they last. Such considerations, for example, prompted omission of much of the detailed lore of the electron theory of metals, but inclusion of similar material relating to semiconductors. The sections are arranged as follows : Section 1 introduces some mathematical concepts that are used in a number of places later in the chapter; Sections 2 through 5 deal with formulas in which a solid is treated as a continuum; Sections 6 through 8 deal with formulas involving the atomic but not the electronic structure of solids; Sections 9 and 10 deal with free electrons; Section 11 contains miscellaneous isolated formulas from all these areas. Most of the subsections contain references to publications where derivations and more detailed expositions of the formulas can be found; these of course do not usually represent the original source of the formulas, but have been selected as sources most likely to be accessible and convenient for the reader. The formulas presented here are not always identical with those in the references, however, since it sometimes seemed expedient to introduce minor generalizations and refinements.

1. Crystal Mathematics

1.1. Translations. In any crystal there exists a set of translations $\boldsymbol{t}_i$ such that the environment of any point $\boldsymbol{r}$ in the crystal is identical with that of the point $\boldsymbol{r} + \boldsymbol{t}_i$. These translations form an additive group of infinite order called the *translation group* of the crystal. There always exists a set of three translation vectors $\boldsymbol{t}_1$, $\boldsymbol{t}_2$, $\boldsymbol{t}_3$ (not necessarily unique, however) such that for any $\boldsymbol{t}_i$

$$\boldsymbol{t}_i = l_i\boldsymbol{t}_1 + m_i\boldsymbol{t}_2 + n_i\boldsymbol{t}_3, \quad (l_i, m_i, n_i \text{ integers})$$

These are called *fundamental translations.*

1.2. The unit cell and the *s* sphere. A *unit cell* is defined as any region of space R with the two properties :

a. Region R does not overlap any of the regions resulting from displacement of it by a translation vector $\boldsymbol{t}_i$.

b. Region R and these translated regions fill all space. There are many possible shapes for a unit cell; one of the most convenient ways of constructing a unit cell is to let R consist of all the points reachable from the origin without crossing any of the planes which are perpendicular bisectors of the various $\boldsymbol{t}_i$. The volume Ω of a unit cell is always that of the parallelepiped formed by any three fundamental translations.

$$\Omega = \boldsymbol{t}_1 \cdot \boldsymbol{t}_2 \times \boldsymbol{t}_3 \tag{1}$$

For crystals whose atoms all occupy equivalent positions a concept useful in some types of theoretical work is that of the *s*-sphere, defined as a sphere centered on an atom and having a volume equal to the volume per atom of the crystal.

The following table gives, for some of the commoner crystal structures, values of the volume Ω of the unit cell, the number S of atoms per unit cell, the radius r_s of the *s*-sphere, and the half-distance $r_{\min}$ between nearest neighbor atoms.

Lattice type	Parameters	Ω	S	r_s	$r_{\min}$
Body-centered cubic	Cube-side d	$d^3/2$	1	$\sqrt[3]{(3/8\pi)}d = 0.49237d$	$(\sqrt{3}/4)d = 0.43301d$
Face-centered cubic	Cube-side d	$d^3/4$	1	$\sqrt[3]{(3/16\pi)}d = 0.39080d$	$(\sqrt{2}/4)d = 0.35355d$
Diamond type	Cube-side d	$d^3/4$	2	$\sqrt[3]{(3/32\pi)}d = 0.31017d$	$(\sqrt{3}/8)d = 0.21651d$
Close-packed hexagonal	Fundamental translations a in basal plane, c along hexagonal axis	$\frac{1}{2}\sqrt{3}\,ca^2$	2	$\sqrt[3]{(3^{3/2}/16\pi)}\sqrt[3]{ca^2} = 0.46932a\sqrt[3]{c/a}$	$a/2$ if $c/a > \sqrt{8/3}$, $\frac{1}{2}\sqrt{a^2/3 + c^2/4}$ if $c/a < \sqrt{8/3}$
Ideal case of close-packed hexagonal	Same with $c/a = \sqrt{8/3}$	$\sqrt{2}a^3$	2	$\sqrt[3]{(3/2^{5/2}\pi)}a = 0.55267a$	$a/2$

1.3. The reciprocal lattice. If $\boldsymbol{t}_1$, $\boldsymbol{t}_2$, $\boldsymbol{t}_3$ are any three fundamental translation vectors of a given crystal lattice, the vectors $\boldsymbol{g}_1$, $\boldsymbol{g}_2$, $\boldsymbol{g}_3$ defined by

$$\boldsymbol{g}_1 = \frac{\boldsymbol{t}_2 \times \boldsymbol{t}_3}{\boldsymbol{t}_1 \cdot \boldsymbol{t}_2 \times \boldsymbol{t}_3}, \quad \boldsymbol{g}_2 = \frac{\boldsymbol{t}_3 \times \boldsymbol{t}_1}{\boldsymbol{t}_1 \cdot \boldsymbol{t}_2 \times \boldsymbol{t}_3}, \quad \boldsymbol{g}_3 = \frac{\boldsymbol{t}_1 \times \boldsymbol{t}_2}{\boldsymbol{t}_1 \cdot \boldsymbol{t}_2 \times \boldsymbol{t}_3} \tag{1}$$

are called fundamental translations of the corresponding *reciprocal lattice*, and the reciprocal lattice itself is defined as the set of all vectors of the form

$$\boldsymbol{g}_j = l_j \boldsymbol{g}_1 + m_j \boldsymbol{g}_2 + n_j \boldsymbol{g}_3, \quad (l_j, m_j, n_j \text{ integers}) \tag{2}$$

If $\boldsymbol{t}_i$ is any translation vector of the original lattice, $\boldsymbol{t}_i \cdot \boldsymbol{g}_j$ is an integer for any $\boldsymbol{g}_j$.

Any function of position which has the same periodicity properties as the original lattice can be written in the form of a Fourier series

$$\sum_j a_j \exp (2\pi i \boldsymbol{g}_j \cdot \boldsymbol{r})$$

and conversely any such series has the periodicity of the original lattice.

The unit cell contained within the perpendicular bisectors of the vectors $2\pi \boldsymbol{g}_j$ is called the *first Brillouin zone* (see also § 10.7).

1.4. Periodic boundary conditions. In problems involving wave motion, potentials, vibrations, etc., in crystals, the size of the region which must be studied is sometimes reduced to finite dimensions by imposition of periodic boundary conditions, a device which avoids the introduction of boundary surfaces where physical conditions differ from those in the rest of the crystal. This device consists in requiring that in an infinite crystal all physical properties be trebly periodic with the periods $G_1\boldsymbol{t}_1$, $G_2\boldsymbol{t}_2$, $G_3\boldsymbol{t}_3$, where $\boldsymbol{t}_1$, $\boldsymbol{t}_2$, $\boldsymbol{t}_3$ are fundamental translations of the crystal lattice, and G_1, G_2, G_3 are three very large integers. Thus specification of physical conditions over the volume v of the parallelepiped formed by $G_1\boldsymbol{t}_1$, $G_2\boldsymbol{t}_2$, $G_3\boldsymbol{t}_3$—called the *fundamental volume*—specifies conditions throughout all space.

Any function of position satisfying the periodic boundary conditions can be expanded into a Fourier series of the form $\Sigma_\nu A_\nu \exp (i\boldsymbol{k}_\nu \cdot \boldsymbol{r})$, where the vectors $\boldsymbol{k}_\nu$ run over a closely spaced lattice of points in the space of the reciprocal lattice, the allowed values of the $\boldsymbol{k}_\nu$ being simply 2π times the vectors of the lattice reciprocal to that of $G_1\boldsymbol{t}_1$, $G_2\boldsymbol{t}_2$, $G_3\boldsymbol{t}_3$. The number of $\boldsymbol{k}_\nu$ per unit volume $\Delta k_x \Delta k_y \Delta k_z$ of k-space is

$$\rho = \frac{v}{8\pi^3} \tag{1}$$

and the number lying within the first Brillouin zone (see § 1.3) is $N = v/\Omega$, the number of unit cells in the fundamental volume.

2. Elastic Constants

2.1. Stress and strain components. The components of the stress-tensor $p_{\mu\nu}$ and the symmetrical part of the strain-tensor $u_{\mu\nu}$ can each be designated by a single suffix running from 1 to 6, thus :

$$p_1 = p_{xx}, p_2 = p_{yy}, p_3 = p_{zz}, p_4 = p_{yz} = p_{zy}, p_5 = p_{xz} = p_{zx}, p_6 = p_{xy} = p_{yx};$$

$$u_1 = u_{xx}, u_2 = u_{yy}, u_3 = u_{zz}, u_4 = u_{yz} + u_{zy}, u_5 = u_{xz} + u_{zx}, u_6 = u_{xy} + u_{yx}$$

We shall use the sign convention that p_{xx} is positive for a tensile stress.

Since relations involving the p's and u's depend on the orientation of the coordinate axes relative to the crystal lattice, it is customary in elasticity and piezoelectricity to use " natural " crystallographic axes, conventions for which have been laid down by the Piezoelectric Crystals Committee of the IRE (Ref. 11). According to these conventions, the x, y, and z axes always form a right-handed system. For crystals of the cubic system these axes are to be chosen parallel to axes of fourfold symmetry, or if such are lacking, to axes of twofold symmetry. For crystals of the trigonal and hexagonal systems the z axis is to be chosen along the three- or sixfold axis, the x axis along a twofold axis or perpendicular to a plane of symmetry if either exists; when the latter criterion does not suffice to locate the x direction uniquely in any 60° sector, it is to be chosen in the direction of one of the shortest fundamental translations. For crystals of lower symmetry, Ref. 11 should be consulted.

2.2. Elastic constants and moduli. The *elastic constants* c_{ij} are defined by

$$p_i = \sum_{j=i}^{6} c_{ij} u_j \tag{1}$$

in any elastic deformation. The numerical values of the c_{ij} may depend on the nature of the auxiliary constraints under which the elastic deformation is carried out (e.g., adiabatic or isothermal conditions, etc.). Energetic considerations require the matrix c_{ij} to be symmetrical ($= c_{ji}$) and positive definite (see § 2.5 for analytical expressions of this criterion).

The *elastic moduli* or *compliance coefficients* s_{ij} are the components of the matrix reciprocal to that of the elastic constants, so that

$$u_i = \sum_{j=1}^{6} s_{ij} p_j \tag{2}$$

The matrix s_{ij} is also symmetrical and positive definite.

2.3. Forms of c_{ij} or s_{ij} for some common crystal classes (Refs. 14 and 27). With the "natural" crystallographic axes described in § 2.1, the restrictions imposed by crystal symmetry enable the values of c_{ij} for arbitrary indexes, i and j to be expressed in terms of a small number of independent components, thus :

Cubic system

$$ij \quad \begin{matrix} c_{11} & c_{12} & c_{12} & 0 & 0 & 0 \\ & c_{11} & c_{12} & 0 & 0 & 0 \\ & & c_{11} & 0 & 0 & 0 \\ & & & c_{44} & 0 & 0 \\ & & & & c_{44} & 0 \\ & & & & & c_{44} \end{matrix}$$

Hexagonal system

$$ij \quad \begin{matrix} c_{11} & c_{12} & c_{13} & 0 & 0 & 0 \\ & c_{11} & c_{13} & 0 & 0 & 0 \\ & & c_{33} & 0 & 0 & 0 \\ & & & c_{44} & 0 & 0 \\ & & & & c_{44} & 0 \\ & & & & & \frac{1}{2}(c_{11} - c_{12}) \end{matrix}$$

Isotropic body

$$ij \quad \begin{matrix} \lambda + 2\mu & \lambda & \lambda & 0 & 0 & 0 \\ & \lambda + 2\mu & \lambda & 0 & 0 & 0 \\ & & \lambda + 2\mu & 0 & 0 & 0 \\ & & & \mu & 0 & 0 \\ & & & & \mu & 0 \\ & & & & & \mu \end{matrix}$$

For the corresponding matrices for crystals of lower symmetry see Refs. 14 and 27. The corresponding matrices of the elastic moduli for cubic and hexagonal crystals are obtained by simply substituting s's for c's in the above, except that the coefficient of $(s_{11} - s_{12})$ in the 66 position for hexagonal crystals is 2 instead of $\frac{1}{2}$.

2.4. Relation of elastic constants and moduli. For cubic crystals

$$c_{11} = \frac{s_{11} + s_{12}}{(s_{11} - s_{12})(s_{11} + 2s_{12})}, \quad c_{12} = \frac{-s_{12}}{(s_{11} - s_{12})(s_{11} + 2s_{12})}, \quad c_{44} = \frac{1}{s_{44}} \tag{1}$$

For hexagonal crystals, with $D = (s_{11} + s_{12})s_{33} - 2s_{13}^2$,

$$\left.\begin{aligned} c_{11} &= \frac{s_{11}s_{33} - s_{13}^2}{D(s_{11} - s_{12})}, \quad c_{12} = \frac{s_{13}^2 - s_{12}s_{33}}{D(s_{11} - s_{12})} \\ c_{13} &= \frac{-s_{13}}{D}, \quad c_{33} = \frac{s_{11} + s_{12}}{D}, \quad c_{44} = \frac{1}{s_{44}} \end{aligned}\right\} \tag{2}$$

All these equations remain valid if s's and c's are interchanged.

2.5. Forms taken by the condition of positive definiteness, for some common crystal classes. For cubic crystals,

$$c_{44} > 0, \quad c_{11} > | c_{12} |, \quad c_{11} + 2c_{12} > 0$$

For hexagonal crystals,

$$c_{44} > 0, \quad c_{11} > | c_{12} |, \quad (c_{11} + c_{12})c_{33} > 2c_{13}^2$$

The elastic moduli s_{ij} satisfy identical inequalities.

2.6. Relation of c_{ij} and s_{ij} to other elastic constants (Ref. 14). The volume compressibility κ, is given by

$$\kappa = \sum_{ij=1}^{3} s_{ij} \tag{1}$$

For a specimen of a cubic substance whose long axis has direction cosines α, β, γ, with respect to the crystal axes, Young's modulus E is given by

$$E = (s_{11} - 2s\Gamma)^{-1} \tag{2}$$

where $s = s_{11} - s_{12} - \frac{1}{2}s_{44}, \quad \Gamma = \alpha^2\beta^2 + \alpha^2\gamma^2 + \beta^2\gamma^2$

The longitudinal linear compressibility is

$$\kappa^{(l)} = s_{11} + 2s_{12} = \kappa/3 \tag{3}$$

If such a specimen has a circular cross section, the mean shear modulus, as measured for example in simple torsion, is

$$G = (s_{44} + 4s\Gamma)^{-1} \tag{4}$$

For a specimen of a hexagonal substance whose long axis makes an angle θ with the hexagonal axis, Young's modulus is

$$E = [s_{11} \sin^4 \theta + s_{33} \cos^4 \theta + (2s_{13} + s_{44}) \cos^2 \theta \sin^2 \theta]^{-1} \tag{5}$$

and the longitudinal linear compressibility is

$$\kappa^{(l)} = s_{11} + s_{12} + s_{13} - (s_{11} - s_{33} + s_{12} - s_{13}) \cos^2 \theta \tag{6}$$

If the cross section is circular, the mean shear modulus is

$$G = [s_{44} + (s_{11} - s_{12} - \tfrac{1}{2}s_{44}) \sin^2 \theta + 2(s_{11} + s_{33} - 2s_{13} - s_{44}) \cos^2 \theta \sin^2 \theta]^{-1} \tag{7}$$

2.7. Thermodynamic relations (Refs. 16 and 27). Let the superscripts *ad* and *is* denote, respectively, adiabatic and isothermal coefficients, let T be the absolute temperature, let $u_i (i = 1 \text{ to } 6)$ be the strain components as defined in § 2.1, and let $\alpha_i = \partial u_i/\partial T$ at zero stress be a generalized expansion coefficient. Then

$$c_{ij}^{(ad)} = c_{ij}^{(is)} + \sum_{r,s=1}^{6} \frac{c_{ir}^{(is)} c_{js}^{(is)} \alpha_r \alpha_s T v}{C_v}, \quad s_{ij}^{(ad)} = s_{ij}^{(is)} - \frac{\alpha_i \alpha_j T}{C_p} \tag{1}$$

where v is the volume and C_v and C_p the constant volume and constant pressure heat capacities, respectively, of a standard amount of the crystalline material (e.g., 1 mole). For cubic crystals the adiabatic and isothermal shear constants are identical, while the volume compressibilities κ satisfy

$$\kappa^{(ad)} = \kappa^{(is)} - \frac{9v\alpha^2 T}{C_p} \tag{2}$$

where $\alpha = \alpha_1$ is the linear expansion coefficient.

3. Dielectrics and Piezoelectricity

3.1. Piezoelectric constants (Refs. 5 and 16). Let p_i, $u_i (i = 1$ to $6)$ be, respectively, the stress and strain components as defined in § 2.1. Let E_α, P_α ($\alpha = 1$ to 3) be the components of electric field and electric polarization, respectively. The *piezoelectric constants* or *stress coefficients* $e_{\alpha i}$ and the *piezoelectric moduli* or *strain coefficients* $d_{\alpha i}$ are defined by

$$e_{\alpha i} = \left(\frac{\partial P_\alpha}{\partial u_i}\right)_E = -\left(\frac{\partial p_i}{\partial E_\alpha}\right)_{u's} \tag{1}$$

$$d_{\alpha i} = \left(\frac{\partial P_\alpha}{\partial p_i}\right)_E = \left(\frac{\partial u_i}{\partial E_\alpha}\right)_{p's} \tag{2}$$

If the temperature is held constant in the differentiations just written, these equations define the *isothermal* constants and moduli; if the entropy is kept constant, they define the *adiabatic* quantities. In either case

$$d_{\alpha i} = \sum_{j=1}^{6} s_{ji} e_{\alpha j}, \quad e_{\alpha j} = \sum_{i=1}^{6} c_{ij} d_{\alpha i} \tag{3}$$

where c_{ij}, s_{ji} are the elastic constants and moduli, respectively (see § 2.2), defined for the case $E = 0$, and isothermal or adiabatic according to whether the piezoelectric quantities are isothermal or adiabatic, respectively.

The equalities of the partial derivatives used in the above definitions of $e_{\alpha i}$ and $d_{\alpha i}$ are exact when the initial state of the crystal is one with $P = E = 0$, as is normally the case in work with crystals without a permanent polarization; for this case the stresses p_i represent simply the stresses imposed on the crystal by external tractions or inertial reactions. When the derivatives are evaluated for states with finite fields, as is the case for crystals with a permanent moment, the equations as written are not exactly correct, although usually only a negligible error is involved in using them, with the p_i interpreted in the manner just mentioned. The equations can be made exactly correct for this case by replacing $(\partial P_\alpha/\partial u_i)_E$ and $(\partial P_\alpha/\partial p_i)_E$ by $(1/v)[\partial(vP_\alpha)/\partial u_i]_E$ and $(1/v)[\partial(vP_\alpha)/\partial p_i]_E$, respectively, where v is the volume of the crystal, and interpreting the stresses p_i as the set whose surface tractions and body forces equal the difference of the mechanically imposed forces and the tractions and body forces due to the Maxwellian field-stress tensor

$$p_{\alpha\beta}^{(f)} = \frac{E_\alpha D_\beta}{4\pi} - \frac{E^2\delta_{\alpha\beta}}{8\pi} \tag{4}$$

Many other equally valid sets of definitions and formulas can of course be given.

3.2. Dielectric constants (Refs. 5 and 16). The *dielectric constant tensor* $\epsilon_{\alpha\beta}$ and the *susceptibility tensor* $\eta_{\alpha\beta}$ are ordinarily defined as

$$\eta_{\alpha\beta} = \frac{\partial P_\alpha}{\partial E_\beta} \tag{1}$$

$$\epsilon_{\alpha\beta} = \delta_{\alpha\beta} + 4\pi\eta_{\alpha\beta} = \frac{\partial D_\alpha}{\partial E_\beta} \tag{2}$$

For piezoelectric crystals different susceptibilities and dielectric constants result according to whether the derivatives are evaluated at constant strain (clamped crystal) or at constant stress (free crystal), and for pyroelectric crystals the isothermal and adiabatic values are different (see § 3.5). These different kinds of susceptibilities and dielectric constants will be denoted by superscripts designating which of the quantities u (strain) and p (stress) are to be kept constant, and *ad* or *is* for adiabatic or isothermal conditions.

Relations exactly valid for crystals without a permanent polarization (derivatives evaluated at $E = P = 0$) and approximately valid even for those with a permanent moment are

$$\epsilon_{\alpha\beta} = \epsilon_{\beta\alpha}, \quad \eta_{\alpha\beta} = \eta_{\beta\alpha}, \quad \text{(for any set of conditions)}$$

$$\epsilon_{\alpha\beta}^{(p)} = \epsilon_{\alpha\beta}^{(u)} + 4\pi \sum_{i=1}^{6} e_{\alpha i} d_{\beta i} \tag{3}$$

the last equation being valid when either isothermal or adiabatic quantities are used throughout.

For crystals with a permanent polarization $\eta^{(p)}_{\alpha\beta}$ is not in general exactly equal to $\eta^{(p)}_{\beta\alpha}$, though the difference is usually small. However, if we define

$$\eta'^{(p)}_{\alpha\beta} = \frac{1}{v}\left[\frac{\partial(vP_\alpha)}{\partial E_\beta}\right]_{p's} \tag{4}$$

we have

$$\eta'^{(p)}_{\alpha\beta} = \eta'^{(p)}_{\beta\alpha} = \eta^{(u)}_{\alpha\beta} + \sum_{i=1}^{6} e_{\alpha i} d_{\beta i} \tag{5}$$

exactly.

3.3. Pyroelectricity and the electrocaloric effect (Ref. 5). The temperature derivatives $(\partial P_\alpha/\partial T)_{E,p's}$ of the components of the polarization vector P at constant (usually zero) field and stress are called *pyroelectric coefficients.* They are related to the *electrocaloric effect*: adiabatic application of an electric field E causes the temperature of a pyroelectric crystal to change by an amount measured by

$$\left(\frac{\partial T}{\partial E_\alpha}\right)_{S,p's} = -\frac{T[\partial(v_m P_\alpha)/\partial T]_{E,p's}}{C_p^{(E)}} \approx -\frac{Tv_m(\partial P_\alpha/\partial T)_{E,p's}}{C_p^{(E)}} \tag{1}$$

where v_m is the volume of a standard amount of material (e.g., a gram or a mole) and $C_p^{(E)}$ is the specific heat associated with the same amount of material, at constant stress and constant field E. Here as in § 3.1 the stresses p_i are for all practical purposes to be identified with the stresses applied by purely mechanical external forces, although rigorously they differ from these by small terms due to the Maxwell stresses.

3.4. Elastic constants of piezoelectric crystals (Ref. 5). The elastic constants c_{ij} and moduli s_{ij} of a piezoelectric crystal are defined, just as for ordinary crystals (see § 2.2), by

$$c_{ij} = \left(\frac{\partial p_i}{\partial u_j}\right) = c_{ji}, \quad s_{ij} = \left(\frac{\partial u_i}{\partial p_j}\right) = s_{ji} \tag{1}$$

where p_i, u_j represent respectively the stress and strain components as defined in § 2.1. This definition leads to several different elastic constants according to whether the differentiation is carried out under isothermal or adiabatic conditions and according to which of the electric field quantities E, D, P is held constant. These different elastic constants will be denoted by attaching as superscripts the symbols of the quantities to be held constant.

The relation of isothermal to adiabatic constants is as given in § 3.5. For either isothermal or adiabatic constants we have the relations, exactly true for materials without permanent polarization, and usually true to within a negligible error for permanently polarized substances,

$$\left.\begin{aligned} c_{ij}^{(D)} &= c_{ij}^{(E)} + 4\pi \sum_{\alpha,\beta=1}^{3} e_{\beta i}(\epsilon^{-1})_{\beta\alpha} e_{\alpha j} \\ s_{ij}^{(D)} &= s_{ij}^{(E)} - 4\pi \sum_{\alpha,\beta=1}^{3} d_{\beta i}(\epsilon^{-1})_{\beta\alpha} d_{\alpha j} \\ c_{ij}^{(P)} &= c_{ij}^{(E)} + \sum_{\alpha,\beta=1}^{3} e_{\beta i}(\eta^{-1})_{\beta\alpha} e_{\alpha j} \\ s_{ij}^{(P)} &= s_{ij}^{(E)} - \sum_{\alpha,\beta=1}^{3} d_{\beta i}(\eta^{-1})_{\beta\alpha} d_{\alpha j} \end{aligned}\right\} \quad (2)$$

where $(\epsilon^{-1})_{\beta\alpha}$, $(\eta^{-1})_{\beta\alpha}$ are the matrices reciprocal, respectively, to those of the dielectric constant $\epsilon_{\alpha\beta}$, and the susceptibilities $\eta_{\alpha\beta}$, and $e_{\alpha j}$, $d_{\beta i}$ are the piezoelectric constants and moduli as defined in § 3.1. The small errors in these equations for permanently polarized media are of the same order as the ambiguities introduced into the definitions of the elastic constants by the Maxwell stresses, i.e., by forces of electrostatic origin.

3.5. Relations of adiabatic and isothermal piezoelectric and dielectric constants (Ref. 16). For pyroelectric crystals there is a difference between the adiabatic and isothermal values of the piezoelectric and dielectric constants, as defined in § 3.1 and § 3.2, respectively. Using the superscripts *ad* and *is* to denote, respectively, adiabatic (constant entropy) and isothermal quantities, we have

$$d_{\alpha i}^{(ad)} = d_{\alpha i}^{(is)} - \left[\frac{\partial(v_m P_\alpha)}{\partial T}\right]_{E,p's} \frac{T(\partial u_i/\partial T)_{E,p's}}{C_p^{(E)}} \quad (1)$$

where v_m is the volume of a standard amount of material (e.g., a gram or a mole), $C_p^{(E)}$ is the specific heat associated with the same amount of material at constant stress and field, u_i is a strain component as defined in § 2.1, so that $(\partial u_i/\partial T)_{E,p's}$ is a generalized expansion coefficient, and the quantity in square brackets can usually be closely approximated by v_m times the pyroelectric coefficient $(\partial P_\alpha/\partial T)_{E,p's}$. For the dielectric constants the relation

$$\epsilon_{\alpha\beta}^{(p,ad)} = \epsilon_{\alpha\beta}^{(p,is)} - \frac{4\pi T v_m}{C_p^{(E)}}\left(\frac{\partial P_\alpha}{\partial T}\right)_{E,p's}\left(\frac{\partial P_\beta}{\partial T}\right)_{E,p's} \quad (2)$$

is ordinarily a very close approximation to the truth.

4. Conduction and Thermoelectricity

4.1. Conductivity tensor of a crystal. When Ohm's law is obeyed, the electric field $\boldsymbol{E}$ and current density $\boldsymbol{j}$ in a homogeneous crystal at constant temperature are related by

$$j_\alpha = \sum_\beta \sigma_{\alpha\beta} E_\beta \tag{1}$$

Similarly the heat flux $\boldsymbol{q}$ and the gradient of temperature T are related, in the absence of electric currents, by

$$q_\alpha = \sum_\beta \kappa_{\alpha\beta} \frac{\partial T}{\partial x_\beta} \tag{2}$$

The conductivity tensors have the symmetry of the crystal, and in the absence of magnetic fields Onsager's principle of microscopic reversibility requires that they satisfy in addition (Ref. 6)

$$\sigma_{\alpha\beta} = \sigma_{\beta\alpha}, \quad \kappa_{\alpha\beta} = \kappa_{\beta\alpha} \tag{3}$$

4.2. Matthiessen's rule. The presence of any sort of impurities or lattice imperfections usually increases the resistivity ρ of a metal above the value $\rho^{(0)}$ characteristic of a perfect crystal. In most cases it is found that over a considerable temperature range

$$\rho - \rho^{(0)} = \text{constant independent of temperature} \tag{1}$$

This is called *Matthiessens's rule.*

4.3. Thomson effect. When a current of density $\boldsymbol{j}$ (in direction of equivalent flows of positive charge) flows in homogeneous material in the presence of a temperature gradient, the rate q at which heat is developed per unit volume contains a term linear in $\boldsymbol{j}$ and ∇T.

$$q = \rho j^2 - \tau \boldsymbol{j} \cdot \nabla T \tag{1}$$

where ρ is the resistivity and τ is called the *Thomson coefficient.* For crystals of lower than cubic symmetry, τ, like ρ, must be replaced by a tensor.

4.4. Seebeck effect. The *absolute thermoelectric power* ϵ of any electronic conductor measures the emf set up by the presence of a temperature gradient in a homogeneous material, when the current density j vanishes. Explicitly, for a cubic or isotropic substance (Ref. 10),

$$e\epsilon = \left(\frac{d\bar{\mu}}{dT} \right)_{j=0} \tag{1}$$

where e is the magnitude of the electronic charge and $\bar{\mu}$ is the electrochemical potential or partial molar free energy per electron, which for metals (as opposed to semiconductors) is for all practical purposes a constant minus $e\Phi$, where Φ is the electrostatic potential. For metals the quantity ϵ obeys the thermodynamic relation (Refs. 7 and 10)

$$\epsilon = \int_0^T \frac{\tau}{T'} dT' \tag{2}$$

where τ is the Thomson coefficient (see § 4.3). In metals of lower than cubic symmetry this integral may be used as a definition of ϵ, with ϵ and τ replaced by tensors. For non-cubic semiconductors the ϵ-tensor is best defined by (1) and (2) of § 4.6

A thermocouple made of two electronic conductors A, B, with junctions at temperatures T_1, T_2, develops an emf (*Seebeck effect*)

$$\text{emf} = \int_{T_1}^{T_2} (\epsilon_A - \epsilon_B) dT' \tag{3}$$

If either conductor is of lower than cubic symmetry, the thermoelectric emf is in general dependent on the shape and orientation of the conductor; for a filamentary shape the expression just written can be used if each ϵ is interpreted as $\epsilon_{\alpha\alpha}$, where the α direction is along the filament.

4.5. Peltier effect. The *Peltier coefficient* $\Pi_{AB} = -\Pi_{BA}$ between two electronic conductors A, B, is defined as the heat developed at the junction of A and B per unit current (positive charge) flowing from B to A. It is given by (Ref. 7)

$$\Pi_{AB} = T(\epsilon_B - \epsilon_A) \tag{1}$$

where T is the absolute temperature of the junction and the ϵ's are thermoelectric powers as defined in § 4.4. In crystals of lower than cubic symmetry the ϵ's are of course tensors, and the heat developed per unit area is

$$T \sum_{\alpha,\beta=1}^{3} [(\epsilon_B)_{\alpha\beta}(j_B)_\alpha - (\epsilon_A)_{\alpha\beta}(j_A)_\alpha] n_\beta \tag{2}$$

where $\boldsymbol{j}_A$, $\boldsymbol{j}_B$ are the current densities in the two conductors, and $\boldsymbol{n}$ is the unit normal to the surface.

4.6. Entropy flow and Bridgman effect (Refs. 4 and 10). If $\epsilon_{\alpha\beta}$ is the absolute thermoelectric power tensor (see § 4.4) and $\boldsymbol{j}$ the electric current density (equivalent current of positive charge) in any conductor, the flow of current is accompanied by a reversible flux of entropy whose direction and magnitude (entropy per unit area per unit time) are given by the vector with components

$$\eta_\alpha = \sum_{\beta=1}^{3} \epsilon_{\beta\alpha} j_\beta \tag{1}$$

In an isothermal specimen

$$\boldsymbol{\eta} = \frac{1}{T}\left(\boldsymbol{W} + \frac{\bar{\mu}\boldsymbol{j}}{e}\right) \tag{2}$$

where $\boldsymbol{W}$ is the energy flux vector, $\bar{\mu}$ the electrochemical potential per electron, and e the magnitude of the electronic charge. Thus when the direction of $\boldsymbol{j}$ changes during passage of current through a crystal of lower than cubic symmetry, a heating or cooling analogous to the Peltier effect occurs, and is called the *Bridgman effect.*

4.7. Galvanomagnetic and thermomagnetic effects. Let $\boldsymbol{j}$, $\boldsymbol{q}$ be the vector densities of electric current and heat current, respectively, and let $\boldsymbol{H}$ be the magnetic field strength. Let $\boldsymbol{E}_t$, $\boldsymbol{\nabla}_t T$ be the projections of the electric field vector and the temperature gradient, respectively, on the plane normal to $\boldsymbol{j}$ or $\boldsymbol{q}$, whichever is nonvanishing. Then the Hall coefficient R, the Nernst coefficient Q, the Ettingshausen coefficient P, and the Righi-Leduc coefficient S are defined, respectively, by

Hall : $\boldsymbol{E}_t = R\boldsymbol{j} \times \boldsymbol{H}$
Nernst : $\boldsymbol{E}_t = Q\boldsymbol{\nabla}T \times \boldsymbol{H}$ under condition $\boldsymbol{j} = 0$
Ettingshausen : $\boldsymbol{\nabla}_t T = P\boldsymbol{j} \times \boldsymbol{H}$ under condition $\boldsymbol{j} \cdot \boldsymbol{\nabla}T = 0$, $\boldsymbol{q} = 0$
Righi-Leduc : $\boldsymbol{\nabla}_t T = S\boldsymbol{H} \times \boldsymbol{\nabla}T$ under condition $\boldsymbol{j} = 0$

These definitions may be used for substances of lower than cubic symmetry if $\boldsymbol{E}_t$, $\boldsymbol{\nabla}_t T$ are interpreted as the changes in these quantities when a magnetic field is applied; for such substances R, Q, P, S are in general functions of the directions of $\boldsymbol{H}$ and $\boldsymbol{j}$ or $\boldsymbol{q}$. We have the thermodynamic relation (Ref. 4)

$$P = TQ/\kappa \tag{1}$$

where κ is the thermal conductivity.

5. Superconductivity

5.1. The London equations (Ref. 13). According to F. and H. London the charge density ρ and current density $\boldsymbol{j}$ in superconducting matter can each be written as a sum of a " normal part (superscript n) and a " superconducting " part (superscript s), in such a way that

$$\frac{\partial \rho^{(n)}}{\partial t} + \boldsymbol{\nabla} \cdot \boldsymbol{j}^{(n)} = 0, \quad \frac{\partial \rho^{(s)}}{\partial t} + \boldsymbol{\nabla} \cdot \boldsymbol{j}^{(s)} = 0 \tag{1}$$

and at the same time

$$j^{(n)} = \sigma E, \quad \frac{\partial(\Lambda j^{(s)})}{\partial t} = E, \quad \nabla \times (\Lambda j^{(s)}) = -\frac{B}{c} \tag{2}$$

where E, B are, respectively, the electric field in esu and the magnetic induction in emu, c is the velocity of light, Λ is a temperature-dependent constant of the material with dimensions (time) ^{2}, and σ is a conductivity which is finite at all temperatures. In addition we have the Maxwell equations (see also Chapter 13),

$$\left.\begin{array}{c} \nabla \times E = -\frac{1}{c} \cdot \frac{\partial B}{\partial t}, \quad \nabla \times H = \frac{1}{c} \cdot \frac{\partial D}{\partial t} + \frac{4\pi(j^{(s)} + j^{(n)})}{c} \\ \nabla \cdot D = 4\pi\rho, \quad \nabla \cdot B = 0 \end{array}\right\} \tag{3}$$

It is customary to assume further that $D = \epsilon E$, $B = \mu H$, where ϵ and μ are practically unity.

5.2. Field distribution in a steady state (Ref. 13). When all field quantities are independent of time, the equations of § 5.1 lead to

$$E = 0, \quad \rho = \rho^{(n)} + \rho^{(s)} = 0 \tag{1}$$

When in addition the superconducting matter is homogeneous, so that Λ is constant, the vectors B, H, and $j = j^{(s)}$ all obey the differential equation

$$\nabla^2 F = F/\lambda^2 \tag{2}$$

where $\lambda = c\sqrt{\Lambda/4\pi}$ is a temperature-dependent length known as the *penetration depth.* In a superconducting specimen of dimensions $\gg \lambda$ all these field quantities become practically zero in the deep interior, and near the surface are of the form

$$F = \text{tangential vector} \times e^{-z/\lambda}$$

where z is the depth beneath the surface.

Any steady-state solution of the equations of § 5.1 is uniquely determined within a superconducting body by the values, over the surface of the body, of the tangential component of H or of the tangential component of j.

5.3. The energy equation (Ref. 13). In any isothermal process taking place in a superconductor we have, in the notation of § 5.1,

$$\frac{\partial}{\partial t}\left[\frac{E \cdot D + H \cdot B}{8\pi} + \frac{\Lambda j^{(s)2}}{2}\right] + \sigma E^2 + \frac{c}{4\pi} \nabla \cdot (E \times H) = 0 \tag{1}$$

The quantity in square brackets thus plays the role of a free-energy density.

5.4. Critical field and its relation to entropy and specific heat (Ref. 13). At any absolute temperature T there exists a critical value H_c of the magnetic field strength H, such that any region of a specimen of dimensions $\gg$ the penetration depth λ of § 5.2 loses its superconductivity when the value of H at the boundary of this region exceeds H_c. The value of $H_c \to 0$ as $T \to T_c$, the temperature above which superconductivity disappears in the absence of a field, while as $T \to 0$, $dH_c/dT \to 0$.

At any temperature $T < T_c$, the transition from the superconducting to the normal state in the presence of a magnetic field $H_c(T)$ has a latent heat given by

$$Q = T(S^{(n)} - S^{(s)}) = \frac{-Tv}{4\pi} H_c \frac{dH_c}{dT} \tag{1}$$

where $S^{(n)}$, $S^{(s)}$ are the entropies in the normal and superconducting phases, respectively, of any standard amount of the material, e.g., a mole, and v is the volume of this same amount. As in § 5.1, the field H_c is supposed measured in absolute electromagnetic units. The specific heats of the two phases, referred to this same amount of material, differ by

$$C^{(n)} - C^{(s)} = \frac{-vT}{4\pi}\left[\left(\frac{dH_c}{dT}\right)^2 + H_c \frac{d^2H_c}{dT^2}\right] \tag{2}$$

We have also

$$Q = \frac{v}{8\pi} H_c^2 \int_T^{T_c} (C^{(n)} - C^{(s)}) dT' \tag{3}$$

5.5. Equilibrium of normal and superconducting phases for systems of small dimensions (Ref. 13). The condition $\mathrm{H} = \mathrm{H}_c$ was given in § 5.4 for equilibrium of a large-scale superconducting region with a neighboring nonsuperconducting region. This is a special case of a more general condition which, for regions separated by a plane boundary but not necessarily thick compared with the penetration depth λ of § 5.2, takes the form

$$\frac{\Lambda}{2} j_t^{(s)2} = \frac{H_c^2}{8\pi} \tag{1}$$

where Λ is the fundamental constant of § 5.1, related to the penetration depth in § 5.2, and $j_t^{(s)}$ is the component of superconducting current density tangential to the interface between normal and superconducting regions. If the boundary between the two regions is not plane, a term roughly of the form $\gamma_{ns}(C_1 + C_2)$ must be added to this equation, where γ_{ns} is the surface tension of the interface between the two phases, and C_1, C_2 are the two principal curvatures of the interface.

For a thin film of thickness d in a tangential field the completely non-superconducting state is thermodynamically more stable than the super-conducting state when

$$H > H_c \sqrt{\frac{1 + \Delta\bar{\gamma} \cdot 16\pi/H_c^2 d}{1 - (2\lambda/d) \tanh (d/2\lambda)}}$$

where λ is the penetration depth of § 5.2 and $\Delta\bar{\gamma}$ is the average, over top and bottom faces of the film, of the specific surface free energy of the normal phase minus that of the superconducting phase.

5.6. Multiply connected superconductors (Ref. 13). Let C be any closed curve lying entirely within superconducting matter, S any finite surface bounded by C, and $\boldsymbol{n}$ the local unit normal to S. With the convention that the direction of integration around C be related by the right-hand rule to the direction of $\boldsymbol{n}$, and with the notation of § 5.1, the quantity

$$\Phi_C = \iint_S \boldsymbol{n} \cdot \boldsymbol{B} dS + c \oint_C \Lambda \boldsymbol{j}^{(s)} \cdot d\boldsymbol{s} \tag{1}$$

is called the *fluxoid* through C; it has the properties

a. $d\Phi_C/dt = 0$ in any thermal or electromagnetic change of the system, as long as the neighborhood of C remains at all times superconducting.

b. $\Phi_C = \Phi_{C'}$ for any two curves which can be deformed continuously into each other without passing out of superconducting matter. Thus in a simply connected superconductor every $\Phi_C = 0$, but in multiply connected ones a finite number of nonzero values are possible.

For a multiply connected superconductor whose dimensions (including the dimensions of the holes) are $\gg$ the penetration depth λ of § 5.2, the magnetic flux through any hole is, to a good approximation, constant in time during any thermal or electromagnetic changes, i.e.,

$$\frac{d}{dt} \iint_S \boldsymbol{n} \cdot \boldsymbol{B} dS \approx 0 \tag{2}$$

where S is any surface lying in the nonsuperconducting region and bounded by the hole in question.

Under steady-state conditions the distribution of current and field in and around any multiply connected superconductor is uniquely determined by (1) the distribution of external currents and (2) either the fluxoids $\Phi_1, \ldots, \Phi_p$ for the different classes of closed curves within the superconductor, or the currents $i_1, \ldots, i_p$ in the p circuits of which the multiply connected super-conductor is composed.

5.7. General properties of time-dependent disturbances in superconductors (Ref. 13). Let $\boldsymbol{q}$ represent any of the quantities $\boldsymbol{B}$, $\boldsymbol{E}$, $\boldsymbol{j}^{(s)}$, or $\boldsymbol{j}^{(n)}$, in the notation of § 5.1. Within any homogeneous superconducting region all these quantities obey the differential equation

$$c^2\nabla^2\boldsymbol{q} = \frac{4\pi}{\Lambda}\boldsymbol{q} + 4\pi\sigma\frac{\partial\boldsymbol{q}}{\partial t} + \frac{\partial^2\boldsymbol{q}}{\partial t^2} \tag{1}$$

In actual superconducting metals the last term on the right, which represents the effect of displacement current, is negligible compared to the others at all frequencies at which the theory is usable; the second term on the right is usually sizable only at frequencies in the microwave range and above.

In the absence of charges mechanically introduced from the outside, the volume density ρ of electric charge vanishes at all times in a superconductor.

5.8. A-c resistance of superconductors (Ref. 13). Let a superconducting body of dimensions $\gg$ the penetration depth λ of § 5.2 be subjected to an alternating field containing the time factor $e^{i\omega t}$. Let R_c be the resistance, at the same frequency, of a normal conductor of the same geometry and having a conductivity σ_c large enough to make the skin depth $\ll$ the dimensions of the specimen. Then the resistance of the superconducting specimen is

$$R = R_c\left(\frac{\sigma_c}{\sigma}\right)^{1/2}\frac{\lambda}{\delta}\left[\frac{\sqrt{1+(\lambda/\delta)^4}-1}{1+(\lambda/\delta)^4}\right]^{1/2} \tag{1}$$

where σ is the actual conductivity of the superconducting material as defined in § 5.1 and $\delta = c/(4\pi\sigma\omega)^{1/2}$ is the skin depth which one would compute for a normal conductor of this conductivity. In the superconductor the field and current vary with depth z beneath the surface according to e^{-Kz}, where

$$K = \frac{1}{\lambda}\left[1 + i\left(\frac{\lambda}{\delta}\right)^2\right]^{1/2} \tag{2}$$

These relations are based on the assumption of a homogeneous conductivity σ, and do not take account of the fact that even in normal conductors the effective conductivity is altered when the skin depth becomes comparable with or less than the mean free path of the conduction electrons.

5.9. Optical constants of superconductors. For wavelengths sufficiently far in the infrared one may reasonably expect the equation of § 5.7 to predict the optical constants correctly. The optical constants, n, k are defined so that a plane wave of angular frequency ω progressing in the z direction has an amplitude proportional to

$$\exp\left(i\omega t - \frac{i\omega nz}{c} - \frac{k\omega z}{c}\right)$$

The values given by the equation of § 5.7 are, with neglect of the displacement current term,

$$n = \frac{1}{\omega}\left(\frac{2\pi}{\Lambda}\right)^{1/2}\left[-1 + \sqrt{1 + (\omega\sigma\Lambda)^2}\right]^{1/2} \tag{1}$$

$$k = \frac{1}{\omega}\left(\frac{2\pi}{\Lambda}\right)^{1/2}\left[1 + \sqrt{1 + (\omega\sigma\Lambda)^2}\right]^{1/2} \tag{2}$$

where Λ, σ, have the meanings defined in § 5.1. If $\omega\sigma\Lambda \gg 1$ these reduce to the expressions characterizing a normal conductor (see § 10.12).

6. Electrostatics of Ionic Lattices

6.1. Potential at a general point of space, by the method of Ewald (Ref. 3). Consider first the potential due to a continuous distribution of charge whose density $\rho(\boldsymbol{r})$ is arbitrary except for the requirement of over-all electrical neutrality and the periodicity condition $\rho(\boldsymbol{r} + \boldsymbol{t}) = \rho(\boldsymbol{r})$ where $\boldsymbol{t}$ is any translation of the crystal lattice (see § 1.1). The potential $V(\boldsymbol{r})$ which satisfies Poisson's equation and the periodicity condition and has mean value zero is given by

$$V(\boldsymbol{r}) = V'(\boldsymbol{r},\epsilon) + V''(\boldsymbol{r},\epsilon) \tag{1}$$

where ϵ is a positive number with the dimensions of reciprocal length, which may be chosen at will anywhere in the range $0 < \epsilon < \infty$, and where V' and V'' are, respectively, a sum over the points of the reciprocal lattice of the crystal, and an integral over ordinary space. Explicity, if $\boldsymbol{K}$ is 2π times a general vector of the reciprocal lattice (see § 1.3) and if the Fourier coefficients ρ_K are defined by

$$\rho(\boldsymbol{r}) = \sum_K \rho_K e^{i\boldsymbol{K}\cdot\boldsymbol{r}}$$

we have

$$V'(\boldsymbol{r},\epsilon) = 4\pi \sum_{K\neq 0} \frac{\rho_K}{K^2} \exp\left(-\frac{K^2}{4\epsilon^2} + i\boldsymbol{K}\cdot\boldsymbol{r}\right) \tag{2}$$

$$V''(\boldsymbol{r},\epsilon) = \int_{\substack{\text{all}\\ \text{space}}} \rho(\boldsymbol{r}')\left[\frac{1 - \operatorname{Erf}(\epsilon\,|\,\boldsymbol{r}' - \boldsymbol{r}\,|)}{|\,\boldsymbol{r}' - \boldsymbol{r}\,|}\right] d\tau' \tag{3}$$

where Erf is the error function

$$(2/\sqrt{\pi})\int_0^x e^{-x^2}\,dx$$

Since the sum for V' converges the more rapidly the smaller ϵ, while the integral for V'' converges the more rapidly the larger ϵ, a choice $\epsilon \sim$ (interatomic spacing)$^{-1}$ or a little more is usually best for computation.

For a lattice whose unit cell consists of p point charges of magnitudes e_i at positions $\boldsymbol{r}_i$, with

$$\sum_{i=1}^{p} e_i = 0$$

the preceding expressions specialize to

$$V'(\boldsymbol{r},\epsilon) = \sum_{i=1}^{p} e_i \psi'(\boldsymbol{r} - \boldsymbol{r}_i,\epsilon), \quad V''(\boldsymbol{r},\epsilon) = \sum_{i=1}^{p} e_i \psi''(\boldsymbol{r} - \boldsymbol{r}_i,\epsilon) \qquad (3)$$

with

$$\psi'(\boldsymbol{r},\epsilon) = \frac{4\pi}{\Omega}\sum_{K\neq 0}\frac{\exp(-K^2/4\epsilon^2 + i\boldsymbol{K}\cdot\boldsymbol{r})}{K^2}$$

$$\psi''(\boldsymbol{r},\epsilon) = -\frac{\pi}{\epsilon^2\Omega} + \sum_{t}\frac{1 - \mathrm{Erf}(\epsilon\,|\,\boldsymbol{t} - \boldsymbol{r}\,|)}{|\,\boldsymbol{t} - \boldsymbol{r}\,|}$$

where Ω is the volume of the unit cell of the crystal (see § 1.2) and where the vector $\boldsymbol{t}$ runs over all the translations of the crystal lattice. The function $\psi(\boldsymbol{r}) = \psi'(\boldsymbol{r},\epsilon) + \psi''(\boldsymbol{r},\epsilon)$ represents the potential resulting from a lattice of unit positive point charges combined with an equal amount of negative charge uniformly distributed throughout space; it is therefore sometimes called the *neutralized potential* of the lattice of positive charges.

6.2. Potential acting on an ion, by the method of Ewald (Ref. 3). Consider a crystal lattice whose unit cell contains a point charge e_i at position $\boldsymbol{r}_i$, plus other charges continuously or discretely distributed, the total charge density being $\rho(\boldsymbol{r})$. The work required to remove a single one of the charges of type i to a place of zero potential (defined as the space average of the potential in the lattice) is $-e_iV_i$, where

$$V_i = \lim_{\boldsymbol{r}\to\boldsymbol{r}_i}[V(\boldsymbol{r}) - e_i/r] \qquad (1)$$

We have $V_i = V_i'(\epsilon) + V_i''(\epsilon)$ where, in the notation of § 6.1,

$$V_i'(\epsilon) = -\frac{2e_i\epsilon}{\sqrt{\pi}} + 4\pi\sum_{K\neq 0}\frac{\rho_K}{K^2}\exp\left(-\frac{K^2}{4\epsilon^2} + i\boldsymbol{K}\cdot\boldsymbol{r}_i\right) \qquad (2)$$

$$V_i''(\epsilon) = \int_{\substack{\text{all}\\ \text{space}}}[\rho(\boldsymbol{r}') - e_i\delta(\boldsymbol{r}')]\left[\frac{1 - \mathrm{Erf}\,(\epsilon\,|\,\boldsymbol{r}' - \boldsymbol{r}_i\,|)}{|\,\boldsymbol{r}' - \boldsymbol{r}_i\,|}\right]d\tau' \qquad (3)$$

For the special case where the lattice consists exclusively of point charges, these reduce to

$$V_i'(\epsilon) = -\frac{2e_i\epsilon}{\sqrt{\pi}} + \frac{4\pi}{\Omega} \sum_{K\neq 0} \sum_{j=1}^{p} \frac{e_j \exp[-K^2/4\epsilon^2 + i\boldsymbol{K}\cdot(\boldsymbol{r}_i - \boldsymbol{r}_j)]}{K^2} \tag{4}$$

$$V_i''(\epsilon) = \sum_{R\neq r_i} \frac{e_R}{|\boldsymbol{R} - \boldsymbol{r}_i|} [1 - \mathrm{Erf}(\epsilon\, |\boldsymbol{R} - \boldsymbol{r}_i|)] \tag{5}$$

where $\boldsymbol{R} = \boldsymbol{r}_j + \boldsymbol{t}$ runs over the position vectors of all ions of the crystal except the one $j = i$, $t = 0$, and $e_R = e_j$ is the charge of the ion at $\boldsymbol{R}$.

6.3. Potential due to an infinite linear array, by the method of Madelung (Ref. 3). Let an infinite line array of charges consist of p kinds of charges e_j, the jth kind being located at positions x_j, $x_j \pm t$, $x_j \pm 2t$, etc., along a line, and let the array be neutral, so that

$$\sum_{j=1}^{p} e_j = 0$$

Then we have for the potential at a point whose coordinate along the line is x and whose distance from the line is r,

$$V(x,r) = \frac{4}{t} \sum_{n=1}^{\infty} \sum_{j=1}^{p} e_j K_0\left(\frac{2\pi n r}{t}\right) \cos\left[\frac{2\pi n(x - x_j)}{t}\right] \tag{1}$$

where $K_0(z) = (\pi i/2)H_0^{(1)}(iz)$ is the modified Bessel function of the second kind.

6.4. Potential acting on an ion in a linear array, by the method of Madelung (Ref. 2). For the array of § 6.3 the potential produced at the position of one of the charges of type i by all the other charges is

$$V_i = -\frac{1}{t} \sum_{j\neq i} \left[\Psi\left(\frac{x_j - x_i}{t}\right) + \Psi\left(\frac{t + x_i - x_j}{t}\right)\right] + 2\frac{\gamma e_i}{t} \tag{1}$$

where $\Psi(z) = d \log \Gamma(z)/dz$, and $\gamma = 0.5772$ is Euler's constant.

6.5. Potential due to a plane array, by the method of Madelung (Ref. 2). Let $\boldsymbol{t}_1$, $\boldsymbol{t}_2$ be the fundamental translations of a two-dimensional lattice in the x-y plane, and let the unit parallelogram of this lattice contain charges e_j at positions $\boldsymbol{r}_j (j = 1 \text{ to } p)$ with

$$\sum_{j=1}^{p} e_j = 0$$

Then the potential at any point $\boldsymbol{r} = (x,y,z)$ is

$$V(x,y,z) = \frac{2\pi}{|\boldsymbol{t}_1 \times \boldsymbol{t}_2|} \sum_j \sum_{K\neq 0} \frac{e_j e^{-K|z|} e^{i\boldsymbol{K}\cdot(\boldsymbol{r}-\boldsymbol{r}_j)}}{K} \tag{1}$$

where $\boldsymbol{K}/2\pi$ runs over the lattice of vectors in the x-y plane reciprocal to that generated by $\boldsymbol{t}_1$, $\boldsymbol{t}_2$, i.e., $\boldsymbol{K}\cdot\boldsymbol{t}_1/2\pi = \text{integer}$, $\boldsymbol{K}\cdot\boldsymbol{t}_2/2\pi = \text{integer}$.

7. Thermal Vibrations

7.1. Normal modes of a crystal (Ref. 20). Let $\boldsymbol{r}^{jl}$ be the position vector of the jth atom in the lth unit cell of a crystal in equilibrium, where j runs from 1 to s, where s is the number of atoms per unit cell; let $\boldsymbol{u}^{jl}$ be the displacement of this atom from its equilibrium position. If the atoms are bound to each other by harmonic forces and if they are subjected to periodic boundary conditions (see § 1.4) at the edges of the crystal the normal modes of vibration have displacements u_μ^{ji} $(\mu = 1 \text{ to } 3)$ proportional to

$$u_\mu^{jl}(\boldsymbol{k},n) = \text{Re}\{A_\mu^j(\boldsymbol{q},n) \exp[i(\boldsymbol{q}\cdot\boldsymbol{r}^{jl} - \omega_{qn}t)]\} \tag{1}$$

where *Re* means " real part of," the vector $\boldsymbol{q}$ and the index n label the various normal modes, ω_{qn} is the angular frequency of the normal mode in question, and the $3s$ quantities $A_\mu(\boldsymbol{q},n)$ are determined to within a constant factor by a secular equation involving the atomic masses and the interatomic force constants. The allowed values of $\boldsymbol{q}$ are distributed almost continuously over the first Brillouin zone (see § 1.3) in reciprocal lattice space, with the density $v/8\pi^3$, where v is the volume of the crystal. The index n takes on $3s$ values, corresponding to $3s$ bands or branches of the vibrational spectrum. For three of these, which may be designated by $n = 1, 2, 3$, and for any given direction of $\boldsymbol{q}$,

$$\omega_{qn} \to \text{constant } \boldsymbol{q} \quad \text{as} \quad \boldsymbol{q} \to 0, \quad (n = 1 \text{ to } 3) \tag{2}$$

and

$$A_\mu^j(\boldsymbol{q},n) \sim A_\mu^i(\boldsymbol{q},n), \qquad (\text{for all } i,\, j) \tag{3}$$

These are called the *acoustical branches*. For the other branches $\omega_{\boldsymbol{q},n} \to$ finite limit as $\boldsymbol{q} \to 0$ $(n > 3)$, and the A_μ^j for different j may remain different; these are often called the *optical branches*.

For small $\boldsymbol{q}$ the asymptotic frequencies and A^j_μ of the acoustical branches can be expressed in terms of the elastic constants of the crystal. The secular equation determining the limiting ratios ω_{qn}/q is (Ref. 3)

$$\left| \sum_{\alpha,\beta=1}^{3} c_{\mu\alpha\nu\beta} q_\alpha q_\beta - \rho\omega_{qn}^2 \delta_{\mu\nu} \right| = 0 \tag{4}$$

where μ and ν label the rows and columns of the determinant, ρ is the density of the crystal, and $c_{\mu\nu\alpha\beta}$ is the elastic constant tensor defined by the equation

$$p_{\mu\alpha} = \sum_{\nu,\beta=1}^{3} c_{\mu\alpha\nu\beta} u_{\nu\beta} \tag{5}$$

relating the stress tensor $p_{\mu\alpha}$ to the strain tensor $u_{\nu\beta}$. For cubic crystals the only nonvanishing components of $c_{\mu\alpha\nu\beta}$ are, relative to the "natural" axes of § 2.1, $c_{\alpha\alpha\alpha\alpha} = c_{11}$, $c_{\alpha\alpha\beta\beta} = c_{12}$. $c_{\alpha\beta\alpha\beta} = c_{\alpha\beta\beta\alpha} = c_{44}$, where α and β take on any values from 1 to 3 ($\alpha \neq \beta$) and where the c_{ij} are the usual elastic constants as defined in § 2.2.

7.2. Thermodynamic functions, general case (Ref. 22). At any absolute temperature T the energy U, free energy F, and entropy S of a crystal whose atoms are bound by harmonic forces can be expressed as sums of terms involving the frequencies $\omega_{\boldsymbol{q}n}$ of the various normal modes, as follows

$$U = U_0 + \sum_{qn} \frac{\hbar\omega_{qn}}{\exp(\hbar\omega_{qn}/kT) - 1} \tag{1}$$

$$F = U_0 + kT \sum_{qn} \ln [1 - \exp(-\hbar\omega_{qn}/kT)] \tag{2}$$

$$S = k \sum_{qn} \left\{ -\ln [1 - \exp(-\hbar\omega_{qn}/kT)] + \frac{(\hbar\omega_{qn}/kT)}{\exp(\hbar\omega_{qn}/kT) - 1} \right\} \tag{3}$$

where $\hbar$ is Planck's constant divided by 2π, k is Boltzmann's constant, and U_0 is the energy of the crystal at the absolute zero, including the zero point energy

$$\tfrac{1}{2} \sum_{qn} \hbar\omega_{qn}$$

The molar specific heat C_v is given by

$$C_v = 3sR \left\{ \frac{(\hbar\omega_{qn}/kT)^2 \exp(\hbar\omega_{qn}/kT)}{[\exp(\hbar\omega_{qn}kT) - 1]^2} \right\}_{\text{av on } q,n} \tag{4}$$

where R is the gas constant.

7.3. Thermodynamic functions at high temperatures (Refs. 9 and 24). If $kT < \hbar\omega_{\max}/2\pi$, where $\omega_{\max}$ is the highest frequency occurring for any of the normal modes, the energy and specific heat of the crystals of § 7.2 can be expanded into convergent series in powers of $1/T$. For a crystal containing N unit cells of s atoms each, the series for the energy is

$$U = U_0 + 3Ns\left[kT - \tfrac{1}{2}\langle\hbar\omega\rangle_{\text{av}} + \sum_{p=1}^{\infty}\frac{B_{2p}\langle(\hbar\omega)^{2p}\rangle_{\text{av}}}{2p!(kT)^{2p-1}}\right] \tag{1}$$

where $\langle(\hbar\omega)^{2p}\rangle_{\text{av}}$ is the average over all normal modes k, n of $(\hbar\omega_{kn})^{2p}$, and where B_{2p} are the Bernouilli numbers $B_2 = \frac{1}{6}$, $B_4 = -\frac{1}{30}$, $B_6 = \frac{1}{42}$, $B_8 = -\frac{1}{30}$, $B_{10} = \frac{5}{66}$, ... The molar specific heat can be obtained from this by differentiation, since for the case $Nk = R$, $C_v = \partial U/\partial T$. The corresponding series for the entropy is

$$S = -k\sum_{q,n}\ln(\hbar\omega_{qn}/kT) + 3Nsk\left[1 + \sum_{p=1}^{\infty}\frac{B_{2p}\langle(\hbar\omega)^{2p}\rangle_{\text{av}}}{(2p)^2(2p-2)!(kT)^{2p}}\right] \tag{2}$$

7.4. Thermodynamic functions at low temperatures (Ref. 9). At sufficiently low temperatures the only normal modes to be appreciably excited will be those for which ω_{qn} is practically proportional to q and calculable in terms of the elastic constants by means of the secular equation given in § 7.1. In this low frequency region the number of normal modes with angular frequencies in the range ω to $\omega + d\omega$ is

$$f(\omega)d\omega = \frac{3v}{2\pi^2}\left\langle\frac{1}{V^3}\right\rangle_{\text{av}}\omega^2 d\omega = 9Ns\left(\frac{\hbar}{k\Theta}\right)^3\omega^2 d\omega \tag{1}$$

where v is the volume of the crystal containing N unit cells of s atoms each, V is the velocity ω_{qn}/q of a sound wave, the average being taken over all directions of propagation and over the three states of polarization, and where Θ is an effective Debye temperature (see § 7.5) defined by

$$k\Theta = \hbar\left(\frac{6\pi^2}{\left\langle\dfrac{1}{V^3}\right\rangle_{\text{av}}}\cdot\frac{Ns}{v}\right)^{1/3} \tag{2}$$

In terms of these quantities the asymptotic values of the energy, free energy, entropy, and molar specific heat of the crystal are, respectively

$$U \sim U_0 + \frac{\pi^2}{10}v\left\langle\frac{1}{V^3}\right\rangle_{\text{av}}\cdot\frac{(kT)^4}{\hbar^3} = U_0 + \frac{3\pi^4}{5}\left(\frac{T}{\Theta}\right)^4 Nsk\Theta \tag{3}$$

$$F \sim U_0 - \frac{\pi^2}{30}v\left\langle\frac{1}{V^3}\right\rangle_{\text{av}}\frac{(kT)^4}{\hbar^3} = U_0 - \frac{\pi^4}{5}\left(\frac{T}{\Theta}\right)^4 Nsk\Theta \tag{4}$$

$$S \sim \frac{4\pi^4}{5}\left(\frac{T}{\Theta}\right)^3 Nsk, \quad C_v \sim \frac{12\pi^4}{5}\left(\frac{T}{\Theta}\right)^3 sR \tag{5}$$

7.5. Debye approximation (Refs. 3, 9, and 22). A useful approximation to the distribution of normal modes in frequency is to take for the number of modes in the range ω to $\omega + d\omega$ of angular frequencies

$$\left.\begin{aligned} f(\omega)d\omega &= 9Ns\left(\frac{\hbar}{k\Theta_D}\right)^3 \omega^2 d\omega, \approx (\text{for } \hbar\omega < k\Theta_D) \\ &= 0 \qquad\qquad\qquad\qquad (\text{for } \hbar\omega > k\Theta_D) \end{aligned}\right\} \tag{1}$$

where N is the number of unit cells in the crystal, s is the number of atoms per cell, and Θ_D is a parameter called the *Debye temperature* which is to be chosen empirically. This gives for the energy, free energy, entropy, and molar specific heat, respectively,

$$U = U_0 + 3NskTD\left(\frac{\Theta_D}{T}\right) \tag{2}$$

$$F = U_0 + NskT\left[3 \ln\left(1 - e^{-\Theta_D/T}\right) - D\left(\frac{\Theta_D}{T}\right)\right] \tag{3}$$

$$S = Nsk\left[4D\left(\frac{\Theta_D}{T}\right) - 3 \ln\left(1 - e^{-\Theta_D/T}\right)\right] \tag{4}$$

$$C_v = 3sR\left[4D\left(\frac{\Theta_D}{T}\right) - \frac{3\Theta_D/T}{e^{\Theta_D/T} - 1}\right] \tag{5}$$

where the function $D(x)$ is defined by

$$D(x) = \frac{3}{x^3}\int_0^x \frac{\xi^3 d\xi}{e^\xi - 1}$$

so that $D(0) = 1$, $D(\infty) = 0$.

The asymptotic values of these expressions for U, F, S, and C_v at low temperatures are given by the formulas of § 7.4 with Θ_D substituted for Θ. At temperatures above $\Theta_D/2\pi$,

$$D\left(\frac{\Theta_D}{T}\right) = 1 - \frac{3}{8} \cdot \frac{\Theta_D}{T} + 3\sum_{p=1}^{\infty} \frac{B_{2p}}{(2p+3)2p!}\left(\frac{\Theta_D}{T}\right)^{2p} \tag{6}$$

while at any temperature

$$\left.\begin{aligned} D\left(\frac{\Theta_D}{T}\right) &= \frac{\pi^4}{5}\left(\frac{T}{\Theta_D}\right)^3 + 3 \ln\left(1 - e^{-\Theta_D/T}\right) \\ &\quad - 9\sum_{p=1}^{\infty} \frac{[(T/\Theta_D)p^2 + 2(T/\Theta_D)^2 p + 2(T/\Theta_D)^3]e^{-p\Theta_D/T}}{p^4} \end{aligned}\right\} \tag{7}$$

The zero point energy of the normal modes in the present approximation is

$$\frac{1}{2}\sum_{q,n} \hbar\omega_{qn} = \frac{9}{8}Nsk\Theta_D \tag{8}$$

7.6. Equation of state for a crystal (Ref. 22). If the interatomic forces were strictly harmonic, as has been assumed in the preceding sections, a crystal would show no thermal expansion, and in the equation of state the pressure would be a function of the volume but not of the temperature. The slight departures from harmonicity which actually occur do not, however, necessitate abandoning the formalism of the harmonic approximation; for many purposes they can be taken adequately into account by retaining the preceding expressions for energy, etc., but allowing the frequencies of the normal modes to depend on volume and state of strain. This gives for the pressure corresponding to any volume v,

$$p = -\frac{dU_0}{dv} + \frac{1}{v}\sum_{q,n} \frac{\gamma_{qn}\hbar\omega_{qn}}{\exp(\hbar\omega_{qn}/kT) - 1} \tag{1}$$

where, as before, U_0 is the energy in the absence of thermal vibrations but including zero point energy, and

$$\gamma_{qn} = -\frac{d \ln \omega_{qn}}{d \ln v} \tag{2}$$

A common approximation is to assume that γ_{qn} has the same value γ for all normal modes. For this case we have the Mie-Grüneisen equation of state

$$p = -\frac{dU_0}{dv} + \gamma\frac{(U - U_0)}{v} \tag{3}$$

and the linear thermal expansion coefficient is

$$\alpha = \frac{1}{3v}\left(\frac{\partial v}{\partial T}\right)_p = \frac{\kappa\gamma}{3v_m} C_v \tag{4}$$

where κ is the volume compressibility, v_m the molar volume, and C_v the molar specific heat at constant volume. If the Debye approximation is used, $\gamma = -d \ln \Theta / d \ln v$.

7.7. Long wavelength optical modes of polar crystals (Ref. 15). Consider first a crystal of cubic symmetry containing two ions per unit cell. The normal vibrations of the optical branches (see § 7.1) can then, in the limit of long wavelengths, be characterized as longitudinal (one branch with atomic displacements parallel to the wave vector $\boldsymbol{q}$) or transverse (two branches with displacements perpendicular to $\boldsymbol{q}$). As $\boldsymbol{q} = 2\pi/\text{wavelength} \to 0$, let the angular frequency of the longitudinal branch approach ω_l, that of the transverse branches ω_t. Then if κ, κ_0 represent, respectively, the static dielectric constant and the dielectric constant at frequencies $\gg \omega_l$ and ω_t, but $\ll$ the frequencies of electronic transitions,

$$\frac{\omega_l^2}{\omega_t^2} = \frac{\kappa}{\kappa_0} \tag{1}$$

Let M_1, M_2 be the masses of the two kinds of ions and $\mu = (1/M_1 + 1/M_2)^{-1}$ the reduced mass. Let e_{eff} be the effective charge on an ion, defined by the equation

$$\text{Force} = -\, e_{\text{eff}} E$$

for the force which would have to be applied to each ion to hold it in its original position in the presence of a uniform macroscopic electric field E. Then if Ω is the volume of the unit cell, i.e., the volume per ion pair

$$\mu\omega_t^2 = \frac{4\pi e_{\text{eff}}^2}{\Omega(\kappa - \kappa_0)} \tag{2}$$

The preceding formulas can be applied to noncubic diatomic crystals if the atomic displacements for the two modes considered lie along a symmetry axis, so that for the longitudinal mode q lies along this axis, for the transverse mode at right angles to it. For this case κ and κ_0 must be interpreted as the dielectric constants in the direction of the atomic displacement.

These formulas can also be applied to those polyatomic binary compounds, e.g., those with the fluorite structure, whose crystal symmetry requires all atoms of each element to have the same displacement in an optical mode of infinite wavelength. In such cases M_1, M_2, e_{eff} are to be replaced by the sums of the masses or effective charges, respectively, of all ions of the same element in a unit cell.

7.8. Residual rays (Ref. 8). The reflection coefficient of an ionic crystal for infrared radiation at normal incidence possesses a maximum at a wavelength λ_R, called the residual ray wavelength, somewhat shorter than the wavelength $\lambda_t = 2\pi c/\omega_t$ which resonates with the transverse optical normal mode defined in § 7.7. If the optical constants in the frequency range under consideration can be represented as arising from slightly damped normal vibrations of the transverse optical branch, we have for diatomic cubic crystals

$$1/\lambda_t^2 = 1/\lambda_R^2 - \frac{N^2 e_{\text{eff}}^2 \rho}{2\pi c^2 A_1 A_2 \kappa_0} \tag{1}$$

where N is Avogadro's number, e_{eff} is the effective charge on an ion as defined in § 7.7, ρ is the density, c is the velocity of light, A_1 and A_2 are the atomic weights of the two kinds of ions, and κ_0 is the dielectric constant at frequencies $\gg \omega_t$ but $\ll$ the frequencies of electronic transitions.

This formula can be applied to noncubic and polyatomic binary crystals under the conditions described in § 7.7; for the polyatomic case A_1, A_2, e_{eff} must be replaced by sums of these quantities over all ions of a given element in a unit cell.

8. Dislocation Theory

8.1. Characterization of dislocations (Ref. 18). A *dislocation* in a crystal lattice is a region of departure from the normal lattice arrangement, localized in the neighborhood of an endless line or curve, called the dislocation line, and with the properties : (1) the atomic arrangement in the regions well away from the dislocation line agrees with that in a perfect crystal lattice except for a small elastic distortion, so that each vector $\boldsymbol{t}$ from an atom to one of its near neighbors can be placed in unambiguous correspondence with a vector $\boldsymbol{t}^{(0)}$ of the perfect lattice; (2) if we select any sequence of atomic positions lying along a closed path avoiding the neighborhood of the dislocation line but enclosing this line, then for the sum of the vectors associated with successive pairs of neighboring atoms along this path we have

$$\Sigma \boldsymbol{t} = 0 \quad \text{by definition,} \quad \text{but} \quad \Sigma \boldsymbol{t}^{(0)} = \boldsymbol{t}' \neq 0$$

where $\boldsymbol{t}'$, a translation vector of the undistorted lattice, is the same for all paths encircling the dislocation line in the same sense (paths encircling it in the opposite direction merely give $\Sigma \boldsymbol{t}^{(0)} = -\boldsymbol{t}'$), and is called the *slip vector*, or *Burgers vector*, of the dislocation.

8.2. Force on a dislocation (Ref. 17). Consider any dislocation line and let $\boldsymbol{t}$, $\boldsymbol{\nu}$ be, respectively, the slip vector of the dislocation and the unit vector along the dislocation line, the directions of these vectors being so specified that, in the notation of § 8.1, $\Sigma \boldsymbol{t}^{(0)} = \boldsymbol{t}$ for circuits taken in the right-hand sense with respect to the direction of $\boldsymbol{\nu}$. The force dF on each element of length of the dislocation is defined by setting the change in elastic energy or free energy, which would accompany any virtual shift of the dislocation line, equal to $-\int \delta \boldsymbol{r} \cdot d\boldsymbol{F}$, where $\delta \boldsymbol{r}$ is the arbitrary virtual displacement of any point of the dislocation line and the integration is over all elements ds along the length of the dislocation line. It is given by

$$d\boldsymbol{F} = \boldsymbol{\nu} \times \boldsymbol{T}^{(t)} \,|\, \boldsymbol{t} \,|\, ds \tag{1}$$

where $T^{(t)}$ is the traction exerted across a plane normal to the slip vector $\boldsymbol{t}$ by that portion of the stress field due to sources other than the immediately neighboring parts of the dislocation being considered; explicitly,

$$T_\alpha^{(t)} \mid \boldsymbol{t} \mid = \sum_\beta t_\beta \bar{p}_{\beta\alpha} \tag{2}$$

where if $\boldsymbol{r}$ is a vector measured from a point on the dislocation line and $p_{\beta\alpha}$ is the total stress tensor in the crystal lattice (with the sign convention of § 2.1, which makes tensile stresses positive),

$$\bar{p}_{\beta\alpha} = \lim_{r \to 0} \tfrac{1}{2}[p_{\beta\alpha}(\boldsymbol{r}) + p_{\beta\alpha}(-\boldsymbol{r})] \tag{3}$$

The limit is independent of the direction of $\boldsymbol{r}$ provided $\boldsymbol{r}$ is interpreted in the macroscopic sense, i.e., $\boldsymbol{r} \gg$ atomic dimensions, an interpretation which is in fact necessary if the stress is to be treated as a smoothly varying function of position.

8.3. Elastic field of a dislocation in an isotropic medium. Consider a dislocation line lying along the z axis in an elastically isotropic crystal, and let its slip vector $\boldsymbol{t}$ (defined by the equation of 8.1 for a right-hand circuit about the positive z direction) have components t_x, 0, t_z. In terms of the shear modulus G (equals the μ of § 2.3) and Poisson's ratio σ the stress tensor (defined as in § 2.1) so that tensions are positive) is, at points sufficiently far from the dislocation line for elasticity theory to be applicable,

$$\left.\begin{aligned}
p_{xx} &= \frac{G}{2\pi(1-\sigma)} \frac{t_x y(3x^2+y^2)}{(x^2+y^2)^2} \\
p_{yy} &= \frac{G}{2\pi(1-\sigma)} \frac{t_x y(y^2-x^2)}{(x^2+y^2)^2} \\
p_{zz} &= 0 \\
p_{yz} &= -\frac{G}{2\pi} \cdot \frac{t_z x}{(x^2+y^2)} \\
p_{zx} &= \frac{G}{2\pi} \frac{t_z y}{(x^2+y^2)} \\
p_{xy} &= \frac{G}{2\pi(1-\sigma)} \frac{t_x x(y^2-x^2)}{(x^2+y^2)^2}
\end{aligned}\right\} \tag{1}$$

The elastic displacement $\boldsymbol{u}$ of the medium from its unstrained state has the components

$$\left.\begin{aligned} u_x &= -\frac{t_x}{2\pi}\arctan\frac{y}{x} - \frac{t_x}{4\pi(1-\sigma)}\frac{xy}{(x^2+y^2)} \\ u_y &= \frac{(1-2\sigma)t_x}{4\pi(1-\sigma)}\ln(x^2+y^2)^{1/2} + \frac{t_x}{4\pi(1-\sigma)}\frac{x^2}{(x^2+y^2)} \\ u_z &= -\frac{t_z}{2\pi}\arctan\frac{y}{x} \end{aligned}\right\} \quad (2)$$

These are of course multivalued, since $\boldsymbol{u}$ must change by $\boldsymbol{t}$ in going around the dislocation. The dilatation is

$$\frac{\partial u_x}{\partial x} + \frac{\partial u_y}{\partial y} + \frac{\partial u_z}{\partial z} = \frac{(1-2\sigma)}{2\pi(1-\sigma)}\frac{t_x y}{(x^2+y^2)} \quad (3)$$

9. Semiconductors

9.1. Bands and effective masses. Let some reference state for a single electron be chosen, e.g., the state of rest outside the crystal, and assigned the energy zero. Relative to this reference state the energy ϵ_c of the *bottom of the conduction band* may then be defined for any nonmetallic crystal as the least energy required to take an electron from the reference state and place it in a region of the crystal where there are no lattice imperfections. The energy ϵ_v of the *top of the valence band* is similarly defined as the negative of the least energy required to remove an electron from a perfect region of this type and place it in the reference state. The latter process creates an electron deficiency or *hole* in the crystal. In both cases the extra electron or hole with the least possible energy in the crystal always has zero mean velocity. The minimum energy of creation of an electron or hole with a given infinitesimal mean velocity $\bar{v}$ is, respectively,

$$\epsilon_c + \tfrac{1}{2}m_e^*\bar{v}^2 + O(\bar{v}^4) \quad \text{or} \quad -\epsilon_v + \tfrac{1}{2}m_h^*\bar{v}^2 + O(\bar{v}^4)$$

where m_e^* or m_h^* is called the *effective mass* of the electron or hole, respectively. The effective mass is usually assumed independent of the direction of motion, but may depend on this direction if the crystal is of lower than cubic symmetry or if the band in question is *degenerate*, i.e., if there exist two or more orthogonal quantum states for the electron or hole having the same energy, the same spin, and zero mean velocity.

9.2. Density of states (Refs. 20 and 21). If the conduction band is nondegenerate (see § 9.1) a crystal of volume Ω_N contains $\nu(\epsilon)d\epsilon$ quantum states for an extra or *conduction* electron having energies in the range $\epsilon_c + \epsilon$ to $\epsilon_c + \epsilon + d\epsilon$, where for small ϵ the asymptotic form of $\nu(\epsilon)$ is

$$\left.\begin{aligned} \nu(\epsilon) &= \frac{2^{7/2}\pi m_e^{*3/2}\Omega_N}{h^3}\,\epsilon^{1/2} \\ \frac{\nu(\epsilon)}{\Omega_N} &= 6.814 \times 10^{21}\left(\frac{m_e^*}{m}\right)^{3/2}\left(\frac{\epsilon}{1ev}\right)^{1/2} \text{ per cm}^3 \end{aligned}\right\} \quad (1)$$

per electron volt, where h is Planck's constant and m the true mass of the electron. Half of these states have one direction of spin, half the other. An analogous expression applies for holes.

9.3. Traps, donors, and acceptors. Associated with impurities and other imperfections in the crystal lattice there may be localized discrete energy levels for an electron. If the work ϵ_a required to take an electron from the reference state of zero energy and place it at the imperfection satisfies $\epsilon_v < \epsilon_a < \epsilon_c$, the imperfection is called an *electron trap*; if the work $-\epsilon_i$ required to remove an electron from the imperfection into the reference state satisfies $\epsilon_v < \epsilon_i < \epsilon_c$, it is called a *hole trap*. Of course, electron trap + electron → hole trap, hole trap + hole → electron trap. A trap which is electrically neutral when it is a hole trap, hence positively charged when it is electron trap, is called a *donor center*; one which is negative when a hole trap and neutral when an electron trap is called an *acceptor center*.

9.4. The Fermi-Dirac distribution (Ref. 21). Let i label the members of a set of quantum states for an electron, and let $N_i = 0$ or 1 be the number of electrons in the ith state. Suppose first that all combinations of values of the N_i are statistically possible, and that the dependence of the total energy E of the system on the N_i is given by $E = \text{constant} + \Sigma N_i\epsilon_i$, where ϵ_i is the energy of the ith state. Then in thermal equilibrium at absolute temperature T the fraction of the time that state i is occupied is

$$\langle N_i\rangle_{\text{av}} = f(\epsilon_i,\epsilon_F) = \frac{1}{\exp\,[(\epsilon_i - \epsilon_F)/kT] + 1} \quad (1)$$

where k is Boltzmann's constant and ϵ_F is a quantity known as the *Fermi level* and dependent on the mean total number of electrons in the system. The function f is called the *Fermi-Dirac distribution function.* The quantity ϵ_F is in the present case identical with the thermodynamically defined *electrochemical potential* of the electrons, and must have the same value in any two systems or regions which are in thermal equilibrium with each other. Its value in any large homogeneous region is determined by the requirement that the total number of electrons in all states must be such as to make the region electrically neutral.

The assumptions of the preceding paragraph, though approximately correct for the free electron and hole states enumerated in § 9.2, are not fulfilled by the trap states defined in § 9.3. For example, a donor center of energy ϵ_d may correspond to two quantum states with different spin directions, yet if both of these states were occupied the energy would be $\gg 2\epsilon_d$ because of the electrostatic interaction of the two electrons. To generalize the Fermi distribution to include cases like this let g_0 be the statistical weight of a particular trap t when the trap is empty, let g_1 be the statistical weight when there is one electron in the trap, and suppose for simplicity that other values of the charge on the trap are so improbable statistically that they can be neglected. Then if ϵ_t is the work required to take an electron from the state of zero energy and put it in the initially empty trap, the fraction of the time the trap is occupied under thermal equilibrium conditions is

$$\langle N_t \rangle_{\mathrm{av}} = \frac{1}{(g_0/g_1)\exp\left[(\epsilon_t - \epsilon_F)/kT\right] + 1} \tag{2}$$

9.5. Density of mobile charges (Refs. 20 and 21). When the conduction band is nondegenerate and the density of conduction electrons is sufficiently low so that their mutual interactions can be neglected, the value of this density in thermal equilibrium at any absolute temperature T can be obtained by integrating § 9.2 over the Fermi-Dirac distribution. If ϵ_F is the Fermi level and if $\epsilon_c - \epsilon_F \gg kT$, where k is Boltzmann's constant, this equilibrium density of conduction electrons is well approximated by

$$\left.\begin{aligned} n_e &= \frac{2(2\pi m_e^* kT)^{3/2}}{h^3} \exp\left(\frac{\epsilon_F - \epsilon_c}{kT}\right) \\ &= 1.4843 \times 10^{20} \left(\frac{m_e^*}{m} \cdot \frac{T}{1000}\right)^{3/2} \exp\left(\frac{\epsilon_F - \epsilon_c}{kT}\right) \text{ per cm}^3 \end{aligned}\right\} \tag{3}$$

With corresponding assumptions the equilibrium density of holes, n_h, is given by the same expression with m_h^* substituted for m_e^* and $\epsilon_v - \epsilon_F$ for $\epsilon_F - \epsilon_c$.

9.6. Fermi level and density of mobile charges, intrinsic case (Ref. 21). If the number of traps per unit volume is $\ll n_e$ as given by § 9.5 with $\epsilon_c - \epsilon_F = (\epsilon_c - \epsilon_v)/2$, the energy ϵ_F of the Fermi level and the densities of electrons and holes become independent of the number and nature of the traps and the conduction is called *intrinsic*. Explicitly, for this case and when the other conditions of § 9.5 are fulfilled,

$$\epsilon_F = \frac{\epsilon_c + \epsilon_v}{2} + \frac{3kT}{4} \ln \frac{m_h^*}{m_e^*} \tag{4}$$

$$\left.\begin{aligned} n_e = n_h &= \frac{2(2\pi\sqrt{m_e^* m_h^*}kT)^{3/2}}{h^3} \exp\left[-\frac{(\epsilon_c - \epsilon_v)}{2kT}\right] \\ &= 1.4843 \times 10^{20}\left(\frac{m_e^*}{m} \cdot \frac{m_h^*}{m}\right)^{3/4}\left(\frac{T}{1000}\right)^{3/2} \exp\left[-\frac{(\epsilon_c - \epsilon_v)}{2kT}\right] \text{ per cm}^3 \end{aligned}\right\} \tag{5}$$

9.7. Fermi level and density of mobile charges, extrinsic case. When the condition of § 9.6 is not fulfilled, the position of the Fermi level depends on the densities of the various kinds of traps present and their energies. In the lower parts of the temperature range either the density of mobile electrons will be many times that of mobile holes or the reverse, and the conduction is called *extrinsic*. If electrons predominate, the material is said to be *n-type*, if holes, *p-type*. In all cases, however, the product $n_e n_h$ of electron and hole densities equals the square of the expression in § 9.6, provided the conditions of § 9.5 are fulfilled.

While no simple analytical expression can be given for the density of mobile charges in the most general case, there is a case which can be treated fairly simply and which is still sufficiently broad to include many actual semiconductors. For an n-type specimen this case is one in which : (1) only a single kind of donor center is present; (2) the acceptor centers, present in smaller concentration, all have energies sufficiently low so that throughout the temperature range of interest the number of holes trapped at the acceptors can be neglected; (3) the conditions of § 9.5 are fulfilled. An exactly similar case of course occurs for a p-type specimen when the roles of donors and electrons are interchanged with those of acceptors and holes, respectively.

For an n-type specimen satisfying the conditions just mentioned let n_a, n_d and ϵ_d be, respectively, the density of acceptor centers, the density of donor centers, and the energy of an electron in a donor center, and let g_{0d}/g_{1d} be the ratio of the statistical weights of empty and occupied donor centers.

Define

$$n_{0e}(T) = \frac{2(2\pi m_e^* kT)^{3/2}}{h^3} \frac{g_{0d}}{g_{1d}} \exp\left[-\frac{(\epsilon_c - \epsilon_d)}{kT}\right]$$

$$= 1.4843 \times 10^{20}\left(\frac{m_e^*}{m} \cdot \frac{T}{1000}\right)^{3/2} \frac{g_{0d}}{g_{1d}} \exp\left[-\frac{(\epsilon_c - \epsilon_d)}{kT}\right]$$

Then the actual density of mobile electrons at any temperature is

$$n_e = \frac{1}{2}\left\{\left[1 + \frac{4n_{0e}(n_d - n_a)}{(n_{0e} + n_a)^2}\right]^{1/2} - 1\right\}(n_{0e} + n_a) \tag{1}$$

For a p-type specimen satisfying the analogous conditions let ϵ_a be the energy of an electron in an acceptor level, and let g_{0a}/g_{1a} be defined as the ratio of the statistical weight of an acceptor center when negatively charged to that when neutral. Define

$$n_{0h}(T) = \frac{2(2\pi m_h^* kT)^{3/2}}{h^3} \cdot \frac{g_{0a}}{g_{1a}} \exp\left[-\frac{(\epsilon_a - \epsilon_v)}{kT}\right]$$

$$= 1.4843 \times 10^{20}\left(\frac{m_h^*}{m} \frac{T}{1000}\right)^{3/2} \frac{g_{0a}}{g_{1a}} \exp\left[-\frac{(\epsilon_a - \epsilon_v)}{kT}\right]$$

Then the density of mobile holes is

$$n_h = \frac{1}{2}\left\{\left[1 + \frac{4n_{0h}(n_a - n_d)}{(n_{0h} + n_d)^2}\right]^{1/2} - 1\right\}(n_{0h} + n_d) \tag{2}$$

9.8. Mobility, conductivity, and diffusion (Ref. 21). In the presence of an electric field E an electron in the conduction band will migrate with a time average velocity $\langle v_e \rangle_{av}$ which is to a good approximation proportional to the field if E is not too large. Holes in the filled band behave similarly, with a drift velocity $\langle v_h \rangle_{av}$. The *mobilities* of electrons and holes are designated, respectively, by μ_e and μ_h, and defined by

$$\langle v_e \rangle_{av} = -\mu_e E, \quad \langle v_h \rangle_{av} = \mu_h E$$

In a cubic crystal μ_e and μ_h are scalars, but in crystals of lower symmetry the equations just written take the form of linear relations between components of vectors, with the mobilities represented by symmetric tensors. For simplicity, cubic symmetry will be assumed henceforth. The electric conductivity σ or resistivity ρ of a specimen containing n_e mobile electrons and n_h mobile holes per unit volume is given by

$$\sigma = 1/\rho = e(n_e\mu_e + n_h\mu_h) \tag{1}$$

If the μ's are measured in cm²/volt sec and the n's in cm^{-3},

$$\sigma = 1.6020 \times 10^{-3}\left(\frac{n_e}{10^{16}}\mu_e + \frac{n_h}{10^{16}}\mu_h\right) \text{ohm}^{-1}\,\text{cm}^{-1} \tag{2}$$

The variation of the concentration n_e of mobile electrons with position and time obeys the generalized diffusion equation

$$\frac{\partial n_e}{\partial t} = \nabla \cdot (D_e \nabla n_e) + \nabla \cdot (n_e \mu_e \boldsymbol{E}) - s \tag{3}$$

where $D_e = (kT/e)\mu_e$ is the *diffusion coefficient* for electrons and where s is the rate of disappearance of electrons from the conduction band, per unit volume, because of recombination or trapping, minus the rate of creation of new free electrons by thermal action, light, etc. An analogous equation applies for holes with $\boldsymbol{E}$ replaced by $-\boldsymbol{E}$.

9.9. Hall effect (Ref. 21). When no holes are present and when the density of mobile electrons is not too high, the Hall coefficient R_e (see § 4.7) at any given temperature varies inversely as the electron concentration n_e, i.e., $n_e R_e$ is a function of T independent of the position of the Fermi level. Similarly the Hall coefficient R_h for holes when no electrons are present varies inversely as the hole concentration n_h. When both electrons and holes contribute to the conduction the measured Hall coefficient for a homogeneous specimen is

$$R = \frac{(R_e\sigma_e)\sigma_e + (R_h\sigma_h)\sigma_h}{(\sigma_e + \sigma_h)^2} \tag{1}$$

where $\sigma_e = en_e\mu_e$ and $\sigma_h = en_h\mu_h$ are the respective contributions of electrons and holes to the conductivity σ, and where the grouping of factors in the numerator is to emphasize the fact that $R_e\sigma_e$ and $R_h\sigma_h$ are independent of n_e and n_h at any given temperature. Formulas for these quantities are given in § 9.11; normally $R_e < 0$, $R_h > 0$.

9.10. Thermoelectric effects. The *thermoelectric power* Q, defined as ϵ in § 4.4, measures the change in height of the Fermi level with temperature in an inhomogeneously heated specimen when no current is flowing:

$$\nabla \epsilon_F = eQ\nabla T, \quad (\boldsymbol{j} = 0) \tag{1}$$

When both holes and electrons contribute to the conduction, Q is an average of electron and hole contributions.

$$Q = \frac{Q_e\sigma_e + Q_h\sigma_h}{\sigma_e + \sigma_h} \tag{2}$$

where σ_e, σ_h are the contributions of electrons and holes, respectively, to the conductivity, as defined in § 9.9, and Q_e, Q_h are, respectively, the thermoelectric power which the mobile electrons would have in the absence of holes, and that which the holes would have in the absence of electrons. Formulas for Q_e, Q_h are given in § 9.11; normally $Q_e < 0, Q_h > 0$.

9.11. Mean free time and mean free path (Ref. 21). Let it be assumed that over the energy range of interest the effective mass of an electron or hole (see § 9.1) is independent of its direction of motion, and that the scattering processes which act to randomize the velocities of the mobile charges are such that (1) the energy change suffered by a charge in the course of being scattered through a sizable angle is usually only a small part of the original energy ϵ relative to the band edge, and (2) the probability $W(\theta)$ of being scattered in unit time into unit solid angle in a direction making angle θ with the initial direction of motion is independent of this original direction. Then quantities such as mobility, Hall coefficient, etc., can be expressed as integrals over energy involving the energy-dependent mean free time τ, defined by

$$\frac{1}{\tau(\epsilon)} = \int W(\theta,\epsilon)\,(1 - \cos\theta)d\omega \tag{1}$$

where $d\omega$ ranges over all elements of solid angle. If desired, τ may be eliminated in terms of the mean free path l, defined by

$$l(\epsilon) = v(\epsilon)\tau(\epsilon) \tag{2}$$

where $v(\epsilon) = (2\epsilon/m^*)^{1/2}$ is the speed of an electron or hole of energy ϵ relative to the band edge.

Assume the velocity distribution to be Maxwellian (Fermi level well away from allowed band of energies) and let $f_M(T,\epsilon)d\epsilon$, be the fraction of the charges whose energies lie in the range ϵ to $\epsilon + d\epsilon$, with $\int f_M d\epsilon = 1$. Denoting the Maxwellian average of any quantity F by

$$\langle F\rangle = \int_0^\infty F f_M d\epsilon$$

we have at any absolute temperature T

Mobility

$$\left.\begin{aligned} \mu &= e \cdot \frac{\langle v^2\tau\rangle}{3kT} = \frac{e}{m^*}\,\bar{\tau}_2 = \frac{4e\bar{l}_1}{3(2\pi m^* kT)^{1/2}} \\ &= 2.4036\left(\frac{m}{m^*}\right)^{1/2}\left(\frac{100}{T}\right)^{1/2}\frac{\bar{l}_1}{1\text{A}}\ \text{cm}^2/\text{volt sec} \end{aligned}\right\} \tag{3}$$

where $\bar{\tau}_2$, $\bar{l}_1$ are averages of τ, l with weights proportional to v^2 and v, respectively. Similarly the Hall coefficient, defined as in § 4.7 with E and j in absolute electrostatic units, H in absolute electromagnetic units, is

$$R_{\text{abs}} = \pm \frac{1}{nec} \frac{\langle v^2\tau^2\rangle \langle v^2\rangle}{\langle v^2\tau\rangle^2} \tag{4}$$

where n is the number mobile charges per unit volume, c is the velocity of light, and $\pm$ is $+$ for holes, $-$ for electrons. Also, if T is high enough,

$$\text{thermoelectric power } Q = \pm \left[\frac{\Delta\epsilon_F + \langle\epsilon^2\tau\rangle / \langle\epsilon\tau\rangle}{eT}\right] \tag{5}$$

where $\Delta\epsilon_F$ is the distance $\epsilon_F - \epsilon_v$ or $\epsilon_c - \epsilon_F$ of the Fermi level from the band edge, and where as before $\pm$ is $+$ for holes, $-$ for electrons.

When l is independent of energy, as is the case for scattering by lattice vibrations of the acoustic branch, the formulas reduce to

$$\left.\begin{aligned} R_{\text{abs}} &= \pm \frac{3\pi}{8nec} \quad \text{or} \quad R = \pm\, 7.3540\left(\frac{10^{18}\ \text{cm}^{-3}}{n}\right) \text{cm}^3/\text{coulomb} \\ Q &= \pm \left[\frac{\Delta\epsilon_F}{eT} + \frac{2k}{e}\right] \end{aligned}\right\} \tag{6}$$

while when τ is independent of energy, as is sometimes the case for scattering by lattice vibrations of the optical branch in a polar crystal,

$$\left.\begin{aligned} R_{\text{abs}} &= \pm \frac{1}{nec} \quad \text{or} \quad R = \pm\, 6.2422\left(\frac{10^{18}\ \text{cm}^{-3}}{n}\right) \text{cm}^3/\text{coulomb} \\ Q &= \pm \left[\frac{\Delta\epsilon_F}{eT} + \frac{5k}{2e}\right] \end{aligned}\right\} \tag{7}$$

9.12. The space charge layer near a surface (Ref. 25). Both the free surface of a semiconductor and the interface between a semiconductor and a metal usually carry surface-bound charges, which are compensated by a volume distribution of charge in the regions of the semiconductor immediately beneath surface. This volume charge causes the electrostatic potential ψ to vary with position.

A case of common occurrence is where the following two conditions are fulfilled : (1) the surface charge density q is negative and the semiconductor is n type; (2) either practically all donors are ionized and the change in $e\psi$ between the deep interior and a point just inside the surface is $\gg kT$, or the change in $e\psi$ is $\gg$ the ionization energy of the donors. A symmetrically related case is one where q is positive, the semiconductor p type, and conditions analogous to (1) and (2) are satisfied. For both these cases the volume charge density is nearly constant over the range x_0 of depths x over which most of the change of ψ takes place, at least if the centers are uniformly distributed. We then have, if n_d is the density of donor centers, n_a the density of acceptor centers (assumed all occupied), κ the dielectric constant, and the surface is taken as $x = 0$,

$$\psi(x) - \psi(x_0) = -\frac{2\pi e}{\kappa}(n_d - n_a)(x_0 - x)^2 = -V_b\left(\frac{x_0 - x}{x_0}\right)^2 \tag{1}$$

with
$$V_b = 2\pi q^2/e(n_d - n_a)\kappa,$$

$$x_0 = q/e(n_d - n_a) = \sqrt{\kappa V_b/2\pi e(n_d - n_a)}$$

$$= 1050\sqrt{\frac{\kappa V_b \text{ volts}}{(n_d - n_a)/10^{16}\text{ cm}^{-3}}}\text{ angstroms}$$

These equations apply whether or not an external potential bias has been applied to the contact.

9.13. Contact rectification (Ref. 25). A metal-semiconductor contact will show rectification if the change of potential in the space charge layer is in the direction postulated in § 9.12. Let such a contact be assumed plane and the potential a function only of the distance from this plane interface, and let tunneling of charges through the barrier be negligible. Assume that the field E at the contact ($= 4\pi q/\kappa$ in the notation of § 9.12) and the mean free path l of the electrons or holes satisfy either $|eEl| \gg kT$ (diode case) or $|eEl| \ll kT$ (diffusion case). Assume finally that the current across the interface region is carried predominantly by majority carriers, i.e., by electrons if the semiconductor is n type or by holes if it is p type. Then the relation of current density j to voltage V applied across the contact, i.e., across the space charge region, is

$$j = j_0(E)[\exp(eV/kT) - 1] \tag{1}$$

where j and V are measured positive in the forward (low resistance) direction and where if V is in the forward direction it must be restricted to values appreciably below that necessary to wipe out the space charge barrier. Note that E is in general dependent on V. The dependence of j_0 on E is different for the diode case and the diffusion case. For the diode case,

$$j_0(E) = A\frac{m^*}{m}T^2(1 - \bar{r})\exp\left(-\frac{e\phi}{kT}\right) \tag{2}$$

where
$$A = \frac{4\pi mk^2e}{h^3} = 120\text{ amp/cm}^2\text{ deg}^2$$

is Richardson's thermionic constant, m^*/m is the ratio of the effective mass of the carriers (see § 9.1) to the true electron mass, $\bar{r}$ is the mean reflection coefficient for charges energetically capable of crossing the metal-semiconductor boundary, and $e\phi$ is the barrier height, defined as the difference between the Fermi level of the metal and the bottom of the conduction band (for n type material) or top of the filled band (for p type) at the peak of the space charge barrier. For the diffusion case,

$$j_0(E) \sim \sigma_0|E| \exp(-e|V_b|/kT) \tag{3}$$

where σ_0 is the conductivity of the semiconductor in its deep interior and V_b is the change in electrostatic potential between the inner boundary of the space region and the peak of the space charge barrier. The formula for the diffusion case is written as an approximation because it is based on the assumption that the energy of the band edge varies linearly with position until it differs from its value at the surface by several times kT.

In the formula for the diode case the dependence of j_0 on E occurs only by virtue of the dependence of V_b on E due to the Schottky image effect; treating the semiconductor as a continuum of dielectric constant κ gives

$$V_b(E) = V_b(0) - \sqrt{\frac{eE}{\kappa}} = V_b(0) - 3.79 \times 10^{-4}(E_{\mathrm{v/cm}}/\kappa)^{1/2} \text{ volts} \tag{4}$$

To make a similar allowance for the image effect in the diffusion case one must abandon the assumed linear variation of band edge energy with depth; however, the principal modification of the formula given above is the replacement of V_b by the field-dependent value just given.

For some contacts the current across the contact is carried largely by minority carriers, i.e., by holes if the semiconductor is n type, or by electrons if it is p type (Ref. 1). For such contacts the preceding formulas do not apply, and in most cases a three-dimensional rather than one-dimensional approach must be used.

9.14. Differential capacity of a metal-semiconductor contact. When a small alternating potential is applied to a rectifying contact of the sort described in § 9.12 and § 9.13, the contact behaves like a capacitor in parallel with a resistor, the latter being of course derivable from the d-c current-voltage characteristic by differentiation. If the impurity centers are uniformly distributed and if the potential in the semiconductor can be taken to be a function only of distance from an essentially plane metal interface

$$\text{capacity per unit area} = |\rho_b/E| \tag{1}$$

where E is the electric field strength in the semiconductor just inside the metal boundary and ρ_b is the charge density in this region. If, as is often the case, the donor centers are all ionized at the boundary and the acceptor centers all filled, $\rho_b = e(n_d - n_a)$, where n_d, n_a are the densities of donor and acceptor centers, respectively.

Alternatively, if the charge density at each point throughout the space charge layer can be assumed unaffected by a small change of potential, then whether or not the charge density is uniform we have, if the one-dimensional treatment is applicable,

$$\text{capacity per unit area} = \kappa/4\pi x_0 \tag{2}$$

where κ is the dielectric constant and x_0 is the thickness of the space charge layer. When in addition the assumptions of § 9.12 are satisfied

$$\left.\begin{aligned} \text{capacity per unit area} &= \sqrt{\frac{\kappa e(n_d - n_a)}{8\pi V_b}} \\ &= 8422\kappa^{1/2}\left(\frac{n_d - n_a}{10^{16}\ \text{cm}^{-3}}\right)^{1/2}\left(\frac{1\ \text{v}}{V_b}\right)^{1/2} \mu\mu f/\text{cm}^2 \end{aligned}\right\} \tag{3}$$

where V_b is the potential change across the space charge layer, equal to the sum of the potential change in equilibrium and the applied bias potential.

9.15. D-c behavior of *p-n* junctions (Ref. 21). If the relative concentrations of donor and acceptor centers (see § 9.3) vary with position in a semiconducting specimen it is possible for regions of n and p type conductivity (see § 9.7) to coexist in it, separated by a region of low conductivity called a *p-n junction.* Such a junction manifests a nonlinear resistance and capacitance similar to those of metal-semiconductor contacts. The following assumptions, often realized in practice, will be made : Let the semiconductor be divisible into an n region of uniform impurity concentration, a plane-parallel transition region, and a p region of uniform impurity concentration. At points well away from the junction, let the equilibrium hole density $n_h(n)$ in the n region and the equilibrium electron density $n_e(p)$ in the p region satisfy

$$n_h(n) \ll n_e(n), \quad n_e(p) \ll n_h(p)$$

Let the quantity s, introduced in § 9.8 as the difference between the rates of annihilation and creation of mobile charges per unit volume, be describable in terms of so-called *recombination lifetimes*, thus :

$$\left.\begin{aligned} s_h &= \frac{n - n_h(n)}{\tau_h}, \quad \text{(for holes in the } n \text{ region)} \\ s_e &= \frac{n_e - n_e(p)}{\tau_e}, \quad \text{(for electrons in the } p \text{ region)} \end{aligned}\right\} \tag{1}$$

Let the thickness of the transition region be $\ll L_h$ and $\ll L_e$, where, if D_h, D_e are the diffusion coefficients for holes and electrons respectively,

$$L_h = \sqrt{D_h \tau_h}, \quad L_e = \sqrt{D_e \tau_e}$$

are the so-called *diffusion lengths* for holes and electrons, respectively. Assume the transition region to have values of s comparable with or smaller than those in the n and p regions.

Let two planes be given, one on the p side of the junction and at a distance $d_p \gg L_e$ from it, the other on the n side at a distance $d_n \gg L_h$, yet neither so far away that the ohmic resistance of p material of thickness d_p and n material of thickness d_n is comparable with the junction resistance as given below. Let a direct voltage V, measured positive in the forward direction, be applied between these two planes, and designated as the " voltage across the junction." The resulting current per unit area will then be, to a good approximation

$$\left.\begin{aligned} j &= e\left[\frac{D_h n_h(n)}{L_h} + \frac{D_e n_e(p)}{L_e}\right](e^{eV/kT} - 1) \\ &= \frac{b\sigma_i^2}{(1+b)^2}\left(\frac{1}{\sigma_n L_h} + \frac{1}{\sigma_p L_e}\right)\left[\frac{kT}{e}(e^{eV/kT} - 1)\right] \end{aligned}\right\} \tag{2}$$

where $b = \mu_e/\mu_h = D_e/D_h$, σ_i is the conductivity which the semiconductor would have in the intrinsic state (see § 9.6), and σ_n and σ_p are the conductivities of the n and p regions, respectively. The quantity in square brackets is an effective voltage, the quantity multiplying is an effective conductance per unit area.

9.16. A-c behavior of *p-n* junctions. Let a p-n junction satisfying the conditions of § 9.15 be subjected to a d-c bias V_0, measured positive in the forward direction, and to a small alternating voltage $V_1 e^{i\omega t}$. The alternating part of the current per unit area will then be $AV_1 e^{i\omega t}$, where the complex admittance A per unit area is given by

$$A = (1 + i\omega\tau_h)^{1/2} G_{h0} e^{eV_0/kT} + (1 + i\omega\tau_e)^{1/2} G_{e0} e^{eV_0/kT} + i\omega C_T \tag{1}$$

where in the notation of § 9.15

$$G_{h0} = \frac{b\sigma_i^2}{(1+b)^2 \sigma_n L_h}, \quad G_{e0} = \frac{b\sigma_i^2}{(1+b)^2 \sigma_p L_e} \tag{2}$$

and where C_T is a capacitance associated with the transition region and described below for special cases.

Let κ be the dielectric constant and n_i the density of holes or electrons in intrinsic material (see § 9.6), and let $L_D = (\kappa kT/8\pi e^2 n_i)^{1/2}$ be the corresponding Debye length. If most of the change in potential in the transition region occurs in a region within which the densities n_d of donors and n_a of acceptors satisfy

$$n_d - n_a = ax$$

where x is distance normal to the plane of the junction, and if $a \gg n_i/L_D$, then

$$C_T \approx \frac{\kappa}{8\pi}\left[\frac{8\pi e a}{3\kappa(\psi_0 - V_0)}\right]^{1/3} \tag{3}$$

where ψ_0 is a positive quantity equal to the difference in electrostatic potential between the two sides of the junction when no bias is applied. If, on the other hand, most of the change in potential in the transition region occurs in the regions of uniform impurity concentration, as may happen for large reverse bias,

$$C_T \approx \left\{\frac{\kappa e n_e(n) n_h(p)}{8\pi[n_e(n) + n_h(p)](\psi_0 - V_0)}\right\}^{1/2} \tag{4}$$

where $n_e(n)$, $n_h(p)$ are the equilibrium densities of electrons in the n region and holes in the p region, respectively.

10. Electron Theory of Metals

10.1. The Fermi-Dirac distribution (Ref. 20). Let there be n electrons per unit volume in a metal, and assume that the total energy of the metal can be represented as a constant plus a sum of energies ϵ_i of the individual electrons. Then if i designates any quantum state, i.e., set of orbital and spin quantum numbers, the fraction of the time this state is occupied in thermal equilibrium at temperature T is the Fermi function $f(\epsilon_i, \epsilon_F)$ of § 9.4. For metals, as distinguished from semiconductors, the Fermi level ϵ_F lies in a region of energies where there is a continuous distribution of quantum states, and usually does not vary much with temperature. If a metal specimen of volume Ω_N contains $n\Omega_N$ electrons and $\nu(\epsilon)d\epsilon$ quantum states, the Fermi level at temperature T is

$$\epsilon_F(T) = \epsilon_F(0) - \frac{\pi^2}{6}\left(\frac{d \ln \nu}{d\epsilon}\right)_{\varepsilon=\varepsilon_F(0)}(kT)^2 + O(T^4) \tag{1}$$

where k is Boltzmann's constant and $\epsilon_F(0)$ is determined by

$$\int_{-\infty}^{\varepsilon_F(0)} \nu(\epsilon)d\epsilon = n\Omega_N$$

If the energies of the various quantum states are the same as those of free electrons of mass m^*, $\nu(\epsilon)$ is given by the formula of § 9.2. When electrons of both spins are present equally we have, if the atomic volume $\Omega = (4\pi/3)r_s^3$ contains Z electrons,

$$\left.\begin{aligned}\epsilon_F(0) &= \frac{h^2}{2m^*}\left(\frac{3n}{8\pi}\right)^{2/3} = 3.6867 Z^{2/3}\left(\frac{a_H}{r_s}\right)^2\left(\frac{m}{m^*}\right) \text{ rydberg units} \\ &= 3.6458 \times 10^{-15}\left(\frac{m}{m^*}\right)(n_{\text{cm}^{-3}})^{2/3} e \text{ volts}\end{aligned}\right\} \quad (2)$$

$$\epsilon_F(T) \sim \epsilon_F(0) - \frac{\pi^2}{12} \cdot \frac{(kT)^2}{\epsilon_F(0)}$$

where h is Planck's constant, m the normal electron mass, and a_H the Bohr radius. For this case the maximum wave vector k_m (see § 10.5) defined by $\hbar^2 k_m^2/2m^* = \epsilon_F(0)$, has the value

$$k_m = \left(\frac{3n}{8\pi}\right)^{1/3} = \frac{1.9202 Z^{1/3}}{r_s} \qquad (3)$$

10.2. Averages of functions of the energy (Ref. 23). If $F(\epsilon)$ is any function of the energy of an electron, the sum of F over all electrons in the Fermi distribution is, in the notation of § 10.1,

$$\sum_i F(\epsilon_i)\langle N_i\rangle_{\text{av}} = \sum_{\varepsilon_i < \varepsilon_F(0)} F(\epsilon_i) + \frac{\pi^2}{6}\nu_0\left(\frac{dF}{d\epsilon}\right)_0 (kT)^2 + O(T^4) \qquad (1)$$

where the subscript 0 implies that ν and $dF/d\epsilon$ are to be evaluated at $\epsilon_F(0)$. Note that ν, being the density of quantum states, is, in an unmagnetized metal, twice the density of orbital states.

10.3. Energy and electronic specific heat (Ref. 20). For the model described in § 10.1 the electronic contribution to the molar specific heat is

$$C_v^{(e)} = \frac{\pi^2 k^2 T}{3}\nu_m(\epsilon_F) + O(T^3) \qquad (1)$$

where ν_m is the density in energy of electronic states of both spins, for one mole of material. The term $O(T^3)$ is negligible if $kT(d \ln \nu/d\epsilon)_{\varepsilon=\varepsilon_F} \ll 1$.

If the energies of the various quantum states are the same as those of free electrons of mass m^* and if there are Z such electrons per atom of a monatomic substance,

$$\left.\begin{aligned} C_v^{(e)} &\sim \left(\frac{\pi^2}{2}\right) Z \left(\frac{kT}{\epsilon_F}\right) R \\ &= 2.317 \times 10^{11} \left(\frac{m^*}{m}\right) \frac{Z}{(n_{\mathrm{cm}^{-3}})^{2/3}}\, T \quad \text{cal mol}^{-1}\,\text{deg}^{-1} \\ &= 1.694 \times 10^{-5} Z^{1/3} \left(\frac{r_s}{a_H}\right)^2 \left(\frac{m^*}{m}\right) T \quad \text{cal mol}^{-1}\,\text{deg}^{-1} \end{aligned}\right\} \qquad (2)$$

where R is the gas constant and the other symbols have the meanings explained in § 10.1. For this case of quasi-free electrons the average energy of the occupied levels at the absolute zero is

$$\epsilon_{\mathrm{av}} = \tfrac{3}{5}\epsilon_F(0) \qquad (3)$$

10.4. Spin paramagnetism (Ref. 20). In the presence of a magnetic field a nonferromagnetic metal will have an equilibrium state in which the numbers of electrons with spins parallel and antiparallel to the field are slightly different. The contribution of these unbalanced spins to the molar magnetic susceptibility is, for the model described in § 10.1,

$$\chi_m^{(s)} = \beta^2 \nu_m(\epsilon_F) + O(T^2) \qquad (1)$$

where $\beta = e\hbar/2mc$ is the Bohr magneton, and ν_m is the total number of electronic states of both spins per unit energy range, for one mole of material. The term $O(T^2)$ is negligible if

$$kT(d \ln \nu/d\epsilon)_{\varepsilon=\varepsilon_F} \ll 1$$

If the energies of the various quantum states are the same as those of free electrons of mass m^* and if there are Z such electrons per atom of a monatomic substance

$$\left.\begin{aligned} \chi_m^{(s)} &\sim \frac{3}{2} \cdot \frac{N_0 Z \beta^2}{\epsilon_F} = 1.88 \times 10^{-6} Z^{1/3} \left(\frac{A}{\rho}\right)^{2/3} \left(\frac{m^*}{m}\right) \\ &= 0.9685 \times 10^{-6} Z^{1/3} \left(\frac{r_s}{a_H}\right)^2 \left(\frac{m^*}{m}\right) \end{aligned}\right\} \qquad (2)$$

where N_0 is Avogadro's number, A the atomic weight, ρ the density, a_H the Bohr radius, and r_s the radius of the atomic s-sphere (see §§ 1.2, 10.1).

For the orbital contribution to the susceptibility see § 10.11.

10.5. Bloch waves. Consider the Schrödinger wave equation for a single electron in a potential field possessing the periodicity of a crystal lattice. The solutions satisfying periodic boundary conditions (see § 1.4) may be taken in the form

$$\psi_k = e^{i\boldsymbol{k}\cdot\boldsymbol{r}} u_k(\boldsymbol{r}) \tag{1}$$

where the function u_k possesses the periodicity of the lattice, i.e., $u_k(\boldsymbol{r}+\boldsymbol{t}) = u_k(\boldsymbol{r})$ for all lattice translations $\boldsymbol{t}$. The wave vector $\boldsymbol{k}$ must terminate on one of the closely spaced lattices of points in $\boldsymbol{k}$-space defined in § 1.4; it may, if desired, be specified to lie within the first Brillouin zone (see § 1.3), since if $\boldsymbol{g}$ is any vector of the reciprocal lattice (see § 1.3) the quantity $e^{i\boldsymbol{k}\cdot\boldsymbol{r}}$ in the above equation can be replaced by $e^{i(\boldsymbol{k}+2\pi\boldsymbol{g})\cdot\boldsymbol{r}}$ with substitution of a new periodic function for u_k. If $\boldsymbol{k}$ is thus specified to lie in the first Brillouin zone, it is called the *reduced wave vector* of ψ_k. The set of energies ϵ_k going with a particular reduced wave vector $\boldsymbol{k}$ is discrete, but the variation of each of these ϵ_k's with changes in $\boldsymbol{k}$ is continuous. Explicitly, if ψ_k is the only eigenfunction of reduced wave vector $\boldsymbol{k}$ and energy ϵ_k,

$$\frac{\partial \epsilon_k}{\partial \boldsymbol{k}} = -\frac{\hbar^2}{m}\int \psi_k^* i \nabla \psi_k \, d\tau \tag{2}$$

10.6. Velocity and acceleration. The mean velocity of an electron in a Bloch wave state ψ_k of energy ϵ_k is, if no other state has the same reduced wave vector and the same energy,

$$\boldsymbol{v}_k = \frac{1}{\hbar}\cdot\frac{\partial \epsilon_k}{\partial \boldsymbol{k}} \tag{1}$$

Application of a spatially uniform force $\boldsymbol{F}$ to an electron in such a state causes the wave function and energy to change with time, in a manner which for nearly all practical purposes can be described by saying that the wave vector changes uniformly at the rate

$$\frac{d\boldsymbol{k}}{dt} = \frac{\boldsymbol{F}}{\hbar} \tag{2}$$

10.7. Energy levels of almost free electrons (Ref. 23). For perfectly free electrons $\epsilon_k^{(0)} = \hbar^2 k^2/2m$ varies continuously with k as k goes from 0 to ∞. If the periodic potential field of a crystal is treated as a small perturbation on these free electron levels, ϵ_k acquires discontinuities on certain planes in $\boldsymbol{k}$-space, viz., when for any vector $\boldsymbol{g}$ of the reciprocal lattice (see § 1.3)

$$\boldsymbol{g}\cdot(\boldsymbol{k}-\pi\boldsymbol{g}) = 0$$

The *n*th *Brillouin zone* is defined as that region of $\boldsymbol{k}$-space which can be reached from the origin by crossing $(n-1)$ of these planes in the outward direction. Each point of the first Brillouin zone occurs once and only once among the reduced wave vectors (see § 10.5) of all points in the nth zone.

If $\boldsymbol{k}$ is a point rather closer to the discontinuity plane going with the reciprocal lattice vector $\boldsymbol{g}$ than to any other such plane, the value of ϵ_k given by the present perturbation treatment is approximately

$$\epsilon_k = \frac{\epsilon_k^{(0)} + \epsilon_{k-2\pi g}^{(0)} \pm \sqrt{(\epsilon_k^{(0)} - \epsilon_{k-2\pi g}^{(0)})^2 + 4 \mid V_g \mid^2}}{2} \tag{1}$$

where
$$V_g = \frac{1}{\Omega_N} \int_{\Omega_N} e^{2\pi i \boldsymbol{g} \cdot \boldsymbol{r}} V(\boldsymbol{r}) d\tau$$

is a Fourier coefficient of the potential energy function V, Ω_N being the volume of the specimen, the "fundamental volume" of § 1.4. Let $\boldsymbol{k} = \pi \boldsymbol{g} + \boldsymbol{k}_{\|} + \boldsymbol{k}_{\perp}$ where $\boldsymbol{k}_{\|}$ is parallel to the discontinuity plane, $\boldsymbol{k}_{\perp}$ normal to it. Then since $\epsilon_k^{(0)} = \hbar^2 k^2/2m$ we have, if $k_{\perp} \ll m \mid V_g \mid/\pi \hbar^2 g$,

$$\epsilon_k \sim \frac{\hbar^2 \pi^2 g^2}{2m} + \frac{\hbar^2}{2m} k_{\|}^2 + V_0 \pm \mid V_g \mid \pm \frac{\hbar^2}{2m} k_{\perp}^2 \left(\frac{\hbar^2 \pi^2 g^2}{m \mid V_g \mid} \pm 1 \right) \tag{2}$$

where V_0 is the space average of the perturbing potential, and where it is customary to use the upper sign if $\boldsymbol{k}_{\perp}$ points away from the origin, the lower if toward it. When $k_{\perp} \gg m \mid V_g \mid/\pi \hbar^2 g$,

$$\epsilon_k \sim \frac{\hbar^2 k^2}{2m} + V_0 + \frac{m \mid V_g \mid^2}{\hbar^2 (2\pi \boldsymbol{g} \cdot \boldsymbol{k}_{\perp})} \tag{3}$$

10.8. Coulomb energy (Ref. 20). Since a unit cell of a metal is electrically neutral, a convenient step in calculating electrostatic energies is to calculate the energy of a single unit cell by itself. If the unit cell does not differ too much in shape from the s-sphere (see § 1.2) of equal volume and if the charge of Z conduction electrons is uniformly distributed over the cell, the electrostatic potential due to this distribution of electrons will be approximately the same as that due to a uniform distribution of electrons over an s-sphere, viz.,

$$U(r) = -\frac{3Ze}{2r_s} + \frac{Zer^2}{2r_s^3} \tag{1}$$

where r_s is the radius of the s-sphere. The contribution to the potential energy of an electron is of course $-eU$. The self-energy of this distribution of electrons over an s-sphere is

$$-\tfrac{1}{2} Ze \langle U \rangle_{\text{av}} = \frac{3Z^2 e^2}{5r_s} \tag{2}$$

10.9. Exchange energy (Ref. 20). Let the ground state wave function for an assembly of N free electrons be approximated by a determinant of plane wave functions, half with one spin and half with the other. The total energy will then be the sum of the kinetic energies of the various electrons, the energy of interaction of the electrons with whatever positive charges are present, the Coulomb self-energy of the mean charge density of the electrons, and an exchange term given by

$$-\frac{3^{4/3}}{4\pi^{1/3}}\, e^2 n^{1/3} \cdot N = -\frac{3^{5/3}}{2^{8/3}\pi^{2/3}} \frac{Z^{1/3}e^2}{r_s} \cdot N = -0.458 \frac{Z^{1/3}e^2}{r_s} \cdot N \qquad (1)$$

where $n = N/\Omega_N$ is the number of electrons per unit volume and Z is the number of electrons in a volume $4\pi r_s^3/3$. The change in energy caused by removing an electron from a state with wave vector $\boldsymbol{k}$ is, in the present determinantal approximation, equal to the negative of the kinetic and electrostatic energies of this electron, plus the exchange term

$$\left.\begin{aligned} A_{kk} &= \frac{e^2 k_m}{2\pi}\left(2 + \frac{k_m^2 - k^2}{k k_m} \ln \left|\frac{k + k_m}{k - k_m}\right|\right) \\ &= 1.222 \frac{Z^{1/3}e^2}{r_s}\left[\frac{1}{2} + \frac{k_m}{4k}\left(1 - \frac{k^2}{k_m^2}\right) \ln \left|\frac{1 + k/k_m}{1 - k/k_m}\right|\right] \end{aligned}\right\} \qquad (2)$$

where k_m is the maximum k occurring in the Fermi distribution. The quantity in square brackets has the value 1 at $k = 0$, $\frac{1}{2}$ at $k = k_m$, and 0 at $k = \infty$. Its derivative with respect to k is 0 at $k = 0$, $-\infty$ at $k = k_m$.

10.10. Electrical and thermal conduction (Ref. 20). Let the conduction electrons of a metal be assumed to occupy states of the Bloch type (see § 10.5) and to be scattered by lattice vibrations but not by each other. Suppose further that $T \gg \Theta$, where Θ is the Debye temperature of the lattice (see § 7.5), but that at the same time the electron distribution is highly degenerate, i.e., $kTd \ln \nu/d\epsilon \ll 1$, where ν is the number of electronic states per unit energy. Then the electric conductivity σ and the thermal conductivity κ must be related by the *Wiedemann-Franz law*

$$\frac{\kappa}{\sigma T} = \frac{\pi^2}{3}\left(\frac{k}{e}\right)^2 = 2.45 \times 10^{-8} \text{ watt-ohm/deg}^2 \qquad (1)$$

The Hall constant R, as defined in § 4.7, can be simply related to the electron density only if some special assumptions are made regarding the variation of energy with wave vector and the angular dependence of the scattering probability. The simplest case is that where $\epsilon_k \propto k^2 +$ constant, degeneracy is complete, and scattering is isotropic; for this case

$$R_{\text{abs}} = -\frac{1}{nec} \quad \text{or} \quad R = -6.2422 \cdot \left(\frac{10^{18}\ \text{cm}^{-3}}{n}\right) \ \text{cm}^3/\text{coulomb} \tag{2}$$

where n is the number of electrons per unit volume, c is the velocity of light, and R_{abs} is defined with E and j in absolute electrostatic units, H in absolute electromagnetic units. The same formula applies, with a positive instead of negative sign, to the case where there are n holes per unit volume in a band and the energies of these empty levels satisfy $\epsilon_k \propto \text{constant} - (\boldsymbol{k} - \boldsymbol{k}_0)^2$.

10.11. Orbital diamagnetism (Ref. 20). When a magnetic field is applied to a metal the conduction electrons not only change their spin distribution but also suffer an alteration of their orbital wave functions. The latter effect causes a contribution $\chi_m^{(o)}$ to the molar susceptibility, which must be added to the spin contribution $\chi_m^{(s)}$ of § 10.4. For perfectly free electrons at temperatures approaching the absolute zero

$$\chi_m^{(o)} = -\tfrac{1}{3}\chi_m^{(s)} \tag{1}$$

A band containing a number Δn per unit volume of electrons or holes with a small effective mass m^* contributes a rather larger amount to $\chi_m^{(0)}$, given approximately by

$$\chi_m^{(0)} = -\frac{1}{3}\chi_m^{(s)}\left(\frac{m}{m^*}\right)^2 = -\frac{4\pi m\beta^2}{3h^2}\left(\frac{3\Delta n}{\pi}\right)^{1/3}\left(\frac{m}{m^*}\right) v_m \tag{2}$$

where $\beta = e\hbar/2mc$ is the Bohr magneton and v_m is the molar volume. This formula may be applied to cases where the effective masses m_z^* along and m_x^*, m_y^* transverse to the magnetic field are different, by setting $m^* = (m_x^{*2} m_y^{*2}/m_z^*)^{1/3}$. All these formulas refer to the susceptibility at zero field; when the magnetic field H becomes of the order of kT/β, the susceptibility becomes field-dependent.

10.12. Optical constants (Ref. 20). In any homogeneous isotropic medium the amplitude of a plane electromagnetic wave of angular frequency ω will vary as

$$e^{-k\omega x/c}\begin{pmatrix}\sin\\ \cos\end{pmatrix}\left[\omega\left(\frac{nx}{c} - t\right)\right]$$

where c is the velocity of light, t the time, x the coordinate in the direction of propagation, and k and n are optical constants which are in general functions of ω. Consider the case where the medium consists of an assembly of classical free electrons, of mass m, charge e, and density n per unit volume. Assume the motion of each electron to be damped by a frictional force equal to $-m\omega_\tau$ times its velocity. For this case

$$\left.\begin{aligned} n^2 - k^2 = 1 - \frac{\omega_0^2}{\omega^2 + \omega_\tau}, \quad nk = \frac{\omega_\tau \omega_0^2}{2\omega(\omega^2 + \omega_\tau^2)} \end{aligned}\right\} \tag{1}$$

where

$$\omega_0^2 = \frac{4\pi n e^2}{m} \quad \text{or} \quad \omega_0 = 1.7841 \times 10^{16} \left(\frac{n}{10^{23}\ \text{cm}^{-3}} \right)^{1/2} \quad \text{sec}^{-1}$$

The quantity ω_τ is related to the d-c conductivity σ_0 of this model by

$$\omega_\tau = \frac{ne^2}{m\sigma_0} = 2.8185 \times 10^{13} \left(\frac{n}{10^{23}\ \text{cm}^{-3}} \right) \left(\frac{10^6\ \text{ohm}^{-1}\ \text{cm}^{-1}}{\sigma_0} \right) \text{sec}^{-1}$$

When this model is used as an approximation to actual metals it turns out that $\omega_\tau \ll \omega_0$. When this is fulfilled and $\omega \ll \omega_\tau$, the above formulas reduce to

$$n \approx k \approx \left(\frac{2\pi\sigma_0}{\omega} \right)^{1/2} = 54.75 \left(\frac{\lambda}{1\mu} \right)^{1/2} \left(\frac{\sigma_0}{10^6\ \text{ohm}^{-1}\ \text{cm}^{-1}} \right)^{1/2} \tag{2}$$

This leads to the *Hagen-Rubens relation* for the reflection coefficient R of a metal surface in the infrared.

$$R = 1 - 2\left(\frac{\omega}{2\pi\sigma_0} \right)^{1/2} \tag{3}$$

When $\omega_\tau \ll \omega$, on the other hand, $nk \approx 0$, so if $\omega < \omega_0$

$$n \approx 0, \quad k \approx \left(\frac{\omega_0^2}{\omega^2} - 1 \right)^{1/2}$$

and if $\omega > \omega_0$,

$$n \approx \left(1 - \frac{\omega_0^2}{\omega^2} \right)^{1/2}, \quad k \approx 0 \tag{4}$$

11. Miscellaneous

11.1. Specific heats at constant stress and strain (Ref. 27). Let C_p be the heat capacity of some given amount of crystalline material at constant stress p, and C_v that at constant volume and state of strain. Let v be the volume of this same amount of material. Then if T is the absolute temperature and u_i ($i = 1$ to 6) the strain components as defined in § 2.1, so that $(\partial u_i/\partial T)_p$ are generalized expansion coefficients,

$$C_p - C_v = Tv \sum_{i,j=1}^{6} c_{ij} \left(\frac{\partial u_i}{\partial T} \right)_p \left(\frac{\partial u_j}{\partial T} \right)_p \tag{1}$$

where the c_{ij} are the elastic constants as defined in § 2.2. For cubic or isotropic material this reduces to

$$C_p - C_v = \frac{9Tv\alpha^2}{\kappa} \tag{2}$$

where $\alpha = (\partial u_1/\partial T)_p$ is the linear expansion coefficient and $\kappa = -(1/v)(\partial v/\partial p)_T$ is the isothermal volume compressibility.

11.2. Magnetocaloric effect and magnetic cooling (Ref. 19). Let M be the magnetic moment of a specimen of matter subjected to a magnetic field H due to external sources. If H is changed in such way that the entropy S of the specimen remains constant, and if the state of the specimen is always one of thermal equilibrium in the field H, the absolute temperature T of the specimen will change according to

$$\left(\frac{\partial T}{\partial H}\right)_S = -\frac{T}{C^{(H)}}\left(\frac{\partial M}{\partial T}\right)_H \tag{1}$$

where $C^{(H)} = T(\partial S/\partial T)_H$ is the heat capacity of the specimen at constant H. The equation is valid if all derivatives are taken at constant pressure, or all at constant volume.

11.3. The Cauchy relations (Ref. 3). Let the atoms of a crystal be assumed to interact in pairs, with the interaction energy of each pair a function of radial distance only. Let the crystal, initially in equilibrium at zero stress and the absolute zero of temperature, be subjected to an infinitesimal homogeneous strain described by the tensor $u_{\mu\nu}$, with resultant stress tensor $p_{\mu\nu}$ (as used in § 2.1). Let the symmetry of the lattice be such that the displacement of any atom, originally at position $R^{(i)}$, is simply

$$\sum_{\nu=1}^{3} u_{\mu\nu} R_\nu^{(i)}$$

This condition is satisfied, for example, if each atom is a center of symmetry. Then the elastic constant tensor $c_{\mu\alpha\nu\beta}$, defined by

$$p_{\mu\alpha} = \sum_{\nu,\beta=1}^{3} c_{\mu\alpha\nu\beta} u_{\nu\beta} \tag{1}$$

(as used in § 7.1), must be symmetrical with respect to all interchanges of the indices μ, α, ν, β. The identities which result from this fact go beyond those always required by the symmetry of $c_{\mu\alpha\nu\beta}$ in $\mu \rightleftarrows \alpha$, $\nu \rightleftarrows \beta$ and $\mu, \alpha \rightleftarrows \nu, \beta$, and are called the *Cauchy relations*.

In the notation of § 2.2 these are

$$\left.\begin{aligned} c_{23} &= c_{44} \qquad & c_{56} &= c_{14} \\ c_{31} &= c_{55} \qquad & c_{64} &= c_{25} \\ c_{12} &= c_{66} \qquad & c_{45} &= c_{36} \end{aligned}\right\} \tag{2}$$

For cubic crystals these degenerate into the single relation

$$c_{12} = c_{44} \tag{3}$$

11.4. The Brillouin and Langevin functions (Ref. 26). Let $\beta = e\hbar/2mc$ be the Bohr magneton and let g be the Landé factor for an atom of total angular momentum quantum number J, so that the eigenvalues of the z component of magnetic moment run from $g\beta J$ to $-g\beta J$, in steps of $g\beta$. When such an atom is in thermal equilibrium at absolute temperature T in the presence of a magnetic field H, and in the absence of other orienting influences, its mean magnetic moment is

$$M_{\text{av}} = g\beta J B_J\left(\frac{g\beta JH}{kT}\right) \tag{1}$$

where k is Boltzmann's constant and

$$B_J(y) = \left(\frac{2J+1}{2J}\right) \coth \frac{(2J+1)y}{2J} - \frac{1}{2J} \coth \frac{y}{2J} \tag{2}$$

is called the *Brillouin function.* If J is $\gg 1$ but $g\beta H/kT \ll 1$, M_{av} approaches the value given by the classical statistics, viz., the value obtained by substituting for the function B_J the *Langevin function*

$$L(y) = \coth y - \frac{1}{y} \tag{3}$$

of the same argument. See also, Chapter 26.

11.5. Relation of thermal release to capture of mobile charges by traps. In an insulator or semiconductor let ϵ_c be the energy of the bottom of the conduction band (see § 9.1), ϵ_t the energy required to take an electron from the state of zero energy and place it in an electron trap (see § 9.3). Assume the energy level at the bottom of the conduction band to be nondegenerate, and let m_e^* be the effective mass associated with this band (see § 9.1). Let σ be the cross section for capture of a free electron by the trap, averaged over spin orientations and assumed independent of electron energy. Then the mean lifetime τ of an electron in the trap, defined by rate of thermal release $= (1/\tau) \times$ number in traps, is given by

$$\left.\begin{aligned} \tau &= \frac{h^3(g_1/g_0)}{16\pi m_e^*(kT)^2\sigma} \exp\left(\frac{\epsilon_c - \epsilon_t}{kT}\right) \\ &= 3.332 \times 10^{-12}\left(\frac{m}{m_e^*}\right)\left(\frac{1000}{T}\right)^2\left(\frac{g_1}{g_0}\right)\left(\frac{10^{-16}\ \text{cm}^2}{\sigma}\right)\exp\left(\frac{\epsilon_c - \epsilon_t}{kT}\right) \text{sec} \end{aligned}\right\} \tag{1}$$

where h is Planck's constant, k Boltzmann's constant, m the normal electron mass, T the absolute temperature, and g_1, g_0 are the statistical weights of full and empty traps, respectively.

The same formula applies, under analogous assumptions, to release of holes from hole traps (see § 9.3); for this case m_e^* is replaced by the effective mass m_h^* of holes, g_1 and g_0 refer to states respectively with and without a trapped hole, and $\epsilon_c - \epsilon_t$ is replaced by $\epsilon_t - \epsilon_v$, the energy required to take an electron from the top of the valence band and place it in a trap which has previously captured a hole.

The same formula can be applied to cases where the capture cross section is inversely proportional to the energy of the mobile charge relative to the band edge, if for σ is set the cross section for an energy kT. Similarly it can be applied when the capture cross section is inversely proportional to the velocity, if for σ is set the cross section for a charge with the arithmetic mean thermal speed $v_T = (2^{3/2}/\pi^{1/2})\,(kT/m^*)^{1/2}$.

Bibliography

1. Bardeen, J. and Brattain, W. H., *Phys. Rev.*, **75**, 1208 (1949).
2. Born, M. and Bollnow, O. F., " Der Aufbau der festen Materie," in *Handbuch der Physik*, Vol. 24, Julius Springer, Berlin, 1927. Similar in content to the later article of Born and Goeppert-Mayer (Ref. 3), but with some variation in choice of material.
3. Born, M. and Goeppert-Mayer, M., " Dynamische Gittertheorie der Kristalle," in *Handbuch der Physik*, Vol. 24/2, 2d ed., Julius Springer, Berlin, 1933. An exhaustive review of the classical theory of crystals as lattices of pairwise-interacting atoms or ions.
4. Bridgman, P. W., *Thermodynamics of Electrical Phenomena in Metals*, The Macmillan Company, New York, 1934. The most detailed and penetrating treatise on the phenomenological theory of thermoelectric and related phenomena, but not adapted to quick reference.
5. Cady, W. G., *Piezoelectricity*, McGraw-Hill Book Company, Inc., New York, 1946. Covers in considerable detail not only piezoelectricity but also theoretical and practical aspects of crystal electricity.
6. Casimir, H. B. G., *Revs. Modern Phys.*, **17**, 343 (1945).
7. Epstein, P. S., *Textbook of Thermodynamics*, John Wiley & Sons, Inc., New York, 1937. Chapter 20 gives the standard application of thermodynamics to thermoelectric phenomena.
8. Försterling, K., *Ann. Physik*, **61**, 577 (1920).
9. Fowler, R. H. and Guggenheim, E. A., *Statistical Thermodynamics*, Cambridge University Press, London, 1939. A comprehensive advanced treatise on the derivation of the thermodynamic properties of matter from statistical mechanics.
10. Herring, C., *Phys. Rev.*, **59**, 889 (1941).
11. IRE Committee on Piezoelectric Crystals, *Proc. IRE*, **37**, 1378 (1949).

12. Koehler, J. S., *Phys. Rev.*, **60**, 397 (1941).
13. London, F., *Superfluids*, Vol. 1, John Wiley & Sons, Inc., New York, 1950. A complete and lucid account of the London theory of superconductivity and its applications.
14. Love, A. E. H., *Treatise on the Mathematical Theory of Elasticity*, 3d ed., Cambridge University Press, London, 1920. A comprehensive treatise, of which Chapter 6 is devoted to the elastic constant of crystals.
15. Lyddane, R. H., Sachs, R. G., and Teller, E., *Phys. Rev.*, **59**, 673 (1941).
16. Mason, W. P., *Piezoelectric Crystals and Their Application to Ultrasonics*, D. Van Nostrand Company, Inc., New York, 1950. Covers piezoelectricity, crystal electricity, and associated thermodynamic relations, using the standard IRE notation of Ref. 11.
17. Peach, M. and Koehler, J. S., *Phys. Rev.*, **80**, 436 (1950).
18. Read, W. T. and Shockley, W., " Geometry of Dislocations," in *Imperfections in Nearly Perfect Crystals*, John Wiley & Sons, Inc., New York, 1951.
19. Ruhemann, M. and B., *Low Temperature Physics*, Cambridge University Press, London, 1937. A small, readable book devoted mainly to experimental aspects of the subject.
20. Seitz, F., *Modern Theory of Solids*, McGraw-Hill Book Company, Inc., New York, 1940. A sound and thorough treatise on most aspects of the atomistic theory of solids, especially the electron theory of metals, but too old to include recent developments on semiconductors.
21. Shockley, W., *Electrons and Holes in Semiconductors*, D. Van Nostrand Company, Inc., New York, 1950. Covers authoritatively most, though not all, modern developments in the theory of semiconductors, discussing many of the topics twice—once from an elementary and once from an advanced point of view.
22. Slater, J. C., *Introduction to Chemical Physics*, McGraw-Hill Book Company, Inc., New York, 1939. Covers atomistic and phenomenological theories of the properties of matter, at such a level as to be easily readable.
23. Sommerfeld, A. and Bethe, H., " Elektronentheorie der Metalle," in *Handbuch der Physik*, Vol. 24/2, 2d ed., Julius Springer, Berlin, 1933. Somewhat out of date, but still valuable because of its thoroughness and scholarly approach.
24. Thirring, H., *Physik. Z.*, **14**, 867 (1913).
25. Torrey, H. C. and Whitmer, C. A., *Crystal Rectifiers* (Radiation Laboratory Series, Vol. 15), McGraw-Hill Book Company, Inc., New York, 1948. Though devoted primarily to the application of semiconducting devices to microwave electronics, this book gives a fairly good account of the theory of semiconductors, and especially of rectifying contacts, as of its publication date.
26. Van Vleck, J. H., *Theory of Electric and Magnetic Susceptibilities*, Oxford University Press, New York, 1932. An authoritative and detailed treatise, so soundly written that little of it is out of date.
27. Voigt, W., *Lehrbuch der Kristallphysik*, B. G. Teubner, Leipzig, 1910 (2d ed., 1928). The most exhaustive treatise on all properties of crystals considered as anisotropic continua.

Chapter 26

THE THEORY OF MAGNETISM

BY J. H. VAN VLECK

Hollis Professor of Mathematical Physics and Natural Philosophy,
Dean of Applied Science, Harvard University

The following brief summary comprises some of the major formulas of the atomic theory of magnetism. They have been selected to provide the reader with basic relations and ones most likely to be useful for the research student. It is hoped that the explanatory text will fill in the background necessary for the understanding of the fundamentals. The emphasis is entirely on the atomic or molecular viewpoint, and no attempt is made to include domain theory, or so-called phenomena of " technical magnetization," such as remanence, hysteresis, etc.

1. Paramagnetism

1.1. Classical theory. Langevin's formula for the magnetic moment M per unit volume in a field of arbitrary strength H is

$$M = N\mu L(\mu H/kT) \tag{1}$$

where N is the number of atoms or molecules per unit volume, μ is the magnetic dipole moment of the atom or molecule, and $L(x)$ is the Langevin function

$$L(x) = \coth x - 1/x \tag{2}$$

In weak fields (i.e., $\mu H/kT \ll 1$), the Langevin formula reduces to the following expression for the susceptibility :

$$\chi = M/H = N\mu^2/3kT \tag{3}$$

The proportionality of the paramagnetic susceptibility to the reciprocal of the temperature constitutes Curie's law. The proportionality factor is known as the Curie constant. According to the Langevin formula, the Curie constant is $N\mu^2/3k$.

1.2. Quantum theory. In quantum mechanics, Curie's law is valid if the matrix elements of the magnetic moment exist only between states whose separation is small compared with kT, and if there is a permanent magnetic moment μ. A permanent magnetic moment signifies that the square of the magnetic moment has the same expectation value for all states that possess an appreciable Boltzmann factor. If in addition matrix elements exist connecting states widely spaced compared with kT, the susceptibility will contain a term independent of temperature, i.e.,

$$\chi = N\mu^2/3kT + N\alpha$$

If there are matrix elements joining states separated by intervals comparable to kT, deviations from Curie's law will occur.

a. *Free atoms with multiplets wide compared with kT.* In a field of arbitrary strength, the moment is

$$M = NJg\beta B_J\left(\frac{Jg\beta H}{kT}\right) + N\alpha_J H \tag{1}$$

Here J is the atom's inner quantum number, g is the Landé factor, β is the Bohr magneton $he/4\pi mc = 0.927 \times 10^{-20}$ erg · gauss^{-1}, and B_J is the Brillouin function.

$$\left.\begin{aligned} B_J(y) &= \frac{\sum_{M=-J}^{J} Me^{My/J}}{J\sum_{M=-J}^{J} e^{My/J}} \\ &= \frac{2J+1}{J}\coth\left(\frac{2Jy+y}{2J}\right) - \frac{1}{2J}\coth\frac{y}{2J} \end{aligned}\right\} \tag{2}$$

The last member $N\alpha_J H$ of Eq. (1) is a correction term for the effect of the matrix elements of the magnetic moment which are nondiagonal in J. It is assumed that the Zeeman separations are small compared with the multiplet intervals $h\nu(J',J)$, and that the latter are large compared with kT. The explicit formula for α_J is

$$\alpha_J = \frac{\beta^2}{6(2J+1)}\left[\frac{F(J+1)}{h\nu(J+1,J)} - \frac{F(J)}{h\nu(J,J-1)}\right] \tag{3}$$

where

$$F(J) = \frac{1}{J}\,[(S+L+1)^2 - J^2]\,[J^2 - (S-L)^2]$$

In weak fields ($Jg\beta H \ll kT$), the susceptibility is

$$\chi = \frac{Ng^2 J(J+1)\beta^2}{3kT} + N\alpha_J \tag{4}$$

The following formulas (5) to (8) are given only for the case of weak fields, i.e., with neglect of saturation effects.

b. *Free atoms with multiplets small compared with kT.*

$$\chi = \frac{N\beta^2}{3kT}[4S(S+1) + L(L+1)] \tag{5}$$

c. *Free atoms with multiplet separations comparable to kT*

$$\chi = N \frac{\sum\limits_{J=|L-S|}^{L+S} \left[\frac{g_J{}^2\beta^2 J(J+1)}{3kT} + \alpha_J\right] e^{-E_J/kT}}{\sum e^{-E_J/kT}} \tag{6}$$

Here the E_J are the energies of the various multiplet components of the atom in the absence of a magnetic field. The subscript J is attached to the g-factor to indicate that it depends on J.

d. *Free molecules.* Practically all free molecules except NO have susceptibilities conforming to the " spin-only " formula

$$\chi = \frac{4N\beta^2 S(S+1)}{3kT} + N\alpha \tag{7}$$

Here $N\alpha$ is a small correction term, independent of temperature, arising from the orbital magnetic moment, which is highly nondiagonal.

Nitric oxide is the standard example of a molecule that deviates from Curie's law because the multiplets interval $\Delta\nu$ is comparable with kT. Here

$$\chi = \frac{4N\beta^2}{3kT}\left[\frac{1 - e^{-z} + ze^{-z}}{z(1+e^{-z})}\right] + N\alpha \tag{8}$$

where $$z = \frac{h\Delta\nu}{kT} = \frac{173}{T}$$

e. *Solids of high magnetic dilution.* In such solutions the paramagnetic ions are widely separated. They are usually highly hydrated salts. Such materials can be treated by means of a one-atom model, based on the idea that an ion is subject to a crystalline potential $V(x,y,z)$ which represents the effect of the interatomic forces. Let E_n be the energy of a quantum-mechanical state, including both the Stark energy arising from the crystalline field, and the Zeeman energy caused by the applied magnetic field. The quantum-mechanical formula for the expectation value of the magnetic moment of an arbitrary state n is in general,

$$\langle M_n \rangle_{\text{av}} = -\partial E_n/\partial H \tag{9}$$

The magnetic moment per unit volume is thus

$$M = -N \frac{\Sigma_n (\partial E_n/\partial H) e^{-E_n/kT}}{\Sigma_n e^{-E_n/kT}} \tag{10}$$

In case the energy E_n can be developed as a Taylor's series in H, viz.,

$$E_n = E_n^{(0)} + E_n^{(1)} H + E_n^{(2)} H^2 + \ldots$$

the expression for the susceptibility in weak fields is

$$\chi = \frac{N \Sigma_n [(E_n^{(1)})^2/kT - 2E_n^{(2)}] e^{-E_n^{(0)}/kT}}{\Sigma_n e^{-E_n^{(0)}/kT}} \tag{11}$$

In salts of the iron group, the crystalline potential largely quenches the orbital moment, and the spin-only formula [Eq. (7) of § 1.2] is often a fairly good approximation. Rare-earth salts at room temperatures can usually be treated as having free atoms [Eq. (4) or (6) of § 1.2].

f. *Magnetically compact solids.* These require inclusion of exchange coupling between atoms and cannot be treated on the basis of the one-atom model. Oftentimes the exchange coupling can be approximately represented by means of a Weiss molecular field [see Eq. (1) of § 2.1].

g. *Nuclear effects.* Nuclear effects on the paramagnetic susceptibility are negligible as long as the hyperfine structure is small compared with kT.

h. *Spectroscopic stability.* In general any interaction producing a fine structure small compared with kT does not influence the susceptibility, which is thus the same as if the interaction were completely absent.

2. Ferromagnetism

2.1. Classical theory. The standard model, semitheoretical, semiphenomenological, of ferromagnetism in classical theory is that of Weiss, wherein the field in the argument of the Langevin-function involved in Eq. (1) of § 1.1 is taken to be not the applied field, but rather the field augmented by a " Weiss molecular field " proportional to the intensity of magnetization. The total effective field is then

$$H_{\text{eff}} = H + qM \tag{1}$$

and in place of Eq. (1) of § 1.1, one has

$$M = N\mu L\left[\frac{\mu(H + qM)}{kT}\right] \tag{2}$$

The Curie temperature T_c is that below which spontaneous magnetization is possible, i.e., below which Eq. (2) admits a solution with $H = 0$. It is

$$T_c = N\mu^2 q/3k \tag{3}$$

For $T > T_c$, the susceptibility, apart from saturation corrections, has the form

$$\chi = N\mu^2/3k(T - T_c) \tag{4}$$

2.2. Quantum theory. a. *Heisenberg model.* Heisenberg showed that the origin of the Weiss molecular field is to be found in exchange coupling. In his model each atom contains one or more uncompensated electron spins (Heitler-London model of valence). The exchange effects introduce an interatomic potential of the form

$$V = -2\,\Sigma_{j>i}\mathcal{J}_{ij}\boldsymbol{S}_i \cdot \boldsymbol{S}_j \tag{1}$$

where $\boldsymbol{S}_i$ is the spin-vector of atom i, and $\mathcal{J}_{ij}$ is the exchange integral joining atoms i and j. Usually $\mathcal{J}_{ij}$ is assumed, for simplicity, to have a nonvanishing value $\mathcal{J}$ only between adjacent atoms.

Even with this simplification, an exact analytical expression for the moment is obtainable only in the vicinity of the absolute zero, where the so-called Bloch spin waves can be used. In the region, i.e., $\mathcal{J}/kT \ll 1$, one has for the special case $S = \frac{1}{2}$,

$$M = N\beta\left[1 - A\left(\frac{kT}{\mathcal{J}}\right)^{3/2}\right] \tag{2}$$

where A is a constant, which assumes the value 0.1174 for a simple cubic lattice.

At higher temperatures, great simplification follows from the use of the so-called first approximation of the Heisenberg theory, wherein it is assumed that all states of the same resultant spin for the whole crystal have the same energy. This approximation is questionable from a mathematical standpoint but seems to work fairly well and gives results remarkably similar to those of the Weiss theory. In place of Eqs. (2) and (3) of § 2.1 one has

$$M = gNS\beta B_S\left[\frac{gS\beta(H + qM)}{kT}\right] \tag{3}$$

with $q = 2z\mathcal{J}/g^2N\beta^2$.

$$T_c = \frac{2\mathcal{J}zS(S + 1)}{3k} \tag{4}$$

Here $B_S(y)$ is defined as in Eq. (2) of § 1.2, and z denotes the number of nearest neighbors possessed by an atom. Eq. (4) of § 2.1 is applicable with

$$\mu^2 = g^2\beta^2 S(S+1) \tag{5}$$

More accurate analysis gives a somewhat different formula than Eq. (4) for T_c. An accurate development of the reciprocal of the susceptibility above the Curie point takes the form

$$\frac{1}{\chi} = \frac{3k}{g^2 N\beta^2 S(S+1)}\left(T - \Delta + \frac{a}{T} + \frac{b}{T^2} + \frac{c}{T^3} + \dots\right) \tag{6}$$

Values of the constants, a, b, c have been computed for the case $S = \frac{1}{2}$ by Opechowski, corrected by Zehler.

b. *Stoner's model of "collective electron ferromagnetism."* The Stoner model is the analogue of the Hund-Mulliken theory of valence, and assumes that electrons wander from atom to atom, instead of being bound to a given atom. Besides the intensity of the exchange coupling or molecular field, the conduction band width enters as a disposable constant.

The free energy F, specific heat C_v, and moment M are computed as follows from a characteristic function Γ.

$$F = NkT - kT\Gamma, \quad C_v = \frac{\partial}{\partial T}\left[kT^2\left(\frac{\partial \Gamma}{\partial T}\right)_\eta\right], \quad M = kT\left(\frac{\partial \Gamma}{\partial H}\right)_\eta \tag{7}$$

The Stoner expression for Γ is

$$\left.\begin{aligned}\Gamma = &\int_0^\infty \nu(\epsilon) \ln\left[1 + e^{\eta - (\varepsilon - qM\beta - \beta H)/kT}\right] d\epsilon \\ &+ \int_0^\infty \nu(\epsilon) \ln\left[1 + e^{\eta - (\varepsilon + qM\beta + \beta H)/kT}\right] d\epsilon\end{aligned}\right\} \tag{8}$$

Here $\nu(\epsilon)$ is the number of states in the interval ϵ, $\epsilon + d\epsilon$. The constant η is given in terms of the number of atoms N per unit volume by the relation

$$N = (\partial\Gamma/\partial\eta)_T \tag{9}$$

2.3. Anisotropic effects. These effects, and phenomena such as hysteresis, remanence, etc., are not included in the Heisenberg or Stoner models. Most of these subjects belong to the domain theory of magnetism. The phenomenological energy of anisotropy for a cubic crystal has the from

$$E_{\text{anisotropy}} = K_1(\alpha_1{}^2\alpha_2{}^2 + \alpha_1{}^2\alpha_3{}^2 + \alpha_3{}^2\alpha_2{}^2) + K_2(\alpha_1{}^2\alpha_2{}^2\alpha_3{}^2) \tag{1}$$

where α_1, α_2, α_3 are the direction cosines of the intensity of magnetism relative to the principal cubic axes. The anisotropy constants K_1, K_2 have their origin presumably in spin-orbit interaction, but their theory is at present none too satisfactory.

2.4. Antiferromagnetics. For ferromagnetism it is necessary that the exchange integral J be positive. If instead it is negative and sufficiently great in magnitude, antiferromagnetism can occur. This is substantially a form of paramagnetism rather than of ferromagnetism, since the susceptibility is relatively small and depends little on field strength. There is a Curie point T_c at which the susceptibility is a maximum. Below this Curie temperature there is an antiparallel or staggered ordering of the spins, whence the name antiferromagnetism arises. With simple models, the susceptibility at $T = 0$ is two-thirds of that at the Curie point

$$\chi_{T=0} = \tfrac{2}{3}\chi_{T=T_c} \tag{1}$$

If approximations analogous to those of the Weiss field are employed, the formula for the susceptibility above the Curie point is

$$\chi = \frac{g^2 N\beta^2 S(S+1)}{3(T + cT_c)} \tag{2}$$

The value of the constant c is 1 if one includes only coupling between nearest atomic neighbors, but Néel and Anderson showed that with other, more complicated models, which come closer to reality, c can be as high as 5.

3. Diamagnetism and Feeble Paramagnetism

3.1. Classical theory of diamagnetism. The Langevin-Pauli formula for the diamagnetic susceptibility of an atom is

$$\chi = -\frac{Ne^2}{6mc^2} \Sigma_i \overline{r_i^2} \tag{1}$$

where the bars denote the time average and the summation is over all the electrons in the atom.

3.2. Quantum theory of diamagnetism. a. *Atoms.* Equation (1) of § 3.1 still holds as long as one is dealing with isolated atoms, e.g., a monatomic gas.

b. *Molecules.* For a nonmonatomic molecule, the expression for the diamagnetic susceptibility is

$$\chi = -\frac{Ne^2}{6mc^2} \sum \overline{r_i^2} + 2N \sum_{n'} \frac{|\mu_z(n;n')|^2}{E_{n'} - E_n} \tag{1}$$

Here $\mu z(n;n')$ is an off-diagonal matrix element of the molecule's magnetic moment along the z axis, which we take as the direction of the applied field.

The summation over n' in Eq. (1) is over all the excited states of the molecule. We have supposed the ground state to be nondegenerate. If there is degeneracy, Eq. (1) should be averaged over the different states n associated with the degeneracy.

c. *Free electrons.* Landau's formula for the diamagnetism of free conduction electrons is

$$\chi = -\frac{4m\beta^2}{h^2}\left(\frac{N\pi^2}{9}\right)^{1/3} \tag{2}$$

Classical theory would give instead $\chi = 0$.

3.3. Feeble paramagnetism. A common kind of magnetic behavior may be termed feeble paramagnetism, wherein the susceptibility is considerably smaller than that given by Langevin's formula and substantially independent of temperature. Feeble paramagnetism can be due to one of three causes.

a. *Atoms or ions with matrix elements of magnetic moment existing between, and only between, states whose separation is large compared with kT.* This represents simply a preponderance of the second or paramagnetic part of Eq. (1) of § 3.2 compared with the first term, so that the expression is positive.

b. *Inhibition of the alignment of the spin of conduction electrons by the Fermi-Dirac statistics.* According to Boltzmann statistics, free conduction electrons would have a strong paramagnetism because of their spin. Pauli showed that with the actual or Fermi-Dirac statistics, the resulting paramagnetism is, except for sign, three times the expression (2) of § 3.2, i.e.,

$$\chi = \frac{12m\beta^2}{h^2}\left(\frac{N\pi^2}{9}\right)^{1/3} \tag{1}$$

The total susceptibility hence has a value two-thirds as great as that given in Eq. (1).

c. *Antiferromagnetism.* The susceptibility of an antiferromagnetic is small and sensibly independent of T if $T_c \gg T$ in Eq. (2) of § 2.4.

Bibliography

1. Bozorth, R. M., *Ferromagnetism*, D. Van Nostrand Company, Inc., New York, 1951.
2. Stoner, E. C., *Magnetism and Matter*, Methuen & Co., Ltd., London, 1934.
3. Van Vleck, J. H., *The Theory of Electric and Magnetic Susceptibilities*, Oxford University Press, New York, 1932.
4. Van Vleck, J. H., *J. phys. et radium*, **12**, 262 (1951). A review of antiferromagnetism.

Chapter 27

PHYSICAL CHEMISTRY

BY RICHARD E. POWELL

Professor of Chemistry
University of California

1. Chemical Equilibrium

1.1. Equilibrium constant or " mass action law." If the chemical reaction

$$aA + bB + \ldots = mM + nN + \ldots$$

is at equilibrium, then

$$\frac{(P_M)^m (P_N)^n \ldots}{(P_A)^a (P_B)^b \ldots} = K_p \tag{1}$$

$$\frac{(x_M)^m (x_N)^n \ldots}{(x_A)^a (x_B)^b \ldots} = K_x \tag{2}$$

$$\frac{(C_M)^m (C_N)^n \ldots}{(C_A)^a (C_B)^b \ldots} = K_c \tag{3}$$

where K_p is the equilibrium constant in pressure units; P_i is the partial pressure of the substance i, in atmospheres; K_x is the equilibrium constant in mole fraction units; x_i is the mole fraction of substance i; K_c is the equilibrium constant in concentration units; C_i is the concentration of substance i, in moles per liter. Pressure units are customarily used for equilibrium constants involving gases, though it is possible to use mole fractions or concentrations for gases. Either mole fractions or concentrations may be used for reactions in solution; for reactions in aqueous solution, concentrations are usually used. For a reaction involving both gases and solutions, both pressure units and concentration units may be used in the same equilibrium constant. The concentration of pure solids and pure liquids is taken as unity, and the corresponding factors omitted from the equilibrium constants.

The constants K_p, K_x, and K_c are approximately independent of concentrations. See also Chapters 10 and 11.

1.2. Equilibrium constant from calorimetric data.

$$K = e^{-\Delta F^\circ/RT} = e^{\Delta S^\circ/R}\, e^{-\Delta H^\circ/RT} \tag{1}$$

where ΔF° is the standard free energy change of the reaction, i.e., the free energy change for all reactants at one atmosphere partial pressure (for K_p), or unit mole fraction (for K_x), or one mole per liter (for K_c); ΔS° is the corresponding standard entropy change; ΔH° is the standard enthalpy change. When ΔF° is in calories per mole, R is 1.9865 calories per mole degree.

Since ΔH° is the heat absorbed by the reaction at constant pressure, it can be measured calorimetrically. Alternatively, ΔH° can be obtained by algebraic addition of heats of combustion of the several reactants, or of their heats of formation from the elements.

Here ΔS° can be computed from the tabulated standard entropies of the several reactants,

$$\Delta S^\circ = S^\circ_{\mathrm{M}} + S^\circ_{\mathrm{N}} + \cdots - S^\circ_{\mathrm{A}} - S^\circ_{\mathrm{B}} - \cdots$$

The individual standard entropies are obtained from

$$S^\circ = \int_0^T C_p d \ln T + \sum \frac{\Delta H_{tr}}{T_{tr}} \tag{2}$$

where C_p is the heat capacity at constant pressure, and ΔH_{tr} is the heat of a phase transition occurring at temperature T_{tr}.

If the quantities ΔF°, ΔH°, and ΔS° are known at one temperature and pressure, but required at another temperature or pressure, they can be calculated with the thermodynamic relations,

$$\left.\begin{aligned}
&\left(\frac{\partial \Delta F}{\partial T}\right)_P = -\Delta S, &&\left(\frac{\partial \Delta F}{\partial P}\right)_T = \Delta V\\
&\left(\frac{\partial \Delta H}{\partial T}\right)_P = \Delta C_p, &&\left(\frac{\partial \Delta H}{\partial P}\right)_T = \Delta V - T\left(\frac{\partial \Delta V}{\partial T}\right)_P\\
&\left(\frac{\partial \Delta S}{\partial T}\right)_P = \frac{\Delta C_p}{T}, &&\left(\frac{\partial \Delta S}{\partial P}\right)_T = -\left(\frac{\partial \Delta V}{\partial T}\right)_P
\end{aligned}\right\} \tag{3}$$

1.3. Equilibrium constant from electric cell voltages. The relation between the voltage of a cell and the free energy of the cell reaction is

$$\epsilon = -\frac{\Delta F^o}{n_e\mathcal{F}} - \frac{RT}{n_e\mathcal{F}} \ln \frac{(C_M\gamma_M)^m(C_N\gamma_N)^n \cdots}{(C_A\gamma_A)^a(C_B\gamma_B)^b \cdots} \tag{1}$$

where n_e is the number of electrons flowing when the chemical reaction proceeds as written, and $\mathcal{F}$ is Faraday's constant, 23,059 calories per electron volt. When all reactants are in their standard states, the last term vanishes and

$$\epsilon^0 = -\frac{\Delta F^o}{n_e\mathcal{F}} \tag{2}$$

where ϵ^0 is the " standard potential " of the cell. The equilibrium constant is given by

$$K = e^{n_e\mathcal{F}\varepsilon^0/RT} \tag{3}$$

At 25° C, this becomes

$$\log K = n_e\epsilon^0/0.0591 \tag{4}$$

1.4. Pressure dependence of the equilibrium constant

$$\frac{K_{P_2}}{K_{P_1}} = e^{-\Delta V(P_2-P_1)/RT} \tag{1}$$

where ΔV is the molal volume change of the reaction, not including the volume of any gases consumed or produced. If ΔV is in cubic centimeters and $P_2 - P_1$ is in atmospheres, R is 82.07 cc atm per deg. Because ΔV is usually small, the pressure dependence of most equilibrium constants is small.

1.5. Temperature dependence of the equilibrium constant

$$K = e^{\Delta S^o/R - \Delta H^o/RT} \tag{1}$$

Since ΔS^o and ΔH^o are only slowly varying functions of temperature, they may be treated as constant over a moderate temperature interval. The form

$$\ln K = \frac{\Delta S^o}{R} - \frac{\Delta H^o}{RT} \tag{2}$$

shows that a graph of ln K against $1/T$ will be almost a straight line. Equivalent expressions are

$$\left.\begin{aligned} \left(\frac{\partial \ln K}{\partial T}\right)_P &= \frac{\Delta H^o}{RT^2} \\ \left(\frac{\partial \ln K}{\partial(1/T)}\right)_P &= -\frac{\Delta H^o}{R} \end{aligned}\right\} \tag{3}$$

If the equilibrium constant is K_1 at T_1 and K_2 at T_2, then the average values of ΔH^o and ΔS^o in this temperature interval are

$$\left.\begin{aligned}\Delta H^o &= \frac{4.57 T_1 T_2 \log (K_2/K_1)}{T_2 - T_1} \\ \Delta S^o &= \frac{4.57(T_2 \log K_2 - T_1 \log K_1)}{T_2 - T_1}\end{aligned}\right\} \quad (4)$$

A graph of the left-hand side of the following equation against $1/T$ gives a perfectly straight line, whose slope is $\Delta H^o{}_{T_0}/R$.

$$\ln K - \frac{1}{R}\int_{T_0}^{T} \Delta C_p d \ln T + \frac{1}{RT}\int_{T_0}^{T} \Delta C_p dT = \frac{\Delta S^o{}_{T_0}}{R} - \frac{\Delta H^o{}_{T_0}}{RT} \quad (5)$$

2. Activity Coefficients

2.1. The " thermodynamic " equilibrium constant. The equilibrium constants K_p, K_x, or K_c actually vary somewhat with concentration. To keep them truly constant, we can use " activities " instead of concentrations, each activity being a concentration multiplied by an " activity coefficient," γ.

$$\frac{(P_M\gamma_M)^m(P_N\gamma_N)^n \cdots}{(P_A\gamma_A)^a(P_B\gamma_B)^b \cdots} = K_p \quad (1)$$

$$\frac{(x_M\gamma_M)^m(x_N\gamma_N)^n \cdots}{(x_A\gamma_A)^a(x_B\gamma_B)^b \cdots} = K_x \quad (2)$$

$$\frac{(C_M\gamma_M)^m(C_N\gamma_N)^n \cdots}{(C_A\gamma_A)^a(C_B\gamma_B)^b \cdots} = K_c \quad (3)$$

Such equilibrium constants are called " thermodynamic " or " activity " equilibrium constants, and sometimes written K_a. The γ's are functions of concentration, which vary so as to keep the K_a's exactly constant.

2.2. Thermodynamic interpretation of the activity coefficient

$$\gamma = e^{(F_{\text{real}} - F_{\text{ideal}})/RT} = e^{\Delta F E/RT} \quad (1)$$

The activity coefficient can be calculated from the difference between the free energy of the actual substance and that of an ideal substance at the same concentration. This is sometimes called the " excess " free energy, ΔF^E.

2.3. Activity coefficients of gases. The ideal gas is taken to be one which obeys the law $PV = RT$. The activity coefficient of a real gas is

$$\gamma = e^{\int_0^P \left(\frac{PV}{RT} - 1\right)\frac{dP}{P}} \tag{1}$$

The integral can be evaluated graphically from the P-V-T data for a gas. Alternatively, the integral can be evaluated analytically, with the aid of an empirical equation of state for the gas. Some of these are listed below.

a. *van der Waals, 1873 :*

$$\left(P + \frac{a}{V^2}\right)(V - b) = RT \tag{1}$$

b. *Dieterici, 1899 :*

$$Pe^{a/RTV}(V - b) = RT \tag{2}$$

c. *Berthelot, 1907 :*

$$\left(P + \frac{a}{TV^2}\right)(V - b) = RT \tag{3}$$

also

$$\frac{PV}{RT} = 1 + \frac{9}{128} \cdot \frac{PT_c}{P_c T}\left(1 - 6\frac{T_c^2}{T^2}\right) \tag{4}$$

d. *Kamerlingh Onnes, 1901 :*

$$\frac{PV}{RT} = 1 + \frac{B}{V} + \frac{C}{V^2} + \frac{D}{V^3} + \ldots \tag{5}$$

or

$$\left.\begin{aligned}\frac{PV}{RT} = 1 + B\left(\frac{P}{RT}\right) + (C - B^2)\left(\frac{P}{RT}\right)^2 \\ + (D - 3BC + 2B^3)\left(\frac{P}{RT}\right)^3 + \ldots\end{aligned}\right\} \tag{6}$$

e. *Keyes, 1917 :*

$$\left[P + \frac{a}{(V - f)^2}\right](V - be^{-\alpha/V}) = RT \tag{7}$$

f. *Beattie and Bridgeman, 1927-1928 :*

$$P + \frac{A_0}{V^2}\left(1 - \frac{a}{V}\right) = \frac{RT}{V^2}\left(1 - \frac{c}{VT^3}\right)\left(V + B - \frac{bB}{V}\right) \tag{8}$$

g. *Benedict, Webb, and Rubin, 1940:*

$$\frac{PV}{RT} = 1 + \frac{V^3}{RT}\left(RTB - A - \frac{C}{T^2}\right) \tag{9}$$

where
$$B = B_0 + \frac{b}{V}$$

$$A = A_0 + \frac{a}{V} - \frac{a\alpha}{V^4}$$

$$C = C_0 - \frac{c}{V}\left(1 + \frac{\gamma}{V^2}\right)e^{-\gamma/V^2}$$

The activity coefficient calculated from the Kamerlingh Onnes equation of state (" virial equation ") is

$$\ln \gamma = \frac{BP}{RT} + \frac{(C - B^2)}{2}\left(\frac{P}{RT}\right)^2 + \frac{(D - 3BC + 2B^3)}{3}\left(\frac{P}{RT}\right)^3 + \ldots \tag{10}$$

2.4. Activity coefficient from the " law of corresponding states." The law of corresponding states, which is obeyed fairly well by most gases, says that V/V_c is a universal function of P/P_c and T/T_c, where V_c, P_c, T_c are the critical volume, pressure, and temperature. For gases which obey this law, γ likewise is a universal function of P/P_c and T/T_c. Consequently, a single graph can be prepared, giving γ as a function of P/P_c, for various values of T/T_c (e.g., Newton, 1935). This is an extremely convenient method for evaluating γ for any gas whose critical constants are known.

2.5. Activity coefficients of nonelectrolytes in solution. If the pure liquid is taken as the standard state, an ideal solution is one whose components obey Raoult's law,

$$\frac{P_i}{P_i^0} = x_i \tag{1}$$

where P_i is the vapor pressure of substance i, P_i^0 its vapor pressure when pure, and x_i its mole fraction. The activity coefficient of component i in a real solution is given by

$$\frac{P_i}{P_i^0} = \gamma_i x_i \tag{2}$$

The partial pressures P_i and P_i^0 should also be multiplied by the appropriate activity coefficients for the gases, but this is usually a negligible correction.

Sometimes the infinitely dilute solution of component i is taken as its standard state; in this case, an ideal solution is one which obeys Henry's law,

$$P_i = k_H x_i \tag{3}$$

where k_H is " Henry's-law constant " for that component. (Henry's law can also be written for various other concentration units.) The activity coefficient is then given by

$$P_i = k_H \gamma_i x_i \tag{4}$$

where
$$k_H = \lim_{x_i \to 0} (P_i/x_i)$$

2.6. The Gibbs-Duhem equation. The activity coefficient of a non-volatile component can be computed, if the activity coefficient of the volatile solvent is known over the whole concentration range, by integrating the relation

$$\sum_j x_j d \ln (\gamma_j x_j) = 0 \tag{1}$$

(Gibbs 1876, Duhem 1886, Margules 1895, Lehfelt 1895). For a two-component system this becomes

$$-\ln \gamma_A = \int_0^{x_B} \frac{x_B}{1 - x_B} d \ln \gamma_B \tag{2}$$

2.7. The enthalpy of nonideal solutions. For an ideal solution, there is no heat of mixing, and ΔH^E is zero for all components. For nonideal solutions, the heat of mixing is given approximately by the van Laar (1906), Hildebrand (1927), Scatchard (1931) equation,

$$\Delta H^E = (\delta_2 - \delta_1)^2 (x_1 V_1 + x_2 V_2) \phi_1 \phi_2 \tag{1}$$

where δ is a quantity called the " solubility parameter," x is the mole fraction, V the molal volume, and ϕ the volume fraction of the substance in question. The excess enthalpy for an individual component, $\Delta \bar{H}_1^E$, is

$$\Delta \bar{H}_1^E = (\delta_2 - \delta_1)^2 V_1 \phi_2^{\,2} \tag{2}$$

and $\Delta \bar{H}_2^E$ is given by the same equation with subscripts interchanged. For many solutions, called " regular " solutions, the entropy of solution is ideal, and for these the activity coefficient is

$$\gamma_1 = e^{[(\delta_2 - \delta_1)^2 \mathrm{V}_1/\mathrm{RT}]\phi_2^{\,2}} \tag{3}$$

for component 1, the subscripts being interchanged for component 2.

The solubility parameter, δ, for a substance is given by

$$\delta^2 = \Delta E_{\text{vap}}/V \tag{4}$$

where ΔE_{vap} is the energy change of vaporization of the pure liquid at the temperature in question, and V is the molal volume of the liquid. Solubility parameters for a number of liquids have been tabulated by Hildebrand and Scott (1950).

2.8. The entropy of nonideal solutions. For ideal solutions, the entropy change of mixing is

$$-\frac{\Delta S}{R} = x_1 \ln x_1 + x_2 \ln x_2 \tag{1}$$

For solutions of molecules of different molal volume, the entropy change of mixing is given approximately by the Flory (1941), Huggins (1941) equation,

$$-\frac{\Delta S}{R} = x_1 \ln \phi_1 + x_2 \ln \phi_2 \tag{2}$$

For an individual component, the entropy of mixing is

$$-\frac{\Delta \bar{S}_1}{R} = \ln \phi_1 + \phi_2(1 - V_1/V_2) \tag{3}$$

and the excess entropy is

$$-\frac{\Delta \bar{S}_1^E}{R} = \phi_2(1 - V_1/V_2) + \ln [1 - \phi_2(1 - V_1/V_2)] \tag{4}$$

For a solution with no heat of mixing, the activity coefficient is

$$\gamma_1 = [1 - \phi_2(1 - V_1/V_2)]e^{\phi_2(1-V_1/V_2)} \tag{5}$$

The same equations, with subscripts interchanged, hold for the other component.

These equations were first derived to apply to solutions of high polymers, where the difference in molal volumes of solvent and solute are very great.

If the components have different molal volumes, and there is also a heat of mixing, the Flory-Huggins and the van Laar-Hildebrand-Scatchard equations are combined.

2.9. The activity coefficients of aqueous electrolytes. These are usually obtained by applying the Gibbs-Duhem equation (§ 2.6) to the activity coefficient of the water. The latter can be measured through its vapor pressure, or its freezing point or boiling point. To obtain activity coefficients from freezing points, we first define the " freezing point depression constant," k_F, by

$$k_F = \lim_{C \to 0} (\Delta T/C)$$

where ΔT is the freezing point depression and C the molal concentration of solute. Then the expected freezing point depression for any concentration is $k_F C$. We define j as the fractional amount by which the expected freezing point depression exceeds the actual depression, $j = (k_F C - \Delta T)/k_F C$. Then the activity coefficient of the solute is

$$-\ln \gamma = j + \int_0^C j d \ln C \tag{1}$$

The activity coefficient of an electrolyte can also be determined from the voltage of an electrical cell.

$$\epsilon = -\frac{\Delta F^o}{n_e \mathcal{F}} - \frac{RT}{n_e \mathcal{F}} \ln \frac{(C_M \gamma_M)^m (C_N \gamma_N)^n \cdots}{(C_A \gamma_A)^a (C_B \gamma_B)^b \cdots} \tag{2}$$

Here ΔF^o is evaluated by a suitable extrapolation of the cell voltage to infinite dilution, where all γ's become unity.

The activity coefficient of a single ion cannot be measured; what is actually measured is the " mean activity coefficient " which is often written $\gamma_{\pm}$ to emphazise this fact.

$$\gamma_{\pm} = \Sigma \nu_i \gamma_i / \Sigma \nu_i \tag{3}$$

where ν_i is the number of ions of species i, whose true activity coefficient is γ_i.

2.10. The Debye-Hückel equation. The activity coefficient of a single ion is given approximately by the equation due to Debye and Hückel (1923),

$$-\ln \gamma_i = \left[\frac{e^3}{(DkT)^{3/2}} \sqrt{\frac{2\pi N}{1000}} \right] z_i^2 \sqrt{\mu} \tag{1}$$

where $$\mu = \tfrac{1}{2} \Sigma C_j z_j^2$$

Here e is the charge of the electron, D the dielectric constant of water, k Boltzmann's constant, N Avogadro's number, and z the charge of the ion. The quantity μ is called the " ionic strength." At 25° C, the activity coefficient of a single ion is

$$-\log \gamma_i = 0.509 z_i^2 \sqrt{\mu} \tag{2}$$

and the mean activity coefficient is

$$-\log \gamma_{\pm} = 0.509 \frac{\Sigma\, \nu_i z_i^2}{\Sigma\, \nu_i} \sqrt{\mu} \tag{3}$$

The corresponding mean excess free energy, excess enthalpy, and excess entropy of an ion are, at 25° C,

$$\left.\begin{aligned} \Delta \bar{F}_{\pm}^{E} &= 695 \frac{\Sigma\, \nu_i z_i^2}{\Sigma\, \nu_i} \sqrt{\mu} \quad \text{calories per mole} \\ \Delta \bar{H}_{\pm}^{E} &= 359 \frac{\Sigma\, \nu_i z_i^2}{\Sigma\, \nu_i} \sqrt{\mu} \quad \text{calories per mole} \\ \Delta \bar{S}_{\pm}^{E} &= -1.12 \frac{\Sigma\, \nu_i z_i^2}{\Sigma\, \nu_i} \sqrt{\mu} \quad \text{calories per mole degree} \end{aligned}\right\} \tag{4}$$

The Debye-Hückel equation is applicable only to very dilute solutions. An extended equation, good to somewhat higher concentrations, is

$$-\log \gamma_{\pm} = \frac{0.509(\Sigma\, \nu_i z_i^2/\Sigma\, \nu_i)\sqrt{\mu}}{1 + A\sqrt{\mu}} + B\mu \tag{5}$$

where A and B are adjustable parameters.

3. Changes of State

3.1. Phase rule. If p is the number of phases in a system at equilibrium, c the number of components, and f the number of degrees of freedom, Gibbs' " phase rule " is

$$p + f = c + 2 \tag{1}$$

3.2. One component, solid-solid and solid-liquid transitions. Solid phase transitions and melting occur sharply at a temperature T_{tr}, which can be evaluated from thermal data :

$$T_{tr} = \Delta H_{tr}/\Delta S_{tr} \tag{1}$$

The dependence of the transition temperature on pressure is given by the Clausius-Clapeyron equation,

$$\frac{dT}{dP} = \frac{\Delta V}{\Delta S} \tag{2}$$

where ΔV is the volume change of the transition, and ΔS its entropy change.

3.3. One component, solid-gas and liquid-gas transitions. The partial vapor pressure of a pure liquid or solid is

$$P = e^{\Delta S^\circ/R - \Delta H^\circ/RT} \tag{1}$$

where ΔS^o is the standard entropy change and ΔH^o the standard enthalpy change of the process. Since ΔS^o and ΔH^o are only slowly varying functions of temperature, the vapor pressure is given approximately by

$$\log P = A - \frac{B}{T} \tag{2}$$

and to a somewhat better approximation by

$$\log P = A - \frac{B}{T} + C \log T \tag{3}$$

The partial pressure P in these equations ought to be multiplied by the activity coefficient of the gas, but this is usually a negligible correction.

The dependence of vapor pressure on total pressure is

$$\frac{P_{\text{at total pressure } P_2}}{P_{\text{at total pressure } P_1}} = e^{(P_2 - P_1)V_{\text{liq}}/RT} \tag{4}$$

where V_{liq} is the molal volume of the liquid.

3.4. Two components, solid-liquid transition. The general equation for the solubility of a solid in a solution, or, what amounts to the same process, the freezing of one component out of a solution, is

$$x_A \gamma_A = e^{\Delta S^\circ_A/R - \Delta H^\circ_A/RT} \tag{1}$$

where x_A is the mole fraction in solution of that substance which is also present as solid, γ_A its activity coefficient in the solution, ΔS_A^0 its entropy of fusion and ΔH_A^0 its enthalpy of fusion.

For dilute solutions, the freezing-point law takes the approximate form

$$\left.\begin{aligned} \Delta T &= \frac{RT_A^2}{\Delta H_A{}^o}\, x_B \\ \text{or}\qquad \Delta T &= \frac{RT_A{}^2 M_A}{\Delta H_A{}^o 1000}\, C_B = k_F C_B \end{aligned}\right\} \tag{2}$$

where T_A is the melting point of the solvent, ΔH_A^0 its molal heat of fusion, and M_A its molecular weight; x_B is the mole fraction of solute, and C_B the molal concentration of solute.

The eutectic temperature, which is the temperature at which both solids coexist with solution, can be calculated from the general solubility equations for both components, and the additional condition that $x_A + x_B = 1$.

The solubility of an electrolyte, which on dissolving gives *a* ions A and *b* ions B, is given by

$$(C_A)^a(C_B)^b(\gamma_\pm)^{a+b} = K \tag{3}$$

3.5. Two components, liquid-vapor transition. The partial pressure of each component of a solution is given by

$$\frac{P_A}{x_A\gamma_A} = P_A^0 = e^{\Delta S^\circ_A/R - \Delta H^\circ_A/RT} \tag{1}$$

where γ_A is its activity coefficient in the solution, and ΔS_A^0 and ΔH_A^0 its entropy of vaporization and enthalpy of vaporization, respectively.

The boiling point of a solution is the temperature at which $P_A + P_B = 1$. The boiling point of a mixture of two mutually insoluble liquids is the temperature at which $P_A^0 + P_B^0 = 1$. The vapor composition at the boiling point is $x_A = P_A$, $x_B = P_B$.

If a nonvolatile solute is dissolved in a volatile solvent, the approximate boiling-point elevation in dilute solution is

$$\left.\begin{aligned} \Delta T &= \frac{RT_A{}^2}{-\Delta H_A{}^0} x_B \\ \text{or} \qquad \Delta T &= \frac{RT_A{}^2 M_A}{-\Delta H_A{}^0\, 1000} C_B = k_B C_B \end{aligned}\right\} \tag{2}$$

where T_A is the boiling point of the solvent, ΔH_A^0 its molal heat of vaporization, and M_A its molecular weight; x_B is the mole fraction of solute, C_B its molal concentration.

If x is the mole fraction of one component in the solution, and y the mole fraction of that component in the vapor phase, then Rayleigh's equation (1902) for differential distillation is

$$\ln f = \int_{x_0}^{x} \frac{dx}{y - x} \tag{3}$$

where f is the fraction of the liquid remaining unvaporized when the solution composition has gone from x_0 to x.

3.6. Liquid-liquid transition. If there are two liquid phases, the general condition for equilibrium is that the activity of any component must be the same in both phases.

$$\left.\begin{aligned} x_A\gamma_A &= x_A'\gamma_A' \\ x_B\gamma_B &= x_B'\gamma_B' \end{aligned}\right\} \tag{1}$$

The temperature at which a binary solution separates into two liquid layers, the " consolute temperature," is given approximately by

$$2RT_c = V(\delta_1 - \delta_2)^2 \tag{2}$$

where δ_1 and δ_2 are the solubility parameters of the two pure components (see § 2.7).

3.7. Osmotic pressure. The general expression for osmotic pressure is

$$x_1\gamma_1 = e^{-\Pi V_1/RT} \tag{1}$$

where Π is the osmotic pressure, x_1 the mole fraction of solvent in the solution and γ_1 its activity coefficient there, and V_1 its molal volume. (The effect of pressure on the molal volume has been disregarded.) If Π is in atmospheres and V_1 in cubic centimeters, R is 82.07.

For very dilute solutions, the osmotic pressure law takes the approximate form (van't Hoff's law)

$$\Pi V_1 = x_2RT \tag{2}$$

3.8. Gibbs-Donnan membrane equilibrium. Two solutions are separated by a semipermeable membrane; in one of them is a concentration C_R of an ionic salt AR, the ion R being unable to penetrate the membrane; the solutions also contain a total concentration C_B of a freely diffusible ionic salt AB. If we denote by C_B' the concentration of diffusible salt which at equilibrium is in the solution containing AR, and by C_B'' the concentration of diffusible salt in the other solution, the equilibrium condition is

$$\frac{(C_B')(C_B' + C_R)(\gamma_\pm')^2}{(C_B'')^2(\gamma_\pm'')^2} = 1 \tag{1}$$

For the special case where the activity coefficients are unity, this becomes

$$\frac{C_B''}{C_B'} = \frac{C_B + C_R}{C_B} \tag{2}$$

4. Surface Phenomena

4.1. Surface tension. The surface tension, γ, is defined as the free energy of formation of unit surface area,

$$dF = \gamma\, d\sigma \tag{1}$$

It is usually measured in ergs per square centimeter (dynes per centimeter).

4.2. Experimental measurement of surface tension

a. *Capillary rise*

$$\gamma = \tfrac{1}{2}gh(\rho - \rho_0)/\cos\theta \tag{1}$$

where g is the acceleration of gravity, h the capillary rise, ρ the liquid density, ρ_0 the density of the vapor above it, and θ the contact angle. For a liquid which wets the capillary wall, the contact angle is zero.

b. *Bubble pressure.* The pressure increment across a curved surface, of radius of curvature r, is

$$\Delta P = 2\gamma/r \tag{2}$$

The maximum pressure sustained by a bubble forming at depth h in a liquid is

$$\Delta P = 2\gamma/r + gh(\rho - \rho_0) \tag{3}$$

The differential pressure in a "soap bubble," which has two surfaces, is

$$\Delta P = 4\gamma/r \tag{4}$$

c. *Ring tensimeter*

$$\gamma = Ff/4\pi r \tag{5}$$

where f is the force sustained by the ring, whose radius is r, and F is a correction factor which lies between 0.75 and 1.02 (Harkins and Jordan, 1930).

d. *Drop weight*

$$\gamma = F'mg/4r \tag{6}$$

where m is the mass of a drop, r the outer radius of the tube from which it falls, and F' a correction factor which is approximately unity, but is a function of V/r^3 (Harkins and Brown, 1919).

e. *Hanging drop.* The shape of the drop is measured photographically, and

$$\gamma = g(\rho - \rho_0)(d_e)^2/H \tag{7}$$

where d_e is the diameter of the drop at its equator, and H is a factor which is a function only of the ratio of d_e to the drop diameter at a distance d_e from its bottom (H has been tabulated by Andreas, Hauser, and Tucker, 1938).

4.3. Kelvin equation. The vapor pressure P of a drop of liquid of radius r is

$$\ln \frac{P}{P^0} = \frac{2\gamma}{r} \cdot \frac{V}{RT} \tag{1}$$

where P^0 is the vapor pressure of the liquid in bulk, and V is its molal volume.

4.4. Temperature dependence of surface tension. Since surface tension is a free energy change, it can be expressed in terms of the corresponding enthalpy and entropy changes,

$$\gamma = \Delta h - T\,\Delta s \tag{1}$$

where Δh is the enthalpy of surface formation per unit area, and Δs the entropy of surface formation per unit area. These are slowly varying functions of temperature, so surface tension is approximately a linear function of temperature.

Empirical equations which reproduce the surface tension over a wide range of temperature include

$$\gamma(V)^{2/3} = 2.12(T_c - T - 6) \tag{2}$$

where V is the molal volume and T_c the critical temperature (Eötvös 1886, Ramsay and Shields 1893).

$$\gamma = c(\rho - \rho_0)^4 \tag{3}$$

(McLeod, 1923.)

$$\gamma = \gamma_0(1 - T/T_c)^n \tag{4}$$

where n is approximately 1.21 and γ_0 approximately 4.4 $T_c/V_c^{2/3}$ (Guggenheim, 1945).

4.5. Insoluble films on liquids. If the " surface pressure," π, is $\gamma_{\text{pure liquid}} - \gamma$, and the surface area per molecule (i.e., total area divided by number of molecules) is σ, then the equation of state for a very dilute or " gaseous " layer is

$$\pi\sigma = kT \tag{1}$$

where k is Boltzmann's constant. For a " condensed " layer,

$$\sigma = a - b\pi \tag{2}$$

approximately, where a and b are suitable constants.

4.6. Adsorption on solids. a. *Langmuir isotherm (1916):*

$$\frac{V}{V_M} = \frac{KP}{1 + KP} \tag{1}$$

where V is the volume (at standard conditions) of gas adsorbed per unit amount of solid, V_M the volume adsorbed at saturation, P the partial pressure of adsorbate, and K a suitable constant. The Langmuir isotherm can be derived on the assumption that the adsorbed substance occupies a monolayer, and that the surface is energetically uniform.

b. *Brunauer-Emmett-Teller isotherm (1938):*

$$\frac{V}{V_M} = \frac{KP/P_0}{(1 - P/P_0)(1 - P/P_0 + KP/P_0)} \tag{2}$$

where P_0 is the vapor pressure of the adsorbate in the liquid state. The B-E-T isotherm can be derived on the assumption that the adsorbed substance builds up multilayers, the surface being energetically uniform.

c. *Harkins-Jura isotherm (1946):*

$$1/V^2 = A - B \ln P \tag{3}$$

where A and B are suitable constants. The Harkins-Jura isotherm can be derived on the assumption that the adsorbed substance is a " condensed monolayer."

d. *Freundlich isotherm (1909):*

$$\frac{V}{V_M} = KP^n \tag{4}$$

which has been extended by Sips (1949):

$$\frac{V}{V_M} = \left(\frac{KP}{1 + KP}\right)^n \tag{5}$$

The Freundlich-Sips isotherm can be derived from the assumption of monolayer adsorption on a nonuniform surface characterized by an exponential distribution of adsorption energies. As written here, these adsorption isotherms apply to the adsorption of gases. Equations of the same form, using concentrations instead of pressures, apply to adsorption from solution.

4.7. Excess concentration at the surface. The Gibbs adsorption equation (1878) gives

$$-RT\Gamma_2 = \frac{d\gamma}{d \ln x_2} \tag{1}$$

where Γ_2 is the excess concentration of solute at the surface.

4.8. Surface tension of aqueous electrolytes. For a one-one electrolyte of molal concentration C in water at 25° C, the surface tension is approximately

$$\gamma = \gamma_{H_2O} + 1.0124C \log \frac{1.467}{C} \tag{1}$$

(Onsager and Samaras, 1934).

4.9. Surface tension of binary solutions. According to a theoretical treatment which regards the surface as a monolayer (Schuchowitzky 1944, Belton and Evans 1945, Guggenheim 1945),

$$e^{-\gamma\sigma/kT} = x_1 e^{-\gamma_1\sigma/kT} + x_2 e^{-\gamma_2\sigma/kT} \tag{1}$$

and

$$x_1' = \frac{x_1 e^{-\gamma_1\sigma/kT}}{x_1 e^{-\gamma_1\sigma/kT} + x_2 e^{-\gamma_2\sigma/kT}} \tag{2}$$

where x_1 and x_2 are mole fractions in the bulk solution, x_1' and x_2' are surface mole fractions, and γ_1 and γ_2 are the surface tensions of the pure liquids; σ is the cross-sectional area of a molecule (taken as identical for the two species). All activity coefficients have here been assumed to be unity.

5. Reaction Kinetics

5.1. The rate law of a reaction. The rate of a chemical reaction, as measured by the rate of disappearance of one of its reactants or appearance of one of its products, is in general proportional to the concentration of one or more of its reactants.

$$-\frac{dC_A}{dt} = k_r C_A C_B C_C \ldots \tag{1}$$

This expression is called the "rate law" for the reaction, and k_r is the "specific rate" or "rate constant." The concentration of a substance may, of course, appear in the rate law to a higher power than the first. The substances whose concentrations appear in the rate law are not, in general, exactly identical with those which appear in the balanced equation for the reaction, so it is necessary to determine the rate law by experiment.

5.2. Integrated forms of the rate law. For rate laws involving only a single substance, the integrated forms of some of the simple rate laws are:

Zero order	$-\frac{dC}{dt} = k_0$	$\frac{C}{C_0} = 1 - \frac{k_0 t}{C_0}$
$\frac{1}{2}$ order	$-\frac{dC}{dt} = k_{1/2} C^{1/2}$	$\frac{C}{C_0} = \left(1 - \frac{k_{1/2} t}{2C_0^{1/2}}\right)^2$
First order	$-\frac{dC}{dt} = k_1 C$	$\frac{C}{C_0} = e^{-k_1 t}$
$\frac{3}{2}$ order	$-\frac{dC}{dt} = k_{3/2} C^{3/2}$	$\frac{C}{C_0} = \frac{1}{\left(1 + \frac{C_0^{1/2} k_{3/2} t}{2}\right)^2}$
Second order	$-\frac{dC}{dt} = k_2 C^2$	$\frac{C}{C_0} = \frac{1}{1 + C_0 k_2 t}$

5.3. Half-lives. For rate laws involving only a single substance, the time to half reaction is

Zero order :	$t_{1/2} = C/2k_0$
$\frac{1}{2}$ order :	$t_{1/2} = (2 - 2^{1/2})C_0^{1/2}/k_{1/2}$
First order :	$t_{1/2} = (\ln 2)/k_1$
$\frac{3}{2}$ order :	$t_{1/2} = (8^{1/2} - 2)/C_0^{1/2}k_{1/2}$
Second order :	$t_{1/2} = 1/C_0k_2$

5.4. Integrated form of rate law with several factors. If the rate law is $-dC_A/dt = k_rC_AC_BC_C \ldots$ and the chemical reaction is such that it consumes a molecules of A for b molecules of B for c molecules of C, etc., we write x for the fractional extent of reaction of A, and obtain

$$\int_0^x \frac{a\,dx}{(C_{0A} - ax)\,(C_{0B} - bx)\,(C_{0C} - cx)\ldots} = k_rt \tag{1}$$

where the integral can readily be evaluated by partial fractions.

If the concentration of one substance in a reaction mixture is much smaller than all other concentrations, the others may be taken as constant in integrating the rate law. This is the basis of the experimental technique known as " isolation " or " flooding."

5.5. Consecutive reactions. If a reaction proceeds in two successive steps,

$$A \rightarrow B \rightarrow C$$

the first reaction being kinetically first-order with specific rate k_1 and the second reaction kinetically first-order with specific rate k_2, and the initial concentration of A is C_{0A}, the initial concentration of B and C being zero, then the integration of the rate laws gives

$$\left.\begin{aligned} \frac{C_A}{C_{0A}} &= e^{-k_1t} \\ \frac{C_B}{C_{0A}} &= \frac{k_1}{k_2 - k_1}(e^{-k_1t} - e^{-k_2t}) \\ \frac{C_C}{C_{0A}} &= \frac{k_2(1 - e^{-k_1t}) - k_1(1 - e^{-k_2t})}{k_2 - k_1} \end{aligned}\right\} \tag{1}$$

If either or both of the reaction steps is kinetically second-order, the rate laws can also be integrated (Chien, 1948).

5.6. Multiple-hit processes. The destruction of bacteria by a chemical agent is kinetically first-order ("logarithmic order of death"), but for higher organisms the destruction of more than a single vital spot or cell is supposedly necessary to kill them. If N hits are necessary, each individual offering just N targets, then the fraction of individuals surviving at time t is

$$1-(1-e^{-kt})^N \tag{1}$$

If N hits are necessary, each individual offering an infinite number of targets, the fraction of individuals surviving at time t is

$$e^{-kt}\left[1+kt+\frac{k^2t^2}{2!}+\frac{k^3t^3}{3!}+\dots+\frac{(kt)^{N-1}}{(N-1)!}\right] \tag{2}$$

In these equations k is the first-order specific rate for a single hit.

5.7. Reversible reactions. If the rate of a reaction in one direction is written as $k_f(C_f)$, where the notation (C_f) is understood to indicate the product of concentrations which is the rate law for that reaction, and the rate of the reverse reaction is similarly $k_b(C_b)$, then

$$\frac{k_f}{k_b}=K \tag{1}$$

and

$$\frac{(C_f)}{(C_b)}=\frac{1}{(K)} \tag{2}$$

where K is the numerical value of the equilibrium constant for the reaction, and (K) is the ratio of concentrations which is the equilibrium constant expression.

5.8. The specific rate: collision theory (Arrhenius, 1889). The specific rate for a bimolecular gas reaction is

$$k_r = Ze^{-E/RT} \tag{1}$$

where Z is the "collision number" or "frequency factor," and E is the "activation energy." A graph of log k_r against $1/T$ gives a nearly straight line.

From the kinetic theory of gases, the collision number for two molecules of mass m and diameter σ is

$$Z=\frac{\sigma^2}{NkT}\left(\frac{4\pi}{mkT}\right)^{1/2}10^{15}\text{ mole liter}^{-1}\text{ sec}^{-1}\text{ atm}^{-2} \tag{2}$$

If the molecules are of diameters σ_1 and σ_2, σ is taken to be $(\sigma_1+\sigma_2)/2$; if the molecules have masses m_1 and m_2, the effective mass is

$$m=(\tfrac{1}{2})(1/m_1+1/m_2)^{-1}$$

5.9. The specific rate: activated complex theory (Eyring, 1935). The specific rate for any reaction is

$$k_r = \frac{kT}{h} e^{\Delta S^{\ddagger}/R} e^{-\Delta H^{\ddagger}/RT} \tag{1}$$

where k is Boltzmann's constant, h is Planck's constant, and $\Delta S^{\ddagger}$ and $\Delta H^{\ddagger}$ are the standard entropy and enthalpy of forming the "activated complex" from the original reactants. At 25° C, the factor kT/h is 6.21×10^{12} sec^{-1}. The entropy of activation, $\Delta S^{\ddagger}$, can sometimes be computed a priori by the methods of statistical mechanics, and it can often be estimated approximately by analogy with the entropies of known molecules.

For a unimolecular decomposition, the entropy of activation is near zero, so the frequency factor is expected to be of the order of 10^{13} sec^{-1}. For a bimolecular gas reaction, the activated complex theory can be shown to lead to just the same equation the collision theory does.

5.10. Activity coefficients in reaction kinetics. The relation between the observed specific rate k_r and the specific rate k_r^0 for an ideal solution is (Brønsted 1922, 1925, Bjerrum 1924)

$$k_r = k_r^0 \frac{\gamma_A \gamma_B \gamma_C \cdots}{\gamma^{\ddagger}} \tag{1}$$

For the reaction of an ion of charge z_A with another ion of charge z_B, the Debye-Hückel equation for activity coefficients leads to

$$\log k_r = \log k_r^0 + z_A z_B \sqrt{\mu} \tag{2}$$

at 25° C, for dilute solutions.

If two neutral reactants combine to form an activated complex of radius r and dipole moment $\mu^{\ddagger}$, a formula of Kirkwood (1934) for the activity coefficient of a dipole in an electrolyte of ionic strength μ is

$$-\ln \gamma^{\ddagger} = \frac{4\pi N e^4}{1000 D^2 k^2 T^2} \cdot \frac{\mu^{\ddagger 2}}{r} \mu \tag{3}$$

For water at 25° C, r measured in Ångstrøm units and $\mu^{\ddagger}$ in Debye units,

$$\log k_r = \log k_r^0 + 0.00238 \frac{\mu^{\ddagger 2}}{r} \mu \tag{4}$$

For the reaction of an ion of charge z_A with one of charge z_B, the dependence of the specific rate (extrapolated to zero ionic strength) upon dielectric constant is approximately

$$\ln k_r = \text{constant} - \frac{e^2 z_A z_B}{D r k T} \tag{5}$$

5.11. Heterogeneous catalysis. The rate of a surface-catalyzed reaction, per unit surface area, is often described satisfactorily by

a. *A semi-empirical equation of the Freundlich type,*

$$\text{Rate} = k_r(P_\text{A})^\alpha(P_\text{B})^\beta \ldots \tag{1}$$

where the exponents α and β are arbitrarily chosen to fit the data; or

b. *An equation of the Langmuir type,*

$$\text{rate} = \frac{k_r(P_\text{A})(P_\text{B})(P_\text{C}) \ldots}{1 + K_\text{A}(P_\text{A}) + K_\text{B}(P_\text{B}) + \ldots} \tag{2}$$

where the product in the numerator includes the concentrations of those substances which make up the activated complex, and the summation in the denominator extends over all those substances which are adsorbed on the surface.

5.12. Enzymatic reactions. An enzyme and its substrate often combine to form a relatively stable intermediate (" Michaelis complex," Michaelis and Menten, 1913) previous to the enzymatic reaction itself. The corresponding rate law is

$$-\frac{d\,(\text{substrate})}{dt} = k_r\,(\text{enzyme})\frac{(\text{substrate})}{1 + K_m\,(\text{substrate})} \tag{1}$$

where K_m is the equilibrium constant for the formation of the Michaelis complex. Many enzymes can be reversibly denatured into forms which are catalytically inactive; if K_d is the equilibrium constant for the denaturation reaction,

$$k_r = \frac{k_r^0}{1 + K_d} \tag{2}$$

and the temperature dependence of the rate is given by

$$k_r = \frac{(kT/h)e^{\Delta S^{\ddagger}/R - \Delta H^{\ddagger}/RT}}{1 + e^{\Delta S_d^0/R - \Delta H_d^0/RT}} \tag{3}$$

As this equation indicates, the rate of an enzymatic reaction normally increases with temperature at low temperatures, passes through a maximum, and decreases with temperature at high temperatures.

5.13. Photochemistry. The law of photochemical equivalence (Stark 1908, Einstein 1912) states that one quantum of active light is absorbed per molecule of substance which disappears. The rate of the photochemical primary process is, accordingly, proportional to the intensity of light absorbed.

$$\text{rate} = k_1 I_{\text{abs}} \tag{1}$$

The absorption of light can be measured by direct actinometry, or computed from the Lambert-Beer law,

$$I_{\text{abs}} = I_0(1 - e^{-aCx}) \tag{2}$$

5.14. Photochemistry in intermittent light. If a reactant is photodissociated into two radicals, which can recombine by a bimolecular process to form the original reactant

$$\mathrm{A} \underset{k_2(C_{\mathrm{R}})^2}{\overset{k_1 I_{\text{abs}}}{\rightleftarrows}} \mathrm{R} + \mathrm{R} \tag{1}$$

and it is possible to measure the average concentration of R within a constant factor (e.g. by a chemical reaction of R), the use of intermittent light permits the determination of the mean lifetime of a radical R. Write p for the ratio of dark period to light period, and t for the ratio of light period to mean life of R under steady illumination. Then the ratio of the average concentration of R under intermittent illumination to the concentration of R under steady illumination is (Dickinson, 1941)

$$\frac{1}{p+1}\left\{1 + \frac{1}{t}\ln\left[1 + \cfrac{pt}{1 + \cfrac{2(pt + \tanh t)/(pt \tanh t)}{1 + \sqrt{1 + 4/(pt \tanh t) + 4/(p^2t^2)}}}\right]\right\} \tag{2}$$

6. Transport Phenomena in the Liquid Phase

6.1. Viscosity: definition and measurement. The viscosity η is defined as the shear stress per unit shear rate,

$$\eta = \frac{f}{dx/dt} \tag{1}$$

Methods for its measurement include:

a. *Concentric-cylinder viscometer*

$$\eta = (L/4\pi\omega h)\,(1/r_1^2 - 1/r_2^2) \tag{2}$$

where L is the measured torque, ω is the angular velocity of the rotating cylinder, h the height of the cylinders, and r_1 and r_2 their respective radii.

b. *Capillary flow*

$$\eta = \frac{P\pi r^4}{8lU} \tag{3}$$

where U is the volume rate of flow of liquid through the capillary, l its length, r its radius, and P the pressure difference (Poiseuille, 1844).

c. *Falling ball*

$$\eta = \frac{2\sigma r^2 \Delta o}{9v} \tag{4}$$

where v is the terminal velocity of the sphere falling through the liquid, g the acceleration of gravity, r the radius of the sphere, and $\Delta\rho$ the difference in density between sphere and liquid (Stokes, 1856).

d. *Fiber method (used for glass)*

$$\eta = \frac{mg}{3\pi r^2 V} \tag{5}$$

where V is the fractional rate of extension of a fiber, of radius r, which is loaded by the mass m.

6.2. Diffusion: definition and measurement. The diffusion coefficient $\mathcal{D}$ is defined as the quantity of solute diffusing across unit area in unit time per unit concentration gradient (Fick, 1855).

$$\mathcal{D} = -\frac{\partial n/\partial t}{A\ \partial c/\partial x} \tag{1}$$

Methods for its measurement include:

a. *Diaphragm cell method.* Two stirred solutions are separated by a porous diaphragm; the initial concentration difference is ΔC_0, and after time t the concentration difference is ΔC_t.

$$\mathcal{D} = -\frac{1}{\alpha t} \ln \frac{\Delta C_t}{\Delta C_0} \tag{2}$$

where α is a cell factor.

b. *Sheared boundary method.* At zero time, a solution of concentration C_1 and a solution of concentration C_0 are brought into contact along a plane boundary. The differential equation governing the one-dimensional diffusion (Fick's second law) is

$$\frac{\partial C}{\partial t} = \mathcal{D} \frac{\partial^2 C}{\partial x^2} \tag{3}$$

whose approximate solution for the stated boundary conditions is

$$\frac{dC}{dx} = \frac{C_1 - C_0}{2\sqrt{\pi \mathcal{D}t}} e^{-x^2/2\mathcal{D}t} \tag{4}$$

6.3. Equivalent conductivity : definition and measurement. The equivalent conductivity of an electrolyte is defined as

$$\Lambda = \frac{\kappa}{c} \tag{1}$$

where κ is the specific conductance in mho per centimeter, and c is the concentration of electrolyte in equivalents per cubic centimeter. The equivalent conductivity of a salt is the sum of the equivalent conductivities of its individual ions (Kohlrausch's " law of the independent migration of ions "),

$$\Lambda = \Lambda_+ + \Lambda_- \tag{2}$$

The fraction of the current carried by the ions of one kind, the " transference number," is defined as

$$t_+ = \frac{\Lambda_+}{\Lambda} \quad \text{or} \quad t_- = \frac{\Lambda_-}{\Lambda}; \quad t_+ + t_- = 1 \tag{3}$$

Methods for the experimental determination of transference numbers include :

a. *Hittorf method.* After electrolysis, the cathode compartment and the anode compartment are analyzed, and a correction applied for the amount of electrolyte which was consumed by electrolysis. If Δn_a is the excess loss of electrolyte at the anode, due to migration, and Δn_c is the excess loss of electrolyte at the cathode, in equivalents per faraday, then approximately

$$t_+ = \Delta n_a, \quad t_- = \Delta n_c \tag{4}$$

b. *Moving boundary method.* The velocity of travel of one kind of ion permits the computation of its " ionic mobility " l, the velocity per unit potential gradient in cm^2 sec^{-1} $volt^{-1}$. Then

$$\Lambda_+ = \mathcal{F} l_+ \quad \text{or} \quad \Lambda_- = \mathcal{F} l_- \tag{5}$$

where $\mathcal{F}$ is Faraday's constant, 96,494.

c. *Concentration cell with liquid junction.* This is a cell consisting of two solutions, one of concentration C_1 and the other C_2, the solutions being in direct contact, and each containing one electrode reversible to (say) the cation. The corresponding concentration cell without liquid junction comprises two solutions of concentrations C_1 and C_2, each containing two electrodes—one reversible to the cation and the other to the anion—and connected so their polarities oppose one another. If the voltage of the cell *without* liquid junction is ϵ, and the voltage of the cell *with* liquid junction is ϵ_t, then

$$t_- = \frac{\epsilon_t}{\epsilon} \tag{6}$$

The transference number obtained is that for the ion to which the electrode is not reversible.

6.4. Viscosity of mixtures. The viscosity of a solution of normal liquids is represented fairly closely by the semi-empirical relation

$$\log \eta = x_1 \log \eta_1 + x_2 \log \eta_2 \tag{1}$$

where x_1 may be mole fraction, weight fraction, or volume fraction (Kendall, 1913).

The viscosity of a dilute suspension of spheres is

$$\frac{\eta}{\eta_0} = 1 + 2.5\phi_2 + \ldots \tag{2}$$

where η_0 is the viscosity of the pure liquid and ϕ_2 is the volume fraction of spheres (Einstein, 1906, 1911).

The viscosity of a solution of linear high polymers is

$$\frac{\eta}{\eta_0} = 1 + KM^{\alpha}C \tag{3}$$

where C is the concentration (usually in grams per 100 cc) of polymer, M its molecular weight, K a constant characteristic of a given type of polymer, and α a constant usually falling between 0.6 and 0.8 (Houwink 1940, Flory 1943).

The viscosity of an aqueous electrolyte is given approximately by

$$\frac{\eta}{\eta_0} = 1 + 0.003\mathring{r}\sqrt{\mu} \tag{4}$$

where μ is the ionic strength and $\mathring{r}$ is the mean radius of an ion, in Ångstrøm units (approximate form of an equation due to Falkenhagen, 1929). An empirical equation of the form

$$\frac{\eta}{\eta_0} = 1 + A\sqrt{C} + BC \tag{5}$$

holds over a wider range of concentration.

6.5. Diffusion coefficient of mixtures. The diffusion coefficient of a liquid solution varies with composition, approximately obeying the law

$$\mathcal{D}\eta = (\mathcal{D}\eta)_{\mathrm{av}}\left[\frac{d\ln a_1}{d\ln x_1}\right] \tag{1}$$

where $(\mathcal{D}\eta)_{\mathrm{av}}$ can be the arithmetic mean value, and $a_1 = x_1\gamma_1$ is the activity of component 1. The quantity in brackets, which can be computed from the activity-coefficient data for the liquid system, corrects for the fact that activity rather than concentration is the driving force for diffusion.

The diffusion coefficient of a number of electrolytes is represented, within the experimental error, by

$$\mathcal{D} = 17.86\ 10^{-10}\ T\left(\frac{1}{\dfrac{1}{\Lambda_+}+\dfrac{1}{\Lambda_-}}\right)\frac{1}{\phi_{H_2O}}\left[1+\frac{d\ln\gamma_\pm}{d\ln C}\right]\frac{\eta_0}{\eta} \tag{2}$$

(Gordon, 1937).

The diffusion coefficient of a large spherical molecule is given by Stokes' law,

$$\mathcal{D}\eta = \frac{kT}{6\pi r}$$

where k is Boltzmann's constant and r is the molecular radius. For molecules of the same size as the solvent,

$$\mathcal{D}\eta = \frac{kT}{\lambda} \tag{4}$$

where λ is of the order of a molecular dimension (Eyring, 1936).

6.6. Dependence of conductivity on concentration. The conductivity of a partially ionized substance is given approximately by

$$\frac{\Lambda}{\Lambda_0} = \alpha \tag{1}$$

where α is the degree of dissociation and Λ_0 is the conductivity at infinite dilution. More exactly, the relation is

$$\frac{\Lambda}{\Lambda_{(\mathrm{Onsager})}} = \alpha \tag{2}$$

where $\Lambda_{(\mathrm{Onsager})}$ is the limiting ionic conductivity, corrected approximately for " ionic atmosphere " effects (Onsager and Fuoss, 1932).

At 25° C, $\Lambda_{(\text{Onsager})}$ for various types of electrolytes is

$$\left.\begin{aligned}
&\text{1-1} \quad \Lambda_0 - \sqrt{C}(59.86 + 0.2277\Lambda_0) \\
&\text{2-2} \quad \Lambda_0 - \sqrt{C}(239.4 + 1.822\Lambda_0) \\
&\text{3-3} \quad \Lambda_0 - \sqrt{C}(538.7 + 6.148\Lambda_0) \\
&\text{2-1} \quad \Lambda_0 - \sqrt{C}\left(155.6 + \frac{1.796\Lambda_0}{(1+t_1) + 0.816\sqrt{1+t_1}}\right) \\
&\text{3-1} \quad \Lambda_0 - \sqrt{C}\left(293.3 + \frac{4.280\Lambda_0}{(1+2t_1) + 0.866\sqrt{1+2t_1}}\right) \\
&\text{3-2} \quad \Lambda_0 - \sqrt{C}\left(634.5 + \frac{11.88\Lambda_0}{(1+0.5t_2) + 0.775\sqrt{1+0.5t_2}}\right)
\end{aligned}\right\} \tag{3}$$

where t_i is the transference number of the i-valent ion.

6.7. Temperature dependence of viscosity, diffusion, and conductivity. Approximately,

$$\eta = A_\eta e^{+E_\eta/RT} \tag{1}$$

$$\mathcal{D} = A_{\mathcal{D}} e^{-E_{\mathcal{D}}/RT} \tag{2}$$

$$\Lambda = A_\Lambda e^{-E_\Lambda/RT} \tag{3}$$

where the A's and E's are suitable constants. A graph of log η against $1/T$ gives an almost straight line, and similarly for the other properties.

According to one theory of these phenomena (Eyring, 1936)

$$\eta = \frac{h}{\lambda^3} e^{-\Delta S_\eta^{\ddagger}/R} e^{\Delta H_\eta^{\ddagger}/RT} \tag{4}$$

$$\mathcal{D} = \lambda^2 \frac{kT}{h} e^{\Delta S_{\mathcal{D}}^{\ddagger}/R} e^{-\Delta H_{\mathcal{D}}^{\ddagger}/RT} \tag{5}$$

$$\Lambda_0 = \frac{\mathcal{F}\lambda^2 ze}{h} e^{\Delta S_\Lambda^{\ddagger}/R} e^{-\Delta H_\Lambda^{\ddagger}/RT} \tag{6}$$

where λ is a distance of the order of molecular dimensions, h is Planck's constant, k is Boltzmann's constant, and $\Delta S^{\ddagger}$ and $\Delta H^{\ddagger}$ are the entropy of activation and enthalpy of activation for the respective processes. Since the unit processes are not quite identical in the three cases, the values of $\Delta S^{\ddagger}$ and $\Delta H^{\ddagger}$ may be slightly different. For normal liquids, $\Delta S^{\ddagger}$ is small and $\Delta H^{\ddagger}$ is about one-third or one-fourth the heat of vaporization.

Chapter 28

BASIC FORMULAS OF ASTROPHYSICS

BY LAWRENCE H. ALLER

University of Michigan Observatory

Astrophysics is the borderline field between astronomy and physics. Much of astrophysics is related to the interpretation of atomic spectra. Hence, useful formulas will also appear in Chapters 19, 20, and 21, and the sections on thermodynamics and statistical mechanics also have a relationship to the subject, as has the more specialized chapter on physical chemistry.

1. Formulas Derived from Statistical Mechanics

1.1. Boltzmann formula (Ref. 1, Chap. 4). Let there be N_n atoms in level n of excitation potential χ_n and $N_{n'}$ atoms in level n' of excitation potential $\chi_{n'}$. Let the statistical weights of level n and n' be $\tilde{\omega}_n$ and $\tilde{\omega}_{n'}$ respectively. Under conditions of thermal equilibrium

$$\frac{N_n}{N_n{}'} = \frac{\tilde{\omega}_n}{\tilde{\omega}_n{}'} e^{-\chi/kT} \tag{1}$$

where $\chi = \chi_n - \chi_{n'}$, T is the temperature in absolute degrees, and k is Boltzmann's constant. If the total number of atoms in all levels of excitation is N, then

$$\frac{N_n}{N} = \frac{\tilde{\omega}_n}{B(T)} e^{-\chi/kT} \tag{2}$$

where

$$B(T) = \tilde{\omega}_1 + \tilde{\omega}_2 e^{-\chi_2/kT} + \tilde{\omega}_3 e^{-\chi_3/kT} + \ldots = \sum_i \tilde{\omega}_i e^{-\chi_i/kT}$$

is called the partition function. Here χ is the excitation potential above the ground level.

1.2. Ionization formula (Ref. 1, Chap. 4). Let there be N_r, N_{r+1} atoms in the rth and $(r+1)$st stages of ionization per cm³. Let the electron density be N_ε and the temperature be T. If χ_r is the ionization potential from the ground level of the atom in the rth stage of ionization, then

$$\frac{N_{r+1}N_\varepsilon}{N_r} = \left(\frac{2\pi mk}{h^2}\right)^{3/2} \frac{2B_{r+1}(T)}{B_r(T)} T^{3/2} e^{-\chi_r/kT} \tag{1}$$

where B_r and B_{r+1} represent the partition functions for the rth and $(r+1)$st stages of ionization. If we use the electron pressure

$$P_\varepsilon = N_\varepsilon kT$$

and substitute numerical values we find

$$\log \frac{N_{r+1}}{N_r} P_\varepsilon = -\frac{5040}{T}\chi_r + \frac{5}{2}\log T + \log \frac{2B_{r+1}(T)}{B_r(T)} - 0.48 \qquad (2)$$

where P_ε is expressed in dynes cm^2 and χ_r is expressed in electron volts.

1.3. Combined ionization and Boltzmann formula (Ref. 1, Chap. 4). If $N_{r,s}$ is the number of atoms/cm^3 in the sth level of the rth stage of ionization, $N_{r,s}$ may be expressed in terms of the number of atoms in the $(r+1)$st stage of ionization, viz.,

$$\log \frac{N_{r+1}P}{N_{r,s}} = -\frac{5040}{T}(\chi_r - \chi_s) + \frac{5}{2}\log T + \log \frac{2B_{r+1}(T)}{\tilde{\omega}_s} - 0.48 \qquad (1)$$

where χ_s is the excitation potential of the level s of statistical weight $\tilde{\omega}_s$ in volts.

1.4. Dissociation equation for diatomic molecules (Ref. 1, Chap. 4). Let two elements X and Y combine to form the diatomic molecule XY, viz.,

$$\mathrm{X} + \mathrm{Y} \rightleftarrows \mathrm{XY}$$

Then the concentration of the atoms X, Y, and the molecule XY will be governed by an equation of the form

$$\frac{N_\mathrm{X} N_\mathrm{Y}}{N_\mathrm{XY}} = \frac{\tilde{\omega}_\mathrm{X}\tilde{\omega}_\mathrm{Y}}{\tilde{\omega}_\mathrm{XY}}\left(\frac{2\pi M}{h^2}\right)^{3/2} \frac{h^2}{8\pi^2 I}(kT)^{1/2}(1 - e^{-hW/kT})e^{-D/kT} \qquad (1)$$

Here $\tilde{\omega}_\mathrm{X}$, $\tilde{\omega}_\mathrm{Y}$, and $\tilde{\omega}_\mathrm{XY}$ denote the statistical weights of the ground levels of atoms X, Y, and molecule XY.

$$M = \frac{M_\mathrm{X} M_\mathrm{Y}}{M_\mathrm{X} + M_\mathrm{Y}} = \text{“ reduced mass ” expressed in grams.}$$

$I = M r_0^2$ where r_0 is the separation of atoms X and Y in cm

W = fundamental vibration frequency of the molecule in units of sec^{-1}

D = dissociation energy from lowest vibrational level in cgs units

The right-hand side of the equation corresponds to the dissociation “ constant ” of ordinary chemical reaction formulas.

2. Formulas Connected with Absorption and Emission of Radiation

2.1. Definitions (Ref. 1, Chap. 5 and 8). If $I_\nu(\theta,\phi)$ is the specific intensity of the radiation, the flux through a surface S is defined by

$$\mathcal{F} = \int_{\theta=a}^{\pi} \int_{\phi=0}^{2\pi} I(\theta,\phi) \cos\theta \sin\theta \, d\theta \, d\phi \tag{1}$$

where θ is the angle between the ray direction and the normal to the surface, and ϕ is the azimuthal angle. If I does not depend on ϕ, and we write $\mu = \cos\theta$, then

$$\mathcal{F} = 2\pi \int_{-1}^{+1} I(\mu)\mu \, d\mu \tag{2}$$

The energy density is given by

$$u(T) = \frac{1}{c} \int I(\theta,\phi) d\omega \tag{3}$$

where the integration is carried out over all solid angle. For isotopic radiation

$$u(T) = \frac{4\pi}{c} I \tag{4}$$

The radiation pressure is

$$p(T) = \frac{1}{c} \int I(\theta,\phi) \cos^2\theta \, d\omega \tag{5}$$

For isotopic radiation

$$p(T) = \tfrac{1}{3} u(T) \tag{4}$$

2.2. Specific intensity (Ref. 1, Chaps. 5 and 8). The dependence of intensity upon frequency for blackbody radiation is given by the Planck formula

$$I_\nu(T) = \frac{2h\nu^3}{c^2} \frac{1}{e^{h\nu/kT} - 1} \tag{1}$$

or in wavelength units

$$I_\lambda = \frac{2hc^2}{\lambda^5} \cdot \frac{1}{e^{hc/\lambda kT} - 1} \tag{2}$$

From these relations are derived Wien's law and Stefan's law (see Chapters 10 and 11).

2.3. Einstein's coefficients (Ref. 1, Chaps. 5 and 8). The atomic coefficients of absorption and emission are defined in the following way. If N_n atoms are maintained in the upper level of a transition of frequency $\nu(nn')$, the number of spontaneous downward transitions/cm³/sec will be

$$N_n A_{nn'}$$

where $A_{nn'}$ is the Einstein coefficient of spontaneous emission. If radiation of intensity I_ν is present there also will be induced emissions whose number is given by

$$N_n B_{nn'} I_{\nu(nn')} \quad \text{per cm}^3/\text{sec}$$

More correctly these induced emissions should be called negative absorptions since the induced quantum is emitted in the same direction as the absorbed quantum. The number of transitions from level n' to n produced by the absorption of quanta by the atoms in the lower level is

$$N_{n'} B_{n'n} I_{\nu(nn')}$$

The relations between these coefficients are

$$\tilde{\omega}_n B_{nn'} = \tilde{\omega}_{n'} B_{n'n} \tag{1}$$

$$A_{nn'} = B_{nn'} \frac{2h\nu^3}{c^2} \tag{2}$$

2.4. Oscillator strength (Ref. 1, Chaps. 5 and 8). The relation between the Einstein A coefficient and the oscillator strength or Ladenberg f is

$$A_{nn'} = \frac{\tilde{\omega}_{n'}}{\tilde{\omega}_n} \frac{8\pi^2\epsilon^2\nu^2}{mc^3} f_{n'n} \tag{1}$$

or

$$A_{nn'} = 3\frac{\tilde{\omega}_{n'}}{\tilde{\omega}_n} f_{n'n}\gamma_c \tag{2}$$

where γ_c is the classical damping constant.

2.5. Absorption coefficients (Ref. 1, Chaps. 5 and 8). The absorption coefficient for a single atom at rest is

$$\alpha_\nu = \frac{\pi\epsilon^2}{mc} f \frac{\Gamma}{4\pi^2} \frac{1}{(\nu - \nu_0)^2 + (\Gamma/4\pi)^2} \tag{1}$$

where Γ is the quantum mechanical damping constant. For pure radiation processes, we can usually write

$$\Gamma = \Gamma_r = \Sigma A_{nn'} \tag{2}$$

where the summation is taken over all lower levels. If collisional broadening also occurs, we can define a

$$\Gamma = \Gamma_r + \Gamma_{\text{col}} \tag{3}$$

where Γ_{col} represents the effects of collisions.

$$\Gamma_{\text{col}} = 2\pi r_0^2 N_p v \tag{4}$$

where r_0 is the effective radius of the perturbing particles which number

N_p per cm³. The relative velocity of the radiating atom and the perturbing atom is v.

The profiles of all lines are broadened by the Doppler effect. The shape of the absorption coefficient of a line broadened by Doppler effect only is

$$\alpha_\nu = \frac{\pi\epsilon^2}{mc} f \frac{c}{v_0 \nu \sqrt{\pi}} e^{-[c(\nu-\nu_0)/v_0\nu_0]^2}$$

Usually both types of broadening operate together and the absorption coefficient given by the integral

$$\alpha_\nu = \alpha_0 \frac{a}{\pi} \int_{-\infty}^{+\infty} \frac{e^{-\chi^2}}{a^2 + (u-\chi)^2} d\chi \tag{6}$$

where

$$\chi = \frac{v}{v_0}, \quad u = \left(\frac{\nu - \nu_0}{\nu_0}\right)\frac{c}{v_0}, \quad a = \frac{c\Gamma}{4\pi\nu_0 v_0},$$

$$\alpha_0 = \frac{\tilde{\omega}_n}{\tilde{\omega}_{n'}} A \frac{\lambda^3}{8 v_0 \pi^{3/2}}$$

Here v_0 is the most probable velocity of the atoms. The integral must be evaluated numerically, and tables have been published by Mitchell and Zemansky, Hjerting, and Daniel Harris. The arguments are usually a and u and with the aid of the tables, α/α_0 may be found at once. These formulas do not hold for Stark broadening in hydrogen and helium.

2.6. Line strengths (Refs. 4 and 12). The A or f-value may be expressed in terms of the " strength " of the line. Thus, for an electric dipole transition between 2 atomic levels γSLJ and $\gamma' SL'J'$,

$$A_e(\gamma SLJ;\gamma' SL'J') = \frac{1}{2J+1} \frac{64\pi^4\nu^3}{2hc^3} S_e(\gamma SLJ;\gamma' SL'J') \tag{1}$$

where

$$S_e(\gamma SLJ;\gamma' SL'J') = S(\gamma SLJ;\gamma' SL'J')\sigma^2(nl;n'l')$$

and S is the relative strength.

$$\sigma = \frac{\epsilon}{\sqrt{4l^2-1}} \int_0^r rR(n,l)R(n'l')dr \tag{2}$$

where l is the azimuthal quantum number; R is the radial wave function. For magnetic dipole radiation between two levels of the same configuration,

$$A_m(J,J') = 35{,}320\left(\frac{\nu}{\nu_R}\right)^3 \frac{S_m(J,J')}{2J+1} \text{ sec}^{-1} \tag{3}$$

where $S_m(J,J')$ is the magnetic dipole strength in atomic units $\epsilon h^2/16\pi^2 m^2 c^2$; ν_R = frequency of Lyman limit (3.28×10^{15} sec^{-1}). The electric quadrupole transition probability is

$$A_q(J,J') = 2648\left(\frac{\nu}{\nu_R}\right)^5 \frac{S_q(J,J')}{2J+1} \text{ sec}^{-1} \tag{4}$$

Here $S_q(J,J')$ is expressed in atomic units $\epsilon^2 a^4$ (a = radius of first Bohr orbit) and may be written as

$$S_q(J,J') = C_q(J,J')S_q^{\,2}(nl,nl)$$

where

$$S_q = c_e \int_0^r r^2 R^2(nl)dr$$

and $c_e = 2/5$ for p electrons. The values of $C_q(J,J')$ have been tabulated by Shortley and collaborators. If both magnetic dipole and electric quadrupole radiation are permitted for a line

$$A = A_q + A_m \tag{5}$$

2.1. Definition of *f*-values for the continuum (Ref. 7).

$$\alpha_\nu = \frac{\pi\epsilon^2}{mc} \cdot \frac{df}{d\nu} \tag{1}$$

3. Relation Between Mass, Luminosity, Radii, and Temperature of Stars

3.1. Absolute magnitude (Ref. 10). Relation between absolute magnitude M, apparent magnitude m, and distance r is

$$M = m + 5 - 5 \log r \tag{1}$$

The distance r is given in parsecs.

$$1 \text{ parsec} = 3.084 \times 10^{18} \text{ cm}$$

which is 206,265 times the distance of the earth from the sun. If the star is dimmed by A magnitudes due to space absorption, m must be replaced by $m - A$.

3.2. Color index (Ref. 1, Chap. 6; Ref. 15, Chap. 6). The difference between the photographic and photovisual magnitudes is called the color index,

$$C = m_{\text{ptg}} - m_{\text{vis}} \tag{1}$$

If the star is undimmed by space absorption, color index and temperature are related by

$$T = \frac{8200}{C + 0.68} \tag{2}$$

The difference between the observed color index and the true color index appropriate to the spectral class and temperature of the star is called the *color excess.*

$$E = C_{\text{obs}} - C \tag{3}$$

In most regions of the Milky Way one can take

$$A_{pg} = 4E \tag{4}$$

If $M_{\text{vis}} =$ absolute visual magnitude, $R =$ radius in terms of the sun as 1.0, $T =$ temperature in absolute degrees,

$$\log R = \frac{5700}{T} - 0.05 - 0.2M_{\text{vis}} \tag{5}$$

For high-temperature stars this formula must be modified, viz.,

$$\log R = \frac{5700}{T} - 0.05 - 0.2M_{\text{vis}} + 0.5 \log [1 - 10^{-14,700/T}] \tag{6}$$

The surface gravity is

$$g = g_0 \frac{M}{R^2}$$

where $g_0 = 2.74 \times 10^4$ cm/sec^2 is the surface gravity of the sun, M and R are the mass and radius, respectively, in terms of the corresponding quantities for the sun. For main sequence stars, Russell has given the following empirical formula dependence of surface gravity on temperature.

$$\log_{10} \frac{g}{g_0} = -0.65 + \frac{3250}{T} \tag{8}$$

For the giants

$$\log_{10} \frac{g}{g_0} = +0.76 - \frac{11250}{T} \tag{9}$$

3.3. Mass-luminosity law (Ref. 11). The empirical relation between mass M and luminosity L (expressed in terms of the corresponding quantities for the sun) is

$$\log M = 0.26 \log L + 0.06 \tag{1}$$

for stars which do not differ greatly in brightness from the sun.

3.4. The equation of transfer for gray material (Ref. 2)

$$\mu \frac{dI}{d\tau} = I - J(\tau) \tag{1}$$

where $I(\mu,\tau)$ is the intensity; $\mu = \cos\theta$; θ is the angle between the ray and the outward directed normal. Here $d\tau = k\rho dx$ where dx is the element of geometrical depth, $\rho =$ density, $k =$ coefficient of continuous absorption.

$$J(\tau) = \tfrac{1}{2}\int_{-1}^{+1} I(\mu,\tau)d\mu = \tfrac{1}{2}\int_{0}^{\infty} E_1(|\, t - \tau\,|)J(t)dt \tag{2}$$

where $E_1(x)$ is the exponential integral

$$E_1(x) = \int_1^{\infty} e^{-yx}\frac{dy}{y}$$

The solution of the equation of transfer is

$$I(0,\mu) = \frac{\sqrt{3}}{4} FH(\mu) \tag{3}$$

where $I(0,\mu) =$ intensity of emergent ray making an angle θ with outward directed normal, πF is the flux, and

$$H(\mu) = 1 + \tfrac{1}{2}\mu H(\mu)\int_0^1 \frac{H(x)}{\mu + x}dx \tag{4}$$

This equation may be solved by an iteration procedure. For gray material in thermal equilibrium the dependence of temperature in optical depth is given by

$$T^4 = \tfrac{3}{4}T_e^{\,4}[\tau + q(T)] \tag{5}$$

where $T_e =$ effective temperature.

Here $q(T)$ is a monotonic function increasing from $1/\sqrt{3}$ at $\tau = 0$ to 0.71045 at $\tau = \infty$. In the Eddington approximation the dependence of T on τ was given as

$$T^4 = \tfrac{3}{4}T_e^{\,4}(\tau + \tfrac{2}{3}) \tag{6}$$

An approximation of sufficient accuracy for most purposes has been given by D. Labs.

$$T^4 = \tfrac{3}{4}T_e^{\,4}(\tau + B - Ae^{-\alpha\tau}) \tag{7}$$

where $A = 0.1331$, $B = 0.7104$, $\alpha = 3.4488$.

3.5. Non-gray material (Ref. 1, Chap. 7). Element of optical depth is defined by

$$d\tau_\nu = \kappa_\nu \rho dx \tag{1}$$

where κ_ν is continuous absorption coefficient.

For large optical depths the mean absorption coefficient is the Rosseland mean

$$\bar{\kappa} = \frac{\int_0^\infty [dB_\nu/(\rho dx)]d\nu}{\int_0^\infty (1/\kappa_\nu)[dB_\nu/(\rho dx)]d\nu}$$

where B_ν is the Planck function. Also, $\bar{\kappa}$ may be defined by

$$\bar{\kappa} = \frac{1}{F}\int_0^\infty \kappa_\nu F_\nu d\nu$$

where πF_ν is the monochromatic flux. Chandrasekhar suggests that at small optical depths we employ the net monochromatic flux of radiation of frequency ν in a gray atmosphere. If

$$\bar{\tau} = \int \bar{\kappa}\rho\, dx$$

the temperature dependence on $\bar{\tau}$ is assumed to be the same as in gray atmosphere with τ identified with $\bar{\tau}$.

3.6. Model atmosphere in hydrostatic equilibrium (Ref. 1, Chap. 7; Ref. 13).

$$\frac{dP}{d\tau} = \frac{g}{\kappa} \tag{1}$$

$\kappa(P_\varepsilon,T)$ can be expressed as $\kappa(P_g,T)$ when P_g is known as a function of P_ε, T. This depends only on the chemical composition. Here g = surface gravity.

If the mechanical force exerted by radiation is important, Eq. (1) may be written as

$$\frac{dP_g}{d\tau} = \frac{g}{\kappa} - \frac{\sigma_r}{c} T_e^4$$

where P_g is the gas pressure and σ_r is the Stefan-Boltzmann constant.

3.7. Formation of absorption lines (Ref. 2, p. 321; Ref. 1, Chap. 8). The fundamental equation

$$\cos\theta \frac{dI_\nu}{dt_\nu} = I_\nu - \mathcal{J}_\nu(t) \tag{1}$$

where $dt_\nu = (\kappa_\nu + l_\nu)dx$, κ_ν = coefficient of continuous absorption at the line, l_ν = coefficient of line absorption.

$$\eta_\nu = l_\nu/\kappa_\nu, \quad \lambda_\nu = \frac{1+\epsilon\eta}{1+\eta} \tag{2}$$

where ϵ expresses the role of thermal processes in the line, $\epsilon = 1$ for line formed by thermal emission and absorption processes, $\epsilon = 0$ for pure scattering.

$$\mathcal{J}_\nu(t_\nu) = \lambda B_\nu(t_\nu) + (1 - \lambda_\nu) J(t_\nu) \tag{3}$$

Then
$$I_\nu(0,\mu) = \int_0^\infty \mathcal{J}(t_\nu) e^{-t/\mu} \frac{dt_\nu}{\mu} \tag{4}$$

The intensity in the continuum is

$$I_\nu^c(0,\mu) = \int_0^\infty B_\nu(T_\nu) e^{-\tau_\nu/\mu} \frac{d\tau_\nu}{\mu} \tag{5}$$

The residual intensity in the line

$$r_\nu = \frac{I_\nu(0,\mu)}{I_\nu^c(0,\mu)} \tag{6}$$

For $\eta =$ constant and $B_\nu(t_\nu) = B_0 + B_1 t_\nu$ an exact solution is available. For an arbitrary variation of η and B_ν, the equation is solved by a process of iteration (Strömgren) or trial and error (Pannekoek).

3.8. Curve of growth (Ref. 1, Chap. 8; Ref. 6; Ref. 14). If r_ν is the residual intensity at a point ν in a line profile,

$$W_\nu = \int (1 - r_\nu) d\nu \quad \text{and} \quad W_\lambda = \frac{\lambda^2}{c} W_\nu \tag{1}$$

If we regard the lines as being formed in a reversing layer which overlies a photosphere that radiates a continuous spectrum (Schuster-Schwarzschild model, then to a good approximation

$$r_\nu = \frac{1}{1 + N\alpha_\nu} \tag{2}$$

where $N =$ number of atoms above the photosphere, $\alpha_\nu =$ atomic absorption coefficient including both collisional, radiative, and Doppler broadening. The relation between W_λ and the number of atoms is given by

$$\frac{W}{\lambda} = \frac{vX_0\sqrt{\pi}}{c}\left(1 - \frac{X_0}{\sqrt{2}} + \frac{X_0^2}{\sqrt{3}} - \dots\right) \sim \frac{vX_0\sqrt{\pi}}{c} \tag{3}$$

when $N\alpha_\nu < 1$. Here

$$X_0 = N \frac{\pi\epsilon^2}{mc} f \frac{1}{\sqrt{\pi}} \cdot \frac{c}{v\nu_0} \tag{4}$$

When $\ln X_0 \gg 1$,

$$\frac{W}{\lambda} = 2\frac{v}{c}(\ln X_0)^{1/2}\left[1 - \frac{\pi^2}{24(\ln X_0)^2} - \frac{7\pi^4}{384(\ln X_0)^4} + \dots\right] \tag{5}$$

When X_0 is very large,

$$\frac{W}{\lambda} = \frac{\pi^{1/4}}{2}\left(\frac{v}{c}\right)^{1/2}\left(X_0 \frac{\Gamma}{\nu}\right)^{1/2} \tag{6}$$

A different set of curves is obtained for each different value of the ratio Γ/ν.

3.9. Equations governing the equilibrium of a star (Ref. 15, Chaps. 1 and 2; Ref. 3). Let M_r be mass within a distance r of the center of the star; L_r be the total amount of energy developed in a sphere of radius r. The structure of the star is governed by the following equations.

$$\left.\begin{aligned} &P = \frac{\rho RT}{\mu} + \frac{aT^4}{3}, && \text{(gas + radiation pressure)} \\ &\mu = \mu(\rho, T, \mathcal{A}), && \text{(molecular weight)} \\ &\kappa = \kappa(\rho, T, \mathcal{A}), && \text{(mean absorption coefficient or opacity)} \\ &\epsilon = \epsilon(\rho, T, \mathcal{A}), && \text{(energy generation)} \end{aligned}\right\} \tag{1}$$

Here $\mathcal{A}$ denotes the relative abundances of the elements or the chemical composition.

$$\left.\begin{aligned} &\frac{dP}{dr} = -G\frac{M_r\rho}{r^2}, && \text{(hydrostatic equilibrium)} \\ &M_r = \int 4\pi r^2 \rho\, dr \\ &\frac{dL_r}{dr} = 4\pi r^2 \epsilon\rho, && \text{(energy generation)} \end{aligned}\right\} \tag{2}$$

For the domain in radiative equilibrium

$$\frac{d(aT^4)}{dr} = -\frac{3\kappa\rho}{c}\cdot\frac{L}{4\pi r^2} \tag{3}$$

For the domain in adiabatic equilibrium, we neglect radiation pressure and have

$$P = K\rho^{\gamma} \tag{4}$$

The equations can then be reduced to the form

$$\frac{d}{d\theta}\left(\frac{d\xi}{d\theta}\theta^2\right) + \theta^2\xi^n = 0, \quad \text{(Emden's equation)} \tag{5}$$

$$n = \frac{1}{\gamma - 1}, \quad \theta^2 = r^2\left[\frac{1}{1+n}\cdot\frac{\mu}{R}4\pi G\left(\frac{R}{\mu}\cdot\frac{1}{K}\right)^n\right]T_c^{\,n-1}, \quad T = \xi T_c$$

where T_c = central temperature, and n is called the polytropic index.

3.10. Boundary conditions (Ref. 15, Chaps. 1 and 2; Ref. 3).

$$\left.\begin{array}{ll} r=0, \quad M_r=0, \quad L_r=0, & \text{(center of star)} \\ r=R, \quad M_r=M, \quad L_r=L, \quad \rho=0, \quad T=0, & \text{(surface of star)} \end{array}\right\} \qquad (1)$$

3.11. Theoretical form of mass-luminosity law (Ref. 15, Chaps. 1 and 2; Ref. 3).

$$L = \text{const}\,\frac{1}{\kappa_0}\cdot\frac{M^{5+s}}{R^s}(\mu\beta)^{+7+s} \qquad (1)$$

where $\kappa = \kappa_0\rho T^{-3+s}$, $\beta =$ ratio of gas pressure to total pressure. This equation must be solved in conjunction with the equation governing the energy output.

$$\epsilon = \epsilon_0(\mathcal{A})\rho^m T^n, \quad \text{(energy generation law)} \qquad (2)$$

$$L = 4\pi\int_0^R \epsilon_0(\mathcal{A})\rho^{m+1}T^n r^2 dr \qquad (3)$$

Bibliography

1. ALLER, L. H., *Astrophysics : The Atmospheres of the Sun and Stars,* Ronald Press Co., New York, 1953.
2. CHANDRASEKHAR, S., *Radiative Transfer*, Oxford University Press, New York, 1950. The mathematical theory of the flow of radiation through matter, and scattering of light in extended atmospheres.
3. CHANDRASEKHAR, S., *Stellar Structure*, University of Chicago Press, Chicago, 1940. A comprehensive account of the theory of stellar interiors.
4. CONDON, E. U. and SHORTLEY, G. H., *Theory of Atomic Spectra*, Cambridge University Press, London, 1935.
5. LABS, D., *Z. Astrophys.*, **27**, 153 (1950).
6. MENZEL, D. H., *Astrophys. J.*, **84**, 462 (1936).
7. MENZEL, D. H. and PEKERIS, C. L., *Monthly Notices Roy. Astron. Soc.*, **96**, 89 (1935), Equation (2.1).
8. MENZEL, D. H. and SEN, H. K., *Astrophys. J.*, **110**, 1 (1949).
9. ROSSELAND, S., *Theoretical Astrophysics*, Oxford University Press, New York, 1937. A text on theoretical astrophysics and selected topics of theoretical physics.
10. RUSSELL, H. N., DUGAN, R. S. and STEWART, J. A., *Astronomy*, Vol. 2, Ginn & Company, Boston, 1927.
11. RUSSELL, H. N. and MOORE, C. E., *The Masses of the Stars*, University of Chicago Press, Chicago, 1940.
12. SHORTLEY, G. H., BAKER, J. G., ALLER, L. H. and MENZEL, D. H., *Astrophys. J.*, **93**, 178 (1941).
13. STRÖMGREN, B., *Pub. Copenhagen Obs. 138* (1944).
14. UNSÖLD, A., *Physik der Sternatmosphären*, Julius Springer, Berlin, 1938. A general text on stellar atmospheres.
15. ALLER, L. H., *Astrophysics : Nuclear Transformations, Stellar Interiors, and Nebulae*, Ronald Press Co., New York, 1954.

Chapter 29

CELESTIAL MECHANICS

By Edgar W. Woolard

Naval Observatory, Washington, D. C.

The basic equations of celestial mechanics are essentially those of ordinary classical mechanics. In the applications of these equations to the motions of celestial bodies, however, the technique adopted by the astronomer differs somewhat from that ordinarily employed by the physicist who is working on the average problem of classical dynamics. The distinction in general arises from the necessity, for astronomical purposes, of obtaining solutions of the equations of motion that will represent the motions over very long intervals of time with the high accuracy of precise astronomical observations, and in a form adapted to the practical numerical computation of the motion as an explicit function of the time. The emphasis is principally on indefinite integrals. Moreover, necessity demands that a solution which meets the needs of astronomy be obtained regardless of the mathematical difficulty or even impossibility of a general abstract solution in the current state of mathematical knowledge.

These considerations have resulted in the characteristic methods used in celestial mechanics, the more important of which are given in the following summary of formulas for the different types of motion that must be treated.

1. Gravitational Forces *

At any point external to a body with mass M and principal moments of inertia A, B, C, the Newtonian gravitational attraction exerted by the body is **grad** U, where to the *second order* inclusive in the ratio of the linear dimensions of the body to the distance r of the point from the center of mass, the Newtonian gravitational potential U is

$$U = k^2 \frac{M}{r} + k^2 \frac{A + B + C - 3I}{2r^3} \tag{1}$$

* See also Chapter 5.

in which I is the moment of inertia about r, and k^2 is the constant of gravitation. In cgs units, $k^2 = 6.673 \times 10^{-8}$ cm^3 g^{-1} sec^{-2}.

For symmetrical distributions of mass, this expression for U is accurate to the *third* order. For homogeneous or concentrically homogeneous spherical distributions, the expression reduces to the first term k^2M/r, as if the entire mass M were concentrated in a particle at the center of mass. For any body for which $A = B$, e.g., a concentrically homogeneous oblate spheroid of revolution, the value of I is $A + (C - A) \sin^2 d$, where d is the angle between r and the plane of the principal axes of A and B, and

$$U = k^2 \frac{M}{r} + k^2 \frac{C - A}{2r^3} (1 - 3 \sin^2 d) \tag{2}$$

On every element of mass dm of another body, the body M exerts a force for which the force function is Udm. When m is a rigid body, the action of this system of forces is the same as if the resultant $\boldsymbol{F}$ of the forces, which has a force function $\int_m Udm$, were applied to a particle of mass m at the center of mass, and a couple, with a moment equal to the resultant $\boldsymbol{G}$ of the moments of the forces about the center of mass, were applied to the body. The consequent motion of m under the action of M is a translation at velocity $\boldsymbol{V}$ in which the rate of change of the linear momentum is

$$m \frac{d\boldsymbol{V}}{dt} = \boldsymbol{F} \tag{3}$$

and a rotation around an axis through the center of mass in which the rate of change of the angular momentum $\boldsymbol{H}$ about the center of mass is

$$\frac{d\boldsymbol{H}}{dt} = \boldsymbol{G} \tag{4}$$

When both M and m are homogeneous or concentrically homogeneous spherical bodies, or when the distance r from M to m is so great that higher powers of $1/r$ may be neglected,

$$\int_m Udm = k^2 \frac{Mm}{r} \tag{5}$$

a function of r only, and hence the force exerted on m by M is

$$F = -k^2 \frac{Mm}{r} \tag{6}$$

directed toward M; an equal and oppositely directed force is exerted on M by m, and the resultant couples vanish.

Under these conditions, relative to an inertial rectangular coordinate system with arbitrary origin, in which the coordinates of the center of mass of m are

x', y', z', and those of M are X', Y', Z', the motion of the center of mass of m is represented by

$$\frac{d^2x'}{dt^2} = -k^2M\frac{x' - X'}{r^3}, \quad \cdots \tag{7}$$

Likewise, M under the action of m moves in accordance with the equations

$$\frac{d^2X'}{dt^2} = +k^2m\frac{x' - X'}{r^3}, \quad \cdots \tag{8}$$

Consequently, in a rectangular system with *origin at* M and axes in fixed directions in space, in which the position of m relative to M is represented by the coordinates $x = x' - X'$, ..., the equations of motion are

$$\frac{d^2x}{dt^2} = -k^2(M + m)\frac{x}{r^3}, \quad \cdots \tag{9}$$

The integration of this system of equations gives the *motion of m relative to M*; the coordinate system is *noninertial.*

2. Undisturbed Motion

Each of two homogeneous or concentrically homogeneous spherical masses, M and m, under the action of their mutual Newtonian gravitational attractions, undisturbed by any other forces, moves about their common center of mass in an orbit which has the form of a conic section with one focus at this center of mass. The orbit of either body relative to the other is likewise a conic section with one focus at the center of mass of this other body. This is the general form of Kepler's first law of planetary motion; only for undisturbed motion are Kepler's laws valid.

The form, size, and orientation in space of an undisturbed Newtonian gravitational orbit are fixed by the position and velocity of the body at any one instant, and are invariable. The orbit of m relative to M is an ellipse, a parabola, or a hyperbola according as

$$V^2 \lesseqqgtr k^2\mu\frac{2}{r}$$

where V is the linear speed *relative to* M at distance r, and μ is the sum of the masses, $M + m$.

The exact form of the orbit is specified by the eccentricity e, which, for a given initial speed and distance, depends on the initial direction of motion. The size of the orbit is specified by the semimajor axis a (or, for a parabola, by the minimum value q of r) which, for a given initial direction of motion at a given distance, depends on the initial speed in accordance with the relation

$$V^2 = k^2\mu\left(\frac{2}{r} - \frac{1}{a}\right) \tag{1}$$

hence $a \begin{smallmatrix} > 0 \\ = \infty \\ < 0 \end{smallmatrix}$ according as the orbit is an ellipse, a parabola, or a hyperbola. The position of the orbital plane in space is determined by the initial position and direction of motion; it is usually specified by its inclination i to the plane of the ecliptic and the longitude ☊ of its ascending node on the ecliptic reckoned from the vernal equinox. The orientation of the orbit in this plane is specified by the longitude $\tilde{\omega}$ of the extremity of the major axis that is the nearer to the central mass M, defined as the sum of the angle ☊ along the ecliptic and the arc of the orbit from the node to the apse; $\tilde{\omega}$ therefore lies in two different planes. The major axis is known as the *line of apsides.**

The five constants e, a (or q), i, ☊, $\tilde{\omega}$, fix the orbit of m; the position of m in its orbit is fixed by the position at any one instant, e.g., by the time T of passage through the apse nearer to M. These six quantities are called the *elements* of the orbit; their numerical values must be determined from observation, and their determination is equivalent to the evaluation of the constants of integration in the solution of the differential equations of motion.+

The position of m in its orbit at any instant t is represented by the radius vector r from M, and the angle f at M between r and the line of apsides, reckoned in the direction of motion from the apse nearer M. This angle f is known as the *true anomaly*; the value which it would have were m to move around M at a uniform angular rate n equal to the mean value of df/dt is called the *mean anomaly* g.

The motion of m in its orbit is in accordance with the law of areas for the rate at which the radius vector sweeps out the area of a sector in the orbital plane.

$$\tfrac{1}{2}r^2\frac{df}{dt} = \tfrac{1}{2}k\sqrt{\mu p}, \quad \text{(a constant)} \tag{2}$$

(Kepler's second law), where p is the semilatus rectum of the conic.

* For applications to the trajectories of projectiles, and to interplanetary trajectories, see *Am. J. Phys.*, **13**, 253 (1945) and **19**, 52 (1951); also Astronomical Society of the Pacific, *Leaflets 168* (1943) and *201* (1945).

+ For the integration of the equations of motion, and the expressions for the orbital elements in terms of the constants of integration and the initial conditions, see MOULTON, F. R., *Celestial Mechanics*, 2d ed., The Macmillan Company, New York, 1914, pp. 140-149. For the general principles of the determination of the elements of an undisturbed orbit from observation, see WOOLARD, E. W., *Nat. Math. Mag.*, **14**, 1-11 (1940); and for the detailed practical procedures, see HERGET, P., *The Computation of Orbits*, published by the author, 1948.

2.1. Elliptic motion

Period of revolution:

$$P = \frac{2\pi a^{3/2}}{k\sqrt{\mu}} \tag{1}$$

Mean motion:

$$n = 2\pi/P = \frac{k\sqrt{\mu}}{a^{3/2}} \tag{2}$$

Kepler's third law:

$$n^2a^3 = k^2\mu \quad \text{(a constant)} \tag{3}$$

Kepler's third law is the basis for the definition of the fundamental astronomical unit of length. The *astronomical unit* is the unit of distance in terms of which, in Kepler's third law, the semimajor axis a of an elliptic orbit must be expressed in order that, with n in radians, the numerical value of k may be exactly 0.01720209895 when the unit of mass is the mass of the Sun and the unit of time is the mean solar day. In these units, k is known as the Gaussian constant; and $k^2 = 0.00029591221$. With n in seconds of arc per mean solar day, $k = 3548.1876069651$.

Mean anomaly: $$g = n(t - T)$$

or more generally, $g = g_0 + n(t - t_0)$ where g_0 is the mean anomaly at any arbitrary epoch t_0. The quantity $f - g$ is called the *equation of the center.*

Kepler's equation: In an elliptic orbit, the angle E in the usual parametric equations of the ellipse ($x = a \cos E$, $y = b \sin E$) is called the *eccentric anomaly.* It is related to the mean anomaly by Kepler's equation,

$$g = E - e \sin E$$

and its value at any time t may be found from g by solving this equation; for practical methods of solution see Herget, P., *op. cit.*, p. 33, and Bauschinger-Stracke, *Tafeln zur theoretischen Astronomie*, 2d ed.

Position in the orbit

Finite formulas:

$$\left.\begin{aligned}
&\tan \tfrac{1}{2}f = \sqrt{\frac{1+e}{1-e}} \tan \tfrac{1}{2}E \\
&r = a(1 - e\cos E) = \frac{a(1-e^2)}{1 + e\cos f} \\
&q = a(1 - e) \\
&r \sin f = a\sqrt{1-e^2} \sin E, \quad r\cos f = a(\cos E - e)
\end{aligned}\right\} \tag{4}$$

Series developments :

$$\frac{r}{a} = 1 + \tfrac{1}{2}e^2$$

$$-\left[2\left(\frac{e}{2}\right) - 3\left(\frac{e}{2}\right)^3 + \ldots\right] \cos g \tag{5}$$

$$-\left[2\left(\frac{e}{2}\right)^2 - \frac{16}{3}\left(\frac{e}{2}\right)^4 + \ldots\right] \cos 2g \tag{6}$$

$$-\left[3\left(\frac{e}{2}\right)^3 - \ldots\right] \cos 3g \tag{7}$$

$$-\left[\frac{16}{3}\left(\frac{e}{2}\right)^4 - \ldots\right] \cos 4g \tag{8}$$

$$- \ldots \ldots \ldots \ldots \ldots \ldots$$

$$f = g + \left[4\left(\frac{e}{2}\right) - 2\left(\frac{e}{2}\right)^3 + \ldots\right] \sin g \tag{9}$$

$$+\left[5\left(\frac{e}{2}\right)^2 - \frac{22}{3}\left(\frac{e}{2}\right)^4 + \ldots\right] \sin 2g \tag{10}$$

$$+\left[\frac{26}{3}\left(\frac{e}{2}\right)^3 - \ldots\right] \sin 3g \tag{11}$$

$$+\left[\frac{103}{6}\left(\frac{e}{2}\right)^4 - \ldots\right] \sin 4g \tag{12}$$

$$+ \ldots \ldots \ldots \ldots \ldots \ldots$$

For tables of elliptic motion, see Bauschinger-Stracke, *op. cit.*, p. 5.*

The semimajor axis a is usually called the *mean distance*; but it is the mean value of r with respect to E, not with respect to the time

$$a = \frac{1}{2\pi} \int_0^{2\pi} r dE \tag{13}$$

The average in time is $a(1 + \tfrac{1}{2}e^2)$.

* For the calculation of the heliocentric coordinates of a planet or comet from r, v, and the orbital elements, and the computation of the position on the celestial sphere as seen from the Earth, see Smart, W. M., *Spherical Astronomy*, Cambridge University Press, London, 1931, pp. 122-129; also Moulton, F. R., *op. cit.*, pp. 182-189. On the characteristics of the apparent path on the sphere, see Herget, P., *Popular Astronomy*, June-July, 1939; also Herget, P., *op. cit.*, pp. 37-39.

The quantity $L = \tilde{\omega} + g$ is called the *mean orbital longitude*; substituting the expression for g gives the form

$$L = nt + \epsilon$$

where the constant ϵ is the mean longitude at the epoch $t = 0$ from which the time is reckoned, and is often used instead of T or g_0 as the element which fixes the position of m in its orbit.

2.2. Parabolic motion

$$\tan \tfrac{1}{2}f + \tfrac{1}{3}\tan^3 \tfrac{1}{2}f = \frac{k\sqrt{\mu}(t-T)}{\sqrt{2}q^{3/2}} \tag{1}$$

Solution for f with auxiliaries s and w:

$$\tan s = \frac{2^{3/2}}{3k\sqrt{\mu}}\frac{q^{3/2}}{t-T}, \quad \tan w = \sqrt[3]{\tan \tfrac{1}{2}s}, \quad \tan \tfrac{1}{2}f = 2 \cot 2w \tag{2}$$

For solution by successive approximation, see Herget, P., *op. cit.*, p. 32; for tables, see Bauschinger-Stracke, *op. cit.*

$$r = q \sec^2 \tfrac{1}{2}f$$

2.3. Hyperbolic and nearly parabolic motion. See Herget, P., *op. cit.*, pp. 34-37; Bauschinger-Stracke, *op. cit.*

In the cases to which the foregoing equations of undisturbed motion are applied in practice (especially for parabolic and hyperbolic motion), M is usually unity and m is commonly neglected, whence $\mu = 1$. The unit of time is often taken to be $1/k$ mean solar days; k then does not appear explicitly in the equations.

2.4. Relativity correction. The only observable effect on the motion of m from the correction to the Newtonian law of gravitation that is required by the general theory of relativity is a rotation of the orbit within its plane, which causes a variation of $\tilde{\omega}$. The rate of rotation, in radians per revolution of m, is

$$24\pi^3 \frac{a^2}{c^2P^2(1-e^2)} \tag{1}$$

in which c is the velocity of light.*

* See Clemence, G. M., *Revs. Modern Phys.*, **19**, 361 (1947).

3. Disturbed Motion

The actual motion of any celestial body is determined by the gravitational attractions of all the other bodies in the system of which it is a part, and in general conforms only more or less approximately to the foregoing equations of undisturbed motion. In the solar system, the motions of the planets, although dominated by the action of the Sun, are each disturbed by the attractions of the other planets; and the motions of the Moon and many other satellites are appreciably affected by the oblateness of the planets around which they revolve, and by the disturbing attraction of the Sun. The orbits are therefore complex and ever varying curves; however, with few exceptions, the motions do not depart widely from undisturbed elliptic motion, and it is advantageous for many purposes to represent the actual motion mathematically in terms of its departures, or perturbations, from an undisturbed elliptic motion which approximates it.

3.1. The disturbing function. When the motion of m around M is disturbed by the action of a third mass m', the vector difference between the attractions of this disturbing mass on m and M produces a motion of m relative to M additional to the motion produced by the action of M, and causes a departure from the elliptic motion that would occur relative to M under the attraction of M alone. When all three bodies may be considered as concentrically homogeneous spheres, the force function for this disturbing force on m that is added to the attraction of M is

$$R = k^2 m' \left[\frac{1}{\Delta} - \frac{r}{r'^2} \cos(r, r') \right] \tag{1}$$

where Δ is the distance of m' from m, and r, r', are, respectively, the radii vectores of m, m', from M.

When the central mass M is not a concentrically homogeneous sphere, a disturbing force likewise acts, equal to the vector difference between the actual attraction and the attraction that a particle of the same mass M at the center of mass would exert. When M is an oblate ellipsoid of revolution, with equatorial and polar radii a_0 and c_0 and flattening $f = (a_0 - c_0)/a_0$, for which the surface is in equilibrium with gravity (no hypothesis about the interior is then necessary), we have $C - A = \frac{2}{3} M a_0^2 (f - \frac{1}{2}\kappa)$, where κ is the ratio of the centripetal acceleration of rotation at the equator to gravity on M; and the force function for the disturbing force, to the first order in f and the second order in a_0/r, is

$$R' = k^2 M (f - \tfrac{1}{2}\kappa) \frac{a_0^2}{r^3} (\tfrac{1}{3} - \sin^2 d) \tag{2}$$

in which d is the angle between r and the equatorial plane of M.

In a rectangular coordinate system with origin at M and axes in fixed directions in space, the equations of motion of m relative to M are

$$\frac{d^2x}{dt^2} + k^2(M + m)\frac{x}{r^3} = \frac{\partial \Omega}{\partial x}, \quad \cdots \tag{3}$$

where Ω is the sum of the disturbing functions R and R' for all the bodies acting on m; the force function Ω is not a potential. When Ω consists only of the disturbing function R for a single mass m', the motion of m is represented by

$$\frac{d^2x}{dt^2} + k^2(M + m)\frac{x}{r^3} = k^2 m'\left(\frac{x' - x}{\Delta^3} - \frac{x'}{r'^3}\right), \quad \cdots \tag{4}$$

The first term on the right (the principal, or direct, term) represents the attraction of m' on unit mass of m, and the second term (indirect term) is the attraction of m' on unit mass of M; their difference imparts to m the acceleration additional to the acceleration which is imparted by the mutual attractions of m and M represented by the second term on the left, and which alone would give undisturbed elliptic motion.

3.2. Variations of the elements. Because of the acceleration from the disturbing forces additional to the acceleration from the force that a single particle of mass M would exert, the variations of the position and velocity of m from one instant to another are different from the variations that would maintain m in motion in a fixed ellipse. The position and velocity at any particular instant mathematically determine an elliptic orbit in which, in undisturbed motion around M, the elliptic position and velocity *at this instant* would be the same as the actual position and velocity, but this orbit is different at different instants, i.e., the orbital elements are variable instead of being constants. The actual motion may be represented as elliptic motion in an orbit which is continually changing form, size, and position in space under the action of the disturbing forces; at each instant, the motion is the resultant of elliptic motion in the instantaneous orbit and the further motion due to the variations of the orbit.*

Under the action of the total disturbing force, with a disturbing function Ω, the rates of variation of the five elements that characterize the orbital curve are

$$\frac{da}{dt} = \frac{2}{k}\sqrt{\frac{a}{\mu}}\frac{\partial \Omega}{\partial \epsilon} \tag{1}$$

* For simple geometrical derivations of the qualitative effects of the disturbing forces on the orbital elements, see HERSCHEL, Sir John, *Outlines of Astronomy*, Chaps. 12-14.

$$\frac{de}{dt} = -\frac{1}{ke}\sqrt{\frac{1-e^2}{\mu a}}\frac{\partial\Omega}{\partial\tilde{\omega}} - \frac{1}{k}\sqrt{\frac{1-e^2}{\mu a}}\cdot\frac{e}{1+\sqrt{1-e^2}}\cdot\frac{\partial\Omega}{\partial\epsilon} \tag{2}$$

$$\frac{di}{dt} = -\frac{1}{k\sin i\sqrt{\mu a(1-e^2)}}\cdot\frac{\partial\Omega}{\partial\Omega} - \frac{1-\cos i}{k\sin i\sqrt{\mu a(1-e^2)}}\left(\frac{\partial\Omega}{\partial\tilde{\omega}} + \frac{\partial\Omega}{\partial\epsilon}\right) \tag{3}$$

$$\frac{d\Omega}{dt} = \frac{1}{k\sin i\sqrt{\mu a(1-e^2)}}\frac{\partial\Omega}{\partial i} \tag{4}$$

$$\frac{d\tilde{\omega}}{dt} = \frac{1}{ke}\sqrt{\frac{1-e^2}{\mu a}}\cdot\frac{\partial\Omega}{\partial e} + \frac{1-\cos i}{k\sin i\sqrt{\mu a(1-e^2)}}\cdot\frac{\partial\Omega}{\partial i} \tag{5}$$

The elliptic position in the instantaneous orbit is fixed by the mean orbital longitude $L = nt + \epsilon$. The rate of motion *in mean longitude*,

$$\frac{dL}{dt} = n + \left(t\frac{dn}{dt} + \frac{d\epsilon}{dt}\right) \tag{6}$$

is the result partly of the instantaneous elliptic motion *in the orbit* at rate n, and partly of the addition to this elliptic motion by the *variation* of the orbit, which causes variations of n and ϵ.

$$\left.\begin{aligned} \frac{dL}{dt} &= n - \frac{2}{k}\sqrt{\frac{a}{\mu}}\frac{\partial\Omega}{\partial a} + \frac{e}{k\sqrt{\mu a}}\frac{\sqrt{1-e^2}}{1+\sqrt{1-e^2}}\frac{\partial\Omega}{\partial e} \\ &\quad + \frac{1-\cos i}{k\sin i\sqrt{\mu a(1-e^2)}}\frac{\partial\Omega}{\partial i} \end{aligned}\right\} \tag{7}$$

where in the disturbing function Ω the quantities n and ϵ appear explicitly only in arguments of sines and cosines in the form $nt + \epsilon$, and in the differentiations n is formally regarded as constant and independent of a.

In the integral of the right member, since it follows from Kepler's third law and the equation for da/dt that

$$\frac{dn}{dt} = -\frac{3}{2}\frac{n}{a}\frac{da}{dt} = -\frac{3}{a^2}\frac{\partial\Omega}{\partial\epsilon} \tag{8}$$

we have

$$\int n\,dt = -3\iint\frac{1}{a^2}\frac{\partial\Omega}{\partial\epsilon}\,dt^2 \tag{9}$$

which represents the total amount of motion in the disturbed orbit, and is equal to $\bar{n}t$ where $\bar{n}$ is the mean value $(1/t)\int n\,dt$ of the continually varying rate of motion in the orbit.

Denote the integral of the remaining terms by ϵ'. Then the mean longitude in disturbed motion may be expressed in the form :

$$L = \bar{n}t + \epsilon' \tag{10}$$

instead of in terms of the instantaneous elliptic quantities n and ϵ; and in Ω and its derivatives, $\bar{n}$ and ϵ' may be used in place of n and ϵ in all the preceding equations for the variations of the elements.

3.3. Perturbations of the coordinates. In general, the elements have periodic variations about a mean value that itself has a progressive secular change. The coordinates in space or on the celestial sphere at any time may be calculated from the *instantaneous* values of the elements by means of the formulas for undisturbed elliptic motion; or they may be obtained by calculating elliptic coordinates from *arbitrarily adopted* values of the elements, and adding the variations produced in the coordinates by the variations of the elements from these adopted values. In practice, short-period variations of the elements are often represented by equivalent perturbations of the coordinates, while secular and long-period perturbations are left expressed in the form of variations of the orbital elements; the actual position is then represented in terms of its irregularly varying departure from the elliptic position in a slowly changing orbit. See Clemence, G. M., *Astro. J.*, **52**, 89 (1946).

The elliptic orbit to which the actual irregular motion is referred is known as the *mean orbit*, and its elements are called *mean elements*. This mean reference orbit is defined mathematically; it is mathematically arbitrary, and depends on the particular methods adopted for integrating the equations of motion and evaluating the constants of integration from observation. It is often defined differently in different theories; but in defining it for the Moon or for a planet, the semimajor axis is calculated by Kepler's third law from the actually observed mean rate $\bar{n}$ of the disturbed motion.*

3.4. Mean orbit of the Earth. The *observed* mean motion of the Earth, which in this section will be denoted simply by n, is the mean value of the disturbed motion of the center of mass of the Earth-Moon system; $n = 3548''.193$ per mean solar day. The semimajor axis a of the mean orbit is computed from this mean motion, and the total mass of the system, by Kepler's law

$$k^2\left[1 + E\left(1 + \frac{M}{E}\right)\right] = n^2a^3 \tag{1}$$

* The coordinates may also be obtained directly by numerical integration of the equations of motion, without the intermediary of a mean orbit. See CLEMENCE, G. M. and BROUWER, D., *Sky and Telescope*, **10**, 83-86 (1951).

in which E is the mass of the Earth and M the mass of the Moon in terms of the mass of the Sun as the unit.

This mean distance a is 1.0000 0003 astronomical units. To obtain its equivalent in physical units of length, the value of the solar parallax is required. The mean equatorial horizontal solar parallax p is the angle subtended by the equatorial radius of the Earth a_0 at a distance of one astronomical unit : 1 a.u. $= a_0/\sin p$.

In the expression for a obtained from Kepler's law, we may put $k^2E = \rho_1{}^2G_1$ in which ρ_1 is the radius of the Earth at the latitude φ_1 where the gravitational attraction G_1 of the Earth is the same as if the entire mass E were concentrated at the center; φ_1 is very nearly $\sin^{-1}\sqrt{\frac{1}{3}}$, and in terms of gravity g_1 at this latitude

$$G_1 = g_1(1 + \kappa_1 \cos \varphi_1) \tag{2}$$

in which κ_1 is the ratio of the centripetal acceleration of rotation to gravity. We then have from Kepler's law,

$$\sin p = \frac{a_0}{\rho_1}\left[\frac{E + M}{1 + (E + M)} \cdot \frac{n^2\rho_1}{\pi^2 l_1(1 + \kappa_1 \cos \varphi_1)\,(1 + M/E)}\right]^{1/3} \tag{3}$$

where l_1 is the length of the seconds pendulum at latitude φ_1, and n must be expressed in radians/second.

The solar parallax is related to the velocity of light c by the expression for the length of time τ required for light to travel unit distance,

$$\tau = \frac{a_0}{c \sin p} \tag{4}$$

where τ is called the equation of light. Hence p is also related to the aberration of light that is caused by the motion in the mean orbit; in terms of the constant of aberration, which is defined as

$$\alpha = \frac{na}{c\sqrt{1 - e^2}} \tag{5}$$

we have

$$\sin p = \frac{a_0 n}{\alpha c\sqrt{1 - e^2}} \tag{6}$$

In disturbed motion, the constant part or mean value $\bar{r}$ of the disturbed radius vector is not equal to the mean distance a, because of variations of the instantaneous eccentricity and line of apsides which change the average distance without altering a. In the mean orbit of the Earth

$$\bar{r} = a + 0.0000\,0020 \tag{7}$$

3.5. Mean orbit of the Moon. The mean distance a of the Moon from the Earth is defined in terms of the observed mean motion n of the Moon by Kepler's law.

$$n^2a^3 = k^2E(1 + M/E) \tag{1}$$

From the gravitational theory of the motion of the Moon,

$$\frac{1}{a} = \frac{1}{r_0}(1 - 0.0009068) \tag{2}$$

where $1/r_0$ is the constant term in the expression for the disturbed inverse radius vector. The ratio of the equatorial radius of the Earth a_0 to r_0 is the constant part or mean value of the sine of the equatorial horizontal lunar parallax. At this distance r_0 at which the lunar parallax has its mean value P, we have, with n expressed in radians/second,

$$\sin P = 1.0009076 \frac{a_0}{a} \tag{3}$$

$$= 1.0009076 \frac{a_0}{\rho_1}\left[\frac{1}{1 + M/E} \cdot \frac{n^2\gamma_1}{\pi^2 l_1(1 + \kappa_1 \cos \varphi_1)}\right]^{1/3} \tag{4}$$

$$= 3422''.54 \sin 1'' \tag{5}$$

where $P = 57'02''.70$, and $r_0 = 60.2665\ a_0$. Both r_0 and a differ from the average value $\bar{r}$ of the radius vector.

The solar and lunar parallaxes are related by

$$\sin p = 0.9990932 \sin P\left[\frac{E + M}{1 + (E + M)}\left(\frac{n_\oplus}{n_☾}\right)^2\right]^{1/3} \tag{6}$$

3.6. Mass of a planet from the mean orbit of a satellite. From the observed apparent motion of a satellite relative to the planet around which it revolves, a mean orbit for the satellite may be derived and its secular variations determined. From the elements and their variations, the mass and the flattening of the planet may be found. In particular, in terms of the observed mean motion n of the satellite, and the semimajor axis a of its orbit derived from the *directly measured* apparent mean angular distance from the planet, the mass of the planet is

$$m = \left(\frac{n}{n_\oplus}\right)^2 \frac{a^3}{1 + (a_0/a)^2(f - \frac{1}{2}\kappa)}(1 + E) \tag{1}$$

in which a_0, f, and κ denote, respectively, the equatorial radius, flattening, and ratio of centripetal acceleration to gravity at the equator, of the planet, and a is in astronomical units.*

4. The Rotation of the Earth

The motion of the Earth relative to its center of mass is the resultant of three components. First, it rotates around an axis that always passes through the center of mass. However, this axis does not coincide exactly with the axis of figure. Second, the Earth is continually changing its position slightly in space relative to the axis of rotation by a motion known as the Eulerian nutation, which causes the axis of figure to describe an irregular variable conical surface in space around the axis of rotation while the direction of the axis of rotation remains sensibly constant in space. Hence the axis of rotation lies in successively different positions on a conical surface within the Earth. At the same time, under the gravitational attractions of the Sun and Moon, the axis of rotation possesses a conical motion in space in which the Earth as a whole participates without any change in its position relative to the axis. All three motions are affected by elastic and plastic deformations of the Earth, and by transfers of mass on and within the Earth in geophysical phenomena; in particular the rate of rotation has secular, irregular, and periodic variations.

4.1. Poisson's equations. The lunisolar motion of the axis of rotation in space is due to the inequalities of the principal moments of inertia of the Earth. To a high degree of approximation, it is the same as if the Earth were a rigid body.

As a result of the consequent motion of the plane of the equator, the inclination θ of the equator to the fixed ecliptic of an adopted epoch is continually varying, and the ecliptic is intersected at a continually different point. Neglecting the departures of the Earth from perfect rigidity, and assuming the equatorial moments of inertia A and B to be equal, we find that the variations of θ and of the angular distance ψ of the intersection *westward* from its position at the epoch $t = 0$, caused by the action of the mass M' of the Sun or the Moon at distance r and declination δ, are

$$\frac{d\theta}{dt} = + \frac{1}{C\omega \sin\theta} \frac{\partial V}{\partial \psi}, \quad \frac{d\psi}{dt} = - \frac{1}{C\omega \sin\theta} \frac{\partial V}{\partial \theta} \tag{1}$$

* On the general theory of disturbed motion, see Brown, E. W. and Shook, C. A., *Planetary Theory*, Cambridge University Press, London (1933); and Brown, E. W., *Introductory Treatise on the Lunar Theory*, Cambridge University Press, London (1896).

in which ω is the angular rate of rotation of the Earth, and

$$V = -k^2 \frac{3M'(C-A)}{2r^3} \sin^2 \delta \tag{2}$$

where C is the principal moment of inertia with respect to the axis of figure. The variations depend upon $(C - A)/C$, called the *dynamical flattening*, not upon the geometric figure of the Earth.*

The motion is the resultant of a steady progressive secular part, which is called the *lunisolar precession*, and a large number of periodic components that are collectively called the *lunisolar nutation.*

The actual motion of the equinoxes along the ecliptic, and the variation of the obliquity of the ecliptic, are the result of both this lunisolar motion of the equator and a slow secular motion of the ecliptic caused by the secular perturbations of the orbital motion of the Earth. The westward motion of the equinoxes along the ecliptic, called the *general precession* in longitude, results from both the lunisolar precession and the *planetary precession* caused by the motion of the ecliptic.+

4.2. The Eulerian nutation. Kinematically, the daily rotational motion of the Earth, instead of being a simple rotation around a fixed diameter, results from a conical surface within the Earth, with vertex at the center of mass and axis along the axis of figure, rolling on another very much smaller conical surface *in space.* The line of contact of the two cones is the instantaneous axis of rotation; it describes the circumference of the small cone each day, and after each circuit it is displaced within the Earth along the circumference of the large cone by the length of the perimeter of the small cone. This motion is a dynamical consequence of the lack of coincidence of the axis of rotation with the axis of figure. It leaves the position of the small cone in space unchanged; and the angular opening of this cone is too small for the daily conical oscillation of the axis of rotation in space to be observable. The Earth as a whole is therefore displaced in space relative to the axis of rotation, while this axis is practically unchanged

* For the solution explicitly in terms of the masses and the orbital elements of the Sun and Moon, see TISSERAND, F., *Traité de mécanique céleste*, Vol. 2, Gauthier-Villars & Cie., Paris, 1891. See also HILL, G. W., *Collected Mathematical Works*, Vol. 4, Carnegie Institution, Washington, 1907, p. 11.

\+ The principal term in the nutation is due to the action of the Moon; its coefficient is called the constant of nutation. The coefficient of the principal term in the precession is the constant of precession. The expressions for these constants in terms of the masses and orbital elements of the Earth and the Moon, and the dynamical flattening, are given by HILL, G. W., *loc. cit.*; conversely, $(C - A)/C$ and $M/(E + M)$ may be expressed in terms of the constants of precession and nutation.

in space and hence lies in a different position within the Earth; the displacement of the Earth in space causes the axis of figure to describe a cone in space around the axis of rotation.

Unlike the lunisolar precession and nutation, the Eulerian motion is greatly affected by the departures of the Earth from perfect rigidity. Were the Earth an invariable rigid body with $A = B$, the axis of rotation would describe a slightly sinuous circular cone within the Earth around the axis of figure, at a nearly uniform rate with a mean period of

$$T = \frac{2\pi}{(C - A)\omega/A} = 303 \text{ days}$$

the sinuosities are due to a daily oscillation with a variable amplitude that may reach $0''.02$, which is caused by the lunisolar forces. Actually, because of deformations of the Earth, and the continual disturbances from meteorological and other geophysical processes, the period is lengthened to an average of about 14 months, and the motion is highly irregular and variable, with a superimposed annual component. The consequent irregular motion of the geographic poles over the surface of the Earth is confined within an area about 50 feet in radius, and causes the phenomenon frequently termed "variation of latitude."

Bibliography

1. Bacon, R. H., "Motion Relative to the Surface of the Rotating Earth," *Am. J. Phys.*, **19**, 52-56 (1951).
2. Bauschinger, J., *Tafeln zur theoretischen Astronomie*, 2d ed., with G. Stracke, W. Engelmann, Leipzig, 1934.
3. Clemence, G. M., "The Relativity Effect in Planetary Motions," *Revs. Modern Phys.*, **19**, 361-364 (1947).
4. Clemence, G. M. and Brouwer, D., "The Motions of the Five Outer Planets," *Sky and Telescope*, **10**, Feb., (1951).
5. Herget, P., *The Computation of Orbits*, published by the author, 1948.
6. Herget, P., "Planetary Motions and Lambert's Theorem," *Popular Astronomy*, June-July, 1939.
7. Herrick, S., "Rocket Navigation," *Navigation*, **2**, 259-272 (1950).
8. Herschel, Sir John, *Outlines of Astronomy*, many different editions and publishers.
9. Hill, G. W., *Collected Mathematical Works*, Vol. 4, Carnegie Institution, Washington, 1907.
10. Moulton, F.R., *Celestial Mechanics*, 2d ed., The Macmillan Company, New York, 1914.
11. Richardson, R. S., *Celestial Target Practice*, Leaflet 168, Astronomical Society of the Pacific, 1943.
12. Richardson, R. S., *Rockets and Orbits*, Leaflet 201, Astronomical Society of the Pacific, 1945.

13. Scarborough, J. B., "The Actual Path of a Projectile in a Vacuum," *Am. J. Phys.*, 13, 253-255 (1945).
14. Smart, W. M., *Spherical Astronomy*, Cambridge University Press, London, 1931.
15. Tisserand, F., *Traité de mécanique céleste*, Vol. 2, Gauthier-Villars & Cie., Paris, 1891.
16. Woolard, E. W., "The Calculation of Planetary Motions," *Nat. Math. Mag.*, 14, 1-11 (1940).

Chapter 30

METEOROLOGY

By Richard A. Craig

Geophysics Research Directorate
Air Force Cambridge Research Center

Meteorology comprises the branch of geophysics that treats of the earth's atmosphere and its phenomena. However, meteorology, as presently constituted, does not concern itself with the electromagnetic and photochemical phenomena that are important in the upper 1 per cent by mass of the atmosphere. Some of the following formulas are not generally applicable to this upper region.

The basic physical laws of atmospheric behavior derive from other branches of physics. The first section below discusses the four basic equations that govern the large-scale flow patterns in the atmosphere. The second section presents certain auxiliary equations derived from these basic ones.

1. Basic Equations for Large-Scale Flow

1.1. The hydrodynamic equation of motion. The hydrodynamic equation of motion is usually written for a frame of reference that is rotating with the earth so that it takes the form

$$\frac{d\boldsymbol{v}}{dt} = \frac{\partial \boldsymbol{v}}{\partial t} + \boldsymbol{v} \cdot \nabla \boldsymbol{v} = -2\Omega \times \boldsymbol{v} - \frac{1}{\rho} \nabla p - \nabla \Phi + \boldsymbol{F} \tag{1}$$

The terms on the left-hand side give the accelerations, where $\boldsymbol{v}$ is the average velocity (the mode of averaging is discussed below) at a particular location, and t the time. The first term on the right is the so-called Coriolis force, or deflecting force of the earth's rotation. The vector $\boldsymbol{\Omega}$ is directed northward, parallel to the axis of rotation of the earth, and has the magnitude ω, the angular speed of rotation of the earth. This term arises because the frame of reference is fixed to the earth; it cannot change the speed of an air parcel, but only the direction of its motion relative to the earth. The second term on the right is the pressure-gradient term, where ρ is the density and

p the pressure. The third term is the gravitational force, with Φ the gravitational potential. This force has an unbalanced component in the vertical only, whose magnitude we usually regard as a constant. This constant is called g and is defined by

$$g = GM/a^2$$

where G is the gravitational constant, M is the mass of the earth, and a is the earth's radius. The vertical extent of the atmosphere is so small relative to the earth's radius that this approximation is valid in all practical cases in meteorology.

The last term on the right side, $\boldsymbol{F}$, includes the molecular viscosity and the eddy stresses. These latter are not always clearly defined. They arise because the atmosphere is a turbulent fluid, whose rapidly varying motions we can express only in terms of a time and space average. At any given instant and point in the atmosphere, however, $\boldsymbol{v}$ will ordinarily differ from the average value that is presumed to apply to that given instant and point. The nonlinear terms in the expression $\boldsymbol{v} \cdot \nabla \boldsymbol{v}$ then give rise to stresses that depend on the correlations between the velocity components.

A meteorological observation, as usually reported, automatically involves an average that depends on the instrumentation. The scale of the average is typically a few minutes in time and a few hundred meters in space. The stress terms that arise from this scale of averaging are assumed to be negligible for the larger-scale motions and are treated in turbulence theory by a statistical or phenomenological approach.

A second scale of averaging is fixed by the density and frequency of observations. This scale may involve a few hours, or a few hundred kilometers, and the stresses that arise have never been subjected to a consistent study because the relevant observations are not available.

Finally, the analyst may purposely introduce an averaging process on still longer time or distance scales, in which case the consequent stresses must be included in the term $\boldsymbol{F}$.

1.2. Conservation of mass. Conservation of mass is expressed by the equation of continuity:

$$\frac{\partial \rho}{\partial t} + \nabla \cdot \rho \boldsymbol{v} = 0 \tag{1}$$

1.3. Equation of state. Air is a mixture of gases, each of which, to a good degree of approximation, obeys the equation of state for an ideal gas.

$$p = \rho \frac{R}{m} T \tag{1}$$

where R is the universal gas constant, m the molecular weight of the gas, and T the absolute temperature. According to Dalton's law, the sum of the partial pressures of gases in a mixture is equal to the total pressure of the mixture. Consequently, the equation of state for air has the same form as for an ideal gas, as long as we define m in terms of the molecular weights of the individual gases in the air. The appropriate value of m for air turns out to be 28.97, so that the equation of state is generally used in the form

$$p = \rho R' T \tag{2}$$

where

$$R' = R/m = 2.87 \times 10^6 \text{ cm}^2 \text{ sec}^{-2} \text{ deg}^{-1}$$

In the strictest sense, this applies to dry air only. Water vapor is always present in air to an extent that varies widely with time and space. To apply the slight correction for the presence of water vapor, replace T by T^*, the virtual temperature, defined by

$$T^* = \frac{T}{(1 - 0.379e/p)}$$

where e is the partial pressure of the water vapor and p is the total pressure of the dry air and water vapor.

1.4. First law of thermodynamics. The first law of thermodynamics for unit mass of an ideal gas is

$$dq = c_p\, dT - \frac{1}{\rho}\, dp \tag{1}$$

where dq is the heat added to or taken from the unit mass, and c_p is the specific heat of the gas at constant pressure.

2. Derived Equations

Section 1 contains a set of four equations, two of hydrodynamic and two of thermodynamic character, which describe the state of the atmosphere. These equations involve five unknowns, namely, $\mathbf{v}$, p, ρ, T, and q. In principle, at least, one should be able to specify a fifth equation to define q, in terms of heat absorbed directly from the sun, heat added to the atmosphere from the earth's surface by conduction or convection, and heat transferred within the atmosphere by phase changes of water. Since we can describe the boundary of the earth's surface and specify the initial state of the atmosphere, the equations are, in theory, soluble. However, in practice, the specification of the heat exchange and the boundary conditions is so extremely complex, and the mathematical difficulties inherent in nonlinear, partial differential equations are so great, that an exact analytical solution will probably never be possible.

Consequently, meteorological theory tends toward the derivation of other relationships from the four basic equations. One type of derivation has involved the deletion of small terms from the four equations to obtain descriptive formulas. These approximations characteristically ignore terms that, while small in magnitude, are vital for the prediction of changes in the atmosphere. A second type of derived equation transforms the original equations into a form that might be suitable for purposes of prediction or that might lend itself to physical interpretation.

These equations are given here in the coordinate system commonly used in meteorology. This is a Cartesian system, rotating with the earth, with its x-y plane tangential to the earth at the origin, and the z axis directed away from the earth. The x axis is positive toward the east, the y axis is positive toward the north. To simulate the Coriolis deflection, the x-y plane is presumed to be rotating around the z axis with an angular velocity appropriate to the latitude in question. This system achieves some mathematical simplification, but is inappropriate when large areas of the earth's surface are under consideration. In this case, spherical coordinates with their origin at the center of the earth are the natural system to use.

2.1. Geostrophic wind. The Coriolis force and the pressure-gradient force are much larger in magnitude than the other terms in the horizontal components of the equation of motion. The eastward speed, u, and the northward speed, v, obtained by equating these terms, are

$$\left.\begin{aligned} u &= -\frac{1}{2\rho\omega\sin\varphi}\cdot\frac{\partial p}{\partial y} \\ v &= \frac{1}{2\rho\omega\sin\varphi}\frac{\partial p}{\partial x} \end{aligned}\right\} \qquad (1)$$

where φ is the latitude. These so-called "geostrophic" wind components describe the actual wind field in the free atmosphere within the accuracy of wind observations. Near the surface, the wind has a measurable component toward low pressure as a result of friction.

2.2. Hydrostatic equation. In the vertical component of the equation of motion, the acceleration of gravity is balanced almost entirely by the pressure gradient. Thus

$$\frac{\partial p}{\partial z} = -\rho g$$

With the aid of the equation of state, this gives for the pressure at a distance z above a reference level with pressure p_0,

$$p = p_0 \exp\left(-\int_0^z \frac{g\,dz}{R'T}\right)$$

This equation gives the vertical distribution of pressure in the atmosphere within the accuracy of observation.

2.3. Adiabatic lapse rate. If an air parcel gains or loses no heat, its temperature is related to its pressure by the adiabatic form of the first law of thermodynamics,

$$c_p\,dT = \frac{1}{\rho}\,dp \tag{1}$$

In particular, for vertical motion,

$$\frac{\partial T}{\partial z} = \frac{1}{c_p \rho} \cdot \frac{\partial p}{\partial z} = -\frac{g}{c_p} \tag{2}$$

with the help of the hydrostatic equation, and because the density of the parcel is not greatly different from that of its surroundings. This variation of temperature in the vertical is observed in cases where air is heated from below or is thoroughly mixed by turbulence, if the water in the air does not change phase.

In the case where the water does change phase, as in clouds, the latent heat released or used by the water reduces this lapse rate.

2.4. The circulation theorem. The circulation C around a closed curve is defined as the line integral of the velocity component tangential to the curve.

$$C = \oint (u\,dx + v\,dy + w\,dz) \tag{1}$$

With the help of the equation of motion (without the stress terms), this equation reduces to the form common in meteorology, namely,

$$\frac{dC}{dt} = -\oint \frac{dp}{\rho} - 2\omega\,\frac{dA}{dt} \tag{2}$$

where A is the projected area of the closed curve on the equatorial plane.

This equation is valuable mainly because of the insight it affords into atmospheric motions. The first term may be interpreted as the increase in circulation caused by the angle between the isosteric (constant specific volume) and isobaric (constant pressure) surfaces. For an autobarotropic atmosphere, i.e., one wherein the spatial distribution of ρ is always the same function of p only, this term vanishes. The second term represents the effect of the earth's rotation on the circulation.

2.5. The vorticity theorem. As the area of the curve around which the circulation is computed is reduced to zero, the circulation divided by the area approaches the vorticity as a limit. The vorticity is the curl of the velocity.

The " vorticity theorem " as commonly used in meteorology really concerns only the vertical component of the vorticity. This equation is the vertical component of the curl of the equation of motion. For horizontal motion in an autobarotropic frictionless fluid, the theorem states that

$$\frac{d}{dt}(\zeta + 2\omega \sin \varphi) = -(\zeta + 2\omega \sin \varphi)\left(\frac{\partial u}{\partial x} + \frac{\partial v}{\partial y}\right) \tag{1}$$

where ζ is the vertical component of vorticity for the motion of the air parcel relative to the earth. Note that $2\omega \sin \varphi$ is the vertical component of vorticity resulting from the earth's rotation.

This equation is practically the only one in meteorology that has shown any prognostic value. The past few years have seen numerous attempts to integrate this equation (and variants of it) by numerical methods. These experiments offer significant hope for improvement of weather forecasting.

2.6. The energy equation. The scalar product of the equation of motion and the velocity is

$$\frac{d}{dt}(K + W) = -\frac{1}{\rho}\,\boldsymbol{v} \cdot \nabla p + \boldsymbol{v} \cdot \boldsymbol{F} \tag{1}$$

Here K is the kinetic energy and W the potential energy of an air parcel. This combines with the first law of thermodynamics to give the energy equation,

$$\frac{dq}{dt} = \frac{d}{dt}(K + W + I) + p\frac{d(1/\rho)}{dt} + \frac{1}{\rho}\,\boldsymbol{v} \cdot \nabla p - \boldsymbol{v} \cdot \boldsymbol{F} \tag{2}$$

where I is the internal energy $c_v T$.

2.7. The tendency equation. To a close approximation, the pressure at a level z is given by the weight of the overlying air column,

$$p_z = \int_z^\infty g\rho\, dz \tag{1}$$

Therefore the rate of pressure changes, or pressure " tendency," is

$$\left(\frac{\partial p}{\partial t}\right)_z = -\int_z^\infty g\left(\frac{\partial \rho u}{\partial x} + \frac{\partial \rho v}{\partial y}\right) dz + g(\rho w)_z \tag{2}$$

since ρw is assumed to vanish at the upper limit. This is called the tendency equation.

The term under the integral sign, when the indicated differentiation is accomplished, indicates two physical processes that might produce a pressure change. These are advection of air of different density, and velocity divergence. In addition the term outside the integral shows that the pressure at a level may change as a result of a mass transport through the level. These terms are always small in the atmosphere. Note that for horizontal, geostrophic motion, no pressure change would occur. Moreover, the mass divergence in the atmosphere usually changes sign with elevation, so that the net pressure change at the surface represents a slight unbalance among the nearly compensating values of mass divergence at upper levels.

2.8. Atmospheric turbulence. Near the surface of the earth, the variation of the wind with elevation depends largely on the term $\boldsymbol{F}$ in the equation of motion. If the air flow were laminar, $\boldsymbol{F}$ would depend on the molecular viscosity μ, and would be given approximately by

$$\boldsymbol{F} = \frac{1}{\rho} \cdot \frac{\partial}{\partial z}\left(\mu \frac{\partial \boldsymbol{v}}{\partial z}\right) \tag{1}$$

since the variation of $\boldsymbol{v}$ in the horizontal is small.

In the atmosphere, the motion is turbulent and the eddy stresses are far larger than the viscous stresses. These eddy stresses are often represented by a similar formula

$$\boldsymbol{F} = \frac{1}{\rho} \cdot \frac{\partial}{\partial z}\left(\mu_e \frac{\partial \boldsymbol{v}}{\partial z}\right) \tag{2}$$

The eddy viscosity, μ_e, is a property of the flow and not of the fluid. Its magnitude varies widely, depending principally on distance from the earth's surface, wind speed, and the variation of temperature in the vertical. With a dry adiabatic lapse rate and average wind speed, μ_e seems to increase approximately linearly from a value of zero near the ground to a maximum value of about 10^6-10^7 μ a few hundred meters above the ground. When temperature increases with height and the wind is light, μ_e may not exceed 10^4-10^5 μ at any level.

Bibliography

1. American Meteorological Society (MALONE, T., ed.), *Compendium of Meteorology*, Waverly Press, Inc., Baltimore, 1951. A collection of authoritative summaries of the state of knowledge of many detailed meteorological topics.
2. BERRY, F. A., Jr., BOLLAY, E. and BEERS, N. R. (eds.), *Handbook of Meteorology*, McGraw-Hill Book Company, Inc., New York, 1945. A valuable reference book, containing comprehensive coverage of various broad fields of meteorology.

3. BJERKNESS, V., BJERKNES, J., SOLBERG, H. and BERGERON, T., *Physikalische Hydrodynamik*, Julius Springer, Berlin, 1933; reprinted by Edwards Brothers, Inc., Ann Arbor, 1943. Particularly applicable to meteorological problems.
4. *BRUNT, D., *Physical and Dynamical Meteorology*, Cambridge University Press, London, 1939.
5. BYERS, H. R., *General Meteorology*, McGraw-Hill Book Company, Inc., New York, 1944. A general survey of meteorology; contains short section on dynamic meteorology.
6. *ERTEL, H., *Methoden und Probleme der dynamischen Meteorologie*, Julius Springer, Berlin, 1938; reprinted by Edwards Brothers, Inc., Ann Arbor, 1943.
7. *EXNER, F. M., *Dynamische Meteorologie*, Julius Springer, Vienna, 1925.
8. GOLDSTEIN, S. (ed.), *Modern Developments in Fluid Dynamics*, Oxford University Press, London, 1938. Useful to meteorologists primarily in problems of turbulence.
9. *HAURWITZ, B., *Dynamic Meteorology*, McGraw-Hill Book Company, Inc., New York, 1941.
10. HEWSON, E. W. and LONGLEY, R. W., *Meteorology Theoretical and Applied*, John Wiley & Sons, Inc., New York, 1944. Concerned with a general survey of meteorology; contains short section on dynamic meteorology.
11. *HOLMBOE, J., FORSYTHE, G. E. and GUSTIN, W., *Dynamic Meteorology*, John Wiley & Sons, Inc., New York, 1945.
12. HUMPHREYS, W. J., *Physics of the Air*, McGraw-Hill Book Company, Inc., New York, 1940. Deals with acoustical, electrical, optical, and other such physical phenomena of the atmosphere.
13. *KOSCHMIEDER, H., *Physik der Atmosphäre*, Vol. 2, " Dynamische Meteorologie," Akademische Verlagsgesellschaft m. b. H., Leipzig, 1951.
14. LAMB, H., *Hydrodynamics*, Dover Publications, New York, 1945. Useful to meteorologists primarily in problems of perturbation theory and stability.
15. LETTAU, H., *Atmosphärische Turbulenz*, Akademische Verlagsgesellschaft m. b. H., Leipzig, 1939; reprinted by Edwards Brothers, Inc., Ann Arbor, 1944. Deals primarily with atmospheric turbulence.
16. SUTTON, O. G., *Atmospheric Turbulence*, Methuen & Co., Ltd., London, 1949. Deals primarily with atmosphric turbulence.

* These books discuss, with varying emphasis, the statics, thermodynamics, kinematics, and dynamics of the atmosphere.

Chapter 31

BIOPHYSICS

BY JOHN M. REINER

Director, Simon Baruch Research Laboratories
The Saratoga Spa

Introduction

Biophysics is the analysis of biological phenomena in physicomathematical terms. It includes all formal theories of the behavior of living organisms and their parts, especially such theories as attempt a reduction of biological to physical (including chemical) concepts. Thus this chapter embraces such topics as enzyme kinetics, a molecular theory of cell forms and cell division, and the mathematical theory of aggregates of cells or of organisms.

1. Energy Relations

A living system is a spatially circumscribed phase (or aggregate of such phases) in contact with another phase or set of phases, the environment. It is in constant communication with the environment; both matter and energy pass between the two. Living systems, while they display the characteristics that mark them as living, are never in thermodynamic equilibrium. To describe their energy relations requires a generalization of classical thermodynamics. We divide substances found in living systems into two groups: those that normally do not leave the cell (the " permanent " constituents) and those that circulate between cell and environment. Variables pertaining to the two classes are distinguished by subscripts 1 and 2 respectively.

We define a number of symbols.

m_a = mass density of substance a in gm cm^{-3}

m = total mass density $\left(= \sum_a m_a\right)$

V_a = velocity of substance a

C_a = concentration of substance a in moles gm^{-1}

M_a = molecular weight of substance a
R_a = chemical reaction rate of substance a in gm cm^{-3} sec^{-1}
$\mathcal{P}$ = stress tensor
$\boldsymbol{F}$ = external force
H = total energy per unit volume
$\boldsymbol{q}$ = vector of heat flow
p = hydrostatic pressure

All these quantities except the M_a are functions of coordinates x, y, z of points in the cell or its environment relative to any arbitrarily chosen coordinate system, and of the time t.

We define the mean velocity of the system at a point, relative to the coordinate system, by

$$m\boldsymbol{V} = \sum_a m_a \boldsymbol{V}_a \tag{1}$$

The mean velocity of substances of class 1 is defined by

$$m_1 \boldsymbol{V}_1 = \sum_\alpha m_\alpha \boldsymbol{V}_\alpha, \quad (\alpha \text{ ranges over substances of class 1}) \tag{2}$$

and similarly for $\boldsymbol{V}_2$, with $m_1 = \sum_\alpha m_\alpha$ over class 1, etc.

The diffusion velocity of substance a is then $\boldsymbol{U}_a = \boldsymbol{V}_a - \boldsymbol{V}_1$.
We define

$$R_1 = \sum_a R_\alpha, \quad (\alpha \text{ over class 1})$$

$$R_2 = \sum_i R_i, \quad (i \text{ over class 2})$$

$$\boldsymbol{J}_a = mC_a \boldsymbol{U}_a$$

$$\boldsymbol{J} = m\boldsymbol{U} = \sum_a M_a \boldsymbol{J}_a$$

Here M_a and C_a are related by $m_a = mM_aC_a$, and $\boldsymbol{U} = \boldsymbol{V} - \boldsymbol{V}_1$. The internal energy per gram, ϵ, is defined by

$$m\epsilon = H - \tfrac{1}{2}mV^2 \tag{3}$$

The differential equation corresponding to the first law of thermodynamics is then

$$m\frac{d\epsilon}{dt} = (\mathcal{P} \cdot \nabla) \cdot \boldsymbol{V} - \nabla \cdot \boldsymbol{q} - \Sigma\, \nabla \cdot (\mu_a \boldsymbol{J}_a) + \epsilon \nabla \cdot \boldsymbol{J} \tag{4}$$

where $\mu_a = \partial\epsilon/\partial C_a$ and the operator d/dt is given by

$$\frac{d}{dt} = \frac{\partial}{\partial t} + \boldsymbol{V}_1 \cdot \nabla$$

This operator gives the rate of change at a given point in the cell, moving with velocity $\boldsymbol{V}_1$.

Auxiliary equations are the diffusion and continuity equations,

$$\frac{dm}{dt} = -m\nabla \cdot \boldsymbol{V}_1 - \nabla \cdot \boldsymbol{J}, \quad m\frac{dC_a}{dt} = \frac{R_a}{M_a} - \nabla \cdot \boldsymbol{J}_a + C_a\nabla \cdot \boldsymbol{J} \tag{5}$$

and the hydrodynamic equations

$$m\frac{d\boldsymbol{V}}{dt} = \nabla \cdot \mathcal{P} + \boldsymbol{F} - (\boldsymbol{J}\cdot\nabla)\boldsymbol{V}, \quad m_1\frac{d\boldsymbol{V}_1}{dt} = \nabla \cdot \mathcal{P}_1 + \boldsymbol{F}_1 - R_1\boldsymbol{V}_1 \tag{6}$$

The differential equation corresponding to the second law is

$$\left.\begin{aligned} m\theta\frac{d\eta}{dt} = (\mathcal{P}\cdot\nabla)\cdot\boldsymbol{V}_1 + (\mathcal{P}\cdot\nabla)\cdot\boldsymbol{U} + p\nabla\cdot\boldsymbol{V}_1 - \sum_a \mu_a\frac{R_a}{M_a} - \nabla\cdot\boldsymbol{q} \\ -\sum_a \boldsymbol{J}_a\cdot\nabla\mu_a + \left(\epsilon + pv - \sum_a \mu_a C_a\right)\nabla\cdot\boldsymbol{J} \end{aligned}\right\} \tag{7}$$

where η is the entropy and θ the absolute temperature.

Defining the Gibbs free energy as usual by

$$\psi = \epsilon - \theta\eta$$

we have for this function the equation

$$\left.\begin{aligned} m\frac{d(\psi/\theta)}{dt} = -\frac{m\epsilon}{\theta^2}\cdot\frac{d\theta}{dt} + \frac{1}{\theta}\Bigg[-p\nabla\cdot\boldsymbol{V}_1 + \sum_a \mu_a\frac{R_a}{M_a} - \sum_a \mu_a\nabla\cdot\boldsymbol{J}_a \\ + \left(\sum_a \mu_a C_a - pv\right)\nabla\cdot\boldsymbol{J}\Bigg] \end{aligned}\right\} \tag{8}$$

Equations of the same form as the above hold for the environment (in fact, one set holds for each phase if there are more than two phases). At interfaces, we have boundary conditions of two sorts: those prescribing the stress $\mathcal{P}$ at the boundary, and those prescribing the diffusion flux. The latter are of the form

$$\boldsymbol{J}_i = \boldsymbol{J}_{iS}, \quad (i \text{ over class 2})$$

$$\boldsymbol{J}_\alpha = 0 \quad (\alpha \text{ over class 1})$$

The quantity $\boldsymbol{J}_{iS}$ is generally given by

$$\boldsymbol{J}_{iS} = \boldsymbol{n}(a_i C_{iS} - a'_i C'_{iS})$$

the subscript S denoting surface values, the primes denoting the " external " or adjoining phase, and $\boldsymbol{n}$ being the unit external normal to the surface of the phase.

The cell shape is related to the system as follows : if the equation of the cell surface is $S(x,y,z,t) = 0$, then

$$\frac{dS}{dt} = \frac{\partial S}{\partial t} + \boldsymbol{V}_1 \cdot \nabla S = 0 \tag{9}$$

This equation can be solved if $\boldsymbol{V}_1$, the solution of the second hydrodynamical equation, is obtained. Since $\boldsymbol{V}_1$ depends on R_1, the cell shape is thus related to its metabolism.

Of interest in connection with the problem of growth are the equations for the total mass M and total volume V_0 of any region ($d\tau$ = element of volume).

$$\left.\begin{aligned} \frac{dM}{dt} &= \frac{d}{dt}\int m\,d\tau = -\int \nabla \cdot \boldsymbol{J}\,d\tau \\ \frac{dV_0}{dt} &= \frac{d}{dt}\int d\tau = \int \nabla \cdot \boldsymbol{V}_1\,d\tau \end{aligned}\right\} \tag{10}$$

For a region sufficiently small to be approximately homogeneous, those take the simpler form

$$\left.\begin{aligned} \frac{dM}{dt} &= -V_0 \nabla \cdot \boldsymbol{J} \\ \frac{dV_0}{dt} &= V_0 \nabla \cdot \boldsymbol{V}_1 \end{aligned}\right\} \tag{11}$$

See Refs. 3, 11, and 12.

2. Kinetics of Enzyme Catalyzed Reactions

2.1. Simple reactions (Refs. 4 and 5). The basic assumption of the theory is that enzyme and substrate form a complex, which then reacts to yield the product or products together with the free enzyme, which can now enter another cycle. The simplest possible case has been described in equations first derived by Victor Henri (frequently incorrectly attributed to Michaelis and Menten).

Denote the substrate by S, product by P, free enzyme by E, enzyme-substrate complex by C, total enzyme by E_0 (all expressed as concentrations, e.g., in moles gm^{-3}). The stoichiometric relations are

$$S + E \underset{k'_1}{\overset{k_1}{\rightleftarrows}} C, \qquad C \xrightarrow{k_2} E + P$$

We have, moreover,

$$E_0 = E + C$$

The further assumptions that the first reaction is in equilibrium and that the overall reaction rate is determined by the transformation of C to E and P give

$$V = k_2 C = k_2 \frac{S}{K + S} E_0 \tag{1}$$

where $K = k'_1/k_1$.

Haldane's modification of the theory assumes (instead of equilibrium of the complex-forming reaction) a steady state for the complex. That is,

$$dC/dt = 0$$

This yields for the reaction rate

$$V = k_2 \frac{S}{K' + S} E_0 \tag{2}$$

where $K' = K + k_2/k_1$. The functional form is the same, but K' no longer has the significance of the dissociation constant of the complex, so that $1/K'$ does not measure exclusively the affinity of enzyme for substrate.

2.2. Inhibitors (Refs. 1, 2, 7, 13). The effect of substances that inhibit enzymatic reactions is due to their action on the free enzyme molecules, on enzyme-substrate complex, or on both. Such reactions can be treated if stoichiometric combination or its formal equivalent is assumed. The equations are

$$\left.\begin{aligned} &E + S \overset{1}{\rightleftarrows} C \overset{2}{\rightarrow} P + E \\ &E + I \overset{3}{\rightleftarrows} E_I \\ &C + I \overset{4}{\rightleftarrows} C_I \end{aligned}\right\} \tag{1}$$

where I is the free inhibitor, E_I is the enzyme-inhibitor complex, C_I is the enzyme-substrate-inhibitor complex, and the other symbols are as before.

We have the conservation equations

$$\left.\begin{aligned} E_0 &= E + C + E_I + C_I \\ I_0 &= I + E_I + C_I \end{aligned}\right\} \tag{2}$$

(assuming combination in 1 : 1 proportions as above and representing total inhibitor by I_0).

We take C in the steady state as before, and assume that reactions involving inhibitor are in equilibrium (which is true for many but not necessarily for all inhibitions). Thus we have

$$ES = K_1C, \quad EI = K_3E_I, \quad CI = K_4C_I \tag{3}$$

where $K_1 = k'_1/k_1 + k_2/k_1$, $K_3 = k'_3/k_3$, $K_4 = k'_4/k_4$.

This solution of this system gives for the inhibited reaction rate,

$$V_i = k_2C = \frac{1}{2}\cdot\frac{k_2}{k}\left[-\left(\frac{k}{m}-\Delta\right)+\sqrt{\left(\frac{k}{m}-\Delta\right)^2+4\frac{k}{m}E_0}\right] \tag{4}$$

where $k = K_1/S + 1$, $m = K_1/SK_3 + 1/K_4$, $\Delta = E_0 - I_0$.

It is also convenient to plot results of inhibition experiments in terms of the fractional inhibition i or the fractional residual activity ρ, defined by

$$i = \frac{E_I + C_I}{E_0}$$

$$\rho = V_i/V$$

where V is the uninhibited rate as determined in the preceding section. These quantities are related by $i + \rho = 1$. The theoretical equations are

$$I_0 = iE_0 + \frac{k}{m}\cdot\frac{i}{1-i} \tag{5}$$

for the plot of I_0 against i, and

$$E_0 = \frac{I_0}{1-\rho} - \frac{k}{m}\cdot\frac{1}{\rho} \tag{6}$$

for the plot of E_0 against ρ, or

$$I_0 = (1-\rho)E_0 + \frac{k}{m}\frac{1-\rho}{\rho} \tag{7}$$

for I_0 against ρ.

The theory demands in general an infinite value of I_0 for complete inhibition, and an infinite value of E_0 for the complete absence of inhibition.

Some special cases of interest have been worked out in the past, and are readily obtained from the above results. If the inhibitor reacts only with free enzyme, we have what is usually called competitive inhibition, since it is believed that substrate and inhibitor compete for the same grouping on the enzyme. In this case $1/K_4 = 0$, $k/m = K_3(1 + S/K_1)$. If this is substituted in the i, I_0 relation,

$$I_0 = iE_0 + K_3\left(1 + \frac{S}{K_1}\right)\frac{i}{1-i} \tag{8}$$

and the amount of inhibitor required to produce a given fractional inhibition increases with the concentration of substrate.

If inhibitor combines impartially with E and C and has the same affinity for both, $K_3 = K_4$. In this case, $k/m = K_3$, and the relation of I_0 to i is independent of S. This sort of inhibition has been termed noncompetitive.

So-called " uncompetitive " inhibition results if inhibitor combines only with C. Then

$$1/K_3 = 0 \tag{9}$$

and

$$\frac{k}{m} = K_4\left(\frac{K_1}{S} + 1\right) \tag{10}$$

The i, I_0 equation now reads

$$I_0 = iE_0 + K_4\left(\frac{K_1}{S} + 1\right)\frac{i}{1-i} \tag{11}$$

Increasing the substrate concentration now decreases the amount of inhibitor required to produce a given degree of inhibition, as should be expected.

If the combination of inhibitor with E and C is irreversible, we have $K_3 = K_4 = 0$, and therefore $k/m = 0$. In this case, substitution in the i, I_0 equation gives $i = I_0/E_0$.

Moreover, the relation of reaction rate to E_0 takes the special form of a broken line. For $0 \leq E_0 \leq I_0$, $V_i = 0$, while for $E_0 > I_0$,

$$V_i = \frac{k_2}{k}(E_0 - I_0) \tag{12}$$

This form of inhibition has been referred to as " titration " of the enzyme by the inhibitor. The same result is obtained with competitive and noncompetitive inhibition if $K_3 = 0$, and for uncompetitive inhibition if $K_4 = 0$.

3. The Cell

3.1. Metabolism and concentration distributions. The simplest theoretical model of a living cell is based on the minimal set of characteristics which all such cells have in common. Nutrient metabolites diffuse into the cell from the environment, the chemical reactions that constitute metabolism go on inside the cell, and products of metabolism diffuse out of the cell into the environment.

The occurrence of these characteristics can be expressed by a modified form of the classical partial differential equation of diffusion. For a substance undergoing no chemical reactions, this equation has the form

$$\frac{\partial C}{\partial t} = -\nabla \cdot \boldsymbol{J} \tag{1}$$

where $C[= C(x,y,z,t)]$ is the concentration of the substance in gm cm^{-3} (or moles cm^{-3}) and $\boldsymbol{J}$ is the vector of diffusion flux in gm cm^{-2} sec^{-1} (or moles cm^{-2} sec^{-1}). When chemical reactions also occur, they are embodied in a term for " sources " and " sinks," and the equation is

$$\frac{\partial C}{\partial t} = -\nabla \cdot \boldsymbol{J} + Q \tag{2}$$

where Q is the net rate of reaction producing the substance in gm cm^{-3} sec^{-1} (or moles cm^{-3} sec^{-1}). If the substance in the aggregate is removed by reaction rather than supplied, $Q < 0$. In general, one must consider groups of substances which are related to one another by chemical transformations. Thus, one would have simultaneous systems of equations like the foregoing for a set of concentrations $C_1, C_2, \ldots, C_n$. Moreover, Q will in this general case be different in each equation, and each Q_i will be a function $Q_i(C_1, C_2, \ldots, C_n)$ of several or all of the functions C_j. However, much information may be obtained even from the oversimplified case in which each substance is treated independently, i.e., in which $Q_i = Q_i(C_i)$ or $Q_i = \text{constant} = q_i$. (Such a situation may hold approximately for at least one of a group of related substances if all the others are present in sufficient excess.)

To solve the diffusion equation, it is necessary to find an expression for the flux vector $\boldsymbol{J}$. In many cases a satisfactory form is given by Fick's law,

$$\boldsymbol{J} = -D\nabla C$$

where D is a constant known as the diffusion coefficient, and is in general different for each substance (and for each kind of cell or tissue). With this relation, the diffusion equation becomes

$$\frac{\partial c}{\partial t} = D\nabla^2 C + Q \tag{3}$$

As was indicated in Section 1, a separate equation holds for each distinct phase (e.g., for the cell and for its environment). At the surface separating the phases, boundary conditions hold. For the diffusion problem, these express the condition that the flux into the surface from one side equals the flux across the surface equals the flux away from the surface on the other side. Thus for two phases, the interior of a cell and its environment, denoting the corresponding C functions by C_i and C_e, and by $\partial/\partial \nu$ the normal derivative (with respect to the external normal to the surface), we have

$$-D_i \frac{\partial C_i}{\partial \nu} = -D_e \frac{\partial C_e}{\partial \nu} = J_S \quad \text{(at the surface)} \tag{4}$$

The surface flux is generally of the form

$$J_S = h_i C_i - h_e C_e$$

where h_i and h_e are constants (for each substance and each cell). A simple approximation to this, which is frequently used, occurs if $h_i \simeq h_e$, so that

$$J_s = h(C_i - C_e)$$

and h is termed the permeability coefficient. In many cases, the solution of the diffusion equation, $C(x, y, z, t)$, with increasing time approaches a stationary value $C(x, y, z)$ which represents a solution of the equation

$$D\nabla^2 C + Q = 0$$

obtained from the more general equation by setting $\partial C/\partial t$ equal to zero. To estimate the time required to reach practically this stationary state, one can perform an approximate calculation which shows that the time-dependent transient term of $C(x, y, z, t)$ is proportional to e^{-Dt/a^2}, where a is a measure of the linear dimensions of the cell. Since D for a number of important metabolites is known to be $\sim 10^{-7}$ cm^2 sec^{-1}, for a cell of linear dimensions $\sim 10^{-3}$ cm, we have $D/a^2 \sim 10^{-1}$ sec^{-1}. In this case the transient term will drop to $1/e$ of its initial value in 10 seconds, and become virtually negligible after 1 minute. Thus many problems may be treated satisfactorily in terms of the stationary diffusion equation.

A solution satisfying the boundary conditions is readily found if the cell has a spherical shape. For the case where Q is a constant q, the solution is given by

$$\left.\begin{aligned} C_e &= C_0 + \frac{q r_0^3}{3D_e} \cdot \frac{1}{r} \\ C_i &= C_0 + \frac{q r_0}{3h} + \frac{q}{6D_i}(r_0^2 - r^2) + \frac{q r_0^2}{3D_e} \end{aligned}\right\} \quad (5)$$

where the coordinate r is the radial distance from the center of the cell, r_0 is the radius of the cell, and C_0 is the limiting concentration of the substance at a great (strictly speaking, infinite) distance from the cell. For $q > 0$, the concentration distribution has a maximum at the center of the cell, and decreases as one moves outward, with a discontinuity of $q r_0/3h$ at the surface. For $q < 0$, there is a minimum at the center of the cell and an increase as one moves outward.

For nonspherical cells, the solution of the boundary value problem rapidly becomes unmanageable, or at best so cumbersome as not to justify the effort expended. Rashevsky introduced a method of approximation that permits most problems to be handled with relative ease (Ref. 10). Consider a cell of roughly oblong shape, with " half-width " r_2 and " half-length " r_1. Let the mean concentration of metabolite, halfway between periphery and center, be $\bar{c}$. Let the average peripheral concentration inside the cell at the ends be c_1, at the " sides " be c_2, when the corresponding values just outside the cell are c'_1 and c'_2. Finally let δ be a length, of the order of magnitude of the cell dimensions, that distance from the cell in which the concentration changes from c'_1 and c'_2 to the limiting value c_0. The boundary conditions (two sets, one for the ends and one for the sides) take the form

$$\left.\begin{aligned} 2D_i(\bar{c}-c_1) &= r_1 h(c_1 - c'_1) \\ 2D_i(\bar{c}-c_2) &= r_2 h(c_2 - c'_2) \\ \frac{2D_i}{r_1}(\bar{c}-c_1) &= \frac{D_e}{\delta}(c'_1 - c_0) \\ \frac{2D_i}{r_2}(\bar{c}-c_2) &= \frac{D_e}{\delta}(c'_2 - c_0) \end{aligned}\right\} \qquad (6)$$

The (nonstationary) diffusion equation becomes the equation of continuity.

$$\frac{d\bar{c}}{dt} = q - 3D_i\left(\frac{\bar{c}-c_1}{r_1^{\,2}} + 2\,\frac{\bar{c}-c_2}{r_2^{\,2}}\right) \qquad (7)$$

With the help of the boundary conditions this takes the form

$$\frac{d\bar{c}}{dt} = q - \frac{\bar{c}-c_0}{\Lambda} \qquad (8)$$

where

$$\Lambda = \frac{r_1 r_2}{3hD_iD_e} \times \frac{(2D_iD_e + 2\delta D_i h + r_1 hD_e)(2D_iD_e + 2\delta D_i h + r_2 hD_e)}{2(2D_iD_e + 2\delta D_i h + r_1 hD_e)r_1 + (2D_iD_e + 2\delta D_i h + r_2 hD_e)r_2}$$

is termed the total diffusion resistance of the cell.

The solution of the continuity equation is

$$\bar{c} = c_0 + \Lambda q - C\Lambda e^{-t/\Lambda} \qquad (9)$$

where C is a constant of integration. In the stationary state,

$$\bar{c} = c_0 + \Lambda q$$

3.2. Diffusion forces and cell division (Refs. 10 and 15). The relation of cell movements and cell division to metabolic activity is based on the production of concentration gradients and differences by metabolism. All concentrations become equal to c_0 if $q = 0$, and the discontinuity $c_i - c_e$ at $r = r_0$ likewise vanishes with q. The presence of gradients and surface discontinuities for nonvanishing q leads to volume forces and surface pressures of " osmotic " character. The surface pressure is given by

$$p_0 = \frac{RT}{M}(c_i - c_e) \qquad (1)$$

where c_i and c_e are evaluated at the cell surface; R is the gas constant, T the absolute temperature, and M the molecular weight of the solute. The volume force is derivable from a pressure which in the first instance is given by

$$p = \frac{RT}{M} c, \quad F_V = -\frac{RT}{M} \nabla c \tag{2}$$

A more refined calculation takes into account the modification of the distribution c by the molecule or particle subjected to this thermal bombardment (e.g., an enzyme or protein molecule). Thus the next approximation gives

$$F_V = -\frac{3}{2} \cdot \frac{RT}{M} \alpha V \nabla c \tag{3}$$

for the force on a particle of volume V, where α is a constant ~ 1. The dependence of c on q then leads to the general result that the volume and surface forces are directed outward for $q > 0$ and inward for $q < 0$.

The possibility that these forces will cause division of the cell can be analyzed by calculating the energy change ΔE which results when a spherical cell of radius r_0 divides into two equal spherical cells of radius $r_1 = 0.8 r_0$. The calculation makes use of the well-known device of an imaginary expansion of the cell to infinity followed by condensation to two half-cells. The first component of the energy change is due to the surface tension, the second to the surface pressure, and the third to the volume force on the enzyme molecules, giving

$$\Delta E = \Delta E_S + \Delta E_m + \Delta E_V = 1.12 \pi \gamma r_0^2 - \frac{\pi RT q r_0^4}{2Mh} - \frac{3}{20} \cdot \frac{\pi RT \alpha \mu q r_0^5}{DM} \tag{4}$$

where γ is the surface tension in ergs cm^{-2}, D is an average of D_i and D_e, and μ is the relative volume occupied by the enzyme particles. For small r_0, $\Delta E > 0$; for larger values $\Delta E < 0$. There is thus a critical value r_0^* of r_0 for which $\Delta E = 0$, where the cell becomes unstable (if $q > 0$). Then r_0^* is the solution of the cubic equation

$$1.12\gamma - \frac{RT q r_0^2}{2Mh} - \frac{3}{20} \cdot \frac{RT \alpha \mu q r_0^3}{DM} = 0 \tag{5}$$

The exact solution is cumbersome, but two simple limiting cases are easily studied. If h is very large,

$$r_0^* = \sqrt[3]{\frac{7.5 \gamma DM}{RT \alpha \mu q}} \tag{6}$$

If D is very large,

$$r_0^* = \sqrt{\frac{2.24 \gamma Mh}{RTq}} \tag{7}$$

With plausible values of the constants ($\gamma \sim 1$; $\alpha\mu = 1$; $q = 10^{-6}$ gm cm^{-3} sec^{-1}; $M = 100$; and $D = 10^{-7}$ cm^{2} sec^{-1}, $h = \infty$, or $h = 10^{-4}$ cm sec^{-1}, $D = \infty$), we get $r_0^* \sim 10^{-3}$ cm, which corresponds well to average cell sizes. Relatively large variations in the constants, however, result in relatively much smaller changes in r_0^*.

A more precise analysis of the stability of the cell uses as a criterion the virtual work of small arbitrary deformations of the cell, taking into account the redistribution of concentrations due to the deformation. The condition of instability leads to more complex expressions for r_0^*, but gives essentially the same numerical values. The condition is (n an integer)

$$\frac{RT}{M}\alpha\mu\frac{2hqr_0^2 + D_e(n+1)qr_0}{D_iD_en(n+1) + h[D_e(n+1) + D_in]r_0}(n-1)$$

$$+\frac{2}{3} \times \frac{RT}{M} \times \frac{[D_in(n-1) - D_e(n^2-1)]qr_0}{D_0D_en(n+1) + h[D_e(n+1) + D_in]r_0} > \frac{2(n-1)(n+2)}{r_0^2}\gamma$$

A novel result arises if $q < 0$, for now, if certain relations among the constants hold, the condition of instability may be satisfied in a region between the lower and the higher values of r_0. Within this range an infinitesimal elongation of the cell results in a decrease of energy. But we have seen that for $q < 0$ the division of the cell gives an increase of energy. Thus the energy cannot continue to decrease as the deformation goes on, and an intermediate, nonspherical equilibrium shape must result. Neither of these calculations is adequate to predict the entire course of deformation of a cell and its eventual division or stabilization in a nonspherical shape. This can be done by applying the laws of plastic flow, in combination with the approximation method for diffusion in nonspherical cells. A theorem of Betti, first applied to the problem by G. Young (Ref. 15), gives for the average relative rate of change of any dimension of a body of any shape the following sort of expression.

$$\left.\begin{aligned}\frac{1}{l_z}\cdot\frac{dl_z}{dt} = \frac{1}{3\eta V}\Bigg\{\iiint_V [zZ - \tfrac{1}{2}(yY + xX)]dV +\\ \iint_S [zZ_\nu - \tfrac{1}{2}(yY_\nu + xX_\nu)]dS\Bigg\}\end{aligned}\right\} \quad (8)$$

where l_z is the length of the body at time t in the direction of the z axis, X, Y, and Z are the components of the volume force in the x, y, and z directions, and X_ν, Y_ν, and Z_ν are the components of the surface pressure, and the integrals are extended over the volume V and surface S, respectively, of the body, whose viscosity is η.

For the volume force we use the previously cited expression,

$$\boldsymbol{F} = -\frac{3}{2} \cdot \frac{RT\alpha\mu}{M} \nabla c$$

while the surface pressures on the ends and sides of the cell respectively are

$$\left.\begin{aligned} p_1 &= \frac{RT}{M}(c_1 - c'_1) \\ p_2 &= \frac{RT}{M}(c_2 - c'_2) \end{aligned}\right\} \tag{9}$$

We put the z axis along the largest dimension of the cell, so that $l_z = r_1$. Solving for the concentrations by means of the approximate method as before, we obtain

$$\frac{1}{r_1} \cdot \frac{dr_1}{dt} = \frac{RT}{2M\eta} \cdot \frac{[3\alpha\mu\delta h + (3\alpha\mu - 2)D_e]hD_iD_e(r_1 - r_2)(\bar{c} - C_0)}{(2D_iD_e + 2\delta D_ih + r_1hD_e)(2D_iD_e + 2\delta D_ih + r_2hD_e)} \tag{10}$$

A more general relation is obtained if we take into account the effect of surface tension, which produces at the " ends " of the cell a surface force $-2\gamma/r_2$ and along the " sides " a force $-\gamma(1/r_1 + 1/r_2)$, which results in a contribution to the relative rate of elongation of $-(\gamma/2\eta)(r_1 - r_2)/r_1r_2$. Introducing the approximate stationary value Λq for $\bar{c} - c_0$, we get, finally,

$$\frac{1}{r_1} \cdot \frac{dr_1}{dt} = \frac{RT}{6M\eta} \cdot \frac{[3\alpha\mu\delta h + (3\alpha\mu - 2)D_e]r_1r_2(r_1 - r_2)q}{2(2D_iD_e + 2\delta D_ih + r_1hD_e)r_1 + (2D_iD_e + 2\delta D_ih + r_2hD_e)r_2}$$

$$-\frac{\gamma}{2\eta} \cdot \frac{r_1 - r_2}{r_1r_2} \tag{11}$$

Since $r_1 - r_2 > 0$, then for $q > 0$ one necessary condition for elongation to occur (since usually $3\alpha\mu - 2 < 0$) is

$$\delta > \frac{2 - 3\alpha\mu}{3\alpha\mu} \cdot \frac{D_e}{h}$$

Since δ is of the order of the cell size (e.g., $\delta \simeq r_2$), this means that elongation will occur for sufficiently large cell sizes. As r_1 increases, r_2 decreases. In fact, if the cell volume remains approximately constant during the elongation, r_2 can be expressed in terms of $r_1 (r_2 \sim 1/\sqrt{r_1})$ by virtue of the approximate expression for the cell volume.

$$V = \frac{4\pi}{3} r_1 r_2^2 \tag{12}$$

Thus for very large values of r_1 (where $\delta \sim r_2$), dr_1/dt varies as $Ar_1^{1/2} - Br_1^{3/2}$ where A and B are constants. This expression will vanish for some sufficiently large value of r_1, so that the elongation will proceed only to a finite extent. However, Betti's formula gives only the average rate of elongation. In point of fact, the middle of the cell, which is subject to the maximum force, will elongate and constrict more rapidly than the ends, and the process may continue at the middle even when the average elongation has reached its limit. The final stages of cell division may then be treated approximately in terms of a dumbbell-shaped figure, essentially two spheres of radius r_2'', whose centers are separated by a distance r_1'' and connected by a cylindrical " neck " of radius r. The spheres are pulled apart by diffusion forces, due to metabolites produced in each sphere and acting on the other sphere, giving the effect of a repulsion between the spheres. An approximate expression for the total force is

$$F = \frac{RT\pi\alpha\mu q(r_2'')^6}{6MD_e(h_1'')^2} \tag{13}$$

This force is applied to the total surface of the end of the neck, πr^2, giving a surface pressure $F/\pi r^2$. The surface forces due to surface tension in the neck are $-2\gamma/r$ dynes cm^{-2} at the ends, and $-\gamma/r$ on the lateral surface. Thus Betti's theorem gives

$$\frac{1}{l}\cdot\frac{dl}{dt} = \frac{1}{3\pi\eta}\frac{F - \pi r\gamma}{r^2} \tag{14}$$

Since for a viscous incompressible body the relative lateral constriction is half the relative elongation,

$$\frac{1}{r}\cdot\frac{dr}{dt} = -\frac{1}{2l}\cdot\frac{dl}{dt} \tag{15}$$

Thus we have

$$\frac{dr}{dt} = P - \frac{Q}{r}$$

where

$$P = \frac{\gamma}{6\eta}, \quad Q = \frac{RT\alpha\mu q r_2''^6}{36\eta D_e M r_1''^2}$$

For constriction to occur, we must have always

$$Q/r > P$$

The differential equation has the solution

$$P(r - r') + Q \ln\frac{Q - Pr}{Q - Pr'} = P^2 t \tag{16}$$

where r' is the initial value of r. From this it can be seen that r vanishes and division is complete at a time τ given by

$$P^2\tau = Q \ln\frac{Q}{Q - Pr'} - Pr' \tag{17}$$

It is easy to see that τ is real and positive if $Q - Pr' > 0$ and that τ decreases as $Q - Pr'$ increases. Thus the time required to complete division is smaller, among other things, as the metabolic rate q increases. It is also obvious that division will never occur if $q < 0$, for in this case $dr/dt > 0$ always.

3.3. Cell polarity and its maintenance (Ref. 10). A model for the self-regulation of cell polarity depends on the effect of diffusion forces on a negative catalyst. Consider a spherical cell whose hemispheres have mean concentration $\bar{c}_1$, and $\bar{c}_2$ of some metabolite. The reaction rate is q. The treatment of the problem is as usual, except that the internal flux $\pi r_0 D(\bar{c}_1 - \bar{c}_2)$ must be taken into account. We get finally

$$\bar{c}_1 - \bar{c}_2 = \frac{r_0^2(2D + r_0 h)(q_1 - q_2)}{3D(2D + 3r_0 h)} \tag{1}$$

which vanishes if $q_1 = q_2$. The diffusion forces will act on colloidal particles of mean concentration n, volume V, and molecular weight M, to produce a concentration ratio in the two hemispheres

$$\frac{n_1}{n_2} = e^{-\bar{\alpha}(\bar{c}_1 - \bar{c}_2)} \tag{2}$$

where

$$\bar{\alpha} = \frac{3}{2} \cdot \frac{NV\alpha}{M}$$

Putting $x = \bar{c}_1 - \bar{c}_2$, and noting that $n = (n_1 + n_2)/2$, we have

$$n_2 - n_1 = 2n \tanh(\tfrac{1}{2}\bar{\alpha}x) \tag{3}$$

Suppose the particles act as negative catalysts on the reaction rate, so that for example,

$$q = q_0 - an$$

Then

$$q_1 - q_2 = a(n_2 - n_1) \tag{4}$$

A representation of an asymmetric distribution of the particles follows from the elimination of the q's and n's from the above relations.

$$x = 2Aan \tanh(\tfrac{1}{2}\bar{\alpha}x)$$

where

$$A = \frac{r_0^2(2D + r_0 h)}{3D(2D + 3r_0 h)}$$

Approximately, for small $\bar{\alpha}x$, this is

$$x = Aan\bar{\alpha}x(1 - \frac{1}{12}\bar{\alpha}^2 x^2)$$

This has a root (besides $x = 0$),

$$x_* = \frac{2}{\bar{\alpha}} \sqrt{\frac{3(Aan\bar{\alpha} - 1)}{Aan\bar{\alpha}}}$$

which is real and positive if $Aan\bar{\alpha} > 1$.

This root corresponds to a stable configuration, so that the asymmetry will be maintained against disturbances such as division of the cell. A similar result holds for a cell with impermeable membrane, in which the metabolite is produced at rate q and consumed at rate bc, except that the constant A is now given by

$$A = \frac{r_0^2}{r_0^2 b + 3D}$$

3.4. Cell permeability (Ref. 12). An analysis of interface and membrane permeability in terms of kinetic theory requires a calculation of the velocity distribution in the presence of a concentration gradient. An adaptation of a procedure used by Lorentz in the theory of conductivity was used. If the Maxwell distribution of velocities c is $f_0(c)$, the perturbed distribution is approximated by

$$f = f_0 + uF(c) \qquad (1)$$

where u is the component of c in the direction of the gradient. The equation of Boltzmann is used to evaluate the correction term, giving

$$F(c) = -\left(\frac{L}{c}\right) \partial f_0 / \partial x \qquad (2)$$

where L is the mean free path, and the x axis of a rectangular coordinate system has been placed in the direction of the gradient. We can now evaluate the diffusion current J.

$$J = \iiint_{-\infty}^{+\infty} ufdudvdw = -\frac{L}{3}\left(\frac{8kT}{\pi m}\right)^{1/2} \partial n / \partial x \qquad (3)$$

where m is molecular mass, T absolute temperature, n is concentration at x, and k is Boltzmann's constant. This is identical with Fick's law if the diffusion coefficient D is

$$D = \frac{L}{3}\left(\frac{8kT}{\pi m}\right)^{1/2}$$

At a phase boundary, the integral splits into two parts, since the parameters of the distribution for molecules approaching from one phase are in general different from those for molecules approaching from the other side. We denote values at the boundary in the "left" and "right" phases by subscripts 1 and 2 respectively.

If a field with potential $V(x)$ acts inside a phase, it adds $-Mn\partial V/\partial x$ to the expression for J, where the mobility $M = D/kT$. At the boundary, V may undergo a finite change, and a potential barrier may also occur. Let the potential in phase 1 at the boundary be V_1, in phase 2 V_2, and the barrier V. Then the potential jump going from 1 to 2 is $U_1 = V - V_1$, and from 2 to 1 is $U_2 = V - V_2$. The lower limits of the velocity integrals for J all given now by $\frac{1}{2}mc^2 = U_1$ and $\frac{1}{2}mc^2 = U_2$. The diffusion current at the boundary is therefore

$$J_S = a_1 n_1 - a_2 n_2 \tag{4}$$

with

$$a_1 = a\phi_1/[1 - \tfrac{1}{2}(\phi_1 + \phi_2)]$$

$$a_2 = a\phi_2/[1 - \tfrac{1}{2}(\phi_1 + \phi_2)]$$

$$a = \tfrac{1}{2}(2\pi kT/m)^{1/2}$$

$$\phi_1 = e^{-U_1/kT}(1 + U_1/kT)$$

$$\phi_2 = e^{-U_2/kT}(1 + U_2/kT)$$

The constants a_1 and a_2 are called the coefficients of permeability. It is readily shown that values of the potentials can be chosen such that the flow will have a sign opposite to that of $n_1 - n_2$ ("anomalous" diffusion, diffusion against a gradient).

In the case of a membrane of finite but small thickness d, we can apply the foregoing results. The potential barriers at the two boundaries are V and W, and the boundary potentials in the membrane are V_{m_1} and V_{m_2}. We write $U_1 = V - V_1$, $U_2 = W - V_2$, $U_{m_1} = V - V_{m_2}$, $U_{m_2} = W - V_{m_2}$. The diffusion current in the membrane is, to a good approximation,

$$J_m = \frac{D_m(n_{m_1} - n_{m_2})}{d} \tag{5}$$

where D_m is the diffusion coefficient in the membrane. Noting that the left and right boundary fluxes are equal to each other, to J_m, and to J_S (continuity of flux across the membrane),

$$J_{S_1} = J_{S_2} = J_m = J_S$$

we get, finally,

$$J_S = \frac{(a_1/a_{m_1})n_1 - (a_2/a_{m_2})n_2}{1/a_{m_1} + 1/a_{m_2} + d/D_m}$$

with
$$\left.\begin{aligned}
a_1 &= \frac{a\phi_1}{1-\frac{1}{2}(\phi_1+\phi_{m_1})}, & a_2 &= \frac{a\phi_2}{1-\frac{1}{2}(\phi_2+\phi_{m_2})} \\
a_{m_1} &= \frac{a\phi_{m_1}}{1-\frac{1}{2}(\phi_1+\phi_{m_1})}, & a_{m_2} &= \frac{a\phi_{m2}}{1-\frac{1}{2}(\phi_2+\phi_{m_2})} \\
\phi_1 &= e^{-U_1/kT}(1+U_1/kT), & \phi_2 &= e^{-U_2/kT}(1+U_2/kT) \\
\phi_{m_1} &= e^{-U_{m_1}/kT}(1+U_{m_1}/kT), & \phi_{m_2} &= e^{-U_{m_2}/kT}(1+U_{m_2}/kT)
\end{aligned}\right\} \quad (6)$$

4. The Neurone and Behavior

4.1. Excitation and conduction in the neurone (Ref. 10). The biophysical theory of nerve activity is a modification by Rashevsky of a theory introduced by Blair. The central concept of the theory is that of a pair of antagonistic " factors," referred to as " excitatory " and " inhibitory " and denoted by ϵ and j, respectively. The nature of the factors is unspecified, though the analogy of antagonistic ions is very suggestive.

If an exciting current I is applied, it is assumed that both ϵ and j increase at a rate proportional to I, and decrease at a rate proportional to the excess of ϵ and j over their respective resting values ϵ_0 and j_0. Thus

$$\frac{d\epsilon}{dt} = KI - k(\epsilon-\epsilon_0), \quad \frac{dj}{dt} = MI - m(j-j_0) \qquad (1)$$

where K, M, k, and m are constants. The condition for excitation of the nerve is $\epsilon \geq j$; hence, of course, $\epsilon_0 < j_0$. If a constant current is applied at $t = 0$, the solution is

$$\left.\begin{aligned}
\epsilon &= \epsilon_0 + \frac{KI}{k}(1-e^{-kt}) \\
j &= j_0 + \frac{MI}{m}(1-e^{-mt})
\end{aligned}\right\} \qquad (2)$$

Under the conditions

$$m \ll k, \quad M \ll K, \quad \frac{K}{k} \leq \frac{M}{m}, \quad \frac{K}{k} \sim \frac{M}{m}$$

excitation will occur at the cathode only when the current is established, and at the anode when it is broken, provided I is sufficiently great. The intensity-time curve for excitation at the cathode at make (from $\epsilon = j$) is

$$I = \frac{j_0 - \epsilon_0}{(K/k)(1-e^{-kt}) - (M/m)(1-e^{-mt})} \qquad (3)$$

and at the anode at break,

$$I = \frac{j_0 - \epsilon_0}{(M/m)e^{-mt} - (K/k)e^{-kt}} \tag{4}$$

The threshold or rheobase values of the current at cathode and anode, respectively (from $\epsilon = j$ and $d\epsilon/dt = dj/dt$), are

$$R_c = \frac{j_0 - \epsilon_0}{(K/k)[1 - (M/K)^{k/(k-m)}] - (M/m)[-- (M/K)^{m/(k-m)}]} \tag{5a}$$

$$R_a = \frac{j_0 - \epsilon_0}{(M/m)(M/K)^{m/(k-m)} - (K/k)(M/K)^{k/(k-m)}} \tag{5b}$$

with the approximate value

$$R_c \sim [(j_0 - \epsilon_0)/K]k, \; R_a \sim [j_0 - \epsilon_0)/M]m$$

The solution for a slowly rising current, $I = \lambda t$, is

$$\left.\begin{aligned} \epsilon &= \epsilon_0 + \frac{K\lambda}{k}\left\{ t - \frac{1}{k}(1 - e^{-kt}) \right\} \\ j &= j_0 + \frac{M\lambda}{m}\left\{ t - \frac{1}{m}(1 - e^{-mt}) \right\} \end{aligned}\right\} \tag{6}$$

For sufficiently small λ, no excitation occurs as long as $K/k \leq M/m$. For alternating current, $I = I_0 \sin \omega$, a solution obtained under the condition $K/k = M/m$ gives an empirically verifiable relationship between the threshold value of I_0 and the frequency ω.

$$\frac{I_0}{R_c} = \sqrt{\left(1 + \frac{\omega^2}{k^2}\right)\left(1 + \frac{m^2}{\omega^2}\right)} \tag{7}$$

where $$R_c = \frac{j_0 - \epsilon_0}{K - M} k$$

This case has also been solved without the restriction $K/k = M/m$. Another interesting relation derivable from the theory is that between the duration $\bar{t}$ of a constant current pulse and the threshold intensity I required to produce anodic excitation at break

$$I_c = \frac{(1 - e^{-k\bar{t}})^{1/[(k/m)-1]}}{(1 - e^{-m\bar{t}})^{1/[1-(m/k)]}} \left(\frac{k}{m}\right)^{1/[(k/m)-1]} \tag{8}$$

The theory of excitation is at present largely phenomenological, as is evident from the foregoing. The theory of conduction of the excitation along the nerve is a simple physical one, however, and is essentially the theory of a core conductor. The nerve is pictured as a cylinder with a core of radius r and specific resistance ρ, surrounded by a sheath of thickness δ and specific resistance $\bar{\rho}$. Also $\delta \ll r$. To a first approximation, neglecting the distributed capacity of the fiber, the distribution of current is given at $t = 0$ by

$$i(x) = Ie^{-\alpha x} \tag{9}$$

where I is the current at the initially excited region, x is distance from the excited region to a point along the nerves, and

$$\alpha = \sqrt{\frac{\gamma + 1}{\gamma} \frac{2\rho}{\delta \bar{\rho} r}}$$

where γ is the ratio of resistance per unit length of the core to resistance per unit length of the sheath.

The distribution is propagated along the nerve, so that at any later time we have at any point a distribution,

$$i(S) = Ie^{-\alpha S} \tag{10}$$

where S is the distance between the point considered and the excited region at the moment t. If the velocity of propagation is $v(t)$, then at a point x_0 we have

$$S = x_0 - \int_{t_1}^{t} v(t)dt = x_0 - u(t)$$

where t_1 is the time from application of current I to occurrence of excitation at the electrode, and is given by

$$t_1 = \frac{1}{k} \log \frac{KI}{KI - k\epsilon_1}$$

where $\epsilon_1 = \epsilon^* - \epsilon_0$, and ϵ^* is the value of ϵ at the electrode when $\epsilon = j$. From $t = 0$ to t_1, the current at x_0 is $Ie^{-\alpha x_0}$. After t_1, it varies according to

$$i(x_0,t) = Ie^{-\alpha x_0 + \alpha u(t)} \tag{11}$$

Excitation at the point x_0 by the local current $i(x_0,t)$ obeys the differential equations:

$$\left.\begin{aligned} \frac{d\epsilon}{dt} &= Ki - k(\epsilon - \epsilon_0) \\ \frac{dj}{dt} &= Mi - m(j - j_0) \end{aligned}\right\} \tag{12}$$

Solving, and putting $\epsilon(x_0,t) = j(x_0,t)$ for excitation, we finally obtain the differential equation

$$\alpha \frac{dv}{dt} = -\alpha^2 v^2 - \left(m + k - \frac{K - M}{j_0 - \epsilon_0} I\right)\alpha v - \left(mk + \frac{Mk - Km}{j_0 - \epsilon_0} I\right) \tag{13}$$

If (as is probably the case, from available values of the constants),

$$\Delta = a^2 - 4b > 0$$

the right side of the differential equation has two real roots,

$$\alpha v_1 = \tfrac{1}{2}(a - \sqrt{\Delta}), \quad \alpha v_2 = \tfrac{1}{2}(a + \sqrt{\Delta}) \tag{14}$$

where

$$-a = m + k - \frac{K - M}{j_0 - \epsilon_0} I, \quad b = mk + \frac{Mk - Km}{j_0 - \epsilon_0} I$$

The velocity $v(t)$ is given by

$$v = \frac{v_1 - A v_2 e^{\sqrt{\Delta} t}}{1 - A e^{\sqrt{\Delta} t}} \tag{15}$$

where

$$A = e^{-\sqrt{\Delta} t_1} \frac{(m + \alpha v_2)[j_1(m + \alpha v_1) - MI]}{(m + \alpha v_1)[j_1(m + \alpha v_2) - MI]}$$

$$j_1 = j_* - j_0$$

At $t = t_1$,

$$v_1 < v < v_2$$

With increasing t_1, v approaches v_2, which is a stable value.

4.2. Behavior and the structure of the central nervous system (Ref. 10). The biophysical theory of the behavior of organisms with a central nervous system is based on what might be called the network postulate : that the units of the central nervous system follow the same simple laws as isolated peripheral neurones, and that the complexities of behavior result from the interaction of such units arranged in networks of varying degrees of complexity.

It is known that a continuous physiological stimulus produces a volley of nerve impulses rather than a single impulse. The frequency ν of the volley increases with the intensity S of the stimulus. The intensity I of the impulses is independent of S according to the "all-or-none law."

We define the intensity of excitation of a fiber, E, by

$$E = I\nu \tag{1}$$

and write as an approximate expression for the relation between ν and S,

$$\nu = \alpha(S - h)$$

where h is the threshold of the fiber and α a constant of the fiber. Thus

$$E = \alpha I(S - h) = \beta(S - h) \tag{2}$$

The neuroelement produces factors ϵ and j according to the differential equations

$$\frac{d\epsilon}{dt} = AE - a\epsilon, \quad \frac{dj}{dt} = BE - bj \tag{3}$$

The neuroelements may be divided into two classes, excitatory and inhibtory, according as the asymptotic values of ϵ exceed those of j or vice versa, which depends on certain relations among the constants. A simplified version of this classification occurs if the neuroelements produce only one factor, either ϵ or j alone; such neuroelements are termed purely excitatory or purely inhibitory.

One further postulate is required to estabish the influence of the neuroelements in the network on one another. We consider the neuroelements as linear (possibly with collateral branches). They are polar : one end receives the stimulus, and this is propagated along the element to its other end. This end may make a connection with the stimulus-receiving and of a second neuron. Such connections may be multiple, i.e., more than one neuroelement may enter or leave such a connection. We now postulate that at any connection, if $\epsilon > j$, then $\epsilon - j$ acts as the stimulus intensity S for any neuroelement leaving the connection. (It is understood that, if several neuroelements enter the connection, their contributions to ϵ and j are additive.)

Space will permit only a few illustrations of the many applications of this scheme which have been made.

a. *Reaction time.* Consider a network in which two elements I and III converge in a connection to an element II. Let I be purely excitatory and III be simply excitatory. Suppose a warning stimulus S_3 is applied to III at a time t_w units before S_1 is applied to I. Then the reaction time t_r for response to S_1 via I and II is related to t_w by

$$t_r = t_0 - \frac{1}{a_1} \log \left[M + J(e^{-b_3 t_w} - e^{-a_3 t_w})\right] \tag{4}$$

where
$$M = 1 - \frac{a_1 h_2}{A_1 E_1}, \quad J = \frac{A_3 E_3 a_1}{A_1 E_1 a_3}$$

and t_0 is the constant time due to conduction on the efferent side and delays at the end organs.

b. *Discrimination.* Discrimination problems of various sorts are analyzed in terms of networks with fundamentally similar characteristics : series of excitatory neuroelements run parallel to one another, and send collateral branches, both excitatory and inhibitory, to each other's connections. A simple example consists of n elements I connecting with n elements II at connections $c_i(i = 1,\ldots,n)$. A branch of each element i of I connects at c_i to a set of inhibitory elements III which join every connection $c_h(h \neq i)$. Thus every c_i receives an excitatory path from the periphery and $n - 1$ inhibitors from other neuroelements. If all stimuli have the same intensity S, we have for $\epsilon - j$ at c_i (asymptotically)

$$\epsilon - j = \left(\frac{A_e}{a_e} - \frac{B_e}{b_e}\right)E_1 + (n-1)\left(\frac{A_j}{a_j} - \frac{B_j}{b_j}\right)E_3 \tag{5}$$

with

$$E_1 = \alpha_1 I_1(S - h_1)$$

$$E_3 = \alpha_3 I_3[P\alpha_1 I_1(S - h_1) - h_3]$$

$$P = \frac{A_e}{a_e} - \frac{B_e}{b_e}$$

The subscripts e and j refer to excitatory and inhibitory parameters, the subscripts 1 and 3 to element I and III. If

$$h_1 < S < h_1 + \frac{h_3}{P\alpha I}$$

then $E_3 = 0$ and $\epsilon - j > 0$. If also

$$S > h_1 + \frac{h_2}{P\alpha_1 I_1}$$

which is possible only if $h_2 < h_3$, then $\epsilon - j > h_2$, and all II pathways are excited. But if

$$S > h_1 + \frac{h_3}{P\alpha_1 I_1}$$

then, for sufficiently large n, $\epsilon - j < 0$; i.e., if

$$n > 1 + \frac{P}{Q} \cdot \frac{\alpha_1 I_1}{\alpha_3 I_3} \cdot \frac{S - h_1}{P\alpha_1 I(S - h_1) - h_3}$$

where

$$Q = -\left(\frac{A_j}{a_j} - \frac{B_j}{b_j}\right)$$

In this case complete inhibition occurs at all c_i. But if $m < n$ of the pathways are stimulated with $S' > S$, then at the c_i^m connections of these m paths

$$(\epsilon - j)_m = PE'_1 - (m-1)QE'_3 - (n-m)QE_3 \tag{6}$$

while at the other $n - m$ connections c_i^{n-m},

$$(\epsilon - j)_{n-m} = PE_1 - (n-m-1)QE_3 - mQE'_3 \tag{7}$$

where

$$E'_1 = \alpha_1 I_1(S' - h'), \quad E'_3 = \alpha_3 I_3(PE'_1 - h_3)$$

and the other symbols are as before. Now

$$(\epsilon - j)_{n-m} < P\alpha_1 I_1(S - h_1) - (n-1)Q\alpha_3 I_3[P\alpha_1 I_1(S - h_1) - h_3] \tag{8}$$

since $S' > S$. Thus $(\epsilon - j)_{n-m} < 0$ for the same conditions as made $\epsilon - j < 0$ before. But $(\epsilon - j)_m > h_2$ whenever

$$S' > h_1 + \frac{h_2 + Q\alpha_3 I_3[(n-m)P\alpha_1 I_1(S - h_1) - (n-1)h_3]}{P\alpha_1 I_1[1 - (m-1)Q\alpha_3 I_3]}$$

Thus, if S' is sufficiently greater than S, the m pathways will respond, while the $n - m$ fail to respond to S.

c. *Self-exciting circuits.* Consider a closed circuit consisting of pure excitatory elements I and II. The differential equations are

$$\frac{d\epsilon_1}{dt} = AE_2 - a\epsilon_1, \quad \frac{d\epsilon_2}{dt} = AE_1 - a\epsilon_2 \tag{9}$$

The approximate relation $E = \alpha I(S - h)$ leads to the physically absurd result that E_1 and E_2 become infinite if the circuit is excited at all. The next best approximation is

$$E = \frac{I}{\theta}[1 - e^{-\alpha\theta(S-h)}]$$

giving in this case

$$\left.\begin{aligned} \frac{d\epsilon_1}{dt} &= \frac{AI_2}{\theta_2}[1 - e^{-\alpha\theta_2(\varepsilon_2 - h_2)}] - a\epsilon_1 \\ \frac{d\epsilon_2}{dt} &= \frac{AI_1}{\theta_1}[1 - e^{-\alpha\theta_1(\varepsilon - h_1)}] - a\epsilon_2 \end{aligned}\right\} \tag{10}$$

An analytic solution is not known. But a graphical analysis is readily carried out in terms of ϵ_1 and ϵ_2 as Cartesian coordinates in a plane. Then, setting $d\epsilon_1/dt = 0$ and $d\epsilon_2/dt = 0$, we derive two curves in this plane, which in general intersect in two points. One of these points represents a stable equilibrium and the other an unstable one, while a third stable point is $\epsilon_1 = \epsilon_2 = 0$. There is a curve passing through the unstable point, which divides the positive quadrant of the plane into two regions, such that, starting at any point in one region, one passes to the origin, while from any point in the second region one arrives at the stable nonzero equilibrium. Thus, if the circuit is sufficiently excited by some external stimulus, it will arrive at a stable excitatory equilibrium, in which it will remain unless externally inhibited.

d. *Conditioned reflexes.* Consider two pathways, one consisting of elements I^u and II^u, the other of elements I^c and II^c, with I-II connections c_u and c_c, respectively. Let II^u and II^c converge at a connection c, which leads by further paths to a response R. A collateral of I^u leads to c_c. Also connected to c_c is a self-exciting circuit C of the type just described; the external excitation needed to start C is h^*, and the stable excitation value of C is ϵ_0. Pathway I^c has threshold h_c, while II^c has threshold h'. We use for E_u and E_c the exponential expression of the preceding paragraph; the values of the constants are such that the limiting values of E_u and E_c, I_u/θ_u and I_c/θ_c, satisfy

$$P\frac{I_c}{\theta_c} < h', \quad P = \frac{A_e}{a_e} - \frac{B_e}{b_e}, \quad P\frac{I_c}{\theta_c} < h^*, \quad P\frac{I_u}{\theta_u} < h^*$$

but

$$P\left(\frac{I_u}{\theta_u} + \frac{I_c}{\theta_c}\right) > h^*, \quad P\frac{I_c}{\theta_c} + \epsilon_0 > h'$$

Now if $S_u > h_u$ is applied to I^u, R results. But S_c applied to I^c, no matter how strong, does not give R. But if S_u and S_c are applied simultaneously for a sufficient time, $\epsilon - j$ at c_c will be $P(E_u + E_c)$; and for sufficiently large S_u and S_c to bring E_u and E_c close to their limiting values I_u/θ_u and I_c/θ_c, this $\epsilon - j$ will exceed h^*. Now C is in an excited state with $\epsilon = \epsilon_0$, even when external stimuli are removed. If S_c is now applied alone, ϵ at c_c is $PE_c + \epsilon_0$; and by the last inequality, for sufficiently large S_c, this will exceed h', and elicit R_1. This is a simple scheme which contains the essential features of the conditioned reflex. Various modifications have been worked out which account for the finer details of the phenomenon.

e. *Learning.* The biophysical theory of learning utilizes the properties of the self-exciting circuit, contained in a larger cycle which has the property that has been rather loosely compared with feedback in electronic networks. If one of two alternatives is to be learned, as in many experimental setups in psychology, consider a pair of parallel pathways, containing several elements in series, one path originating in stimulus S_c and terminating in response R_c (" correct " response to choice) the other going from S_w to R_w (" wrong " response to choice). (The usual cross-inhibitory elements run from the I-II connections c_c and c_w to higher connections in the pathways.) Let R_c produce the event R_1, and R_w produce R_2. Here R_1 (" reward ") acts as stimulus to a pathway which includes a self-exciting circuit C, and terminates with an excitatory element at c_c; R_2 (" punishment ") serves as stimulus to a path which includes a self-exciting circuit C' and terminates with an inhibitory element at c_w. (C and C' actually consist of two large groups of circuits arranged in parallel, and having a distribution of threshold values, so that they will not all be activated at once, but will be activated in increasing numbers with repetition of the stimulus to them from R_1 and R_2.) Now S_c and S_w are presented simultaneously on many successive occasions. Response is random at first, but C and C' are progressively activated, so that the strength of response R_c is reinforced and that of R_w is weakened. The relation between number of wrong responses w and number of trials n is

$$w = \frac{1}{k(b-\beta)} \log \frac{2be^{k(\varepsilon_{0c}-\varepsilon_{0w})}}{2be^{k(\varepsilon_{0c}-\varepsilon_{0w})} - (b-\beta)(1-e^{-kbn})} \tag{11}$$

Here ϵ_{0c} and ϵ_{0w} are the initial values of ϵ at C_c and C_w, b is the increase in ϵ at c_c per correct response, β is the decrease in ϵ at c_w per wrong response, and k is a constant.

A generalization for N choices, with M associations to be learnt, with an allowance for prompting by the experimenter in a fraction $(1-f)$ of the trials, and taking into account the effect of M on the parameter b, gives

$$w = \frac{(N-1)e^{\varphi M}}{\eta A} \log \frac{N}{e^{-\eta n e^{-\varphi M}} + N - A} \tag{12}$$

where $$A = Nf - f - \beta/b$$

and η and φ are constants.

The logical calculus of neural nets : the foregoing work on the biophysics of behavior consists essentially in constructing networks and seeing what kind of behavior they will give. An alternative treatment by McCulloch and Pitts is capable of solving the inverse problem : for a given behavior pattern, to determine the corresponding network. This treatment employs the analogy between two-valued logic and the all-or-none character of nerve activity. Numbering the neurones, we represent by " $N_1(t)$ " the proposition " Neurone #1 fires at time t." In the same way we write " $\sim N_2(t)$ " for " Neurone #2 does not fire at time t," the symbol $\sim$ being the classical negation sign of symbolic logic in the Russell-Whitehead notation. We shall also use " V ", the classical disjunctive symbol (" ... or ..., or both "). It is convenient to take the synaptic delay as the unit of time. It is also convenient to assume that inhibition is absolute; i.e., if any inhibitory neurone terminates on a second neurone, its firing will always inhibit the second neurone. However, it can be shown that nothing would be essentially altered in the results if one abandons this assumption, which merely simplifies the symbolic manipulations. The threshold of a neurone, taken to be an integer θ, is for simplicity identified with the number of terminal bulbs, synapsing on it from other (excitatory) neurones, which must be excited simultaneously in order to stimulate it. This assumption facilitates diagrammatic representation of networks, but is otherwise not essential; there is, however, some evidence for its reality. Consider now that neurone 1 terminates on neurone 2 with a number of terminal bulbs equal to θ for #2. The necessary and sufficient condition for #2 to fire at t is simply that #1 fired at $t-1$.

$$N_2(t). \equiv .N_1(t-1) \tag{13}$$

where $\equiv$ is the logical sign of equivalence (" if and only if "), and the dots follow the dot punctuation conventions of Russell and Whitehead. If $\theta = 2$, and neurons 1 and 2 terminate on 3 with only one terminal bulb each, both must fire at once

$$N_3(t). \equiv .N_1(t-1) \cdot N_2(t-1) \tag{14}$$

If 1 and 2 synapse on 3 with two bulbs each, and $\theta = 2$, the firing of either will excite 3.

$$N_3(t). \equiv .N_1(t-1) V N_2(t-1) \tag{15}$$

If 1 synapses on 3 with 2 bulbs ($\theta = 2$), and 2, an inhibitory neurone, synapses on 3, then 1 must fire while 2 is not firing to excite 3.

$$N_3(t). \equiv .N_1(t-1) \cdot \sim N_2(t-1) \tag{16}$$

These basic circuits are useful in constructing more complex ones, as will be seen. It is convenient to introduce the functor (operator) " S ", defined by

$$SN_1(t). \equiv .N_1(t-1)$$

so that a sentence like $N_2(t). \equiv .N_1(t-1)$ becomes

$$N_2(t). \equiv .SN_1(t) \tag{17}$$

Repetitions of the operation are represented by powers. Thus

$$S[SN_1(t)]. \equiv .S^2N_1(t) \tag{18}$$

Obviously, the operator S commutes with . and V.

Any network can be represented by a number of equivalences, as just illustrated, one for each neurone in the net except the initial ones (the peripheral afferents, defined by the fact that no neurone of the net terminates on them). (We neglect nets containing cycles in this presentation, since their theory is a far more elaborate one). Anormal form is readily obtained. If the equivalence for $N_i(t)$ contains on the right side N_j, where $j(\neq i)$ is not a peripheral afferent, then N_j can be eliminated by means of its own equivalence. This elimination can be carried out consistently and with a unique result, until only the N's of peripheral afferents appear on the right sides (since no cycles occur in the nets). The resulting form, called a temporal propositional expression, expresses each $N_i(t)$ as a disjunction of conjunctions of propositions of the form $S^n N_k(t)$ and their negations, where $n \geq 1$ and k is a peripheral afferent. No term in the disjunction can consist wholly of negations.

To illustrate the application of the above, we treat the " illusion of heat and cold." If a cold object is touched briefly to the skin and removed, a sensation of heat is felt; only cold is felt if the contact is more prolonged. We number the cutaneous heat and cold receptor neurones 1 and 2, the corresponding central neurones whose activity gives the heat and cold sensations 3 and 4, respectively.

The phenomenon can then be expressed by

$$\left.\begin{array}{l} N_3(t) : \equiv : N_1(t-1) \cdot V \cdot N_2(t-3) \cdot \sim N_2(t-2) \\ N_4(t) . \equiv . N_2(t-2) \cdot N_2(t-1) \end{array}\right\} \quad (19)$$

where we have for simplicity assumed the required contact for cold sensation to be two synaptic delays as against one for heat. These relations can be rewritten with the aid of the operator S.

$$\left.\begin{array}{l} N_3(t) . \equiv . S\{N_1(t) V S[(SN_2(t) \cdot \sim N_2(t)]\} \\ N_4(t) . \equiv . S\{[SN_2(t)] \cdot N_2(t)\} \end{array}\right\} \quad (20)$$

The problem is to connect neurones 1, 2, 3, 4, and introduce other neurones if necessary, such that the normal forms for the network will contain the above sentences. To do this, we construct nets for the partial expressions, beginning with those included in the largest number of brackets and proceeding outward.

Introduce a neurone a, upon which two terminal bulbs from neurone 2 synapse (assume for simplicity $\theta = 2$ for all neurones of the net). Then

$$N_a(t) . \equiv . SN_2(t)$$

and we can substitute this expression above. Now let a single bulb from a and a single bulb from 2 terminate on 4. Then

$$N_4(t) . \equiv . S[N_a(t) \cdot N_2(t)] . \equiv . S[(SN_2(t)) \cdot N_2(t)]$$

Introduce neurone b, receiving an inhibitory terminal from 2 and two excitatory terminals from a. Then

$$N_b(t) . \equiv . S[N_a(t) \cdot \sim N_2(t)]$$

which is the square bracket in the expression for $N_3(t)$.

Now let neurones 1 and b each send two terminals to 3. Then

$$N_3(t). \equiv .S[N_1(t) V N_b(t)]. \equiv .S\{N_1(t) V S[(SN_2(t) \cdot \sim N_2(t)]\} \tag{21}$$

This completes the solution of the problem, since our systematically constructed network leads to the desired expression for $N_3(t)$ and $N_4(t)$.

The nature of the logical formalism for cyclic nets may be briefly indicated. If a self-exciting circuit is firing at time t, it is not true, as for simple neurones, that it was stimulated at $t-1$. One can only say that it must have been stimulated at $t-1$ or some earlier moment. We introduce the logical existential operator $\exists$, which is such that $(\exists x)N(x)$ means, "There is an x for which $N(x)$ holds." With the aid of this operator, some simple examples of cyclic nets may be given. Let neurone 1 terminate on neurone 2 with terminals less than θ in number. Let 1 also terminate on a self-exciting circuit (with threshold number of terminals). Each neurone of the circuit sends a branch to 2; the total number of terminals from this source equals or exceeds θ. This circuit is represented by

$$N_2(t) \equiv (\exists x)N_1(t-x-1) \tag{22}$$

Again, let neurone 1 have a branch to a self-exciting circuit, each neurone of which sends a branch to 1. Then

$$N_1(t) \equiv (\exists x)N_1(t-x-2) \tag{23}$$

Thus for cyclic nets we may have N_i expressed in terms of N_i, which is never true for noncyclic nets.

5. The Evolution and Interaction of Populations

5.1. The general laws of populations (Ref. 8). The elementary units of a population may be of quite diverse sorts: molecules, as in chemical kinetics; cells, as in embryology; or organisms, as in demography and ecology. The general character of the laws is the same for all these cases. The laws are differential or integrodifferential equations (or systems of equations), of first order in the time. The dependent variables are quantities which express the number of units, the total mass, or some such extensive property of each species or type of units in the population. Thus we have equations of the form

$$\frac{dX_i}{dt} = F_i(X_1, \ldots, X_n; P) \tag{1}$$

where P represents a set of parameters (e.g., temperature, volume of space available to the population, etc.). In most cases, the time t does not appear explicitly in the F_i. But the parameters P may vary with the time independently of the X_i, as in the case of long-range or seasonal climatic variations, or diurnal variations of temperature; and these variations may not always be neglected. For the moment, however, we ignore them.

These equations define certain steady states, which occur when all the dX_i/dt vanish, so that

$$F_1 = F_2 = \dots = F_n = 0$$

These n equations in general determine one or more sets of values

$$X_1 = C_1, \quad X_2 = C_2, \quad \dots, \quad X_n = C_n$$

for which the system is at rest. Some of these solutions are stable, however, and some unstable. It is convenient to introduce the new set of variables,

$$x_i = X_i - C_i$$

whence the system of equations becomes

$$\frac{dx_i}{dt} = f_i(x_1, \dots, x_n; P) \tag{2}$$

If the functions f_i can be expanded in Taylor series, the general solution of the system can be written

$$x_1 = G_{11}e^{\lambda_1 t} + G_{12}e^{\lambda_2 t} + \dots + G_{1n}e^{\lambda_n t} + G_{111}e^{2\lambda_1 t} + \dots \tag{3}$$

where the G's are constants, of which n are arbitrary and are fixed by the initial conditions. The λ_i are roots of the characteristic equation

$$\left| a_{ij} - \delta_{ij}\lambda \right| = 0 \tag{4}$$

where the a_{ij} are the coefficients of the linear terms in the Taylor series, and δ_{ij} is the Kronecker delta,

$$\delta_{ii} = 1, \quad \delta_{ij} = 0 \quad \text{for} \quad i \neq j$$

If all λ_i are real and negative, the steady state is stable. If some λ_i are complex with negative real parts, damped oscillations occur, but the steady state is eventually approached. Pure imaginary λ_i result in permanent oscillations, however. The steady state is unstable if any λ_i is positive or has a positive real part.

5.2. Equations of biological populations (Ref. 6). In a large number of cases, biological populations are well represented by equations in which the F_i are quadratic in the X_i.

Thus

$$\frac{dX_i}{dt} = \alpha_i + \sum_j \epsilon_{ij} X_j - X_i \sum h_{ij} X_j, \quad (i = 1, \ldots, n) \tag{1}$$

The α_i may represent immigration and emigration at constant rates. The linear terms represent increase due to excess of births over deaths, and to movements from one species to another. The quadratic terms represent interactions between members of the same or different species; they may be due to parasitism, predatory activity, metabolic products, physical conflict, competition for food, or the like. If we neglect transition between groups, which might result from mutation, metamorphosis, etc., and confine ourselves to closed populations, a useful and not too special case results.

$$\frac{dX_i}{dt} = X_i(\epsilon_i - \sum_j h_{ij} X_j), \quad (i = 1, \ldots, n) \tag{2}$$

The ϵ_i, termed coefficients of multiplication, may be interpreted as excess of birth rate over death rate. There are 2^n possible steady states. The simplest is

$$C_1 = 0, \quad C_2 = 0, \quad \ldots, \quad C_n = 0 \tag{3}$$

This is stable only if all $\epsilon_i < 0$, and so is not very significant. There are n states of the type

$$C_k = \frac{\epsilon_k}{h_{kk}}, \quad C_i = 0 \quad \text{for} \quad i \neq k \tag{4}$$

These are stable if

$$\epsilon_k > 0, \quad h_{kk} > 0, \quad \epsilon_s h_{kk} < h_{sk} \epsilon_k, \quad (s \neq k)$$

There are $n(n-1)/2$ states like

$$C_1 = \frac{\epsilon_1 h_{22} - \epsilon_2 h_{21}}{h_{11} h_{22} - h_{12} h_{21}}, \quad C_2 = \frac{\epsilon_2 h_{11} - \epsilon_1 h_{12}}{h_{11} h_{22} - h_{12} h_{21}}, \quad C_3 = 0, \quad \ldots, \quad C_n = 0 \tag{5}$$

One can continue in this fashion, finally arriving at a steady state in which none of the groups vanishes. This is given by the solutions C_i of the linear equations:

$$\sum_j h_{ij} C_j = \epsilon_i, \quad (i = 1, \ldots, n) \tag{6}$$

This is stable if all the roots of the secular equation are negative or have negative real parts. The secular equation is of course

$$\left| \frac{\partial F_i}{\partial C_j} - \delta_{ij} \lambda \right| = 0 \tag{7}$$

where $\partial F_i / \partial C_j$ stands for $\partial F_i / \partial X_j$ evaluated at $X_1 = C_1, \ldots, X_n = C_n$.

Thus in the present case

$$\left.\begin{aligned}\frac{\partial F_i}{\partial C_i} &= \epsilon_i - 2h_{ii}C_i - \sum_{j\neq i} h_{ij}C_j = -h_{ii}C_i \\ \frac{\partial F_i}{\partial C_j} &= -h_{ij}C_i, \quad (i \neq j)\end{aligned}\right\} \tag{8}$$

5.3. Simple populations; effect of wastes, nutriment, and space (Ref. 9). If p is the number of elements of a simple closed population,

$$\dot{p} = \epsilon p - hp^2 \tag{1}$$

The solution is

$$p = \frac{Cp_0}{p_0 + (C - p_0)e^{-\varepsilon t}} \tag{2}$$

where p_0 is the value of p at $t = 0$, and $C = \epsilon/h$ is the stationary value of p. This is the so-called logistic law of growth. If $h \ll \epsilon$, C is large, and

$$p \simeq p_0 e^{\varepsilon t} \tag{3}$$

the Malthusian law of growth. If the accumulated metabolites are toxic, we get

$$\dot{p} = \epsilon p - hp^2 - cp \int_0^t K(t-\tau)p(\tau)d\tau \tag{4}$$

Putting for simplicity

$$K(t-\tau) = 1$$

we get

$$\dot{p} = \epsilon p - hp^2 - cpP \tag{5}$$

where
$$P(t) = \int_0^t p(\tau)d\tau$$

The solution is obtained in parametric form.

$$p = \left(p_0 - \frac{\epsilon}{h} - \frac{c}{h^2}\right)e^{-hP} + \frac{\epsilon}{h} + \frac{c}{h^2} - \frac{c}{h}P = F(P) \tag{6}$$

$$t = \int_0^P \frac{dS}{F(S)}$$

Now $p = 0$ for a finite value of P attained as $t \to \infty$. But if $p_0 < \epsilon/h$, p increases for small t. Hence p has a maximum p_m, which is given by

$$p_m = \frac{\epsilon}{h} - \frac{c}{h^2} \log \frac{c + \epsilon h - p_0 h^2}{c} < \frac{\epsilon}{h} \tag{7}$$

We can find approximate representations of p.

$$\left.\begin{aligned} p &\cong \frac{p_0 p_m}{p_0 + (p_m - p_0)e^{-\varepsilon t}}, \quad (t < t_m) \\ p &\cong \frac{p_m}{ch^2 \dfrac{c(t - t_m)}{2}}, \quad (t > t_m) \end{aligned}\right\} \tag{8}$$

Space is one of the important limiting factors for a population. Suppose the space occupied per unit volume by living or dead members is s, the effective volume of a living member α, that of a dead member β. The birthrate is n, death rate m. Births are proportional to p and available free space $1 - s$, deaths to p and to s. Then

$$\left.\begin{aligned} \dot{p} &= pn(1 - s) - nps - hp^2 \\ s &= p\alpha + m\beta \int_0^t p(u)s(u)du \end{aligned}\right\} \tag{9}$$

The solution in parametric form is

$$p = \frac{n}{h} - ZS_0 e^{-\varphi(Z)}, \quad t = \int_Z^{Z_0} \frac{du}{F(u)p(u)} \tag{10}$$

where

$$F(Z) = \alpha h Z^2 + Z(h - \alpha n - \alpha m + \beta m) - (m + n)$$

$$\varphi(Z) = \int_{Z_0}^{Z} \frac{\alpha h u - \alpha n - \alpha m + \beta m}{F(u)} du$$

and the parameter Z is defined by $Z = (n - hp)/hs$.

An interesting treatment in the case where nutriment is the only limiting factor is that of Monod. He writes in general

$$\frac{dp}{dt} = \epsilon(C)p \tag{11}$$

where C is the concentration of the limiting metabolite. He assumes further

$$\epsilon(c) = \epsilon_0 \frac{C}{K_1 + C}$$

where ϵ_0 and K_1 are constant. This expression, proposed by Monod as an approximation to the solution of the differential equation

$$\frac{d\epsilon}{dC} = B(1 - \epsilon) \tag{12}$$

is interesting for its formal resemblance to the rate of an enzyme-catalyzed reaction limited by substrate.

The final relation needed is

$$-\frac{dC}{dt} = K\frac{dp}{dt} \tag{13}$$

which is an obvious assumption for the relation of food consumption to growth rate. In integrated form,

$$C - C_0 = K(p_0 - p)$$

it expresses the constancy of the "material efficiency of growth." The final solution, after C is eliminated, is

$$(1 + P)\ln\frac{p}{p_0} - P\ln\left(Q - \frac{p}{p_0}\right) = \epsilon_0 t + P\ln\frac{Kp_0}{C_0} \tag{14}$$

$$P = \frac{K_1}{C_0 + Kp_0}, \quad Q = \frac{C_0 + Kp_0}{Kp_0}$$

The asymptotic stationary value of p is

$$p_\alpha = p_0 Q$$

The curve has an inflection point, with a p value of

$$p_i = p_0 Q[1 + P - \sqrt{P(1 + P)}]$$

and in general is not symmetrical, as is the Verhulst logistic.

5.4. Interaction of two species (Refs. 8 and 14). The interaction of groups in a population has been analyzed principally by Lotka and Volterra. An interesting case is that in which all members of both groups compete for some common necessity like food. Let the effect of this competition on the food supply be $F(p_1, p_2)$. Then

$$\left.\begin{aligned} \frac{dp_1}{dt} &= p_1[\epsilon_1 - \gamma_1 F(p_1, p_2)] \\ \frac{dp_2}{dt} &= p_2[\epsilon_2 - \gamma_2 F(p_1, p_2)] \end{aligned}\right\} \tag{1}$$

where the constants γ_1 and γ_2 represent the effect of the food curtailment on the growth of the two groups. An integral of this pair of equations is

$$\frac{p_1^{\gamma_2}}{p_2^{\gamma_1}} = Ce^{(\gamma_2\varepsilon_1 - \gamma_1\varepsilon_2)t} \tag{2}$$

where C is a constant of integration. If $\gamma_2\epsilon_1 > \gamma_1\epsilon_2$, the system approaches a steady state where

$$p_2 = 0, \quad F_1(p_1, 0) = \epsilon_1/\gamma_1$$

If $\gamma_2\epsilon_1 < \gamma_1\epsilon$, the steady state reverses the fates of p_1 and p_2. If species 1 is the sole food of the predatory species 2 (neglecting for simplicity the intragroup competition), we have

$$\left.\begin{aligned} \frac{dp_1}{dt} &= p_1(\epsilon_1 - h_{12}p_2) \\ \frac{dp_2}{dt} &= p_2(-\epsilon_2 + h_{21}p_1) \end{aligned}\right\} \qquad (3)$$

where the negative sign before ϵ_2 takes cognizance of the fact that species 2 would die out in the absence of its prey. Integration yields (with C a constant of integration)

$$p_1^{\varepsilon_2} p_2^{\varepsilon_1} e^{-h_{21}p_1 - h_{12}p_2} = C$$

This represents a family of nonintersecting closed curves. The system is therefore periodic. If terms for intragroup competition are included, however, the oscillations are damped, and the system spirals into a steady state. In the above case, p_1 will never be completely wiped out by the predator if its initial value is positive. But suppose a third group is present, also a prey for group 2. Then

$$\left.\begin{aligned} \frac{dp_1}{dt} &= p_1(\epsilon_1 - h_{12}p_2) \\ \frac{dp_2}{dt} &= p_2(-\epsilon_2 + h_{21}p_1 + h_{23}p_3) \\ \frac{dp_3}{dt} &= p_3(\epsilon_3 - h_{32}p_2) \end{aligned}\right\} \qquad (4)$$

Consider, for instance, in the neighborhood of the p_3 axis the approximate relation

$$\frac{dp_1}{dp_2} = \frac{p_1\epsilon_1}{p_2(-\epsilon_2 + h_{23}p_3)}$$

This is positive for sufficiently large p_3. The integral curve in that case has a positive slope, and may therefore intersect the $p_2 - p_3$ plane; that is, p_1 may become extinct. That the presence of an alternative prey may have such an effect has been experimentally verified, and the mechanism is obvious upon reflection.

5.5. Embryonic growth (Ref. 6). Consider a free embryo in the presence of a limited supply of nutriment (yolk). Suppose that the rate at which it consumes this is $ap + bpn$, where n is the nutriment at time t.

Let the toxic effect of wastes be $-cpP$, where

$$P = \int_0^t p\,dt$$

The differential equations of the system are

$$\left.\begin{aligned} \frac{dp}{dt} &= \tau(ap + bpn) - hp^2 - cpP \\ \frac{dn}{dt} &= -ap - bpn \end{aligned}\right\} \quad (1)$$

The solution in parametric form is

$$\left.\begin{aligned} n &= \left(n_0 + \frac{a}{b}\right)e^{-bP} - \frac{a}{b} \\ p &= \frac{\tau(n_0 b + a)}{h - b}(e^{-bP} - e^{-hP}) + \left(p_0 - \frac{c}{h^2}\right)e^{-hP} + \frac{c}{h^2} - \frac{cP}{h} = F(P) \\ t &= \int_0^P \frac{dS}{F(S)} \end{aligned}\right\} \quad (2)$$

The function n vanishes when

$$P = \frac{1}{b}\log\left(1 + \frac{n_0 b}{a}\right)$$

If the reserve n_0 is so inadequate that

$$\tau(n_0 b + a) < p_0 h$$

then $dp/dt < 0$ at $t = 0$ and the embryo dies. If the converse inequality holds, p increases to a maximum before decreasing. It is reasonable to assume that the egg is mature and hatches at or near the maximum. If this is also to correspond to the time of disappearance of n, we have a relation between p_0 and n_0.

$$p_0 = \frac{1}{h}\left[-\left(\frac{c}{h} + \frac{ab\tau}{h - b}\right)\left(1 + \frac{n_0 b}{a}\right)^{h/b} + \frac{h\tau(n_0 b + a)}{h - b} + \frac{c}{h}\right] \quad (3)$$

Bibliography

1. Ackermann, W. W. and Potter, V. R., *Proc. Soc. Exp. Biol. Med.*, **72**, 1 (1949).
2. Ebersole, E. R., Guttentag, C. and Wilson, P. W., *Arch. Biochem.*, **3**, 399 (1944).
3. Eckart, C., *Phys. Rev.*, **58**, 269-275 (1940).
4. Haldane, J. B. S., *Enzymes*, Longmans, Green & Co., London, 1930.
5. Henri, V., *Lois générales de l'action des diastases*, Hermann & Cie., Paris, 1903.

6. Kostitzin, V. A., *Biologie mathématique*, Librairie Armand Colin, Paris, 1937.
7. Lineweaver, H. and Burk, D. J., *J. Am. Chem. Soc.*, **56**, 658 (1934).
8. Lotka, A., *Elements of Physical Biology*, Williams & Wilkins Company, Baltimore, 1925.
9. Monod, J., *Recherches sur la croissance des cultures bactériennes*, Hermann & Cie., Paris, 1942.
10. Rashevsky, N., *Mathematical Biophysics*, rev. ed., University of Chicago Press, Chicago, 1948.
11. Reiner, J. M., *J. Phys. Chem.*, **49**, 81-92 (1945).
12. Reiner, J. M., *Philosophy of Science*, **8**, 105 (1941).
13. Reiner, J. M., Unpublished.
14. Volterra, V., *Leçons sur la théorie mathématique de la lutte pour la vie*, Gauthier-Villars & Cie., Paris, 1935.
15. Young, G., *Bull. Math. Biophys.*, **1**, 31, 75 (1939).

INDEX

Printed in Belgium